WHO NEEDS WINGS TO FLY?

Certainly not the VT2 Hovercraft — this British invention is carried to a highly versatile conclusion by Vosper Thornycroft. The VT2 design is aimed at providing a robust craft with a high level of reliability and good load carrying performance.

To Fly Navy is true of the VT2 — the logistic support version, illustrated, is now in service with the Royal Navy. It has taken part in several naval exercises, operating independently and maintained and serviced by the on-board crew.

Amphibious hovercraft such as the 60-knot VT2 have opened up new opportunities in the defence field. Hovercraft are independent of conventional harbours since bases can be set up on any convenient beach.

In the logistic support role the VT2 can transport 130 troops and their vehicles. A strike version carries an armament comparable to that of a large patrol craft. A multi-role version combines several duties.

Vosper Thornycroft have also designed a smaller 18m Patrol Hovercraft which can be adapted to a number of different roles, including coastal patrol, customs, coastguard, military, rescue and fire fighting operations. The maximum speed of the 18m Patrol Hovercraft is 60 knots.

Please contact us if you require further information.

Top illustration: VT2 Hovercraft in Royal Navy service

Illustrated left: The 18m Hovercraft utilizes the technology developed in the VT2

  VOSPER THORNYCROFT (UK) LIMITED

223 Southampton Road, Paulsgrove, Portsmouth, England. Tel: Portsmouth (0705) 379481. Telex: 86115. Cables: Repsov, Portsmouth.

A Member of British Shipbuilders

Floating wings.

Modern ship designs call for light, high-speed diesel engines and gearboxes to match. Despite its exacting role, the gearbox must not be heavy. Its range of efficiency should be wide. It should be capable of long service life – dependable to a degree. And for good measure, quiet-running and simple to maintain.

ZF – Europe's No. 1 gearbox specialist – has developed a series of modern marine reversing gearboxes which meet the requirement precisely. They are compact, surprisingly light – give outstanding performance in ratings from 5 to 8000 hp. Gearboxes of this quality demand first-class materials – backed by uncompromising manufacturing and inspection standards. For instance, gears are of forged, case-hardened alloy steel with ground tooth flanks. They are inspected with meticulous care.

ZF gearboxes utilise every ounce of engine power in the hydrofoil. If you'd like the facts, ZF will be happy to fill you in.

Zahnradfabrik Friedrichshafen AG
D-7990 Friedrichshafen 1
P.O. Box 2520, W.-Germany

The sign of progress

JANE'S
SURFACE SKIMMERS
1981

LM 500

GAS TURBINE ENGINE

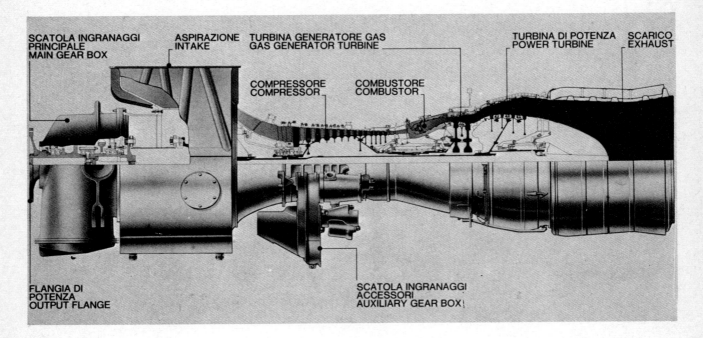

SCATOLA INGRANAGGI PRINCIPALE MAIN GEAR BOX — ASPIRAZIONE INTAKE — TURBINA GENERATORE GAS GAS GENERATOR TURBINE — COMPRESSORE COMPRESSOR — COMBUSTORE COMBUSTOR — TURBINA DI POTENZA POWER TURBINE — SCARICO EXHAUST — FLANGIA DI POTENZA OUTPUT FLANGE — SCATOLA INGRANAGGI ACCESSORI AUXILIARY GEAR BOX

STATUS

The LM 500 Gas Turbine is a cooperative effort of FIAT AVIAZIONE, of Torino, (Italy) and GENERAL ELECTRIC (USA).

As a compact high-performance marine and industrial power unit in the 3000-6000 SHP Class, the LM 500 demonstrated the highest efficiency and is suited for marine applications requiring light weight and fuel economy.

The LM 500 is derived from the TF34 high bypass turbofan aircraft engine used on the U.S. Navy S-3A and the U.S. Air Force A-10 aircraft. It is a simple-cycle, two-shaft gas turbine engine with a free power turbine.

A variable stator compressor with an excellent stall margin capability is driven by a two-stage, air-cooled turbine.

Current plans for the LM 500 include tests at FIAT AVIAZIONE facilities with a 3600 RPM gearbox and a 1560 RPM gearbox variant.

The engine is in production from mid 1980 for delivery thru 1981.

PERFORMANCE AND CHARACTERISTICS

Power output	: up to 4475 KW (6080 CV) at 300 °K (27 °C) and standard inlet and exhaust losses - liquid fuel
Specific fuel consumption	: 0,273 Kg/KWh (0,200 Kg/CVh)
Output speed	: 7000 RPM direct drive
	1500 ÷ 3600 RPM with FIAT Reduction Gearbox
Lenght	: 2190 mm for Basic Engine 3300 mm for standard Engine
Weight	: 590 Kg for Basic Engine 1100 Kg for Standard Engine
Fuel	: Natural Gas, Liquid fuel, Dual fuel

APPLICATIONS

- Landing Crafts ● Hydrofoils ● Hovercrafts
- FPB ● Cruise propulsion for larger ships
- Generator sets on board, Industrial or Mobile use
- Drives for pipeline transmission

Marine & Industrial Projects Dept

FIAT AVIAZIONE S.p.A.
Torino - Via Nizza 326
Tel. 637287 - Tlx 221320 FIATAV

JETCAT JC-F1

CATAMARAN

**ECONOMY
SIMPLICITY
VERSATILITY
PROFITABILITY**

The prototype Jetcat JC-F1 001 high-speed catamaran ferry on trials November 1980

AN EXCEPTIONAL SPECIFICATION!

The welded-aluminium-alloy Jetcat JC-F1 offers for the first time in a high-speed ferry all the following important features:

* Engines: two MTU 12V 396 high-speed diesels
* Payload capacity: over 200 passengers on a single deck
* 30 knots cruising speed
* 40 seconds to reach cruising speed
* Excellent operating economics
* Exceptional quietness
* Propulsion: two KaMeWa water-jet units
* Superb manoeuvrability
* Very shallow draught: less than 1·2m (3ft 11in)
* Highly stable platform
* Excellent ride
* Very low wash
* Detachable hulls on anti-vibration mountings

JETCAT MARKETING LIMITED
31 Southampton Row,
London WC1B 5HJ
England.

Tel: 01 404 4321
Telex: 892465 EPICO G
Cables: EPICAX LONDON WC1

28A St. Thomas Street,
Lymington,
Hampshire SO4 9NE,
England.

Tel: 0590 75098
Telex: 47674 MATCOM G

81 08516

Alphabetical list of advertisers

A

Avon Industrial Polymers (Melksham) Ltd
Bumpers Way, Bristol Road, Chippenham,
Wiltshire SM14 6NF, England .... [16]

B

Bell Aerospace Textron
Division of Textron Inc, Buffalo,
New York 14240, USA .... [18]

Breda Meccanica Bresciana SpA
Via Lunga 2, 25100 Brescia, Italy .... [14]

British Hovercraft Corporation
East Cowes, Isle of Wight, England .... [6] & [7]

F

FIAT Aviazione SpA
Marine & Industrial Projects Department,
Via Nizza 326, Turin, Italy .... [2]

J

Jetcat Marketing Ltd
31 Southampton Row, London WC1B 5HJ,
England .... [3]
&
28a St Thomas Street, Lymington, Hampshire
SO4 9NE, England .... [3]

M

Mitsui Engineering & Shipbuilding Company Ltd
6-4 Tsukiji 5-chome, Chuo-ku,
Tokyo, Japan .... [9]

Motoren-und Turbinen-Union
Friedrichshafen GmbH (MTU)
Postfach 2040, D-7990 Friedrichshafen,
Federal Republic of Germany .... [5]

N

Northern Rubber Company Ltd
Victoria Works, Retford,
Nottinghamshire DN22 6HH, England .... [9]

O

OTO Melara SpA
Via Valdilocchi 15, 19100 La Spezia, Italy .... [12]

R

Rodriquez Cantiere Navale SpA
Via S Raineri 22, 98100 Messina,
Italy .... *inside front cover*

S

SEPA SpA
Lungo Stura Lazio 45, 10156 Turin, Italy .... [20]

V

Vosper Thornycroft Ltd
223 Southampton Road, Paulsgrove,
Portsmouth, Hampshire PO6 4QA, England
facing inside front cover

Z

Zahnradfabrik Friedrichshafen AG
P O Box 2520, D-7990 Friedrichshafen 1,
Federal Republic of Germany ...... *front endpaper iv*

Portrait of a Corporate Enterprise

Name

The MTU Group is formed by two companies, namely Motoren- und Turbinen-Union München GmbH and Motoren- und Turbinen-Union Friedrichshafen GmbH.

Headquarters

The main plants are located in Munich and Friedrichshafen, with a branch factory in Peißenberg/Obb.

Workforce

11,600 people on the payroll.
Service mechanics and engineers, lathe operators and data processors, toolmakers and salesmen, and a multitude of other vocations for a large variety of important tasks.

Turnover

More than 1 billion DM – Proof of the prominent position of leadership maintained by the MTU Group.

Products

Whether railroad or marine, vehicular or special-purpose, stationary or mobile applications – MTU Friedrichshafen's high-performance diesels are well known and highly appreciated throughout the world.

MTU München excels in the development, production and technical support of aircraft propulsion systems: Gas turbines for helicopters, turboprop engines, jet engines for commercial and military aircraft.

History

MTU is closely related to the beginning of motorization. Diesel, Daimler, Benz, and Maybach are the big names behind MTU. Daimler-Benz, Maybach, BMW, and M.A.N. are the technical and organizational roots of the MTU Group which was established in 1969.

Peculiarities

Through consistent engineering advancement and development of the high-performance diesel into an economical, ecology-oriented and powerful prime mover, MTU Friedrichshafen has set an example of modern technology usage.

Intensive research and testing in the development of advanced jet engines, use of up-to-date production and quality control techniques, and handling of materials technology tasks are featured functions of MTU München.

---

mtu

MOTOREN- UND TURBINEN-UNION GESELLSCHAFTEN
MÜNCHEN UND FRIEDRICHSHAFEN

Classified list of advertisers

The companies advertising in this publication have informed us that they are involved in the fields of manufacture indicated below

ACV manufacturers
Bell Aerospace Textron
British Hovercraft Corporation
Vosper Thornycroft

ACV research and design
Bell Aerospace Textron
British Hovercraft Corporation

Catamaran displacement craft
Jetcat

Diesel engines
Mitsui Engineering
Motoren-und Turbinen-Union
Zahnradfabrik

Electronic equipment
SEPA

Finished machine parts
British Hovercraft Corporation

Gas turbine engines
FIAT Aviazione

Glass fibre resins
British Hovercraft Corporation

Guided missile ground handling equipment
OTO Melara

Guns and mountings
Breda Meccanica
OTO Melara

Hovercraft command staff training
British Hovercraft Corporation

Hovercraft consultants
Bell Aerospace Textron
British Hovercraft Corporation

Hovercraft interior design
British Hovercraft Corporation

Hovercraft interior furnishings
British Hovercraft Corporation

Hovercraft manufacturers
Bell Aerospace Textron
British Hovercraft Corporation
Mitsui Engineering
Vosper Thornycroft

Hoverpallet manufacturers
British Hovercraft Corporation

Hydrofoil boats and ships
Rodriquez Cantiere Navale

Hydrofoil interior design
Rodriquez Cantiere Navale

Hydrofoil interior furnishing
Rodriquez Cantiere Navale

Hydrofoil missile / gun boats combat systems
OTO Melara

Günther Jörg, a West German aeronautical engineer, with his twin-aerofoil ram-wing craft, Jörg III. Built in glass fibre and powered by a 225-325hp Ford engine, the craft seats four to six passengers and cruises at 135km/h (84mph). An earlier, but similar, craft has flown more than 11,000km along West German rivers and around the Mediterranean

JANE'S SURFACE SKIMMERS

FOURTEENTH EDITION

EDITED BY
ROY McLEAVY

1981

JANE'S YEARBOOKS

''Jane's'' is a registered trade mark

Published in the United Kingdom by
Jane's Publishing Company Limited, 238 City Road, London EC1V 2PU

ISBN 0 7106-0719-9

Published in the United States of America by
Jane's Publishing Incorporated, 730 Fifth Avenue, New York, NY 10019

ISBN 0 531-03969-2

CONTENTS

FOREWORD   [15]

ACV MANUFACTURERS AND DESIGN GROUPS   1
  Australia   1
  Brazil   5
  Bulgaria   5
  Canada   5
  China, People's Republic   9
  Czechoslovakia   12
  Finland   12
  France   14
  Germany, Federal Republic   23
  Indonesia   25
  Japan   25
  Korea, Republic   34
  New Zealand   34
  Poland   35
  Singapore   35
  Spain   35
  Trinidad   37
  Union of Soviet Socialist Republics   38
  United Kingdom   61
  United States of America   109

ACV OPERATORS   147
  Abu Dhabi   147
  Australia   147
  Bahrain   147
  Belgium   147
  Brazil   147
  Canada   147
  China, People's Republic   148
  Egypt   148
  Finland   148
  France   148
  Hong Kong   148
  Iran   149
  Iraq   149
  Israel   149
  Italy   149
  Japan   149
  Jordan   149
  Netherlands   149
  New Zealand   149
  Nigeria   149
  Pakistan   149
  Philippines   149
  Portugal   150
  Saudi Arabia   150
  Union of Soviet Socialist Republics   150
  United Kingdom   150
  United States of America   153
  Venezuela   153
  Zaire   153

ACV TRAILERS AND HEAVY LIFT SYSTEMS   155
  Australia   155
  Canada   155
  France   158
  Japan   160
  Union of Soviet Socialist Republics   160
  United Kingdom   162
  United States of America   168

TRACKED SKIMMERS   175
  Brazil   175
  France   175
  Germany, Federal Republic   183
  Japan   186
  Union of Soviet Socialist Republics   189
  United States of America   190

**AIR CUSHION APPLICATORS, CONVEYORS
AND PALLETS**   193
  Australia   193
  France   193
  Germany, Federal Republic   194
  Trinidad   194
  Union of Soviet Socialist Republics   195
  United Kingdom   196
  United States of America   201

HYDROFOILS   211
  Bolivia   211
  Canada   211
  China, People's Republic   214
  France   214
  Israel   216
  Italy   217

HYDROFOILS cont
  Japan   239
  Poland   239
  Romania   240
  Singapore   240
  Switzerland   240
  Union of Soviet Socialist Republics   256
  United States of America   274

SAILING SKIMMERS   295
  Japan   295
  Poland   296
  United Kingdom   297
  United States of America   298

HYDROFOIL OPERATORS   301
  Albania   301
  Argentina   301
  Australia   301
  Austria   301
  Belgium   301
  Bolivia   301
  Brazil   301
  Bulgaria   301
  Canada   301
  China, People's Republic   301
  Cuba   301
  Denmark   301
  Egypt   301
  Finland   301
  France   301
  Germany, Democratic Republic   301
  Germany, Federal Republic   301
  Greece   302
  Hong Kong   302
  Hungary   302
  Indonesia   302
  Iran   302
  Ireland   302
  Israel   302
  Italy   302
  Japan   303
  Korea, Republic   303
  Morocco   303
  New Zealand   303
  Norway   303
  Pakistan   303
  Philippines   303
  Poland   303
  Romania   303
  Spain   303
  Sri Lanka   304
  Sweden   304
  Tanzania   304
  Turkey   304
  Union of Soviet Socialist Republics   304
  United Kingdom   304
  United States of America   305
  Uruguay   305
  Venezuela   305
  Yugoslavia   305
  Zaire   305

FAST CATAMARANS   307
  Norway   307
  United Kingdom   308

SEMI-SUBMERGED CATAMARANS   309
  Japan   309
  United States of America   310

POWER PLANTS AND PROPULSION SYSTEMS   313
  Canada   313
  France   314
  Germany, Federal Republic   316
  Italy   319
  Union of Soviet Socialist Republics   322
  United Kingdom   324
  United States of America   328

LICENSING AUTHORITIES   341

CLUBS AND ASSOCIATIONS   343

ACV AND HYDROFOIL CONSULTANTS   345

GLOSSARY   350

BIBLIOGRAPHY   362

ADDENDA   368

INDEX   377

[13]

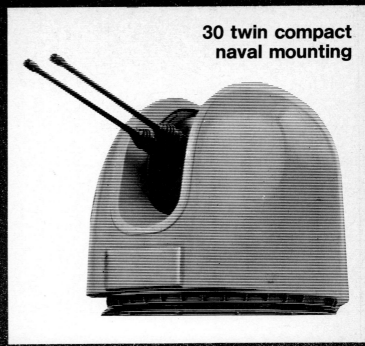
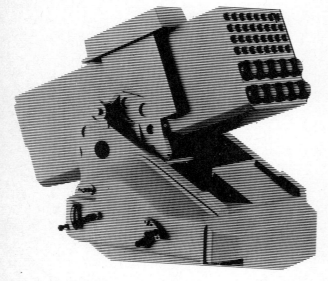

FOREWORD

Time to advance the technology

Most predictions firmly agree that hovercraft sales, both commercial and military, will rise at an unprecedented rate throughout the present decade. A promising sign that the marketing forecasts may be squarely on target is that by early January 1981 advanced orders placed for Western hovercraft for delivery up to the mid-1980s had already reached the all-time record of £100 million.

Even more encouraging is the long-term growth prospect, which should result in a substantial number of major orders for fast hoverferries, freighters and warships from the West and for a variety of specialist and multi-duty vehicles to help open up the hinterlands of the Third World countries. The new orders will provide the industry with much-needed funds and could well mark a vital turning point in the industry's fortunes; but there is no doubt that its future success will depend increasingly on the degree to which the companies and governments alike are prepared to advance the state of the technology.

As the acceptance of the hovercraft widens, so will the expectations of the potential clients tend to broaden. To meet their requirements in many cases significant improvements in a number of design areas will be expected. For too many years modification has been the traditional means of keeping existing hovercraft in the current sales list. Within the industry "make-do and modify" has become almost a way of life to avoid the cost of investing in entirely new designs.

In the early 1960s there was considerable enthusiasm for the potential of hovercraft which resulted in substantial sums being invested in research and development by both government and private industry. It was perhaps unfortunate that the world's first 2/3 seat man-carrying hovercraft, the SR.N1, was such an immediate success. In a blaze of publicity it crossed the Channel within weeks of first hovering. This rate of progress was extrapolated, but it was not fully appreciated that the SR.N1 was an experimental craft which merely confirmed that cross-Channel commercial operations might be viable.

Subsequently, the apparently slow rate of progress in bringing large seagoing hovercraft into fruition towards the end of the 1960s resulted in a reduction of expenditure, particularly on research. It has been estimated that over the life of the UK hovercraft industry on average only £1 million per year has been spent on research. Had this figure been ten to fifteen times as great it is probable that by now startling advances in the technology would have been made which would have more than paid for themselves by greatly improved sales.

Significant advances could have been made in ride quality, controllability, noise reduction, spray reduction, first cost and operating costs. With the exception of the first item, improvements would have been achieved by tackling the problems methodically and matching the cost of achieving the improvements against the increase in the general acceptance of hovercraft in all roles. In the case of ride quality, however, a fundamentally different approach has been more appropriate. There may be a strong parallel in the three-dimensional active control system of the Jetfoil. In the late 1950s the father of hovercraft, Sir Christopher Cockerell, envisaged the use of automatic control systems to improve the ride when operating over rough surfaces. As an electronics engineer he was not too concerned with the difficulty of producing the appropriate "black boxes", but could foresee problems in fitting hovercraft with the physical devices for controlling the pitch, roll and vertical displacement. However, small-scale experimental installations have shown that there are several methods of control which could be used to improve the ride quality of hovercraft to a point where it offers positive improvements.

There is a minimum level of funding which, if applied to improving the qualities referred to, would make the craft more attractive to military and civil operators and to the public. This level of expenditure has not been achieved and in recent years this has resulted in static, or even falling, sales. There is considerable evidence that more advanced levels of ACV activity exist outside the United Kingdom and United States which should justify a drastic revision of the official attitude to the hovercraft's potential for defence operations and as a means of improving communications.

Industrial research and development has been called many things. In North America, for example, every R & D dollar spent is regarded as a worthy investment in the future of that particular industry or market sector. Within the agricultural community, R & D has been described as the "fertiliser in the field of opportunity". Most industrialists recognise that without adequate funding for research and development there is a constant danger that the customers' demands or expectations will exceed the capabilities of the product. When this occurs the customer is forced to look elsewhere and a supplier, possibly of several years' standing, loses both a customer and a major market advantage.

R & D on grand scale

Those sectors of industry and commerce most often associated with research and development on a grand scale can be easily listed: pharmaceuticals, aerospace, motor vehicles, electronics and computers. All these spend vast sums on R & D. No one is greatly concerned about how much duplication of time and effort may be expended by these industries on similar and sometimes identical avenues of investigation. For them research and development is a fact of life and one which is becoming more and more important. A glance at the annual reports of British and US organisations engaged in these fields will indicate just how much money each company is prepared to commit. The total sums invested in R & D in the five industries mentioned in the UK for 1978 and the United States for 1977 appear in Tables 1 and 2.

Table 1

UK investment in R & D in selected industries during 1978*

	Industrial and private sources £ million	Government share of total funding £ million
Aerospace	424·9	307·2
Computers	125	22
Electronics	525·2	289·2
Motor vehicles	130	5·5
Pharmaceuticals	163·8	—

*Most recent year for which figures were available

[16]

Table 2
US investment in R & D in selected industries during 1977*

	Industrial and private souces $ million	Government share of total funding $ million
Aerospace	7,078	5,496
Computers	2,758 ⎫	
Electronics	3,607 ⎭	2,696
Motor vehicles	3,302	414
Pharmaceuticals	1,153	—

*Most recent year for which figures were available

On a worldwide scale the total sums committed to active industrial research and development are immense, even omitting the expenditure for the Soviet Union, Eastern bloc and the People's Republic of China. No figures are available, but one can only conclude that the sums involved in these countries must be similar to those spent by their Western counterparts.

Reports to the US Congress, though costing hundreds of thousands of dollars to prepare, have rarely advanced the cause of R & D activities in the United States and, more often than not, have served only to delay essential decisions. Ironically, many of the findings when subsequently published have been collected by the Soviet Union and the Eastern bloc and have provided yardsticks against which their own progress can be measured. References to the more informative reports appear in the appendices to books published in the Soviet Union on the very subjects of air cushion vehicles and surface effect ships.

For a decade or more there has been concern that the sources of research and development funding for the skimmer industries have been extremely limited and frequently reliant on public sources. Whether the product is an ACV, SES or fully-submerged hydrofoil, the potential is invariably linked with the funding available to create an attractive design. If the source of the funding is military, the likelihood is that the design will develop only towards a military application; if the source or funding is private venture capital the initial market will almost certainly be civil. When the two markets meet—a rare occurrence these days—the compromise is often such that it is readily apparent that neither design is entirely suitable for either of the applications and simply confuses the potential customer.

UK activities

UK activities appear to be still concerned with consolidation rather than innovation. Ironically, the only major programme of a new type to emerge during 1980 has been API-88, a possible replacement for the ageing SR.N6 which has rendered sterling service in virtually every role in which it has been deployed. Despite the promise of the Vosper Hovermarine 500 series and the company's 700 series, which employs the deep cushion concept, few steps had been taken to bring either type closer to the market place or operational status until recently.

In the USA the Carter administration's uncertainty over the future roles of the amphibious assault landing craft, convoy escort and logistics support vessel had taken its toll. The successor to the AACC—the Landing Craft Air Cushion (LCAC)—has now progressed to the extent that six pre-production prototypes are being built, but it is unlikely that the first of these will emerge for two or three years and that fleet utilisation will develop earlier than 1985. The case of the LACV-30 is slightly more encouraging. Within the next few years there is a strong suggestion that up to three US Marine Corps companies, each having twelve craft, will be established; already the procurement of the first twelve LACV-30s has been planned with Bell Aerospace Textron receiving contracts worth around $60 million.

The future of the large SES (LSES) of 5,000 to 10,000 tons is less certain. Following the Carter administration's cancellation of the 3KSES programme the prospects of further work have appeared

bleak. It is only in the 100 to 1,000-ton SES range that future US Naval SES activity is likely to be concentrated. Even here, the emphasis will be on low cost/low risk designs which capitalise on existing knowledge obtained through the early SES work undertaken by Rohr Marine Inc, and supplemented by operational data obtained through the evaluation of the SES-100A and SES-100B. Nonetheless, the new Reagan initiative for advanced defence systems, particularly those in the naval sphere, seems likely to raise the priority of future LSES projects, although the 3KSES itself is unlikely to be resurrected in its projected configuration. Despite the value of the support of the US Navy's former Chief of Naval Operations, Admiral Elmo R Zumwalt, for a "100-knot Navy" the present environment suggests that rather lower targets—perhaps 80 knots, with a 1,000-ton SES—might meet the revised requirements. Also the technological risks involved would be considerably less and the costs substantially more controllable at this size. Many in the defence community in the United States have been uneasy about the allocation of large sums of money to the production of yet another prototype, although it might be of 1,000 tons and capable of high speeds. The adjustment of funding towards a "first step" LSES with a slightly lower speed but which would have open sea capability, is likely to be far more acceptable. Some progress towards confirmation of the goal is likely to come from US Coast Guard experiments with the extended BH 110 demonstrator recently purchased by the US Navy and which derives much from Bell Aerospace Textron's involvement over several years in the SES programme.

Whatever the immediate outcome, US Navy planners are unlikely to lose sight of a prime long-term need: large, fast logistics transports with transoceanic range which would permit the US armed services to reduce the number of personnel based overseas without compromising the ability to respond immediately in an emergency.

Two such craft are already in the preliminary design stage at Rohr Marine Inc. The first is an LSES with a displacement of 11,500 tons and the second is an amphibious assault SES displacing 5,200 long tons. The LSES is intended primarily for the rapid resupply of units in the field. It would be propelled by waterjets and employ technology developed for the 3KSES. It would be 627 feet long, have a beam of 126 feet and a draft of 24 feet. Cruising speed would be 50 knots in sea state 3. Range would be 3,500n miles and payload 3,200 short tons. Cost is estimated at $230 million at 1980 rates and if ordered during 1981, delivery of the first craft could be made in the late 1980s. The amphibious assault SES is seen as having a wide range of potential roles. In logistical support configuration it would carry eight ACV lighters, two helicopters and 100 containers or vehicles, artillery pieces or palletised cargo. Length would be 393 feet, beam 106 feet and cushion depth 18 feet. Speed at full load would be about 50 knots; average cruising speed would be 75 knots. Ferry transit range would be 4,750n miles.

Understandably, the US Navy is keeping its options open. But whether the next SES prototype is big or small, it is to be hoped that the final funding does not suffer the same ridiculous bureaucratic vacillations as the 3KSES. Taking the 3KSES funding for 1978 as being typical, the initial US Navy request for that fiscal year to develop the vehicle was $68·9 million. The House Armed Services Committee voted only $43·9 million; the Senate Armed Services Committee reduced it still further to $33·9 million; the Joint Armed Services Committee raised it back to $43·9 million; the House Appropriations Committee felt it was worth only $6·0 million; the Senate Appropriations Committee then raised it once again to $43·9 million, which was the final figure.

Arbitrary policy, as opposed to realistic planning, has for too long been the overriding force in political decision making in Washington and Whitehall, this time to the detriment not only of commercial growth in the field, but more vitally, to national defence.

Combat readiness

During 1980 before the November elections the Republican

Bell hardware: here and now

This impressive array of ACV/SES craft demonstrates Bell's ability to translate concepts into successful working hardware. Whatever the requirement; a 100 mph research SES, a rugged commercial flatbed, the LACV-30 serving the U.S. Army's Logistics Over The Shore mission or the 60-ton payload JEFF (B), precursor of the Navy's Operational LCAC of the late eighties, Bell has been there with hardware to fulfill it. As new international requirements emerge, Bell will be there with a hardware oriented team to meet them.

Bell Aerospace **TEXTRON**

Division of Textron Inc.
Buffalo, New York 14240 U.S.A.

Party's Study Group in Defence suggested that the Carter administration's decision to cancel the 3KSES programme would compound mistakes made in the maritime arena in the past. The group cited a past example when the US government had refused to subsidise the initial steamship building programme in the early 1800s. The failure of the government of the day to grasp the significance of the new steamship and steel shipbuilding technology led to the loss of the earlier maritime leadership which the United States had achieved by utilising the clipper ship technology. Admiral Zumwalt has been advising the incoming Reagan administration on the defence posture which should be adopted during the next four years and there are strong indications that he has advised the resumption of SES and ACV funding as a method of maintaining both a technological lead and in some areas parity with Soviet developments.

The Republicans have pledged to make the combat readiness of the US armed forces and the preparedness of the industrial base a top priority.

However, nearly all this effort has either been funded directly by US government contracts or has indirectly benefited from study programmes contracted to Bell and others active in this field.

In France the scene has been far more difficult in terms of both funding and the continuity of effort. After several years of research aimed at the development of a viable SES design which would be capable of ASW duties on the Western Approaches and along the French Atlantic coastline, the French Naval Ministry appears to be resigned to observation and not production. In terms of fully amphibious ACVs the Dubigeon-Normandie/SEDAM partnership has been hard at work refining the premier French ACV project, the Naviplane N 500. The commercial prospects for delivery appear as volatile as ever, although it is to Dubigeon-Normandie's credit that a continuation of the SEDAM research and development programme exists at all. Some feel that perhaps Dubigeon-Normandie might emerge as a more successful supplier of ACVs or Aéroglisseurs to the Arab world where recent contracts have permitted French companies to secure an unprecedented share of orders for weapon systems and naval hardware. Whether this pace can be attained by sales of ACVs remains very much a matter for conjecture, especially since the French experience is regarded as limited and is still beset by problems related to skirt systems and payload capability.

Canada, for long a centre of interesting developments within the spheres of low-speed and specialised-use ACVs, has suffered from some setbacks. The low-speed hoverferries which have been applied in various provinces to solving year-round river transit problems caused by flooding rivers and ice floes have not all made the grade. But mechanical rather than air-cushion technology problems appear to have been the root cause. In terms of Canadian progress with the air cushion icebreaking technique, no further developments of note have emerged although interest in the area remains high and there are indications that both Finland and the Soviet Union have benefited from Canadian work.

Finland and China

Finland and China are two recent cases where the governments have grasped the importance of hovercraft technology to their national economies and are now supporting domestic programmes with both determination and sustained financing. Although Finland's initial activity was based on the development of ACV icebreaking techniques this has now been expanded to include amphibious hoverbarges, lighters and passenger vehicle ferries designed to operate in low temperatures across stretches of sea, water, ice and broken ice during winter conditions in the Finnish archipelago (see Addenda). Oy Wärtsilä Ab is building these craft at its Helsinki shipyard. The company is best known for its icebreakers and is the biggest builder of these vessels in the world. Most have been sold to the Finnish government and the Soviet Union. The ACV programme is aimed at the same markets although it should offer business potential in other arctic regions, from Alaska and Northern Canada to possibly arctic and antarctic expeditions.

Chinese ACV research and development programmes have been under way since 1970 and, as in the Soviet Union, cover a broad range of types, including wing-in-ground-effect machines. At present Chinese interest is focused on amphibious craft in the 10 to 300 ton range which are required for a variety of military and civil applications, including the operation of fast passenger/vehicle ferry services over river networks with route distances of up to 240 to 320km (150 to 200 miles). A 70-ton assault hovercraft resembling a scaled-down SR.N4 began its trials in August 1979. Unconfirmed reports suggest that an export variant is already being offered in the Middle East.

Soviet air cushion activity during the 1980s is likely to be massive and spectacular in comparison with the efforts of the Western World. Part of this activity will be devoted to meeting Soviet military needs but in the main it will be devoted to the development and construction of amphibious personnel carriers and snow and marshgoing vehicles capable of providing year-round transport in the Soviet North and North-eastern regions where a number of vital development projects are under way.

Only a small percentage of the freight required can be delivered to these areas by Mi-6 helicopter. Estimates of the Institute of Integrated Transport Problems, operating under the USSR Gosplan Institute have indicated that the use of ACVs, apart from speeding up the construction of important facilities under difficult conditions, will enable the cost of haulage over difficult routes of the North and North-east to be reduced by one-third. Savings in transportation expenditure for the work volume forecast for the Eleventh Five Year Plan will be 1,200-1,500 million roubles annually because of this.

The Institute of Integrated Transport Problems is considering under Gosplan the data of 25 Soviet Ministries and has ascertained the requirement for developing the North and North-eastern regions of the USSR. It has been established that for the level of haulage forecast for the long-term, 6,000 to 6,500 self-propelled and towed amphibious air cushion transporters and about 3,500 fully-amphibious passenger craft and mixed traffic ferries will be necessary. From the forecast it is apparent that fully amphibious ACVs will become more common in the Soviet Union than sidewall ACVs. This is because the latter lack all-terrain capability, require waterway depths of at least 1 metre and can be employed only seasonally because of winter ice.

Soviet commercial air cushion vehicles could well be made available on the world markets before long. Oleg Kropotov, Director General of Sudoimport, the organisation responsible for the export sales of Soviet ships, marine equipment and hydrofoils, has announced that the Soviet Union "is now prepared to hold negotiations for the sale of licences for the construction of (Soviet designed) hovercraft".

Amphibious landing capability

On the military side, the expansion of the Soviet Navy's amphibious landing capability continues, not only with the continued production of the 270-ton Aist and the 90-ton Lebed, but also with the introduction of a completely new design, reported to be similar in size, configuration and performance to the 55-ton BHC BH.7 and incorporating a bow door and central load well.

One new Soviet concept which is creating a great deal of interest in the West is a projected class of icebreaker/transport-cum-supply vessel which will carry a 50-ton capacity self-propelled hoverbarge as standard equipment. The object is to provide the vessels with the means to discharge their cargoes onto shores where no offloading facilities exist. The supply vessel will stop 10 to 20 miles offshore, launch the platform and then load it with the cargo to be taken ashore. A photograph of the prototype self-propelled hoverbarge appears on page 161.

Wing-in-ground-effect machines and ram-wings in a wide variety of configurations have been under development in the Soviet Union for more than 15 years. It is anticipated that at least one of these designs will enter production during the 1980s. In this particular branch of ACV technology the Soviet Union is acknowledged as leading the rest of the world.

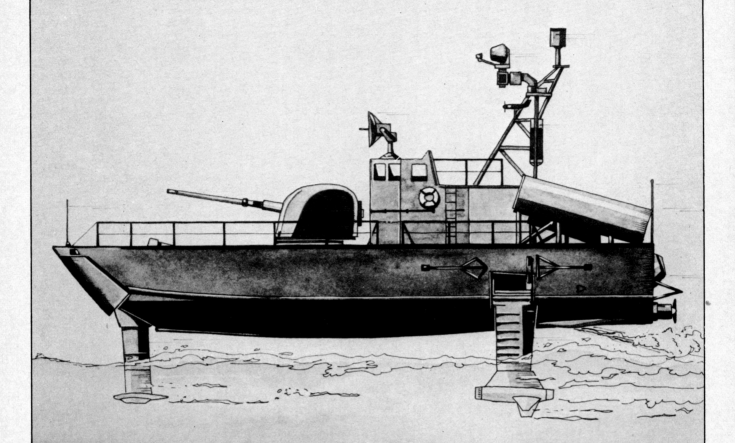
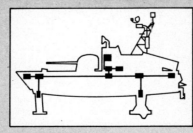

For some time the activities of the Japanese Self-Defence Force have seemed ideal for application of the SES. However, the force has been reluctant to make such a major change and the efforts of a few far-sighted advocates of SES naval technology seem unlikely to change Japanese decisions. Perhaps the need will become more pressing when deployment of additional Soviet Far East Fleet vessels of the Ivan Rogov type, able to transport up to two Lebeds or three Guses, is complete. Mitsui, the only active producer of Japanese fully-amphibious ACVs, has shown no interest publicly in naval versions of its MV-PP15 design although it is conceivable that Mitsui's activities with semi-submerged catamarans (SSC) could lead to the introduction of these craft in an ASW role in Japanese waters.

For those who have been in the industry since its inception, the evolution and introduction of the hovercraft into commercial and military service has been a long, uphill struggle. But having marshalled its resources and successfully laid the foundations of a totally new technology, the industry is now in sight of achieving its goal—the replacement of the traditional displacement ship by a vehicle which, in dozens of roles, is more efficient. In amphibious form it can replace other vehicles too. Its market is vast and worldwide.

After such a promising start to the hovercraft's third decade it would be a tragedy not only for the United Kingdom and United States, but also for the Western World as a whole, if a really determined effort was not made now to exploit this vast technical asset and to begin building up the new technology needed for craft of the next generation.

Roy McLeavy   January 1981

ACKNOWLEDGEMENTS

The Editor wishes to acknowledge his indebtedness to the following correspondents for their readiness to supply information and their many helpful suggestions.

Baron Hanns von Schertel, Supramar; R Wheeler and Mike McSorley, British Hovercraft Corporation; Dr Leopoldo Rodriquez and Giovanni Falzea, Rodriquez Cantiere Navale SpA; Elaine H Heise, Bell Aerospace Textron, Niagara Frontier Operations; Alan Bingham and A Winter, Vosper Thornycroft; Peter Mantle; Captain Carl C Drenkard, USN, Project Manager, Surface Effect Ships Project; Dr William R Bertelsen, Bertelsen Manufacturing Company; L Flammand, Bertin & Cie; M W Beardsley, Skimmers Inc; Franklin A Dobson, Dobson Products Co; T Akao, Hitachi Shipbuilding and Engineering; Neil MacDonald; Donald E Kenney, Bell Aerospace Textron, New Orleans Operations; R V Taylor, Taylorcraft Transport Pty Ltd; Audoin de Dampierre, Dubigeon-Normandie; C D J Bland and P H Winter, Air Vehicles Ltd; Andre Clodong, United Aircraft of Canada; Rhoda G Stolk, Stolkraft Pty Ltd; Chuck Srock, Scorpion Inc; Richard Catling, Rolls-Royce (1971) Ltd; W G Eggington and Jacqueline Jenerette, Rohr Industries Inc; B H Wright, Rolair; Kenneth Cook, Hydrofoils Inc; Masahiro Mino, Nihon University; Mike Pinder, Pindair Ltd; Georges Hennebutte, Ets Georges Hennebutte; Admiral Alexander Snead, USN (Retd), Victor Croizet and Walter Wohleking, Grumman Aerospace, Marine Division; S Morita, De Havilland Aircraft of Canada; Robert Bateman, P B Dakan and Bob Edwards, Boeing Marine Systems; Ralph Wortmann, AiResearch Mfg; Christopher Fitzgerald, Neoteric Engineering; Masaya Nakamura, Nakamura Seisakusho Co Ltd; J L Benson and B C Swanson, US Navy Amphibious Ship Acquisition Project; Vernon W McKay, Hovermac Hovercraft Aust; H B Standen, Light Hovercraft Company (Australia); Pedro G Ferrandes, F M Aerodeslizadores; Peter Venn, Australian Light Hovercraft Services; W B Griffin, Space Hovercraft Ltd; William C House, Maritime Dynamics Inc; Wärtsilä Helsinki Shipyard; John Van Veldhuizen, Air Cushion Systems; Günther W Jörg; Haruo Yamane, Mitsui Engineering & Shipbuilding; R C Gilbert, Air Cushion Equipment (1976) Ltd; Edward F Davison, Aerojet Liquid Rocket Company; D G Kinner, Mears Construction Ltd; Shoichi Fukumitsu and Yutaka Matsuyama, Kanazawa Institute of Technology; Donald E Kenney, Bell-Halter; Marilyn Walsh, Aero-Go Inc; Jukka Tervamäki; R J Windt, Universal Hovercraft; Esko Hietanen, Pintaliitäjäpalvelu; Jalmari Lukkarila; Paul W Esterle, Venture Aero-Marine; Marvin F Proctor, Alaska Hovercraft; J T Darwood, Skidaddle Leisure Products; B R Crouch, Rotork Marine Ltd; G J Nutt, Hoverservices Hovercraft; C C Harris, Tropimere; Bill Baker, Bill Baker Vehicles Ltd; David J Cline, Dynafoil Inc; George C Dagher, North American Hovercraft Corporation; R F King, Surface Craft Ltd; Paul Guienne; Robert Motte, Angevinière; Jacques Thilloy.

Finally he would like to acknowledge the tremendous assistance by David Rose of Jane's Yearbooks, by Sian Prior who assisted in checking the galleys and page proofs and indexed this edition, by Erica Lock for typing the manuscript and to the production team, headed by Glynis Long, for their enthuasiasm and hard work.

ACV MANUFACTURERS AND DESIGN GROUPS

AUSTRALIA

AUSTRALIAN LIGHT HOVERCRAFT SERVICES

1 Leon Street, Thorneside, Queensland 4158, Australia
Telephone: 207 2934
Officials:
Peter Venn, *Manager*

Australian Light Hovercraft Services markets ACV plans and components for homebuilders and also offers an aquatic and terrestrial weed control service with the aid of a modified Scarab II hovercraft (see UK section under Hoverservices). The craft can be fitted with various types of spraying systems to cope with many types of weeds.

Examples include:
4·87m (16ft) long spray boom with two rows of jets, capable of delivering chemicals at rates of 9-90 litres (2-20 gallons) per acre;
2·43m (8ft) boom, employed above small dams infested with salvinia and similar weeds;
for high volume application a centrifugal pump can be fitted which draws water from the dam or lake via a revolving caged foot valve;
by employing a venturi system and a high pressure pump, groundsel and other terrestrial weeds along river banks can be sprayed.

The Scarab II is capable of spraying approximately 20 hectares (50 acres) in an 8-hour day. On average 8 tonnes of mixed chemical are consumed every 8 hours. The cost of hiring the craft for weed control is A$2 to A$7 per acre, plus the cost of the chemical.

Scarab II modified for aquatic and terrestrial weed spraying by Australian Light Hovercraft Services

Scarab II being employed to spray salvinia. The weed is floating on about 11m of water. On later crop-spraying variants instrumentation and controls have been raised to facilitate operation from the standing position

HOVERMAC HOVERCRAFT AUSTRALIA

Green Glades, Old Gympie Road, Narangba, Queensland 4504, Australia
Telephone: 07 204 1210
Officials:
Vernon W McKay, *Manager*

Hovermac Hovercraft was founded by Vernon W McKay in 1977. It supplies plans for three different designs for the recreational hovercraft market, Hovermac I, II, III and IV. A new craft, with six-eight seats and powered by a Volkswagen engine, is under development. The company is also a representative for Cyclone Hovercraft Ltd, the UK-based light ACV manufacturer, and is currently marketing the Simple Cyclone.

HOVERMAC 1

First craft designed by Hovermac, this machine incorporates many features first introduced by light hovercraft designers in the United Kingdom. Built in ply it was intended as a development craft for the Hovermac II and III fibreglass-hulled designs, but it performed so successfully that it is being offered for home construction.

First prototype, Hovermac I single-seat light amphibious hovercraft

LIFT AND PROPULSION: Lift is supplied by a vertically mounted 4bhp two-stroke driving a five-blade axial fan with blades set at 30 degrees. The lift fan duct is in fibreglass and built into the forward hull. Thrust is furnished by a 12·5bhp Kec 225 two-stroke driving via a toothed belt a 600mm (1ft 11½in) diameter ducted axial fan.

CONTROLS: Aerodynamic rudders set in the thrust fan slipstream provide directional control.

HULL: Built in 3 and 4mm exterior grade ply with 20mm square wooden stringers. Sealed buoyancy chambers are built into the hull and can be filled with polyurethane foam. Joints and skids on hull underside are reinforced with fibreglass.

DIMENSIONS
Length: 3m (9ft 10½in)
Width: 1·78m (5ft 10in)
Height on landing skids: 1·05m (3ft 5¾in)
WEIGHTS
Normal payload: 100kg (220lb)
PERFORMANCE
Max speed across land and calm water: 48km/h (29·82mph)
Fuel consumption: 6-9 litres (1·3-2 gallons)/h

Hovermac II grp-hulled two-seater

HOVERMAC II

A lightweight grp-hulled two-seater, Hovermac II can be hovered onto a trailer and towed behind a small car. It can be launched and landed from beaches, sloping river banks or across mud flats and marshes.

LIFT AND PROPULSION: Lift is provided by a vertically mounted 4bhp two-stroke driving a five-blade axial fan with blades set at 30 degrees pitch. 4bhp is the minimum recommended installed lift power. Thrust is supplied by either one or two 20-40bhp engines each driving via a toothed belt transmission a 600mm (1ft 11½in) diameter ducted Breza axial fan.

CONTROLS: Aerodynamic rudders set in the thrust fan duct provide directional control.

HULL: Built in grp with expanded polyurethane foam for buoyancy.

SKIRT: Simple loop type fabricated in 430g/m² polyurethane-coated nylon.

DIMENSIONS
Length: 3·1m (10ft 2in)
Beam: 1·78m (5ft 10½in)
Height on landing pads: 1·1m (3ft 7¼in)
WEIGHTS
Normal payload: 135kg (304lb)
PERFORMANCE
Max speed across land and calm water (dependent on installed power): 60-80km/h (37-49mph)
Vertical obstacle clearance: 200mm (8in)
Fuel consumption (dependent on power installed): approx 10 litres (2·2 gallons)/h

HOVERMAC III

This is a lengthened version of Hovermac II seating a driver forward and two passengers side-by-side aft of the driving seat.

LIFT AND PROPULSION: Lift is supplied by a vertically mounted 8bhp two-stroke driving a five-blade axial fan with 30 degree pitch. Thrust is provided by twin 40bhp engines each driving a 600mm (1ft 11½in) diameter Breza axial fan via a toothed belt transmission.

HULL AND SKIRT: As for Hovermac II.

DIMENSIONS
Length: 3·5m (11ft 5¾in)
Beam: 1·78m (5ft 10½in)
Height on landing pads: 1·1m (3ft 7¼in)
WEIGHTS
Normal payload: 200kg (441lb)

Hovermac IV two-three-seater designed for home construction. Fitted with two 40bhp thrust engines it can attain nearly 80km/h (50mph) over calm water

PERFORMANCE
Max speed across land and calm water (dependent on installed power): 60-80km/h (37-49mph)
Vertical obstacle clearance: 185mm (7¼in)

HOVERMAC IV

Intended primarily for home construction this two-three seater is of simple layout and is easily built from readily available materials. Three prototypes were built to test various power arrangements.

LIFT AND PROPULSION: Lift is supplied by a single 8hp two- or four-stroke driving either a five- or ten-blade axial fan with blades set at 30 degrees. Thrust is furnished by either one or two 40bhp engines, each driving via a toothed belt transmission a 600mm (2ft) or 730mm (2ft 4¾in) diameter axial-flow ducted fan.

HULL: Exterior grade ply structure with 20 × 20mm wooden stringers. Built-in sealed buoyancy chambers can be filled with polyurethane foam. Joints and skids on underside reinforced with fibreglass.

SKIRT: Simple loop type fabricated in 430g/m² polyurethane-coated nylon.

DIMENSIONS
Length: 3·6m (11ft 9¾in)
Beam: 1·8m (5ft 11in)
Height on landing skids: 1·2m (3ft 11¼in)
WEIGHTS
Normal payload: 150kg (4ft 11in)
PERFORMANCE
Max speed across land and calm water (dependent on installed power): 60-80km/h (37-49mph)
Vertical obstacle clearance: 175mm (7in)
Fuel consumption (dependent on installed power): approx 10 litres/h

---

LIGHT HOVERCRAFT COMPANY

11 Hayward Street, Stafford, Queensland 4053, Australia
Telephone: 59 7006
Officials:
H B Standen, *Manager*

Light Hovercraft Company was founded in Brisbane, Australia, in 1971. Its first product was a small transportable ACV but series production of this particular craft ended in 1973.

Currently, Light Hovercraft is concentrating on the sale of plans to homebuilders and producing light hovercraft tailor-made to the needs of

individual purchasers. At the time of going to press the company was offering plans for twelve different craft ranging in seating capacity from one to sixteen.

The majority of the company's clients reside in Australia, New Zealand, the Pacific Islands and South America.

NEOTERIC ENGINEERING AFFILIATES PTY LTD

Box 2438, GPO Melbourne 3001, Australia
Telephone: (03) 391 3639
Officials:
Christopher J Fitzgerald, *Managing Director*
Robert K Wilson, *General Manager*
Alan Fitzgerald, *Company Accountant*

Neoteric Engineering Affiliates Pty Ltd specialises in the development of the Neova II light hovercraft, and the company is at present concentrating on marketing two-seat models which are available in kit or ready-built form.

In 1975 Neoteric-USA Incorporated was established at the Fort Harrison Industrial Park, Terre Haute, Indiana 47804. Details of the Neova range of light hovercraft will be found in this edition under the entry for Neoteric-USA Inc.

Neoteric Neova light hovercraft

STOLKRAFT PTY LTD

52 Hilltop Road, Clareville Beach, New South Wales 2107, Australia
Telephone: 918 3620
Cables: Stolkraft Sydney
Officials:
Rhoda Gladys Stolk, *Managing Director*
Clive M Backhouse, *Chairman*
Richard M Jones, *Director*
Adrian W Stolk, *Director*
Consultant:
Noel Riley, Commercial Marine Design, 24 Thomas Street, Chatswood, New South Wales 2067, Australia
International Marketing Consultants:
Capt R W Ware, World Logistics Pty Ltd, GPO Box 1270, Sydney, New South Wales 2001, Australia

Leo D Stolk's Stolkraft concept of optimising the benefits of air lubrication on a planing hull can be summarised as follows:

At speed an appreciable amount of aerodynamic lift is built up by a ram-air cushion at the bow, and this, combined with air fed through twin bow intakes, creates a second ram-air cushion and lifts the craft in order to reduce frictional resistance.

A feature of the concept is the absence of trim variation. The craft rises bodily, parallel to the surface and has no tendency to porpoise. At speed it creates neither bow-wash nor hull spray outward. The aerodynamic lift reduces fuel consumption.

Recently a series of tests were undertaken with a 2·4m (8ft) model at the Netherlands Ship Model Basin, Wageningen, the Netherlands. The performance of this model was monitored in the high speed tank, and actual sea tests with 4·95m (16ft) and 8·45m (28ft) vessels provided additional data.

These tests fully supported Leo Stolk's earlier theoretical predictions as to the applicability of this design concept to larger vessels such as passenger ferries, naval craft, cargo offshore services, and work boats.

INCEPTOR II SK.16 Mk 1

The prototype of the company's first production runabout is the fibreglass-hulled Inceptor II SK.16 Mk 1.
PROPULSION: A Volvo Aquamatic stern-drive of either 170 or 225hp, drives a water screw for propulsion. Alternatively twin outboards can be fitted. Fuel is carried in two 20-gallon tanks located amidships, port and starboard.
HULL: Stepped trimaran configuration. Moulded fibreglass construction with bulkheads in fibreglass-covered seaply. Craft has eight foam-filled airtight compartments for positive buoyancy.
ACCOMMODATION: Open cockpit for driver and six adults and up to two children.

Stolkraft Mk III, 14-seat test craft

Prototype of Stolkraft's first production runabout, the Inceptor II. Power for this seven-seater is provided by a 170hp Volvo Aquamatic stern drive engine. Twin bow intakes feed pressurised air to a ventilated transverse step and thence to a second air cushion created beneath the hull aft

Stolkraft SK.16 Mk 1 at speed demonstrating absence of wave formation, bow wash and outward hull spray

DIMENSIONS
Length overall: 4·95m (16ft 3in)
Beam: 2·13m (7ft)
Width overall: 2·44m (8ft)
WEIGHTS
Normal load: 550kg (1,200lb)
Max load: 680kg (1,500lb)
PERFORMANCE
PROTOTYPE, INCEPTOR II
Max speed/load 600lb/170hp: 80km/h (50mph)

STOLKRAFT Mk III

This new 8·53m (28ft) addition to the Stolkraft range was built for a series of tests at the Netherlands Ship Model Basin. These tests fully supported earlier theoretical predictions regarding stability and performance.

The large cockpit space makes the craft suitable for a variety of utility applications, including rescue, diving platform, naval, police and fisheries patrol.

The prototype is powered by three 200hp outboard engines.
DIMENSIONS
Length: 8·53m (28ft)
Beam: 4·26m (14ft)
PERFORMANCE
Max speed: in excess of 40 knots

25 METRE COMMUTER FERRY

Latest addition to the Stolkraft range is this 110-tonne passenger ferry, designed at the request of the Public Transport Commission of New South Wales for consideration and evaluation for fast commuter services across Sydney Harbour. One of the main attractions of the Stolkraft concept is the absence of wave formation in the wake and consequently the lack of erosion along the foreshores.

LIFT AND PROPULSION: Motive power is supplied by two marinised gas turbines, each developing 3,500hp. Output is transmitted to two waterjets which discharge through area nozzles beneath the transom. Watertight bulkheads separate the engine room from the waterjet pumps. At 22 knots and upwards aerodynamic lift is built up by a ram-air cushion at the bow and this, combined with air fed through twin bow intakes and vented from a transverse step beneath the hull aft, creates a second ram-air cushion and raises the craft in order to reduce frictional resistance. Stability is inherent and a stable platform is provided.

Despite pitch and heave forces in choppy seas, extensive tests have shown that this type of craft can self-regulate its riding attitude. Recovery from wave-induced perturbation is rapid and smooth and optimum trim is resumed. Direction (yaw) and transverse (roll) stability is always maintained.

HULL: Hull and superstructure are in marine grade weldable aluminium alloy. Subdivisions are incorporated in accordance with international safety regulations for passenger ferries.

ACCOMMODATION: Passengers are accommodated in an aft saloon on the main deck, seating 166, and a forward saloon, on the main foredeck, seating 54. Thirty standing passengers can be accommodated on short runs, giving a total capacity of 250 passengers. The captain is accommodated in a raised wheelhouse located between the forward and main saloons. Access to the passenger cabins is via four doors (two port, two starboard) each 1·35m (4ft 5in) wide by 2·1m (6ft 10½in) high, sited on the main deck, and located to ensure an equal flow through both entrances. Entrance to the engine rooms is via hatches in the main deck aft of the main passenger saloon.
DIMENSIONS
Length overall: 24·45m (80ft 5½in)
Beam: 9·9m (32ft 6in)
Width overall: 11·1m (36ft 5in)
Deck length: 23·85m (78ft 3in)
    width: 10·85m (35ft 7in)
Total deck area: 258m² (2,784ft²)
Passenger deck area: 189·3m² (2,140ft²)
Draft hullborne: 1·95m (5ft 5in)
Draft cushionborne at cruising speed: 0·9m (3ft)
WEIGHTS
Empty: 68·25 tonnes
Operating: 93 tonnes
Normal operating: 110 tonnes
PERFORMANCE
Cruising speed, sea state 3: 35 knots
Max speed: 39 knots

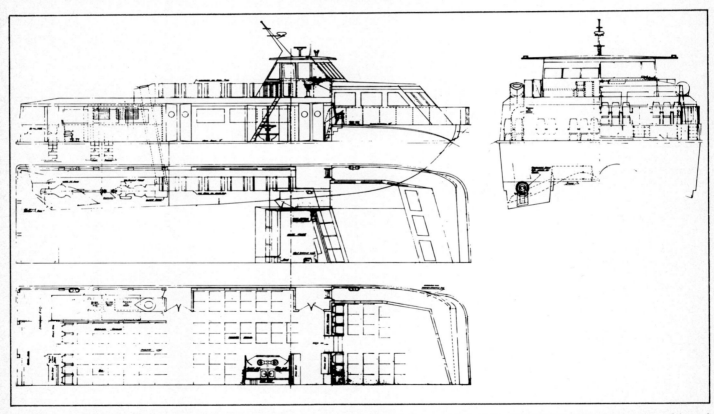

Stolkraft study for a 25 metre, 220-seat high-speed commuter ferry, prepared for the Public Transport Commision of New South Wales. Displacement of the craft fully loaded would be 109 tonnes and its cruising speed, in sea state 3, would be 35 knots

---

TAYLORCRAFT TRANSPORT PTY LTD

Airport, Parafield, South Australia 5106, Australia
Telephone: (08) 258 4787
Telex: AA 88777

Taylorcraft Transport Pty Ltd has been active in ACV research and development since 1966. It ceased operation in 1980, but R V Taylor the company's founder and managing director, is available as a consultant on ACV matters and may be contacted at the above address, or telephone and telex numbers.

Drawings and design information for the range of ACVs developed by the company may be made available at cost to anyone interested in manufacturing the craft.

Details of the range of ACVs, Trailaire hovertrailers and the Taylorcraft Liftaire industrial skirt system will be found in *Jane's Surface Skimmers 1980* and earlier editions.

BRAZIL

FEI
FACULTY OF INDUSTRIAL ENGINEERING

Research Vehicle Department (DEPV), Faculty of Industrial Engineering, São Bernado do Campo, Avenido Oreste Romano 112, São Paulo, Brazil

Telephone: 443 1155

Officials:

Eng Rigoberto Soler Gisbert, *Director of Vehicle Research*

The Vehicle Research Department of the FEI was founded in 1968. Its first major task was to conduct a full-scale investigation into Brazil's transport problems and its likely future requirements. An outcome of this was the design and construction by students and faculty of a 15·54m (51ft) long prototype of a tracked ACV, the TALAV.

Since then the Department, under the direction of Eng Rigoberto Soler Gisbert, has designed, built and tested a number of light amphibious ACVs, including the VA and the VA-1, which it is expected will be put into production by a Brazilian industrial concern.

VA

A glass fibre-hulled amphibious two-seater, the VA is powered by a single Volkswagen VW 1300 automotive engine and has a top speed of about 80km/h (50mph).

VA-1

The VA-1 is a four-seat utility vehicle designed for use in a variety of projects aimed at opening up and developing areas of the Amazon and traversing the swamps of the Mato Grosso. Details will be found in *Jane's Surface Skimmers 1980* and earlier editions.

BULGARIA

OKRUJNAYE POLYTECHNIC
Plovdiv, Bulgaria

ICARUS II

Relatively little news has been forthcoming over the years on hovercraft activities in the smaller countries of the Eastern bloc. That interest is probably just as keen in these parts as it is in the West is indicated by the accompanying photograph. Described as "an automobile that rides on an air-cushion", Icarus II was designed and built by students of the Okrujnaye Polytechnic, Plovdiv, Bulgaria, under the guidance of Christel Christov.

The vehicle has been demonstrated extensively at exhibitions dedicated to the achievements of engineering students and is reported to have made an appearance in the Soviet Union.

Icarus II

CANADA

ACV SALES INC

Box 11107 Royal Centre, 1055 West George Street, Vancouver, British Columbia V6E 3P3, Canada

Officials:

Andrew Robertson, *President*

ACV Sales Inc builds the Mark V Turbo amphibious hovercraft designed to meet year-round climatic conditions in the Canadian north. The company can also supply small sports and utility vehicles.

TURBO SUPER HOVER Mk 5

This multiduty ACV has been designed for a variety of commercial and military applications in the more remote areas of North America and Canada. It carries a driver and up to four passengers or 453kg (1,000lb) of freight. Built in moulded high impact fibreglass, it is powered by a single 390hp V8 water-cooled engine and has a top speed over ice and snow of 35-40mph.

LIFT AND PROPULSION: Integrated system powered by a single 390hp V8 water-cooled engine with heat exchanger. Mounted inboard, the engine drives two axial-flow fans mounted at opposite ends of a transverse shaft. Both fans are enclosed in ducts to eliminate any danger from moving parts. Airflow is ducted beneath the craft for lift and via outlets aft for thrust. Fuel recommended is Hi-Test gasoline. Cushion area is 14·86m² (160ft²). Cushion pressure, 0·28kg/cm² (4psi).

CONTROLS: Craft heading is controlled by multiple rudders in the airjet outlets aft. Driving controls comprise a steering wheel, which actuates the rudders, an electric starter, automatic choke and a throttle lever for lift and thrust. Reverse thrust is applied for braking and stopping.

HULL: Moulded fibreglass and corrosion resistant aluminium construction. Buoyancy, 150%.

ACCOMMODATION: Access to the enclosed cabin is via twin gull-wing doors, one port and one starboard.

Driving position showing instruments, controls and steering wheel which actuates rudders

Aft view of Turbo Super Hover Mk 5 showing fan ducts and multiple rudders in airjet outlets

DIMENSIONS
Length overall: 5·79m (19ft)
Beam overall: 3·5m (11ft 6in)
Height, cushionborne: 2·33m (7ft 8in)
WEIGHTS
Empty: 1,310kg (2,890lb)

Payload, freight: 453kg (1,000lb)
Gross: 1,882kg (4,150lb)

PERFORMANCE
Max speed: 64·37km/h (40mph)
Range: 201-244km (125-150 miles)

Endurance: 4½ hours
Distance for emergency stopping: 15m (50ft)
Normal stopping distance: 45m (150ft)
Gradient capability: 8·7%
Craft can climb long 20% gradients and short
   30% gradients, including river banks.

AIR CUSHION INDUSTRIES LTD

Head Office: Suite 206, 77 City Centre Drive,
Mississauga, Ontario L5B 1M5, Canada
Telephone: (416) 270 8780
Works: Unit 3, 9 Lime Bank Road, Ottawa,
Ontario, Canada
Mailing address: PO Box 660, Ontario K1G
3N3, Canada
Telephone: (613) 521 1647

AC 800

This is a multi-purpose amphibious ACV
designed to carry a driver and four passengers or
up to 362·85kg (800lb) of freight. Built in reinforced high impact strength fibreglass, it is powered by a single V8 engine and cruises over ice
and snow at 56·32km/h (35mph).
LIFT AND PROPULSION: Integrated system
powered by a single 230hp water-cooled V8
engine. Mounted inboard, the engine drives two
centrifugal-flow fans mounted at opposite ends of
a transverse shaft. Both fans are enclosed in ducts
to eliminate any danger from moving parts.
Airflow is ducted beneath the craft for lift and via
outlets aft for thrust. Fuel recommended is standard gasoline. Fuel capacity, 109·1 litres (24
imperial gallons).

AC 800 utility hovercraft

CONTROLS: Craft heading is controlled by
rudders in the airjet outlets aft.
HULL: Moulded fibreglass, with steel engine
mounting and frame. Aluminium and stainless
steel fittings. Buoyancy 150%.
DIMENSIONS
Length, overall: 5·79m (19ft)
Beam, overall: 3·5m (11ft 6in)
   skirt deflated for trailering: 2·28m (7ft 6in)

Height, skirt inflated: 2·33m (7ft 8in)
   on landing pads: 1·72m (5ft 8in)

WEIGHTS
Empty: 1,043·2kg (2,300lb)
Payload: 362·85kg (800lb)

PERFORMANCE
Cruising speed: 56·32km/h (35mph)
Hard structure clearance: 355mm (1ft 2in)

BELL AEROSPACE TEXTRON, CANADA
(A division of Textron Canada Ltd)

PO Box 160, Grand Bend, Ontario NOM 1TO,
Canada
Telephone: (519) 238 2333
Telex: 064 7268

Officials:
Norton C Willcox, *President*
Joseph R Piselli, *Vice President*
John W McKinney, *Vice President*
James G Mills, *Managing Director*

In January 1971, Bell Aerospace Textron
Canada acquired facilities at Grand Bend,

Ontario, for the development and production of
its Model 7380 Voyageur heavy haul ACV, and
the smaller 17-ton Viking multi-duty craft.
The facilities at Grand Bend Airport include
two buildings with a total of 3,350m² (30,000ft²)
of floor space on a 21-hectare (52-acre) site.
The company has worked closely with the
Canadian Department of Industry, Trade and

Upper left and right: For two years, Voyageur 001 was operated by KAPS
transport in the Mackenzie Delta region of Northern Canada on oil exploration
logistics support missions. Typical loads were a caterpillar tractor and a
Nodwell seismic driller weighing 46,000lb, a 3,300 imperial gallon fuel tank
(filled) and miscellaneous items of earth moving equipment. **Bottom left:**
Voyageur 004 hauls a cargo container from a freighter to ice-locked communities along the St Lawrence river in Quebec. **Bottom right:** Voyageur 003
carrying oil tanks to a drilling site in North Alaska

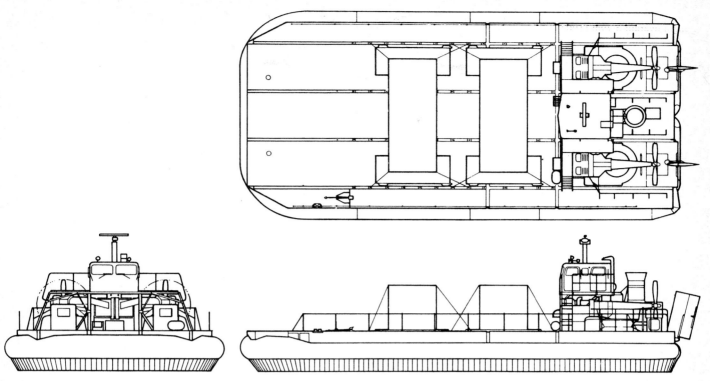

Bell AL-30, commercial derivative of the US Army's LACV-30, intended for rapid transfer of containers from ships to shore and other port cargo handling

Commerce in planning a programme which has led to the establishment in Canada of a commercially viable air cushion industry to meet the growing requirements for Coast Guard, remote area cargo hauling, high speed passenger ferry services and other specialised applications.

The first two 40-ton Voyageurs were built under a joint agreement between the company and the Canadian Department of Industry, Trade and Commerce. The prototype, Voyageur 001, differs from later craft insofar as it is fitted with two GE LM100 engines, as opposed to the ST6T-75 Twin-Pac gas turbines which are now standard.

The Voyageur features a basic flatbed hull of all-welded extruded marine aluminium that can be adapted to a variety of operational needs by adding the required equipment and superstructure.

Construction of Voyageur 001 started in March 1971. It began operational trials and certification testing in November 1971. Voyageurs have operated in the Canadian and American arctic regions on oil industry exploration logistics support. Voyageur 002 is owned and operated by the Canadian Coast Guard and since March 1975 has worked as an ACV icebreaker. Ice in excess of 1·01m (3ft 4in) thick has been successfully broken.

A stretched version of the Voyageur, the

Model 7467 LACV-30, has been built to meet US Army requirements for a high speed amphibious vehicle for LOTS (Logistics-Over-The-Shore) operations. The LACV-30 is intended to replace conventional vessels of the LARC-5 and LARC-15 types by 1981. Details will be found in the entry for Bell Aerospace Textron, USA.

Bell Aerospace Textron Canada provides major components of the LACV-30. The Model 7380 has been succeeded in production by the Bell AL-30, the commercial variant of the US Army's LACV-30. Details of the Model 7380 Voyageur may be found in *Jane's Surface Skimmers 1980* and earlier editions.

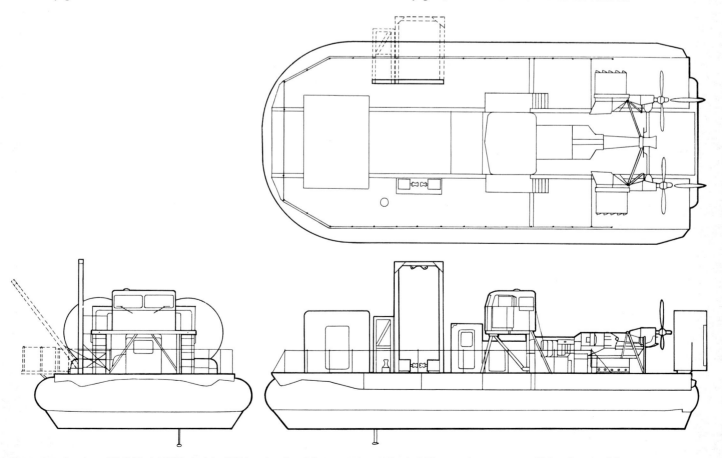

Three-view drawing of Bell Model 7505 stretched Viking showing A frame gantry, walkout platform and passenger and laboratory modules

BELL AL-30

A commercial derivative of the US Army's LACV-30, the Bell AL-30 amphibious lighter is intended for use in port cargo handling systems and is particularly suited to the rapid transfer of containers from ships to shore. Fully amphibious, it can carry a 30-ton payload, ranging from vehicles to break-bulk type cargo. In an integrated lighterage cargo transfer system the AL-30 can offload ships independently of existing berth and dock facilities and will permit the direct transfer of cargo from the ship into the transport system of the country, hence speeding its arrival at its final destination.

LIFT AND PROPULSION: Integrated system powered by two Pratt & Whitney ST6T Twin-Pac gas turbines mounted aft, one at each side of the raised control cabin. Each engine is rated at 1,800shp maximum and 1,400shp at normal output. The output of each is absorbed by a three-bladed Hamilton Standard 43D50-363 reversible-pitch propeller and a 2·13m (7ft) diameter, twelve-bladed, fixed pitch light aluminium alloy, centrifugal lift fan. Cushion pressure at maximum gross weight, 267kg/m² (54·7lb/ft²).

FUEL SYSTEM: Recommended fuel is standard aviation kerosene, Jet A1, JP4, JP5 or light diesel fuel oil. Main fuel usable capacity is 9,419 litres (2,272 US gallons). Fuel ballast/emergency fuel capacity, 6,960 litres (1,531 US gallons). Estimated fuel consumption during lighterage missions, 454kg/h (1,000lb/h) (147 US gallons/h).

SYSTEMS, ELECTRICAL: Starter generators: Four gearbox driven brushless, 28V dc, 200A each. Batteries: Two nickel cadmium, 28V dc, 40A each.

DIMENSIONS

Length overall, on cushion, without optional swing crane: 23·3m (76ft 6in)
Beam overall, skirt inflated: 11·2m (36ft 8in)
Height overall, on landing pads: 7·86m (25ft 9in) on cushion: 8·83m (29ft)
Length, cargo deck: 15·7m (51ft 6in)
Width, cargo deck: 9·9m (32ft 6in)
Height, cargo deck, off cushion: 1·2m (3ft 11½in)
Cushion height: 1·22m (4ft)

WEIGHTS
Gross: 52,163kg (115,000lb)

Model 7505 stretched Viking, with hull length increased to 16·9m (55ft 6in)

PERFORMANCE
Max speed (calm water, zero wind, at 52,163kg (115,000lb) gross weight),
normal rating: 74km/h (46mph)
max rating: 90km/h (56mph)

MODEL 7505 STRETCHED VIKING

Bell engineers have designed an improved version of the earlier Viking (see *Jane's Surface Skimmers 1978* and earlier editions) by stretching the hull. The following details apply to the baseline configuration, with the hull stretched by 3·35m (11ft) to 16·9m (55ft 6in).

DIMENSIONS
Length overall: 16·9m (55ft 6in)

Beam overall: 7·9m (26ft)
Height overall: 6·1m (20ft)
Cargo deck area: 102·2m² (1,100ft²)
Deck height, off cushion: 1·2m (3ft 11in)

WEIGHTS
Empty: 11,475kg (25,299lb)
Max permissible gross: 19,051kg (42,000lb)

PERFORMANCE
Calm water: 94km/h (58mph)
Continuous gradient capacity: 11 degrees
Ditch crossing width: 2·7m (9ft)
Endurance with max fuel: 10·5 hours
Max wave height: in excess of 1·8m (6ft)
Max range: 1,020km (550n miles)

HOVER-FLIGHT CANADA LTD

7686 Kimbel Street, Unit 15, Mississauga, Ontario L56 1E9, Canada
Officials:
D Gertsbein

CHINOOK

This is a lightweight amphibious single-seater with a maximum payload capacity of about 147·41kg (325lb). Built in fibreglass reinforced plastics it is 3·42m (11ft 3in) long and sufficiently small and light to be transported on the roof of a family car.

Maximum speed over water is 48·28km/h (30mph).

LIFT AND PROPULSION: Cushion air is supplied by a 5hp Tecumseh two-cycle engine driving a 0·6m (2ft) diameter ten-bladed polypropylene fan. A 26hp Kohler 295-2AX, two-cycle engine drives a 0·6m (2ft) diameter, ten-bladed ducted polypropylene fan for thrust. Fuel capacity is 22 litres (5 imperial gallons). Fuel recommended is gasoline and oil mixed 30:1.

HULL: Moulded in fibreglass reinforced plastic.

SKIRT: Bag type in neoprene impregnated nylon.

ACCOMMODATION: Open cockpit with single seat for driver.

DIMENSIONS
OVERALL
Length: 3·42m (11ft 3in)
Beam: 1·52m (5ft)
Height: 1·09m (3ft 7in)

WEIGHTS
Normal empty: 129·26kg (285lb)

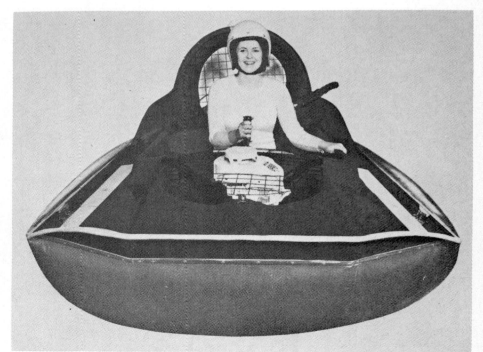
Chinook single-seater with payload of 147·41kg (325lb)

Max payload: 147·41kg (325lb)
PERFORMANCE (at normal operating weight)
Max speed, over calm water: 48·28km/h (30mph)
over land: up to 64·37km (40mph)

over ice and snow: up to 72·42km (45mph)
Still air range and endurance at cruising speed: 4·5-5 hours
Max gradient, static conditions: 20 degrees
Vertical obstacle clearance: 203mm (8in)

SPACE HOVERCRAFT LIMITED

Box 660, RR5 Ottawa KIG 3N3, Canada
Telephone: (613) 733 3296
Officials:
W S Griffin, *President and General Manager*
J H McKinnon, *Vice President*
J Martiniello, *Director*

ODYSSEY 700

This fibreglass-hulled four-seater has been designed as an all-terrain, all-season runabout. It is claimed to be quiet in operation and easy to control. The average person can learn to operate the craft over varied terrain in only six hours.

In March 1980 the Canadian Coast Guard took delivery of an Odyssey 700 to provide transport for lighthouse keepers at Long Point, Lake Erie, Ontario and for navigation aids servicing.

LIFT AND PROPULSION: Motive power is supplied by a single 188hp water-cooled engine which drives both the lift system and the ducted propeller aft. Fuel capacity is 104·5 litres (23 imperial gallons). Fuel consumption is 21 litres (4·5 gallons) per hour.

CONTROLS: Craft direction is controlled by three air rudder-vanes hinged at the aft end of the propeller duct. A reverse thrust system is installed for braking.

HULL: Moulded glass fibre. Buoyancy 150% of all-up weight. Bilge blower fitted as standard.

ACCOMMODATION: Fully enclosed cabin for driver and three passengers or a 317kg (700lb) load when operated for freight carrying. Access to the cabin is via two gull-wing doors, port and starboard.

Odyssey 700 utility hovercraft designed for all-terrain and all-season operation

DIMENSIONS
Length overall, on cushion: 5·48m (17ft 10in)
  on landing pads: 5·18m (16ft 10in)
Width overall, on cushion: 3·4m (11ft 2in)
  on landing pads: 2·28m (7ft 6in)
Height, on cushion: 2·38m (7ft 10in)
  on landing pads: 2·08m (6ft 10in)

WEIGHTS
All-up weight: 952·5kg (2,100lb)
Payload: 317·5kg (700lb)
PERFORMANCE
Speed, depending on wind and surface conditions: 56-64km/h (35-40mph)
Vertical obstacle clearance: 304mm (1ft)

TRANSPORT CANADA
Air Cushion Vehicle Division

Tower A, Place de Ville, Ottawa, Ontario K1A 0N7, Canada

Officials:
T F Melhuish, *Chief ACV Division*

The Air Cushion Vehicle Division, Transport Canada, was established in 1968 as part of the Marine Administration. The Division is responsible to the Director, Canadian Coast Guard Ship Safety Branch for all aspects of air cushion vehicle certification and regulation.

On the operations side, the Division has direct responsibility to the Director, Canadian Coast Guard Fleet Systems Branch to advise and assist Coast Guard in its air cushion vehicle activities. Included in this is the use of air cushion technology for ice-breaking and the Division has been responsible for the development of this new technology within the Canadian Coast Guard.

There is also close collaboration with Transport Canada's Policy and Planning Branch, Surface Administration and Research and Development Centre.

The division participates actively with the National Research Council's Research Group on Air Cushion Technology, and participates as Canada's representative on the US SNAME Panel MSI on High Speed Craft. Close liaison is maintained with industry, government and military organisations both in Canada and abroad.

CHINA (People's Republic)

An ACV research and development programme has been underway in China since 1970. Much of the experimental work appears to have been undertaken at a shipyard in the Shanghai area which has constructed a small number of test craft, one of which is being operated from Chungking on a passenger ferry service. It is understood that this particular craft is fully amphibious, is powered by one aircraft piston-engine and operates at between 25 and 30 knots. The craft is constructed in aluminium and steel and the skirt is of simple bag type. Although the skirt has proved adequate for this craft it is clear that a great deal of development work has to be undertaken in this area of ACV technology before Chinese-designed amphibious ACVs can operate satisfactorily across open waters.

At present Chinese interest in amphibious craft is focused on vehicles in the SR.N6 to SR.N4 size range (approximately 10-300 tons). These are required for a variety of military and civil applications, including the operation of fast passenger ferry services over river networks with route distances of up to 240-320km (150-200 miles).

Initially interest was limited to craft of approximately 10-60 tons but this is because the smaller craft present fewer problems when selecting power plants, in addition to which they can be built more easily by smaller shipyards.

Largest hovercraft to be built in China so far is a 70-ton assault landing craft prototype which was launched at Tianjin in August 1979. It is understood that the craft, which resembles a scaled-down SR.N4, is undergoing evaluation trials.

ACV passenger ferry prototype designed by a hovercraft research unit at Shanghai. Power is supplied by three radial aircraft engines. Two drive two-bladed propellers for thrust while the third, mounted centrally aft, drives via a right-angle drive a lift fan at the rear of the cabin superstructure

Considerable interest is also centring on sidewall type ACVs with moulded grp hulls, and wing-in-ground-effect machines of various types for high-speed, long-distance river services.

70-TON ASSAULT LANDING CRAFT

Largest ACV to be built in the Chinese People's Republic so far, this 70-ton vehicle has been designed specifically for a range of naval and military applications. The prototype is currently being evaluated in the amphibious initial assault role. In overall appearance the craft resembles a scaled-down BHC SR.N4.

Design was undertaken by the Shanghai 708 Shipbuilding Research Institute and the craft was built at the Dagu Shipyard with the assistance of some 52 other specialist engineering, technical and military groups. Construction began in December 1977 and the craft was launched in August 1979. The start of the initial trials programme, which began on 3 September 1979, was attended by 400 heads of committees, institutes, government and municipal bureaus, state councils, ministries and military units.

The vehicle is described as being capable of operating over water, land, grasslands, marshlands, lakes, shallows and beaches. It can clear vertical obstacles 1m (3ft 3in) high and ditches up to 5m (16ft 4in) wide.

LIFT AND PROPULSION: Published material refers to cushion lift being provided by twin engines, probably diesels, mounted one each side of the central cargo deck aft and each driving three centrifugal fans. Air for the engines appears to be drawn in through filtered roof intakes. Fan air, which is taken through three large filtered ducts each side of the superstructure is discharged into the cushion via a continuous peripheral loop skirt with segmented fringes. Thrust is supplied by two pairs of variable-pitch, pylon-mounted propellers, the aft pair being powered by gas turbines.

CONTROLS: It is believed that craft heading is controlled by swivelling the forward propeller pylons, operating them in conjunction with the twin aerodynamic rudders aft. Reverse thrust is applied for braking and reversing. Elevator provides pitch trim at cruising speed.

HULL: Riveted skin and stringer structure employing alloy sheet. Main hull is formed by a buoyancy raft based on a grid of longitudinal and transverse frames which form a number of flotation compartments. Two main longitudinal vertically stiffened bulkheads run the length of the craft separating the central load deck from the outer sidestructures which contain the lift fan engines, lift fans, transmissions and auxiliary power systems. The freight deck is reinforced to permit the carriage of armoured troop carriers and heavy vehicles. A stern door and bow loading door/ramp provide a drive-on, drive-off through-loading facility. Separate side doors, port and starboard, give access to the two cabins which flank the load deck forward.

SKIRT: Loop and segment type tapered skirt, similar to that of the SR.N6, fabricated in coated nylon fabric.

ARMAMENT: Machine gun turret on bow port quarter.

DIMENSIONS
Length overall: 21·94m (72ft)
Beam overall: 7·92m (26ft)
Height: 7·62m (25ft)
WEIGHTS
Normal gross: about 70 tonnes
Payload: 12-15 tonnes
PERFORMANCE
Max speed: 55-60 knots
Vertical obstacle clearance: 1·5m (5ft 3in)

THREE-ENGINED AMPHIBIOUS PASSENGER FERRY

One of a number of development craft designed and built by the Shanghai 708 Research unit, this machine is powered by three radial aircraft engines. Two of the engines drive two-bladed propellers for thrust while the third, mounted centrally, aft, drives a lift fan at the rear end of the cabin superstructure via a shaft extending forward externally to a right-angle drive above a horizontally-mounted centrifugal lift fan.

The skirt is of fingered bag configuration similar to that of the BHC SR.N5.

The hull is of the light alloy buoyancy type. Twin aerodynamic rudders provide directional control and an elevator set high on the twin fins aft provides pitch trim at cruising speed.

JING-SAH RIVER TEST CRAFT

Before constructing the ACV passenger ferry prototype described above, the Shanghai 708 Shipbuilding Research Institute built a small scale version powered by two 270bhp Type 604-1 air-cooled radial engines.

In elevation the craft is not unlike a scaled-down SR.N5 with a radial engine mounted on each of its twin fins, each radial driving a two-bladed propeller. However, the power sharing arrangement is unique. A shaft with a universal joint extends from each of the propeller hubs and both meet in a mixing gearbox and right-angle

Model of the experimental three-engined amphibious passenger ferry

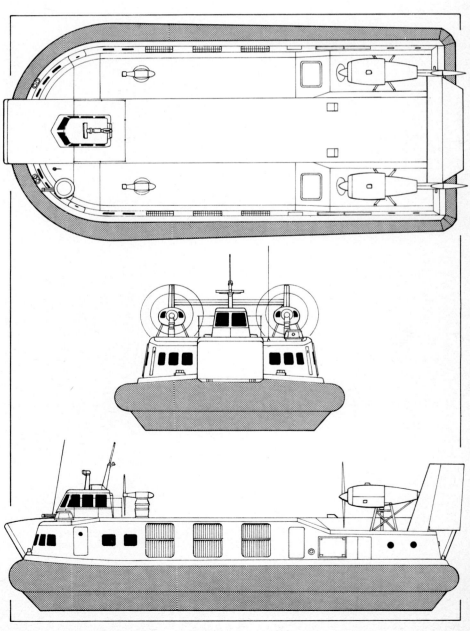

Three-view of new 70-ton amphibious assault landing craft being tested by the Chinese Navy

drive above a horizontally-mounted centrifugal lift fan located behind the cabin. The skirt is of continuous peripheral loop type with segmented fringes.

DIMENSIONS
Length overall: 11·74m (38ft 6¼in)
Beam overall: 5·1m (18ft 8¾in)
Height overall: 3·76m (12ft 4in)
WEIGHTS
Empty: 2·96 tonnes
Payload: 0·84 tonnes
PERFORMANCE
Max speed: 54 knots
Range: 300km (162n miles)

JING-SAH RIVER PASSENGER FERRY

One of the largest air cushion vehicles under development in China is this 70-seat rigid sidewall passenger ferry which is similar to the Hovermarine 218 but has a higher length-to-beam ratio. Like the Hovermarine 218 the craft is diesel-powered and propelled by waterscrews. It was built during 1979 and began trials in 1980.
LIFT AND PROPULSION: Motive power for the lift fan is provided by a 380bhp 12V135CZ marine diesel. Propulsive thrust is supplied by two identical 12V135CZ high-speed marine diesels driving waterscrews.
SKIRT: Finger seal at bow and rigid balanced seal aft.
DIMENSIONS
Length overall: 22·3m (73ft 2¼in)
Beam overall: 6·4m (21ft)
Height overall: 4·27m (14ft 0¼in)
WEIGHTS
Empty: 21 tonnes
Loaded: 30 tonnes
PERFORMANCE
Max speed: 31 knots
Range: 269km (145n miles)

Gas turbine-powered amphibious 70-ton assault landing craft of the Chinese Navy

Jing-Sah amphibious research hovercraft

Jing-Sah research hovercraft, powered by two 270bhp 604-1 radial aero-engines

Tests have been undertaken with the Jing Sah 12m research craft in the role of fast patrol boat. Note the weapons hatch in the cabin roof

Jing-Sah 70-seat river hoverferry

NAVAL INLAND WATER CRAFT

Rigid sidewall hovercraft are being developed as river patrol craft for the Chinese Navy. One of the first to be built has an all-up weight of 15 tons and is being used to test the viability of waterjet propulsion on China's main inland waterways.

The craft is smaller than the 70-seat sidewall passenger ferry illustrated, but appears to employ the same basic hull design. It was built during 1977.

LIFT AND PROPULSION: Motive power for the lift system is supplied by two 350bhp 12V150Z high-speed diesels. A third engine, of identical design, powers the waterjet system. Cushion pressure is reported to be 230kg/m².

SKIRT: Loop and segment type at bow; planing rigid type seal aft.

DIMENSIONS
Length overall: 17·3m (56ft 9½in)
Beam overall: 4·1m (13ft 6in)
Height overall: 4·27m (14ft)

WEIGHTS
Empty: 12 tonnes
Payload: 3 tonnes
All-up: 15·2 tonnes

PERFORMANCE
Max speed: 26·5 knots
Range: 500km (270n miles)

Diesel-powered waterjet-propelled sidewall hovercraft operated by the Chinese Navy

CZECHOSLOVAKIA

AERO VODOCHODY

The V-66, an amphibious three-seat hovercraft, was displayed in public for the first time in September 1978 at the Bino Svazaim airfield, at an "air day" sponsored by the magazine *Science and Technology for the Younger Generation.*

Design and construction was undertaken by a group of young workers employed by the state aircraft manufacturer Aero Vodochody. The engineer in charge was V Leiniveter. The powerplant, a 115hp four-cylinder, air-cooled M-1104 from an HC-2 helicopter, was built at the Avia works under the direction of J Dopita.

DIMENSIONS
Length: 4·5m (14ft 9in)
Beam: 2·5m (8ft 2in)
Height: 2·1m (6ft 10in)

WEIGHTS
Max weight, with three persons: 820kg (1,808lb)
Normal operating weight: 580kg (1,235lb)

PERFORMANCE
Max speed: 60km/h (37·28mph)
Vertical obstacle clearance: 250mm (9·8in)

V-66 amphibious three-seater on display at Bino Svazaim airfield, Czechoslovakia

FINLAND

LUKKARILA

Lohtaja Commune, Kokkola, Gulf of Bothnia, Finland
Telephone: 968 57044

Jalmari Lukkarila, whose hobbies include seal hunting and building fibreglass boats, has developed a number of craft which can be operated across sea, ice and water. His designs include a number of air boats driven by air propellers and wheeled drives. One employs a toothed wheel aft which bites into the sea ice for propulsive thrust. These vehicles have been used frequently on his

hunting trips in the Gulf of Bothnia, some of which have lasted for several weeks. It was during one of these hunting vacations that he first became interested in air cushion vehicles.

Mr Lukkarila's first hovercraft was built in 1973 in conjunction with P Karhula and T Virkola. This machine had two 45hp VW 1600 industrial engines, one for lift and one for propulsion. A three-seater, it was used successfully across both ice and water until the owners sold it to a new owner in North Finland where it was destroyed in an accident. This occurred when the

driver failed to follow at high speed one of the curves in the meandering Kani river.

LUKKARILA TWO-SEATER

The latest air cushion vehicle designed by Jalmari Lukkarila is a fully amphibious two-seat runabout with an estimated speed of 50km/h (31mph) over water and 70-80km/h (43-50mph) across flat ice. The craft was first tested in 1976, since when a number of modifications have been introduced to improve its performance.

LIFT AND PROPULSION: Lift air is supplied by a 30hp Kohler engine driving an axial fan. For thrust the craft is fitted with a four-bladed propeller driven by a 30hp Sachs engine aft of the enclosed cabin.

CONTROLS, HULL: Details not available at the time of going to press.

DIMENSIONS

Length overall: 3·5m (11ft 6in)

Width overall: 2·7m (8ft 10¼in)

WEIGHTS

Empty: 250kg (551lb)

PERFORMANCE

Max speed over water: 50km/h (31mph)

over ice: 70-80km/h (43-50mph)

This 80km/h (50mph) two-seater is the latest hovercraft to be built by Finnish designer Jalmari Lukkarila

PINTALIITÄJÄPALVELU (HOVERCRAFT SERVICE)

Paattistentie 141, SF-20360 Turku 36, Finland

Telephone: 921 472376

Officials:

Esko A Hietanen, *Director*

Ari Hietanen, *Director*

This company was formed in 1971 to design and manufacture light hovercraft capable of operation in extreme winter conditions in Finland when other forms of surface transport are either too expensive, too slow, or incapable of operation across wide expanses of snow and ice. The company's first product is the four-seat Amficat 4, of which only the prototype has been built so far. Since March 1975 this machine has been in continuous service as a high-speed amphibious taxi between Turku and the islands in the Turku archipelago.

The prototype has proved to be extremely reliable and economical and the service is expected to continue until two new craft come into service—the more powerful Amficat 4b, which is intended for series-production, and the larger Amficat 10, a ten-seater. The company is seeking a licensing agreement with a manufacturer prepared to undertake series production.

AMFICAT 4 PROTOTYPE

A light amphibious ACV powered by a single 45hp Volkswagen engine, the Amficat 4 is of wooden construction and seats a driver and three passengers. Directional control is good and by employing special speed brakes the craft is easily stopped and reversed.

An operating certificate has been granted by the Finnish Board of Navigation for running passenger services with the craft. Registered as the M/S Pinturi, and operated by Pintaliitäjäpalvelu, the craft began taxi runs in the Turku archipelago on 21 March 1975. Most of the operations have been undertaken during the spring and winter months when other forms of surface transport have proved either inoperable, because of ice or snow conditions, or too expensive. Since then the craft has visited over fifty different points in the archipelago. By early summer 1978, it had completed 11,000km (6,214 miles) in 1,300 operations and carried nearly 1,000 passengers.

LIFT AND PROPULSION: Integrated system powered by a single Volkswagen 1600 industrial engine developing 45hp at 3,200rpm. Power is absorbed by a single 600mm (23in) diameter centrifugal lift fan and a three-bladed grp propeller mounted forward in an NACA duct. Fuel is carried in two separate tanks, one forward and one amidship. Total fuel capacity is 90 litres (19·8 gallons). Recommended fuel is Super Grade gasoline.

CONTROLS: Craft heading is controlled by triple aerodynamic rudders operating in the propeller slipstream. Other controls include a speed brake, a reverse system and an electronically operated pitch trim system.

HULL: Wooden hull frame covered with marine quality ply. Integral buoyancy chambers. Structure designed for loads of up to 6g and for operation in moderate sea conditions.

Amficat 4, Finland's 30-knot amphibious hover-taxi. Features include the ducted propeller for thrust, the novel cabin layout with the driver seated in a raised position aft, and the triple fins to control craft heading. A ten-seat derivative with a 160hp aero-engine is under construction

SKIRT: Bag type, 0·41m deep, fabricated in pvc fabric.

ACCOMMODATION: Fully-enclosed cabin seating a driver and three passengers. Two passengers sit side-by-side at the front of the cabin with the third passenger and driver seated immediately behind in tandem. Cabin is both heated and ventilated. Entry is via two access doors on the left side. Emergency equipment includes life jackets, distress rockets and fire extinguishers.

SYSTEMS, ELECTRICAL: 500W alternator.

DIMENSIONS

EXTERNAL

Length overall, power off: 6m (19ft 8in)

skirt inflated: 5·9m (19ft 4in)

Beam overall, power off: 2·9m (9ft 6in)

skirt inflated: 3·1m (10ft 2in)

Height overall on landing pads, power off: 2·1m (6ft 11in)

skirt inflated: 2·5m (8ft 2in)

Draft afloat: 0·07m (3in)

Cushion area: 13m² (140ft²)

Skirt depth: 0·41m (1ft 4in)

INTERNAL

Cabin length: 2·4m (7ft 10in)

Max width: 1·15m (3ft 9in)

Max height: 1·48m (4ft 10in)

WEIGHTS

Normal empty: 650kg (1,433lb)

All-up weight: 900kg (1,984lb)

Normal payload: 250kg (551lb)

Max payload: 370kg (816lb)

PERFORMANCE

Max speed over calm water: 30 knots

Cruising speed: 26 knots

Turning circle diameter: 150m (164yds) on ice 100m (109yds) on water

Wave capability on scheduled runs: 0·6m (1ft 11in)

Max survival sea state: state 2

Still air range and endurance at cruising speed: 360km (223 miles)

Max gradient, static conditions: 1:7

Vertical obstacle clearance: 0·3m (12in)

PRICE: Approximate cost of craft fob FMk 120,000.

AMFICAT 4b

Almost identical to the Amficat prototype but with small improvements in the light of operating experience. Modifications include a more powerful engine and entry doors on both sides of the cabin. The craft is intended for series production.

AMFICAT 10

This is a high performance 10-seater based on the Amficat 4. Designed for both civil and military applications, it is powered by a 160hp aero engine.

FRANCE

ANGEVINIÈRE SA

63 avenue de Villiers, 75017 Paris, France
Telephone: 227 0094
Telex: 290 995 F

Angevinière is building and marketing the PSL 003, an inflatable amphibious three-seater based on the Hoveryak, a craft employed by the French explorer and ethnologist Michael Peissel for travelling along Himalayan rivers during an expedition in 1972. Thirty PSL 003s have been supplied to Libya for para-military applications while others have been sold to Iraq and Tunisia.

Angevinière is planning a series of new designs: the C3, a five-seater; the C4, a six-seater; the C5, an eight-seater and the C6 for 16. The latter, in conjunction with Thomson-Brandt, would be available in an armed patrol craft configuration and would be suitable for frontier surveillance, especially where the lines of the national frontiers cross inland waterways and marginal terrain.

Two new air cushion vehicles were added to the Angevinière range in 1979, the PGA 1 Intercepteur, designed by Paul Guienne, and the Gardan G 10, developed and manufactured by Avions Yves Gardan.

PSL 003

LIFT AND PROPULSION: Integrated system powered by a single BMW 900cc motorcycle engine which delivers 60hp at 6,500rpm.

CONTROLS: Craft heading is controlled by triple aerodynamic rudders hinged to the rear of the propeller duct.

HULL: Inflatable type, with four separate buoyancy compartments. Aluminium floor.

SKIRT: Bag type skirt, fabricated in neoprene plastic.

ACCOMMODATION: Open cockpit with side-by-side seating for a driver and two passengers.

DIMENSIONS

Length overall: 3·96m (12ft 11⅞in)

Beam overall: 2·2m (7ft 2in)

Height overall: 1·3m (4ft 3⅛in)

WEIGHTS

Empty: 300kg (661lb)

PERFORMANCE

Max speed continuous: 60km/h (37mph)

Endurance: 2-3 hours

Clearance height: 480mm (1ft 7in)

PGA 1 INTERCEPTEUR

Paul Guienne, one of the best known French hovercraft engineers, was responsible for much of the design of the N 500. His latest design, the PGA 1 is a fully-amphibious seven-seater, intended for applications ranging from waterway ambulance to light coastal and river patrol duties.

LIFT AND PROPULSION: Power for the lift system is supplied by a single Citroen 25hp automotive engine. Thrust is provided by a Citroen 65hp automotive engine driving a ducted four-bladed propeller aft. Normal fuel capacity is 60 litres, but an additional fuel tank can be fitted to extend the range.

CONTROLS: Craft heading is controlled by twin aerodynamic rudders hinged to the rear of the propeller duct.

HULL: Semi-inflatable structure with aluminium floor.

ACCOMMODATION: To suit customer's requirements. Standard model is fitted with two front seats, one for the driver, the other for a passenger. Floor can be modified on request.

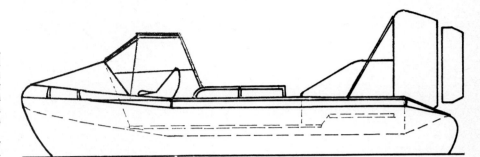

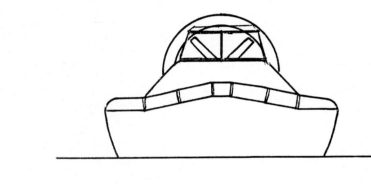

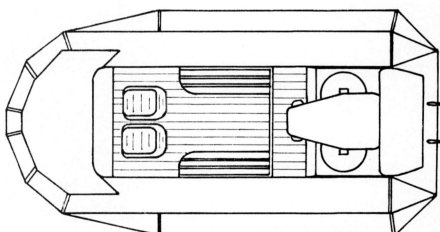

General arrangement of Angevinière PGA 1 utility ACV

Angevinière's PGA 1 semi-inflatable ACV, designed by Paul Guienne

DIMENSIONS
Length: 6·4m (21ft)
Width: 3·35m (11ft)
Width for road transport: 2·4m (7ft 10in)
WEIGHTS
Empty: 600kg (1,322lb)
Useful: 550kg (1,212lb)
Total: 1,150kg (2,535lb)
PERFORMANCE
Max speed, calm water: 70km/h (43·5mph)
Cruising speed, calm water: 50km/h (31mph)
Endurance at cruising speed: 6 hours

GARDAN G 10

Designed for a variety of utility applications, the Gardan G 10 has a payload capacity of just under 1 tonne. Light armament can be fitted enabling the craft to undertake light patrol duties.

LIFT AND PROPULSION: Integrated system powered by a single 140hp Peugeot, Renault or Volvo six-cylinder automotive engine. Power is transmitted to an axial-flow fan for lift and a four-bladed ducted fan aft for propulsion. A variable and reversible-pitch propeller can be fitted as an optional extra. Fuel capacity is 150 litres, but additional tanks can be installed if required.
CONTROLS: Craft heading is controlled by twin rudders at the rear of the propeller duct.
HULL: Semi-inflatable structure with strong aluminium floor.
SKIRT: Bag-type with finger fringe at bow.
ACCOMMODATION: Open cockpit with three seats forward, the driver sitting in the centre. A light cabin structure can be supplied as an optional extra. As a light transport, seats can be provided for a driver and up to eleven passengers. As an amphibious ambulance, the craft will carry a driver, a doctor and up to six litter cases.
DIMENSIONS
EXTERNAL
Length overall: 7·7m (25ft 3in)
Beam overall: 4·25m (13ft 11in)
Height, skirt inflated: 2·75m (9ft)
Beam for road transportation: 2·4m (7ft 11in)
Cushion area: 23m² (247·5ft²)
Cushion depth: 0·4m (1ft 4in)
INTERNAL: CABIN
Length: 3·6m (11ft 9in)
Width: 1·9m (6ft 3in)
Height: 1·4m (4ft 7in)
Cargo area, length: 2·5m (8ft 2in)
    width: 1·9m (6ft 3in)
WEIGHTS
Empty: 750kg (1,653lb)
Useful load: 950kg (2,094lb)
Loaded: 1,700kg (3,748lb)
PERFORMANCE
Max speed, calm water: 35 knots
Cruising speed, calm water: 30 knots
Range in calm conditions with 10 aboard (endurance/distance): 140 min/260km (161 miles)
    3 aboard: 850 min/1,550km (963 miles)
Max wave height: 0·8m-1m (2ft 7in-3ft 3in)

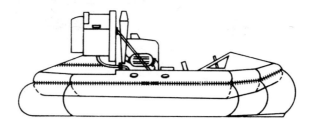
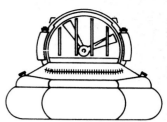

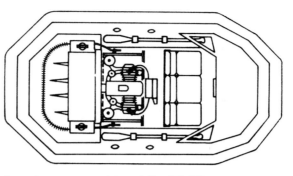

General arrangement of Angevinière PSL 003

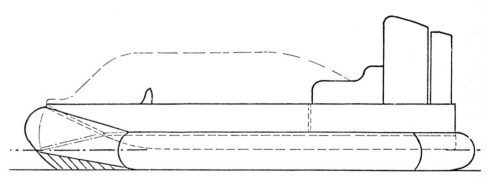

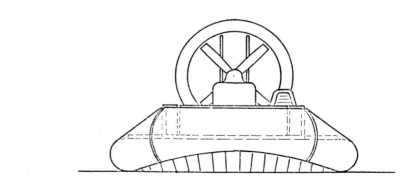

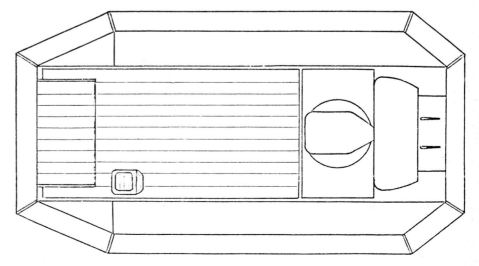

Gardan G 10R light utility craft with a bow loading ramp. Driver's seat is located on the port side to provide unobstructed access from the bow to the load deck

Stern view of PGA 1 Intercepteur. Useful load of the craft is 550 kg. Maximum speed across calm water is 70km/h

BERTIN & CIE

BP 3, 78370 Plaisir, France
Telephone: 056 25 00
Telex: 696231
Officials:
Fernand Chanrion, *President, Director General*
Michel Perineau, *Director General*
Georges Mordchelles-Regnier, *Director General*

Société Bertin & Cie has been engaged in developing the Bertin principle of separately fed multiple plenum chambers surrounded by flexible skirts since 1956. A research and design organisation, the company employs a staff of more than 500, mainly scientists and design engineers who are involved in many areas of industrial research, including air cushion techniques and applications.

Société de l'Aérotrain is responsible for the construction and development of Bertin tracked air cushion vehicles (Aérotrain) and SEDAM is responsible for developing the Naviplane and Terraplane vehicles. Designs based on the Bertin technique are described under the entries for these two companies in this volume.

The Bertin principle of multiple air cushions has also led to numerous applications in the area of industrial handling and aeronautics. These applications, developed by Bertin, are described in the sections devoted to Air Cushion Applicators, Conveyors and Pallets in this edition, and Air Cushion Landing Systems in *Jane's Surface Skimmers 1980* and earlier editions.

GEORGES HENNEBUTTE

Société d'Exploitation et de Développement des Brevets Georges Hennebutte
Head Office: 43 avenue Foch, 64200 Biarritz, France
Works: 23 impasse Labordotte, 64200 Biarritz, France
Telephone: 23 03 70
Officials:
G Hennebutte, *Managing Director*

Ets G Hennebutte was founded in 1955 to design and build inflatable dinghies. Its Espadon series of sports craft is used extensively by French lifeguard patrols and the French Navy.

The Espadon 422 is the only inflatable craft to have crossed the Etal Barrier.

Development of the Espadon to meet a range of special requirements led to the construction of a number of experimental craft, including one equipped with foils, one with hydroskis and a third with an inflatable parasol delta wing for aerodynamic lift. Several of these have been described and illustrated in earlier editions.

Georges Hennebutte's latest released craft is a further variant of the Espadon 422 inflatable sports craft equipped with hydroskis, wings and an air-propeller for thrust. A preliminary description of this new project, designated the Etel 422 Swordfish, will be found in the Hydrofoil section of this edition.

Z O ORLEY

1 allée du Capitaine Dupont, 94260 Fresnes, France

GLIDERCRAFT

Z O Orley and Ivan Labat have designed a range of lightweight recreational craft employing the glidercraft air cushion system invented by M Orley. The object of the system is to reduce the loss of cushion air by fully skirted vehicles when crossing uneven surfaces.

Beneath the hard structure of the glidercraft is an air cushion chamber in rubberised fabric, the base of which is divided into a number of small cell compartments.

Each cell is equipped at the lower end with a perforated shutter.

A short surface sensor protruding beneath each shutter is designed to open up, to deliver cushion air fully, whenever the cell encounters an obstacle rising above the general plane of the reaction surface, and reduce cushion air delivery when crossing a hollow.

A design study is being undertaken for a small commercial craft for operations in South America to carry twelve passengers and freight.

M Orley and his partner will build to order commercial and military prototypes employing his system for use over arctic and tropical terrain. Illustrations of a dynamic model incorporating the glidercraft air cushion system appears in *Jane's Surface Skimmers 1973-74* and earlier editions.

ESCAPADE

M Orley and M Labat, who was a member of the N 500 design team, have projected a 100km/h

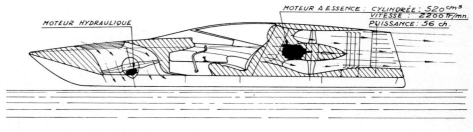

Inboard and outboard profiles of two-seat Orley Escapade

(62mph) two-seater, the Escapade.

A feature of the design is the combination of a petrol engine for thrust and a hydraulic drive for the lift fan. This arrangement allows a continuous sharing of the power output between the lift and propulsion systems.

Aircraft-style seating and furnishing is provided for the driver and passenger.

DIMENSIONS
Length overall: 5·5m (18ft)
Hull beam: 2·7m (8ft 10¼in)
Folded width for transport: 1·9m (6ft 2¾in)
Height overall, on cushion: 1·15m (3ft 9¼in)

WEIGHTS
Craft with fuel: 240kg (529lb)
Loaded for operation on air cushion: 390kg (860lb)
Loaded for operation as hydroplane: 420kg (926lb)

PERFORMANCE
Max speed, calm water: 90km/h (55mph)
over land: 100km/h (62mph)
Cruising speed over calm water: 70km/h (43·5mph)
Max gradient, static conditions: 15%
Vertical obstacle clearance: 0·3m (1ft)

DUBIGEON-NORMANDIE SHIPYARDS

15 boulevard de l'Amiral Bruix, 75116 Paris, France
Telephone: 502 12 20
Telex: 612921 F DUBINOR
Officials:
M Perreau, *Deputy General Manager*
A de Dampierre, *Sales Manager, Hovercraft*

SEDAM

Technical Office: 80 avenue de la Grande Armée, 75017 Paris, France
Telephone: 574 41 69
Telex: 612921F DUBINOR
Telegrams: DUBINOR Paris
Officials:
P Guienne, *Technical Adviser*
R Anger, *Works Director*
G Herrouin, *Head of Technical Department*

All technical and commercial activities of Société d'Etudes et de Développement des Aéroglisseurs Marins, Terrestres et Amphibies (SEDAM) have been taken over by Dubigeon-Normandie, the French shipbuilding concern, which will be responsible in future for the development and construction of all Naviplanes.

SEDAM was incorporated on 9 July 1965, to study, develop and test the Naviplane series of amphibious ACVs based on principles conceived by Bertin & Cie. In April 1968, the company was vested with similar responsibilities for the Terraplane wheeled ACVs based on identical principles. The company holds the exclusive world licence for Bertin patents involving both the Naviplane and Terraplane series.

In 1965 the 5-ton Naviplane BC 8 was completed, after which SEDAM built several small research craft, including the N 101, a quarter-scale manned research model of the 30-ton, 90-passenger N 300. Two N 300s were completed in the winter of 1967/68 and operated along the Côte d'Azur up to the summer of 1971. One has since been operated by the Département of Gironde as a passenger/car ferry across the Gironde estuary and is available for charter operation.

Following its reorganisation in late 1972, the company has been concentrating on three main objectives: the final design, construction and marketing of the 260-ton N 500 Naviplane series; incorporation of improvements on the N 300; and the introduction of a series of air cushion barges. Details of the latter are to be found in this edition in the section devoted to ACV Trailers and Heavy Lift Systems.

Two firm orders have been received for the N 500 from SNCF (French National Railways) for operation across the English Channel on the Boulogne-Dover route.

On 3 May 1977, N 500-01, named 'Côte d'Argent', was severely damaged by fire while minor skirt modifications were being undertaken and was subsequently 'written off'.

N 500-02 named 'Ingenieur Jean Bertin' made its first 'in service' flight on 5 July 1978 and has since been operating in conjunction with British Rail Hovercraft Ltd's Seaspeed service. The approval in principle for ordering N 500-03 was decided at an SNCF board meeting on 25 June 1978.

During 1980 it was announced that N 500-03 will be fitted with bi-conical skirts which will increase the cushion area by at least 10%. Payload will be increased without the power being increased. Trials of the new skirt configuration are being undertaken with the aid of a ¹/₇th scale free-flying model of the N 500-03.

Another of the company's current activities is the development of the N 300 Mk II, a fast patrol craft based on the N 300, but modified in the light of experience gained from the N 500. Major differences include the relocation of the wheelhouse and thrust propellers, and a redesigned hull and skirt system. Alternative military uses include coastal patrol, salvage, rescue and assault landing craft. A further variant of the N 300 Mk II is an amphibious passenger ferry with alternative seating configurations for either 137 or 146 passengers.

N 300 Naviplane, 90-seat passenger ferry

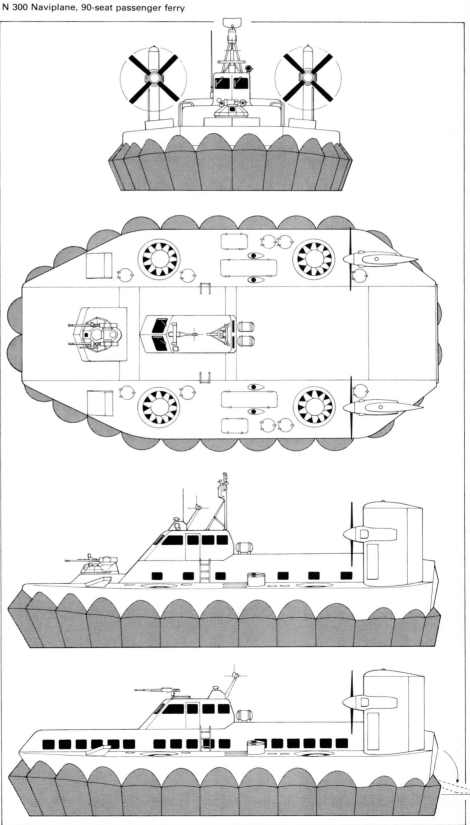

N 300 Mk II (Military) in fast patrol boat and amphibious assault landing craft configuration. Note the new SEDAM bi-conical skirt

The company is also undertaking feasibility studies for surface effect warships of 4-5,000 tons and more for the French Navy.

In July 1972, in response to an EEC request, SEDAM completed a study for a 4-5,000 tonnes mixed-traffic sidewall vessel propelled by water-jets. Model tests have been undertaken at the Paris towing tank.

NAVIPLANE N 300

A 27-ton multi-purpose transport for amphibious operation, the N 300 was the first full-scale vehicle in the Naviplane series designed for commercial use.

The first two N 300s were built at Biarritz at the Breguet factory and started tethered hovering and preliminary handling trials in December 1967. Afterwards they were transported by sea to the SEDAM test centre at l'Etang de Berre. In September 1968 N 300-01 and -02 went to Nice for a series of experimental services and tests conducted by the French armed services.

During the summer of 1970 the two craft operated a scheduled passenger service along the Côte d'Azur. One N 300 was later acquired by the Gironde Département for the operation of a passenger/car ferry service across the Gironde estuary between Blaye and Lamarque. The craft, which was operated by the Bordeaux Port Authority, carried up to four cars and 35 passengers per crossing. It operated 30 crossings per day, seven days a week.

The passenger version seats 90 in a lightweight cabin structure above the open deck.

LIFT AND PROPULSION: Motive power is provided by two Turboméca Turmo IIIN3 gas turbines located in separate engine rooms, port and starboard and drawing filtered air from plenum compartments behind the forward fan ducts. Each engine is coupled via a main gearbox located directly beneath each propeller pylon to a three-bladed Ratier-Figeac 3·6m (11ft 10in) diameter, variable and reversible pitch propeller and via a secondary gearbox to two 11-blade 1·9m (6ft 3in) diameter axial lift fans. The main gearboxes are cross-connected by a shaft so that in the event of one engine failing or malfunctioning the four fans and two propellers can all be

Close-up of N 500-02 *Ingenieur Jean Bertin* showing the forward load door/ramp and the loading system

driven by the remaining engine. The fans deliver air to eight individual Bertin skirts, each 2m (6ft 7in) deep and with a hemline diameter of 3·09m (10ft 2in). These are in turn surrounded by a single wrap-around skirt.

CONTROLS: The wheelhouse, which seats a captain and navigator, is located above a bridge spanning the foredeck to provide a 360 degree view. The main driving controls and the instrumentation are positioned in front of the port seat.

The wheel of a control column varies the pitch of the two propellers differentially and fore and aft movement of the column alters pitch collectively.

HULL: The hull is a raft-like structure built in marine corrosion resistant aluminium alloys. Main buoyancy compartments are beneath the freight deck. Fans and machinery are installed in separate structures on either side of the freight/passenger deck, port and starboard.

ACCOMMODATION: Aircraft-type seats are

provided for 100-120 passengers. Baggage areas are provided in the centre of the passenger saloon, port and starboard, and at the rear of the saloon where there is also a dinghy stowage area. Access to the passenger compartment is by steps built into the bow and stern ramp/doors.

DIMENSIONS
Length overall: 24m (78ft 9in)
Beam: 10·5m (34ft 5in)
Height overall: 7·5m (24ft 7in)
Skirt depth: 2m (6ft 7in)
Cabin floor area: 80m² (861ft²)
Cushion area: 160m² (1,722ft²)
WEIGHTS
Basic: 14 tons
Passenger version: 100-120 passengers
Freight version: 13 tons
Normal all-up weight: 27 tons
PERFORMANCE
Max speed: 57-62 knots
Cruising speed: 44-50 knots
Endurance: 3 hours

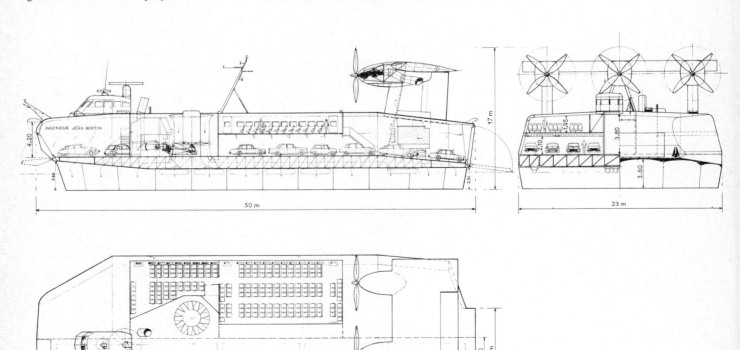

General arrangement of N 500, powered by five 3,200hp Avco Lycoming TF40 marinised gas turbines, two for lift and three for propulsion

NAVIPLANE N 300 Mk II (MILITARY)

In June 1977, SEDAM announced that plans were under way for an improved model of the N 300, known as the N 300 Mk II. This is intended for a variety of military roles, from fast patrol to search and rescue and amphibious assault landing craft.

The chief differences between this craft and its predecessor lie in the resiting of the wheelhouse at the bow, the location of the two thrust propellers aft and the redesigned hull and skirt system.

The bow door has been removed and the entire bow has been redesigned for improved rough water performance. The stern ramp/door is retained. Gross weight will be 37 tonnes. A military version, powered by two 1,200kW Turboméca Turmo XII gas turbines, is envisaged. Armament would comprise a SAMM fully automatic twin 30mm naval gun mount at the bow and a further SAMM automatic gun mount aft. Full air-conditioning would be installed in the living and working spaces of the tropicalised version.

DIMENSIONS
EXTERNAL

Length overall: 23m (75ft 6in)
Beam overall: 12·2m (40ft)
Height, on cushion to tips of fins: 8m (26ft 3in)

NAVIPLANE N 300 Mk II (FAST FERRY)

This new derivative of the N 300 is a fully amphibious passenger ferry with seats for 137-146 passengers. Chief external differences between the N 300 Mk II and the N 300 are the location of the two thrust propellers on fins aft of the passenger cabin, the resiting of the raised wheelhouse forward and the completely re-designed bow.

The bow ramp/door has been removed and the bow and bow skirt have been redesigned for improved rough weather performance. The loading ramp/door aft has been retained for passenger and crew access. The passenger cabin is fully air-conditioned and can be equipped with a refreshment bar.

Power is supplied by two 1,200kW Turboméca Turmo XII gas turbines.

DIMENSIONS
EXTERNAL

Length overall: 22·97m (75ft 4¼in)
Beam overall: 12m (39ft 5in)
Height on landing pads: 7·15m (23ft 5½in)

Details of weights and performance on application.

NAVIPLANE N 500

The N 500 is a 265-tonne, mixed-traffic hover-ferry with a payload capacity of 85 tonnes and a maximum speed of 130km/h (70 knots) in calm conditions. The first two craft were built for SNCF (French National Railways) to operate under the Seaspeed banner on a service across the English Channel, between Boulogne and Dover, starting in 1978.

N 500-01 started trials on 19 April 1977 but on 3 May 1977 was severely damaged by fire during minor skirt repairs and the craft was subsequently 'written off'. N 500-02, 'Ingenieur Jean Bertin', began trials on the English Channel in November 1977 and made its first official 'in service' flight on 5 July 1978. The SNCF board took the decision in principle to order N 500-03 at a meeting on 25 June 1978. N 500-03 and subsequent craft will be fitted with SEDAM's new bi-conical skirt which will increase the cushion area by at least 10%. This should enable the craft to carry 418 passengers and 65 cars without the power being increased. The specification of the craft will change only slightly. The width will be increased by 1·5m and the loaded weight will be increased from 265 to 310 tonnes.

LIFT AND PROPULSION: Motive power is supplied by five Avco Lycoming TF40 marinised gas turbines, two for lift and three for propulsion. Maximum output of the TF40 is 3,000hp; maximum intermittent output is 3,400hp and maximum continuous is 3,200hp. Specific fuel consumption is 247 gallons/h. Each lift engine drives via a reduction system and bevel gear a 4m (13ft 1½in) diameter, 13-bladed, axial-flow fan of laminated construction. The fans, built by Ratier-Forest, are based on experience gained with the N 300 series, and the blades can be adjusted, when stopped, to suit flight conditions. Revolution speed is 900rpm and the tip speed is limited to 200 metres/second to avoid excessive noise. Each fan weighs 800kg (1,764lb) and their rated input power is 2,150kW.

Fan air intakes are located immediately aft of the wheelhouse, one each side of the longitudinal centreline. Cushion air is drawn into two wells reaching down through the passenger and car decks, into a plenum beneath the latter, from which it is fed to the multiple skirts. The flow of air to each group of skirts is controlled by air valves.

Both fans deliver air to a common plenum and in the event of either having to be shut down, the remaining unit has sufficient capacity to enable the craft to take-off and operate in waves up to 2·5m (8ft 3in) high.

Lift and propulsion systems are totally independent of each other in order to reduce gearing to a minimum. The three propulsion engines, each contained in a separate nacelle, are mounted on a horizontal stabiliser aft, where each TF40 drives a 6·3m (20ft 8in) diameter, four-bladed variable- and reversible-pitch propeller at a maximum rotation speed of 640rpm. Three reduction units reduce the nominal engine speed of 15,400rpm to 622rpm at the propeller. The second of these units is equipped with a brake to stop propeller rotation in case of engine failure. The propellers, designed and built by Hawker-Siddeley Dynamics, are similar to those used on the BH.7. The blades consist of a duralumin spar, forged and machine-finished, and covered with a glass fibre and epoxy resin shell to NACA Series 16 and 64 modified profiles. Tractive power is 15 tonnes at zero speed and 11·5 tonnes at 36 metres/second.

The horizontal stabiliser is designed to counteract pitching during take-off and create sufficient lift to compensate the tail-load moment induced by the aerodynamic forces acting on the craft.

CONTROLS: Craft directional control is provided by pedal-operated aerodynamic rudders and differential propeller pitch. In the event of either outboard propeller being stopped, yawing moment is compensated by the use of rudders. Pitch control is provided by elevators on the horizontal stabiliser, and fuel is transferred between forward and aft tanks to adjust fore and aft static trim.

HULL: Modular structure built in simple light alloy units. The main platform structure is made up of welded longitudinal and transverse girder boxes which also form buoyancy chambers. The main longitudinal box girder is the central lane

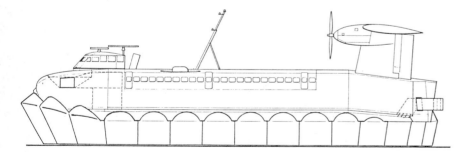
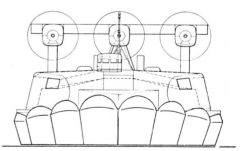

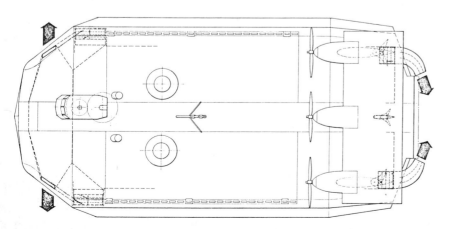

N 500-03 will be fitted with SEDAM's new bi-conical skirt system, illustrated in the three-view above. The new skirt system will increase the cushion area by at least 10%. Trials of the bi-conical skirt have been undertaken with the aid of manned dynamic models of the N 500-03 and have shown very satisfactory behaviour in all flight configurations. Forward and aft thrust ports, port and starboard, aid directional control at low speeds

for coaches and heavy vehicles. Beneath each car
deck is a structure made up by welded trellis-type
lateral beams. The main hull platform supports
the box-like coach compartment on the longitudinal centreline and the two car decks, one each
side of the coach deck. On land, off-cushion, the
craft rests on small cylindrical inflated pads. Lifting jacks are employed to raise the craft off the
ground for inspection and servicing. Both the
forward and aft load door/ramps can accommodate three vehicles abreast for loading and offloading.

SKIRTS: Arrangement based on that adopted
for the N 300. Planform of the N 500's hull is a
rectangle, elongated at the bow by a semicircle.
The skirt system comprises 48 identical skirts,
each of 4m (13ft 1½in) diameter, arranged
around the outer perimeter of the hull base in a
continuous double ring. The skirts are in Tergal
(Terylene) covered with synthetic rubber. Air is
fed to the skirts in groups, giving a labyrinth
effect. It is also fed into the central cushion area
direct.

ACCOMMODATION: In the mixed-traffic
version, passengers are accommodated in two
saloons on two upper half-decks on either side of
the box structure containing the coach passageway. The arrangement is claimed to give passengers greater safety, since they are on a different
level from the vehicles; as well as greater comfort
as their location is in the centre of the craft. Since
their seats are sited above the spray they will also
have a better view. The payload of 85 tonnes
would comprise 400 passengers and 45 medium-
sized cars, or 280 passengers, 10 cars and five
coaches. The wheelhouse, located above the
forward end of the longitudinal coach box,
accommodates a crew of three—captain, co-pilot
and radio operator/navigator. Access is via a
companionway at the base of the starboard lift
engine compartment and a vertical ladder from
the passenger saloon.

SYSTEMS, ELECTRICAL: Electrical supply is
provided by two turbo-alternators, each comprising a Deutz T216 gas turbine driving an Auxilec
1602 alternator.

NAVIGATION: Two Decca radars, one 10cm,
one 3cm plus one gyro and one magnetic compass.

DIMENSIONS

EXTERNAL

Length overall: 50m (164ft 1in)
Beam overall: 23m (75ft 1½in)
Height overall, on cushion: 17m (55ft 9in)
Cushion length: 45m (147ft 8in)
Cushion beam: 22m (72ft 2in)

INTERNAL

Cargo deck length, inboard: 46m (150ft 11in)
  width, inboard: 22m (72ft 2in)
  area: 960m² (10,332ft²)

WEIGHTS

Empty: 160 tonnes
Fuel etc: 20 tonnes
Payload: 85 tonnes
Total gross: 265 tonnes

PERFORMANCE

Max speed, calm water: 75 knots, attainable in
  less than 200 seconds
Cruising speed, 1·5m (5ft) waves: 58 knots
  2·5m (8ft) waves: 48 knots
Endurance over 2·5m (8ft) waves: 5 hours
Max wave height: 4m (13ft 2in)
Normal stopping distance from
  70 knots: 1,000m (3,280ft)
  emergency: 500m (1,640ft)
  vertical acceleration: 0·15g

MN.2 RESEARCH CRAFT

While conducting design studies for the N 500,
SEDAM made extensive use of data gathered
from models. Wind tunnel tests were undertaken
at the Eiffel research centre with a 1:50 scale
model, and a 1:20 model was tested at the
Carènes tank to measure aerodynamic and hydrodynamic resistance.

Two manned, dynamic research craft employed were the MN1 and the MN2. The former, a
1:9 scale, 6m (19ft 8in) long model was designed
for testing the fans and multiple skirt system,
while the latter was built for handling and man-

N 500-02, which made its first official flight 'in service' on 5 July 1978, operates under the Seaspeed banner on the Boulogne-Dover cross-Channel route. Named after the French hovercraft pioneer *Ingenieur Jean Bertin*, the craft is seen above on the hoverpad at the British Rail hovercraft terminal, Western Docks, Dover

Control cabin of the N 500. Basic manning requirement is for a crew of three—captain, first officer and radio operator/navigator

Dynamic model of the 4-5,000 ton SES undergoing tank tests at the Bassin des Carènes, Paris

One of the configurations of a 5,000-ton SES for the French Navy being studied by Dubigeon-Normandie in conjunction with Société des Ateliers et Chantiers de Bretagne (ACB). Alternative propulsion systems under consideration include four turbofans, four hydrojets and four semi-submerged propellers

oeuvrability trials. In addition, a number of tests were conducted with scale model skirts, singly and in groups.

4,000-5,000 ton SES

A study for a 4,000-5,000 ton surface effect ship for the French Navy is being undertaken by SEDAM in conjunction with Société des Ateliers et Chantiers de Bretagne (ACB). The study has been requested by the Centre de Prospective et d'Evaluations (CPE) of the Ministry of Defence.

The configuration selected is known as the AQL, an abbreviation of the French term for sidewall craft—aéroglisseur à quilles latérales.

The studies are being undertaken at the Bassin des Carènes, Paris, with the aid of models equipped with rigid sidewalls integral to the hull structure and flexible seals fore and aft to contain the air cushion.

Several versions of the projected vessel are envisaged. An ASW variant appears to be high on the list of the French Navy's requirements. In ASW configuration, the craft would carry VDS and could also be fitted with auxiliary medium depth sonar enabling it to conduct attacks with its own weapons. In addition it could carry ASW helicopters on its aft deck which could locate distant targets and conduct attacks on their own.

All versions of the projected vessel would be equipped with defensive armament based on naval automatic guns, surface-to-air missiles and electronic warfare systems.

Long-range offensive patrols, the transport of helicopter-borne assault forces and escort destroyer are among the other applications foreseen.

PROPULSION: Various alternative methods of propulsion are being examined, including four hydrojets, four semi-submerged propellers and four turbofans. The power output necessary to operate the vessel is estimated as follows:

MN.2 manned dynamic research craft has been employed to test the new bi-conical skirt for N 500-03

Operation hullborne: 110,500CV 84mW
Operation on air cushion: 190,000CV 140mW
Power to operate lift fans and generate cushion: 30,000CV 22mW
Electricity: 4,000-22,000CV 3-16mW

The specification below applies to the hydrojet-propelled variant.
DIMENSIONS
Length overall: 119·4m (392ft)
Beam overall: 47m (154ft)
Beam across sidewalls: 31m (98ft)
Width of each sidewall: 8m (26ft 3in)
Cushion length: 100m (328ft)
  width: 37m (121ft)

height: 10m (32ft 9in)
  area: 3,700m² (39,826ft²)
WEIGHTS
Empty: 2,900 tons
Fuel: 1,500 tons
Weapons and equipment: 600 tons
Total gross: 5,000 tons
PERFORMANCE
Max speed hullborne: 16 knots
  on cushion in force 3 winds, wave height 1-1·5m: 60 knots
  force 3, wave height 3m: 55 knots
In waves higher than 5m, the vessel would operate in displacement condition.

JACQUES M THILLOY

25 rue Neuve, Ostwald, 67400 Illkirch Graffenstaden, France

LESTES 03

This craft was completed in July 1979 and is now operational. It has performed well over land and water and is likely to be put on sale commercially in kit form for home assembly.
LIFT AND PROPULSION: A single JLO 198cc engine, rated at 7·3bhp at 4,500rpm drives a 600mm diameter, five-bladed Multiwing axial lift

fan. Blades have 30 degree pitch. A single Hirth twin-cylinder 438cc engine rated at 32bhp at 5,600rpm is employed for propulsion. This drives via a notched belt a 1·1m diameter two-bladed ducted propeller. Cushion pressure of the craft loaded is estimated at 45kg/m² (10lb/ft²). The craft can carry 30 litres of fuel for cruising.
CONTROLS: A throttle lever controls the lift engine and a twist-grip throttle controls the propulsion engine. Twin aerodynamic rudders, operated by handlebar, provide directional control.

HULL: All-wooden hull built in 4mm marine plywood with wooden stringers. The fuel tank and battery are situated under the seat. Closed compartments along each side of craft packed with polyurethane foam provide 150% buoyancy.
SKIRT: Segmented type fabricated in 5oz/yd² polyurethane-coated nylon material. Loop and segment type on commercial model.
ACCOMMODATION: Although designed as a single-seater, the craft is capable of carrying two persons in tandem.

DIMENSIONS
Length overall: 3·6m (11ft 9in)
Width overall: 1·9m (5ft 11in)
Height overall, hovering: 1·75m (5ft 9in)
  at rest: 1·5m (4ft 11in)
WEIGHTS
Empty: 160kg (353lb)
All-up weight, one person: 245kg (540lb)
PERFORMANCE
Max speed estimated: 85-90km/h (53-56mph)
Endurance: 2 hours
Obstacle clearance: 0·25m (10in)

Lestes 03, light amphibious single/two-seater designed and built by Jacques M Thilloy

Lestes 03 light amphibious hovercraft operating as a two-seater

TRANSFUTUR SA

18 rue Marbeuf, 75008 Paris, France
Telephone: 924 15 48
Officials:
Laurent Hasson, *President*

First hovercraft to be built by this Paris-based company is the Windlord, an amphibious, grp-hulled four-seater powered by a 64hp Citroen car engine. Designed in 1977 by Robert Trillo Limited, the craft is now in production.

WINDLORD

LIFT AND PROPULSION: Integrated system employing a single 64bhp Citroen GSX3 automotive engine which drives via a toothed-belt and two flexible couplings a single eight-bladed, 1·25m (4ft 1¼in) diameter ducted fan. The primary airflow is ducted aft for propulsion while the secondary airflow is ducted into the plenum below for cushion lift. Fuel capacity is 42 litres.
CONTROLS: Craft heading is controlled by four rudders hinged to the rear of the propeller duct and activated by a control column. A hand lever is provided for engine throttle control.
HULL: Glass-reinforced polyester plastic structure built in two halves, upper and lower, and bonded together. Spaces between the two hull shells are filled with closed-cell polyurethane foam. Reinforced areas are provided for four lifting points, three landing pads, one towing point and one for the engine mounting.
SKIRT: HDL loop and segment type fabricated in polyurethane coated nylon fabric.
DIMENSIONS
Length hard structure: 4·95m (16ft 4in)
Beam: 2·48m (8ft 1½in)
Height off cushion: 1·7m (5ft 7in)
  cushion inflated: 2·0m (6ft 7½in)
WEIGHTS
Empty: 650kg (1,435lb)
Fuel: 42 litres (9·24 imperial gallons), 34kg (75lb)
Payload including driver: 350kg (773lb)
Normal gross weight: 1,034kg (2,283lb)
PERFORMANCE (at normal gross weight, calm conditions)

Transfutur's grp-hulled four-seater, the Windlord

Windlord being employed by a film unit in the Carmargue

Cruising speed: 55km/h (30 knots)
Max speed: 70km/h (37·8 knots)
Range: 300km (186 miles)
Endurance: 5 hours

Max gradient: 1:10
Vertical obstacle clearance: 25cm (10in)
Max wave capability: 0·6-1m (2ft-3ft 3in)

GERMANY, FEDERAL REPUBLIC

HORST FALKE

Dasnochel 46, 5600 Wuppertal-1, Federal Republic of Germany

RACING HOVERCRAFT

This two-seat amphibious sports hovercraft was completed in 1979. It has competed in several West German hovercraft rallies, including meetings held in Munich and Bainberg.

LIFT AND PROPULSION: Power for the lift system is provided by a 9hp two-stroke ahead of the open cockpit and directly coupled to an axial lift fan. Thrust is furnished by a 40hp Hirth engine driving two ducted fans via toothed belts.

CONTROLS: Craft heading is controlled by twin rudders, one hinged to the rear of each thrust duct. Handlebars control rudder movement.

HULL: Laminated polyester.

SKIRT: Segmented skirt, fabricated in neoprene and pvc coated nylon.

DIMENSIONS

Length overall: 3·4m (11ft 2in)

Beam overall: 1·8m (5ft 11in)

Horst Falke in his amphibious sports hovercraft

RHEIN-FLUGZEUGBAU GmbH (RFB)

(Subsidiary of VFW-Fokker GmbH)

Head Office and Main Works: Flugplatz, Postfach 408, D-4050 Mönchengladbach, Federal Republic of Germany

Telephone: (02161) 662031

Telex: 08/52506

Other Works: Flughafen Köln-Bonn, Halle 6, D-5050 Porz-Wahn, Federal Republic of Germany and Flugplatz, D-2401 Lübeck-Blankensee, Federal Republic of Germany

Officials:

Dipl-Volkswirt Wolfgang Kutscher, *Executive Director*

Dipl-Ing Alfred Schneider, *Executive Director*

Founded in 1956, this company holds 100% of the stock of Sportavia-Pützer.

RFB is engaged in the development and construction of airframe structural components, with particular emphasis on wings and fuselages made entirely of glassfibre-reinforced resins. Research and design activities include studies for the Federal German Ministry of Defence.

Current manufacturing programmes include series and individual production of aircraft components and assemblies made of light alloy, steel and glassfibre-reinforced resin for aircraft in quantity production, as well as spare parts and ground equipment. The company is also active in the fields of shelter and container construction.

Under contract to the West German government, RFB services certain types of military aircraft, and provides target-towing flights and other services with special aircraft.

The X-113 Am Aerofoil Boat was built and tested under the scientific direction of the late Dr A M Lippisch. Flight tests of the 6-7 seat RFB X-114 have been successfully completed and after some hydrodynamic modifications, including the fitting of hydrofoils beneath the sponsons, it is undergoing a new series of tests.

RFB X-113 Am during a flight demonstration over the Wattenmeer

6-7 seat RFB X-114 Aerofoil Boat. Powered by a 200hp Lycoming IO-360 driving an RFB ducted fan, the X-114 cruises in ground effect at 150km/h (93mph) and has a maximum range of 2,150km (1,336 miles). A retractable wheel undercarriage is fitted enabling the craft to operate from both land and water

RFB (LIPPISCH) X-113 Am AEROFOIL BOAT

The Aerofoil Boat was conceived in the United States by Dr A M Lippisch. The first wing-in-ground-effect machine built to Lippisch designs was the Collins X-112, which was employed by Lippisch to examine the stability problems likely to be encountered in the design of larger machines of this type.

Since 1967 further development of the concept has been undertaken by RFB with government backing. The single-seat X-113 has been built as a test craft to provide data for the design of larger craft of the same type.

The X-113 Am underwent its first airworthiness test from Lake Constance in October 1970.

During the first series of tests, the craft demonstrated its operating ability on water as well as

flight capability at very low altitudes. These tests were followed in the autumn of 1971 by a second series of trials during which performance measurements were taken. A cine camera built into the cockpit recorded instrument readings and a camera built into the lateral stabilisers took pictures of small threads on the upper wing surface for current flow analysis.

The earlier trials on Lake Constance were followed in November/December 1972 by a third series of tests in the North Sea in the Weser estuary area.

Apart from various performance measurements, the aim of these trials was to investigate the machine's capabilities in roughish weather conditions. Although the machine was originally designed for only a brief general demonstration on calm water, it proved capable of take-offs and landings in a moderate sea.

Remarkably good sea behaviour was shown from the outset. Take-offs and landings in wave heights of about 0·75m (2ft 6in) presented no problem. During the course of these tests, flights were made in the coastal region, and sometimes on the Wattenmeer, in wind forces of up to 25 knots, without any uncontrollable flying tendencies being observed in low-level flight.

The flight performance measurements gave a gliding angle of 1 : 30, which cannot be greatly improved by enlarging the machine. It is also of interest to note that the relatively thin outer laminate of the gfr wing sandwich, with a thickness of 0·4mm, stood up to the loads involved in taking off in a roughish sea and also remained watertight throughout the whole period of trials.

Towards the end of the trials, in order to reduce noise and give the airscrew better protection from spray, the machine was converted to pusher propulsion.

The company envisages a range of Aerofoil craft for a variety of civil and military purposes, from single-seat runabouts to cargo transporters with payloads of up to 10 tons. As transports they could be employed on coastal, inter-island and river services. Military variants could be used as assault craft, FPBs and ASW vessels.

Flight tests, including a series performed over rough water in the North Sea near Bremerhaven, have established that 50% less power is required in ground effect, enabling operations in excess of 50-ton-miles per gallon of fuel at speeds in the 90-180 knot range.

RFB X-114 AEROFOIL BOAT

Evolved from the X-113, this 6-7-seater has a maximum take-off weight of 1,500kg and is fitted with a retractable wheel undercarriage, enabling it to operate from land or water.

Power is provided by a 200hp Lycoming IO-360 four-cylinder horizontally-opposed air-cooled engine driving a specially-designed Rhein-Flugzeugbau ducted fan. Range, with 100kg (220lb) of fuel is more than 1,000km (621 miles). Operational speed is 75-200km/h (46-124mph).

An initial trials programme was successfully completed in 1977. A new series of trials is now being undertaken after hydrodynamic modifications that included the fitting of hydrofoils beneath the sponsons.

The vehicle is designed to operate over waves up to 1·5m (4ft 11in) in ground effect and can therefore be used without restriction during 80% of the year in the Baltic Sea area and 60% of the year in the North Sea. On days with high seas of more than 1·5m (4ft 11in) takeoff and landing takes place in waters near the coast. Flying is virtually unrestricted, providing due allowance is made for the loss in economy.

Fuel consumption costs, while flying in ground effect, are lower than those for cars. RFB states that its economics cannot be matched by any other form of transport aircraft.

Although built primarily as a research craft to extend the experience gained with the X-113 Am single-seater. Aerofoil Boats of the size of the X-114 are suitable for air-taxi work along coastlines, the supervision of restricted areas, patrol, customs and coastguard purposes and search-and-rescue missions.

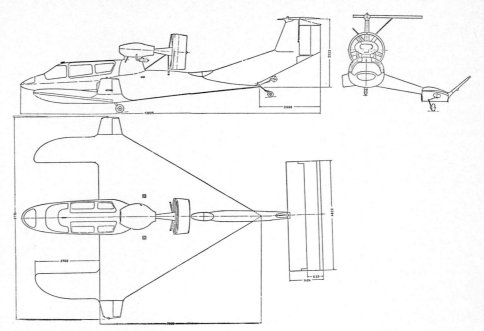

General arrangement of RFB X-114

During the second test phase the X-114 was equipped with hydrofoils, raising its maximum take-off weight to 1,750kg. In this configuration it is known as the X-114H

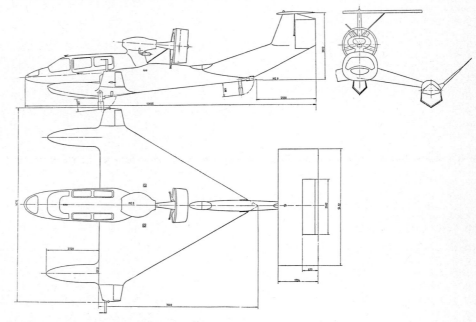

RFB X-114H showing retractable vee foil undercarriage

Without any significant new research the construction of a vehicle with a takeoff weight of approximately 18,000kg is possible. On a vehicle of this size, the ratio of empty weight to takeoff weight is less than 50%.

DIMENSIONS
Length overall: 12·8m (42ft)
Wing span: 7m (22ft 11⅝in)
Height overall: 2·9m (9ft 6⅛in)

WEIGHTS
Max takeoff: 1,500kg (3,307lb)
Payload: 500kg (1,102lb)

PERFORMANCE
Max cruising speed: 200km/h (124mph)
Cruising speed in ground effect: 150km/h (93mph)
Max flight range: 2,150km (1,336 miles)

INDONESIA

LAPAN
LEMBAGA PENERBANGAN
DAN ANTARIKSA NASIONAL
(The National Institute of Aeronautics and Space)

Head Office: Jalan Pemuda Persil No 1, Jakarta Timur, Indonesia
Mailing Address: PO Box 3048, Jakarta, Indonesia
Telephone: (021) 48 28 02; (021) 48 51 25
Telex: 45675 LAPAN IA
Cable: LAPAN JAKARTA
Officials:
Air Vice Marshal J Salatum, *Chairman*
Prof Wiranto Arismunandar, *Vice Chairman*

PUSAT TEKNOLOGI DIRGANTARA
(Aerospace Technology Centre)
Rumpin Airfield, Bogor, West Java
Dr Haryono Djojodohardjo, *Head, Aerospace Technology Centre*

Ir Jaidun Kromodihardjo, *Manager, Aerospace Technology Development*

Lapan was established in 1963 with the object of pioneering indigenous capabilities in aeronautics and space in support of the National Five Year Plan. At the beginning of 1978 Lapan had 527 personnel, out of which there were 195 university graduates and bachelors of science, divided into the Space Applications Centre (Jakarta), the Aerospace Technology Centre (Rumpin Airfield near Bogor), the Atmospheric and Space Research Centre (Bandung) and the Aerospace Study Centre (Jakarta).

In 1977 Lapan undertook the design and construction of an experimental hovercraft designated XH-01.

LAPAN XH-01
Lapan's first research craft is a two-seater with a moulded fibreglass hull.

LIFT AND PROPULSION: A McCullough 6hp engine drives a 70mm (2ft 3½in) fan at 6,000rpm for cushion lift. Propulsion is supplied by two 6hp McCullough engines aft, each driving a 60cm (1ft 11½in) ducted fan for propulsion.

CONTROLS: A single rudder in each thrust duct provides the craft with directional control.

HULL: Moulded glass reinforced plastic with integral bouyancy.

ACCOMMODATION: Side-by-side seating for two persons is provided in an open cockpit.

DIMENSIONS
Length overall: 3m (9ft 10in)
Beam overall: 1·5m (4ft 11in)

WEIGHTS
Empty: 250kg (550·66lb)
Max all-up: 370kg (815lb)

PERFORMANCE: Not available at the time of going to press.

JAPAN

FANBIRD HOVERCRAFT
Head Office: 4F Nakauchi Bld 1-7-6, Nihonbashi Chuo-ku, Tokyo 103, Japan
Telephone: (03) 278-0227
Officials:
Jiichiro Yokota, *Director*
Yoshimichi Kushida, *Director*
Consultant:
Masahiro Mino
Fanbird Shikoku Division
164-1 Samukawa-cho, Iyomishima-shi Ehime 799-04
Kazunori Takahashi, *Director*
Fanbird Kohchi Division
2490-11 Niida, Kohchi-shi Kohchiken 781-01
Arioshi Armitsu, *Director*

Fanbird Hovercraft was formed in May 1976. It is currently engaged in the design, development and manufacture of light hovercraft, which are available in plan and kit form to Japanese amateur hovercraft constructors. The company also publishes *The Light Hovercraft Handbook* and holds stocks of materials for homebuilders including fans, propellers, engines, ducts, completed skirts and skirt material, shafts, pulleys, belts, mounts,, wood for ribs and stringers and marine ply.

Abbreviated specifications of eight of the company's designs appear in the accompanying table.

"UHO" a 1·8m diameter saucer-shaped ACV designed by Fanbird Hovercraft. It can be purchased in either plan or kit form. A variety of engines can be fitted, from 4 to 8 hp

Fanbird FB24 Mosquito single-seat sports hovercraft

Fanbird FB26 Mini single-seat sports hovercraft

Type	l × w (m)	l × w on cushion (m)	Seats	Type	Engine power (hp)	Empty weight (kg)	Total (kg)	Max speed (km/h)	Hover gap (m)	Skirt type
UHO	1·8	2·3	1	—	4-8	60	120	20	0·25	Finger
FB24	2·4 × 1·2	2·6 × 1·6	1	L/P	8-15	60	120	30	0·18	Bag
FB26 Mini	2·6 × 1·6	2·8 × 2·0	1	L/P	12-20	80	145	40	0·2	Bag
FB26 Super Mini	2·6 × 1·6	2·8 × 2·0	1	L/P	20-30	100	170	45	0·2	Bag
FB32 Std	3·2 × 1·8	3·4 × 2·2	1	L/P	30-40	120	195	40	0·23	Bag
FB32 Sports	3·2 × 1·8	3·4 × 2·2	1	L + P	6-30	150	225	50	0·23	Bag
FB36 Sd	3·6 × 1·8	3·8 × 2·2	2	L + P	8-40	190	340	50	0·25	Bag
FB36 TD	3·6 × 1·8	3·8 × 2·2	2	L + P	15-65	220	390	65	0·25	Bag

Number of plans/number of craft sold by March 1978:
UHO 30/12; FB24 42/24; FB26 Mini 208/118; FB26 Supermini 32/11; FB32STD 202/113; FB32 Sports 251/123; FB36SD 108/58; FB36TD 38/20; Total 911/479

Fanbird FB32 single-seat sports runabout

Fanbird FB36 two-seat sports hovercraft

Fanbird FB32 in standard configuration. Maximum speed of this amphibious single-seater is 40km/h

Fanbird FE36 TD with twin ducted thrust fans powered by a single 65hp engine

FUN VEHICLE CO LTD

Nakauchi Building 3F, 1-7-6 Nihonbashi, Chuo-ku, Tokyo 103, Japan Z.C.
Telephone: (03) 278 0225
Officials:
Hiroshi Suzuki, *President*
Isao Ishii, *Managing Director*
Haruo Ota, *Design Director*
Yoshimichi Kushida, *Technical Director*
Kouji Mizauo, *Marketing Director*
Kazutoshi Okamato, *Marketing Service Director*
Masahiro Mino, *Consultant*
Yasuyo Minemura, *Secretary*

Fun Vehicle Co Ltd was founded in June 1977 to undertake the development, manufacture and marketing of sports and utility vehicles, with particular emphasis on hovercraft and air boats.

Its first product is the FV-10 Newpole, an amphibious single-seater with separate lift and propulsion systems. The company is selling this craft in Japan, throughout South-east Asia and in the USA. It is available as a kit, a kit with completed hull or as a finished craft, 'ready-to-fly'.

FV-10 NEWPOLE

Development of this grp-hulled single-seater began in 1976 and six prototypes were built and tested before the craft was finally put into production in late 1977. Maximum speed across land and water is 50km/h (31·2mph).

LIFT AND PROPULSION: Lift is provided by a single Fuji EC-17D two-stroke, rated at 6·5hp at 5,000rpm and driving a 480mm (19in) five-bladed, 30 degree pitch ducted fan. Thrust is supplied by a single Kyoritsu KEC 225cc two-stroke, rated at 12·5hp at 5,500rpm, driving a 580mm (23in) diameter five-bladed, 30 degree pitch fan.

CONTROLS: Handlebar-operated air rudder mounted in the fan duct controls craft heading. Twist-grip throttle for propulsion engine on handlebar.

HULL: Complete hull structure is built in self-coloured glass-reinforced plastics. Polyurethane

First production machine to be marketed by Fun Vehicle Co, the FV-10T Newpole amphibious single-seater

FV-10Ts under construction at Fun Vehicle's Isezaki factory

foam, contained in the underside of the hull, provides 200% buoyancy.

SKIRT SYSTEM: Simple bag skirt, fabricated in polyurethane-coated nylon fabric provides 0·19m (7½in) obstacle clearance.

ACCOMMODATION: Driver sits astride a central bench in an open cockpit.

DIMENSIONS
Length overall, on cushion: 3·09m (10ft 6in)
   on landing pads: 2·9m (9ft 6in)
Width overall, on cushion: 1·98m (6ft 6in)
   on landing pads: 1·6m (5ft 3in)
Height, on cushion: 1·09m (3ft 7in)
   on landing pads: 0·9m (3ft)

WEIGHTS
Empty: 140kg (308lb)
All-up: 210kg (463lb)

PERFORMANCE
Max speed, calm water: 50km/h (31·2mph)
Hard structure clearance: 0·19m (7½in)

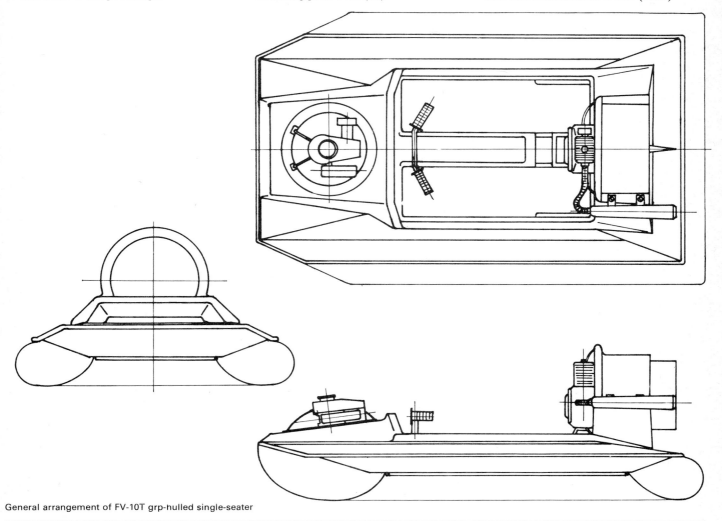

General arrangement of FV-10T grp-hulled single-seater

HOVERMARINE PACIFIC CO, LTD

Head Office: Fuji Building 4F 5-3, 1-Chome, Yayesu, Chuo-ku, Tokyo 103, Japan
Telephone: (03) 278 0821
Telex: 2228198 (HOVPAC J)
Works: c/o Sasebo Heavy Industries Co Ltd, Tategami-cho, Sasebo 857, Japan
Telephone: (0956) 24 2111
Telex: 748219 (SSK J)
Officials:
T Nakabe, *President*
K Hishiya, *Senior Managing Director*
A Okiyoshi, *Customer Service Manager*
T Nakamae, *Marketing Manager*
K Hayashi, *Sales Manager*

Hovermarine Pacific is a joint venture by Vosper Hovermarine Ltd, Taiyo Fishery Co Ltd, Sasebo Heavy Industries Ltd, and Fairfield International Limited. Taiyo is the world's biggest fish processing company, with an annual sales revenue in excess of US$2,000 million and Sasebo is the world's tenth largest shipbuilder. Fairfield International is a private company with extensive interests in shipping. The company was established on 9 April 1976 with a capital of Y100,000,000.

Hovermarine is licensed by Hovercraft Development Ltd, an agency of the National Research Development Corporation, under various world-wide patents relating to air cushion technology.

The company imported a 65-seat HM.2 Mk III from Vosper Hovermarine Ltd in 1976. Named Hovsterm it has been in service as a passenger

Five Vosper Hovermarine HM.2 Mk 4s had been built by Hovermarine Pacific Co Ltd by December 1979. The first and second craft built at Sasebo are seen here

ferry on the Lake of Biwa for the past two years.

The company's first craft, a 93-seat HM.2 Mk 4, was completed in 1978 at Hovermarine Pacific's factory at Sasebo, on the Japanese island of Kyushu. The craft was in passenger ferry service in 1979 connecting Fukuoka and the Isle of Iki, some 41 miles in 90 minutes. Five craft had been built up to December 1979. One craft has recently been chartered for the Mihara-Imabari route.

The company is also undertaking the marketing of HM.5 and HM.2 Mk 4 based fireboats, crewboats and patrol boats. Future plans include the building of the 100-ton payload Hoverfreighter, a joint technical development with Vosper

Hovermarine Ltd. The Hoverfreighter, designated HM.100F, will have all of the characteristics of the basic Hovermarine designs and is intended to meet the need for heavy cargo transportation where limited harbour facilities exist and speed of movement is a primary requirement.

Hovermarine Pacific is currently working on the preliminary design of HM.100F Car Ferry. Dimensions will be approximately 70-75m (230-246ft) long and 14·5m (47ft) wide. It will have a maximum speed of 40 knots, a cruising speed of 32 knots and range of 320n miles. The craft will be able to carry 350 passengers, 30 cars and 4 buses or trucks.

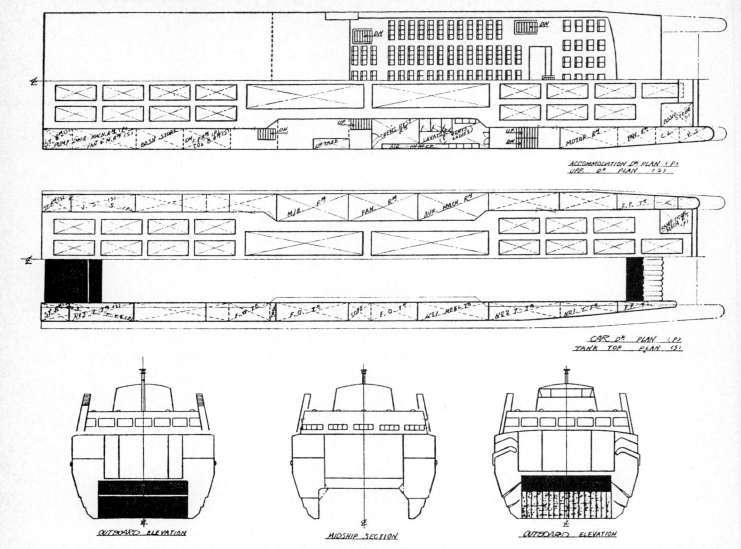

General arrangement of HM.100F Car Ferry, showing the through loading arrangement via bow and stern ramp/loading doors forward and aft on the main deck

KANAZAWA INSTITUTE OF TECHNOLOGY

Hydrodynamic Laboratory, Department of Mechanical Engineering, Kanazawa Institute of Technology, Kanazawa South, Ishikawa 921, Japan
Telephone: (0762) 48-1100
Officials:
Mutsushige Kyoto, *President*
Shoichi Fukumitsu, *Programme Manager*
Dr Yoshio Fujimura, *Chairman of Dept of Mechanical Engineering*

WATER SPIDER II

The Department of Mechanical Engineering, Kanazawa Institute of Technology, is conducting a research programme aimed at determining the performance potential of ACVs operating across snow-covered terrain. The programme is being conducted in conjunction with the Japanese National Ship Research Institute and Nihon University at Narashino.

In Japan the specific gravity of snow is between 0·1 and 0·5 and Kanazawa is an area which generally experiences heavy annual snowfalls. The Department of Mechanical Engineering at the Kanazawa Institute of Technology built its first hovercraft, the Water Spider I, in 1976. An improved model, the Water Spider II, was completed the following year.

LIFT AND PROPULSION: Lift is provided by a 30hp Fuji Subaru EK-33 two-cycle, twin-cylinder air-cooled automobile engine located ahead of the cockpit and driving a five-bladed axial fan. Thrust is supplied by an identical engine driving a ducted Yashima Kogyo seven-bladed axial fan aft. Two fuel tanks are fitted, one for each engine. Total fuel capacity is 20 litres (2·64 gallons).

Water Spider I, first hovercraft to be built by the Department of Mechanical Engineering at the Kanazawa Institute of Technology

CONTROLS: Craft direction is controlled by single aerodynamic rudder hinged to the rear of the thrust fan duct and operated by a handle bar.
HULL: Wooden construction in aircraft-grade plywood.
SKIRT: Bag type, 20cm (8in) deep, fabricated in nylon satin material.
DIMENSIONS
Length overall, power off: 3·9m (12ft 9½in)
  skirt inflated: 4·12m (13ft 6¼in)
Beam overall, power off: 2·0m (6ft 6¾in)
  skirt inflated: 2·44m (8ft)

Height overall on landing pads, power off: 1·1m (3ft 7¼in)
  skirt inflated: 1·3m (4ft 3⅛in)
Draft afloat: 24cm (9½in)
Skirt depth: 20cm (7⅞in)

WEIGHTS
Normal empty: 242kg (534lb)
Normal all-up: 250kg (551lb)
Normal gross: 320kg (706lb)
Normal payload: 70kg (154lb)
Max payload: 100kg (220lb)

PERFORMANCE
Max speed over calm water: 30km/h (18mph)
over snow: 25km/h (15mph)
Vertical obstacle clearance: 20cm (7⅞in)

Water Spider II research hovercraft operating across 457mm (1ft 6in) deep snow in Kanazawa

MITSUI ENGINEERING & SHIPBUILDING CO LTD

6-4, Tsukiji 5-chome, Chuo-ku, Tokyo 104, Japan
Telephone: 544-3451
Telex: J22821, J22924

Officials:
Isamu Yamashita, *Chairman*
Kazuo Maeda, *President*
Kazuo Hamano, *Senior Managing Director*
Hiromasa Kikuchi, *Senior Managing Director*
Ryoji Kawazura, *Managing Director*
Shunkichi Matsuoka, *Managing Director*
Isshi Suenaga, *Managing Director*
Fumio Makino, *Managing Director*
Hideo Matsushima, *Managing Director*
Yoshio Ishitani, *Managing Director*
Koji Arase, *Managing Director*
Tetsujiro Tomita, *Director*
Yoshikatsu Ochi, *Director*
Kanemi Tsujino, *Director*
Shonosuke Ishii, *Director*
Takashi Furuno, *Director*
Kotaro Kishi, *Director*
Koichi Takano, *Director*
Niro Harano, *Director*
Satoru Ohashi, *Director*
Shogo Saeki, *Director*
Saburo Yanagi, *Auditor*
Takeo Takayanagi, *Auditor*
Masataro Takami, *Auditor*
Fusao Hongo, *Auditor*
Masatomo Ishibashi, *Manager, Ship Sales and High Speed Craft Department*
Taku Kono, *Manager, Ship Sales Department*

Mitsui's Hovercraft Department was formed on 1 May 1964, following the signing of a licensing agreement in 1963 with Hovercraft Development Ltd and Vickers Ltd, whose ACV interests were later merged with those of British Hovercraft Corporation. In addition, the company was licensed by Westland SA in 1967, following the formation of BHC.

The company has built two 11-seat MV-PP1s, one of which has been supplied to the Thai Customs Department, 14 MV-PP5s and four MV-PP15s.

The MV-PP5 was put into production at the initial rate of four craft a year. In the summer of 1969 the craft was put into service by Meitetsu Kaijo Kankosen Co Ltd, between Gamagoori and Toba, Ise Bay.

Since October 1971 three MV-PP5s designated Hobby 1, 2 and 3 have been operated by Oita Hoverferry Co Ltd on a coastal route linking Oita airport with the cities of Oita and Beppu. The three craft complete a total of 16 round trips per day to link with flight schedules at the airport.

Other PP5 operators include Japanese National Railways (two craft) and Yaeyama Kanko Ferry Co Ltd (one craft).

The company has also developed the MV-PP05, a five-seater and the MV-PP5 Mk II, a 76-seat stretched variant of MV-PP5. Two existing PP5s have been converted to Mk IIs and one new Mk II is in service with Japanese National Railways.

Mitsui's MV-PP15 50-ton passenger ferry, powered by twin 1,950hp Avco Lycoming TF25 gas turbines. The craft seats 155 passengers and has a top speed of 65 knots. Seen in these photographs are the raised control cabin, the pylon mounted propellers, lift fan air intakes and the thrust ports beneath the passenger door entrances, port and starboard

MV-PP15

Developed from the earlier PP5, the Mitsui MV-PP15 is designed for high speed passenger ferry services on coastal and inland waterways. Accommodation is provided for 155 passengers and a crew of five. Four craft of this type have been completed so far.

LIFT AND PROPULSION: Two Avco Lycoming TF25 gas turbines, each with a maximum continuous output of 2,200hp at 15°C, drive the integrated lift/propulsion system. Each turbine drives a 2·3m (7ft 6in) diameter, 13-bladed centrifugal fan and a 3·2m (10ft 6in) diameter, four-bladed variable-pitch propeller. Power is transmitted via a main gearbox, propeller gearbox, fan gearbox and an auxiliary gearbox, all connected by shafting and flexible couplings. Auxiliary systems, such as hydraulic pumps for propeller pitch and lubricating oil pumps, are driven directly by auxiliary gears. Fuel is carried in two flexible tanks located immediately ahead of the lift fan assemblies. Total volume of the fuel tanks is 6m³ (21·2ft³).

CONTROLS: Twin aerodynamic rudders in the propeller slipstream and differential propeller pitch provide directional control. The rudders are operated hydraulically by a wheel from the commander's position. In addition, two retractable wheels, located aft, one each side of the main buoyancy tank, can be extended downwards into the water to prevent drift when turning and assist braking at high speeds. On land, the wheels assist manoeuvring and help to reduce skirt wear.

A thrust port air bleed system provides lateral control at slow speeds. Four ports are located beneath the passenger door entrances, port and starboard. A water ballast system is provided for longitudinal and transverse centre of gravity adjustment.

HULL: Construction is primarily in corrosion resistant aluminium alloy. The basic structure is the main buoyancy chamber which is divided into watertight sub-divisions for safety, and includes the fore and aft ballast tanks. Overall dimensions of the main buoyancy raft structure are 19·8m (64ft 10½in) long by 7·1m (23ft 3½in) wide by 0·7m (2ft 4in) high. Sidebodies of riveted construction are attached to the sides of the main buoyancy structure. The outer shell of the main buoyancy chamber, machinery deck space, the forward deck and passageways around the cabin interior, are all constructed in honeycomb panels with aluminium cores. The lift fan air intake, inner window frames and hood for the electric motor that rotates the radar scanner are in glass fibre reinforced plastics.

Six rubber-soled landing pads are fitted to the hull base, together with jacking pads. Four lifting eyes for hoisting the craft are provided in the buoyancy chamber.

SKIRT: 1·6m (5ft 3in) deep fingered-bag skirt of Mitsui design, fabricated in nylon-based sheet and coated both sides with synthetic rubber. Two transverse stability bags are included in the skirt system to minimise pitch and roll.

ACCOMMODATION: The passenger cabin, containing 155 seats, is located above the forward part of the main buoyancy chamber. The seats are arranged in three groups and divided by two longitudinal aisles. Seats in the two outer sections are arranged in rows of three abreast, and in the centre section, six abreast.

The four cabin entrance doors, two port, two starboard, are divided horizontally, the top section opening upwards and the lower section opening sideways. A lavatory, toilet unit, pantry and luggage room are provided aft, and a second luggage room is located forward. Lockers are sited close to the forward entrance doors. The control cabin is located above the passenger cabin superstructure and provides a 360 degree view. It is reached from the passenger saloon by a companion ladder. An emergency exit is provided on the starboard side.

The cabin has a total of four seats, one each for the commander and navigator, plus two spare ones of the flip-up type. The wheel for the air rudders, the two propeller pitch-control levers, instrument panel and switches are arranged on a console ahead of the commander; and the radio, fuel tank gauge, water ballast gauge and fire warning system are arranged ahead of the navigator.

On the cabin roof are the radar-scanner, mast for navigation lights, a siren and a searchlight.

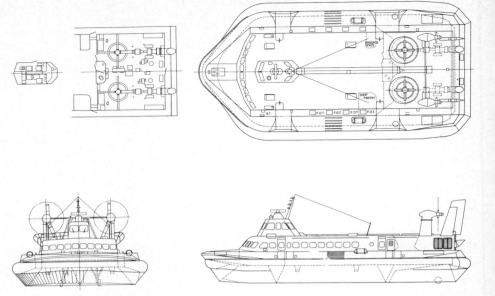

Mitsui MV-PP15 155-seat hoverferry. Twin Avco Lycoming TF25 gas turbines power the integrated lift and propulsion system and give the craft a maximum speed of about 65 knots

SYSTEMS, ELECTRICAL: 28·5V dc. Two 9kW generators are driven directly by the main engines. One 24V 175Ah battery is employed for starting, and another for control. Both are located in the engine room and are charged by the generators when the main engines are operating. A shore-based power source is used for battery charging when the main engines are not in use.

RADIO/NAVIGATION: Equipment includes one 10in radar, compass, radio and one 22cm, 250W searchlight.

AIR CONDITIONING: Two Daikin RKA 1000R-PP15 air coolers, each with a capacity of 20,000 Kcal/h. Compressors are driven by belts from the auxiliary gearboxes and cooled air is supplied via air-conditioning ducts. Four ceiling ventilators are provided, each equipped with a 40W fan.

SAFETY: Remotely-controlled BCF or BTM fire extinguishers provided in the engine room. Portable extinguishers provided in the passenger cabin. Inflatable life boats, life jackets, automatic SOS signal transmitter and other equipment carried according to Japanese Ministry of Transport regulations.

DIMENSIONS
EXTERNAL
Length overall, on cushion: 26·4m (86ft 8in)
  on landing pads: 25·09m (82ft 4in)
Beam overall, on cushion: 13·9m (45ft 7in)
  on landing pads: 11·1m (36ft 5in)
Height, on cushion: 7·9m (25ft 11in)
  on landing pads to tip of propeller blade: 6·9m (22ft 8in)
Skirt depth: 1·6m (5ft 3in)
INTERNAL
(Passenger cabin including toilet, pantry and locker rooms):
Length: 14·14m (46ft 5in)
Max breadth: 7·06m (23ft 2in)
Max height: 2·1m (6ft 11in)
Floor area: 93m² (1,001ft²)

WEIGHTS
All-up: about 50 tons

PERFORMANCE
Max speed: about 65 knots
Cruising speed: about 50 knots
Fuel consumption: about 280g/shp/h at 15°C
Endurance: about 4 hours

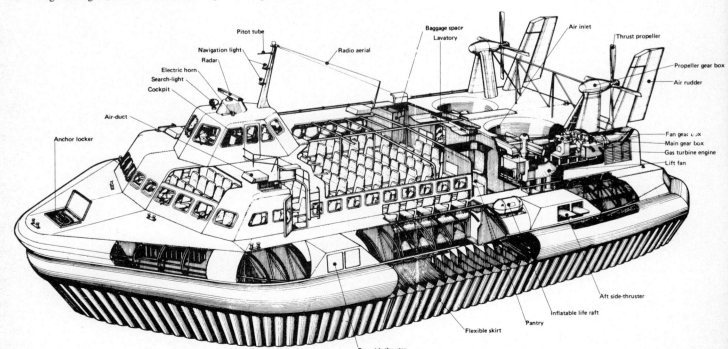

Cutaway of the Mitsui MV-PP15, showing the seating arrangements for the 155 passengers. Seats are arranged in three groups, divided by two longitudinal aisles. In the two outer sections they are arranged in rows of three abreast, and in the centre, six abreast

MV-PP5

Mitsui's first large hovercraft, the 50-seat MV-PP5, is a gas-turbine powered craft intended primarily for fast ferry services on Japanese coastal and inland waters.

LIFT AND PROPULSION: All machinery is located aft to reduce to a minimum the noise level in the passenger cabin. A single IHI IM-100 gas turbine (licence-built General Electric LM100) with a maximum continuous rating of 1,050hp at 19,500rpm drives the integrated lift/propulsion system. Its output shaft passes first to the main gearbox from which shafts extend sideways and upwards to two three-bladed Hamilton/Sumitomo variable-pitch propulsion propellers of 2·59m (8ft 6in) diameter. A further shaft runs forward to the fan gearbox from which a drive shaft runs vertically downwards to a 2·27m (7ft 7in) 13-bladed lift fan mounted beneath the air intake immediately aft of the passenger saloon roof. The fan is constructed in aluminium alloy and the disc plate is a 40mm (1½in) thick honeycomb structure.

To prevent erosion from water spray the propeller blades are nickel plated.

Fuel is carried in two metal tanks, with a total capacity of 1,900 litres (416 gallons), located immediately ahead of the lift fan assembly.

CONTROLS: Twin aerodynamic rudders in the propeller slipstream and differential thrust from the propellers provide directional control. The rudders are controlled hydraulically from the commander's position. In addition two retractable water rods, located slightly aft of amidships on each side of the main buoyancy tank, can be extended downwards to prevent drift when turning and these also assist braking at high speeds. The water rods are operated hydraulically by foot-pedals. When used in conjunction with the rudders, the turning radius is reduced to about a third of that taken when only air rudders are used.

A thrust-port air bleed system provides lateral control at slow speeds. The thrust ports are actuated by air extracted from the engine compressor and are located beneath the passenger door entrances, port and starboard.

HULL: Construction is primarily of high strength AA502 aluminium alloy suitably protected against the corrosive effects of sea water. The basic structure is the main buoyancy chamber which is divided into eight watertight subdivisions for safety, and includes fore and aft trimming tanks. Two further side body tanks, each divided into three watertight compartments, are attached to the sides of the main buoyancy chamber. To facilitate shipment the side body tanks can be removed, reducing the width to 3·75m (12ft 4in).

The outer shell of the main buoyancy chamber, the machinery deck space, the forward deck and the passage decks around the cabin exterior are all constructed in honeycomb panels with aluminium cores.

The lift fan air intake, radar cover, part of the air conditioning duct, and inside window frames are in glass fibre-reinforced plastic.

Design loads are as required by the Provisional British ACV Safety Regulations.

SKIRT: The flexible skirt was designed by Mitsui in the light of research conducted with aid of the RH-4 (MV-PP1 prototype). It is made of 0·8mm (¹/₃₂in) thick chloroprene-coated nylon sheet. A fringe of finger type nozzles is attached to the skirt base at the bow and on both sides. At the stern a D-section bag skirt is used to avoid scooping up water.

Two transverse and one longitudinal stability bags are fitted.

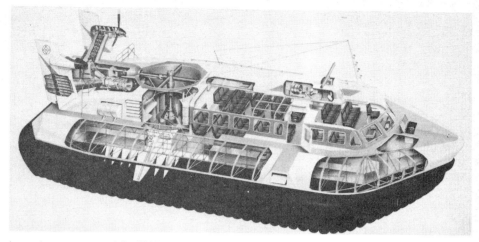
Internal arrangement of the MV-PP5 showing passenger accommodation and the gas-turbine powered lift/propulsion system aft of the cabin

MV-PP5 02 *"Hakucho No 2"* in service with Meitetsu Kaijo Kankosen KK

ACCOMMODATION: The passenger cabin is sited above the forward end of the main buoyancy chamber. Seats for the two crew members are on a raised platform at the front of the cabin. All controls, navigation and radio equipment are concentrated around the seats. The windows ahead are of reinforced tempered glass and have electric wipers.

The two cabin entrance doors are divided horizontally, the lower part opening sideways, the top part upwards. The standard seating arrangement is for 42 passengers but ten additional seats can be placed in the centre aisle.

In accordance with Japanese Ministry of Transport regulations a full range of safety equipment is carried, including two inflatable life rafts, 54 life jackets, one automatic manually activated fire extinguisher for the engine casing and two portable fire extinguishers in the cabin. Other standard equipment includes ship's navig-ation lights, marine horn, searchlight and mooring equipment, including an anchor. The twelve side windows can be used as emergency exits and are made of acrylic resin.

SYSTEMS, ELECTRICAL: Two 2kW, 28·5V ac/dc generators driven by belts from the main gearbox. One 24V, 100Ah battery for engine starting.

HYDRAULIC/PNEUMATIC SYSTEMS: A 7kg/cm² (99·56lb/in²) hydraulic system pressure

for water rods and 4·7-7kg/cm² (56·8-99·5lb/in²)
pneumatic system for thrust port operation.
COMMUNICATIONS AND NAVIGATION:
Equipment includes a radio and radar.
DIMENSIONS
EXTERNAL
Length overall: 16m (52ft 6in)
Beam overall: 8·6m (28ft 2in)
Height overall on landing pad: 4·81m (15ft 9in)
Skirt depth: 1·2m (3ft 11in)
Draft afloat: 0·2m (8in)
Cushion area: 88m² (741ft²)
INTERNAL
Cabin:
Length: 7·1m (23ft 4in)
Max width: 3·8m (12ft 6in)
Max height: 1·9m (6ft 3in)
Floor area: 26m² (280ft²)
Doors:
Two 0·65 × 1·4m (2ft 1½in × 4ft 6in), one each
   side of cabin
Baggage-hold volume: 0·6m³ (24ft³)
WEIGHTS
Normal all-up: 16·3 tons
Normal payload: 4·3 tons
PERFORMANCE
Max speed, calm water: 102km/h (55 knots)
Cruising speed, calm water: 83km/h (45 knots)
Still air range and endurance at cruising speed:
   about 160n miles, 4 hours approx
Vertical obstacle clearance: 0·6m (2ft) approx

MV-PP5 Mk II

This is a "stretched" version of the MV-PP5
fast passenger ferry. Lift and propulsion systems
and power arrangements are identical to those of
the standard MV-PP5, but the hull has been
lengthened by 2·18m (7ft 2in) raising the maximum passenger seating capacity from 52 to 76.
Maximum speed in calm water is 52 knots. Cruising speed and endurance are unaffected.

Two PP5s have been converted to Mk II

Mitsui MV-PP5 Mk II, a new version of the MV-PP5 employing identical lift and propulsion arrangements, but
with the hull stretched by 2·18m, raising the maximum seating capacity from 52 to 76

configuration and one of these is in service with
Japanese National Railways.
DIMENSIONS
Length overall: 18·18m (59ft 7in)
Beam overall: 8·6m (28ft 2in)
Height overall on landing pad to top of mast:
   4·81m (15ft 9in)
Skirt depth: 1·2m (3ft 11in)
Draft afloat: 0·2m (8in)
Cushion area: 104m² (1,120ft²)
WEIGHTS
Normal all-up: 19·3 tons
Normal payload: 7·2 tons
PERFORMANCE
Max speed, calm water: approx 52 knots
Cruising speed, calm water: approx 45 knots
Endurance at cruising speed: approx 4 hours
Passenger capacity, max: 76

MV-PP1

The MV-PP1 is a small peripheral jet ACV
built for river and coastal services and fitted with
a flexible skirt. It seats a pilot and ten passengers
and cruises at 40 knots.

Two craft of this type have been built to
date—the prototype, which was completed in
July 1964 and has been designated RH-4, and the
first production model, the PP1-01.

The latter was sold to the Thai Customs
Department, for service in the estuary of the
Menam Chao Phya and adjacent waters, and has
been named Customs Hovercraft 1. It has been in
service with the Thai Customs Department since
September 1967.

Details of construction, weights, performance,
etc will be found in *Jane's Surface Skimmers
1970-71* and earlier editions.

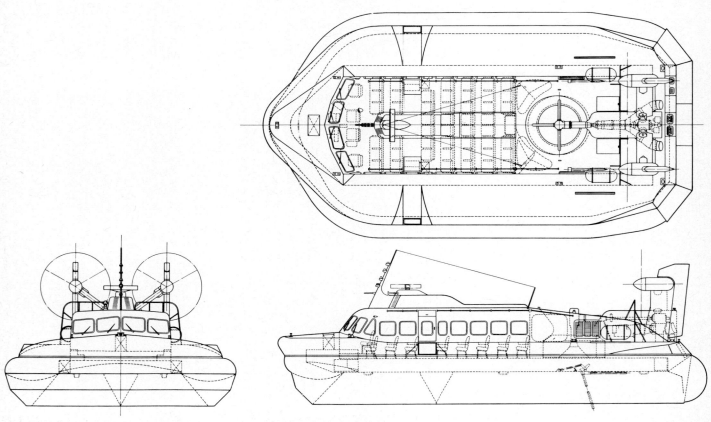

Mitsui MV-PP5 50-seat hovercraft, designed for fast ferry services on Japanese coastal and inland waters

NIHON UNIVERSITY, NARASHINO

Aerodynamics Section, Nihon University at Narashino, 7-1591 Narashinodai, Funabashi, Chiba-Ken, Japan
Telephone: 0474 66 1111 4
Officials:
Masahiro Mino, *Senior Director*
Toyoaki Enda, *Director*

The Aerodynamics Section of the Physical Science Laboratory, Nihon University, is conducting an extensive ACV research programme, which includes the construction and test of four small experimental craft: the Pastoral light amphibious single-seater, the Mistral, propelled by either waterscrew or waterjet, the Floral, a two-seat sidewall craft and the N73.

An air boat, the Ripple, is employed as a "chase" craft to record on film the behaviour of these light ACVs over water.

Nihon University's ACV design group works in close co-operation with similar groups at the Institute of Technology, Ashikaga, and the University of Aoyama Gakuin. Pastoral, in modified form, is now being employed in a research programme conducted by the Institute of Technology, Ashikaga.

The LJ-10 Jimny, a combined ground effect machine and wheeled vehicle, has been completed by Nihon in conjunction with Aoyama Gakuin University.

FLORAL 1

This experimental two-seater was completed in February 1971, and was the first sidewall craft to be built in Japan. In calm water the performance has proved to be superior to that of standard displacement runabouts of similar size and output. The craft was reconstructed in 1972 when the twin outboard propulsion units were replaced by a single unit, and a new stern skirt and trim flaps were introduced. Instrumentation includes trim, roll angle and speed indicators and gauges for measuring pressure in the plenum chamber.
LIFT AND PROPULSION: Lift is provided by a single 8hp ZD-305 two-cycle single-cylinder air-cooled engine, located aft of the open cockpit and driving an F S Anderson 710-20-3L plastic fan. Propulsion is provided by a single Penta 550 outboard engine driving a waterscrew.
CONTROL: Engine/propeller unit turns for steering.
DIMENSIONS
Length overall: 5·2m (17ft 1in)
Beam overall: 1·8m (5ft 11in)
Height overall: 0·8m (2ft 7½in)
WEIGHTS
Normal gross: 540kg (1,191lb)
PERFORMANCE
Max speed over calm water: 62·7km/h (39mph)
Max speed, 0·4m (16in) waves: 52·1km/h (32mph)

MISTRAL 2

Developed jointly by Nihon University, Masahiro Mino and the Institute of Technology, Ashikaga, the Mistral 2 is an experimental waterscrew propelled single-seater derived from the SEA-NAC.
LIFT AND PROPULSION: A single 8hp Fuji ES-162DS- two-cycle single-cylinder air-cooled engine mounted immediately aft of the cockpit drives a 580mm (22⅞in) S11-03-FS03 five-bladed aluminium alloy fan for lift. Propulsion is supplied by either a 22hp Fuji KB-2 or 50hp Mercury 500 driving a waterscrew.
HULL: Moulded glass fibre, with inflated fabric-reinforced neoprene sidebody/skirt.
CONTROLS: Engine/propeller unit turns for steering.
DIMENSIONS
Length overall: 4·1m (13ft 5in)
Beam overall: 1·8m (5ft 11in)
Height overall: 1·09m (3ft 7in)
WEIGHTS
Normal gross: 310kg (664lb)
PERFORMANCE
Max speed over calm water: 67·5 km/h (42mph)
0·6m (2ft) waves: 45·5km/h (28mph)

Floral 1, two-seater sidewall ACV, built by students of the Aerodynamics Section of Nihon University, Narashino, Japan

Mistral 2 single-seat research ACV

N 73 amphibious runabout during trials. Built by the Aerodynamics Section, Nihon University, the craft has attained 90km/h (55mph) over water

N 73

This experimental single-seater has attained 90km/h (55mph) over water and 60km/h (37mph) during trials over land.
LIFT AND PROPULSION: A single 13hp Daihatsu two-cycle, single-cylinder air-cooled engine immediately ahead of the cockpit drives a 560mm (22in) diameter Multiwing fan for lift. Propulsion is supplied by a 40hp Xenoah G44B two-cycle twin-cylinder engine driving a 1·2m (3ft 11¼in) diameter two-bladed propeller.
CONTROLS: Craft heading is controlled by twin aerodynamic rudders hinged to the rear of the propeller shroud and operated by a handlebar.

HULL: Moulded glass fibre with inflated fabric-reinforced neoprene sidebody/skirt.
DIMENSIONS
Length overall: 4·5m (14ft 9in)
Beam overall: 1·8m (5ft 10⅞in)
Height: 1·55m (5ft 1in)
WEIGHTS
Normal empty: 340kg (750lb)
Normal payload: 215kg (474lb)
PERFORMANCE
Max speed, over water: 90km/h (55mph)
over land: 60km/h (37mph)
Range: 150km (93·2 miles)

KOREA, REPUBLIC

KOREA TACOMA MARINE INDUSTRIES LTD

Korea Tacoma, the South Korean associate of Tacoma Boatbuilding Co, Tacoma, Washington, USA, has built a variety of fast patrol boats for the South Korean Navy since 1976. These include three 250-ton PSMM multi-mission patrol ships and four 71-ton CPIC coastal patrol interdiction craft.

In 1979 the company began marketing three metal-hulled surface effect ships for a variety of commercial applications. Lengths of the three craft are 8, 15 and 18 metres, respectively, and each can be fitted with a range of alternative power plants according to performance requirements. preliminary details are given below.

KOREA TACOMA 8m SES

This is the first of a new series of multi-purpose surface effect craft. Passenger ferry, freight and crewboat versions are projected.

LIFT AND PROPULSION: Motive power for the lift system is provided by a single 80hp automotive engine. Thrust is supplied by two water propellers powered by twin outboards or diesel outdrive units of 80, 100 or 150hp.
CONTROLS: Craft direction is controlled by twin water rudders aft or rotation of the engine/propeller units.
HULL: Primary structure built in welded marine aluminium alloy.
SKIRT: Segmented skirt at the bow and stern.
ACCOMMODATION: Choice of seating arrangements for five, ten or fifteen passengers.
DIMENSIONS
Length overall: 8·2m (26ft 11in)
Beam overall: 4·4m (14ft 5in)

Draft, hullborne: 0·6m (2ft)
  on cushion: 0·1m (4in)
WEIGHTS
Normal all-up (according to power arrangements and passenger load): 3·5-4·5 tons
PERFORMANCE
Max speed, twin 80hp engines: 30 knots
  twin 100hp engines: 40 knots
  twin 150hp engines: 45 knots
Range: 120n miles

KOREA TACOMA 15m SES

This new high speed passenger ferry/freighter is capable of operating at speeds up to 50 knots. In passenger/crewboat configuration accommodation is provided for up to 50 seated passengers.
LIFT AND PROPULSION: Motive power for the lift system is provided by a single marinised diesel engine of 200-300hp. Power for the propulsion system is provided by twin diesels of 350, 500 or 800hp, according to the performance required, each driving a water propeller via a reversing gearbox and an inclined shaft.
CONTROLS: Twin water rudders aft, one on each sidehull. Differential propeller thrust for slow speed manoeuvring.
HULL: Main structure in welded marine grade aluminium alloy.
SKIRT: Flexible segmented skirt at the bow and stern.
ACCOMMODATION: Configurations for 35, 40 and 50 passengers according to route requirements.
DIMENSIONS
Length overall: 15m (49ft 2½in)
WEIGHTS
Normal all-up (according to power arrangements and passenger load): 17-20 tons

PERFORMANCE
Max speed, twin 350hp diesels: 35 knots
  500hp diesels: 40 knots
  800hp diesels: 50 knots

KOREA TACOMA 18m SES

Largest of this new range of high-speed SES passenger ferries, the 18m (59ft) design has buoyant catamaran-type sidewalls almost identical in shape to those of the two smaller craft.

LIFT AND PROPULSION: Power for the lift system is provided by a single marine diesel in the 400-500hp range. Power for the propulsion system is provided by twin diesels of 650, 800 or 1,300hp, each driving a water propeller via a reversing gearbox and an inclined shaft.
CONTROLS: Twin water rudders aft, one on each sidehull. Differential propeller thrust for slow speed manoeuvring.
HULL: Main structure built in welded marine aluminium alloy.
SKIRT: Segmented skirt at the bow and stern.
ACCOMMODATION: Seating arrangements for 60, 80 and 90 passengers according to route requirements.
DIMENSIONS
Length overall: 18m (59ft 1in)
Beam overall: 9m (29ft 7in)
Draft, hullborne: 1m (3ft 3in)
  on cushion: 0·4m (1ft 3¾in)
WEIGHTS
Normal all-up weight: 36 tons
PERFORMANCE
Max speed, twin 650hp diesels: 35 knots
  twin 800hp diesels: 40 knots
  twin 1,300hp diesels: 50 knots

NEW ZEALAND

HOVER VEHICLES (NZ) LTD

PO Box 10, Ohau, New Zealand
Telephone: 80792 LEVIN
Officials:
Roy Blake, *Director*
David Clemow, *Director*
Jim Pavitt, *Director*
Ron Wadman, *Director*
Brian Shaw, *Director*
Mel Douglas, *Director*
D Hammond Murray, *Managing Director*

Hover Vehicles (NZ) Ltd has been formed by a group of New Zealand pilots, engineers and businessmen in association with Roy Blake, winner of the "Hovernaut of the Year" title in the United Kingdom in 1968, who afterwards emigrated to New Zealand.

The company plans to build vehicles which can be employed either on light utility applications or as recreational craft. The first craft under development is the H.V.4, a 6·4m (21ft) long amphibious six-seater, the final design for which has been completed. Initial tests of the prototype began in May 1975, when speeds of up to 80·46km/h (50mph) were recorded over land. Good stability and handling qualities were observed.

It is envisaged that several pre-production models will be built before consideration is given to putting the craft into full-scale production.

Apart from the design and construction of the H.V.4 the company has built and tested its own variable- and reversible-pitch fibreglass airscrew which will be used for ACV propulsion.

Government financial assistance was provided

During initial trials, Hover Vehicles' H.V.4 attained speeds of up to 80·46km/h (50mph) over land

for the first prototype. Preliminary details of the company's first craft are given below.

H.V.4

The prototype of this attractive six-seat recreational ACV is complete. It is intended as a quiet, easily controlled craft which can be driven by an "above average" car driver after two hours training. The craft can be towed on a trailer behind most six-cylinder cars.
LIFT AND PROPULSION: Power for the integrated lift/propulsion system is provided by a single 185hp Rover V8 automobile engine which drives a 914mm (3ft) diameter centrifugal lift fan

and two 914mm (3ft) diameter variable-pitch shrouded airscrews.
ACCOMMODATION: Seats are provided for a driver and five passengers in a fully enclosed cabin.
DIMENSIONS
Length overall: 6·4m (21ft)
Beam overall: 3·04m (10ft)
Reduced for transport by road: 2·43m (8ft)
Ground clearance: 609mm (2ft)
WEIGHTS
Normal loaded: 1,360·77kg (3,000lb)
PERFORMANCE
Max speed: 80·46km/h (50mph)

POLAND

WARSAW YOUNG TECHNICIANS CENTRE

Warsaw, Poland

Authorities in the Soviet Union and Eastern Europe are encouraging the construction and operation of light recreational hovercraft by schools, colleges, universities and other youth groups.

Although no official association has yet been formed, encouragement is also being given to the staging of national and international race meetings. Reviewing the light hovercraft scene in 1980, one aviation magazine stated, "Given that successful prototype mini-ACVs have been successfully built in the Soviet Union, Czechoslovakia, Bulgaria, Romania and Poland, competitions between socialist countries are highly likely."

The Polish press has reported the existence of a number of nationally-designed and constructed ACVs, from large-scale prototypes for agricultural, industrial and maritime uses, to small sports and leisure craft.

Brief descriptions of two light hovercraft have been published, the SMT-1 and the Horizonty Technicki.

SMT-1

This amphibious single-seater was designed and built by students at the Warsaw Young Tech-

nician's Centre. It has operated successfully over land, ice and water. The prototype, built in 1964, was underpowered. A more powerful version, fitted with a modified modern wood-saw, motorcycle or PF 126P car engine, is under consideration as a production model.

LIFT AND PROPULSION: Lift is supplied by a single S-1 125cc motorcycle two-stroke driving a six-bladed duct-mounted axial fan. Power for the propulsion system is provided by a second S-1 125cc two-stroke.

CONTROLS: Craft direction is controlled by an aerodynamic rudder operated by a rudder bar.

DIMENSIONS
Length: 2·2m (7ft 2in)
Beam: 1·4m (4ft 7in)
Height: 1·2m (3ft 11in)
PERFORMANCE
Speed (prototype with 125cc S-1 motorcycle engine powering thrust system): 25km/h (15mph)

HORIZONTY TECHNICKI

This is either a single or two-seater, the prototype of which was built in 1971. A sketch of the craft appears alongside.

LIFT AND PROPULSION: Integrated system. Motive power is supplied by a single motorcycle two-stroke rated at 10kW.

CONTROLS: Directional control is supplied by an aerodynamic rudder.

Above: SMT-1 amphibious single-seater and below: impression of Horizonty Technicki two-seater

DIMENSIONS
Length: 3·5m (11ft 6in)
Beam: 1·9m (6ft 2in)
Height: 1·7m (5ft 7in)
WEIGHTS
Empty: 200kg (441lb)
Loaded: 300kg (661lb)
PERFORMANCE
Max speed: 60km/h (37mph)

SINGAPORE

SEACONSTRUCT

Rohr Marine Inc, of Chula Vista, California, and the Singapore-based shipbuilder, Seaconstruct, are jointly investigating the possibility of building the Rohr-designed Light Multi-purpose Surface Effect Ship (LMSES) in Singapore. The craft, which would be built in aluminium, would be 46·3m (152ft) long and have a beam of 14·6m

(48ft). Its range would be 750 nautical miles at a speed of about 60 knots.

In passenger ferry configuration the LMSES would accommodate up to 360 persons, but alternative versions would be available for a range of duties including offshore servicing, in which it would carry a mixed payload of passengers and freight of up to 100 tons.

Initial marketing studies have suggested that

among the suitable routes are Singapore-Jakarta, Singapore-Kuching, Surabaya-Balikpapan and Port Kelang-Penang.

Further details and an illustration of the LMSES will be found in the entry for Rohr Industries Inc, USA, in the ACV section.

It has been reported that should an order be forthcoming, work on the first craft would begin in late 1980 with delivery in late 1981.

SPAIN

FM-AERODESLIZADORES

Avda de España 10, 4°B, Albacete, Spain
Officials:
Pedro Garcia Ferrández, *Engineer*
Julián Martin Sanz, *Engineer*

VAM-F1B

Trials of this interesting new Spanish craft began in the summer of 1979 and proved the craft's ability to carry three persons. At the present time it is undergoing various alterations which have shown themselves desirable in the light of tests and modifications. It has an open cockpit and is fitted with a bag skirt.

LIFT AND PROPULSION: A single Volkswagen engine provides power for both the lift and propulsion systems, with a centrifugal clutch for the centrifugal lift fan. Thrust is supplied by a five-bladed axial fan driven by toothed belt.

CONTROLS: Craft direction is controlled by twin rudder vanes in the thrust fan slipstream and operated by a wheel.

HULL: Glass fibre structure, reinforced where necessary with aluminium tube.

SKIRT: Bag type, fabricated in neoprene/nylon fabric. Use of a loop and segment type skirt is under consideration.

ACCOMMODATION: Open cockpit for driver and two passengers.

SYSTEMS, ELECTRICAL: 6V battery for starting and services.

DIMENSIONS
Length overall: 3·1m (10ft 2in)
Width, sidebodies: 2·48m (8ft 1in)
sides folded for transport: 1·04m (3ft 5in)
Height, skirt inflated: 1·26m (4ft 1½in)
PERFORMANCE
Max speed, estimated: 60km/h (37·3mph)

VAM-F1B three-seater light ACV

G1 CARGO HOVERCRAFT

This craft is designed to carry a variety of cargoes to estuarial, riverside and coastal ports for transhipment.

DIMENSIONS
Length: 6m (19ft 8in)
Width: 3m (9ft 10in)
WEIGHTS
Max payload: 500kg (1,102kg)
PERFORMANCE
Max speed over water: 45km/h (28mph)
over land: 60km/h (37mph)
Max vertical obstacle clearance: 0·4m (15¾in)
Endurance: 2 hours

G2 CARGO HOVERCRAFT

A larger variant of the G1 Cargo Hovercraft, the G2 will carry a 1 tonne payload.

DIMENSIONS
Length: 8m (26ft 3in)
Width: 4m (13ft 1½in)

WEIGHTS
Max payload: 1,000kg (2,204lb)

PERFORMANCE
Max speed over water: 45km/h (28mph)
over land: 60km/h (37mph)
Max vertical obstacle clearance: 0·4m (15¾in)
Endurance: 2 hours

FM-AXZ-001

This is a design study for a high-speed amphibious two-seater powered by a 385hp gas turbine.

LIFT AND PROPULSION: Motive power is supplied by a single 385hp Allison 250B17 gas turbine. This drives two centrifugal lift fans and two ducted variable-pitch fans for thrust.

HULL: Mixed fibreglass reinforced plastics and aluminium construction.

CONTROLS: Craft direction is controlled by twin rudders aft of the propeller ducts. Pitch stability is provided by a horizontal stabilizer.

ACCOMMODATION: Enclosed cabin fitted with two side-by-side seats.

SKIRT: Fingered bag type.

DIMENSIONS
Length overall: 5·5m (18ft 2in)
Width: 2·85m (9ft 4in)
Max height: 2m (6ft 7in)
Skirt height: 0·53m (1ft 9in)

WEIGHTS
Total payload: 1,150kg (2,535lb)
Empty furnished: 590kg (1,300lb)
Payload: 220kg (485lb)

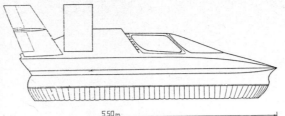
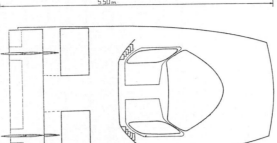

General arrangement of FM-AXZ-001

INTERCEPTOR 1

This fully amphibious four-seater is intended for coast guard, military patrol and ambulance applications on estuaries and navigable rivers.

LIFT AND PROPULSION: Integrated system. A single air-cooled engine drives a centrifugal lift fan and two multi-bladed fixed-pitch thrust fans.

CONTROLS: Two rudders placed in the thrust fan slipstreams provide directional control. Pitch stability is provided by a horizontal stabiliser.

HULL: Aluminium structure. Sealed tanks provide reserve buoyancy.

SKIRT: Open loop type with segments in the stern. Will be provided with conical ducts for avoiding water collection. Skirt material is nylon covered neoprene.

ACCOMMODATION: Enclosed cabin seats four. As an ambulance or rescue craft the cabin interior could accommodate a stretcher beside the driver.

DIMENSIONS
Length overall: 4·8m (15ft 9in)
Beam overall: 2·2m (7ft 3in)
Height without inflated skirt: 1·6m (5ft 3in)

WEIGHTS
Empty: 650kg (1,433lb)
Max payload: 1,000kg (2,204lb)

PERFORMANCE
Max speed over water: 55km/h (34mph)
  over land: 70km/h (43mph)
Endurance: 5 hours
Max vertical obstacle clearance: 0·40m (15¾in)

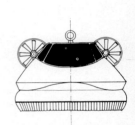
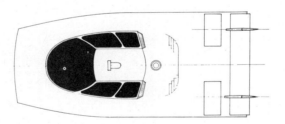

Interceptor 1 for coast guard, military patrol and ambulance applications

ALBERTO GIMENEZ DE LOS GALANES

Reyes 7, Madrid 8, Spain
Telephone: (341) 231 5289
Officials:
Jorge Gomez Gomez
Eduardo Sanchiz Garrote

After several years of studying the theoretical aspects of hovercraft at the Escuela Tecnica Superior de Ingenieros Aeronauticos in Madrid, a group of aeronautical engineers decided, in September 1979, to verify their technical predictions by constructing a small craft. Initially the craft — named Furtivo I — will be used to provide confirmation of earlier theoretical studies, but a later design will be developed which is likely to incorporate certain improvements such as the HDL Skirt Shift system. Furtivo I performed its first flight in February 1980. Its construction started in December 1979.

FURTIVO I

LIFT AND PROPULSION: A single Rotax or Sachs Wankel will drive two ducted fans and a single McCulloch MC-91 engine, rated at 8hp, will provide power for an axial lift fan mounted in the craft forward structure.

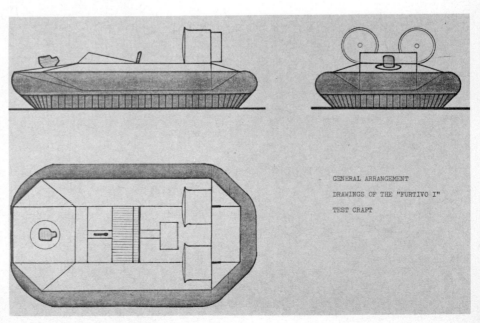

GENERAL ARRANGEMENT DRAWINGS OF THE "FURTIVO I" TEST CRAFT

General arrangement of Furtivo I

CONTROLS: Air rudders located in the rear of each propulsion duct provide directional control and are activated by a control stick located in the cockpit.

HULL: The hull is constructed from plywood with certain items in glass-reinforced plastic.

SKIRT: The skirt, of the loop and segment design, is made of a polyurethane coated nylon material. Cushion pressure is estimated at 10lb/ft².

ACCOMMODATION: Seating is provided for two persons sitting side by side in an open cockpit amidships.

DIMENSIONS
Length overall, power off: 4m (13ft 2in)
Beam overall, power off: 2m (6ft 7in)
Height overall, skirt inflated: 1·5m (4ft 11in)
Draft afloat: 8·5cm (3⅓in)
Cushion area: 7·5m² (80·7ft²)
Skirt depth: 0·3m (12in)

WEIGHTS
Normal empty weight: 197kg (434·3lb)
Normal payload: 183kg (403·4lb)

PERFORMANCE
Max speed, over calm water: 35km/h (21·75mph)
    over land: 45km/h (28mph)
Vertical obstacle clearance: 0·3m (12in)

Furtivo I two-seat research hovercraft

TRINIDAD

COELACANTH GEMCO LTD

1 Richardson Street, Point Fortin, Trinidad
Telephone: Point Fortin 2439
Cables: Coelacanth, Trinidad
Officials:
Nigel Seale, *Director*
Kelvin Corbie, *Director*
R Varma, *Secretary*

Coelacanth Gemco Ltd, the first company to specialise in the design and construction of air cushion vehicles in the West Indies, has been granted Pioneer Status for the manufacture of hovercraft in Trinidad by the government-controlled Industrial Development Corporation. The company has obtained the approval of the Town and Country Planning Commission to construct an ACV factory and a hoverport at Guapo Beach, Trinidad. Guapo Bay and the neighbouring Antilles Bay will be used by the company for sea tests and a disused runway adjacent to the site will be used for overland tests.

The company also plans to build a two-mile long, 100ft wide ACV roadway between Guapo Beach and the Point Fortin Industrial Estate.

Meetings have been held with the Trinidad Government to negotiate a right-of-way over Government-owned land.

A freight operation is planned with ACVs taking aboard finished goods from the factories, and delivering them to Port of Spain, 40 minutes away at a speed of 60 knots.

Craft at present under development by the company are the Pluto, Jupiter, Venus, Arcturus and Mars, and a military ACV.

Progress is also being made with the development of a hover truck, with a payload of 3 tons, for carrying sugar cane from the Trinidad cane fields in wet weather.

PLUTO Mk I AND II

The Pluto is a two-seat test vehicle, built in marine ply, and designed to provide data for a sport and recreational craft which will be marketed under the same name.

The production prototype, which is based on the existing hull and designated Pluto Mk II is undergoing trials. A four-seat version, Pluto Mk III, is due to go into production.

Two and four-seat versions are planned. A standard feature of the production models will be a two-berth cabin and cooking facilities, which will allow the craft to be used for cruising to the northwest of Trinidad in the Gulf of Paria.

LIFT AND PROPULSION: Lift power on Pluto Mk II is supplied by two 6hp Briggs and Stratton motor-mower engines driving two Rotafoil fans.

Pluto Mk II, a manned test model of Coelacanth Gemco Pluto series, puts to sea for a test run off Point Fortin, Trinidad

Pluto Mk III undergoing tests

Thrust is supplied by two 250cc Velocettes driving two 0·685m (2ft 3in) diameter ducted Hordern-Richmond propellers at 5,000rpm.

DIMENSIONS
EXTERNAL
Length: 4·87m (16ft)
Width: 2·38m (7ft 10in)
Height: 1·82m (6ft)

WEIGHTS
Empty: 498·92kg (1,100lb)
Loaded two-seat model: 680·35kg (1,500lb)

PERFORMANCE
Speed, over water: 35·4km/h (22mph)
    over land (with one person): 62·76km/h (39mph)
Vertical obstacle clearance: 203mm (8in)

PLUTO Mk III

Developed from Pluto Mk II, Mk III is a four-seater runabout and yacht.

The production prototype was launched on 26 July 1975 at Point Fortin beach.

LIFT AND PROPULSION: Lift is provided by a single 20hp Sachs Wankel rotary engine driving two Rotafoil fans, and propulsion by two 250cc Velocettes driving two 0·685m (2ft 3in) diameter ducted Hordern Richmond propellers at 5,000rpm.

All series production craft will be powered by three Sachs Wankel engines—one for lift and two for propulsion. Fuel is carried in two standard marine power boat tanks, mounted amidships on the outer hull periphery.

Plans are being made to power a de luxe model with a 120hp engine driving a hydraulic pump which will, in turn, drive three hydraulic motors. Two of these will power the propulsion system and the third will power the lift system.

CONTROLS: Craft heading is controlled by twin rudders aft operating in the slipstreams of the two propellers. Thrust ports are fitted port and starboard, fore and aft, to provide additional control at slow speeds when approaching and leaving jetties.

HULL: First production craft will be in ³/₁₆in mahogany marine ply, with the bottom and sides sheathed to 152mm (6in) above the waterline in glass fibre.

ACCOMMODATION: The cabin accommodates a family of four—two adults and two children—and stores for an overnight stay. The seats are removable and can be used on the beach. On board the craft, the position of the seats can be altered if necessary to adjust craft trim. Built-in steps are provided on each side of the hull to simplify access to the craft after bathing. A hatch is provided aft for baggage items and stores and another forward to facilitate the handling of mooring lines and the anchor. The cabin windows, in ³/₁₆in plexiglass, slide rearwards in their frames for access to the cabin.

DIMENSIONS

EXTERNAL

Length: 5·48m (18ft)
Width: 2·38m (7ft 10in)
Height, inflated skirt: 1·82m (6ft)
Cushion depth: 381mm (1ft 3in)
Freeboard in displacement mode: 0·76m (2ft 6in)

INTERNAL

Cabin floor area (total usable area): 3·71m² (40ft²)

WEIGHTS

Empty: 566·9kg (1,250lb)
Normal gross (4 passengers and 20 gallons of petrol): 884·5kg (1,950lb)

PERFORMANCE

Speed over water: 40·23 km/h (25mph)
  over land: 64·37km/h (40mph)

VENUS

This craft has been designed principally for carrying oil company executives to and from wells in the Gulf of Paria, in Soldado and other areas in the West Indies. Ten- and fifteen-seat versions will be built, and like the Jupiter, the craft will be available in either amphibious form with a continuous skirt or as a rigid sidewall type with bow and stern skirts.

Nigel Seale, designer of Pluto Mk III, stands at the side of the craft as it is put through static hovering trials in Coelacanth Gemco's workshop. Hatches in the cabin roof and at the bow enable mooring lines to be handled more easily

A manned scale model hull of the craft was completed in November 1968. This craft is also being used as a test bed for the two- and four-seat Pluto series.

JUPITER

A projected four-seat ACV runabout, Jupiter is designed around the basic hull of the company's Super Bee cabin cruiser, and will be available either as an amphibious craft, with a continuous peripheral skirt, or as a rigid sidewall type with bow and stern skirts.

Lift will be provided by a 75hp modified outboard driving two Rotafoil fans, and propulsive thrust by a 90hp modified outboard driving a reversible-pitch ducted propeller.

DIMENSIONS

Length: 5·48m (18ft)
Beam: 3·04m (10ft)
Height: 2·13m (7ft)

WEIGHTS

Including fuel: 1,275kg (2,810lb)

PERFORMANCE

Max speed (estimated): 50 knots

ARCTURUS

The Arcturus is a 35-seat amphibious ACV designed by Nigel Seale. Motive power for the lift and propulsion system will be supplied by high speed diesel generators driving Lear Siegler Electric Motors.

Work has started on a manned scale model but activity has been suspended temporarily while the company concentrates its resources on the development of the Pluto series.

MARS

Coelacanth Gemco's first military design is the 10·66m (35ft) long Mars, a 10-ton patrol craft designed to operate in sheltered waters. It will carry seven fully armed men. A manned scale model capable of testing hovering performance has been built.

Construction will be in grp, with aluminium extrusions and panels. Six Rotafoil fans will be employed in the integrated lift/propulsion system.

A feature of the craft will be the employment of stabilisers to reduce drift.

DIMENSIONS

Length: 10·66m (35ft)
Beam: 4·57m (15ft)
Height: 4·57m (15ft)

WEIGHTS

Normal all-up: 10 tons

PERFORMANCE

Cruising speed: 35 knots

UNION OF SOVIET SOCIALIST REPUBLICS

CENTRAL LABORATORY OF LIFESAVING TECHNOLOGY (CLST)

Moscow, USSR

Officials:

Yury Makarov, *Chief Engineer*
A W Gremyatsky, *Project Leader*
Evgeniy P Grunin, *Designer*
N L Ivanov, *Designer*
S Chernyavsky
Y Gorbenko
A Kuzakov, *Consultant*
V Shavrov, *Consultant*
A Baluyev, *Director of Flight Trials*

The Central Laboratory of Rescue Techniques (CLST), a division of OSVOD—the Rescue Organisation for Inland Waters—has designed a small aerodynamic ram-wing machine, capable of 140km/h (86mph), which will be used to answer distress calls on the Soviet lakes, rivers and canals. The vehicle, which is available in several versions, is the ESKA—an abbreviation of Ekranolyetny Spasatyelny Kater-Amphibya (Surface-effect Amphibious Lifeboat). It has also been referred to as the Ekranolet and the Nizkolet (skimmer).

Apart from meeting emergency situations on waterways, the craft, which is amphibious, is capable of operating in deserts, tundra, arctic icefields and steppeland. Derivatives are to be employed as support vehicles for geologists, communications engineers and construction groups.

In Soviet publications emphasis has been given to the potential value of such craft in opening up the mineral wealth of Siberia, the Soviet Far-east, Far-north and other virgin territories.

As with the X-113 Am and other machines of this type, the vehicle operates on the principle that by flying in close proximity to the ground, the so-called image flow reduces induced drag by about 70%. Flight in ground effect inhibits the downwash induced by wing lift, thus suppressing the induced drag. Whereas an average aircraft at normal flight altitude carries about 4kg (9lb) per hp of engine output, the wing-in-ground-effect machine, on its dynamic air cushion carries up to 20kg (44lb), an improvement of more than 400%. Weight efficiency of the craft (ratio of useful load to all-up weight) is 25 to 50% depending on size.

At angles of attack of 2-8 degrees near the ground, its lift is 40-45% greater than when flying out of ground effect. In addition the supporting surface hinders the vortex flow from the lower wing surface to the upper surface which decreases induced drag.

Control of the ESKA is said to be easy and pilots require no special training. Within ground effect it is no more complicated to control than a car.

The design, which has been strongly influenced by the Lippisch "aerofoil boat" concept, employs an almost identical short span, low aspect ratio reversed delta wing with anhedral on the leading edge, dihedral tips and wing floats. A description of ESKA-1 follows, together with illustrations of other aerodynamic machines designed at the CLST, including the saucer-shaped E-120 single-seater; the AN-2E, which incorporates the fuselage, engine and cabin of the Antonov AN-2W seaplane, and a two-seater powered by a 210hp Walter Minor engine.

One of the Ekranoplan's designers has been quoted as saying: "Craft of this type are destined to become, in the not-too-distant future, as popular as hydroplanes, hovercraft and helicopters."

ESKA-1

Research on aerodynamic ram wings began at CLST during 1971. During 1971-72 a series of small scale models were built, followed by the construction of five different full-size craft, including one with a circular planform.

The initial design of the ESKA-1 was prepared by Evgeniy Grunin between September and December 1972. In December 1972 the CLST section specialising in the provision of transport rescue facilities gave the design its full approval and accepted it for construction without additions or alterations.

Several free-flying models of the design were built and tested. In February 1973 A Gremyatsky was nominated leader of the project, and test-flew the first prototype in August of that year. Flight tests were subsequently undertaken by A A Baluyev.

Keynotes of the design were low cost, the use of advanced technology wherever possible and overall reliability in operation. In addition the craft had to be easily broken down for storing and transport by road. Analysis of these and other requirements and conditions led to the decision to build the craft in wood, using 1mm thick aviation ply, plastic foam, glass fibre, glues and varnishes. The resulting machine operated for more than four years in various conditions.

The designers state that although the ESKA-1 is similar aerodynamically to the late Dr Alexander Lippisch's X-112, X-113Am and X-114, the basis of ensuring longitudinal stability and the hydrodynamics at take-off differ. They add, "In the absence of data on the results of tests for those designs, we relied on our own experience and used the results obtained in our own experiments with model ram wings".

Practical help in the preparation of the initial design was given by A Kuzakov, designer of the MAK-15 glider, and the late V B Shavrov (1899-1976), designer of the Sh-2. Another well-known Soviet aircraft designer, V B Gribovsky acted as a consultant in solving the design problems presented by certain joints and structural members.

The basic aerodynamic design and construction of ESKA-1 has provided sufficient data for it to be recommended as a rescue/patrol and communications craft for certain national assignments. The test results show a case for continuing development work on two-three ESKA-1 prototypes, built with modern materials. It has shown considerable operational potential.

POWER PLANT: Single 32hp M-63 four-stroke two-cycle motorcycle engine drives via a two-stage reduction gear a wooden SDW-2 series 1·6m (5ft 3in) diameter constant pitch propeller. Engine is mounted on tubular steel tripod in dorsal position behind the cockpit. ST-4 electric starter mounted on engine block and driving the camshaft via a gear mounted on the extension shaft.

HULL: Built mainly of pinewood frames and longerons, with a box keel in plywood. Structure covered in aviation plywood with exterior clad in glass cloth saturated with ED-6 epoxy resin. Finished with white emulsion and synthetic varnish.

ACCOMMODATION: Cabin contains two aircraft seats in tandem with safety belts and space for parachutes. The rear seat for a passenger or observer is placed close to the centre of gravity which means that no additional trimming is necessary when flying without a passenger.

WINGS: Cantilever shoulder-wing monoplane. Wooden monospar construction with leading edge covered in 1mm ply to form torque box. Dihedral tips each carry a wooden slotted aileron.

TAIL UNIT: Trapezium shaped, strutted T-tailplane mounted on top of fin by sheet metal fixtures. All-wooden single box spar structure. Fixed-incidence, single full-span elevator. Elevator and tailplane covered with AST-100 glass cloth. Wooden rudder secured to fin at two points.

LANDING GEAR: Wing-tip floats are made in pvc foam and covered with a single layer of

Model of ESKA-1 ram wing built by S T Chernyavsky

ESKA-1's effective flying height in ground effect is 0·3-1·5m (1-5ft). The vehicle, a two-seat aerodynamic ram wing, is employed as an experimental, high-speed rescue and liaison craft on the Soviet Union's inland waterways

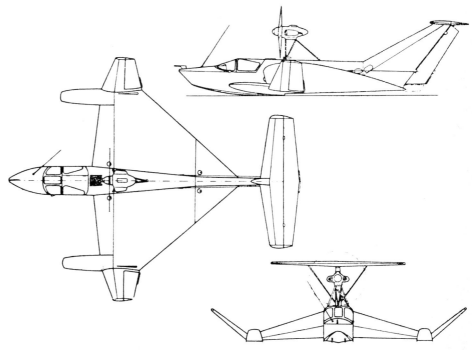

General arrangement, ESKA-1 aerodynamic ram-wing

ASTT3b/-S1 glass cloth. Each is attached to wing by four steel bolts.

CONTROLS: Single aircraft-type control column, incorporating engine throttle, located in the centre of cockpit ahead of pilot's seat. Conventional foot-operated bar to control rudder.

TESTING AND RECORDING EQUIPMENT: In addition to basic aircraft-type instrumentation, the prototype ESKA-1 carried the following test equipment to record pitch and bank angles of up to 40 degrees: K12-51 oscilloscope; GS-6W equipment to measure pitch and angles of bank; synchronising equipment and an electrical supply pack, comprising an SAM28 27V battery and a PT-0.125-36/100 3F alternator.

RADIO: A modified portable 21 RTN-2-4M transmitter receiver provides a continuous radio link between ESKA-1 and the shore up to a distance of 2·5-3km (1½-1¾ miles).

DIMENSIONS
Wing span overall: 6·9m (22ft 5⅝in)
Length: 7·55m (24ft 7in)
Height: 2·5m (8ft 2½in)
Wing area: 13·85m² (148·13ft²)
Tail area: 3m² (32·4ft²)
WEIGHTS
All-up weight: 450kg (992lb)
Empty: 230kg (507lb)
Useful load: 220kg (485lb)
Weight efficiency: 48·879%
PERFORMANCE
Speed, displacement condition: 30-40km/h (18-24mph)
　planing on water: 50-60km/h (31-37mph)
　ram flight at a height of 0·3-3m (11¾in-9ft 10in): 100-140km/h (62-86mph)
　at altitude, 100-300m: 120-130km/h (74-80mph)
　take-off: 55km/h (34·17mph)
　landing: 50-55km/h (31-34mph)
Take-off run from water: 80-100m (260-300ft)
　from snow: 50-60m (162-195ft)
Landing run on water (without braking parachute): 40m (131ft)
Most effective flying height in surface effect: 0·3-1·5m (1ft-4ft 11in)
Max altitude, with 50% load, for obstacle clearance: up to 50m (164ft)
Range with full fuel supply: 300-350km (186-217 miles)
Wing loading: 32·5kg/m² (6·67lb/ft²)
Power loading: 15kg/hp (33lb/hp)
Limiting weather conditions—can operate in force 5 winds.

CLST ANTONOV An-2E

This adaptation of the well-known An-2 multi-duty 12-seat biplane was built in 1973 to the design of E P Grunin. It incorporates several major components of the Soviet-built floatplane version, the An-2W, including the forward fuselage, cabin and engine—a 1,000hp Shvetsov ASh-621R nine-cylinder radial air-cooled engine, driving a four-bladed variable-pitch metal propeller.

The craft is intended for a range of utility applications in addition to carrying passengers and freight. Like the RFB X-114, currently undergoing trials in the German Federal Republic, the An-2E has a retractable wheeled undercarriage enabling it to operate from land as well as rivers, lakes and coastal waters.

DIMENSIONS
Span: 15·75m (51ft 8in)
Length: 18·65m (61ft 2in)
Height: 8·1m (26ft 7in)
Lift area: 94m² (1,011ft²)
WEIGHTS
All-up weight: 7,000kg (15,435lb)
PERFORMANCE
No details available at the time of going to press.

R-1001 MANTA

In 1974 the Central Laboratory of Lifesaving Technology developed a two-seater ekranoplan for light liaison duties with the Soviet fishing fleet. Visually the craft bears signs of having been influenced by the late Dr Alexander Lippisch's design studies for a 300-ton Aerofoil boat, a

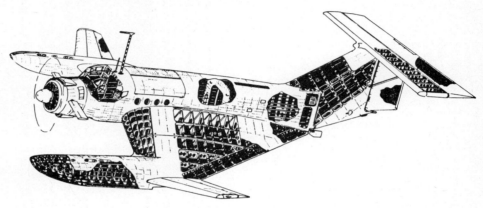

ESKA-1 has been strongly influenced by the Lippisch "Aerofoil boat" concept, and employs an anhedral, reversed delta wing, dihedral tips and wing floats

Cutaway of the CLST ekranoplan adaptation of the 12-seat Antonov An-2W floatplane

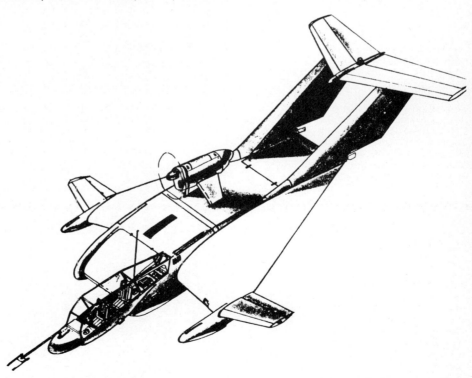

R-1001 MANTA two-seater employed for light liaison duties with the Soviet fishing fleet

major departure from the Lippisch concept being the asymmetrically located cabin jutting ahead of the broad aerofoil-shaped hull on the port side. Reports suggest that in building the wings and hull extensive use was made of grp laminate reinforced with carbon fibres.

Power is supplied by a 210hp Walter Minor VI engine, of Czechoslovak manufacture, and the

craft has an all-up weight of 1,460kg (3,219lb).

Dynamic models were used to gather design data on stability, manoeuvrability and performance.

CLST ESKA EA-06

A developed version of ESKA-1, believed to be a four-seater, began its trials in September

1973, one month after ESKA-1 made its first flight. Photographs of a radio-controlled model of the EA-06 indicate that its lines are similar to those of ESKA-1, major differences being a wider cabin with a full-view windscreen and an aft fuselage angled upwards to support the fin and high-mounted tailplane well clear of the water.

The dynamically similar model was built to ¼ scale and had a wing span of 1·75m (5ft 9in). Power was supplied by a two-cylinder motor, developing 1·8hp at 12,500rpm, and driving a 300mm (11·81in) diameter laminated airscrew. Laminated balsawood construction was employed.

CLST EKRANOLET E-120

No technical details have been released concerning this novel, circular planform WIG single-seater. One of a number of experimental wing-in-ground-effect machines designed by the CLST, it was built in 1971.

PARAWING EKRANOPLANS

The originator of the idea of applying Rogallo-type flexible delta wings to light ekranoplans is Evgeniy Grunin, one of the designers of the ESKA-1. The parawing is well known for its outstanding aerodynamic qualities and stability and is convenient for transport and storage. Grunin, assisted by S Chernyavsky and N Ivanov, fitted a flexible wing to the fuselage of the Czechoslovak Let L-13J Blanik, a powered version of the well known two-seat, all-metal sailplane. Power is supplied by a 42hp Jawa M-150 piston-engine driving a 1·1m (3ft 7¼in) diameter

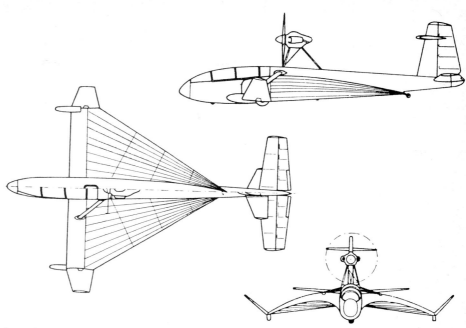

General arrangement of E-0773 Bumblebee 1 parawing ekranoplan

Avia V210 propeller on a tripod mounting aft of the cockpit, an arrangement almost identical to that employed on ESKA-1. The craft was designated the E-0773 Shmiel (Bumblebee). Profiting from the encouraging results of the flight trials,

the team has designed a number of small ekranoplan projects incorporating flexible wings, including a modified version of the An-2W, the floatplane version of the Antonov An-2, single-engine general-purpose biplane.

Four additional ESKA configurations proposed by E Grunin

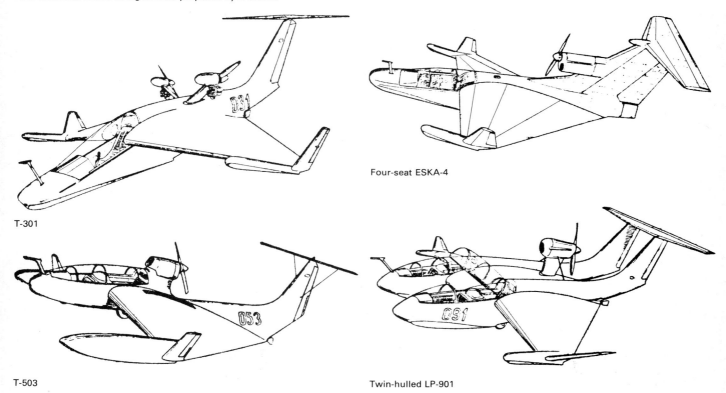

T-301

Four-seat ESKA-4

T-503

Twin-hulled LP-901

KRASNOYE SORMOVO

Gorki, USSR

This shipyard began work in the ACV field by building a five-passenger air cushion river craft known as the Raduga in 1960-61. Since then it has built the Sormovich, a 30-ton peripheral jet ACV for 50 passengers, and the Gorkovchanin, a 48-seat prototype sidewall craft for shallow, winding rivers. It is believed that the Gorkovchanin, Zarnista, Orion, Chaika and Rassvet were all designed by the Gorki Institute of Water Transport Engineers.

The production version of the Gorkovchanin, the Zarnitsa, of which more than 100 have been built, is employed on almost all the river navigation lines of the Russian Federative Republic as

Aist, the Soviet Navy's biggest initial assault amphibious landing craft, is capable of traversing water, beaches and marginal terrain to deliver tanks, armoured transporters, equipment and personnel to assembly points well beyond the shore line

well as on the rivers of the Ukrainian, Moldavian, Byelorussian and Kazakhstan Soviet Socialist Republics.

The design of an 80-seat rigid sidewall ferry, the Orion, was approved by the Soviet Ministry of Inland Waterways in 1970. Construction of the prototype began in 1972 and a trial operation was successfully undertaken in 1975. The craft is now in series production.

A third sidewall vessel is the Rassvet, designed to carry up to 80 passengers along local sea routes. Like Zarnitsa, the craft is able to run bow-on to flat sloping beaches and does not require piers or specially prepared moorings. The prototype, Chaika-1, is undergoing trials. Work is also in hand aimed at evolving a substantially bigger sidewall ACV ferry which has been given the name Turist (Tourist). This particular craft has a design speed of 36 knots and is intended for use along waterways of limited depth and unsuitable for hydrofoils. Two variants are projected, a 300-seat passenger ferry and a mixed-traffic model for 15 cars and 100-120 passengers.

Series production is due to begin in 1981 at the Nakhodka yard following the completion of new facilities.

Work is expected to have been completed during the early 1980s on a variety of sidewall ACV projects including the following:
1. A 120-150 seat river ferry
2. A passenger ferry for very shallow rivers
3. A freight vessel for both narrow and major rivers, including rivers with limited navigation seasons
4. A 120-150 seat seagoing craft
5. A high-speed mixed-traffic ferry for long distance routes

In 1969, prototypes of two fully skirted hovercraft made their debut: the Breeze, a light utility craft, and the Skate, a 50-seat passenger ferry with an all-up weight of 27 tons and a cruising speed of 57·5 mph. While there is no evidence of the Skate going into production, a military version, known in the West by the Nato code name Gus, is in widespread service with the Soviet marine infantry and army. Gus was designed by a special Soviet Navy High Speed Ship Design Bureau, located in Leningrad, which is also thought to have been responsible for the design of the Soviet Union's biggest skirted hovercraft, known in the West as Aist. About ten are in service with the Soviet Navy as amphibious assault landing craft. Aist is generally similar in shape, size and performance to the BHC SR.N4 Mk 2.

Among the latest military air cushion vehicles to enter production for the Soviet armed forces are a 90-ton amphibious assault landing craft, similar in certain respects to the Royal Navy's Vosper Thornycroft VT 2 but smaller, and known by the Nato code name Lebed, and what is believed to be a successor to Gus. It is not unlikely that the latter will appear in a variety of configurations to suit it to a range of military

Seen in this photograph are Aist's rear loading door/ramp, turbine tail pipes and twin skirt flaps. These could be sacrificial strips, since they are just below the tail pipes, rear bag feed ducts or possibly the rear ends of twin keels. Atop the main superstructure is the curved transverse component of the T-shaped duct system supplying air to the main engines. Also clearly seen are the vertical drive shafts which transmit power to the upper gearboxes of the pylon-mounted propellers

duties from assault craft to reconnaissance and fast attack craft. The Soviet Navy is understood to be examining the potential of surface effect ships and is employing at least one sidewall craft for research and development.

The Sormovo yard is likely to have been responsible for building the world's largest air cushion vehicle — a wing-in-ground-effect machine capable of carrying 800-900 troops at speeds up to 300 knots. In 1972 it was announced that plans were in hand to build wing-in-ground-effect machines capable of navigating rivers at a speed of about 250km/h (155mph). A number of these craft are understood to be in experimental service.

Soviet air cushion activity over the next ten years is likely to be massive in comparison with the efforts of the Western World. Part of this activity will be devoted to meeting Soviet military needs, but in the main it will be devoted to the development and construction of amphibious carriers and snowgoing and marshgoing vehicles capable of providing reliable year-round transport in the Soviet North and North-eastern regions where a number of vital development projects are under way.

Only a small percentage of the freight required can be delivered to these areas by Mi-6 helicopter. Estimates of the Institute of Integrated Transport Problems, operating under the USSR Gosplan Institute, have indicated that the use of

air cushion vehicles, apart from speeding up the construction of important facilities under difficult conditions, will enable the cost of haulage over difficult routes of the North and North-east to be reduced by one-third. Savings in transportation expenditure for the work volume forecast for the Eleventh Five-Year Plan will be 1·2-1·5 billion roubles annually because of this.

The use of amphibious ACVs in agricultural production will enable such operations as the application of fertilisers, herbicides, weeding and a number of other operations to be conducted regardless of weather.

Large-load air-cushion platforms will allow beets, potatoes and other crops to be removed from fields regardless of soil conditions. Expenditure for the chemical treatment of fields using self-propelled ACVs will be half the cost of employing an AN-2 aircraft for this work and will be one-third of the cost of an Mi-2 helicopter.

The Institute of Integrated Transport Problems, in considering under Gosplan the data of 25 Soviet ministries, has ascertained the requirement for transport equipment for developing the North and North-eastern regions of the USSR. It was established that, for the level of haulage forecast for the long term, 6,000-6,500 self-propelled and towed amphibious air cushion transport vehicles and about 3,500 fully amphibious ACV ships will be necessary.

From the forecast it is apparent that fully

Side view of Aist hullborne. Major differences between this craft and earlier variants lie in the increased length of the control cabin, the provision of two 30mm fully automatic AA cannon mounts at the bow and the lengthening of the two fins

amphibious ACVs will become more common in the Soviet Union than sidewall ACVs. This is because they lack all-terrain capability, require waterway depths of at least 1m, and can only be employed seasonally because of winter ice.

Soviet air cushion vehicles are expected to be available on the world markets before long. Oleg Kropotov, Director General of Sudoimport, the organisation responsible for the export sales of Soviet ships and shipping equipment and hydrofoils, has announced that the Soviet Union "is now prepared to hold negotiations for the sale of licences for the construction of hovercraft".

270-ton NAVAL ACV
NATO Code Name AIST

The first large amphibious hovercraft to be built in the Soviet Union, Aist is entering service in increasing numbers with the Soviet Navy. Reports suggest that about ten have entered service to date. Built in Leningrad it is similar in appearance to the SR.N4 Mk 2 Mountbatten though giving the impression of being very much heavier than the British craft. It is likely that the bare weight, equipped but no payload, crew or fuel is as much as 170 tons.

Several variants have been built and differ externally in fin height, overall length, superstructure detail and defensive armament.

Since delivery to the Soviet Navy, craft of this type have been employed largely as an amphibious assault landing and logistic supply craft, delivering mechanised infantry, self-propelled weapons, and main battle tanks to simulated beach-heads. Alternative military uses for amphibious craft of the Aist type would be mine countermeasures and fast patrol.

LIFT AND PROPULSION: Integrated system with motive power supplied by two NK-12MV marinised gas turbines, each of which is likely to be rated at 12-14,000hp. Each gas turbine drives two 3·65m (12ft) diameter variable-pitch axial fans and two identical, pylon-mounted propellers, arranged in a facing pair, with the pusher propeller forward and the puller aft. The propellers, which are of the four-bladed variable- and reversible-pitch type are mounted so closely as to be virtually contraprops. Diameter of each propeller is thought to be about 5·79m (19ft).

Air for the main engines appears to be supplied by a curved spine-like trunk above the longitudinal centre line, about 60-70ft long and terminating in a T-piece running athwartships across the stern superstructure between the two fins.

Additional intakes appear to be sited in the sides of the superstructure towards the stern.

An auxiliary gas turbine is located at the rear end of the combat information centre (CIC) at the back of the cabin superstructure.

CONTROLS: Deflection of twin aerodynamic rudders aft, differential propeller pitch and the employment of fore and aft thrust ports provide steering control. Rudders are controlled by a wheel and propeller pitch by levers. All controls are located in a raised bridge located well forward on the superstructure.

HULL: Built mainly in welded marine corrosion resistant aluminium alloys. Structure appears to follow standard practice for large amphibious ACVs. The main hull is formed by a buoyancy raft based on a grid of longitudinal and transverse frames which form a number of flotation compartments. Two main longitudinal vertically stiffened bulkheads run the length of the craft separating the central load deck from the outer or side-structures, which contain the gas turbines and their associated exhausts, lift fans, transmissions, auxiliary power systems and seating for half a company of troops in cabins in the forward port and starboard quarters.

A full width ramp is provided at the bow and a second at the stern, providing through loading facilities.

Typical vehicle loads include two T-62 or T-72 tanks or four to five PT-76 tanks; mobile radio trucks, armoured troop carriers, supply vehicles and ambulances.

ACCOMMODATION: Crew accommodation includes the control cabin or commander's cabin (Aist is described as being the sole warship type in the Soviet fleet in which the commander himself is responsible for steering), galley, radio room, sleeping and living quarters; engine mechanic's watch room and combat information centre (CIC). Naval infantrymen are seated in cabins on both sides of the central vehicle deck. During exercises the standard dress of the Soviet naval infantryman has been steel helmets, black jackets, trousers tucked into short boots, with automatic rifles across their chests and shovels strapped to their sides.

SKIRT: Double bag type in rubberised fabric

Aist unloading two PT-76 amphibious tanks during exercises with a Gus in the background

Forward port quarter of Aist showing the long cabin superstructure which contains the control cabin, crew galley, radio room, engineer's watch room and combat information centre (CIC)

with finger fringe beneath. Features include a high bow skirt line to protect the bow loading door against wave impact.

SYSTEMS, WEAPONS: Two twin 30mm fully-automatic dual-purpose mountings, controlled by Drum Tilt radar for close-in AA defence and by optical sighting and manual control for surface targets, including the suppression of LMG and rifle-fire during beach assaults.

DIMENSIONS (estimated)
Length overall, off cushion: 47·8m (156ft 10in)
Beam overall, off cushion: 17·5m (57ft 5in)
Height, control cabin: 1·98m (6ft 6in)
Length, control cabin: 10·5m (34ft 6in)
Width, bow ramp: 4·41m (14ft 6in)
    rear ramp: 4·87m (16ft)

WEIGHTS (estimated)
Bare weight: 170 tons
Crew, fuel, AFVs or two main battle tanks and ½ company of naval infantry or troops: 90 tons
All-up weight: 260-270 tons

PERFORMANCE (estimated)
Max speed: about 65-70 knots
Endurance: about 5 hours
Hard structure clearance when hovering: 1·2-1·5m (3ft 11in-4ft 11in)

BREEZE

This interesting light amphibious ACV has external features which are reminiscent of the Vickers VA-2 and VA-3.

It was developed by a design group led by German Koronatov, a graduate of the Leningrad Shipbuilding Institute and was completed in 1968. The craft was built to enable the problems of operating a lightweight hovercraft to be understood more clearly and to help assess its economic viability.

The design incorporates the cabin and propulsion system of the Kamov KA-30 Aerosled. Its basic dimensions were dictated partly by the requirement that it should be transportable by rail and trailer.

Trials began during the first half of 1969, during which speed and manoeuvrability tests were conducted over water, snow and ice. Instrumentation was installed in the passenger saloon. In calm water, against a 1-2 metre per second wind,

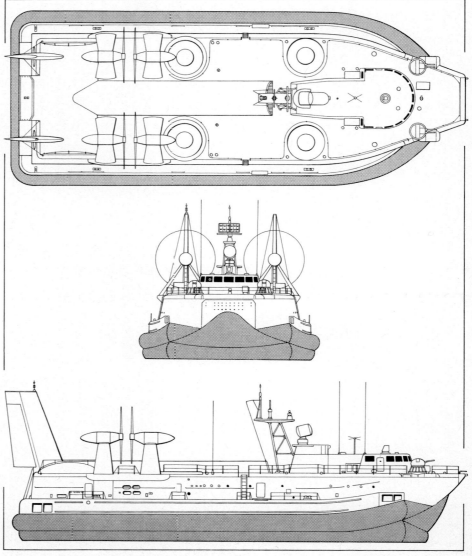

General arrangement of 270-ton Aist amphibious ACV

the measured speed was 70km/h (43·5mph). In similar conditions across ice, the speed was 82km/h (57mph). During winter trials the craft operated over snow 50cm (1ft 8in) deep and shrubs 1m (3ft 3in) high. On the river Neva, when the ice was moving, Briz travelled at 60km/h (37mph) across the icefloes.

In August 1973, extensive trials were undertaken on the rivers and lakes of the Carolia Isthmus and on the basins of the Neva and Ladoga. Briz was transported on a trailer to the Burna estuary and made its way to the source. It also negotiated the Lozevsk rapids and continued on up the river Vuoks until it reached the famous waterfall. It negotiated this, also, then returned to the Burna estuary according to plan. During this endurance test, the craft successfully navigated blocked rivers, stony banks, rapids and raging torrents.

The next series of trials took place in a very busy shipping area, across Lake Lagoda to the Neva and thence back to Leningrad. During this phase, the Briz completed a distance of 1,000km (621 miles). According to the Soviet authorities, the experience gained with Briz confirmed that craft of this type may well have great economic potential.

LIFT AND PROPULSION: Thrust is provided by a 220hp AI-14RS radial piston engine, driving an AV-59 three-bladed metal, controllable and reversible-pitch propeller. Lift is supplied by two 33hp Moskvich MZMA-407 automobile engines mounted aft on the sidestructures, one port and one starboard, each driving a set of four 400mm diameter axial fans mounted on a cardan shaft. The fans are of welded light alloy construction. Cushion pressure is 150kg/m².

CONTROLS: Directional control over most of the speed range is provided by twin aerodynamic rudders operating in the slipstream. Low speed control is assisted by thrust ports fore and aft. Braking and reversing is achieved by reversed propeller pitch.

HULL: Riveted, buoyancy raft-type structure in corrosion resistant V84-4 light alloy. Engine mountings, strengthening members in the hull base and landing pads are in welded AlMg-5 alloy. Hull is divided by four transverse and two longitudinal bulkheads into eight watertight compartments for buoyancy.

SKIRT: Fingered bag type in rubberised fabric. Longitudinal keel and athwartship stability bags for pitch and roll stiffness. Skirt and fingers easily replaceable.

ACCOMMODATION: Fully enclosed cabin, seating operator and six passengers. If required, seating in the passenger saloon can be removed for transporting cargo.

SYSTEMS, ELECTRICAL: The thrust engine drives a 1·5kW, 27V dc generator, type GSK-1500. The lift engines drive a 0·2kW, 12V generator each. The circuitry enables the GSK-1500 to work in parallel with two GST 54 batteries connected in series.

DIMENSIONS
Length overall, cushionborne: 8·4m (27ft 6in)
Hull length: 7·8m (25ft 7in)
Beam overall: 4·1m (13ft 5in)
Height overall, cushionborne: 3m (9ft 10⅛in)
Draft, displacement condition: 0·3m (11¾in)
Skirt depth: 0·4m (1ft 3¾in)
WEIGHTS
All-up weight: 3,100kg (6,835lb)
PERFORMANCE
Max speed over land and water: 100km/h (62mph)

CHAYKA-1 (GULL-1)

This is the name given to the prototype Rassvet, 80-seat sidewall ACV ferry, designed for service in coastal areas with limited water depth. Details will be found in the entry for the Rassvet.

GORKOVCHANIN

The Gorkovchanin is a waterjet-propelled, 48-seat, rigid sidewall ACV, designed for water-bus services on secondary rivers with a guaranteed depth of 0·5m (1ft 8in). In view of the winding nature of these rivers, the craft operates at the relatively low speed of 30-35km/h (19-

Breeze light amphibious ACV for six passengers. Thrust is supplied by a radial aircraft engine driving a three-bladed airscrew, and lift by twin Moskvich 407 automotive engines, each driving a set of four centrifugal fans mounted in series on a common shaft. Fan air is drawn through fixed louvres

Passengers boarding the Breeze. To facilitate access to the cabin a panel is removed from the lift fan cowl ahead of the engine and a handrail and steps are slotted into position

Gorkovchanin rigid sidewall waterbus

22mph). No marked reduction of speed is necessary in water up to 0·5m (1ft 8in) deep.

The craft has been developed from a ten-seat scale model built at the experimental yard of the Institute of Water Transport Engineers at Gorki in 1963, and the pre-production prototype was completed in September 1968. Design was undertaken by a team at the Volgobaltsudoproekt special design office.

Preliminary trials were conducted in September and October 1968, and official trials were completed on the Sura river in May and June 1969. During speed tests over a measured mile with a full complement of passengers aboard, 36·6km/h (22·75mph) was attained. The main engine developed 265hp of which approximately 30hp was used to drive the centrifugal fan.

The craft has covered the journey from Gorki to Moscow (1,016km (622 miles)) and back in 31 and 27 running hours respectively at an average speed of approximately 35km/h (22mph) and has good manoeuvrability when running both ahead and astern. In 1970 the Gorkovchanin was succeeded in production by a developed version, the Zarnitsa.

LIFT AND PROPULSION: Integrated system powered by a 3D6H diesel engine rated at 250hp continuous. The engine is mounted aft and drives a 960mm (3ft 1¾in) diameter six-bladed centrifugal fan for lift, and a 410mm (1ft 4½in) diameter single stage waterjet rotor for propulsion. Fan air is taken directly from the engine

compartment. Skirts of rubberised fabric are fitted fore and aft. The bow skirt of production craft is of segmented type. Cushion pressure is 180kg/m².

The waterjet intake duct is located 100mm (4in) below the displacement water level to prevent air entry, with a consequent reduction in the navigable draft.

CONTROLS: Vanes located in the waterjet stream provide directional control. Thrust reversal is achieved by the use of waterflow deflectors.

HULL: Similar in appearance to that of the Zarya, the hull is in riveted D16 corrosion resistant aluminium alloy. The hull bottom and sides have transverse frames and the sidewalls and superstructure top longitudinal frames. Thickness of plating on sides and bottom is 1·5mm (¹/₁₆in) (2·5mm (³/₃₂in) in the bow section); and on the sidewalls 1mm (³/₆₄in) (up to 5mm (¹³/₆₄in) in the bow section). Deck plates are 1mm (³/₆₄in) thick and the top of the superstructure is in 0·8mm (¹/₃₂in) plating.

Acoustic and thermal insulation includes use of 100mm (4in) thick foam polystyrene sheeting.

ACCOMMODATION: Seats are provided for a crew of two, who are accommodated in a raised wheelhouse, and 28 passengers. Access to the passenger saloon, which is equipped with airliner-type seats, is through a single door located at the bow in the centre of the wheelhouse. The craft runs bow-on to flat sloping banks to embark and disembark passengers.

SYSTEMS, ELECTRICAL: One 1·2kW, 24V dc, engine-operated generator and batteries.
COMMUNICATIONS: Car radio in wheelhouse and speakers in passenger saloon.
DIMENSIONS
Length overall: 22·3m (73ft 2in)
Beam overall: 4·05m (13ft 3½in)
Hull beam: 3·85m (12ft 7⅝in)
Height of hull to top of wheelhouse: 3·3m (10ft 9⅞in)
Height of sidewalls: 0·45m (1ft 5¾in)
Draft afloat: 0·45m (2ft 1⅝in)
Draft cushionborne: 0·65m (1ft 4⅞in)
WEIGHTS
All-up weight with 48 passengers, crew and fuel: 14·3 tons
PERFORMANCE
Normal service speed: 30-35km/h (19-22mph)
Distance and time from full ahead to full astern: 60m (197ft) and 14 seconds

KIROV RIVER FIREFIGHTING ACV

The Kirov shipyard has launched a rivergoing firefighting ACV. It can embark a tracked or wheeled fire engine and transfer it, together with its firecrew, to the site of a disaster. The craft operates at 50km/h (31mph) in the shallowest water and can dock directly onto the river bank.

LEBED

This new amphibious, multi-duty hovercraft is the latest to enter service with the Soviet Navy. Its primary roles are those of amphibious initial assault landing craft and high speed vehicle for LOTS (Logistics-Over-The-Shore) operations. It provides Soviet naval infantry with a rapid lift capability to move personnel and equipment from the well-decks of landing ships across water, beaches and marginal terrain to assembly points well above the shore line.

Smaller than both the US Navy's Jeff (A) and (B) and the Royal Navy's Vosper Thornycroft VT2, Lebed has an overall length of about 25m, a gross weight of about 90 tons and a maximum speed of approximately 55-60 knots.

Three Lebeds or various combinations of Lebeds and Gus type craft up to a total of three can be carried in the well deck of the Soviet Navy's new LPD, the 13,100-ton *Ivan Rogov,* which also accommodates up to a batallion of naval infantry, up to forty tanks and a range of supporting vehicles. The Lebeds were demonstrated in South Yemen when the vessel called there on the way to the Soviet Far East in 1979. Lebed is believed to have been in production for several years. If production rates have been similar to those of Gus, ie 2-4 units per year, it is likely that some 10-12 units are now operational. For use in the initial assault role, Lebeds would be preloaded before the *Ivan Rogov* sailed. Design of Lebed is though to have been undertaken by the Soviet Navy's High Speed Ship Design Bureau in Leningrad.

LIFT AND PROPULSION: Integrated system powered by two marinised gas turbines mounted one each side of the cargo deck aft. Engines are probably two AI-20s, each rated at about 3,600 shp continuous. Air for the two main engines appears to be drawn in through two rectangular, filtered intakes then fed aft through a curved spine-like trunk above the longitudinal centreline and terminating between the two fins. Each engine drives via a main gearbox and shaft a variable-pitch axial lift fan in light alloy. The fans deliver air to the cushion via a continuous peripheral loop skirt with segmented fringes. A second shaft from each main gearbox transmits power via bevel gears to a pylon-mounted four-bladed variable-pitch propulsion fan. The two propulsion fans are contained within aerodynamically shaped ducts which are partly submerged in the hull sidestructures. Apart from attenuating noise the ducts protect the fans from accidental damage. Exhaust covers are provided for both gas turbines aft at the rear of the port and starboard sidestructures.
CONTROLS: The control cabin is located well forward above the port sidestructure and provides a 360 degree view. Directional control at

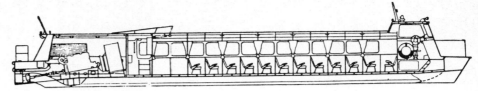
Inboard profile of Gorkovchanin sidewall craft, powered by a single 250hp 3D6H diesel

Bow view of Lebed showing the bow door/loading ramp with its overlapping hatch cover. Above the cabin is a folded mast and navigation radar protected against weather during the voyage by waterproof covering

Air for the Lebed's twin gas turbines appears to be drawn in through two rectangular intakes, one each side of a curved spine-like trunk running above the longitudinal centreline. The intakes for the axial-flow lift fans are outboard of the two gas turbine air intakes

Starboard view showing the twin pylon-mounted thrust fans. The drive arrangement appears to be similar to that employed on Aist with a vertical drive shaft located between the two supports transmitting power to the upper gearboxes

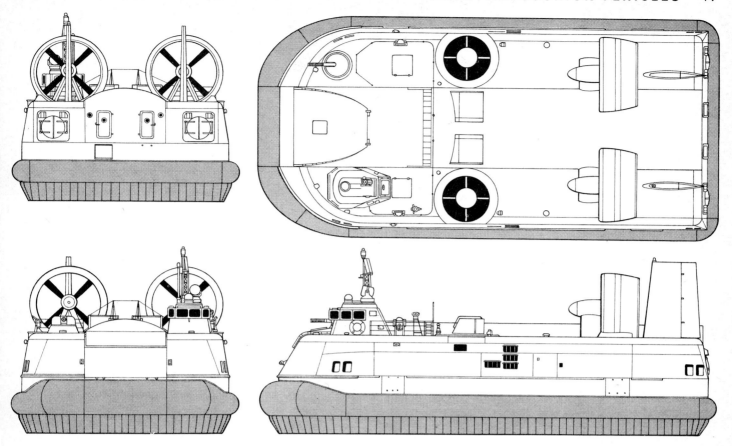

General arrangement of Lebed, the Soviet Navy's latest amphibious initial assault landing craft and logistics-over-the-shore vehicle

normal operating speeds is effected by twin aerodynamic rudders aft of the thrust fan ducts and operating in the fan slipstreams. Differential pitch to the propulsion units augments the turning moment provided by rudder operation. Reverse thrust is applied for braking and reversing. Forward and aft thrust ports, port and starboard, aid directional control at low speeds.

HULL: Riveted skin and stringer structure employing alloy sheet. Structure follows standard practice for large and medium size amphibious ACVs. The main hull is formed by a buoyancy raft based on a grid of longitudinal and transverse frames which form a number of flotation compartments. Two main longitudinal vertically stiffened bulkheads run the length of the craft separating the central load deck from the outer sidestructures which contain the gas turbines and their associated exhausts, lift fans, transmissions and auxiliary power systems. The freight deck is reinforced to permit the carriage of tanks, armoured troop carriers, self-propelled guns, rocket launchers and heavy vehicles. Drive-on, drive-off loading facility is provided by a full-width hydraulically-operated bow door/loading ramp. This is hinged from the base and has an overlapping hatch cover. Photographs suggest that six landing pads are built into the craft undersurface.

SKIRT: Loop and segment type with raised hinge line at the bow.

ARMAMENT: One multi-barrelled remotely-controlled automatically-operated Gatling-type 30mm cannon in barbette on forward quarter of the starboard sidestructure. Probably employed in conjunction with fire-control radar for close-in anti-aircraft and anti-missile defence and with optical sighting and manual control for surface targets including suppressing LMG and rifle fire during beach assaults.

DIMENSIONS
Length overall: 25m (82ft)
Beam overall: 11·2m (36ft 9in)
WEIGHTS
Max all-up weight: 90 tons
Max payload: 40 tons
PERFORMANCE
Max speed, calm conditions: 55-60 knots

Lebed unloading a PT-76 tank. Note the raised control cabin in the port sidestructure and the multi-barrelled remotely controlled automatically operated Gatling-type cannon in the barbette on the forward quarter of the starboard superstructure. The hydraulically-operated bow door/loading ramp has an overlapping hatch cover

NAVAL RESEARCH HOVERCRAFT

A 15-ton experimental ACV has been employed by the Soviet Navy since 1967 to assess the potential of hovercraft for naval applications and investigate controllability and manoeuvrability. Lift is provided by a single 350hp radial aircraft engine driving a centrifugal fan and propulsion by two pylon-mounted radials of the same type driving controllable-pitch airscrews.

DIMENSIONS
Length: 21·33m (70ft)
Beam: 9·14m (30ft)

WEIGHTS
Displacement: 15 tons
PERFORMANCE
Max speed: 50 knots

NAVAL AMPHIBIOUS ASSAULT CRAFT

A larger follow-on design to Gus is believed to be in production for the Soviet Navy. It is reported to be similar in size, configuration and performance to the BHC BH.7 Mk 4 and incorporates a bow door and central load well. Size constraints would be dictated by the dimensions of the well decks of the *Ivan Rogov* and possible follow-on classes.

Like the BH.7, the new craft is fully amphibious and has an all-up weight of 50-55 tons.

LOGISTIC SUPPORT ACV
NATO Code Name "GUS"

The craft is a variant of the Skate, which was designed as a 50-seat amphibious passenger ferry, but which does not appear to have been put into production. Gus is now employed extensively by the Soviet Naval Infantry. During 1978 it was announced that the Soviet Navy's latest and largest amphibious landing ship, the *Ivan Rogov,* is capable of carrying three amphibious assault ACVs of the Gus type. Each of these craft can carry a fully-armed platoon onto a landing beach at speeds of up to 92km/h (57mph). It is thought that thirty to thirty-five of these 27-ton vehicles are in service.

LIFT AND PROPULSION: Motive power is provided by three 780hp TVD 10 marine gas turbines mounted aft. Two drive three-bladed variable and reversible-pitch propellers for thrust and the third drives an axial lift fan. Cushion air is drawn through a raised intake aft of the cabin superstructure.

CONTROLS: Craft direction is controlled by differential propeller pitch, twin aerodynamic rudders and forward and aft puff ports. Elevator provides pitch trim at cruising speed.

HULL: Hull and superstructure are in conventional corrosion-resistant marine light alloy. Basic structure comprises a central load-carrying platform which incorporates buoyancy tanks and outer sections to support the side ducts and skirt. The cabin, fuel tanks, lift fan bay engines and tail unit are mounted on the platform.

ACCOMMODATION: Up to 25 troops are accommodated in an air-conditioned cabin. Commander and navigator are seated in a raised wheelhouse. Battle crew of six, including two responsible for opening the two entry/exit doors forward and amidship.

DIMENSIONS

EXTERNAL

Length overall, power on: 21·33m (69ft 11½in)
Beam overall, power on: 7·3m (23ft 11⅜in)
Height to top of fin: 6·6m (21ft 8in)

WEIGHTS

Normal operating: 27 tons

PERFORMANCE

Cruising speed: 92·5km/h (57·5mph)
Normal cruising range: 370km (230 miles)

ORION-01

Design of the Orion, a rigid sidewall ACV with seats for 80 passengers, was approved in Moscow in the autumn of 1970. The prototype, built in Leningrad, began her trials in October 1973, and arrived at her port of registry, Kalinin, in late 1974, bearing the serial number 01.

The craft is intended for passenger ferry services along shallow rivers, tributaries and reservoirs, and is capable of landing and taking on passengers, bow-on from any flat sloping bank. It is both faster than the Zarnitsa and is less affected in terms of comfort and performance by choppy conditions. Cruising speed of the vessel, which is propelled by waterjets, is 53km/h (32·3mph). It belongs to the R class of the Soviet River Register.

Consideration is being given to the introduction of several variants, including a 'stretched' model seating 100 passengers on shorter routes, a mixed passenger/freight model, an all-freight model and an 'executive' version for carrying government officials.

Experimental operation of the Orion-01 was organised by the Port of Kalinin, Moscow River Transport, the initial run being Kalinin—1st May Factory, a distance of 99km (61·5 miles), of which 45km (28 miles) is on the Volga, 42km (26 miles) on the Ivanov reservoir and 12km (7·5 miles) on the shallow waters of the Soz. The experience of the first weeks of operation was that there was an insufficient flow of passengers on this particular route.

The vessel was then employed on public holi-

This 15-ton research craft has been employed by the Soviet Navy to assess the potential of the skirted air cushion vehicle for naval applications

Gus assault landing craft of the Soviet Naval Infantry during a beach landing exercise. Note the large bellmouth intake for the lift fan amidship. These are early production models with twin elevators for pitch trim

Each Gus carries up to 25 naval infantrymen in an air-conditioned cabin. A battle crew of six is carried, including two responsible for opening the two entry/exit doors forward and amidship, port and starboard

days only for carrying holiday makers and day trippers on such runs as Kalinin—Putlivo 31km (19 miles), Kalinin—Kokoshky 19km (12 miles) and Kalinin—Tarbasa 28km (17·3 miles), and subsequently on a regular schedule to Putlivo.

Finally, Orion-01 was used on the Kalinin—Kimry run, a distance of 138km (85·7 miles), of which 70km (43·4 miles) passes through the Ivanov reservoir and 68km (42 miles) on the Volga.

In all, in 1975, the vessel spent 168 days undergoing trials; of these, it was fully operational on 90 days, and 49 days were spent on repairs or modifications or awaiting work to be undertaken. Time spent underway amounted to 493 hours, during which 7,800 passengers were carried.

Particular attention was paid to assessing the reliability of the skirt. The side sections of the lower part of the bow skirt were badly chafed and split due to contact with the skegs when coming onto the shore. Upper parts of the skirt were not damaged. Problems were also experienced with the aft skirt made from a balloon type fabric. Layers of rubber in the aft part of the segments peeled off; chafing was caused by securing washers and splitting was experienced in the vicinity of the fastenings.

In order to reduce the time spent on repairs, sections of the stern skirt were attached to removable frames. Later a new stern skirt was introduced, based on panels made from a 12mm (0·47in) thick conveyor belt. This enabled the stern draft, on cushion, to be reduced by 10cm (3⅞in) and the speed to be increased by1·5km/h (⅞mph). It also improved the reliability of the craft. During the 200 hours underway from the time the skirt was fitted until the end of the vessel's trials, there was no damage.

It was considered that, in the main, the Orion met the requirements of the Soviet operators for the rapid transport of passengers on R Class rivers and reservoirs. The elimination of the defects revealed during the experimental operation will make it possible to improve the vessel's operational characteristics and increase its reliability.

Series production of vessels of this type is being undertaken at the Sosnovska Shipbuilding Yard in Kirovskaya Oblast.

LIFT AND PROPULSION: Integrated system powered by two 520hp 3D12N-520 diesels mounted in an engine room aft. Each engine drives a Type Ts 39—13 centrifugal fan for lift, and via a cardan shaft, a semi-submerged single-stage waterjet rotor for propulsion. Fan air is fed via ducts to the bow skirt, a transverse stability slot and to the fingered bag skirt aft. Casing of the waterjet system which is removable, forms the stern section of the vessel. In order to reduce vibration the waterjets are mounted on shock absorbers.

Gus 27-ton initial assault amphibious hovercraft during a beach landing

Gus, the Soviet Union's 27-ton amphibious assault landing craft, is entering service in growing numbers with the Soviet Naval Infantry

ORION—Stopping and starting characteristics	Shallow water	Deep water
Distance run by vessel from Full Ahead to Stop		
Metres	136	120
Time in seconds	67	40
Distance run by vessel from Full Ahead to Full Astern		
Metres	84	65
Time in seconds	23	20
Distance necessary for attainment of Full Speed from Stop		
Metres	250	330
Time in seconds	60	80

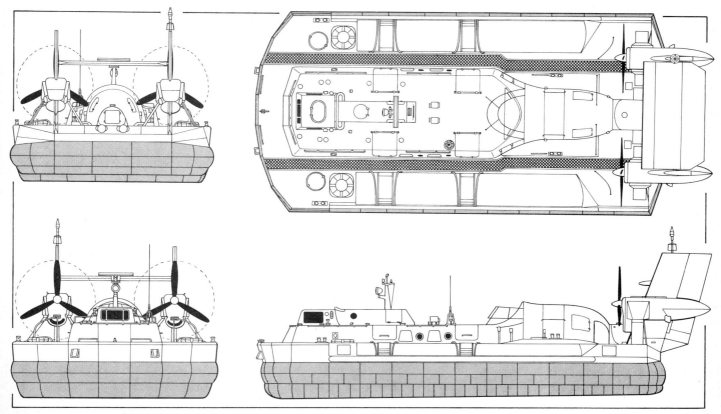

General arrangement of the Gus amphibious assault landing craft. About 35 are in service

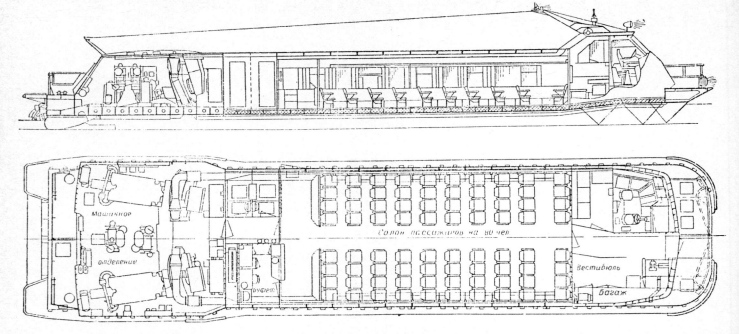

General arrangement of the Orion, 80-seat sidewall ACV passenger ferry. Power is supplied by two 520hp 3D12N-520 marine diesels, each driving a centrifugal fan and a semi-submerged single-stage waterjet rotor

HULL: Similar in overall appearance to Zarya and Zarnitsa types. All-welded structure in AlMg-61 aluminium-magnesium alloy. Lateral framing employed throughout hull with the exception of the bow and stern decks, where longitudinal frames have been fitted. Superstructure and wheelhouse are of welded and riveted duralumin construction on longitudinal framing.

ACCOMMODATION: Seats are provided for the operating crew of 3, who are accommodated in a raised wheelhouse, a barman, two seamen and 80 passengers. At the aft end of the passenger saloon are two toilet/washbasin units and a bar. There is also an off-duty cabin for the crew. Access to the passenger saloon is via a single door at the bow, in the centre of the wheelhouse. A ram-air intake provides ventilation while the craft is underway. Stale air is drawn out by the lift fans aft.

CONTROLS: Rudders located aft of the waterjet inlets and two waterjet deflectors control craft direction. Rudder and flap movement is effected by cables.

SYSTEMS, ELECTRICAL: Two G-73Z engine-driven generators, linked with two sets of STK-18M batteries, provide 28V, 1,200W. One battery set is employed for engine starting, the other for supplying current for the ship's systems.

COMMUNICATIONS: Standard equipment comprises an R-809MZ radiotelephone, a Kama-3 UHF radio and an Unja cabin announcement system.

DIMENSIONS
Length overall: 25·8m (84ft 7¾in)
Beam overall: 6·5m (21ft 4in)
Height overall to mast top: 5·27m (17ft 3½in)
Height to top of wheelhouse: 3·97m (13ft 0¼in)
Draft, displacement condition, fully loaded:
 0·84m (2ft 9⅛in)
 empty: 0·76m (2ft 5⅞in)
Draft, cushionborne, bow: 0·1m (4in)
 stern: 0·5m (1ft 8in)

WEIGHTS
Loaded displacement: 34·7 tonnes
Light displacement: 20·7 tonnes

PERFORMANCE
Max speed: 60km/h (37·25mph)
Cruising speed, full load: 53km/h (33mph)
Max wave height on scheduled runs: 1·2m (4ft)
Range: 400km (249 miles)
Diameter of turn to port: 182m (597ft)
Time to complete turn with rudders at 33 degrees: 187 seconds
Time taken from start of berthing procedure to completion: 1 min approx
Time taken to attain cruising speed from leaving berth: 2 min approx

Impression of the Skate 50-seat amphibious hoverferry

EKRANOPLAN EXPERIMENTAL ("CASPIAN SEA MONSTER")

A giant Soviet experimental wing-in-ground-effect machine, with a span of 40m (131ft 3in) and a length of nearly 91·4m (300ft), is undergoing tests on the Caspian Sea. Trials began in 1965 and are continuing in the company of proportionally smaller models.

The machine, which operates at heights of 3·5-14m (11ft 6in-46ft) above the water, has a potential speed in excess of 300 knots. Power is supplied by eight marinised gas turbines mounted above a stub wing forward, and two 'booster' turbines installed at the base of the dihedral tailplane aft. All ten engines are employed at take-off, when thrust has to be 2·5-3·5 times greater than

that required to maintain cruising conditions in flight.

At take-off the thrust from the eight forward engines is deflected downwards to create additional cushion pressure beneath the wing. After take-off the jet exhaust is directed above the upper surface of the wing again to create additional lift.

The general configuration of the vehicle is indicated in the accompanying impression. It is reported that the machine has been fitted with endplates at the tips of its wings to enhance its aerodynamic characteristics and that the two "booster" jets aft are now fitted to a short vertical fin between the top of the hull aft and the base of the dihedral tailplane.

Giant Soviet ten-jet experimental Ekranoplan which is currently undergoing tests on the Caspian Sea

The system of blowing air beneath the machine's wing enables it to be lifted out of the water and onto a beach at low speeds of about 10-15 knots. Research undertaken in the United States into power augmented ram-wings (PAR) indicates that vehicles of WIG type can be lifted onto their air cushions by blowing air beneath the wings with installed thrust ratios of 0·175 or even lower.

For maximum fuel efficiency, the "Caspian Sea Monster" is probably fitted with turbofan engines such as the 15,000lb st D-30. Its total take-off weight is estimated to be about 313 tonnes and its payload is likely to be at least that of a Western wide-bodied airliner like a Boeing 747, which is roughly 30 per cent of the take-off weight. This gives a payload of about 94 tonnes.

On this basis early claims that the "Sea Monster" can carry 900 or more fully armed troops are probably correct, providing internal dimensions permit.

Like the smaller ekranoplans under development in the Soviet Union, the "Sea Monster" can fly in and out of ground effect wherever necessary to clear shipping, shorelines and port installations, bends in rivers, bridges and fogbanks. In full flight it manoeuvres in exactly the same way as an aircraft, but once out of ground effect its economic advantages are lost, since in order to gain and maintain height, it has to operate at increased power.

When flying in and out of ground effect, pitch stability and longitudinal pitch control are provided by a T-tail, similar in general configuration to that of the C-5A and mounted sufficiently high as to be unaffected by ground effect. Within ground effect the machine seeks its own stability height above rough water.

Soviet experts maintain that craft of this type should be able to negotiate sand spits, shallows, marshes, ice, snow, relatively even and gently sloping banks and low obstacles. Low bridges have been mentioned. They are also stated to be sufficiently seaworthy to operate in rough seas. Wide employment of this type of vessel is foreseen, particularly in the Soviet Navy, which has suggested that they will be invaluable in amphibious operations.

Large numbers of troops could be carried to the selected landing zones with little regard to the condition of the sea, tidal currents, underwater obstacles and minefields, none of which would constitute a hazard.

Advantages in the battle zone will include high speed manoeuvring, and a considerable reduction in the time taken to undertake a mission compared with conventional landing craft.

The capacity of the WIG craft, Ekranoplan machines as they are known in the Soviet Union,

Model of a power augmented ram-wing design patented in the name of the late Robert Oros di Bartini

Likely configuration of a production version of the Bartini concept. Up to forty passengers are seated in each of the twin hulls

will enable them to carry the biggest items of military equipment. Another application for this type of vehicle, according to its designers, is ASW patrol, where its considerable range and endurance will prove an advantage.

References have been made in Soviet technical publications to vehicles with chords of 30-40m (98ft 6in-131ft 2in) and speeds of 400 knots being under consideration. This suggests that research is being aimed at a number of alternative configurations including flying wings and delta wings.

BARTINI T-WINGS

The Ministry of the River Fleet announced in April 1972 that it planned to build craft of the Ekranoplan (WIG) type "which will travel within several metres of a river surface at speeds of some 250km/h (155mph)".

It seems probable that in order to avoid navigation problems in busy river port areas these craft will be of smaller overall dimensions than the 40m (131ft 3in) span machine described earlier. Low aspect ratio wings are likely to be employed and it is possible that these early production craft are of 5-6 tons displacement. A number of these machines were reported to be in experimental service in 1973.

On Moscow television in July 1973, a programme commemorating Soviet Navy Day traced the progress of high speed water transportation and confirmed that Ekranoplanes are being developed in the Soviet Union. The craft were described by the commentator as "ground gliders", capable of operating over land, water, snow and ice. A small machine built in Odessa in the early 1960s was shown to viewers, together with a completely new research craft of much larger size believed to have been designed by the late Robert Oros di Bartini.

The craft, a derivative of an earlier design patented in Bartini's name, is of catamaran configuration and carries up to forty passengers in each of the twin hulls. The crew and operating controls are accommodated in a central pod jutting ahead of the wing leading edge.

Thrust is provided by three pairs of pylon-mounted marinised gas turbines, one pair located aft on the vehicle's longitudinal centreline and two mounted forward beneath the leading edge, between the central cabin pod and the inner faces of the two hulls.

The four forward-mounted engines blow air beneath the wing for take-off and landing. By directing the exhaust gases under the wing leading edge, the vehicle is lifted out of the water. The system enables it to take-off and land on both rough and calm water and from dry land.
DIMENSIONS
Length: approx 30·48m (100ft)
WEIGHTS
All-up: 50 tonnes
Payload: 20 tonnes
Empty: 30 tonnes
PERFORMANCE
Max speed: 300-350 knots
Cruising speed: 170-200 knots

RADUGA

This experimental amphibious ACV was completed at the Krasnoye Sormovo shipyard in the summer of 1962 and is reported to have attained a speed of 100km/h (62mph). Lengthy trials of the Raduga provided positive results and the data obtained was used as a basis for the design and construction of the 36-tonne Sormovich.

Built originally as a peripheral jet type, it is now being used to develop control techniques, and provide amphibious experience and data on skirt design.
LIFT AND PROPULSION: The craft is powered by two 220hp air-cooled radial engines. One, mounted amidships, drives a 1·8m (5ft 11in) 12-bladed lift fan; the second, mounted on a pylon at the stern, drives a two-bladed propeller for propulsion. The fan delivers air to the cushion via a continuous peripheral skirt, the bow and side sections of which are of the fingered bag type.

Raduga experimental air cushion vehicle

CONTROLS: Directional control is provided by an aerodynamic rudder operating on the propeller slipstream.
HULL: Riveted aluminium construction.
ACCOMMODATION: The cabin seats five.
DIMENSIONS
Length: 9·4m (30ft 10in)
Beam: 4·12m (13ft 6in)
WEIGHTS
Operating weight: 3 tons
PERFORMANCE
Max speed: 120km/h (75mph)
Endurance: 3 hours

RASSVET (DAWN)

A waterjet-propelled sidewall passenger ferry, Rassvet is designed for local sea routes of limited water depth. It is an offshore counterpart to the Orion sidewall ACV. Plans call for the Rassvet to serve resort routes in the Crimea, on the Caspian and in the Baltic as well as on large lakes and reservoirs. Like the Orion and Zarnitsa, its two predecessors, it can run bow-on to flat, sloping beaches to embark and disembark passengers. Landing on a beach is facilitated by an articulated gangway with a hydraulic drive.

Rassvet's features include shallow draft, good manoeuvrability and relatively simple construction.

The waterjet reversing/steering system is specially protected to enable the craft to moor alongside existing berths built originally for small conventional displacement ferries.

The Rassvet prototype, named Chayka-1 (Gull-1), is at present undergoing trials. News of the existence of Chayka-1 was given in Moscow for the first time in December 1974 when it was reported that the vessel was the first of thirty of this type, all of which would be built at the Sosnovska Shipyard in Kirovskaya Oblast for the Black Sea Shipping Line. In January 1976 it was stated that the vessel was the first seagoing passenger ACV to be built in the Soviet Union. The

extent of the remote control, automation and monitoring provided for the power plant and systems generally is sufficient to permit the craft to be operated by one person, with intermittent attendance to the machinery space.

Rassvet is designed to carry 80 passengers during daylight hours on coastal routes in conditions up to force 4. It complies with USSR Registration classification KM✳II⃞ Passenger ACV Class.
LIFT AND PROPULSION: Power for the waterjet system is provided by two 3D12N-520 lightweight (3·54kg/kW) irreversible, high-speed four-cycle V-type marine diesels each with a gas-turbine supercharger and a rated power of 383kW at 1,500rpm. Each powers a two-stage waterjet impeller. Water inlet scoops are arranged in the sidewalls and the pump ports, each of which comprises two rotors and two straightening devices are installed in the sidewalls behind the transoms. Cushion air is generated by a single 110kW PD6S-150A diesel driving an NTs6 centrifugal fan via a universal joint and a torque-limited coupling.
CONTROLS: Craft direction is controlled by twin balanced rudders operating in the water discharged by each of the two waterjets. Reversal is achieved by applying rotatable deflectors to reverse the waterflow.
SKIRT: Double-row segmented type at bow; two-tier bag type skirt aft. Repair or replacement of sections of the bow skirt can be undertaken with the bow run on to a flat, gently sloping beach. The stern skirt is secured to special hinged sections which permit inspection and maintenance while still afloat.
HULL: Hull and superstructure are built in aluminium magnesium alloy. The hull is of all-welded construction in AlMg-61 and the decks, superstructure, pilot house and partitions are in AlMg-5 alloy. Hull, superstructure and pilot house have longitudinal frames. Single-piece pressed panels are employed for the lower sections of the sidewalls. Corrugated sheets are used

Chayka-1 sidewall type ACV passenger ferry, prototype of the new Rassvet class. The craft has an air-conditioned passenger saloon and will operate between resorts in the Crimea and Caucasus

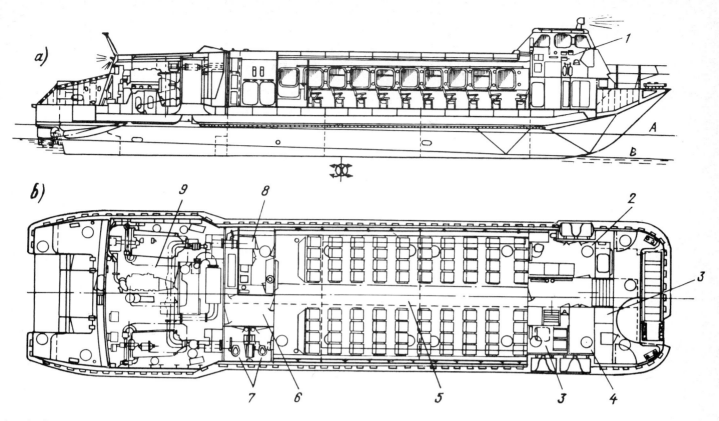

Longitudinal cross section (a) and passenger deck plan (b) of the Chayka sidewall hovercraft
A waterline in displacement condition; B waterline underway on air cushion; 1 pilot house; 2 crew's off-duty cabin; 3 storeroom; 4 baggage compartment; 5 passenger lounge; 6 companionway; 7 toilets; 8 buffet; 9 machinery space

for the hull bottom. Below the passenger deck the hull is sub-divided by transverse bulkheads into seven watertight compartments, access to which is via hatches in the passenger deck. The craft will remain afloat in the event of any one compartment flooding.

ACCOMMODATION: Rassvet seats 80 passengers in a single fully ventilated and heated saloon amidships. Comfortable airliner-type seats are provided, beneath each of which a lifejacket is located. Decks in the passenger cabin, pilot house and crew's off-duty cabin are covered with synthetic carpet and the floors of the companionways with a colourful pvc linoleum. Pavinol aircraft-type leather substitute is employed to decorate the deckheads. Large windows are provided to give passengers a good view. At the aft end of the cabin are a small buffet and two toilets. At the forward end of the cabin are the wheelhouse, a duty crew restroom and a vestibule. A six-man operating crew is carried comprising captain, engineer, motorman, radio operator, seaman and one barman. Passenger embarkation at piers designed for the berthing of small ferries of the local services takes place across the section of open deck forward of the pilot house. At points where conventional berthing facilities do not exist the craft runs bow-on to a flat sloping bank where landing facilities are provided by an articulated gangway with a hydraulic drive.

SYSTEMS, ELECTRICAL: Power supply requirements are met by a 28 volt, KG-2·9 2·9kW generator driven by a power take-off shaft from the main engine and three 28 volt, 1·2kW G-732 charging generators mounted on the main engine. Two banks of storage batteries are installed. One, comprising two Type 6STK-180M storage batteries, supplies dc power when the craft is operating. The second bank, comprising four batteries of the same type are employed for engine starting and also for energising the diesel engine control circuits and the emergency alarm systems. An inverter is installed to meet the needs of navigation and other equipment requiring ac supplies. An auxiliary circuit can be connected to shore systems for a 220 volt single-phase 50Hz ac supply.

SAFETY EQUIPMENT: PSN-10M and PSN-6M inflatable liferafts are installed in containers

along each side of the craft. The number of rafts is designed to meet the requirements of all passengers and crew. Liferaft release is remotely controlled from the landing positions at the bow and stern. Individual lifesaving devices, lifebelts and lifejackets are also provided.

FIREFIGHTING, HYDRAULICS, BILGE, BALLASTING, WATER SUPPLY: Complete systems installed as standard.

COMMUNICATIONS: Lastochka radio telephone transceiver for ship-to-shore and ship-to-ship communications; Kater uhf transceiver and Plot-M portable emergency portable transceiver. Ryabin passenger announcement and broadcast relay system. Omega radar fitted for navigating along shorelines, in narrow waterways and in poor visibility.

ANCHOR: Single 100kg (220lb) Matrosov anchor operated by a hydraulic winch.

DIMENSIONS
Length overall: 26·7m (87ft 3in)

Landing on unprepared, sloping beaches is facilitated by an articulated gangway with a hydraulic drive

Beam, max: 7·1m (23ft 3in)
  amidship: 6·0m (19ft 8in)
Height overall, hull: 2·2m (7ft 3in)
  sidewall only: 1·5m (4ft 11in)
Draft hullborne: 1·27m (4ft 2in)
  cushionborne at bow: 0·1m (4in)
  stern: 0·8m (2ft 7½in)
WEIGHTS
Loaded displacement: 47·5 tonnes
Passenger capacity: 80 persons
PERFORMANCE
Cruising speed: 23 knots
Max speed: 29 knots
Range: 352km (190n miles)

SIDEWALL PASSENGER FERRIES
Details of two new Soviet surface effect ship (SES) passenger ferry projects were published in Leningrad in late 1979, one seating 120 passengers, the other 150. Preliminary specifications of each are given below.

23.5m SES PASSENGER FERRY

LIFT AND PROPULSION: Integrated system, powered by two 1,000hp diesels.
CONTROLS: Craft heading is controlled by water rudders.
HULL: Welded marine aluminium.
ACCOMMODATION: 120 passengers.
DIMENSIONS
Length overall: 23·5m (77ft)
Max beam: 7m (23ft)
Sidewalls, height: 1·5m (4ft 11in)
  breadth: 1m (3ft 3in)
Air cushion, length: 20m (65ft 7in)
  breadth: 5m (16ft 4in)
  area: 100m² (1,076ft²)
WEIGHTS
Empty: 15·3 tonnes
All-up weight: 48·6 tonnes
Displacement tonnes/passenger: 0·406
PERFORMANCE
Max operating speed: 32 knots

25.6m SES PASSENGER FERRY

LIFT AND PROPULSION: Integrated system, probably similar to that employed on Chayka and Turist, powered by two 1,000hp marine diesels.
CONTROLS: Craft direction is controlled by water rudders.
HULL: Welded marine aluminium.
ACCOMMODATION: Seats are provided for 150 passengers.
DIMENSIONS
Length: 25·6m (84ft)
Max beam: 7m (23ft)
Air cushion, length: 22·5m (73ft 10in)
  breadth: 5m (16ft 5in)
  area: 110m² (1,184ft²)
WEIGHTS
Empty: 18 tonnes
All-up weight: 52·8 tonnes
Displacement tonnes/passenger: 0·354
PERFORMANCE
Max operating speed: 31 knots

SORMOVICH

Launched in October 1965, the Sormovich is a 50-passenger ACV designed by Valeri Schoenberg, Chief Constructor of the Krasnoye Sormovo Shipyard, with the assistance of the N E Zhukovski Central Institute of Aerodynamics.

In general layout, the craft represents a "scale-up" of the configuration tested with the Raduga.

In 1970 the craft, which can attain 65 knots, was equipped with a 4ft deep flexible skirt. Several experimental services have been operated with the craft. In 1979 it as revealed that the longest of these services, operated between Gorki and Kazan, lasted for several years. At the end of this period, however, it was felt that amphibious ACVs of this type have insufficient directional stability and control for use on main line rivers where there are many other ships and small craft. Frequently, it became necessary to reduce speed and in general to operate at low speeds, thus robbing the ACV of its basic asset — high speed. The considerable noise of its air propellers was also a drawback when operating close to populated areas.

The experimental operation of the Sormovich led ultimately to the decision to adopt rigid sidewall craft rather than amphibious ACVs for ferry services on Soviet inland waterways, and several craft of this type are now in series production.

Reports indicate that the Sormovich has also been employed as a 'tug' for large power platforms in the Soviet hinterlands.
TESTS: Rigorous acceptance trials included a special programme of runs between Gorki and Gorodets, Gorki and Lyskovo, Gorki and Vasilsursk, and also on the Gorki Reservoir.

These trials confirmed the craft's ability to operate across shoals, sandy spits and dykes, and run on to dry land for cargo handling and repairs.

In the air-cushion mode, her ability to maintain course up- and downwind is satisfactory, and controlled entirely by the rudders. In sidewinds, control is by combined rudder movement and differential propeller pitch. Steering during turns

Sormovich ACV passenger ferry, powered by a single 2,300hp Ivchenko AI-20K gas turbine

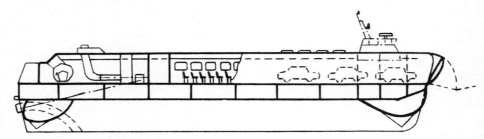

Inboard profile of the car ferry version of the Turist rigid sidewall hovercraft. Propulsive thrust appears to be supplied by two gas turbine driven waterjets, one in each sidewall. Note the fingered bag skirts fore and aft

by rudders alone is unsatisfactory, the turning-circle diameter being 2,500-3,000m (2,734-3,280 yards) with substantial drift. Turning is improved if the manoeuvre is accomplished by varying propeller pitch. The distance from the inception of the manoeuvre to securing a 180 degree course then drops to 700-1,000m (765-1,093 yards) and the diameter of the subsequent turning circle falls to 150m (164 yards).

Collision avoidance manoeuvres with a floating object employing rudder deflection, showed that avoidance is feasible at a distance of not under 500m (546 yards). This distance can be reduced, however, if the manoeuvre is accomplished with variable propeller pitch. Successful undertaking of this manoeuvre depends largely on the skill of the operator.

In the air-cushion mode, while accelerating to 60-70km/h (37-43mph) and turning through 180 degrees in both directions, stability is adequate in any of the load conditions investigated, and passengers may move about freely.

In addition to the basic flight-trial programme, tests were made to check vehicle response to sudden splash-down in case of the emergency shutdown of the main engine while underway. The splash-down tests were conducted at various speeds and drift angles, and showed that the loads imposed are not excessive and that the passengers were not alarmed. In 1·2m (4ft) waves the craft operates at reduced speed, but steering control and satisfactory passenger comfort are maintained.

Since late 1970, Sormovich has been in experimental service with the Volga United Steamship Company.

While operating on the Gorki-Cheboksary run in light conditions and with passengers aboard during the 1971 season, various problem areas were identified. In particular, it was found necessary to improve the reliability of the airscrew and fan drive transmission; improve the design of the flexible-skirt and select a stronger material from which it can be manufactured; find ways of reducing engine noise and improve its operation and maintenance; render more effective the devices employed to reduce craft drift during high speed turns; and raise the overall economic efficiency of the craft.

After modification, the vehicle returned to experimental service on the Gorki-Cheboksary-Gorki passenger run in 1972, with flights scheduled for daylight hours only, in winds not over 10-12m/s (32-39ft/s) and at speeds not above 80km/h (50mph). The route selected was generally beyond that negotiable by a conventional vessel, with depths not less than 0·5m (1ft 8in).

Two crew training flights and 42 passenger flights were undertaken during this particular service. Some 5,655 people were carried a total of 25,000km (15,534 miles).

However, experimental operation of the craft during the 1972 season was a financial loss. The economic viability of Sormovich, as in the previous season, was impaired by the craft being withdrawn from service to eliminate main transmission reduction gear defects and attend to various other repair and maintenance jobs.

A passenger survey indicated that noise levels in the rear of the saloon are acceptable, but high external noise levels are a nuisance to shore personnel and members of the public in the vicinity.

During the 1972/73 off-season period, measures were being taken to eliminate the shortcomings revealed, replace the reduction gear, improve flexible-skirt nozzle elements, and undertake various other modifications found necessary.

LIFT AND PROPULSION: All machinery is located aft behind a sound-proof bulkhead to keep down the noise level in the passenger compartments. A single 2,300hp Ivchenko AI-20K shaft-turbine, at the extreme stern, drives the integrated lift/propulsion system. Its output shaft passes first to a differential gearbox from which shafts extend sideways to the two four-blade ducted variable pitch propellers. A further shaft runs forward from the differential to a bevel gearbox from which a drive-shaft runs vertically upward to the 12-blade variable pitch lift-fan mounted under the intake on the rear of the roof of the vehicle. The gas turbine operates on diesel fuel. Cushion area is 220m².

CONTROLS: Each propeller duct contains two hydraulically-actuated rudders, working in the slipstream.

HULL: Light alloy buoyancy type, with air feeding to the cushion through a peripheral slot. Fore and aft stability slots are located on each side parallel to and about 1·5m (5ft) inboard of the peripheral slot.

ACCOMMODATION: The crew compartment, forward, contains two seats and is separated from the main cabin by a partition containing a door. The front two rows of seats in the cabin are only four-abreast to facilitate entry through the forward door on each side. The remaining 42 seats are six-abreast, in three-chair units with centre aisle. Aft of the cabin is a wardrobe on the port side, with a buffet opposite on the starboard side. Then comes the main entry lobby, with a passenger door on the port side and service door opposite, followed by a toilet (port) and baggage hold (starboard).

An unusual feature of the Sormovich is that it is fitted with retractable wheels which can be lowered to avoid damage to the hull when the craft operates over uneven ice or rough country. The wheels are carried on lightly-sprung legs, enabling them to ride easily over obstructions.

The craft is equipped for navigation at night.

Zarnitsa, a derivative of the Gorkovchanin, is now in series production

DIMENSIONS
Length: 29·2m (96ft)
Beam: 10m (32ft 9½in)
Height to top of hull, on cushion: 7m (22ft 11½in)
WEIGHTS
Normal loaded: 36·5 tonnes
PERFORMANCE
Max cruising speed: 120km/h (74·56mph)

TURIST

The Central Scientific Research Institute has completed the design of a new sidewall ACV ferry, the Turist (Tourist). The vessel, which is based on extensive experience gained from the operation of the Zarnitsa, Orion, and Rassvet, is virtually a scaled-up version of the latter. It has a design speed of 36 knots and is intended for use along waterways of limited depth and unsuitable for hydrofoils. Two variants are projected, a 250-300 seat passenger ferry and a mixed traffic variant for 10-15 cars and 100-120 passengers. As this edition went to press reports were circulating in the Soviet Union that Turist will be put into series production in 1981 at the Nakhodka yard following the completion of new shipbuilding facilities there.

Recent reports suggest that, as a result of detailed assessments undertaken in the Soviet Union over a period of years, a range of large sidewall hovercraft is being developed for the conveyance of freight. It appears that designs of 2,000 to 4,000 tons are under consideration.

ZARNITSA

Evolved from Gorkovchanin, the Zarnitsa is a 48-50 seat waterjet-propelled rigid sidewall ferry designed to operate on shallow rivers, some less than 0·7m (2ft 3in) deep. Series production is underway, and large numbers have been delivered.

The prototype was put into trial service on the Vyatka river, in the Kirov region, in the summer of 1972, and the first production models began operating on shallow, secondary rivers later in

the year. During 1973-74, Zarnitsas entered service on tributaries of the Kama, Lena and Volga. More than 100 are currently employed on almost all the river navigation lines of the Russian Federative Republic as well as on the rivers of the Ukrainian, Moldavian, Byelorussian and Kazakhstan Soviet Socialist Republics.

LIFT AND PROPULSION, CONTROLS, HULL: Arrangements almost identical to those of the Gorkovchanin.

ACCOMMODATION: Seats are provided for two crew members, who are accommodated in the raised wheelhouse, forward, and 48-50 passengers. Access to the passenger saloon is via a single door located at the bow in the centre of the wheelhouse. The craft runs bow-on to flat sloping banks to embark and disembark passengers.

DIMENSIONS
Length: 22·3m (72ft 3in)
Beam: 3·85m (12ft 8in)
Skeg depth: 0·45m (1ft 6in)
WEIGHTS
Light displacement: 9 tonnes
All-up weight, with 48 passengers, crew and fuel: 15 tonnes
PERFORMANCE
Service speed: 33-35km/h (20-22mph)

ZARYA (DAWN)

Experiments with high speed "aéroglisseur" (literally air skimmer) waterbuses, capable of negotiating the many shallow waterways in the Soviet Union, began in 1961.

The object was to develop a vessel for services on shallow waters, with depths of only 0·5m (20in), at speeds of at least 21·5 knots. The prototype Zarya, called the Opytnye-1 (experimental), was put into experimental operations on the river Msta in 1963. During trials the craft attained a speed of 42km/h (26mph) and proved to have a turning radius of 40-70m (44-76 yards). The craft runs bow-on to any flat, sloping bank to embark passengers.

Built with a strong aluminium alloy hull and equipped with a well protected waterjet, the craft

Passenger saloon in the Zarnitsa, looking aft

Zarnitsa 48-50 seat waterjet-propelled rigid sidewall ferry for shallow rivers

is unharmed by floating logs, even when they are encountered at full speed.

Variants include models with a flat load deck in place of the passenger cabin superstructure amidships, and used as light freight vessels. A total of 149 units of the first model of the Zarya were built.

Zarya was designed by a team at the Central Design Office of the Ministry of the River Fleet, Gorki, working in conjunction with the Leningrad Water Transport Institute. Series production is under way at the Moscow Shipbuilding and Ship Repair Yard of the Ministry of the River Fleet.

Given the design prefix P83, Zarya conforms to Class P of the River Register of the USSR.

The latest model is distinguished by its trimaran bow configuration, which gives improved performance in waves and enables the craft to be routed on major waterways. Apart from the large number of Zaryas in service in the USSR, a number have been supplied to Czechoslovakia, Poland and the German Democratic Republic.

LIFT AND PROPULSION: Power is provided by a single M401A-1 four-stroke, water-cooled, supercharged, 12-cylinder V-type diesel with a normal service output of 870-900hp at 1,450-1,500rpm and a maximum output of 1,000hp. It has a variable-speed governor and reversing clutch and drives a single 0·7m (2ft 2½in) diameter variable-pitch, four-bladed waterjet impeller.

The waterjet is of single-stage type, with a semi-submerged jet discharge. The impeller, which is made in brass, sucks in water through an intake duct which is covered by a protective grille. The discharged water flows around two balanced rudders which provide directional control. Two reversal shutters, interconnected by a rod and operated by cable shafting, are employed to reverse the craft or to reduce the waterjet thrust when variations in speed are necessary.

A localised ram-air cushion, introduced by an upswept nose and contained on either side by shallow skegs, lifts the bow clear of the water as the craft picks up speed. The airflow also provides air/foam lubrication for the remainder of the flat-bottomed hull.

CONTROLS: Irrespective of load, the radius of turn is between 30-50m (98-164ft) with the rudder put hard over at an angle of 30 degrees. This can be decreased if necessary by either throttling down the engine or closing the valves of the reversing system. At slow speed the craft is capable of pinwheeling. The time required to stop the vessel is 8-10 seconds, the coasting distance being between 50-60m (164-196ft). Manoeuvrability of the craft is such that it is able to navigate small winding rivers with waterways of 12-15m (39-49ft) wide with the radii of windings varying between 40-70m (131-229ft) without slowing down.

The vessel can easily pull into shore without landing facilities, providing the river bed slope is no steeper than 3 degrees. The time required for pulling in, embarking passengers, then leaving, averages 1·5 minutes. Steps to facilitate access are located at the bow, port and starboard, and lowered by a control in the wheelhouse.

HULL: Hull and superstructure are of all-welded aluminium alloy plate construction, the constituent parts being joined by argon-shielded arc welding. Framing is of mixed type, with transverse framing at the sides and the main longitudinal elements within the hull bottom. The outside shell and bottom plating is 5mm (¹³⁄₆₄in) thick, except for the base at the bow where it is 6mm (¹⁵⁄₆₄in) thick. The wheelhouse is in moulded glass-reinforced plastic. The waterjet duct and nozzle are in grade Cr3 steel and are riveted to the hull.

ACCOMMODATION: Three transverse bulkheads and two recesses divide the hull into six compartments. Behind the forepeak and wheelhouse (frames 0-3) is the passenger cabin (frames 3-27) and aft of this is a compartment housing a small bar and toilet (frames 27-30). A soundproof cofferdam (frames 30-31) follows, aft of which is the engine room (frames 31-41) and steering compartment (frames 41 to stern). The raised wheelhouse, located at the bow, gives

Zaryas in series production at the Moscow Shipbuilding and Ship Repair Yard

Zarya is powered by a 1,000hp M401A-1 four-stroke turbocharged diesel driving a single-stage waterjet. Cruising speed is about 40km/h (25mph)

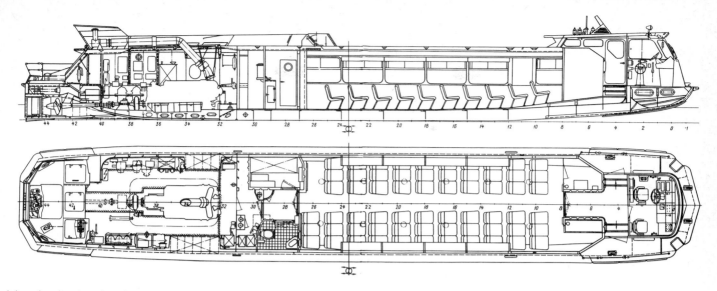

Inboard and outboard profiles and deck views of the latest export model of the Zarya waterjet-propelled passenger ferry

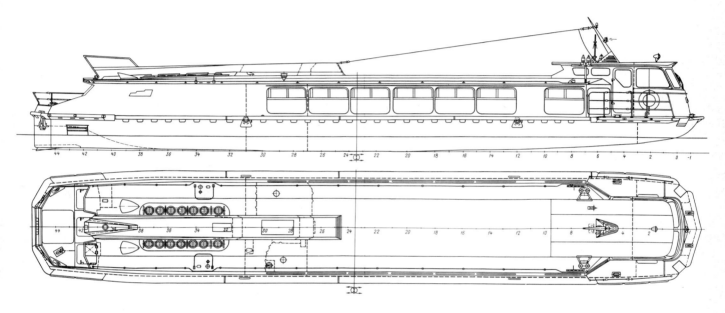

360 degree visibility. The latest export model of the Zarya seats 63 in the passenger cabin, plus another four, without luggage, in two recesses. On routes of up to 45 minute duration an additional 20 standing passengers can be carried. Life jackets for passengers are stowed in lockers in the baggage compartment and under seats at the rear of the cabin.

The crew off-duty room contains a sofa, table, wall-mounted cupboard, folding stool and a mirror. The toilet contains a wash basin, a bowl, mirror and soap tray.

The wheelhouse has rotating seats for the captain and engineer, two sun visors and there are two windscreen wipers.

Both the passenger cabin and wheelhouse are heated by warm air produced by hot water from the closed circuit main engine cooling system. Warm air is admitted into the passenger cabin and wheelhouse through a perforated chamber at the bulkhead. The engine room is heated by two 1·2kW electric heaters and the crew room by a 0·6kW electric heater. Windows of the wheelhouse and the wheelhouse itself are heated by a 330kW electric heater.

SYSTEMS, ELECTRICAL: Main engine driven 3kW, 28V dc generator, charges the storage batteries and meets the demands of 24V circuits while the vessel is underway. Four lead-acid batteries supply 24V for monitoring and alarm circuitry and starting the main engine.

Equipment supplied for charging the storage batteries, operating electric heater, engine room and service space heaters from a shore-based 220V source.

Compared with earlier variants, this new model of the Zarya is distinguished by its trimaran bow, introduced for improved seakeeping. The new bow design allows the vessel to be routed into major waterways

FIRE-FIGHTING: Two tanks containing fire-extinguishing compound and hoses for fighting an outbreak in the engine room. System can be brought into operation either from the engine room or from the wheelhouse. Engine room is also provided with two portable carbon dioxide fire extinguishers. Another of the same type is provided in the wheelhouse and two foam fire extinguishers are standard equipment in the main cabin.

FUEL: Craft is refuelled through a filling hose and a neck on the port side of the superstructure. Fuel is fed to the main engine from a service tank with a capacity of $4 \cdot 13m^3$, sufficient to enable a vessel to cruise for 8 hours without refuelling. In addition, there is a 400-litre storage tank which contains a 2 hour reserve to be used in an emergency. The same tank supplies fuel to a water heater.

COMPRESSED AIR: Starting system for main engines comprising three 45-litre air-cylinders, valves (safety, shut-off, pressure reducing and starting) and piping. Pressure 150-75kgf/cm². Two cylinders in operation, one standby.

DIMENSIONS
Length overall: 23·9m (78ft 5in)
Beam overall: 4·13m (13ft 7in)
Freeboard up to undetachable parts at mean draft of 0·44m (1ft 5½in): 3·2m (10ft 6in)

Mean draft, light: 0·44m (1ft 5½in)
   loaded: 0·55m (1ft 9½in)
WEIGHTS
Empty: 16·68 tonnes
Weight with 60 passengers, and stores for 8 hour trip: 24·78 tonnes
Max weight of cargo that can be stowed in luggage recesses: 1 tonne
Fuel capacity: 3·8 tonnes
PERFORMANCE
Speed (in channel of 0·8m depth): 45km/h (27·96mph)
Range: suitable for service distances of 150km (93 miles) and above
Endurance at cruising speed: 8 hours

MARIISKY POLYTECHNICAL INSTITUTE

Ioshka-Ola, USSR
Officials:
Stanislav F Kirkin, *Leader, Student Design Group*
Anatoli Loskutov, *Engineer*
Valeri Vedernikov, *Engineer*
Vladimir Akulov, *Engineer*

To meet the need for light personal modes of transport capable of operating under winter conditions in the virgin territories of the USSR, the student design group at the Mariisky Polytechnical Institute has developed a range of small ACVs and other vehicles capable of operation over snow, ice and—in the case of the amphibious models—over water. One of the group's first designs was the MPI-4, a "strap-on" system of air propulsion for individual skiers. Known as the "satchel aero-propelling unit" it comprised a 5hp Ural circular-saw engine, a 5-litre petrol tank and an 80cm diameter propeller rotating inside a protective circular duct. Under favourable conditions it propelled the wearer at up to 50km/h across snow or hard-frozen snow crust. This was followed by the MPI-6 air propelled snow motorcycle, capable of running across any kind of snow at speeds up to 65km/h. This vehicle was basically a lightweight motorcycle frame with a sprung, steerable main ski forward and a second main ski aligned with it, aft. An 18hp IZH-Planeta motorcycle engine driving a 1·2m diameter propeller was located behind its driving saddle.

Other concepts included a variety of aerosledges, some with open cockpits and more sophisticated models with fully-enclosed and heated cabins. Two of the group's more recent designs are the MPI-15 and MPI-18, brief descriptions of which appear below.

MPI-15 CASPIAN

Derived from the MPI-10 snowmobile-amphibian, this new design has undergone tests at the Chief Directorate of the Fishing Industry's sea fishing posts on the Caspian Sea and is being prepared for series production. A single-seater, the Caspian can move at speeds of up to 75km/h across snow, frozen snow, ice and water; traverse smaller ice hummocks and climb gradients of up to 20 degrees from a standing start and up to 50

MPI-15 Caspian snowmobile amphibian

MPI-18 cross-country ACV, designed to carry passengers and freight

degrees at speed. Power is supplied by a 25hp petrol engine driving a 2m diameter two-bladed propeller. The craft is capable of towing a trailer with a payload of up to 80kg.

MPI-18

Described as a snow glider-cum-amphibious air cushion vehicle, this 70km/h cross-country vehicle is designed to carry passengers or freight across snow, water and swamps. Air is fed into the cushion by a forward-mounted axial lift fan. Propulsive thrust is supplied by a rear-mounted petrol engine driving a two-bladed propeller. An aerodynamic rudder controls craft heading.

KHARKOV MOTOR TRANSPORT TECHNICAL SCHOOL

AERO-GLIDER

Built by V Kalekin, a teacher at Kharkov Motor Transport Technical School, this 5m long air-propelled sled has been in use since 1972, during which time it has travelled more than 15,000km, including long stretches of mountain rivers. According to its designer, it has performed particularly well during long-distance journeys over water.
DIMENSIONS
Length overall: 5m (16ft 5in)
Beam: 1·86m (6ft 1in)
WEIGHTS
Payload: 500kg (1,102lb)
Fuel capacity: 260 litres (57 gallons)
PERFORMANCE
Range: 1,000km (621 miles)

Aero-Glider, 5m air-propelled sled built by V Kalekin of the Kharkov Motor Transport Technical School

NEPTUN CENTRAL DESIGN BUREAU

Moscow, USSR

Officials:
Igor Alexandrovich Martynov, *Head of Design Bureau*
G Andreyev, *Chief Engineer*
Alexander Sergeyevich Kudryavtsev, *Chief Designer, AKVPR project*
Valeriy V Protsenko, *Designer*
Alexander V Rubinov, *Test Engineer*

The Neptun Central Design Bureau is concerned primarily with the design of small launches, yachts and runabouts for leisure and commercial application on Soviet inland and coastal waters.

The AKVPR-001 airjet-propelled amphibious ACV, Neptun's first attempt at designing and building a hovercraft, is intended for research only. Several variants are under development including the BARS-1 (Snow Leopard) which is destined for service in Siberia and other under-developed areas of the Soviet Union. A 20-seat derivative has been suggested and the bureau has a four-seater, the Gepard, on the drawing board.

AKVPR-001 multi-purpose amphibious five-seater

NEPTUN AKVPR-001

This multi-purpose amphibious five-seater is being used to explore the possibilities of employing craft of this size to support geological expeditions and provide communications in the Soviet Far north and Siberia. It would also be employed by the river rescue services and other authorities to provide emergency services when ice is forming and breaking up on inland waterways. The nomenclature AKVPR signifies "Amphibious Air Cushion Craft, Airjet, Rivergoing". A film of the craft taken during trials in the winter of 1977 and spring of 1978 showed the craft successfully operating across broken ice, negotiating ice hummocks at speed and crossing boggy terrain and marshes.

LIFT AND PROPULSION: Integrated lift/propulsion system, believed to be similar to that of Cushioncraft CC-7. Power is supplied by a single automotive engine, aft of the cabin. Power is transmitted via a gearbox to two transverse shafts at the opposite ends of which are axial fans. Air is fed downwards into the cushion and through circular thrust outlets aft for propulsion.

CONTROLS: Craft heading is controlled by interconnected rudder vanes set in the airjet ducts aft and operated by a wheel. Airflow for braking and reversing is provided by deflecting thrust air upwards and through forward facing roof apertures.

Impression of the BARS-1 (Snow Leopard) a derivative of the AKVPR-001. BARS-1 seats ten or carries 800kg of freight and is intended for communications in Siberia, the Soviet North and Far East

HULL: Built mainly in corrosion resistant light alloy. Basic structure is the main hull which is divided into watertight sub-divisions for safety.
DIMENSIONS AND WEIGHTS: Not available at the time of going to press.
PERFORMANCE: Has achieved 50km/h (31mph) across calm water over a measured mile.

BARS-1 (SNOW LEOPARD)

This enlarged version of the AKVPR-001 seats ten and has been designed primarily for communications duties in Siberia, the Soviet North and Far East. Reports state that it will operate across marshes, ditches and snow plateaus and can negotiate inclines of 30-40 degrees at speed. It is powered by a 450-500hp engine and carries up to 800kg (1,760lb) of freight.
DIMENSIONS AND WEIGHTS: Not available at the time of going to press.
PERFORMANCE
Max speed, calm water: 60km/h (37·28mph)

A N TUPOLEV

TUPOLEV A-3 AMPHIBIOUS AEROSLEDGE

The provision of year-round transport in under-developed areas of the Soviet North, Far East and Siberia would be impossible without the assistance of special vehicles. To reach communities in some of the more inaccessible regions means traversing deep snow, hummock ice, marshes that never freeze and natural waterways overgrown with reeds.

The diversity of the conditions in which transport has to operate, the demand for increased speed and the ability to cross all types of out-back terrain complicate in the extreme the development of a suitable vehicle.

In intermediate navigational seasons when the ice is melting and unsafe, during the winter freeze-up when large chunks of ice drift along rivers and when strips of unfrozen water abound in frozen or semi-frozen rivers, there is not, generally speaking, a single means of terrestrial transport which can provide reliable year-round communications.

One answer to the problem is the amphibious aerosledge, designed under the direct control of one of the Soviet Union's best known aircraft designers, A N Tupolev. Employed for the carriage of mail, passengers, light freight, medical supplies and hospital cases, the craft has the appearance of a small speedboat powered by a

Tupolev A-3 operating over snow

radial engine driving an airscrew. It can carry a payload of half a ton over a distance of 300-500km (186-310 miles) at a cruising speed of 50-70km/h (31-43mph). At speed, when traversing snow, the slightly upturned bow of the hull together with the difference of pressure between the upper and lower surfaces of the craft, generate an aerodynamic lifting force. At 80km/h (50mph) and above, aerodynamic lift reduces by almost one-third the pressure of the craft on snow. The depth of its furrow becomes negligible and resistance to the motion of the craft decreases accordingly. On water the large area of the hull bottom, with its small keel, makes it a stable, shallow-draft craft.

Additionally, the smooth lines of the hull's underside enable it to cross stretches of water overgrown with water weeds without difficulty and glide across areas of shallow water with a depth no greater than 50mm (2in). More than 200 vehicles of this type are in service in the Soviet Union in addition to which many have been exported to Eastern Europe and elsewhere.

PROPULSION: Early production aerosledges were fitted with a single 100hp, five-cylinder M-11 aircooled radial. Later this was replaced by the more powerful 260hp AI-14R radial. The engine is mounted aft on a tubular frame with shock-absorbers and drives a two-bladed wooden airscrew. The engine compartment is covered by an easily removable cowling. Above the compartment and beneath the cowling is the oil tank and pipes for the oil system. Fuel is carried in two tanks, concealed one on each side of the cabin. Filler caps are in wells in the decking.

CONTROLS: Craft direction is controlled by twin aerodynamic rudders aft operating in the propeller slipstream. For operation over snow or ice, positive control is obtained by steel runners fitted to the base of the rudders which maintain surface contact. When moving the rudder wheel to make a turn, upper (air) and lower sections of the rudder operate simultaneously. If the wheel is pulled towards the driver the rudders turn outwards to form a brake. If it is turned and drawn towards the driver only one rudder operates—the one on the inside of the turn. This assists turning when the aerosledge is crossing expanses of water overgrown with reeds or weeds.

HULL: Riveted metal alloy construction employing 2mm D-16T plates and profiles. Ribs, stringers and plates are in D-16T duraluminium. A radial chine runs for 66% of the overall length of the craft from the bow. Transverse bulkheads divide the hull into three watertight compartments. The craft will remain afloat in the event of any one compartment flooding. Double plating is employed on the hull bottom to strengthen it for

Tupolev A-3 with forward baggage compartment hatch and gull-wing cabin doors open

Tupolev A-3 operating over water

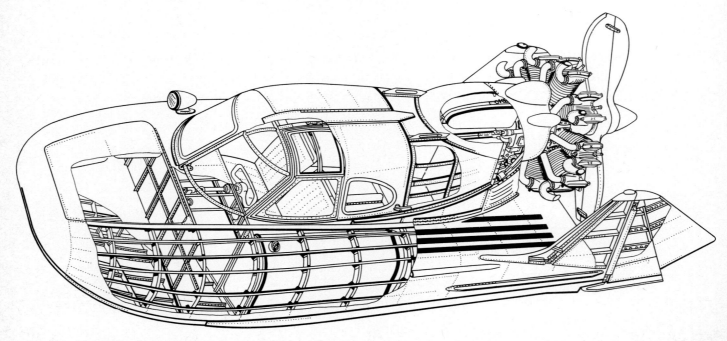

Cutaway showing basic structural components of the Tupolev A-3

crossing ice, snow mounds and ice hummocks. Low friction 3.5mm polyethylene is stuck to the bottom of the plates which are removable for replacement when necessary. Three stainless steel runners are fitted to the hull base, one on the central keel and one on each side. These ensure that the craft is able to hold a given course and prevent it from side-slipping on sheet ice when it is well heeled over.

ACCOMMODATION: In mail-carrying form the Aerosledge carries a driver, postman and mail weighing up to 650kg (1,433lb) in winter and 300kg (661lb) in summer. Driver and passenger sit in swivelling armchairs which are foam padded and covered with aircraft type leather substitute. As a passenger vehicle it carries a driver and up to four passengers. Ahead of the passenger cabin is a hermetically-sealed hatch providing access to a baggage compartment.

DIMENSIONS
Length overall: 6·11m (20ft 1in)
Hull length: 4·01m (13ft 2in)
Beam: 2·14m (7ft)
Cabin height: 1·35m (4ft 5in)
Airscrew diameter: 1·87m (6ft 2in)
WEIGHTS
Empty: 815kg (1,797lb)
Payload: 650kg (1,433lb)

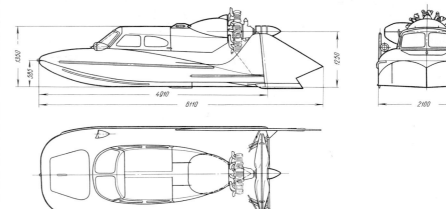

General arrangement of Tupolev A-3 amphibious Aerosledge. The aerofoil-shaped hull generates aerodynamic lift at 80km/h and above. Maximum speed is in excess of 180km/h

PERFORMANCE
Max speed over snow: 120km/h (74·6mph)
    over water: 65km/h (40·4mph)
Max permitted wave height: 0·6m (2ft)

UNITED KINGDOM

AIRHOVER LTD

Hoverplane Works, Main Road, Alresford, Colchester, Essex CO7 8DB, England
Telephone: 020 636 356
Officials:
R P Wingfield, *Managing Director*

Airhover Ltd is marketing the Aero Sabre Mk I and AS-2 light hovercraft—both open single- or two-seaters—and the more sophisticated Aero Sabre III high performance sports ACV.

Latest addition to the line is the Mk IV, a luxury four-seater with ducted fan propulsion.

AERO SABRE Mk I

The new Aero Sabre Mk I is a high performance amphibious light sports hovercraft. It is in production and is available either complete or in kit form.

LIFT AND PROPULSION: Power for the integrated lift/propulsion system is provided by a 15bhp modified Kyoritsu engine, although a wide choice of alternative power plants is available ranging from 6 to 40bhp Kyoritsu. The primary airflow from the eight-bladed axial-flow fan is ejected through a propulsive slot aft of the fan duct, and the secondary airflow, for the cushion, passes downwards into the plenum chamber.

CONTROLS: Throttle twist grip control, with dummy grip opposite and ignition cutout switch. Steering is by kinesthetic control (body movement). The manufacturer points out that as the performance is "very lively," experience at low speeds is desirable before attempting high speed runs.

HULL: Mixed aluminium, glass fibre and wooden construction. Basic hull structure is built from light alloy square section tubing with curved members in laminated wood. The nose fairing, tandem seat and fuel tank form a single unit. These and the streamlined duct aft are in moulded grp. The upper surface is covered with lightweight nylon, impregnated on both sides with pvc for tear resistance. Fuel tank is integral with glass fibre superstructure with filler neck aft of driver's seat. Fuel capacity is 9·09 litres (2 gallons).

SKIRT: Made in extra strong nylon fabric and reinforced with double skin of pvc. Skirt is in eleven segments and is stitched with rot-proofed thread. Skirt attachment rails provided.

ACCOMMODATION: Open motorcycle type upholstered seating for one or two in tandem.

DIMENSIONS
Length: 2·74m (9ft)
Beam: 1·82m (6ft)
Height: 0·914m (3ft)

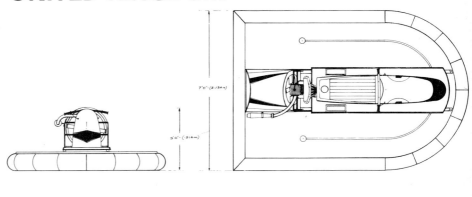

General arrangement of Aero Sabre Mk I

AS-2 built from an Airhover kit by members of 2476 Squadron, Air Training Corps. This particular craft is powered by a 30hp twin cylinder horizontally-operated Citroen engine and has been displayed at a number of air shows

WEIGHTS
Unladen: 68·03kg (150lb)
Max payload: 181·43kg (400lb)
PERFORMANCE
Designed speed, land: 72·42km/h (45mph)
   water: 48·28km/h (30mph)
Fuel consumption: 4·5 litres/h (1 gallon/h)
Obstacle clearance: 15·24cm (6in)

AERO SABRE AS-2

A modified version of the Mk I, the AS-2 has
been produced for Education Authorities and
youth training organisations which include
hovercraft design amongst their educational projects. Like the Mk I SP, which it replaces, it is
available in kit form and can be constructed without recourse to complicated tools and equipment.

A number of alternative power plants can be
installed, from a 10bhp, 210cc Rowena to any
suitable twin-cylinder engine of about 22bhp,
depending on the performance required. With
22hp installed the maximum speed in calm conditions is about 96km/h (60mph).

On this model the fan duct, fin and rudder are
of alloy reinforced glass reinforced plastics. The
duct contains an adjustable "splitter" plate
enabling the airflow fed into the cushion and
ejected through the propulsive slot aft to be
shared as required.
DIMENSIONS
Length, overall: 4·57m (15ft)
Beam, on cushion: 2·43m (8ft)
Height to top of rudder: 1·37m (4ft 6in)
WEIGHTS
Empty: 80·73kg (178lb)
Load: 236·76kg (522lb)
PERFORMANCE
Max speed: up to 96·56km/h (60mph)
Vertical obstacle clearance: 0·22m (9in)

AERO SABRE Mk III

The prototype of this exceptionally elegant
two-seater is undergoing tests. One of the aims of
the designers has been to produce a high-
performance light ACV which combines the lines
of a racing aircraft with the comfort of a modern
sports car. Various alternative layouts are available to suit commercial applications. Performance depends upon the power installed, but the
designed maximum speed is 95·56km/h (60mph).
LIFT AND PROPULSION: The lift engine, a
20hp MAG type 1031 two-stroke is located forward of the cabin beneath a protective metal
mesh panel and drives a 0·53m (1ft 9in) diameter
fan with blades set at 30 degrees. Each blade is
detachable to facilitate replacement. Located aft
of the cabin, the propulsion engine, a 33hp MAG
2062-SRB twin cylinder two-stroke, drives a
0·914m (3ft) diameter two-bladed variable-pitch
propeller. The entire thrust unit will be surrounded by a plated protective mesh guard. Both
engines have electric starters.
CONTROLS: Heading is controlled by a single,
swept back aerodynamic rudder operating in the
propeller slipstream. Aircraft-type wheel,
instrumentation, switches and throttles.
HULL: Built in high grade marine ply and incorporating three watertight buoyancy compartments. In the event of either one or two of these
sustaining damage, the remaining compartments
will keep the craft afloat. The superstructure,
which includes the canopy, forward decking and
air intake is a one-piece moulding in grp. Windows and windshields are in perspex. Cabin
access is via two light alloy gull-wing doors which
are raised electrically.
SKIRT: Conventional bag-type, 304mm (1ft)
deep.
CABIN: Access is via gull-wing doors. Semi-
reclining, upholstered seats are provided side-
by-side for driver and passenger. Panels and
pillars are finished in matching colours.
DIMENSIONS
Length, overall: 5·18m (17ft)
Beam, overall: 2·43m (8ft)
Height to top of rudder (on landing pads): 1·52m
  (5ft)
Skirt depth: 406mm (1ft 4in)

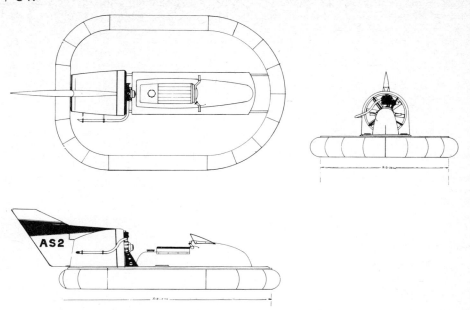

Three-view of Aero Sabre AS-2. Alloy brackets ahead of the fan air duct permit the installation of a wide
choice of engines

Aero Sabre Mk III, a 96·56km/h (60mph) amphibious two-seater, combines elegance and high performance
with the comfort of a modern sports car

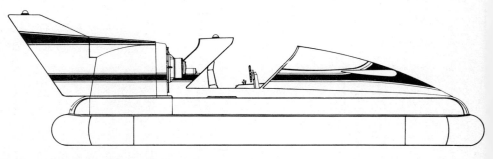

Aero Sabre Targa, two-seat sports ACV under development by Airhover Ltd

WEIGHTS
Unladen: 308·42kg (680lb)
Payload: 272·14kg (600lb)
PERFORMANCE
Max speed: 96·56km/h (60mph)
Obstacle clearance: 304mm (12in)

AERO SABRE Mk IV

Work on the prototype of this luxury four-
seater is currently in progress.

One of the main objectives has been to provide
a fast, amphibious vehicle suitable for business
executives working in countries with a dry and
dusty environment. Simplicity of construction
and ease of maintenance are two of the design
keynotes.
LIFT AND PROPULSION: Power for the integrated lift/propulsion system is provided by a
single Rolls-Royce Continental aero-engine
rated at 100hp. This drives a single 1·16m (3ft
10in) diameter, four-bladed ducted fan, the
primary airflow from which is ejected through a
propulsive slot aft, while the secondary airflow is
ducted downwards into the plenum chamber for

lift. Fuel is carried in two tanks of 35 litre (7·7
gallon) capacity.
CONTROLS: Craft heading is controlled by tri-
ple rudders in the airjet outlet aft. The two outer
units are uncoupled for braking and reverse
thrust.
HULL: Mixed grp and light alloy construction.
ACCOMMODATION: Totally enclosed cabin
fitted with four semi-reclining seats. Aircraft
style instrumentation.
DIMENSIONS
Length: 6·4m (21ft)
Beam: 2·74m (9ft)
Height: 1·21m (4ft)
WEIGHTS
All-up: 521·5kg (1,150lb)
Payload: 294·82kg (650lb)

TARGA

Latest light ACV to be announced by Airhover
Ltd is the Targa two-seat sports craft which emp-
loys many of the hull components of the Aero
Sabre Mk IV.
LIFT AND PROPULSION: Lift is supplied by

an 18bhp engine located forward of the cabin, driving an axial fan. Two 40bhp engines, mounted in twin ducts, one each side of the rear superstructure, provide thrust.

CONTROLS: Craft heading is controlled by twin rudders operating in the fan slipstream. An aerofoil-shaped spoiler in the nose operates at high speed to control craft pitch.

HULL: Mainly moulded grp construction, with the exception of the midhull section which follows light aircraft practice with ply bulkheads and stringers.

ACCOMMODATION: Open cockpit with twin lightweight semi-reclining sports car type seats with headrests. Throttle controls and trim quadrant mounted on a central console. Full width instrument panel and full range of instruments provided. Design permits the cockpit to be enclosed. The canopy would comprise a light alloy frame fitted with a pair of gull-wing doors.

DIMENSIONS
Length overall: 5·18m (17ft)
Beam: 2·13m (7ft)
Height: 1·37m (4ft 6in)

WEIGHTS
Empty: 442·23kg (975lb)
Payload: 181·42kg (400lb)

PERFORMANCE: No details available at the time of going to press

---

AIR VEHICLES LIMITED

Head Office and Works: 1 Sun Hill, Cowes, Isle of Wight, England
Yard: Dinnis' Yard, High Street, Cowes, Isle of Wight, England
Telephone: 0983 293194 and 294739
Telex: 86513 (Hoverwork, Ryde)
Officials:
P H Winter, MSc, *Director*
C D J Bland, *Director*
C B Eden, *Director*

Air Vehicles Ltd was founded in 1968 and has concentrated on the development of small commercial hovercraft and various systems, including skirts and ducted propellers, for larger craft.

The company's main product is the Tiger-S 12-seat hovercraft, several of which have been exported. The first production Tiger was an 8-seater and was delivered to the Canadian Armed Forces.

Air Vehicles Ltd is approved by the Civil Aviation Authority and undertakes design and manufacture of major modifications to larger craft. These have included flat-deck freight conversions for the SR.N5 and SR.N6 and power-assisted rudder packs for both types.

The company is now a leader in the design of low-speed ducted propeller systems and, following the success of the propeller duct fitted to an SR.N6, a smaller unit with integral controls was made for the AV Tiger. Two larger units have been supplied to the United States for a military hovercraft.

Several studies involving the use of hoverbarges have been completed particularly for ship-to-shore operation, and an on-site survey has been undertaken in Indonesia.

Air Vehicles Ltd designed and commissioned the first hoverbarge to operate on the Yukon River, the 'Yukon Princess'.

The company retains a major interest in an SR.N5 craft which is available for charter or purchase.

It is also collaborating with British Hovercraft Corporation in the development of the diesel-powered API-88 multi-duty amphibious hovercraft.

AV TIGER

Developed from the AV2 series, this craft utilises the same hull shape and skirt configuration but employs a ducted propeller for thrust. The prototype AV Tiger was a converted AV2 craft with a Rover V8 3·5 litre engine to drive the integrated lift/thrust system.

The hull of the first production craft was made from welded aluminium, incorporated an AMC 360in³ engine in place of the Rover V8 and had increased hoverheight and inflatable sides.

TIGER-S

This 'stretched' model of the Tiger is the standard production craft. The cabin seats 12 and the non-structural cabin top can be removed for different versions. Fully amphibious, the craft can operate over a variety of surfaces such as mud, ice, sand and shallow water.

LIFT AND PROPULSION: Motive power for the integrated lift/propulsion system is provided by a single AMC 360in³ petrol engine delivering 220hp at 4,000rpm. The engine output is transferred to a 12-bladed centrifugal lift fan and a 1·37m (4ft 6in) diameter, four-bladed, ducted propeller through a notched belt system. Normal fuel capacity is 213 litres (47 imperial gallons).

AV Tiger delivered to Canadian armed forces

Production model of AV Tiger-S 12-seat amphibious hovercraft

CONTROLS: Multiple rudder vanes hinged at the aft end of the propeller duct provide directional control. Elevators provide trim, and when raised fully, assist braking by reducing thrust by 75%.

HULL: Superstructure and all bulkheads are of marine grade aluminium sheet welded to form a strong rigid box structure. Side members are inflatable, giving additional buoyancy and protection for the craft when mooring. By deflating the side members the vehicle can be trailed behind any large car or small truck. Built-in jacking system provided for loading and maintenance.

ACCOMMODATION: Enclosed cabin for driver and up to eleven passengers. Access via sliding doors, one port, one starboard. The driver's seat is forward right; the navigator's forward left. Adequate space is provided for the installation of a radar, radios and navigation equipment ahead of these positions.

SKIRT: Pressurised bag skirt with separate segments. The inflatable sides and skirt are attached to the craft with quick-release piano hinges.

SYSTEMS, ELECTRICAL: 12V dc, negative earth, with engine driven 35A alternator and 60Ah battery.

DIMENSIONS
Length: 8m (26ft 2in)
Width, inflated: 3·85m (12ft 6in)
Transport width: 2·44m (8ft)
Height, static: 2·26m (7ft 5in)
Hoverheight: 50-55cm (20-22in)
12-place cabin: 3·9 × 1·8m (12ft 9in × 6ft)
WEIGHTS
Empty: 1,272kg (2,800lb)
Max: 2,227kg (4,900lb)
Disposable load: 955kg (2,100lb)
PERFORMANCE
Max speed: 65km/h (35 knots)
Cruise speed: 46km/h (25 knots)
Max conditions: 46km/h (25 knot) wind,
    1m (3ft) sea
Speed in 46km/h (25 knot) wind: 37km/h (20
    knots)
Gradient climbing: 1 : 7 (standing start)
Fuel consumption, cruise: 27-45 litres/h (6-10
    imperial gallons/h)
Max: 70 litres/h (15·5 imperial gallons/h)

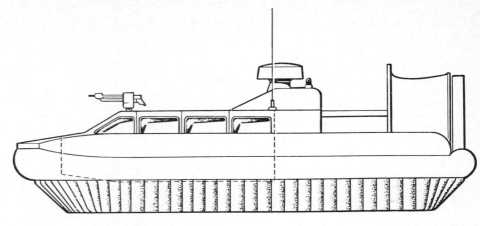

Outboard profile AV Tiger-S 12-seat multi-duty hovercraft. Machine gun and radar are omitted on the civil model

BILL BAKER VEHICLES LTD

1 Stud Farm Cottages, Adderbury, Banbury, Oxon OX17 3NW, England
Telephone: 0295 810624

Bill Baker Vehicles Ltd, designers and manufacturers of the Scarab 10-2 two-seater, the Scarab 10-4 four-seater, and Scarab 11 single-seat racing craft, have licenced Fruitree Ltd, a subsidiary of the Hunting Group, to manufacture and market the Scarab 12. The craft will in future be known as the Jetstream and will be marketed by Skidaddle Leisure Products. The Jetstream is described in this edition under the entry for Skidaddle Leisure Products.

Bill Baker Vehicles Ltd will continue to supply both complete racing hovercraft and kits, as well as supplying Hirth hovercraft motors and various manufactured parts to both amateur and professional manufacturers.

Bill Baker Vehicles' BBV-4 four-seater, complete with cab

SCARAB 10-2

This advanced two-three seat sports/racing craft has been designed for high performance and reliability. It was the winner of the 1977 United Kingdom Hovercraft Society Award.
LIFT AND PROPULSION: Lift is supplied by a single 8bhp Rowena Solo two-stroke driving a 0·53m (21in) multiwing fan. Thrust is supplied by a 42bhp 440cc Hirth twin-cylinder engine driving twin 0·60m (24in) ducted fans via toothed belts. Complete thrust unit is rubber mounted to ensure freedom from vibration. Fuel is carried in a single, centrally-mounted tank with a total fuel capacity of 22·7 litres (5 imperial gallons).
CONTROLS: Craft heading is controlled by twin rudders, one hinged to the rear of each thrust duct. Handlebars control rudder movement.
HULL: Self-coloured grp hull incorporating polystyrene foam buoyancy moulded into floor and sidebodies. Moulded into the hull is the tandem seat which contains the removable 22·7 litre (5 imperial gallon) fuel tank.
SKIRT: Full-flow loop design fabricated in 1802 series nylon coated on both sides with pvc.
ACCOMMODATION: Pillion-style, tandem seating for driver and one to two passengers.
DIMENSIONS
Length: 3·65m (12ft)
Beam: 1·98m (6ft 6in)
WEIGHTS
Unladen: 204kg (450lb)
PERFORMANCE
Max speed, with driver only, calm conditions:
    80·46km/h (50mph)
Normal cruising speed, average conditions, with
    driver and one passenger: 40-48km/h (25-
    30mph)

SCARAB 10-4

The Scarab 10-4 features the same lift and thrust systems as the earlier Scarab 10-2. The grp hull is also of the same design, but has been extended to allow two conventional seats to be

Scarab 11 single-seat racing hovercraft

added aft on either side of the central tunnel. A feature of the craft is that up to four passengers, including the driver, can be carried without altering craft trim.

To ensure a comfortable ride and extend skirt life a new skirt with pressure fed segments is fitted. As wear is experienced, so the segments may be removed from the loop and replaced.

A large number of extras can be fitted to the craft and purpose-built versions can be produced to meet special requirements.
LIFT, PROPULSION, CONTROLS AND HULL: As for Scarab 10-2 above.

SKIRT: Pressure fed segmented skirt system fabricated in neoprene and pvc coated nylon.

DIMENSIONS
Length: 4·67m (15ft 4in)
Beam: 2·13m (7ft)

WEIGHTS
Unladen: 272kg (600lb)

PERFORMANCE
Max speed with driver and three passengers,
    depending upon conditions: 32-48km/h (20-
    30mph)
Hover height: 254mm (10in)

SCARAB 11

This advanced grp-hulled single-seater is one of the fastest of its kind. During its first season of racing in the United Kingdom it finished first and second in the Formula One Championships. It is available either complete and ready to race or in various kits for home assembly. Fitted with smaller engines it is suitable for Formula Two racing.
LIFT AND PROPULSION: Lift is supplied by a single 8hp 210cc Rowena Solo two-stroke directly coupled to a 558mm (22in) multiwing fan. Thrust is provided by a 440cc 42bhp Hirth hovercraft engine driving two 609mm (24in) ducted fans via toothed bells. Fuel is carried in a single centrally-mounted tank with a total fuel capacity of 22·7 litres (5 imperial gallons). Fuel recommended is 95 octane mixed 25:1 with Duckhams outboard oil.
CONTROLS: Craft heading is controlled by twin rudders, one hinged to the rear of each thrust duct. Handlebars control rudder movement.
HULL: Single-piece grp construction complete with foam buoyancy. Motorcycle type seat moulded in. Hull has full hydrodynamic surfaces and internal skirt feed ducts.
SKIRT: Pressure fed segmented skirt system fabricated in neoprene and pvc coated nylon.
DIMENSIONS
Length: 3·35m (11ft)
Beam: 1·96m (6ft 6in)
WEIGHTS
Unladen: 145kg (325lb)
PERFORMANCE
Max speed, calm conditions: 88·51km/h (55mph)
APPROXIMATE PRICE: £2,350.
TERMS: 50% deposit. Balance on delivery.

BRITISH HOVERCRAFT CORPORATION

East Cowes, Isle of Wight, England
Telephone: 0983 294101
Telex: 86761/2
Officials:
B D Blackwell, MA, BSc(Eng), CEng, FIMechE, FRAeS, FBIM, *Chairman*
Sir Christopher Hartley, KCB, CBE, DFC, AFC, BA, *Deputy Chairman*
R Stanton-Jones, MA, DCAe, CEng, AFRAeS, *Managing Director*
R L Wheeler, MSc, DIC, CEng, AFRAeS, *Technical Director*
J M George, BSc(Eng), DCAe, *Sales Director*
J McGarity, *Works Director*
T Bretherton, *Finance*
H W Paice, *Secretary*

The British Hovercraft Corporation is the world's largest hovercraft manufacturer. It was formed in 1966 to concentrate the British hovercraft industry's major technical and other resources under a single management.

The corporation deals with a wide variety of applications of the air cushion principle, the emphasis being on the development and production of amphibious hovercraft. Other activities include the investigation of industrial applications of the air cushion principle.

The capital of the corporation is £5 million, which is wholly owned by Westland Aircraft Ltd.

BHC established the world's first full-scale hovercraft production line in 1964. Currently it is producing the 10-17-ton Winchester (SR.N6) Class craft, the 50-ton Wellington (BH.7) Class craft and the 200-300-ton Mountbatten (SR.N4) Class craft at East Cowes.

At present six Mountbatten Class craft are in service as passenger/car ferries on the Dover/Boulogne and Ramsgate/Calais routes; two with British Rail Hovercraft, and four with Hoverlloyd Ltd.

All four Hoverlloyd craft have been converted to Mk 2 standard, and the Seaspeed craft have been converted from Mk 1 to Mk 3 (Super 4) standard with a daily capacity of 11,650 passengers and 1,550 cars.

The first Super 4 craft, "The Princess Anne", was delivered to British Rail Hovercraft Limited's Seaspeed service on 6 April 1978 and entered service on the Dover-Boulogne-Calais routes on 9 July. During the first six weeks of operation the craft carried more than 100,000 passengers and over 12,000 vehicles. At 300 tons all-up weight Super 4 is the world's largest hovercraft. It has a payload of 418 passengers and 60 vehicles, a cruising speed of 55 knots and a maximum speed of 65 knots.

A military variant, the Military 4, was announced in the autumn of 1980. It can carry a disposable load of up to 165 tons (or 1,000 troops) at a speed of 65 knots and has a maximum endurance of almost 19 hours.

One BH.7 is in service with the Royal Navy's Naval Hovercraft Trials Unit and six have been delivered to the Iranian Navy.

Military and general duty variants of the Warden and Winchester Class hovercraft are now in service with the Naval Hovercraft Trials Unit, Iranian Navy, Italian Interservice Hovercraft Unit, Egyptian Navy and the Canadian and Saudi Arabian Coast Guard.

Winchesters have been employed since 1967 in trials and sales demonstrations in Africa, Canada, Denmark, Finland, India, South America and

British Rail Seaspeed's 300-ton Super 4 "The Princess Anne". A lengthened and refitted BHC SR.N4, the craft entered service on the Dover/Boulogne/Calais route on 9 July 1978. Seaspeed's second SR.N4, "The Princess Margaret", joined her sister craft in May 1979

Interior of the main starboard cabin amidships on the BHC Super 4. Payload of the Super 4 is 54-60 cars and up to 418 passengers

the Middle and Far East, logging well over 250,000 operating hours.

Commercial general purpose variants of the Warden and Winchester are in service with Solent Seaspeed Ltd, Department of Civil Aviation, New Zealand, Department of Transport, Canada, Hovertravel Ltd and Hoverwork Ltd. In recent years the Winchester has been used increasingly for general purpose roles including hydrographic and seismic survey, freighting and search and rescue duties.

Another addition to the BHC range announced during 1980 is the API-88 diesel-powered general-purpose hovercraft. Built in welded aluminium alloy employing shipbuilding techniques, it combines a 7-8 ton payload with a performance equal to that of the SR.N6. As a fast passenger ferry it will seat up to 80 passengers and in troop-carrying form it will seat up to 60 armed troops.

MOUNTBATTEN (SR.N4) CLASS Mk 2

The SR.N4 Mk 2 is a 200-ton passenger/car ferry designed for stage lengths of up to 184km (100n miles) on coastal water routes. It has an average service speed of 40-50 knots in waves up to 3·04m (10ft) in height and is able to operate in 3·7m (12ft) seas at a speed of about 20 knots.
LIFT AND PROPULSION: Power is supplied by four 3,400shp Rolls-Royce Marine Proteus free-turbine, turboshaft engines located in pairs at the rear of the craft on either side of the vehicle deck. Each has a maximum rating of 4,250shp, but usually operates at 3,400shp when cruising. Each engine is connected to one of four identical propeller/fan units, two forward and two aft. The propulsion propellers, made by Hawker Siddeley Dynamics, are of the four-bladed, variable and reversible pitch type 5·79m (19ft) in diameter. The lift fans, made by BHC, are of the 12-bladed centrifugal type, 3·5m (11ft 6in) in diameter.

Since the gear ratios between the engine, fan and propeller are fixed, the power distribution can be altered by varying the propeller pitch and hence changing the speed of the system, which accordingly alters the power absorbed by the fixed pitch fan. The power absorbed by the fan can be varied from almost zero shp (ie boating with minimum power) to 2,100shp, within the propeller and engine speed limitations. A typical division on maximum cruise power would be 2,000shp to the propeller and 1,150shp to the fan; the remaining 250shp can be accounted for by engine power fall-off due to the turbine rpm drop, transmission losses and auxiliary drives.

The drive shafts from the engine consist of flanged light-alloy tubes approximately 2·28m (7ft 6in) long supported by steady bearings and connected by self-aligning couplings. Shafting to the rear propeller/fan units is comparatively short, but to the forward units is approximately 18·27m (60ft).

The main gearbox of each unit comprises a spiral bevel reduction gear, with outputs at the top and bottom of the box to the vertical propeller and fan drive shafts respectively. The design of the vertical shafts and couplings is similar to the main transmission shafts, except that the shafts above the main gearbox are of steel instead of light alloy to transmit the much greater torque loads to the propeller. This gearbox is equipped with a power take-off for an auxiliary gearbox with drives for pressure and scavenge lubricating oil pumps, and also a hydraulic pump for the pylon and fin steering control.

The upper gearbox, mounted on top of the pylon, turns the propeller drive through 90 degrees and has a gear ratio of 1·16:1. This gearbox has its own self-contained lubricating system.

Engines and auxiliaries are readily accessible for maintenance from inside the craft, while engine, propellers, pylons and all gearboxes can be removed for overhaul without disturbing the main structure.

The fan rotates on a pintle which is attached to the main structure. The assembly may be detached and removed inboard onto the car deck without disturbing the major structure.

CONTROLS: The craft control system enables the thrust lines and pitch angles of the propellers to be varied either collectively or differentially. The fins and rudders move in step with the aft pylons. The pylons, fins and rudders move through ±35 degrees, ±30 degrees and ±40 degrees respectively. On Hoverlloyd's craft the rudders have been deleted and on Seaspeed's craft the rudders have been locked relative to the fins.

Demand signals for pylon and fin angles are transmitted from the commander's controls electrically. These are compared with the pylon or fin feed-back signals and the differences are then amplified to actuate the hydraulic jacks mounted at the base of the pylon or fin structure. Similar electro-hydraulic signalling and feed-back systems are used to control propeller pitches.

The commander's controls include a rudder bar which steers the craft by pivoting the propeller pylons differentially.

For example, if the right foot is moved forward, the forward pylons move clockwise, viewed from above, and the aft pylons and fins move anti-clockwise, thus producing a turning movement to starboard. The foregoing applies with positive thrust on the propellers, but if negative thrust is applied, as in the case of using the propellers for braking, the pylons and fins are automatically turned to opposing angles, thus maintaining the turn. A wheel mounted on a control column enables the commander to move the pylons and fins in unison to produce a drift to either port or starboard as required. The control of the distribution of power between each propeller and fan is by propeller pitch lever. The pitch of all four propellers can be adjusted collectively over a limited range by a fore-and-aft movement of the control wheel.

HULL: Construction is primarily of high strength, aluminium-clad, aluminium alloy, suitably protected against the corrosive effects of sea water.

Control cabin of the Super 4 provides virtually 360° vision. The cabin accommodates a commander, an engineer/radio operator and a radio operator/navigator. A seat is provided for a fourth crew member or crew member in training

Hoverlloyd's SR.N4 Mk 2 Swift, en route to Calais in sea state 4

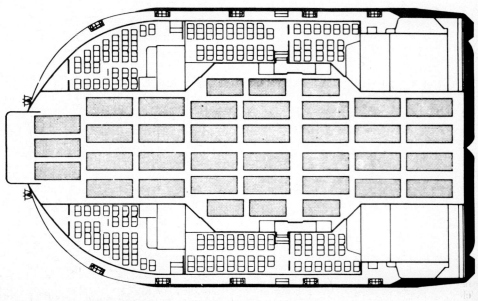

SR.N4 configuration with space for 37 vehicles and 282 passengers

The basic structure is the buoyancy chamber, built around a grid of longitudinal and transversal frames, which form 24 watertight sub-divisions for safety. The design ensures that even a rip from end-to-end would not cause the craft to sink or overturn. The reserve buoyancy is 250%, the total available buoyancy amounting to more than 550 tons.

Top and bottom surfaces of the buoyancy chamber are formed by sandwich construction panels bolted onto the frames, the top surface being the vehicle deck. Panels covering the central 4·9m (16ft) section of the deck are reinforced to carry unladen coaches, or commercial vehicles up to 9 tons gross weight (maximum axle load 5,900kg (13,000lb)), while the remainder are designed solely to carry cars and light vehicles (maximum axle load 2,040kg (4,500lb)). An articulated loading ramp, 5·5m (18ft) wide, which can be lowered to ground level, is built into the bows, while doors extending the full width of the centre deck are provided at the aft end.

Similar grid construction is used on the elevated passenger-carrying decks and the roof, where the panels are supported by deep transverse and longitudinal frames. The buoyancy chamber is joined to the roof by longitudinal walls to form a stiff fore-and-aft structure. Lateral bending is taken mainly by the buoyancy tanks. All horizontal surfaces are of pre-fabricated sandwich panels with the exception of the roof, which is of skin and stringer panels.

Double curvature has been avoided other than in the region of the air intakes and bow. Each fan air intake is bifurcated and has an athwartships bulkhead at both front and rear, supporting a beam carrying the transmission main gearbox and the propeller pylon. The all-moving fins and rudders behind the aft pylons pivot on pintles just ahead of the rear bulkhead.

The fans deliver air to the cushion via a peripheral fingered bag skirt.

The material used for both bags and fingers is nylon, coated with neoprene and/or natural rubber, the fingers and cones being made from a heavier weight material than the trunks.

ACCOMMODATION: The basic manning requirement is for a commander, an engineer/radio operator and a radar operator/navigator. A seat is provided for a fourth crew member or a crew member in training. The remainder of the crew, ie those concerned with passenger service or car handling, are located in the main cabins. The arrangement may be modified to suit individual operator's requirements.

The control cabin is entered by either of two ways. The normal method, when the cars are arranged in four lanes, is by a hatch in the cabin floor, reached by a ladder from the car deck. When heavy vehicles are carried on the centre section, or if for some other reason the ladder has to be retracted, a door in the side of the port forward passenger cabin gives access to a ladder leading onto the main cabin roof. From the roof an entrance door gives access into the control cabin.

The craft currently in service carry 282 passengers and 37 cars.

The car deck occupies the large central area of the craft, with large stern doors and a bow ramp providing a drive-on/drive-off facility.

Separate side doors give access to the passenger cabins which flank the car deck. The outer cabins have large windows which extend over the full length of the craft. The control cabin is sited centrally and forward on top of the superstructure to give maximum view.

DIMENSIONS
EXTERNAL
Overall length: 39·68m (130ft 2in)
Overall beam: 23·77m (78ft)
Overall height on landing pads: 11·48m (37ft 8in)
Skirt depth: 2·44m (8ft)
INTERNAL
Passenger/vehicle floor area: 539m² (5,800ft²)
Vehicle deck headroom-centre line: 3·43m (11ft 3in)

"The Prince of Wales," the fourth 200-ton SR.N4 Mk 2 mixed traffic hovercraft to be delivered to Hoverlloyd Limited. With the addition of the fourth craft, Hoverlloyd has the capacity to carry up to 15,000 passengers and 2,000 vehicles daily

'Super 4' accommodates up to 60 vehicles on its car deck which occupies the central area of the craft

Panels covering the central 4·9m (16ft) of the vehicle decks are reinforced to carry unladen coaches or commercial vehicles up to 9 tons gross weight while the remainder of the deck is designed solely to carry cars and light vehicles

Bow ramp door aperture size (height × width):
3·51 × 5·48m (11ft 6in × 18ft)
Stern door aperture size (height × width): 3·51 ×
9·45m (11ft 6in × 31ft)
WEIGHTS
Normal gross: 200 tons
Fuel capacity: 20,456 litres (4,500 imperial gal-
lons)
PERFORMANCE (at normal gross weight at
15°C)
Max waterspeed over calm water, zero wind
(cont power rating): 70 knots
Average service waterspeed: 40-60 knots
Normal stopping distance from 50 knots: 480m
(525 yards)
Endurance at max cont power on 2,800 imperial
gallons: 2·5 hours
Negotiable gradient from standing start: 1 : 11

SR.N4 Mk 3 'SUPER 4'

The Super 4 differs from earlier Marks of the
SR.N4 primarily in that it is 16·76m (55ft)
longer, increasing the overall length to 56·38m
(185ft) with a beam of 28·04m (92ft).

Modification of an SR.N4 Mk 1 to Super 4
standard necessitates adding a new 16·76m (55ft)
section amidships, widening the existing superstructure and strengthening the original bow and
stern halves to accept the increased stresses
resulting from the 40% increase in length. The
propeller pylons are raised to allow 6·4m (21ft)
diameter propellers to be fitted, the transmission
systems are realigned and four uprated 3,800shp
Rolls-Royce Marine Proteus gas turbines are
installed.

A more efficient low pressure ratio skirt system
with larger fingers is fitted, giving a mean air
cushion depth of 2·7m (9ft). Passenger cabin trim
and seating have been completely revised and
sound-proofing increased.

Compared with the SR.N4 Mk 1, the Super 4
has a 70% greater revenue earning capability,
but costs only about 15% more to operate. The
increased length and advanced skirt system give
both a higher performance in adverse weather
and greatly improved ride comfort for the passengers.

Craft handling and skirt behaviour have
proved entirely satisfactory over the entire
weight range from 212 to 300 tons in sea conditions up to Force 8-9. Measurements taken in the

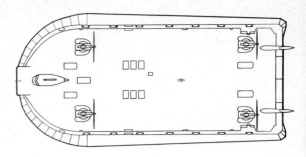
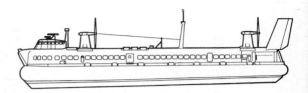

General arrangement of SR.N4 Mk 3 'Super 4'

Typical cruising speeds over water of the BHC Super 4 are 60-65 knots in calm seas, 50-55 knots in moderate seas and 35-45 knots in rough seas. Larger skirt fingers are fitted giving a mean air cushion depth of 2·7m (9ft). Accelerometer measurements in the passenger cabins show a three-fold improvement in ride comfort over the SR.N4 Mk 2

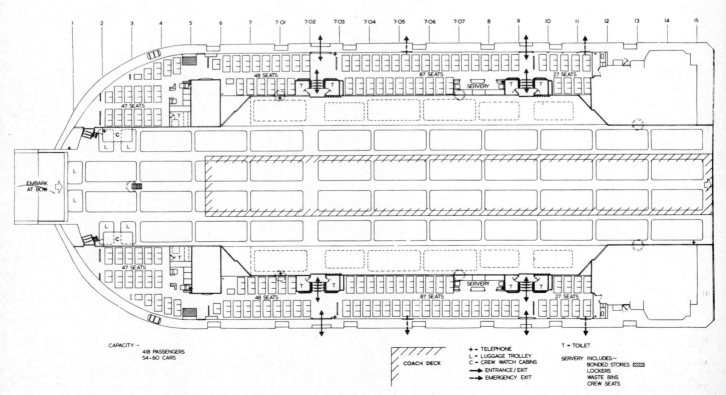

CAPACITY:-
418 PASSENGERS
54-60 CARS

COACH DECK

+ = TELEPHONE
L = LUGGAGE TROLLEY
C = CREW WATCH CABINS
→ ENTRANCE / EXIT
⇢ EMERGENCY EXIT

T = TOILET

SERVERY INCLUDES:-
BONDED STORES
LOCKERS
WASTE BINS
CREW SEATS

Layout of car deck and passenger cabins on BHC SR.N4 Mk 3 'Super 4'

passenger cabins of acceleration forces show a three-fold improvement in ride comfort over the SR.N4 Mk 2. The uprated Rolls-Royce Proteus gas turbines have been completely trouble-free and the new propellers have substantially reduced external noise when operating into and out of hovercraft terminals.

Super 4 has a payload of 418 passengers and 60 vehicles, a laden weight of 300 tons and a top speed in excess of 65 knots.

LIFT AND PROPULSION: Motive power is supplied by four Rolls-Royce Marine Proteus Type 15M/529 free-turbine turboshaft engines, located in pairs at the rear of the craft on either side of the vehicle deck. Each engine is rated at 3,800shp continuous under ISA conditions and is connected to one of four identical propeller/fan units, two forward and two aft. The propellers, made by Hawker Siddeley Dynamics, are of four-bladed, controllable-pitch type D258/485A/2. The lift fans, made by BHC, are of 12-bladed centrifugal type, 3·5m (11ft 6in) in diameter. Maximum fuel tankage, 28·45 tonnes; normal fuel allowing for ballast transfer, 18·29 tonnes.

AUXILIARY POWER: Two Lucas turboshaft engines driving 55kVA 200V, 400Hz Lucas alternators.

DIMENSIONS

Length overall: 56·38m (185ft)
Beam, hardstructure: 23·16m (76ft)
Height overall, on landing pads: 11·43m (37ft 6in)
Bow ramp door aperture size,
    Height: 3·5m (11ft 6in)
    Width: 5·48m (18ft)
Stern door aperture size,
    Height: 3·51m (11ft 6in)
    Width: 9·45m (31ft)
Car deck area: 631m² (6,790ft²)

WEIGHTS

Max laden: 300 tons
Max disposable load: 112 tons
Typical fuel load: 20 tons
Payload: 54-60 cars, 418 passengers

PERFORMANCE

Typical cruise waterspeeds:
Calm (2ft waves, 5 knots wind): 60-65 knots
Moderate (5ft waves, 20 knots wind): 50-55 knots
Rough (8ft waves, 27 knots wind): 35-45 knots
Endurance per ton of fuel: 0·23 hours

API-88 GENERAL PURPOSE HOVERCRAFT

Major advances in hovercraft technology in recent years have enabled British Hovercraft Corporation to offer a 7-8 ton payload craft with a performance equal to that of the well-proven SR.N6. Details of the API-88 (Advanced Project I-88) were first released at the Shanghai Aerospace Exhibition in June 1980. Built in welded aluminium alloy it is powered by air-cooled marine diesels. Not only is it substantially cheaper in first and operating costs but it is considerably more robust than many earlier generation craft of this size. It can be employed in a wide variety of commercial, military and para-military roles including passenger ferrying, search and rescue, geographical surveying, anti-smuggling operations, fire-fighting and logistics.

In its civil passenger form it will seat up to 80 passengers, and in troop carrying form it will seat up to 60 armed troops. In the logistics role the API-88 will carry two LWB Land Rovers, a BV202 Snowcat and trailer or 4,000kg (8,818lb) of stores.

Typical military roles would include amphibious support, logistic support, counter insurgency and police and customs duties. It can also be employed for minelaying and mine countermeasures support. As a fast minelayer it would carry four 1,000kg (2,205lb) mines.

LIFT AND PROPULSION: Lift is supplied by two 258hp 8-cylinder Deutz BF 8L413F air-cooled marine diesels, housed in two box structures flanking the forward end of the cabin superstructure, each driving four 0·84m (2ft 9in) diameter centrifugal fans. Thrust is supplied by

BHC's Super 4 has a payload of 418 passengers and up to 60 cars

Dynamic model of BHC's new diesel powered amphibious general-purpose hovercraft, the API-88

Stern view of API-88 model showing the two ducted 2·6m (8ft 6in) diameter propellers which provide thrust. Max speed in calm water is 55 knots

two 428hp Deutz BF 12L413FC air-cooled marine diesels each driving a 2·6m (8ft 6in) ducted propeller via a system of vee belts. Engine cooling air is ducted from the cushion. Alternative types of diesel engine can be installed if required, including water-cooled types. Maximum fuel capacity, including ballast allowance is 1,705 litres (375 imperial gallons).

CONTROLS: On the passenger ferry version the control cabin is sited at the forward end of the cabin superstructure but is moved aft on the open deck variants. Craft direction is controlled by differential propeller thrust, aided by swivelling bow thrusters and two sets of triple aerodynamic rudder vanes mounted on the rear of the propeller ducts. The bow thrusters contribute to forward thrust in the straight-aft position. Trim is controlled by fuel ballast transfer with additional control available from differential throttling of the lift engines.

HULL: Main hull is formed by a buoyancy raft of welded light alloy construction sub-divided into a number of watertight compartments. Shipbuilding techniques are employed. Box structures forward on each sidedeck house the lift engines and their associated fans and volutes. A loading ramp is fitted at the bow. In the passenger version access doors are provided on each side towards the aft end of the cabin.

SKIRT: Low pressure ratio tapered skirt based on that of the Super 4.

DIMENSIONS
EXTERNAL
Length overall: 20·7m (67ft 10in)
Beam overall: 10·1m (33ft)
Height, on landing pads: 4·3m (14ft)
    hovering: 4·9m (16ft)
Max cushion depth: 1·1m (3ft 7in)
INTERNAL
Cabin, length: 12·8m (42ft)
    beam: 4·4m (14ft 6in)
    headroom: 1·98m (6ft 5in)
Bow ramp width: 2·44m (8ft)
Bow door height: 1·89m (6ft 2in)

WEIGHTS
Max operating: 27,200kg (60,000lb)
Max disposable load
    (open deck version): 8,160kg (18,000lb)

PERFORMANCE
Max speed, calm water: 92km/h (55 knots)
Total fuel consumption at continuous power: 273
    litres/h (60 imperial gallons/h)

WINCHESTER (SR.N6) CLASS
Designed primarily as a fast ferry for operation in sheltered waters, the Winchester can accommodate either 38 passengers or 3 tons of freight.

Fully amphibious, it can operate from relatively unsophisticated bases above the high water mark, irrespective of tidal state.

Directional control is achieved by twin rudders and a thrust port system. Two manually actuated elevators provide pitch trim at cruising speed.

Winchesters have been in regular commercial service since 1965. Current operators include Hovertravel Ltd, Hoverwork Ltd and Solent Seaspeed. A further Winchester is in service with the Civil Aviation Department, Ministry of Transport, New Zealand, as a crash rescue craft at Auckland International Airport. Both the Winchester and its smaller, 7-ton predecessor, the SR.N5 (see *Jane's Surface Skimmers 1971-72* and earlier editions) are in service with the Canadian Coast Guard.

Military variants are in service with the Royal Navy's Hovercraft Trials Unit, Iranian Navy, Italian Navy and the Saudi Arabian Frontier Force and Coast Guard.

LIFT AND PROPULSION: Power for the integrated lift/propulsion system is provided by a Rolls-Royce Marine Gnome gas turbine with a maximum continuous rating at 15°C of 900shp. This drives a BHC 12-blade centrifugal 2·13m (7ft) diameter lift fan, and a Dowty Rotol four blade variable pitch 2·74m (9ft) diameter propeller for propulsion.

DIMENSIONS
EXTERNAL
Overall length: 14·8m (48ft 6in)
Overall beam, skirt inflated: 7·7m (25ft 4in)
Overall height on landing pads: 3·8m (12ft 6in)
Height hovering: 5m (16ft 6in)
Skirt depth: 1·22m (4ft)
INTERNAL
Cabin size (length × width): 6·62 × 2·34m (21ft
    9in × 7ft 8in)
Cabin headroom-centre line: 1·83m (6ft)
Door aperture size (height × width): 1·75 ×
    0·99m (5ft 9in × 3ft 3in)
WEIGHTS
Normal gross: 10 tons

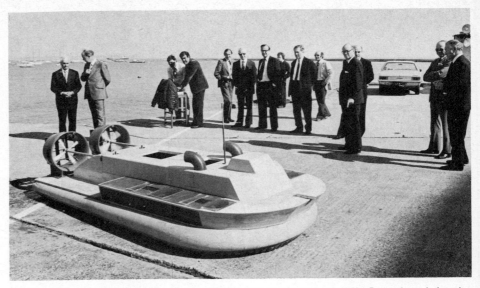

Model of 80-seat fast passenger ferry variant of API-88. Lift is supplied by two 258hp Deutz air-cooled marine diesels housed in two box structures flanking the forward end of the cabin and driving two sets of centrifugal fans

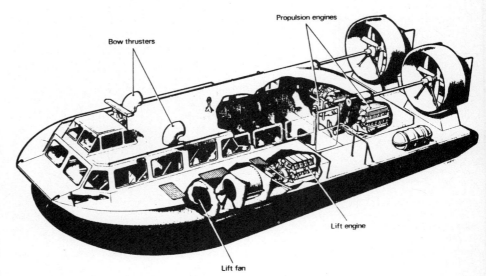

Cutaway showing interior machinery arrangements of API-88

SR.N6 of the Naval Hovercraft Trials Unit setting out on patrol from Hong Kong. Two SR.N6s are employed on patrol duties in Hong Kong to assist in controlling illegal immigration from other countries in South-east Asia

PERFORMANCE (at normal gross weight at 15°C)

Max water speed over calm water zero wind, (cont power rating): 96km/h (52 knots)

Average service water speed in sheltered coastal waters: 55·65km/h (30·35 knots)

Endurance at max continuous power rating on 265 imperial gallons of fuel: 3·6 hours

WINCHESTER (SR.N6) CLASS— PASSENGER FERRY/GENERAL PURPOSE

Since the SR.N6 first entered service as a passenger ferry in 1965, it has carried well over three million fare-paying passengers and is now firmly established in certain areas as an integral part of surface transport networks.

The popularity of these services subsequently led to the introduction of an SR.N6 with a larger carrying capacity, designated the SR.N6 Mk 1S. At 58ft in length, the Mk 1S is 10ft longer than the standard craft and can carry up to 58 passengers as opposed to 35-38 in the standard SR.N6.

Other modifications to this craft include additional baggage panniers, emergency exits and improved cabin ventilation. An additional bonus is a significant increase in ride comfort. To ensure that performance is maintained, the rating of the Rolls-Royce Marine Gnome gas turbine engine has been increased by 100shp to 1,000shp.

Two Mk 1S craft are in service with Solent Seaspeed Ltd, linking Cowes and Southampton, and one Mk 1S is in operation on the Ryde/Southsea route with Hovertravel Limited.

Apart from passenger services, commercial SR.N6s have also made successful inroads into other fields of operation in recent years and typical examples of such applications include freight-carrying, hydrographic/seismographic survey, offshore support operations, general communications, crash rescue and firefighting.

To undertake these duties, craft have been modified either with the fitting of specialised equipment or by structural alterations such as flat-decks.

WINCHESTER (SR.N6) CLASS— MILITARY

Currently, variants of the SR.N6 are in service with a number of the world's military and paramilitary forces on coastal defence and logistic support duties.

The SR.N6 Mk 2/3, for logistic support, features a roof loading hatch and strengthened side-decks for carrying long loads of up to ½ ton. Lightweight armour may be fitted to protect troops being carried in the cabin; the engine; and other vital systems. Defensive armament is provided by a roof-mounted light machine gun (7·62mm or 0·5in).

The craft can carry upwards of 20 fully-equipped troops or supply loads of up to 5 tons. A small auxiliary generator is installed to provide power when the main engine is stopped.

The SR.N6 Mk 4 for coastal defence duties may be fitted with 20mm cannon or short-range wire-guided surface-to-surface missiles. Communications equipment is concentrated behind the rear cabin bulkhead.

SR.N6 Mk 6 GENERAL PURPOSE

The SR.N6 Mk 6 is the latest development in the successful Winchester series and represents significant steps forward in terms of increased

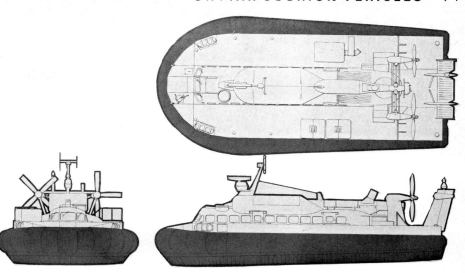

General arrangement of SR.N6 Mk 6

payload, all-weather performance, and increased manoeuvrability, especially in high winds and at low speeds. There is also a significant reduction in the external noise level.

These advances have been achieved by the introduction of twin propellers for thrust, a more powerful engine, wider sidedecks and a redesigned skirt for better seakeeping capabilities. The tapered skirt, which is deeper at the bow than the stern, cushions the effect of operating over larger waves and surface obstacles and enables the craft to operate in winds of up to Beaufort Scale 8 and waves of up to 3·04m (10ft).

The craft, with its large cabin, can carry up to 55 passengers or between five and six tons of equipment. Various options are available including air-conditioning and VIP interior trim.

LIFT AND PROPULSION: Motive power is supplied by a single 1,125hp Rolls-Royce Marine Gnome GN 1301 gas turbine driving a single

2·13m (7ft) diameter BHC lift fan and two 3·05m (10ft) diameter Dowty Rotol variable-pitch propellers. Maximum fuel capacity is 4,840 litres (1,065 imperial gallons).

DIMENSIONS

Length overall: 18·3m (60ft)

Beam overall: 8·5m (28ft)

Height overall, on landing pads: 5·6m (18ft 4in) on cushion: 6·7m (22ft)

WEIGHTS

Max operating: 17,010kg (37,500lb)

PERFORMANCE

Max speed over calm water: 60 knots

Fuel consumption: 410 litres/h (90 imperial gallons/h)

SR.N6 Mk 8

Latest military variant of the ubiquitous SR.N6, the Mk 8 has the same overall measurements as the SR.N6 Mk 6 twin-propeller model

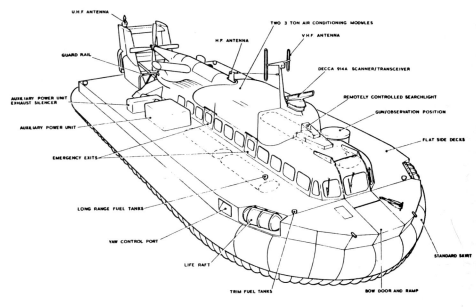

SR.N6 Mk 8 showing main features. In the logistic support role the Mk 8 can carry up to 55 fully-equipped troops or loads up to 6 tons

BHC's SR.N6 Mk 6 general purpose hovercraft, showing the twin-propeller arrangement and tapered skirt. Up to 55 passengers can be carried or between 5 and 6 tons of equipment

but has a single propeller only. Another external difference is the provision of two air-conditioning modules on the cabin roof aft of the driving position.

In the logistic support role the Mk 8 can carry up to 55 fully-equipped troops or loads of up to 6 tons. Access to the cabin, which measures 9·5 × 2·3m (31ft 2in × 7ft 7in), is via a bow door. The floor is fitted with tie-down points for stores and equipment. Loads up to ½ ton which are too long for the cabin may be carried externally on the side-decks.

Operating in the coastal patrol role, the operational flexibility of the SR.N6 is greatly enhanced by its ability to work from beaches and other unprepared sites and to navigate freely in shallow water. At the same time the craft is sea-worthy and can operate in most weather conditions by day or night.

LIFT AND PROPULSION: Integrated system powered by a single Rolls-Royce GN 1301 marine gas turbine rated at 1,050shp at 15°C. Auxiliary power is supplied by a Lucas SS923 gas turbine driving a three-phase alternator. Main fuel tank capacity is 1,204 litres (265 imperial gallons). Long range tanks can be fitted, giving a capacity of 1,818 litres (400 imperial gallons).

ARMAMENT: Either a ring-mounted machine gun (0·5in or 7·62mm) or short range wire-guided surface-to-surface missiles mounted on the side-decks.

DIMENSIONS
Length overall: 18·3m (60ft)
Beam overall: 8·5m (28ft)
Height overall on cushion: 6·7m (22ft)

PERFORMANCE
Max speed, calm water: 50 knots
Endurance, on main tanks: 2·4 hours
    on long-range tanks: 6 hours
A further 1·8 hours endurance can be obtained by using the fuel carried in the craft's trim system giving a maximum endurance of 7·8 hours

WELLINGTON (BH.7) CLASS

BH.7 is a 50-ton hovercraft which was designed specifically for naval and military roles. The prototype, designated BH.7 Mk 2, has been in service with the Royal Navy since 1970 where it has been evaluated in a number of roles including Fishery Protection, ASW and MCM work.

The second and third craft, designated Mk 4 and a further four Mk 5As, are all in service with the Iranian Navy.

LIFT AND PROPULSION: Power for the integrated lift propulsion system on the Mk 2 and Mk 4 is provided by a Rolls-Royce Marine Proteus 15M541 gas turbine with a maximum rating at 23°C of 4,250shp. On the Mk 5A, a 15M549 is installed with a maximum rating of 4,250shp. In both types the engine drives, via a light alloy driveshaft and bevel drive gearbox, a BHC 12-blade, centrifugal 3·5m (11ft 6in) diameter lift fan and an HSD four-blade, variable-pitch pylon-mounted propeller. Propeller diameter on the Mk 4 is 5·79m (19ft) and 6·4m (21ft) on the Mk 2 and Mk 5A. Normal fuel capacity is up to 3,000 imperial gallons.

CONTROLS: Craft direction is controlled by swivelling the propeller pylon angle by a foot-pedal. Thrust ports are fitted at each quarter to assist directional control at low speed, and a hydraulically-operated skirt-shift system helps to bank the craft into turns, thereby reducing drift.

Fuel is transferred between forward and aft tanks via a ring main to adjust fore and aft trim.

HULL: Construction is mainly of corrosion resistant light alloy. Extensive use is made of components which were designed for the N4. The bow structure is a Plasticell base covered with glass fibre.

SKIRT: The fan delivers air to the cushion via a continuous peripheral fingered bag skirt made in neoprene coated nylon fabric. The skirt provides an air cushion depth of 1·68m (5ft 6in). The cushion is divided into four compartments by a full length longitudinal keel and by two transverse keels located slightly forward of amidships.

ACCOMMODATION: The raised control cabin, located slightly forward of amidships on

BH.7 Mk 4 of the Royal Navy's Naval Hovercraft Trials Unit. The craft embodies a bow door and a Sea Rider with a davit

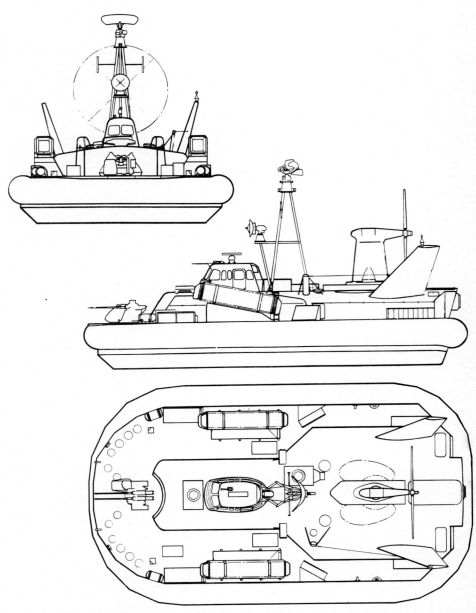

General arrangement of the Wellington (BH.7) Mk 5 combat craft fitted with Exocet launchers and a twin 30mm dual purpose mounting

the hull centre line, accommodates a crew of three, with the driver and navigator/radar operator in front and the third crew member behind. The driver sits on the right, with the throttle and propeller pitch control lever on his right, and the pylon angle footpedal and skirt-shift column in front.

The navigator, on the left, has a Decca radar display (Type 914 on the Mk 5) and compass in front and Decometers in an overhead panel.

The large main cabin area permits a variety of operational layouts. In a typical arrangement, the operations room is placed directly beneath the control cabin and contains communication, navigation, search and strike equipment and associated displays.

The craft has an endurance of up to 11 hours under cruise conditions but this can be extended considerably as it can stay 'on watch' without using the main engine.

Provision can be made for the crew to live aboard for several days.

SYSTEMS, ELECTRICAL: Two Rover IS/90 APUs provide via two 55kVA generators three-phase 400Hz ac at 200V for ac and dc supplies.

DIMENSIONS

EXTERNAL

Length overall: 23·9m (78ft 4in)
Beam overall: 13·8m (45ft 6in)
Overall height on landing pads: 10·36m (34ft)
Skirt depth: 1·67m (5ft 6in)

INTERNAL (Mk 4 only)

Bow door size: 4·18 × 2·2m (13ft 9in × 7ft 3in)
Headroom centre line: 2·38m (7ft 10in)

WEIGHTS

Normal gross: 50 tons
Payload: 14 tons

PERFORMANCE (at max operating weight at 15°C)

Max water speed over calm water (continuous power rating): 60 knots
Average water speed in 1·37m (4ft 6in) seas: 35·5 knots

WELLINGTON (BH.7) Mk 4 LOGISTIC SUPPORT

ACCOMMODATION: In this role, the main hold floor area of 56m² (600ft²) of the Mk 4 provides an unobstructed space suitable for loading wheeled vehicles, guns and military stores.

Two side cabins, filled with paratroop-type seats, can accommodate up to 60 troops and their equipment.

Access at the bow is through a "clamshell" door.

Machine guns can be fitted in gun rings on the roof on either side of the cabin and provision can be made for armour plating to protect personnel, the engine and vital electrical components.

SYSTEMS, ELECTRICAL: Two Rover IS/90 gas turbine APUs provide electrical power independently of the main engine.

TYPICAL MILITARY LOADS: 170 fully equipped troops or three field cars and trailers plus 60 troops or two armoured scout cars or up to 20 NATO pallets.

DIMENSIONS

EXTERNAL

Length overall: 23·85m (78ft 4in)
Beam overall: 13·8m (45ft 6in)
Height overall on landing pads: 10·06m (33ft)

INTERNAL

Main cabin floor area: 56m² (600ft²)
Main cabin headroom—centreline: 2·38m (7ft 10in)
Access door aperture (height × width): 2·2 × 4·2m (7ft 3in × 13ft 9in)

WEIGHTS

Normal gross: 45 tons
Fuel load at 45 tons all-up weight: 9 tons
Max fuel capacity: 12·5 tons

PERFORMANCE (at normal gross weight at 15°C)

Max water speed, calm water, zero wind, continuous power rating: 120km/h (65 knots)
Rough water speed in 1·37m (4ft 6in) seas (depending on heading and wave length): 65-92km/h (35-50 knots)
Endurance at max continuous power rating with 9 tons of fuel (with 10% reserve): 8 hours

WELLINGTON (BH.7) Mk 5 COMBAT

Designed for coastal defence operations, the BH.7 Mk 5 carries medium-range surface-to-surface missiles, such as Exocet, on its sidedecks. Secondary armament consists of a twin 30mm surface/AA radar controlled mounting situated on the foredeck forward of the main centre cabin.

The main central cabin, employed on the BH.7 Mk 4 for load-carrying, is equipped as an operations and fire control room. Since it is fully amphibious, the BH.7 Mk 5 can be operated from relatively unprepared bases on beaches and can head directly towards its target on interception missions regardless of the tidal state and marginal terrain. Also, since none of its solid structure is immersed, it is invulnerable to underwater defences such as acoustic, magnetic and pressure mines and to attack by torpedoes.

Wellington Mk 5A combat/logistic support craft. This particular variant carries medium range ship-to-ship missiles, such as Exocet, on its sidedecks and retains the bow loading door of the Mk 4

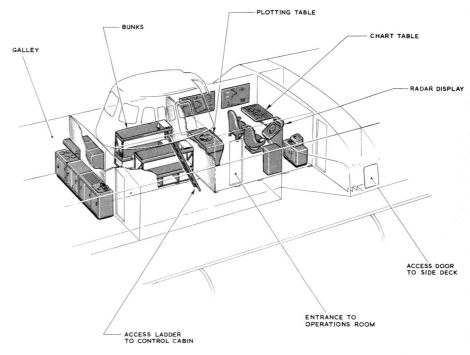
Interior layout of BH.7 Mk 5A Minesweeper

200-ton SR.N4, *Sir Christopher*, accompanied by the 40-knot patrol craft, *Tenacity*, during mine countermeasures trials with the Royal Navy off Portland in May 1976. During these trials the craft reached speeds in excess of 70 knots and covered the 167n miles from Portland back to Ramsgate at an average speed of 51·4 knots

A full range of electronic navigational aids permit the craft to operate by day or night ensuring 'round-the-clock' availability.

WELLINGTON (BH.7) Mk 5A COMBAT/LOGISTICS

Similar to the Mk 5 above, with the exception that the bow door is retained, giving the craft a dual fast attack/logistic capability. Secondary armament can consist of two roof-mounted single 20mm guns.

DIMENSIONS

Length overall: 23·9m (78ft 4in)
Beam overall: 13·9m (45ft 6in)
Height overall, on landing pads: 10·7m (34ft)

WEIGHTS

All-up weight: 55·88 tonnes (55 tons)
Capacity: Up to 5 persons and 7-ton weapon payload

PERFORMANCE

Max speed: 58 knots
Endurance: 8 hours
Long range endurance: 10 hours

BHC MINE CLEARANCE HOVERCRAFT

Minesweeping is one of the most hazardous of all naval activities. Clearance techniques in the past have been very much on a hit or miss basis with craft operating in pairs, one sweeping and the other hunting and destroying the released mines as they surfaced by rifle and machinegun fire. Since the precise location of each mine was unknown, it was not unusual for a released mine to surface in the path of or beneath the hull of the hunter craft.

In the USA in recent years, efforts to reduce the tremendous wastage in lives and craft led to the introduction of the Edo 105 and 106 foil-equipped catamaran minesweeping systems. These not only speed up the process of mine clearance, but since they are towed by helicopter, reduce very considerably the risks to the crews involved.

In the United Kingdom, the Ministry of Defence (Navy) has stated that as hovercraft normally operate clear of the water, they are less vulnerable to possible mine explosions than conventional vessels, and with mine countermeasures equipment they have a potential for this type of work.

The British Hovercraft Corporation has announced plans for both sweeper and hunter versions of the BH.7 and the SR.N4. Descriptions of these vessels are given below.

BH.7 Mk 5A MINESWEEPER

Among the advantages offered by the use of this type of fully amphibious hovercraft for MCM, as opposed to a displacement vessel are five times the transit speed; very low acoustic and magnetic underwater signatures; and virtual immunity to underwater explosions. Additionally, the craft can be used for crew rescue in mined waters. Since the craft is based on the standard BH.7 Mk 5A, and retains its bow loading door, it has logistic support capability when not being employed for minesweeping.

LIFT AND PROPULSION: Integrated lift/propulsion system powered by a single Rolls-Royce Marine Proteus 15M/549 gas turbine with a continuous output at 15°C of 3,800hp at 10,000 turbine rpm. This drives via a light alloy drive shaft and bevel drive gearbox, a BHC 12-blade, centrifugal 3·5m (11ft 6in) diameter, lift fan and an HSD four-blade, variable-pitch 6·4m (21ft) diameter, pylon-mounted propeller.

ACCOMMODATION: Total crew complement is eight men. The raised control cabin accommodates a three-man operating crew, with the captain and navigator in front and the third crew member behind. An off-duty cabin is located immediately beneath, with bunks for four. Ahead of the off-duty cabin is a galley and aft, in the midship cabin, is the operations room with navigation, surface and under surface plotting tables, radar display and data processing equipment. The control cabin is air-conditioned and the rest areas are air-conditioned and soundproofed. Access from the off-duty cabin to the control cabin is via a ladder.

SYSTEMS, MCM EQUIPMENT: Minesweeping equipment, including winches and cable reels, are stowed on the side decks and sides of the superstructure forward. Equipment includes floats, depressors, otters and cutters, venturi acoustic sweeping gear, marker buoys and an inflatable dinghy.

SWEEP DEPLOYMENT: Sweeps are deployed from the port side deck and shackled to the primary tow cable which is permanently attached to the destabilising pulley running on the towing bridle.

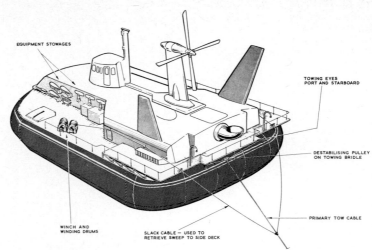

BH.7 Mk 5A equipped for minesweeping

Royal Navy's BH.7 Mk 4 as modified by BHC for the mine countermeasures role, to enable the craft to play a more realistic part in naval exercises. In this particular configuration the craft embodies a bow door, sweep deck extension and a Sea Rider with davit to assist in deployment and recovery

DIMENSIONS

EXTERNAL
Length overall: 23·9m (78ft 4in)
Beam overall: 13·9m (45ft 6in)
Height overall, on cushion: 11·8m (38ft 8in)
  on landing pads: 10·4m (34ft)
INTERNAL
Cabin headroom, on centreline: 2·4m (7ft 10in)
Bow door opening: 4·1 × 2·9m (13ft 9in × 7ft 3in)

WEIGHTS
Starting all-up weight: 53 tons approx
Mean operating: 48 tons approx
MCM payload: 3 tons approx

PERFORMANCE
Cruising speed, knots:

Craft heading	Into wind	Beam wind
Calm water, still air	68	68
Significant wave height/wind speed		
4ft/6 knots	57	59
2ft/11 knots	47	52
3ft/15 knots	38	44

ENDURANCE: Total fuel consumption at max continuous power (includes both APUs): 1·16 tons/hour. Endurance on a nominal 10 ton fuel load: 8·6 hours.

Towing capability: a towing force of 3-5 tons is available at speeds of up to 10 knots in significant waveheights up to 3ft.

BH.7 Mk 5A MINE HUNTER

This version is identical in practically every respect to the minesweeper model and can be reconfigured readily to sweeping duties or logistic support roles. It differs from the sweeper only in the mine disposal equipment carried.

SYSTEMS, MCM EQUIPMENT: A 20mm machine gun mount ahead of the control cabin is optional. Towed or dunking mine detection and classification sonars; remotely piloted mine disposal vehicles; sonar display units; recorders etc; navigation and communications gear.

DEPLOYMENT: Over the sidedecks via davits and swinging A frames. Towing lines are deployed and retrieved by winch and shackled to the primary tow cable which is permanently attached to the destabilising pulley running on the towing bridle.

PERFORMANCE

Cruising and towing speed: as for minesweeper

Endurance: in the case of a sonar being towed at a speed of 5 knots or less, but with the craft in full hover condition, the estimated fuel consumption (ton/hour) is:

Proteus: 0·677 ton/h (ISA conditions)

2 Rover APUs: 0·111 ton/h (assumed requirement)

Total: 0·778 ton/h

On a nominal 10 ton fuel-load, endurance would be 12·9 hours

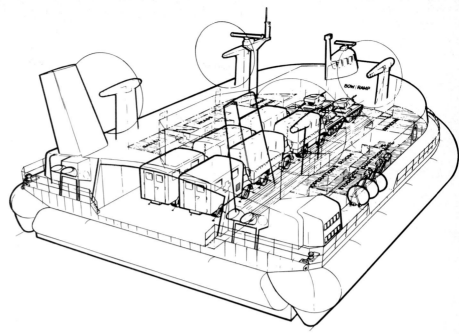

SR.N4 with typical logistic payload

SR.N4 Mk 4

The MCMH version of the SR.N4 is identical in most respects to the Mk 2 commercial craft but has a much larger fuel capacity. A high-speed self-jacking system which would allow the craft to be raised for skirt inspections and repairs on temporary landing sites can be installed if required. At its design maximum all-up weight of 220 tonnes it is capable of carrying up to 60 tonnes of role payload in addition to the fuel for a ten-hour mission.

The craft is able to undertake all the mine clearance tasks currently performed by conventional vessels such as a minesweeper with wire or influence sweeps, or a mine hunter using towed sonar and mine disposal equipment. It can therefore operate either independently or as a unit of a mixed-craft MCM force.

The operations room, crew quarters and workshop can be accommodated in the twin side cabins or alternatively, on the central deck area forward of the winch positions. All major installations in the central area can be erected on palletised modules to facilitate changes of MCM equipment, and conversion for logistic support duties, enabling individual craft to perform any of the proposed MCM roles at short notice.

As with the standard craft, the SR.N4 MCMH has considerable development potential. Most of the future modifications which may be introduced to improve the efficiency of the civil versions will be applicable to the MCMH, including larger propellers, uprated engines and revised skirts. In particular its payload carrying capability could be increased by lengthening as has been undertaken for the Seaspeed craft.

All types of minesweeping gear used by conventional minesweepers—a wiresweep to cut the moorings of tethered mines or influence sweeps, magnetic and acoustic, to detonate influence mines—can be carried by the SR.N4. Additionally in the minehunting role it can tow sonars to locate mines which cannot normally be swept and carry the equipment to destroy them.

Trials with SR.N4 have shown that it maintains a track in winds of at least 20 knots to within a standard deviation of less than eight metres. In the minehunting role, position accuracy as well as track keeping accuracy is required, since relocation may be necessary. These requirements can be met by the provision of two navigation modes. In the primary mode, position fixing could be derived from a high accuracy radio navigation aid. Secondary mode sensors could include a navigation radar with auto extraction, possibly by range-range measurement relative to short scope buoys. Decca Navigator could provide a further mode.

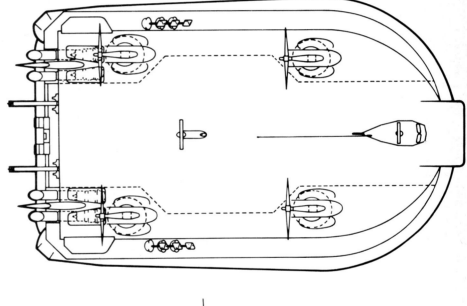

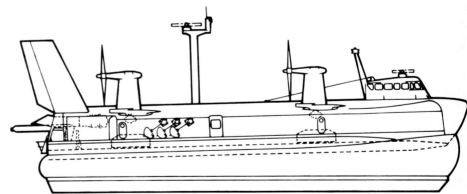

General arrangement of the SR.N4 MCMH, powered by four Rolls Royce Marine Proteus gas turbines, each with a maximum rating of 3,170kW (4,250hp)

It is likely that the SR.N4 MCMH would have an integrated computer-based navigation and action information system. This would have inputs of heading from a gyro compass; velocities from a speed and drift sensor, probably a multibeam doppler radar; position from Hi-fix 6, Decca Navigator and Inboard navigational radar; target position from a towed sonar.

The SR.N4 MCMH would operate from Forward Support Units (FSU) located in the general area of probable mining targets. One such unit could be the force headquarters, providing training facilities and co-ordinating mine clearance operations including, if necessary, those of conventional craft. In the event of a mining attack it may be desirable to establish an additional MCMH base closer to the area of operations. This could be in the form of a Mobile Advanced Base (MAB) able to support up to three craft for a period of 14 days. It is anticipated that MAB sites would be selected in advance of an attack but not necessarily prepared in any way.

Where the situation did not justify a MAB, fuel, sweep spares and crew could be readily transferred at a Temporary Replenishment Point (TRP) which need be no more than a suitable beach area having vehicular access.

It is envisaged that the MCMH force would be responsible for the establishment of any shore based navigation system such as Hi-fix which might be required for operation in particular areas.

INFLUENCE SWEEPER

For operations against the various types of acoustic and magnetic mine the SR.N4 MCMH has sufficient carrying capacity and towing capability to operate existing influence sweeps such as the Osborn Acoustic and the MM Mk 2 Magnetic Loop.

These detonate the mines by reproducing the signature of the intended victim and are usually operated in combination. The relative immunity of the SR.N4 MCMH to underwater explosions gives it a marked advantage in this role.

WIRE SWEEPER

For mine sweeping operations against moored or tethered mines the SR.N4 MCMH can be fitted with the standard Wire Mk 3 Mod 2 Oropesa sweep and associated equipment as used by the Royal Navy Ton Class minesweepers and Hunt Class MCMVs.

The winch has been redesigned for hovercraft use but if desired the standard Type B winch with modified drive arrangements could be accommodated without difficulty.

MOD (N)-sponsored trials with a simulated sweep have been conducted successfully in Coastal Code 5 and it is anticipated that sweeping could be carried out in more adverse conditions, but, as with conventional craft, the actual operating limits may be determined by the ability to stream and recover the sweep gear.

HUNTER/DISPOSAL CRAFT

Mines that cannot be swept using wire, acoustic and magnetic sweeps, such as pressure mines and those yet to be activated, are normally located using sonar devices and then destroyed by explosive charges.

For mine hunting the SR.N4 MCMH can be equipped with a pair of towed sidescan search sonars. Fitted with these the craft can carry out routine surveillance duties more rapidly than most conventional craft.

Relocation of the target can be achieved, if required, by using a dipped sonar and the mine disposal weapon can be delivered by a remotely piloted vehicle (RPC) such as the PAP.104 or the Sperry Catamaran. Alternatively the disposal charge may be placed in position from a manned Gemini dinghy.

MULTI-ROLE CRAFT

The SR.N4 MCMH can carry the full range of equipment associated with the mine sweeping, influence sweeping and hunter/disposal roles at the same time. There is adequate deck space for all the items to be stowed—the central through deck area is about 35m long by 10m wide—and the corresponding craft weight of 227·5 tonnes, which includes fuel for 11 hours endurance, is well within operational limits.

In practice the craft is unlikely to be required to carry all the equipment when operating in a specific role. Wire sweeping can be undertaken with the influence sweeping equipment on board since many components are common. The various mine hunting and disposal systems considered are sufficiently portable to be fitted at the Mobile Advanced Base when needed for specific tasks.

The characteristics of the standard SR.N4 are such that the craft can be adapted to other roles and in particular to those of fast attack craft and anti-submarine craft. As a fast attack craft a typical weapon fit could include at least four surface-to-surface missiles of Exocet or Harpoon type or similar, a 75mm OTO Melara gun and a twin 30mm gun mount for anti-aircraft defence,

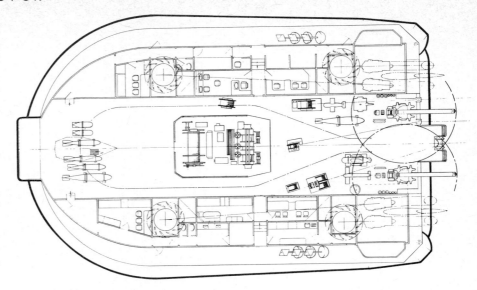

Deck plan of the multi-role version of the SR.N4, which can carry the full range of equipment associated with mine-sweeping, influence-sweeping and hunter disposal roles at the same time

Underwater explosion tests being undertaken with the 35-tonne SR.N3 when operating with the Inter-Service Hovercraft Trials Unit

Top: The N.3, tethered, hovering, unmanned, within the shock dome of the charge
Centre: Rising plume of the explosion
Bottom: The N.3, after the explosion, damaged, but able to return to base under its own power

together with their associated sensors and control equipment. The anti-submarine version could carry upwards of 60 tonnes of equipment enabling it to operate in the hunter/killer role alone or in conjunction with other craft.

LOGISTIC SUPPORT

Should a situation develop which requires large numbers of troops and their equipment to be transported over water at high speed then the SR.N4 MCMH could, by removal of the bulk of the MCM equipment be converted for Logistic Support duties.

Typical loadings up to 90 tonnes:
a) 7 GS trucks; 250 troops
b) 1 battle tank; 2 light tanks; 6 1-tonne land-rovers.
c) 4 light tanks; 2 laden trucks; 2 unladen trucks; 2 ambulances.

Operating around the clock over a 30n mile route in moderate conditions, the craft could, over a 24-hour period, transport approximately 1,500 tonnes of military personnel and equipment.

LIFT AND PROPULSION: Power is supplied by four Rolls-Royce Marine Proteus free turbine turboshaft engines located in pairs at the rear of the craft on either side of the working deck space. Each would operate at 3,800shp when cruising. Each engine is connected to one of four identical propeller/fan units, two forward, two aft. The propellers, made by Hawker Siddeley Dynamics, are of four-bladed, variable and reversible pitch type, 5·8m (19ft) in diameter. The lift fans, made by BHC, are of 12-bladed centrifugal type, 3·5m (11ft 6in) in diameter.

CONTROLS AND HULL: Similar to SR.N4 Mk 2.

ACCOMMODATION: Nominal crew complement is five officers, four senior ratings and six junior ratings. The operations room, crew accommodation and workshop can be fitted into the twin side cabins or alternatively within the central deck area forward of the winch positions. All major installations in the central deck area can be mounted on palletised modules to facilitate the changing over of MCM equipment and conversion to logistic support duties. Fuel for the craft is standard aviation kerosene DERD 2494 (AVTUR). Diesel fuel DEF.2404-4 may be used as an alternative. Capacity of the craft is 10 hours endurance + 10%, 47 tonnes.

SYSTEMS, ELECTRICAL: 2 × 55kVA alternators provide 200V three phase 400Hz power from APU. 28V dc power is provided by two TRUs supplied from 400Hz system. Batteries provide emergency power and APU starting.

PULSE GENERATOR: A gas turbine driven alternator unit provides 500kVA, three phase 400Hz power at voltages required for magnetic-loop sweeps.

DIMENSIONS

EXTERNAL

Overall length: 39·68m (130ft 2in)
Beam: 25·5m (83ft 8in)
Height (masthead): 17·2m (56ft 5in)
Sweepback, length: 24m (78ft 8⅞in)
 beam: 10m (32ft 9¾in)

WEIGHTS

Basic: 113·5 tonnes
Normal max: 220 tonnes
Overload: 240 tonnes

SR.N4 MINELAYER

A high-speed mine laying version of the SR.N4 is now available. This particular variant will carry 110-120 ground mines with their trolleys. A feature of the design is a revised stern door arrangement which will permit mine laying to take place at high speed over all depths of water.

MILITARY 4

A derivative of the Super 4, the Military 4 is the most recent addition to British Hovercraft Corporation's range of large high-speed amphibious hovercraft. In external appearance and dimensions, the two variants are nearly identical, but

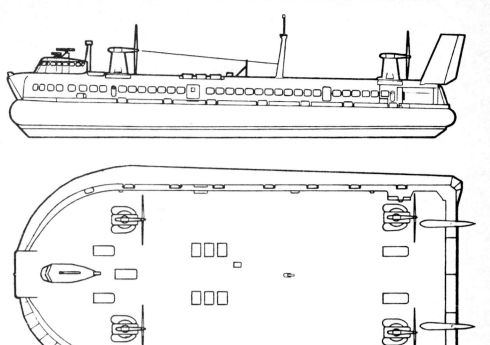

General arrangement of BHC Military 4 high speed amphibious military hovercraft

the Military 4 is capable of carrying almost double the payload of the commercial craft. It can carry a disposable load of up to 165 tons (or 1,000 troops) at a speed of 65 knots and has a maximum endurance of almost 19 hours.

Its high work capacity of more than 10,000 ton nautical miles/hour makes the Military 4 ideal for a variety of military roles in an emergency, in particular logistic support, minelaying and mine countermeasures.

LOGISTICS: As a high-speed logistic craft, it can carry up to 1,000 fully-equipped troops or up to 165 tons of military loads in the form of vehicles or stores. Troops, equipment, stores and vehicles can be loaded and off-loaded from beaches well clear of vulnerable harbour installations.

MINELAYING: By installing mining rails throughout the length of the vehicle deck, the craft can be converted to a high-speed ground minelayer. In this role 160 ground mines can be carried at speeds greatly in excess of conventional minelayers and in all weather conditions, thus permitting instant reaction in the form of offensive or defensive mining.

MINE COUNTERMEASURES (MCM): By the installation of pallet-mounted conventional MCM equipment, the Military 4 can be converted easily into a very effective mine countermeasures vessel. Sweeping and hunting speeds are similar to those of conventional ships, this being a limitation of the MCM gear, but speeds of up to 65 knots can be used in transit to the areas to be swept.

Details of proposed navigational aids and capabilities will be found above under the entry for the SR.N4 Mk 4.

Off-the-shelf mine hunting and sweeping equipment can be pallet-mounted and installed on the vehicle deck, the side and bow passenger cabin being converted to operations rooms, accommodation and messing facilities.

LIFT AND PROPULSION: Motive power is furnished by four marine gas turbines mounted in pairs in two engine rooms at the stern. Each gas turbine is flat rated at 4,500shp and drives a four-bladed 6·4m (21ft) diameter controllable-pitch propeller and a 12-bladed 3·5m (11ft 6in) diameter centrifugal lift fan. The propellers are mounted on rotating pylons which can be turned to change the direction of thrust and so control

craft direction. The aerodynamic rudders mounted aft of the rear propellers provide additional directional control.

The lift fans are mounted one below each propeller pylon. Air is drawn by the fan through intakes on each side of the pylon and directed through plenum chambers under the side cabins into the flexible trunks. From the trunks air is directed inboard beneath the craft to create and maintain the air cushion.

Electrical power is generated by two turbo-shaft engines each driving a 55kVA three-phase alternator. Fuel is standard aviation kerosene DERD 2494 (AVTUR). Diesel fuel, specification DEF 2404-4, may be used as an alternative.

ACCOMMODATION: The control cabin is located on the cabin roof ahead of the two forward pylons and houses the operational crew. Nominal crew would comprise 5 officers, 4 senior ratings and 6 junior ratings. The central main deck accommodates vehicles, logistic loads or troops and there are troop cabins each side of the main deck. At the forward end of the car deck is a hydraulically-operated ramp which when raised completely seals the bow apertures and when lowered enables vehicles and loads to be disembarked. At the aft end of the vehicle deck are hydraulically-operated double doors which extend the full width of the deck.

Additional doors give access to the side cabins thereby enabling troops to be embarked or disembarked concurrently with vehicles.

SKIRT: Tapered BHC skirt. Hemline to solid structure clearance varies from approximately 3m (9ft 10in) at the bow to 2·4m (7ft 10in) at the stern.

DIMENSIONS

EXTERNAL

Length: 56·38m (185ft)
Beam: 23·16m (76ft)
Height, on landing pads: 11·4m (37ft 6in)

INTERNAL

Vehicle deck area: 631m² (6,790ft²)
Beam: 10·0m (32ft 10in)

WEIGHTS

Max operating weight: 375 tons
Max disposable load: 165 tons

PERFORMANCE

Max speed: in excess of 65 knots
Max endurance: 19 hours, plus 10%

CYCLONE HOVERCRAFT

8 Walton Road, Caldecotte, Milton Keynes, Buckinghamshire MK7 8AE, England
Telephone: 0908 64733
Officials:
N R Beale BSc, MSc, *Director*
P J Beale, *Director*

Cyclone Hovercraft has developed a plans, components and design service based upon the experience that won the British National Championships for eight consecutive years.

Their latest enterprise is a simple single-engined hovercraft, plans of which are offered for home construction. This craft is designed around the British-made "Breeza" axial fan, for which Cyclone has been appointed agent. "Breeza" fans employ adjustable pitch blades made from high strength plastic. A glass fibre two-seat version of the craft was scheduled to enter production in late 1979.

SIMPLE CYCLONE

A single-engined design employing a single ducted fan for its integrated lift and propulsion system, Simple Cyclone will carry one adult over water at speeds of up to 48·28km/h (30mph). Over smooth land its payload may be increased to two adults.
LIFT AND PROPULSION: A single Kyoritsu KEC 225cc two-stroke engine, rated at 12·5bhp at 5,550rpm, drives, via a toothed belt, a 600mm (23⅝in) diameter "Breeza" fan. The unit supplies air for both lift and thrust. Any suitable engine of between 10 and 25bhp may be used. The 4·5 litre (1 gallon) fuel tank gives a cruising endurance of more than one hour. A larger capacity tank may be fitted if desired.
CONTROLS: For the utmost simplicity, only two controls are provided, designed for single-handed operation. A lever control for the engine throttle is mounted on the control column which operates the twin rudders.
HULL: The hull is constructed from thin exterior grade plywood with wooden stringers. Polyurethane foam within the hull structure ensures adequate buoyancy. The fan duct unit is laminated from glass reinforced plastic.
SKIRT: The skirt fitted to the Simple Cyclone is a Cyclone-designed extended segment type employing an individual air feed through the hull to every segment.
DIMENSIONS
Length overall: 3m (9ft 11in)
Width overall: 1·83m (6ft)
Height at rest: 0·9m (2ft 11in)
Hard structure clearance: 180mm (7³/₃₂in)

Simple Cyclone, a single-engined light hovercraft employing a single ducted fan with adjustable pitch blades for its integrated lift and propulsion system (*Photo: Nigel Beale*)

Simple Cyclone at speed over water. Maximum speed over land and water is 48·28km/h (30mph)

WEIGHTS
Unladen: 80kg (176lb)
Normal payload: 90kg (198lb)

PERFORMANCE
Max speed over land or water: 48·28km/h (30mph)

GP CONCESSIONAIRES LTD

Worton Hall, Worton Road, Isleworth, Middlesex TW7 6ER, England
Telephone: 01-568 4711
Telex: 477019 CLP
Officials:
John Jobber, *Managing Director*
P D Allnutt, *General Manager*

HOVER HAWK

This two-to-four seat utility ACV is intended for survey and patrol duties as well as the leisure industry. Orders have been placed by countries throughout the world including North and South America, Europe, Scandinavia, South Africa, Australia, the Middle and the Far East.
LIFT AND PROPULSION: Integrated system. A single Volkswagen air-cooled engine drives via a belt a ducted fan aft. Propulsion air is expelled rearwards and lift air is ducted into the plenum below. Fuel capacity is 28 litres (6 imperial gallons). Fuel recommended 93 Octane.
CONTROLS: Single control column operates a single rudder hinged to the rear of the fan duct. Column incorporates a twist-grip throttle for the engine.
HULL: Moulded glass fibre reinforced plastics structure.
SKIRT: Fully-segmented type in neoprene-coated nylon.

Hover Hawk, a grp-hulled, four-seater designed for survey work and light patrol duties

ACCOMMODATION: Open cockpit with seating for driver and up to three passengers.
DIMENSIONS
Length overall: 4·12m (13ft 6in)
Width: 2·44m (8ft)
Height: 1·27m (4ft 2in)
WEIGHTS
Empty: 300kg (650lb)
Payload: 250kg (550lb)
PERFORMANCE
Max speed: 64km/h (40mph)
Gradient capability: 1:7 from static hover
Obstacle clearance: 0·3m (12in)
Endurance, max: 5 hours

PRICE: £3,480 plus VAT. Car trailer for Hover Hawk, £250 plus VAT

Hover Hawk utility ACV with 250kg (550lb) payload

HFL-SEAGLIDE LTD

PO Box 33, London N14 7NS, England
Telephone: 01-368 6013
Telex: 21879 IMP
Officials:
H F Lentge, *Managing Director*
R Bourn, *Director*
H V Lentge, *Director*

HFL-Seaglide Limited was formed in 1976 to build and market the Seabee series of aerodynamic ram-wings designed by Ronald Bourn. The company's first craft is a prototype three-seater with an overall length of 5·18m (17ft). The machine is based on data derived from an earlier delta wing prototype first flown in 1971. Among the range of designs projected by the company are a three-seat fast launch, an eight-seat water taxi or freight carrier and a 35-seat water bus or freighter.

Details of the Seabee 3-seater can be found in *Jane's Surface Skimmers 1980* and earlier editions.

HOVERCRAFT DEVELOPMENT LTD

Head Office: Kingsgate House, 66-74 Victoria Street, London SW1E 6SL, England
Telephone: 01-828 3400
Telex: 23580
Officials:
T A Coombs, *Chairman*
B J Hill, *Director*
Prof W A Mair, *Director*
P N Randell, *Director*
B Bailey, *Secretary*

Hovercraft Development Ltd (HDL) was formed in January 1959 by the National Research Development Corporation (NRDC) to develop, promote and exploit the hovercraft invention. The company uses its large portfolio of patents as the basis of licensing agreements with the principal hovercraft manufacturers in the United Kingdom and overseas, and allows licensees access to work undertaken by its original Technical Group and more recently the Technical Unit at Hythe. HDL may, in certain cases, provide financial backing to assist projects, such as the Hovermarine HM.5, the BHC SR.N4, Pindair Skima 12 and AVL Tiger.

The small technical team employed by the company made assessments of new hovercraft designs and projects in addition to regional and route studies for proposed hovercraft operations. HDL's Technical Unit at Hythe also provided a source of information for government departments, official bodies, potential manufacturers, operators and backers of hovercraft enterprises. Following the recent closure of the Technical Unit at Hythe, members of the technical team have joined Hovercraft Consultants Limited (see entry under ACV Consultants).

HDL SKIRT SHIFT SYSTEM

The HDL skirt shift system is designed to move the centre of pressure of the cushion relative to the craft without altering the total cushion area. Both side skirts are divided into fore and aft panels each of which can be moved in or out by a single cable which actuates an array of cranked ties or chevrons. By transferring the tension in each cable via a form of bell crank to the diagonally opposite skirt panel, loads in the panels become balanced, thus minimising actuation effort. On the small HDL research craft, HD4, the four load balancing cables were connected at the base of a joystick, providing a simple layout for manual operation. When the stick was moved forward the front two panels were drawn in, while

HD4 research craft demonstrating HDL skirt shift system

Pindair Skima 12 fitted with HDL skirt shift system

the rear panels were let out. The craft then tended to pitch forward. The process was reversed for bow up trim. Pushing the stick to the left shifted all four panels to the right, resulting in the desired roll to the left.

The skirt shift system was originally conceived to provide active pitch and roll control for craft having a high centre of gravity. Since then the system has shown itself capable of operating sufficiently rapidly, due to its low inertia, to act as a flying control. It is lighter and more rapid than a ballast system and achieves trim without loss of thrust as occurs with elevators. In addition, trim performance is unaffected by changes in craft weight or thrust levels. The system has also been used successfully as a pitch damper. Potentially dangerous pitch oscillations caused by regular wave encounters can be damped out instantly by a single application of the pitch control.

SKIMA 12

In order to evaluate skirt shift at a larger scale, the system has been fitted to Pindair Skima 12-004. The skirt and chevron layouts are very similar to HD4 although powered actuation is provided by two 12 volt winches, using the standard Skima 12 battery system.

Manoeuvrability and handling of the craft have been improved by the addition of the system, enabling the craft to remain trimmed level even in severe side winds or when the payload is poorly distributed. Correctly banked turns, independent of wind direction, are now easily achieved and the rapid response of the original system has been preserved.
All-up weight: 2,000kg (4,409lb)
Hoverheight: 0·5m (1ft 8in)
Cushion beam: 3·2m (10ft 2in)
CP shift capability as % of cushion beam (roll): ±2·8%
CP shift capability as % of cushion length (pitch): ±1·4%

HOVERSERVICES

24 Hazel Grove, Wallingford, Oxon OX10 0AT, England
Telephone: 0491 37455
Partners:
Graham Nutt
James Lyne
Graham Bran
Overseas Distributors:
Australia (Queensland):
Light Hovercraft Services, 148 Thornside Road, Thornside, Queensland 4158
Telephone: 207 2934
Australia (Western):
Hoverservices (Western Australia), PO Box N1136, Perth, Western Australia 6001
Ireland:
D O'Fahay, 581 Howeth Road, Raheny, Dublin 5

Hoverservices was formed in 1972 to market Scarab hovercraft plans and components. The company now offers a range of light hovercraft plans for the single-seat Scarab I and two-seat Scarab II, in addition to plans for other racing craft such as the Snoopy II and Eccles. All of these plans are marketed worldwide.

The company has a wide range of fans, grp ducts, skirt material and other components in stock and provides a complete engineering service.

SCARAB I (Plans)

This is a simple, lightweight craft, ideal for sheltered water operation. It uses low cost engines and is a useful craft for beginners. Many craft of this type have been selected for school or group hovercraft building projects. It seats one person.
LIFT AND PROPULSION: A single 3·5bhp Briggs & Stratton engine provides power to an axial lift fan of 482mm (19in) diameter, fitted with Multi-wing blades. For thrust the craft employs a JLO 250cc 15bhp engine which drives a 609mm (24in) diameter ducted fan fitted with Multi-wing blades.
CONTROLS: There is a single rudder located in the thrust duct and movement of this control is achieved by a joystick located in the cockpit. A twist grip gives throttle control for the thrust engine and a simple lever controls the lift engine.
HULL: The hull is constructed using a triangulated plywood box technique upon a pine frame and finished with grp tape for extra strength. A full flow skirt of loop design is fitted to the craft.
ACCOMMODATION: A single seat is fitted in the open cockpit.
DIMENSIONS
Length: 3·05m (10ft)
Width: 1·68m (5ft 6in)
Hoverheight: 228mm (9in)

Scarab 8, latest of the range of light hovercraft offered by Hoverservices

WEIGHTS
Empty: 72·57kg (160lb)
Normal payload: 90·72kg (200lb)
Normal all-up weight: 163·29kg (360lb)
PERFORMANCE
Over land or water the craft can achieve speeds of 40·2-48·2km/h (25-30mph)

SCARAB II (Plans)

Scarab II is a two-seater light hovercraft designed for cruising in calm coastal or sheltered estuarial waters. With its larger size it will accept a variety of different engines for lift and propulsion functions.
LIFT AND PROPULSION: A typical lift engine for this craft would be a 5bhp Briggs & Stratton, driving a 558mm (22in) diameter axial lift fan fitted with Multi-wing blades. For propulsion the craft could use various powerplants up to 42bhp driving either 609mm (24in) or 762mm (30in) diameter ducted Multi-wing fans.
CONTROLS: Employs a single rudder positioned in the thrust duct which is activated by a joystick located in the open cockpit. A twist grip throttle is used for the thrust engine and a quadrant type lever is used for lift.
HULL: This is made from triangular plywood boxes upon a framework of pine with grp tape for additional strength for joints etc. A full flow loop skirt is fitted.
ACCOMMODATION: A driver and one passenger can be seated in the craft's open cockpit, sitting side by side.
DIMENSIONS
Length: 3·5m (11ft 6in)
Width: 1·83m (6ft)
Hoverheight: 228mm (9in)

WEIGHTS
Empty: 113·4kg (250lb)
Normal payload: 181·44kg (400lb) (two people)
All-up weight: 294·84kg (650lb)
PERFORMANCE
Over land and water Scarab II craft, with propulsion units of 35-42bhp, can achieve speeds of 48·28-56·32km/h (30-35mph)

SCARAB 8

Latest sports hovercraft to be introduced by Hoverservices, Scarab 8 is ideal for 250cc Formula III racing or for general cruising and exploring otherwise inaccessible backwaters. It is available as a complete kit or as three separate kits which can be made up into the complete craft.
LIFT AND PROPULSION: Power for the integrated lift/propulsion system is provided by a single 12·5bhp KEC 225 single cylinder two-stroke. A tooth belt reduction drive transmits power to a ducted 609mm (24in) fan that provides both thrust and lift.
HULL: Similar to Scarab I. Made from preformed grp sheets with polyurethane foam buoyancy panels to form the hull shape which is then fibreglassed over to make a one piece lightweight hull.
SKIRT: Segmented pressure-fed type similar to that of the Scarab XI.
DIMENSIONS
Length: 3·04m (10ft)
Beam: 1·82m (6ft)
Hoverheight: 228mm (9in)
WEIGHTS
Unladen weight: 68·73kg (150lb)

INGLES HOVERCRAFT ASSOCIATES LTD

Ingles Manor, Castle Hill Avenue, Folkestone, Kent CT20 2TN, England
Telephone: 0303 59055
Officials:
S Sendall-King, BSc, CEng, MRAeS, FSLAET, *General Director*
D G Staveley, BSc, *UK Director*
T J R Longley, TEng(CEI), AMRAeS, *Design Consultant*

Ingles Hovercraft Associates Ltd administer the design and patent rights relating to the hovercraft developed by the Missionary Aviation Fellowship (MAF).

MAF's first craft was the Missionaire, a general purpose amphibious five-seater. This was succeeded by the six-seat River Rover. Following evaluation trials by the Naval Hovercraft Trials Unit, the River Rover was chosen by the 1978-79 British Joint Services Expedition to Nepal. For a period of four months, two Mk 2 craft were successfully used over a 60 mile stretch of the turbulent Kali Gandaki river in support of a medical aid programme.

One of these craft is now in regular use by a mission in Irian Jaya, Indonesia, on the Baliem river and its tributaries.

A Mk 3 version is now in production under an agreement with Dodnor Marine Ltd, Newport, Isle of Wight. Under a separate agreement it is planned that the River Rover will be marketed by Pindair Ltd, as the Skima 6.

RIVER ROVER

Designed as a water-borne counterpart to the Land Rover utility vehicle, River Rover is a sturdily constructed, six-seat cabin hovercraft which has proved its usefulness and reliability in many parts of the world where navigation by conventional boats is difficult or impossible.

The four main requirements for such a craft are:

Low cost, both of manufacture and of operation;

Positive control characteristics, enabling the craft to follow safely the course of a narrow, winding river with the minimum of sideways skidding;

Simple bolt-together unit construction; facilitating transport and simplifying maintenance and repair;

An efficient and reliable skirt system, combining good wear resistance with ease of repair.

The following data refers to the River Rover Mk 3.

LIFT AND PROPULSION: Motive power is provided by a single 100bhp Renault R-20TS automotive engine. This drives a 630mm (25in) diameter lift fan, and two 710mm (28in) thrust fans mounted on either side of the lift fan. Power is transmitted via three Uniroyal HTD toothed belts and pulleys enclosed in streamlined fairings. All three fans are housed in grp ducts. Air from the lift fan is channelled through 90 degrees down beneath the craft via the skirt bag. Fuel consumption at cruising speed is 11·25 litres/h (2·5 gallons/h)

CONTROLS: The primary means of control are two horizontally-pivoted elevons, one in each of the two square-sectioned ducts immediately aft of the thrust fans. Movement of foot pedals rotates the elevons jointly or differentially. Employed together, craft longitudinal trim is adjusted, and when rotated fully, braking is achieved. Used differentially, small deflections of the elevons enable the craft to be banked into a turn, thereby reducing sideways skidding. Greater pedal movement progressively closes the duct on the "inside" of the turn, the outside duct remaining open. Thus differential thrust is added to the bank initially applied to the craft. Conventional vertically-pivoted aerodynamic rudders, controlled by a steering wheel, are fitted immediately aft of the elevons. These are used during operation in crosswinds, in conjunction with the elevons.

HULL: Aluminium alloy angle frame covered with 6mm (¼in) marine grade plywood panels. Engine bay bulkheads and sides are in aluminium alloy sheet. Structure is bolted together for ease of repair and simplicity of breakdown and reassembly. The entire hull is surrounded by an inflatable collar at deck level, providing all-round fendering and additional reserve buoyancy. The sliding cabin canopy is constructed of moulded grp.

ACCOMMODATION: Three bench type seats are provided. These can be folded flat to provide sleeping accommodation for two persons, or, with cushions removed, for the carriage of freight. Alternatively, two stretchers can be carried aft of the front seat.

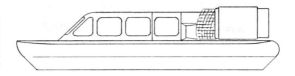
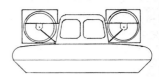
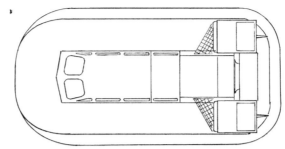

General arrangement of River Rover Mk 2 amphibious 6-seater

Prototype River Rover rounding a buoy at speed. Elevons enable the craft to be banked into a turn, thereby reducing sideways skidding as indicated by the wake

One of two River Rovers employed by the 1978-79 British Joint Services Expedition to Nepal. Capable of 60km/h (37·5mph), the River Rover is powered by a single 100hp Renault R-20TS automotive engine

SKIRT: HDL-type loop and segment skirt fabricated in neoprene-coated nylon.

DIMENSIONS
Length: 6·19m (20ft 3¾in)
Width: 2·62m (8ft 7½in)
Height, off cushion: 1·45m (4ft 9½in)

WEIGHTS
Empty: 670kg (1,477lb)
All-up weight: 1,100kg (2,425lb)
PERFORMANCE
Max speed: 60km/h (37·5mph)
Cruising speed: 48km/h (30mph)

LIGHT HOVERCRAFT COMPANY

Felbridge Hotel & Investment Co Ltd, London Road, East Grinstead, Sussex, England
Telephone: 0342 24424
Officials:
L H F Gatward, *Proprietor*

Light Hovercraft Company has been active in the field of hoverpallets since 1969. It has entered the light sports ACV field with a fibreglass hulled variant of Nigel Beale's Cyclone, which won the British National Hovercraft Championships in 1971 and was joint winner of this event in 1972. In August 1972 a production Cyclone crossed the English Channel from Pegwell Bay hoverport to Calais, a total open sea distance of 56·32km (35 miles).

The company is now concentrating on the production of the four-seat Phantom and the single-seat Turbo.

PHANTOM

This fully amphibious sports/utility craft seats four persons in comfort or will carry up to 300kg (700lb) of cargo or equipment. Keynotes of the design are reliability, ease of maintenance and quiet operation. The ducted fans provide full thrust at low revolutions to maintain a low noise level. The craft is easily hovered onto a trailer for towing by a car.

LIFT AND PROPULSION: Integrated system powered by a single 138hp Ford 2614E V6 engine. Power is transmitted by toothed belts to two ducted axial fans, air from which is used for both lift and propulsion at a ratio of 1:3. Thrust is 130kg (300lb). Fuel capacity is 140 litres (30 gallons).

CONTROLS: Twin rudders hinged to the rear of each thrust duct control craft heading.

HULL: Foam-filled glass fibre structure. Buoyancy is 2,268kg (5,000lb).

SKIRT: 0·73m (2ft 5in) deep, fully-segmented skirt made in rot-proof fabric with an abrasive resistant coating.

ACCOMMODATION: Open cockpit seating a driver and up to three passengers. The cockpit is fitted with dual controls. Standard fittings include a wrap-around tinted perspex windscreen, a convertible hood for use in bad weather and two pairs of upholstered back-to-back seats that fold down to form a sunlounger or bed.

DIMENSIONS
Length overall: 6m (20ft)
Width: 2·2m (7ft 3in)
Height: 1·35m (4ft 6in)
WEIGHTS
Empty weight: 510kg (1,200lb)
Payload: 400kg (900lb)
PERFORMANCE
Max speed: 40 knots
Endurance: 5 hours
Hard structure clearance: 0·3m (1ft)
PRICE: Ex works, £12,000, FOB charge to UK
docks, £240. Terms: payment with order.
Despatch: 12 weeks from confirmation of order.

TURBO

This new one-to-two seater is powered by a
single 46hp Fuji Robin engine and is quieter at
maximum power than most saloon cars are at
cruising speed. Maximum speed of the Turbo is
40 knots.

LIFT AND PROPULSION: Integrated system
powered by a single 46hp 432cc Fuji Robin twin
2-stroke with electric starting and hinged, padded cover. This drives a ducted polypropylene-
bladed axial fan, air from which is used for both
lift and propulsion. Thrust is 60kg (132lb). Fuel
capacity is 25 litres (5 imperial gallons).

CONTROLS: Craft direction is controlled by
multivane rudders hinged to the rear of the thrust
duct and operated by a handlebar.

HULL: Glass fibre construction with four storage
spaces and room in the foot wells for long items
such as fishing rods. Compartments in the
sidebodies contain inflatable buoyancy bags.
Buoyancy ½ ton.

SKIRT: Segmented skirt 0·396m (1ft 4in) deep,
fabricated in neoprene nylon material.

DIMENSIONS
Length: 3·47m (11ft 4in)
Beam: 1·82m (6ft)
Height: 1·17m (3ft 10in)
WEIGHTS
Payload: 180kg (400lb)
PERFORMANCE
Max speed: 40 knots
Hard structure clearance: 0·23m (9in)
Endurance: 2 hours
PRICE: Ex works £2,499 plus VAT

Turbo light ACV with maximum speed of 40 knots

Phantom four-seater sports/utility craft powered by a single 138hp Ford V6 engine

Maximum payload of the Light Hovercraft
Phantom is 400kg (900lb)

MAXCAT HOVERCRAFT

16 Laurieknowe, Dumfries, Scotland
Telephone; 0387 62452
Officials:
Max Houliston, *Proprietor*

The design specification for the Maxcat Hovercraft called for a cabin accommodating four people; facilities for towing and the use of a single
powerplant to power the lift and propulsion systems. Design was undertaken by Paul Davis of
Southampton and the construction of the craft
was supervised by Ivor Verlander. The prototype
is currently operating on the Solway Firth in Scotland.

Maxcat Hovercraft 4-seater showing the lift fan air
intake and bow thrust ports

MAXCAT HOVERCRAFT

Intended primarily for leisure applications, including cruising, the Maxcat Hovercraft is a grp-hulled four-seater powered by a single 150hp aero-engine giving it a maximum speed of 50 knots.

LIFT AND PROPULSION: Power for the integrated lift and propulsion system is provided by a 150hp Lycoming aero-engine mounted behind the cabin. This drives via a shaft and a 2:1 bevel gear box, a 965mm (38in) HEBA/B AL Alloy centrifugal lift fan and a Hoffman variable-pitch 2·0m (6ft 7in) diameter pylon-mounted propeller. The propeller is driven from the main shaft by pulleys and toothed belts. A 36 litre (8 gallon) capacity fuel tank is located behind the rear starboard seat. 91/96 octane is used.

CONTROLS: Craft direction is controlled by twin aerodynamic rudders operating in the airscrew slipstream. Yaw is controlled by thrust ports in the bow of the craft and rudders in the stern.

HULL: The hull comprises two glass reinforced plastic mouldings—lower hull and upper hull including the cabin. Sections are filled with foam and sealed to provide maximum buoyancy. The pylon and other highly stressed parts are in AL alloy or steel.

SKIRT: HDL closed-loop segment type using black 11551 quality material as produced by the Northern Rubber Company.

ACCOMMODATION: Seats are provided for an operator and three passengers. Two gull-wing doors are fitted, one port and one starboard and ventilation is provided in the cabin. In an emergency the cabin windows can be jettisoned. All the necessary gauges and indicators are provided on the dashboard. Pedals are used for

Power for the Maxcat's integrated lift/propulsion system is provided by a single 150hp Lycoming aero engine mounted aft of the cabin. Craft heading is controlled by twin rudders

operating the puff ports. A fireproof and sound-proof bulkhead divides the cabin from the engine bay.

SYSTEMS, ELECTRICAL: A 12V system with an engine driven generator supplies power to the engine and lights.

DIMENSIONS
Length: 5·94m (19ft 6in)

Beam: 2·84m (9ft 4in)
WEIGHTS
All-up weight: 1,270kg (2,800lb)
PERFORMANCE
Max speed: 50 knots
Cruising speed: 35 knots
Endurance at cruising speed: 2 hours
Vertical obstacle clearance: 355mm (1ft 2in)

OSPREY HOVERCRAFT LTD

PO Box 34, Crawley, West Sussex RH10 4TF, England
Telephone: 04446 45791
Officials:
P V McCollum, *Director*
D McCollum, *Director*

This light hovercraft company has been established by P V "Kip" McCollum, previously Technical Director of Surface Flight Ltd. The company is currently concentrating on the production of a range of four craft, Kestrel, Kestrel GT, Falcon and Cormorant.

As part of its development activity Osprey Hovercraft has constructed and tested a four-six seat sidewall design which is currently in the prototype stage. It is envisaged that the sidewall design could become an attractive leisure product and that, in addition, various specialist roles exist for it, including shallow water surveying.

CORMORANT

This addition to the Osprey range originated as a one-off craft to meet a particular customer requirement. After trials it was decided to include the design in the standard range. The chief difference between the Cormorant and the Falcon is the departure from the integrated lift/propulsion system of the latter by the introduction of a separate lift engine and fan. This new arrangement has resulted in a craft with a greater payload capacity and generally increased all-round performance.

LIFT AND PROPULSION: A 15hp one-cylinder two-stroke engine mounted ahead of the cockpit drives a 560mm diameter (22in) polypropylene-bladed axial fan for lift. Thrust is furnished by a 40hp air-cooled twin-cylinder two-stroke driving a ducted 610mm (24in) polypropylene-bladed axial fan via a heavy duty toothed belt. Fuel capacity is 27 litres (6 imperial gallons). Consumption is 9-16 litres/h (2-3·5 gallons/h)

CONTROLS: Craft heading is controlled by twin aerodynamic rudders hinged to the rear of the thrust duct and operated by a handlebar.

HULL: Monocoque construction in self-coloured glass fibre. Preformed sealed

Osprey Hovercraft Ltd's Cormorant twin-engined runabout and light utility hovercraft

polyurethane block at base of craft for buoyancy. Tools and spares compartment provided.

SKIRT: Segmented skirt fabricated in neoprene-coated nylon material.

DIMENSIONS
Length: 3·8m (12ft 6in)
Width: 1·83m (6ft)
Height: 1m (3ft 3in)
WEIGHTS
Empty: 218kg (480lb)
Normal payload: 182kg (400lb)
Max payload: 318kg (700lb)
PERFORMANCE
Max speed over land and water: 56km/h plus (35mph plus)
Cruising speed: 32-40km/h (20-25mph)
Max continuous gradient, standing start: 1 : 8
Max short gradient, at speed: 1 : 4
Vertical hard obstacle clearance: 200mm (8in)

FALCON

Though intended primarily as a two-seat recreational craft, the Falcon is also suitable for a variety of light commercial and utility roles. A keynote of the design is its simplicity. All maintenance can be undertaken by a competent mechanic or handyman.

Falcon is the fastest selling craft in the Osprey range. Some 50 per cent of those sold are being employed for utility purposes. Several have been purchased to act as standby emergency craft in tidal areas and one Falcon is employed in Scotland for harvesting 9·65km (6 miles) of salmon nets. This craft is in use twice daily and is often required to operate at night. One Falcon is being evaluated by the West German army.

A 'stretched' version, with a central driving position forward and a bench seat for two passengers aft, is in the planning stage. This arrangement will increase its ability to carry a larger payload when operating as a utility craft.

LIFT AND PROPULSION: Integrated system powered by a single 40hp air-cooled twin-cylinder two-stroke. This drives via a heavy duty toothed belt a 610mm (24in) diameter polypropylene-bladed ducted fan, air from which is used for both lift and propulsion. Fuel capacity is 27 litres (6 imperial gallons). Fuel recommended is 93 octane, oil mix 25 : 1. Consumption is 11-16 litres/h (2½-3½ gallons/h).

HULL: Monocoque construction in self-coloured glass fibre. All components and fasteners are made from marine quality material. Preformed sealed polyurethane block at base of craft for buoyancy. Tools and spares compartment provided.

SKIRT: Segmented skirt fabricated in neoprene-coated nylon material.

DIMENSIONS
Length: 3·8m (12ft 6in)
Beam: 1·83m (6ft)
Height: 1m (3ft 3in)

WEIGHTS
Empty: 172kg (380lb)
Normal payload: 164kg (360lb)
Max payload: 205kg (450lb)

PERFORMANCE
Cruising speed: 32-40km/h (20-25mph)
Max speed over land and water: 56km/h plus (35mph plus)
Max continuous gradient, standing start: 1 : 8
Max short gradient, at speed: 1 : 2 (45 degrees)
Vertical hard obstacle clearance: 200mm (8in)

Falcon two-seat recreational craft

KESTREL GT

Based on a standard Kestrel hull but fitted with the Falcon's engine and fan system, the Kestrel GT has been designed to meet the need of enthusiasts for a powerful lightweight hovercraft for sport and competitive racing. Due to its high power/weight ratio, it is particularly agile and can negotiate relatively steep slopes with comparative ease.

LIFT AND PROPULSION: Integrated system powered by a single 40hp air-cooled twin-cylinder two-stroke. This drives, via a heavy duty toothed belt, a 610mm (24in) diameter polypropylene-bladed ducted fan, air from which is used for both lift and propulsion. Fuel capacity is 20·25 litres (4·5 imperial gallons). Fuel recommended is 93 octane, oil mix 25:1.

CONTROLS: Twin aerodynamic rudders, operated by a handlebar, control craft heading. Engine throttle mounted on handlebar.

HULL: Monocoque construction in self-coloured glass fibre. Preformed sealed polyurethane block at base of craft for buoyancy. Tools and spares compartment provided.

SKIRT: Fully segmented skirt fabricated in neoprene-coated nylon.

ACCOMMODATION: Open cockpit for driver.

DIMENSIONS
Length: 3·2m (10ft 6in)
Width: 1·83m (6ft)
Height: 1m (3ft 3in)

WEIGHTS
Empty: 164kg (360lb)
Normal payload: 113kg (250lb)
Max payload: 164kg (360lb)

PERFORMANCE
Max speed across land and water: 56km/h (35mph)
Cruising speed: 32-40km/h (20-25mph)
Max continuous gradient, standing start: 1 : 6
Max short gradient, at speed: 1 : 2 (45 degrees)
Vertical hard obstacle clearance: 200mm (8in)

Kestrel GT sports craft, powered by a 40hp air-cooled twin-cylinder two-stroke engine

KESTREL

Designed as a single-seater this fully-amphibious recreational craft has nevertheless operated many times on inland waterways with two aboard in force 5, gusting to force 6. Built on a base of solid foam it will not sink even if badly damaged.

LIFT AND PROPULSION: Integrated system with a single 24hp air-cooled twin-cylinder two-stroke driving one 610mm (24in) polypropylene-bladed ducted fan aft. Fuel capacity is 18 litres (4 imperial gallons). Recommended fuel, 93 octane/oil mix 25 : 1. Consumption, 6·75 to 9 litres/h (1½-2 gallons/h).

CONTROLS: Twin aerodynamic rudders controlled by handlebars. Engine throttle mounted on handlebars.

HULL: Self-coloured glass fibre structure based on a rigid foam block for strength and buoyancy. Built-in tools and spares compartment.

SKIRT: Segmented system fabricated in neoprene-coated nylon.

Kestrel single-seater powered by a single 24hp air-cooled two-stroke engine

DIMENSIONS
Length: 3·2m (10ft 6in)
Beam: 1·83m (6ft)
Height: 1m (3ft 3in)

WEIGHTS
Empty: 127kg (280lb)
Normal payload: 113·5kg (250lb)
Max payload: 136kg (300lb)

PERFORMANCE
Cruising speed: 24-40km/h (15-25mph)
Max speed across land and water: 48km/h (30mph)
Max continuous gradient, standing start: 1 : 7
Max short gradient, at speed: 1 : 2 (45 degrees)
Vertical hard obstacle clearance: 200mm (8in)

PINDAIR LIMITED

Quay Lane, Hardway, Gosport, Hampshire
PO12 4LS, England
Telephone: 070 17 87830
Telex: 86210 Skima G
Officials:
M A Pinder, BSc, CEng, MIMechE, *Managing Director*
A M Pinder, *Director*
J Erickson, *Director*
J Bordes, *Director*
D R Robertson, *Consultant*
E W H Gifford, *Consultant*
T J R Longley, *Consultant*

Pindair Limited was formed in May 1972. It is currently engaged in the design, development, manufacture and sales of a range of small amphibious hovercraft featuring inflatable structures as well as designing for outside manufacture ACV trailers of up to 10 tonnes payload.

The company has supplied hovercraft to over 50 countries for a wide variety of roles ranging from military to recreation. Building on this experience it is currently updating its range of hovercraft to incorporate latest technology, improved production techniques and users' suggestions. The use of inflatable structures is claimed to give a number of advantages including light weight, impact resistance, improved obstacle and wave clearance, low cost transport or storage costs as well as excellent buoyancy.

Special attention has been given to simplicity of maintenance and world-wide spares availability. The smaller portable models are fitted with high performance two-stroke engines whilst the bigger transportable ones use four-stroke automobile units.

SKIMA 2

A low cost two-seat inflatable hovercraft which can be folded and stowed in the luggage compartments of most cars or carried complete on the roof. It can carry two people in reasonable weather conditions but is light enough for two people to carry. The Mark 3 design uses a single engine and fan layout for the first time.

SKIMA 3

A high performance two-three seat version of the Skima 4 (under development).

SKIMA 4

Building on the success of earlier four-seat designs, the Skima 4 Mark 3 now incorporates an electric start and integrated lift and propulsion system for the first time. This new design also features markedly reduced noise levels, more comfortable and spacious passenger accommodation and an improved skirt with snap-on segments and virtually no bow spray. It can be transported on a light trailer or folded inside a pick-up truck and is just light enough for four people to lift.

It is being evaluated by both the Royal Navy and the US Navy. Users include the United Nations, UK Overseas Development Administration, Imperial Chemical Industries, and a number of water authorities, civil engineers, survey groups and pest control organisations.
LIFT AND PROPULSION: Power is provided by a single Hirth engine, fitted with hand and electric starters and driving a six-bladed plastic fan via a high torque toothed belt. Engine and fan are mounted in a grp duct module which also houses the battery. Fuel consumption is approximately 10 litres/h (2·2 gallons/h).
CONTROLS: Craft direction is controlled by a tiller, mounted on the dashboard, which operates four air rudders in the propulsion duct. The engine throttle is mounted on the tiller and a separate lever operates the flow splitter, which varies the proportion of air used for lift and thrust according to conditions.
HULL: The inflatable hull has four compartments and a raised floor, which increases obstacle clearance. The sectional foam sandwich deck is locked in place with aluminium extrusions. The underside is reinforced and fitted with rubber landing skids.

Skima 2 has been designed to be portable and can be carried on a car roof. It is particularly suitable for amphibious operations inland

Skima 3 while racing in Belgium

Pair of Skima 4s under test prior to being shipped to Bangladesh for civil engineering work

TRANSPORT AND ASSEMBLY: For transport or storage the complete hovercraft can be packed into a space of only 2m³ (70ft³), and can be assembled in about one hour.
ACCOMMODATION: Two adjustable bench seats are supplied. Wrap-around windscreen, low cushion pressure and long bow ensure a comfortable and dry ride.
SKIRT: HDL loop and segment type, with snap-on segments.

SKIMA 5

A high performance four-five seat version of the Skima 4 (under development).

SKIMA 6

Conceived as a car-size hovercraft capable of being stored in a domestic garage and towed behind a family car, Skima 6 can carry up to six people at speeds of up to 30 knots over a wide variety of surfaces. Simplicity of maintenance is enhanced by using a Renault R-20TS car engine which has exceptional economy, as well as an excellent power-to-weight ratio. Prototypes (called "River Rovers") have been tested by the British Joint Services Expedition team on the rapid strewn Kali Gandaki River in Nepal, and by missionaries in West Irian, Indonesia as well as by the Royal Navy.

To celebrate the twentieth anniversary of the first cross-Channel hovercraft flight, a Skima 6 crossed from Dover to Calais on 25 July 1979 and later skimmed along the River Seine to Paris.

LIFT AND PROPULSION: Motive power is provided by a single 100bhp Renault R-20TS automotive engine, driving a ten-bladed axial lift fan and two five-bladed thrust fans. Power is transmitted via three high torque toothed belts, enclosed in streamlined fairings. All three fans are housed in grp ducts. Air from the lift fan is channelled through 90 degrees down beneath the craft via the skirt loop. Fuel consumption at cruising speed is 11·25 litres/h (2·5 gallons/h).

CONTROLS: The primary means of control are two horizontally pivoted elevons, one in each of the two square-sectioned ducts immediately aft of the thrust fans. Movement of foot pedals rotates the elevons jointly or differentially. Employed together, craft longitudinal trim is adjusted, and when rotated fully, braking is achieved. Used differentially, small deflections of the elevons enable the craft to be banked into a turn, thereby reducing sideways skidding. Greater pedal movement progressively closes the duct on the "inside" of the turn, the outside duct remaining open. Thus differential thrust is added to the bank initially applied to the craft. Conventional vertically-pivoted aerodynamic rudders, controlled by a steering wheel, are fitted immediately aft of the elevons. These are used during operation in crosswinds, in conjunction with the elevons.

HULL: Aluminium alloy angle frame covered with 6mm (¼in) marine grade plywood panels. Engine bay deck and sides are in aluminium alloy sheet. Structure is bolted together for ease of repair and simplicity of breakdown and reassembly and is surrounded by an inflatable collar. The sliding cabin canopy is constructed of moulded grp.

ACCOMMODATION: Three bench type seats are provided. These can be folded flat to provide sleeping accommodation for two persons, or with cushions removed, for the carriage of freight. Alternatively, two stretchers can be carried aft of the front seat.

SKIRT: HDL loop-and-segment skirt fabricated in neoprene-coated nylon.

SKIMA 12

A semi-inflatable multi-role hovercraft, Skima 12 is capable of carrying up to 12 people or 1 tonne of freight. It combines features of an off-highway vehicle with those of a high-speed workboat. Skima 12 is easily transported on a trailer with the inflatable cylindrical tube around the perimeter of the hull furled or detached and can be shipped in a standard 6 × 2·5 × 2·5m (19ft 8in × 8ft × 8ft) container.

It can be built for a variety of applications, from police, coastguard, pilot and military uses, to pest control, flood relief, air crash rescue and as a passenger ferry or ambulance.

LIFT AND PROPULSION: The engine, toothbelt transmission, and ducted propulsor can be removed quickly for service or repair. Everything is easily accessible for maintenance.

The 5·7 litre GM V8 automobile engine is geared to run at relatively low speed for long life and low noise. The centrifugal aluminium lift fan and ducted four-blade propulsor are also designed to run at low speed to reduce noise and provide more than adequate air flow for good payload and performance.

The low cushion pressure, together with the HDL patented skirt system, generate a low spray pattern, allowing the Skima 12 to be operated with an open cockpit if desired. Individual skirt segments may be quickly replaced when they become worn or damaged without lifting the craft.

HULL: Strong hull built in marine aluminium. It will not corrode or absorb water and if knocked will dent rather than fracture allowing repairs to be made at a convenient time. Separate compartments contain the accommodation, the engine and propulsor, the lift fan, the trim system, batteries, safety equipment and stowage areas.

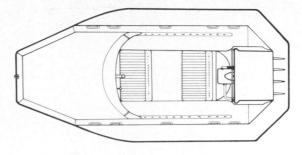
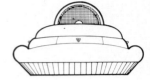
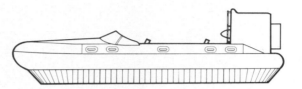

General arrangement of Skima 4

For shipping the Skima 3, 4 and 5 pack into a case of only 2m³ and can be assembled in about one hour

Extra power of Skima 5 allows it to operate in adverse conditions eg climbing weirs

ACCOMMODATION: The standard craft has accommodation for 11-12 passengers and a driver. There are three bucket seats with the driver in the centre at the forward end of the cockpit with a U-shaped bench seat in the cabin. The bench seat is removable to provide a 5m³ load space. Various arrangements can be specified to provide cover for the accommodation. A cruiser-type folding hood with removable sides can be fitted, or a small cockpit cover or an insulated grp hard top with gull-wing doors. Additional equipment such as radio, radar, searchlights, heating and air conditioning can be incorporated. A trailer and lifting gear are available.

SKIMA 18

A stretched version of the proven Skima 12 capable of carrying 18 people or 1½ tonnes is available to special order.

SKIMA 25

This is a projected 25-seat, 2-tonne hovercraft incorporating two proven Skima 12 lift/thrust power units and many other components developed for Skima 12. Alternative layouts are envisaged including versions with a 25-passenger enclosed cabin, an open loadspace with bow ramp for vehicles or freight, firefighting and military configurations.

Skima 6 prototype arriving at Calais Hoverport after crossing the Channel from Dover, to celebrate the twentieth anniversary of the first hovercraft crossing and the seventieth anniversary of the first aircraft crossing

Hardtop model of Skima 12 fitted with radar operating in Rotterdam

View of Skima 4 assembly line with Skima 12 assembly in background

Skima 12 military variant with folding hood operating in the Indian Ocean

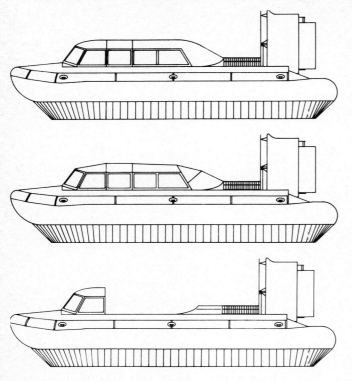

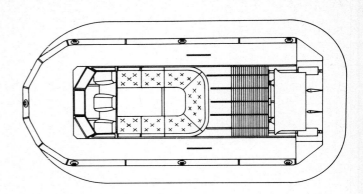

General arrangement of Skima 12 with outboard elevations of the hardtop, folding hood and open-deck rescue versions

Rescue model of Skima 12, carrying sufficient self-inflatable life-rafts for most air crash situations

PINDAIR SKIMA SPECIFICATIONS AND PERFORMANCE

Craft	Skima 2	Skima 3	Skima 4	Skima 5	Skima 6	Skima 12	Skima 18	Skima 25
Length	3·5m	3·8m	4·8m	4·8m	6·19m	7·77m	8·88m	9·99m
Width	1·7m	2m	2m	2m	2·62m	3·5m	3·5m	5m
Height off cushion	1m	1·2m	1·2m	1·2m	1·45m	2·3m	2·3m	2·3m
Unladen weight	100kg	200kg	225kg	250kg	670kg	990kg	1,500kg	2,000kg
Hard structure clearance	25cm	35cm	35cm	35cm	30cm	50cm	50cm	60cm
Shipping dimensions	1 × 1 × 0·75m	1·2 × 1·3 × 1·5m	1·2 × 1·3 × 1·5m	1·2 × 1·3 × 1·5m	6 × 2·3 × 1·3m	6 × 2·5 × 2·5m	7·6 × 2·5 × 2·5m	10 × 3 × 2·5m
Skirt	HDL	HDL	HDL	HDL	HDL	HDL	HDL	HDL
Engine type	2-stroke	2-stroke	2-stroke	2-stroke	4-stroke	4-stroke	4-stroke	4-stroke
Cooling	Air	Air	Air	Water	Water	Water	Water	Water
Cylinders	1	2	2	3	4	V8	V8	2 × V8
Capacity	250cc	440cc	440cc	500cc	2 litres	5·7 litres	5·7 litres	2 × 5·7 litres
Power hp	20	40	40	60	100	250	300	500
Max speed km/h	50	65	60	70	60	70	70	80
Max wind force, Beaufort	4	6	6	6	6	6	6	6
Max range km	100	100	100	100	250	250	250	250

QUANTUM HOVERCRAFT LTD

Head Office: 31 West Street, Wimborne Minster, Dorset, England
Cables: 4M104 (QHL)
Works: 114 Magna Road, Bearwood, Bournemouth, Dorset, England
Telephone: 020 16 3940
Officials:
J R Raymond, *Secretary*
M Charman, *Director*
A G Field, *Director*
N V Charman, *Engineering Manager*

Formed in 1972, Quantum Hovercraft Ltd has been concentrating on the development of light amphibious passenger and utility craft. First vehicles to be marketed by the company are the Islesman 1000 six-seater, the Islesman 1500 nine-seater and the Islesman Utility.

In July 1980 the company announced that a new craft, Islesman 2, is available to order and can be offered in two configurations: as a 12-seater or 907kg (2,000lb) payload light freighter or in stretched form as a 20-seat ferry or 1,814kg (4,000lb) light freighter. Power for the latter may

be supplied by small gas-turbines for greater reliability and improved performance on a single engine.

ISLESMAN 1000

This glassfibre-hulled amphibious hovercraft is designed for a number of duties from six seat water-taxi to light transport and harbour inspection.

LIFT AND PROPULSION: Integrated system powered by a single Lotus 907 two-litre four-cylinder four-stroke aluminium engine rated at

155bhp at 6,500rpm. Cushion air is supplied by a 600mm (2ft) diameter 14-bladed Multi-wing axial-flow fan located at the rear of the craft behind the cabin. Cushion pressure is 22·25kg/m² (15lb/ft²). Thrust is supplied by two 600mm (2ft) diameter 14-bladed axial-flow fans of the same type mounted singly in two propulsion air ducts. Lift and propulsion fans are driven by the single engine via a hydraulic drive system developed by Volvo Hydraulics of Sweden. High pressure oil is piped to a manifold from whence it is diverted to the appropriate hydraulic fan motor by electric solenoid valves. Fuel is carried in four tanks, each with a capacity of 30 litres (8 gallons). Engine oil capacity is 9 pints; hydraulic capacity 56 litres (15 gallons). Engine access is via a large roof hatch and a removable panel in the cabin bulkheads.

CONTROLS: Craft heading is maintained by triple rudder vanes hinged at the rear of each of the propulsion ducts. Reverse thrust for braking is obtained by reversing the rotation of the propulsion fans through the hydraulic drive system, forcing the air forward. A fuel pumping system is used for longitudinal trim.

HULL: Prototype is of wooden construction. Hulls of production craft will be fabricated in coloured, fire retardent glass reinforced plastics. Sidestructure can be detached, bringing width to within 8ft for towing on roads.

SKIRT: 0·45m (18in) deep HDL loop and finger skirt fabricated in neoprene coated nylon fabric supplied by Leyland Rubber of Birmingham.

ACCOMMODATION: Basic version seats a driver and up to five passengers. Seats are secured by quick release fastenings that permit the interior to be cleared to carry stretchers, general cargoes and livestock. Full instrumentation is provided, including fan speed indicators. Access is via two large folding doors, one port and one starboard. Air conditioning can be fitted as an optional extra. Safety equipment includes electrically-operated fire detectors and extinguishing equipment.

SYSTEMS, ELECTRICAL: 12 and 24V systems. Engine driven 24V, 45A alternator.

DIMENSIONS

EXTERNAL

Length overall, power off: 6·12m (20ft 1in)
  skirt inflated: 6·4m (21ft)
Beam overall, power off: 3·5m (11ft 5in)
  skirt inflated: 4·26m (14ft)
Height overall, on landing pads: 1·5m (5ft)
  skirt inflated: 1·92m (6ft 6in)
Draft afloat: 0·08m (3in)
Skirt depth, prototype: 0·48m (1ft 6in)

INTERNAL

Cabin length: 2·43m (8ft)
Max width: 1·45m (4ft 9in)
Max height: 1m (3ft 4in)
Floor area: 3·5m² (36·8ft²)

WEIGHTS

Normal empty: 680kg (1,500lb)
Normal gross: 1,134kg (2,500lb)
Normal payload: 454kg (1,000lb)

PERFORMANCE

Max speed, calm water, max power: 35 knots
Cruising speed, calm water: 35 knots
Still air range and endurance at cruising speed: 400km (250 miles), 6 hours
Max gradient, static conditions: 1 : 8
Vertical obstacle clearance, prototype: 0·45m (1ft 6in)
PRICE: £30,000 ex-works UK

Islesman 1000 amphibious hovercraft, powered by a single 155bhp Lotus 907 four-stroke aluminium engine

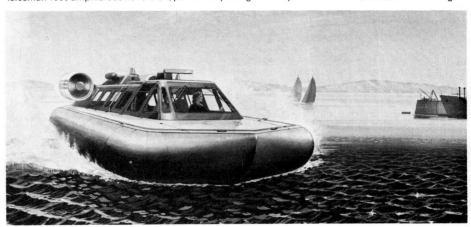

Impression of 12-seat Islesman 2

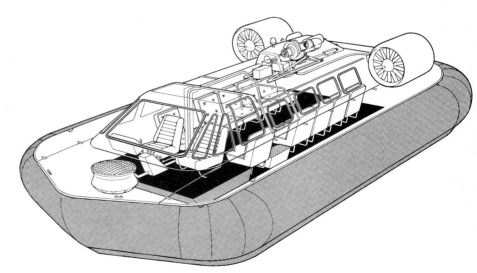

Cutaway showing main features and seating arrangements of Islesman 2. The prototype and production craft will be fitted with two lift fans

---

ROTORK MARINE LIMITED

Head Office: Lake Road, Hamworthy, Poole, Dorset, England
Telephone: 020 13 85581
Telex: 418281
Officials:
J J Fry, *Chairman*
A Moseley, *Managing Director*
D W Smith, *Financial Manager*
R J Cummins, *Marketing Manager*
R J Kretschmer, *Engineering Manager*
S Marshall, *Production Manager*

Formed on 1 March 1966, Rotork Marine initially developed a simple marine-ply 8m planing hull which over the years became standardised and manufactured in grp. The range was extended from 8 to 12m in 1973 and the Series 5, with a revised hull configuration was introduced in 1975. The boats are sold world-wide and are in operation in over 50 countries and in service with 30 nations' defence forces. A key feature of the hull design is the use of air lubrication to reduce hydrodynamic drag. A ram-air cushion, contained by shallow side skegs, raises the bow clear of the water at speed. As the pressurised air flows aft it generates air/foam lubrication for the remainder of the hull, permitting speeds of up to 80·46km/h (50mph) to be achieved. The performance depends upon the payload, installed power and sea conditions. A wide choice of power plants is available, and cabin modules can be supplied for passenger and work crew accommodation. Bow loading ramps are fitted for ease of access and operation from beaches.

The company offers a series of fast assault craft and patrol boats, tactical personnel carriers and logistic support craft, together with a range of general purpose passenger and vehicle ferries, 7·37m (24ft 2in) to 12·65m (41ft 6in) in length. The four basic craft are the 408, 412, 512 and TB106.

ROTORK STW 408 SEA TRUCK WORK-BOAT

This is a heavy duty, multi-purpose workboat designed for high performance and low running costs. It can operate safely in only 304mm (1ft) of water and is equipped with a bow ramp to facilitate the loading of passengers, freight or light vehicles from beaches. The maximum payload is 2,500kg, depending on machinery and optional equipment fitted.

POWER PLANT: Dependent upon payload and performance requirements and whether the craft is to be employed for sheltered water or open sea operation. Engines recommended are 85-235hp OMC OBMs fitted in pairs or single 130hp Volvo Penta AQ D40A/280. Supplied as standard with these units are the control console, and depending on the type of power unit, 227 litres (50 gallons) or 455 litres (100 gallons) fuel tanks in two fully isolated sections, together with separate fuel lines.

HULL: Heavy duty glass fibre reinforced plastics. Buoyancy is provided by closed cell polyurethane foam of TD I type. The skegs are in prestressed cold drawn galvanised steel tube. The ramp, which is manually operated, is in 25·4mm (1in) thick, polyurethane-coated marine ply. It is housed in a galvanised steel frame with galvanised steel capping, and is counter-balanced by a torsion bar.

ACCOMMODATION: As a workboat a grp cabin can be fitted, together with extensions to provide adequate covered crew space and lockers.

SYSTEMS, ELECTRICAL: Heavy duty 12V batteries housed in acid-resistant reinforced plastic battery box mounted at deck level.

FUEL: Fuel is carried in one or more 50 or 100 gallon tanks located to suit customers' layout requirements.

SCUPPERS: Scuppers for the removal of deck water are located in the transom. Discharge capacity is 818·27 litres/min (180 gallons/min).

DIMENSIONS
Length, overall: 7·37m (24ft 2in)
  at waterline: 6·09m (20ft)
Beam: 3m (9ft 10in)
Freeboard, unladen, to deck level: 127mm (5in)
  to top of bulwarks: 0·914m (3ft)
  max load, to deck level: 50·8mm (2in)
  to top of bulwarks: 838·2mm (2ft 9in)
Deck area (with outboard power): 15·81m² (170ft²)
Draft:
unladen, outboard drive up: 177·8mm (7in)
  outboard drive down: 0·584m (1ft 11in)
max load, outboard drive up: 279mm (11in)
  outboard drive down: 0·685m (2ft 3in)
WEIGHTS
Total, light condition, twin OMC OBMs: approx 2,000kg (4,409lb)
  single Volvo Penta AQ D40A diesel: approx 2,500kg (5,512lb)
Max displacement: 4,500kg (9,921lb)
Payload, dependent on engines and fixed equipment: up to 2,500kg (5,512lb)
PERFORMANCE
Performance varies with rig, type of load, installed power and operating conditions. An approximate guide is provided by the accompanying performance graph.

ROTORK STW 412 SEA TRUCK

This 12m variant of the Sea Truck is available in two versions, the STW workboat and the FAC 412 assault craft. The latter variant can carry up to 50 men with a Land Rover at speeds up to 25 knots. It can operate in only 304mm (12in) of water and can unload vehicles, personnel and supplies directly on to a beach.

Rotork STW 408 Sea Truck multi-purpose workboat

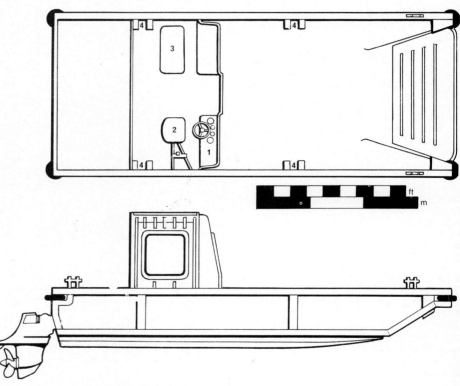

Elevation and deck plan of STW 408 Sea Truck

Rotork STW 412 Sea Truck assault craft version can carry up to 50 men and a Land Rover at speeds of up to 25 knots

PROPULSION (Alternative power plants and weights)

1 OMC 85-235hp OBMs in pairs
2 Single Volvo Penta AQ D40A/280 130hp diesel stern drive unit
3 Twin Volvo Penta AQ D40A/280 130hp diesel stern drive units
4 Single 79hp Deutz air-cooled diesel with Schottel rudder propeller

HULL: Standard Rotork Sea Truck hull in glass fibre reinforced plastics. Reinforcement: E glass chopped strand mat. E glass woven roving. Silane finish. Buoyancy: Closed cell polyurethane foam. Deck has a non-slip bonded grit surface applied to a point load integral with the hull structure. Chassis is of star frame type, integral with the hull structure. Fender frames are in hot-dip galvanised welded mild steel tube 101·6mm (4in) and 127mm (5in) diameter. Rotating fender wheels are fitted as standard at bow and stern. A polyurethane coated and grit bonded 25·4mm (1in) thick marine plywood ramp is fitted at the bow. The ramp is opened and closed manually by galvanised mild steel levers. Fuel tanks are in welded mild steel. Type 1 tanks have a capacity of 227 litres (50 imperial gallons) and are in pannier form for bulwark mounting. Type 2 tanks have a capacity of 455 litres (100 imperial gallons) and are designed for athwartship mounting. Independent fuel lines are provided.

ACCOMMODATION: A grp covered cabin can be supplied together with an extension of the control position, providing additional crew space and lockers.

DIMENSIONS
Length overall: 11·27m (37ft)
    at waterline: 9·8m (32ft 2in)
Beam: 2·99m (9ft 10in)
Freeboards, unladen to deck level: 127mm (5in)
    unladen to top of bulwarks: 914·4mm (36in)
    with max load to deck level: 50·8mm (2in)
    with max load to top of bulwarks: 838·2mm (33in)
Height, of top rail from deck: 787·2mm (31in)
Deck area, overall: 30·85m² (287ft²)
Draft, unladen, outdrive up: 177·8mm (7in)
    unladen, outdrive down: 584·2mm (23in)
    max load, outdrive up: 279·4mm (11in)
    max load, outdrive down: 685·8mm (27in)
WEIGHTS
Total, light condition, twin Volvo Penta AQ D40A/280: approx 4,000kg (8,818lb)
Max displacement: 7,500kg (16,535lb)
Payload, dependent on engines and fixed equipment: up to 4,750kg (10,472lb)

ROTORK 512 RANGE

Seven principal versions of the 512 (12m) craft are in production. The flexibility design concept based on modular layout arrangements allows variations to meet specific user requirements. The range comprises:

Goods Vehicle Ferry (GVF)
General Purpose Launch (GPL)
Passenger Vehicle Ferry (PVF)
Passenger Ferry (SPV)
Sea Truck Workboat (STW)
Logistic Support Craft (LSC)
Fast Patrol Boat (FPB)

The basic hull is constructed in heavy duty grp to British Admiralty specifications and is foam-filled, resulting in the craft being unsinkable, even when fully laden. Extensive use is made of stainless steel, rubber, nylon and other non-corrodible materials for minimum maintenance.

The PVF 512, which is designed for ferrying vehicles, cargo, livestock and passengers in areas where jetties and other landing facilities are not available, was conceived with international safety requirements in mind, enabling, where applicable, local authorities to issue certificates for the operation of these boats under varying conditions.

HULL: Glass reinforced plastic with non-slip bonded grit surface on deck. Superstructure in integrally coloured grp. Stainless steel rolled section gunwales. Full peripheral fendering at gunwale. Solid rubber strake at waterline. Black nylon full length skegs, additional beaching skegs at bow. Winch operated reinforced plastic load-

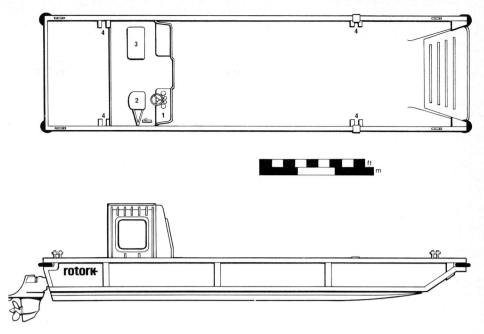

STW 412 Sea Truck

Rotork 512 in general purpose launch configuration

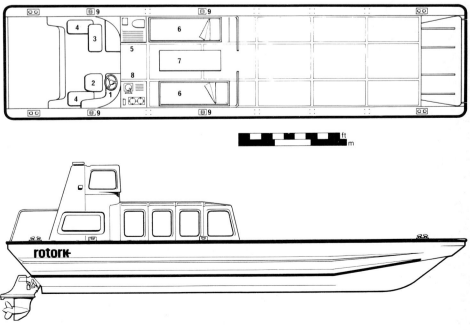

Rotork 512, outboard profile and deck plan

ing ramp with non-slip surface. Scuppers for the removal of deck water located in transom. Fuel is carried in two 200 litre (44 imperial gallon) pannier tanks mounted on internal bulwarks.

ACCOMMODATION: An all-weather grp cabin is provided aft above the gunwale level with a canvas dropscreen giving access to the quarter-deck. Door and steps give access to the welldeck. A seat is provided for the helmsman and a bench seat for two observers. Standard bridge equipment includes navigation lights, searchlight, internal light, klaxon, windscreen wiper, rechargeable fire extinguishers (two) and bilge pump. Personnel accommodation varies according to type. On the SPV 512 it comprises a cabin on deck forward of the bridge, with access doors to the bridge and foredecks, a washroom/toilet unit, galley unit with sink, cooker and 20 gallon fresh water supply system and ferry seating for 36 passengers.

COMMUNICATIONS: Optional. Fully synthesised, 25W VHF radio transceiver, up to 56 channels. SSB. HF radio telephone.

NAVIGATION: Optional. Illuminated helmsman's compass. Short range radar (Decca 060, range 24n miles).

DIMENSIONS
Length, overall: 12·65m (41ft 6in)
    waterline: 10·75m (35ft 3in)
Beam, overall: 3·2m (10ft 6in)
Overall height, hull: 1·487m (4ft 10in)
    with cabins: 2·501m (8ft 2in)
    with flying bridge: 3·525m (11ft 7in)
Height of gunwale above deck: 1m (3ft 3in)
Deck area: 9 × 2·5m = 22·5m² (29ft 6in × 8ft 3in = 243ft²)
Freeboard with max load to gunwale: 1,052·5mm (41·4in)
Draft, unladen: 268mm (10·55in)
    with max load: 420mm (16·5in)
WEIGHTS
Total, light condition, twin Volvo Penta AQ D40A/280: 4,750kg (10,472lb)
Max allowable displacement: 9,000kg (19,842lb)
Payload, dependent on engines and fixed equipment: up to 5,000kg (11,023lb)

ROTORK TB106 TUBE BOAT

The TB106, Tube Boat, is a 7m multi-role combat craft. It can operate in 67cm (26½in) of water when fully laden and has a bow ramp allowing easy access to the shore. The construction is rugged and simple with tiller steering which doubles as a manual tilt mechanism. The hull is made of virtually indestructible mid-density polyethylene.

These materials mean that it can operate in areas where sea bed conditions make beaching of conventional craft hazardous.

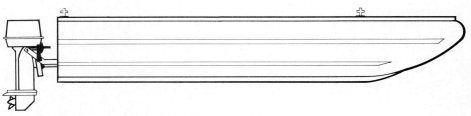

Rotork Tube Boat, outboard profile and plan

Rotork Tube Boat 7m multi-role combat craft

PROPULSION (alternatives):
1 Two 40hp Volvo OBMs
2 Two 55hp Volvo OBMs
3 Two 70hp Volvo OBMs
4 One 115hp Evinrude OBM
5 One 140hp Evinrude OBM
DIMENSIONS
Length overall: 7·26m (23ft 10in)
Beam: 2·70m (8ft 10in)
Height overall to gunwale:1·02m (3ft 4in)
Height of gunwale above deck: 0·61m (2ft)

Deck area: 6·0m² (64·58ft²)
Draft, laden (OBM up): 0·27m (10½in)
    laden (OBM down): 0·67m (26½in)
WEIGHTS
Unladen plus 2 × 40hp OBMs: 1,350kg (2,976lb)
Payload, including fuel and crew: 1,000kg (2,205lb)
PERFORMANCE
Unladen, 2 × 40hp OBMs: 20 knots
Laden, 2 × 40hp OBMs: 15 knots

Performance Guide — UK conditions							
		Speed in knots		Weight light kg	Max payload kg	Draft laden cm drive	
	Light	50%	Laden			up	down
1 GVF or LSC 512 2 × 130hp Diesel/Stern drive Volvo Penta AQ D40A/280 (6 cylinder in line turbocharged)	28	23	15	4,500	4,500	42	93
2 LSC 512 2 × 135hp Diesel/Waterjet GM Detroit diesel 4·53MN (4 cylinder two cycle)	21	18	15	5,500	3,500	42	42
3 STW 412 2 × 130hp Diesel/Stern drive Volvo Penta AQ D40A/280 (6 cylinder in line turbocharged)	29	22	17	4,400	3,100	30	42
4 STW 412 1 × 79hp Deutz Air-cooled Diesel Schottel rudder	10	9	8·5	4,400	3,100	30	120
5 STW 408 1 × 130hp Diesel/Stern drive Volvo Penta AQ D40A/280 (6 cylinder in line turbocharged)	20	12	8	2,500	2,000	30	83
6 FAC 408 2 × 140hp Outboard Motors OMC (Johnson or Evinrude)	35	28	20	2,000	2,500	30	83
7 FAC 408 2 × 235hp Outboard Motors OMC (Johnson or Evinrude)	48	42	35	2,200	2,300	30	83
8 TB106 2 × 40hp Outboard Motors	20	17·5	15	1,350	1,000	27	67

SECTOR HOVERCRAFT LTD

342 Teignmouth Road, Torquay, Devon, England
Telephone: 0803 35641
Telex: 42905 Deeley G
Officials:
E H Grundy, *Director*

Sector Hovercraft Ltd is specialising in the development and marketing of small, reliable and relatively inexpensive ACVs for private and commercial applications. The company's first production designs are the five-seat Seahawk 500 and the ten-seat Seahawk 1000.

SEAHAWK 500

This new amphibious five-seater is suitable for a wide range of commercial and public service applications. It can be supplied with a six-wheel fly-on, fly-off trailer.
LIFT AND PROPULSION: Integrated system powered by a single 240hp Chrysler V8 automotive engine. Cushion air is supplied by a 965mm (3ft 2in) diameter marine alloy centrifugal lift fan. Thrust is supplied by twin 702mm (2ft 3⅝in) diameter axial fans mounted singly in two propulsion ducts.
CONTROLS: Craft direction is controlled by twin rudder vanes hinged at the rear of each of the propulsion ducts. Driving controls include a steering wheel, side-mounted hand-throttle, switch-operated trim system, fuel-tank changeover, flashing beacon, navigation lights and a hydraulically-operated port and starboard thrust reversal system.
HULL: Sandwich construction with glass fibre reinforced marine polyester facings. Sidebodies are of grp construction and hinged to fold up for road or container transportation. Built-in buoyancy tanks. Additional buoyancy tanks fastened beneath each sidebody.
SKIRT: HDL loop and finger type fabricated in coated nylon fabric.
ACCOMMODATION: Basic version seats a driver and up to five passengers. Cabin access is via a gull-wing door located on the starboard side. Seats can be removed to permit cargo to be carried. A lightweight air-conditioning unit can be installed if required.
SYSTEMS, ELECTRICAL: Engine-driven 12V 60A alternator with 12V 68Ah battery providing power for engine starting, trim, bilge and fuel pumps, lights and windscreen wipers.
SAFETY EQUIPMENT: Standard marine safety lighting, engine bay fire-extinguishing system with fire wires lighting warning lamp. Push-button release for engine bay extinguisher. Cabin mounted portable extinguisher. Anchor. Flares. Life jackets and rafts available as optional extras.
RADIO AND RADAR: Available as optional extras.

Sector Seahawk 500 five-seat amphibious multi-duty hovercraft

Stern view of 44-knot Seahawk 500 showing thrust fan ducts and rudder vanes

ROAD TRANSPORT: Custom-built six-wheel fly-on/fly-off trailer can be supplied.
PRICE: Purchase price, Seahawk 500, delivery FOB, port of exit in the United Kingdom, mainland only £38,000. Price includes pilot seat and standard equipment as indicated in the specification. VAT at the prevailing rate is charged if the craft is to be operated in the United Kingdom.
DIMENSIONS
EXTERNAL
Length overall, power off: 6·1m (20ft)
    power on: 6·4m (21ft)
Beam overall, power off: 2·34m (7ft 8¼in)
    power on: 5·08m (16ft 8in)
Height overall, on landing pads: 1·65m (5ft 5in)
    power on: 2·1m (6ft 10⅜in)
Draft afloat: 0·25m (10in)
Cushion area: 21·69m² (234ft²)
Skirt depth: 0·46m (1ft 7in)
INTERNAL
Cabin length: 2·33m (7ft 7¾in)
Max width: 1·55m (5ft 1in)
Max height: 1·24m (4ft 0⅞in)
Floor area, excluding driver's seat: 2·3m² (22ft²)
WEIGHTS
Normal gross: 1,973kg (4,350lb)
Payload, including driver: 522kg (1,151lb)
PERFORMANCE
Max speed over calm water: 44 knots
Cruising speed: 27 knots
Still air range at cruising speed: 270km (168 miles)
Vertical obstacle clearance: 0·46m (1ft 7in)

SKIDADDLE LEISURE PRODUCTS
Division of Fruitree Ltd

15 Holywell Hill, St Albans, Herts AL1 1EZ, England
Telephone: 0727 34171
Telex: 8812915 MORTHO G SKIDADDLE
Officials:
I T Darwood, *Chairman*
D P Vann, *Director*
R W Thornton, FCA, *Director*
B Stairs, FCA, *Director*

Skidaddle Leisure Products has been licenced to build and market throughout the world the Scarab 12, a Bill Baker design which has been renamed Jetstream. It is the intention of the company, with Bill Baker as consultant, to continue the development of the Jetstream and one or two other craft and eventually mass produce them.

Jetstream amphibious two-seat utility hovercraft

JETSTREAM

This 3·65m (12ft) amphibious two-seater is designed for a range of leisure applications, including fishing, shooting, bathing and touring inland waterways. It can also be employed in underdeveloped areas for survey work in marginal terrain and as a light transport vehicle to support expeditions.

On the latest model the freeboard has been increased by 6in, which not only provides a drier craft, but since it required an alteration in hull design, it now has greater structural strength without a large increase in overall weight.

LIFT AND PROPULSION: Integrated system. A single 40bhp Hirth 276 R.6 2-cylinder air-cooled two-stroke drives via a toothed belt a ducted 71cm (28in) six-bladed multiwing fan aft. Propulsion air is expelled rearwards and lift air is ducted into the plenum below. An 18·18 litre (4 gallon) capacity fuel tank is built into the seat. Fuel recommended is 25 : 1 petrol oil mix.

CONTROLS: Craft heading is controlled by a single handlebar-operated rudder hinged to the rear of the fan duct. Handlebars incorporate twist grip throttle for the engine. An electric starter is provided as well as a lockable ignition to prevent theft.

HULL: Moulded grp structure with foam buoyancy.

SKIRT: Fully segmented type fabricated in neoprene-coated nylon.

ACCOMMODATION: Open cockpit with two seats in tandem or with side-by-side seating. In the latter configuration a single central control column is installed enabling the craft to be controlled by either occupant.

DIMENSIONS
Length: 3·68m (12ft)
Beam: 1·98m (6ft 6in)

WEIGHTS
Unladen: 164kg (360lb)

PERFORMANCE
Driver only: 55-65km/h (35-40mph)
Driver and passenger: 40-48km/h (25-30mph)
Max gradient, static conditions: 12·5%
Vertical obstacle clearance: 228mm (9in)

JETSTREAM VARIANTS

A special variant for Scandinavian countries has separate side-by-side seating and increased protection for the face and body through the addition of a higher cockpit moulding and a raised perspex screen. Basic heating is provided by a heat exchanger fitted to the engine exhaust system.

JETSTREAM 4-SEATER

About to enter production is a four-seat variant, known as the Jetstream 4. This particular design is under the direction of Bill Baker, the company's ACV design consultant. A feature of the craft will be separate lift and thrust motors. Wide interest in this design has already been shown by Scandinavian countries. A small light-weight cabin top will be fitted, together with a heating arrangement similar to that employed on earlier Jetstreams supplied to the Scandinavian market.

JETSTREAM 6-SEATER

A six-seat model of the Jetstream is also under development, although the company does not envisage that this will be in production until at least late 1981. Features include a fully-enclosed cabin, twin thrust units and a single lift motor. Tests of a mock-up of the craft are currently underway, using a number of different four-stroke engines.

Standard Jetstream 4-seater with separate lift and thrust systems

Standard Jetstream with large fairing and perspex screen

Jetstream 4 four-seater with single thrust unit and separate lift engine

Jetstream 6-seater with twin thrust units and separate lift engine

SURFACE CRAFT LTD

4 Rubastic Road, Brent Park Industrial Estate, Southall, Middlesex UB2 5LL, England
Officials:
R F King, *Director*
E A Revel
P E King, *Secretary*

NIMBUS Mk III

This inflatable two/three-seater is intended for leisure, commercial and para-military applications. It can be towed on a specially designed trailer fitted with a remotely controlled electric winch. Loading and unloading is a one-man operation which can be undertaken in a matter of minutes.

LIFT AND PROPULSION: Integrated system powered by a single 40bhp Rotax 635cc air-cooled twin-cylinder engine. The primary airflow from the two axial fans is ejected through a propulsion slot aft of the fan duct and the secondary flow, for the cushion, passes downwards into the plenum chamber. Fuel tank capacity 45 litres (10 imperial gallons). Fuel recommended, 90 octane, oil mix 25 : 1.

CONTROLS: Fourteen small rudder vanes in the propulsion slot control craft heading.

HULL: Main structure in colour-impregnated glass fibre. Twin neoprene buoyancy tubes integral with craft structure. Electric bilge pump fitted.

ACCOMMODATION: Open cockpit for two-three passengers, depending on weight and distribution. Access through forward sliding entry door.

DIMENSIONS
Length: 4·41m (14ft 6in)
Width: 2·13m (7ft 2in)
Height: 1·33m (4ft 5in)

WEIGHTS
Normal all-up weight: 498kg (1,100lb)
Max all-up weight: 590kg (1,300lb)
Empty: 362kg (800lb)
Normal payload: 136kg (300lb)
Max payload: 226kg (500lb)
PERFORMANCE
Max speed, land and water: up to 80km/h
  (50mph)
Cruising speed: 48-56km/h (30-35mph)
Range: 280km (175 miles)
Endurance: up to 5 hours
Max gradient: 40 degrees
Vertical hard structure clearance: 229mm (9in)

NIMBUS Mk IV

This is a para-military version of the Mk III
Nimbus with a modified windscreen and light
machine gun mounting ahead of the open cockpit. Three Mk IV craft have been sold for coastguard duties in South Yemen.

NIMBUS Mk V

Introduced in 1978, this new model is very
similar to the Mk III but has an improved power-
to-weight ratio and therefore a generally
enhanced performance.

Nimbus Mk IV, a two-seat hovercraft for para-military use, with a light machine gun mounted forward of the open cockpit

Nimbus, 80km/h (50mph) two-three seater built
by Surface Craft Ltd

TRANSCRAFT LIMITED

Unit 10, Holton Heath Industrial Estate, Poole,
Dorset, England
Telephone: 0202 624284
Officials:
G R Nichol, *Director*
C D Stocks, *Director*
A E Collins, *Director*

Transcraft Limited is currently producing the
Sunrider hovercraft and the Privateer wheeled
amphibious all-terrain vehicle. Although
designed primarily for recreational use the Sunrider is suitable for a range of light 'workhorse'
roles from rescue and surveying inland waterways to harbour inspection.

SUNRIDER

The Sunrider is a popular glass fibre hulled
two-seater, which has been exported to twelve
different countries. Ruggedly constructed, it has
a low noise level and has been operated at speeds
in excess of 80km/h (50mph).
LIFT AND PROPULSION: A 10bhp two-
stroke single-cylinder engine located ahead of
the open cockpit drives a five-bladed fan for cushion lift. Thrust is supplied by a 50bhp two-
cylinder two-stroke driving a ducted 3-bladed fan
aft of the cockpit. Tank capacity, 28 litres (6
imperial gallons). Fuel recommended, 93 octane.
CONTROLS: Single control column operates
twin rudders hinged to rear of fan duct. Column
incorporates a twist-grip throttle for the lift
engine. Electric starter provides for thrust
engine. Recoil hand starter for lift engine. Engine
speed control and propulsive thrust are regulated
by foot-operated throttles on each side of the
cockpit.
HULL: Moulded glass-reinforced plastics. Sides
and bow reinforced by foam plastic beneath.
Closed compartments along each side of craft
packed with low density plastic foam for buoyancy.

Rear view of Sunrider. Thrust is supplied by a 50bhp two-stroke with electric start

SKIRT: Fully segmented skirt in neoprene-
coated nylon. Replaceable segments.
ACCOMMODATION: Open cockpit with
single bench-type seat for driver and passenger.
SYSTEMS, ELECTRICAL: Propulsion engine
has 12V 100W charging circuit for the battery
which supplies electric start and any optional
extras such as lights and gauges.

DIMENSIONS
Length overall: 4m (13ft 2in)
Beam overall: 1·98m (6ft 6in)
Height: 1·11m (3ft 8in)

WEIGHTS
Empty: 300kg (660lb)
Payload: 190kg (420lb)

PERFORMANCE (calm conditions)
Max speed: in excess of 80km/h (50mph)
Normal cruising speed: 56km/h (35mph)
Endurance: 4 hours
Gradient capability: 1 : 8 from static hover
Obstacle clearance height: 23cm (9in)

Sunrider two-seater has been operated at speeds
in excess of 80km/h (50mph)

TRANS-HOVER LTD

109 Wimborne Road, Cole Hill, Wimborne Min-
ster, Dorset BH21 2QR, England
Telephone: 0202 883719
Telex: 418297 CHACOM G
Officials:
Ian F Butler, *Director*
Ian S Primrose, *Director*
Robert Trillo, *Consultant*

T.6

This new design is intended to meet the
demand for a sturdily-built, light amphibious
hovercraft, which is easily controlled and can be
employed for a variety of light military and commercial applications. It is capable of carrying six
persons or a half-ton payload for prolonged
periods over rough terrain, water, ice or snow,
mud, sands, swamps and other marginal terrain.
It can be airlifted to its area of operation by
aircraft or helicopter or transported there by a
road trailer.
LIFT AND PROPULSION: Integrated system.
A 2·6 litre car engine operating on 98 octane
gasoline drives via a toothed belt with flexible
coupling a ducted fan. Propulsion air is expelled
through multiple rudder vanes aft and lift air is
ducted into plenums below. Fuel capacity is 68
litres (15 imperial gallons). Engine compartment
is fitted with a fire extinguisher system remotely
controlled from the dashboard. Fuel tank is fitted
with explosafe.
CONTROLS: Single control column operates
rudders hinged to the rear of the fan duct. Levers
control throttle, elevators, lift and thrust ports.
HULL: Hull, superstructure and all bulkheads
are in welded marine grade aluminium alloy.
Reinforced lifting and towing points.
SKIRT: HDL loop and segment type. Lower
segments integrated with flexible cushion feed
duct and fabricated from neoprene-coated nylon.
SYSTEMS, ELECTRICAL: 12V dc, operating
engine starter, navigation lights, bilge pumps,
wipers, washers, dashboard and cabin illumina-
tion.

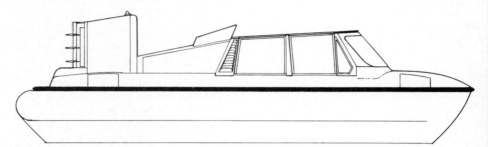

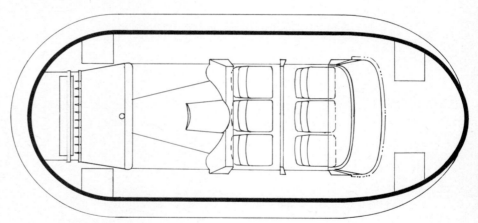

General arrangement of Trans-Hover T.6

ACCOMMODATION: Individual seats in two
rows of three side-by-side are provided for the six
occupants. Cabin or open cockpit versions can be
provided depending on operating needs. A range
of superstructure options is available.

DIMENSIONS
Length, rigid structure: 6·35m (20ft 10in)
Beam, rigid structure: 2·43m (8ft)

Height overall, power on: 1·92m (6ft 3½in)
power off: 1·6m (5ft 3in)
WEIGHTS
Payload: 506·79kg (1,120lb)
PERFORMANCE
Max speed over water: 38 knots
Cruising speed over water: 30 knots
Endurance at cruising speed: 5 hours
Obstacle clearance: 320mm (12½in)

TROPIMERE LIMITED

Head Office: 17 Wigmore Street, London W1H
9LA, England
Telephone: 01-580 5816
Telex: 24637
Factory: Devonshire Road, Millom, Cumbria
LA18 4JT, England
Telephone: 0567 2234-5

Tropimere Limited was formed in 1977, and
has a 15,000 square foot design and production
facility at Millom in Cumbria. In the company's
first year it delivered two ex-Sealand Hovercraft
SH2-4s, one to Abu Dhabi, the other to the
Spanish Army. Tropimere Limited produces two
types of craft; the Dash 6 and the Dash 7, of
which two have been delivered; the Dash 6 to the
Bahrain Coastguard Service, and a Dash 7 for
civil use in Kuwait. Although based on the stan-

dard design several variants are available to suit
many specialised roles. The company offers full
warranty, after sales spares and training schemes
to suit all types of operation.

DASH 6

The Dash 6 is the first of a series of hovercraft
designed to fill the gap between the light recreational machine and the large commercial hovercraft. Twin engines are fitted, providing adequate
power to cope with difficult terrain and sea conditions and at the same time ensuring that the craft
can return safely to base in the event of one
engine failing.
LIFT AND PROPULSION: Integrated system
powered by two Mazda RX-2 Wankel rotary pet-

rol engines. Each engine drives a 1,092mm (3ft
7in) diameter propeller which provides lift and
propulsion. Engines are cooled by a totally
enclosed fresh water system and high efficiency
radiators. Cooling air is drawn through the
radiators by the propellers. An explosion-proof
fuel tank is fitted providing sufficient capacity for
eight hours endurance at cruise setting. Fuel is
drawn through a stainless steel pipework to each
engine via a filter and an electrical solenoid valve
to the carburettor.
CONTROLS: Aerodynamic rudders aft of the
propeller ducts provide heading control and
elevators provide longitudinal trim. Additional
trim is provided by two water tanks, one in the
bow and one aft. Water is transferred from one
tank to the other by electrical pumps.

HULL: Sandwich construction employing expanded PVC foam faced with glass-reinforced marine polyester. Built-in buoyancy compartments with additional buoyancy provided by sidebodies. Sidebodies can be removed from the main hull structure to reduce the overall width for road trailing.

SKIRT: 50/50 fingered bag type fabricated in PVC-coated nylon fabric.

ACCOMMODATION: Two cabin configurations available:

a. In standard configuration the cabin seats ten. By removing seats various combinations of passenger/cargo layouts are possible.

b. Logistics support craft. Open cabin and front loading ramp with rear cabin for driver and radio/radar operator. This arrangement permits the loading of troops or bulky loads.

SYSTEMS, ELECTRICAL: 12V negative earth system, powered by two 12V-63A alternators. Power is stored in two 12V-65Ah batteries providing reserves of power for radar, radio, search-lights etc. Circuit breaker switches protect all essential services.

TRANSPORTATION: To enable the craft to be transported by road over long distances a six-wheeled undercarriage and towbar is provided with each craft, together with a lifting beam and slings to facilitate a total lift.

SAFETY EQUIPMENT: Each craft is supplied with the following: full navigation lighting to IMCO 1972 requirements; a life raft stowed in the bow compartment; life jackets; flares; anchor and fire extinguishers.

NAVIGATION AND COMMUNICATIONS: Radar and radio are optional extras and are fitted to customers' specifications.

DIMENSIONS

EXTERNAL

Length overall, power off: 8·24m (27ft)
　　on cushion: 8·9m (29ft 3in)
Beam overall, power off: 3·5m (11ft 6in)
　　on cushion: 5·8m (19ft)
Height overall, power off, excluding mast: 2·3m (7ft 6in)
　　on cushion: 3·6m (11ft 10in)
Draft afloat, static: 0·2m (8in)
Hard structure clearance: 0·46m (1ft 6in)

INTERNAL

Cabin
　　length: 4·1m (13ft 5in)
　　width: 2·1m (6ft 10in)
　　height: 1·4m (4ft 7in)

WEIGHTS

Max gross: 3,000kg (6,615lb)
Payload: 1,000kg (2,205lb)

PERFORMANCE

Max speed, calm water: 40 knots
Cruising speed: 30 knots
Still air endurance at cruising speed: 8 hours

DASH 7

This is a single-engined light utility hovercraft designed to carry a driver and up to five passengers or a 0·6 tonne payload. It uses many of the systems fitted to the larger Dash 6.

LIFT AND PROPULSION: Integrated system powered by a single 150bhp Mazda RX-2 Wankel rotary engine. Power is transmitted to a 1,082mm (3ft 7in) diameter ducted fan which provides lift and propulsion. Cooling is provided by a totally enclosed fresh water system and high efficiency radiators. Two explosion-proof tanks are provided giving sufficient capacity for six hours endurance at cruise setting. Fuel is drawn through a stainless steel pipework via a filter and electrical solenoid valve to the carburettor.

CONTROLS: Aerodynamic rudders aft of the propeller duct provide heading control and elevators provide longitudinal trim. Additional trim is provided by two ballast tanks, one located in the bow, the other in the stern. Water is transferred from one tank to the other by electrical pumps.

HULL: Sandwich construction employing expanded PVC foam faced with glass-reinforced marine polyester. Built-in buoyancy compartments with additional buoyancy provided by

Tropimere Dash 6 light passenger ferry and multi-duty hovercraft

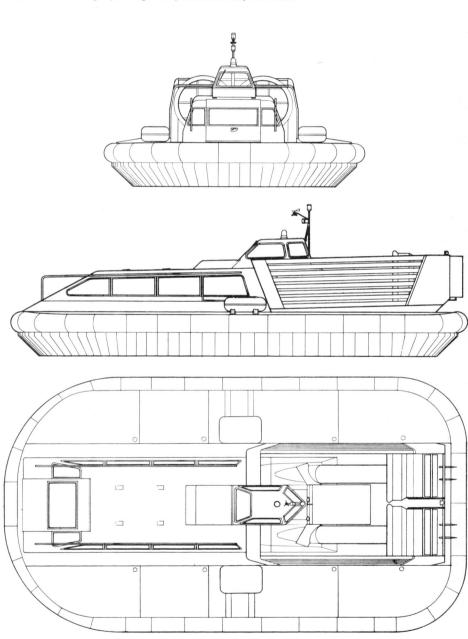

General arrangement of Dash 6 multi-purpose hovercraft

sidebodies. Sidebodies can be removed from the main hull structure to reduce the overall width for road trailing.

SKIRT: 50/50 fingered bag type in PVC-coated nylon fabric.

ACCOMMODATION: In standard configuration the cabin is laid out as a 6-seater. Heating and air-conditioning is supplied. Removal of seats enables various passenger/cargo layouts to

be achieved. Access is via a large gull-wing door. An emergency escape hatch is located on the opposite side of the cabin.

SYSTEMS, ELECTRICAL: 12V negative earth electrical system, powered by one 12V-63A alternator. Power is stored in one 12V-65Ah battery, providing a reserve of power for radio, searchlights, pumps etc, when the engine is shut down.

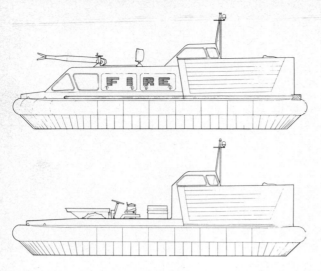

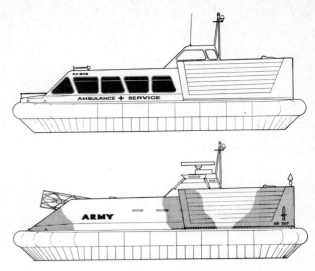

Top left: Tropimere Dash 6 in firefighting configuration: up to 200 gallons of foam-making chemical would be delivered by a roof-mounted monitor. Fitted with lockers for rescue equipment, liferafts for survivors and a searchlight
Bottom left: Utility version with flat deck for harbour or coastal engineering or light inter-island freight and supply carrying applications
Top right: High speed emergency craft for areas with poor communications. Fitted with four stretchers and attendant's seating, oxygen and resuscitation equipment
Bottom right: Patrol model equipped with surface-to-air missiles and a twin machine gun mount. Radar is fitted for night operation. Plastic armour and explosion-proof fuel tanks are available

NAVIGATION AND COMMUNICATIONS:
Radio and radar are optional extras and are fitted to customer's specifications.
BILGE SYSTEM: Cabin is bilged by means of a hand bilge pump, the engine bay being bilged by an electrical pump.
SAFETY EQUIPMENT: Each craft is supplied with the following items: full navigation lighting to IMCO 1972 regulations; a life raft stowed in the bow compartment; life jackets; flares; anchor; fire extinguishers.
TRANSPORT: To permit the craft to be transported by road over long distances, a six-wheeled undercarriage and towbar is provided with each craft. A lifting beam and slings are also provided to facilitate a complete lift.

DIMENSIONS
EXTERNAL
Length overall, power off: 8·68m (28ft 6in)
  on cushion: 8·68m (28ft 6in)
Beam overall, sidebodies removed: 2·8m (9ft 2in)
  on cushion: 5·08m (16ft 8in)
Height overall, power off: 1·65m (5ft 5in)
  on cushion: 2·1m (6ft 10in)
Draft hullborne: 0·25m (10in)
Cushion area: 28·33m² (305ft²)
Hard structure clearance: 0·46m (1ft 6in)
INTERNAL
Cabin
  length, max: 4·19m (13ft 9in)
  width, max: 1·55m (5ft 1in)
  height, max: 1·24m (4ft 1in)
  floor area: 5·2m² (56ft²)
WEIGHTS
Max gross: 2,600kg (5,732lb)
Payload: 600kg (1,323lb)
PERFORMANCE
Max speed, calm water: 40 knots
Cruising speed: 30 knots
Still endurance at cruising speed: 6 hours

Tropimere Dash 7, powered by a single 150hp
Mazda RX-2 Wankel rotary engine

Tropimere Dash 7

VOSPER HOVERMARINE LIMITED

Hazel Wharf, Hazel Road, Woolston, Southampton SO2 7GB, England
Telephone: 0703 443122
Telex: 47141
Officials:
Sir John Rix, *Chairman*
W A Zebedee, *Deputy Chairman*
K D C Ford, *Financial Director*
R L S Blackadder, *Director*
E G Tattersall, *Research and Development Director*
P J Hill, *Operations Director*
E W Furnell, *Production Director*
R R L Wilkins, *Secretary*

Vosper Hovermarine is the most experienced designer and builder of surface effect ships in the world. The Vosper Group purchased a 51% share of Hovermarine Transport, formerly a wholly-owned subsidiary of Hovermarine Corporation, at the beginning of 1980. Vessels are built in two yards in Woolston, Southampton. Total covered area is over 13,000m², including some of the best grp facilities in Europe.

By mid-1980 66 Hovermarine 200 series vessels had been sold to more than 20 countries. The design, which is currently available in 16m, 18m and 21m hull lengths, is type approved in the United Kingdom for Certificates of Construction and Performance/Hovercraft Safety Certificates issued by the Civil Aviation Authority and for Operating Permits issued by the Department of Trade. It has also been certified by Lloyd's Register of Shipping as a Class A1 Group 2 Air Cushion Vehicle and approved by the United States Coast Guard and the Marine Division of the Japanese Government.

The first of the new Hovermarine 500 series surface effect ships is now in an advanced stage of construction at Woolston and will be launched during the latter half of 1981. The 500 series is available in 27m and 33m hull lengths. Both the Hovermarine 200 and Hovermarine 500 series can be fitted out for a variety of requirements including passenger ferry, survey, harbour work, coastguard surveillance, naval patrol and other duties.

Vosper Hovermarine is also working on developments of the Hovermarine 200 and 500 series and the design of a Hovermarine 600 Vehicle Ferry/Freighter. A British Government-funded research and development programme into large, deep cushion surface effect ships has been initiated. Recent 200 series deliveries include six more Hovermarine 218 ferries to the Hongkong & Yaumati Ferry Company (increasing its Hovermarine fleet to 16 vessels), four Hovermarine 218 Port Patrol Boats to the Port of Rotterdam, two Hovermarine 218 ferries to the Jordan Valley Authority and three Hovermarine 218 crewboats to Maraven SA in Venezuela.

HOVERMARINE 216 HYDROGRAPHIC SURVEY VESSEL

The Hovermarine 216 Hydrographic Survey Vessel features a superstructure and equipment designed specifically for the hydrographic survey role. A craft delivered to the Belgian Ministry of Public Works has been used in the River Scheldt estuary since 1972.
POWERPLANTS
Lift: One 206bhp Cummins V555M marine diesel
Propulsion: Two 445bhp General Motors Detroit Diesel Allison 8V92TI marine diesels
DIMENSIONS
Length overall: 15·24m (50ft)
Beam overall: 5·8m (19ft)
Height overall: 4·1m (13ft 4in)
Draft floating, loaded: 1·49m (4ft 10in)
on cushion, loaded: 0·87m (2ft 10in)
Bridge/cabin length: 4·3m (14ft)
  beam: 4·3m (14ft)
  height: 2·0m (6ft 6in)
WEIGHTS
Standard gross: 19,300kg (42,500lb)
Normal disposable payload: 5,600kg (12,300lb)

Vosper Hovermarine 216 hydrographic survey vessel operated on the River Scheldt by the Belgian Ministry of Public Works

One of a fleet of sixteen Vosper Hovermarine 216s and 218s operated by the Hong Kong and Yaumati Ferry Co

Passenger saloon in a Vosper Hovermarine 218

PERFORMANCE
Cruising speed: 35 knots
Standard range at cruising speed: 250n miles

HOVERMARINE 218 FERRY

The Hovermarine 218 Ferry represents a 40% improvement in payload over the earlier Hovermarine 216 Ferry for only a 15% increase in operating costs. It can carry 86-92 passengers at cruising speeds of up to 35 knots. An extended bow skirt permits passenger operations in up to 1·5m (4ft 11in) waves. A computerised roll stabilisation system can be fitted to customer order.

The first Hovermarine 218 ferry went into service in 1976. A major operator of the type is the Hongkong & Yaumati Ferry Company, which has 12 on commuter services within Hong Kong and on an 80n mile international route to Kwang-Chow (Canton) in the People's Republic of China. Other Hovermarine 218 ferries are operating in Japan, Jordan and Nigeria. Production at Woolston since 1977 has been concentrated on the Hovermarine 218 but the smaller Hovermarine 216 will still be built to order.

LIFT AND PROPULSION: Two General Motors Detroit Diesel Allison 8V92TI vee, eight-cylinder marine diesels, each developing 445bhp at 2,300rpm, provide propulsive power. A single Cummins 90 degree vee, eight-cylinder V555M marine diesel rated at 206bhp at 2,800rpm drives the 0·60m (24in) diameter centrifugal lift fans.

The lift engine drives two pairs of forward fans through toothed belts and one aft fan through a hydraulic system. Air for the forward fans is drawn through inlets at each forward cabin quarter and in the base of the wheelhouse structure. Air for the aft fan is drawn through an inlet in the rear companionway.

The two propulsion engines each drive a 0·45m (18in) diameter aluminium bronze three-bladed propeller through a reversing gearbox and 1:1 ratio vee box. Fuel is carried in stainless steel tanks, two beneath the aft companionway and one under the main lift fans. Electrical power for instruments, radio, radar, lighting and air conditioning is supplied by two dc alternators driven by the lift engine.

CONTROLS: Craft direction is controlled by twin balanced stainless steel rudders operated hydraulically by a car-type steering wheel. Additional control is provided by differential use of the water propellers.

HULL: The hull is made up of several grp mouldings and various types of sandwich panels. The mouldings consist of the main deck, deck and superstructure centre section, forward intakes and wheelhouse, inner sidelinings, aft com-

Vosper Hovermarine 218 operated by the Jordan Valley Authority on the Dead Sea featuring roof-mounted luggage modules

Three Vosper Hovermarine 218 crewboats operated on Lake Maracaibo, Venezuela, by Maraven SA

panionway and engine bay cowlings. The first three are joined by a system of transverse frames. The floor panels are bonded to the frames and to the longitudinal intercoastal members.

The complete outer shell of the hull, including the bottom between the sidewalls and under the bow, is moulded in one piece, gunwale to gunwale. The hull moulding incorporates local thickening of the laminate to meet the design load requirements and to facilitate the incorporation

of fittings and apertures. Frames and bulkheads are manufactured from sandwich panels of expanded pvc foam covered with grp. All frames and bulkheads are laminated into the hull.

ACCOMMODATION: The Hovermarine 218 ferry can be operated by a crew of two. Controls are all sited in an elevated wheelhouse, with a 360-degree view, at the forward end of the passenger saloon. The saloon can be fitted out with up to 86 aircraft-type seats or 92 utility seats.

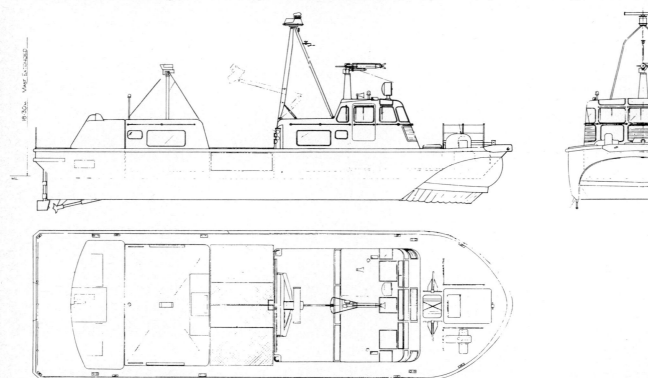

General arrangement of Vosper Hovermarine 218 port patrol craft for the Rotterdam Port Authority

These are normally arranged three abreast in banks of three. Toilet and baggage compartments are located aft. Up to six luggage containers, able to hold a total of 1,500kg (3,307lb), may also be carried on the saloon roof.

Passenger access to the saloon is via a double width door aft. Crew and emergency access is provided forward via two hatch doors, one on each side of the wheelhouse. Knock-out emergency windows are fitted in the passenger saloon. Safety equipment includes life rafts, aircraft-type life jackets under the seats, fire detectors and extinguishers.

SKIRTS: The extended bow skirt consists of a single loop extending from the bow chine to a line just below the base of the main hull. Thirty-two segments are attached to the main loop and connected to the underside of the hull by terylene ropes. An inner loop overlaps the fan volute outlet and causes the bow skirt to inflate.

The rear seal consists of a membrane and loop which is suspended front and rear by transverse continuous sheets of material. It is inflated to a pressure slightly above that of the cushion by the rear fan housed in the starboard propulsion engine room.

DIMENSIONS
Length overall: 18·29m (60ft)
Beam overall: 6·1m (20ft)
Height overall: 4·88m (16ft)
Draft floating, loaded: 1·72m (5ft 6in)
  on cushion, loaded: 1·07m (3ft 5in)
Saloon length: 9·75m (32ft)
  beam: 4·88m (16ft)
  height: 1·93m (6ft 4in)
WEIGHTS
Standard gross: 25,400kg (56,000lb)
Normal disposable payload: 6,578kg (14,500lb)
Normal fuel capacity: 818 litres (180 imperial gallons)
PERFORMANCE
Cruising speed: 35 knots
Acceleration 0-30 knots: 45 seconds
Standard range at cruising speed: 135n miles
Standard endurance at cruising speed: 4 hours

HOVERMARINE 218 CREWBOAT

The Hovermarine 218 crewboat is based on the 218 ferry but the hull is locally reinforced to withstand handling alongside offshore installations and fitted out for both bow and stern loading. Three Hovermarine 218 crewboats are operated on offshore supply duties on Lake Maracaibo, Venezuela, by Maraven SA. Specifications and performance are similar to the 218 ferry.

HOVERMARINE 218 PORT PATROL BOAT

Four Hovermarine 218 Port Patrol Boats were delivered to the Port of Rotterdam Authority in 1979-80. The design features port monitoring and emergency service equipment housed in two superstructure modules. In addition to the standard lift and propulsion engines, an auxiliary Mercedes Benz OM6 36 diesel generating unit driving a single 250V 50Hz single-phase alternator is fitted.

EQUIPMENT: Firefighting equipment capable of delivering seawater, aspirated protein foam, high pressure fog and dry powder. A remote control monitor with foam and seawater nozzles has a range of 46m (151ft) and flow rates of 2,270 litres/minute (500 gallons/minute) for water or water/foam mix and 19,500 litres/minute (4,290 gallons/minute) for aspirated foam. The two deck hydrants can also be supplied with water or water/foam mix. Each has four low pressure outlets and one high pressure outlet for fog generation. The craft also carry hoses, large quantities of protein foam concentrate and a Graviner 100kg (220lb) portable dry powder firefighting system.

Hull and superstructure are protected by a waterskirt drenching system. Other ancillary equipment includes wind speed and direction meters, explosive gas detection apparatus, water temperature monitoring and compressed air breathing equipment. To enable the craft to respond to emergencies requiring medical aid, they are equipped with racks for four stretchers,

Vosper Hovermarine 218 of the Rotterdam Port Authority demonstrating its remote control monitor

Wheelhouse of Vosper Hovermarine 218 ferry and crewboat

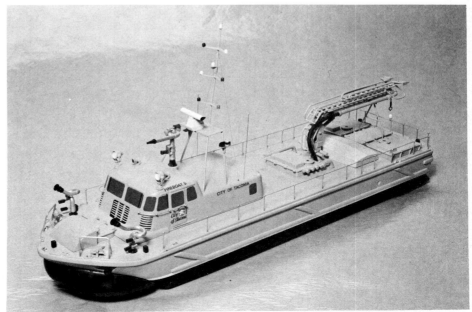

Model of Vosper Hovermarine 221 multi-role harbour service vessel ordered by the City of Tacoma, Washington State

oxygen respiratory equipment and a resuscitation unit. A crew room and galley are also included.

The Hovermarine 218 port patrol boat can be operated on patrol by the commander and a navigating officer. For full duties, there are manning positions for a fire officer, traffic control officer and a working crew of four. Dimensions and powerplants are similar to the Hovermarine 218 ferry.

HOVERMARINE 218 COASTGUARD VESSEL

Based on the standard Hovermarine 218 hull but incorporating a purpose-built superstructure and equipment, the Hovermarine 218 Coastguard Vessel is designed for operations in coastal areas. At a cruising speed of over 30 knots, it has a range of 600n miles, or 1,200n miles at slower patrol speeds up to 10 knots. A ride stabilisation unit is fitted as standard to ensure an exceptionally stable platform at high speeds in heavy seas. Dimensions and main powerplants are similar to the Hovermarine 218 ferry.

HOVERMARINE 218 MEDICRAFT

Another variant based on the Hovermarine 218 hull, the Hovermarine 218 Medicraft is available as a rapid intervention vessel able to provide emergency medical facilities in areas where local conditions necessitate an approach by water. The standard design offers an examination/treatment clinic for medical or dental work, complete with operating table, fitted out with a comprehensive range of equipment.

HOVERMARINE 221 MULTI-ROLE HARBOUR SERVICE VESSEL

The 21m (68ft 10in) Hovermarine 221 is the latest and largest design in the 200 series. Two Multi-role Harbour Service Vessels based on the 221 hull have been ordered by the City of Tacoma, Washington, USA. These will have a comprehensive range of firefighting, rescue, navigation and communications equipment. Much of this, including fire monitors and telescopic ladder, will be remotely controlled.

A single General Motors Detroit Diesel Allison 8V92TI diesel engine will maintain a high pumping rate, enabling the Hovermarine 221s to cope with ship or harbour installation fires. The other three engines are also General Motors Detroit Diesel Allison units: the lift engine will be a 6V92TI and the 8V92TI propulsion engines of the Hovermarine 218 are retained.

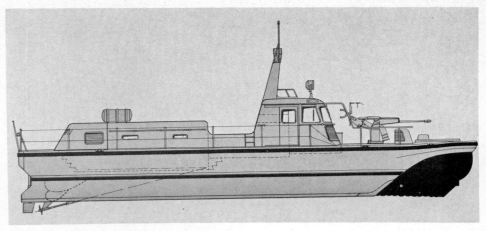

Outboard profile, Vosper Hovermarine 218 coastguard vessel

Vosper Hovermarine 527 ferry

A crewboat version of the Hovermarine 221 could carry both personnel and equipment. The design features a passenger saloon forward and a flat deck cargo area aft.

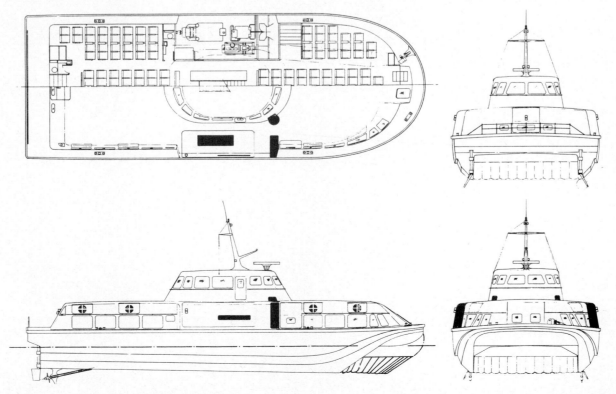

Vosper Hovermarine 527 ferry, general arrangement

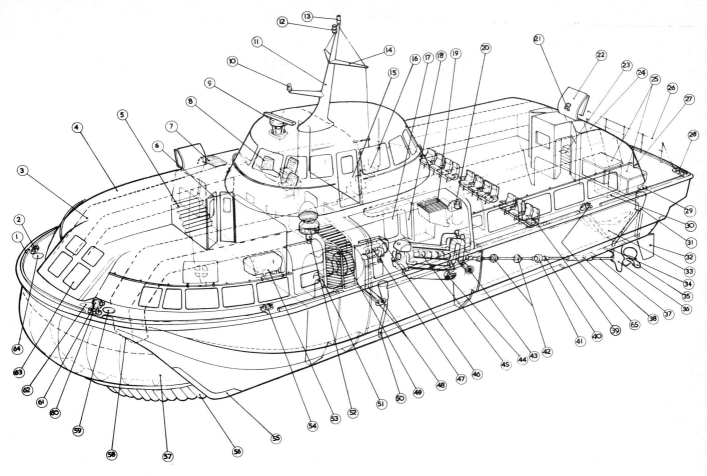

Vosper Hovermarine 527

1. Toe Rail; 2. Mooring Bitt; 3. Air Duct, Forward Skirt Loop Inflation; 4. Superstructure; 5. Forward Saloon Companionway; 6. Forward Saloon Companionway Doors; 7. Intake Grill, Starboard Lift Fan; 8. Commander's Seat; 9. Radar Scanner; 10. Flashing Hoverlight (Yellow); 11. Mast; 12. Masthead Light; 13. Anchor Light; 14. Crosstree; 15. Wheelhouse Door; 16. Stairway, Upper/Lower Decks; 17. Engine Room Door; 18. Air Conditioning Duct; 19. Engine Room Air Intake; 20. Navigation Light; 21. Stern Light; 22. Folding Hatch, Aft Companionway; 23. Aft Companionway; 24. Port Aft Toilet; 25. Fuel Tanks, Port; 26. Stern Rail; 27. Refuelling Point, Port; 28. Mooring Bitt; 29. Access Hatch, Port Aft Sea Water Strainer; 30. Air Duct, Aft Skirt Loop Inflation; 31. Sea Water Strainer; 32. Rudder; 33. Skirt Segment; 34. Aft Sea Water Intake; 35. Propeller; 36. 'P' Bracket/Skeg; 37. Propeller Shaft; 38. Shaft Log; 39. Passenger Seats, Aircraft Type; 40. Shaft Spacer and Coupling; 41. Thrust Bearing; 42. Shaft Bearing; 43. Exhaust, Propulsion Engine; 44. Sea Water Discharge; 45. Port Propulsion Engine; 46. Port Auxiliary Power Unit; 47. Port Lift Engine; 48. Exhausts, Lift Engine and Auxiliary Power Unit; 49. Lift Fan; 50. Forward Sea Water Intake; 51. Lift Fan Volute; 52. Skirt Loop Inflation Fan; 53. Liferaft Stowage in Soft Valise; 54. Mooring Bitt and Slinging Point; 55. Sidewall Impact Blade; 56. Skirt Segment; 57. Skirt Loop (Shown Inflated); 58. Air Duct, Forward Skirt Loop Inflation; 59. Chain Locker Access; 60. Mooring Bitt; 61. Winch (Electric); 62. Davit Mounting; 63. Forward Window and Emergency Exit; 64. Equipment Stowage Hatch; 65. Mooring Bitt and Slinging Point

HOVERMARINE 527 FERRY

The Hovermarine 527 ferry will carry up to 210 passengers at a cruising speed of 35 knots. It will operate on coastal and inland waters in wave heights of up to 3m (9ft 10in) with a payload of 21,000kg (20·7 tons). Normal range is 200n miles. A computerised roll stabilisation system is fitted as standard. Other designs based on the Hovermarine 527 hull include a hydrographic survey vessel and both all-passenger crewboats and mixed payload supply boats for the offshore oil industry. A 33m (108ft) Hovermarine 533 ferry is also projected.

LIFT AND PROPULSION: The marine diesels are housed in two amidships engine rooms. Both accommodate one lift engine, one propulsion engine and one auxiliary power unit. The lift engines are General Motors Detroit Diesel Allison 8V92TIs rated at 435bhp at 2,300rpm. Each drives a lift fan, via a gearbox, to provide plenum air and, via a hydraulic pump and hydraulic motor, a second fan for skirt inflation. The propulsion engines are MTU 12V 936 TB82 diesels rated at 1,400bhp at 1,800rpm. Each incorporates a variable ratio gearbox and drives a single three-bladed propeller via transmission shafting inclined at 13 degrees. The outward rotating propellers operate at up to 1,540rpm. Two Perkins 6·354M marine diesels rated at 115bhp at 2,800rpm drive the ac alternators, dc generators and compressors for the air conditioning system.

Fuel is carried in four tanks in the transom bay, in-line athwartships. Both the two port tanks and two starboard tanks are connected to form two main tanks. Each of these has a fuel capacity of 933 litres (205 gallons) including ballast.

Model of Vosper Hovermarine 527 showing bow loop and segment skirt

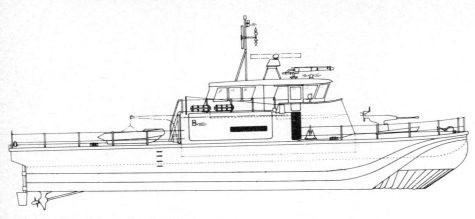
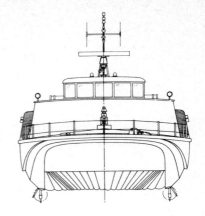

Vosper Hovermarine 527 MC coastguard/rescue craft

CONTROLS: Vessel heading is controlled by power-operated twin water rudders. Additional control is provided by differential use of the propellers.

HULL: A single shell grp moulding with sub-moulding, frames, bulkheads and cabin sole panels bonded together. Materials used include expanded pvc foam, glass fibre, polyester resins, wood and aluminium alloy.

ACCOMMODATION: The bridge accommodates the commander, navigator and third crew member. Passenger access is via doors port and starboard in the forward and aft saloons. Emergency exits are located in both saloons. Four toilet/washbasin units are provided plus a central luggage space. There is also provision for eight luggage containers to be mounted on the roof of the craft. Safety equipment includes liferafts, inflatable life jackets, lifebuoys and line-throwing apparatus.

SKIRTS: The main plenum chamber receives air from two lift fans via ducts located amidships port and starboard. Bow and stern skirts receive air from port and starboard fans, driven hydraulically by lift engine gearbox pumps, via ducts forming part of the superstructure.

The bow skirt is made up of two tailored neoprene/nylon loops suspended in 180 degree arcs sidewall to sidewall. These are joined at their lower edges to form an irregularly shaped inflatable compartment. When inflated, the loops support 20 single fabric segments, attached at the loop joint line, and absorb wave impact shock to a degree. Four additional corner segments are attached on each side by ropes and shackles.

Two similar tailored loops are suspended under the stern. These are joined at their lower edges to form a single inflatable compartment. When inflated, this supports 20 double fabric segments attached to the loop joint line.

DIMENSIONS
Length overall: 27·2m (89ft 3in)
Beam overall: 10·2m (33ft 5in)
Height overall: 4·9m (16ft)
Draft floating, loaded: 2·55m (8ft 4in)
 on cushion, loaded: 1·4m (4ft 7in)
Standard passenger capacity, forward saloon: 95
 aft saloon: 116

HOVERMARINE 527 MC

The Hovermarine 527 MC is a high-speed coastguard/rescue vessel. At a cruising speed of 32 knots, it has a range of 1,600n miles. At a patrol speed of 12 knots, the range increases to 3,000n miles. The MC design combines the hull of the Hovermarine 527 ferry with a purpose-built superstructure. Operational crew is only two officers and three ratings. A double cabin is provided for the officers and a three-berth cabin for the ratings. There is also a first aid/detention room. Armament would be a single 20mm Oerlikon GAM-BOI naval mount on the forward deck and small arms. Dimensions and powerplants are similar to the Hovermarine 527 ferry.

HOVERMARINE 533 OPV

The Hovermarine 533 OPV is intended specifically for patrolling Exclusive Economic Zones. Designed for autonomous patrols of up to seven days' duration, a typical fit-out would

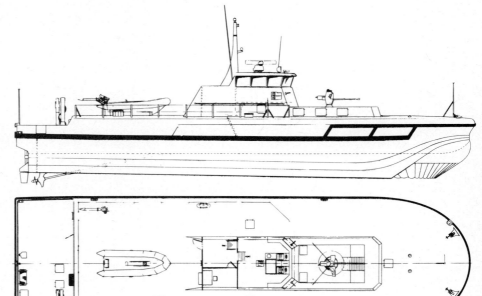

Outboard profile and weather deck plan of Vosper Hovermarine 533 OPV

Vosper Hovermarine 533 offshore patrol vessel

include a 30mm gun, communications and navigation equipment, a firefighting monitor and accommodation for a crew of up to 26 officers and men.

The crew would normally comprise a captain, three officers, four observers or officers under training, three senior ratings, nine junior ratings and six trainees. Accommodation would be air conditioned and include a galley and galley store, captain's suite, ward room, dining hall, and separate sleeping and messing accommodation for the ratings.

Armament would be a single Rarden 30mm cannon on LSE stabilised mount, two light machine guns and small arms. Navigation and communications equipment would include HF,

UHF and VHF radio, Decca Clearscan radar and SPL plotting table, gyrocompass, log, echo sounder and radio position fixing aids.

DIMENSIONS
Length overall: 33·2m (109ft)
Beam overall: 10·2m (33ft 6in)
Draft floating, loaded: 2·55m (8ft 4in)
 on cushion, loaded: 1·40m (4ft 7in)

WEIGHTS
Max gross weight: 110,000kg (242,500lb)

PERFORMANCE
Cruising speed: 35 knots
Range, at 35 knots: 1,400n miles
 at 12 knots: 3,000n miles
Endurance: 7 days

VOSPER THORNYCROFT (UK) LIMITED

Head Office: Fareham House, East Street, Fareham, Hants PO16 0BW, England
Telephone: 0329 283411
Telex: 86669 VT FARE G
Cables: Repsov, Portsmouth
Officials:
W Richardson, *Chairman and Chief Executive*
D E Wilson, *Group Managing Director*
J E C Grant, *Administrative Director*
H W Melvin, *Financial Director*
Dr P A Milne, *Director*
L Peacock, *Personnel Director*
P J Usher, *Managing Director, Woolston Shipbuilding Division*
J A Wilde, *Director*
A L Dorey, *Technical Director*

Vosper Thornycroft (UK) Limited, a member of British Shipbuilders, continues the shipbuilding business originally established over a century ago by two separate companies, Vosper Limited and John I Thornycroft & Co Ltd. These well-known companies merged in 1966 and the organisation has continued the design and construction of warships from fast patrol boats to large frigates. The company was nationalised on 1 July 1977 and is now part of British Shipbuilders.

The company's main activities embrace the design and construction of warships and hovercraft intended primarily for military purposes. Diversified engineering work is also undertaken including the design and manufacture of ship stabilisers and specialised electrical and electronic control equipment for marine and industrial use.

Vosper Thornycroft entered the hovercraft field in 1968 and is currently concentrating its designs on amphibious military hovercraft.

18 METRE PATROL HOVERCRAFT

This 18 metre hovercraft design can be adapted to a number of different roles including coastal patrol, logistic support, coastguard and customs duties. In the logistic support role it is capable of carrying up to 35 troops with their equipment. Fire-fighting and rescue duties can also be undertaken by fitting bolt-on equipment to mountings on the hull structure. A gun of up to twin 30mm calibre can be mounted on a well deck forward. All-up weight of the craft is about 25 tonnes and under normal conditions it will carry a disposable load of about 9 tonnes. Maximum continuous speed for the craft is estimated at 60 knots in calm conditions. Range is about 600n miles at a speed of 50 knots.

LIFT AND PROPULSION: Integrated system powered by a single Avco Lycoming Super TF25 gas turbine rated at 3,000shp maximum and 2,500shp continuous at 15°C. The gas turbine is installed in an engine bay amidship and has easy access for servicing. Power is transmitted to a 3·2m (10ft 6in) diameter ducted controllable-pitch propeller aft, and via a vertical driveshaft, to a bevel drive gearbox beneath from which shafts extend sideways to drive four 1·2m (4ft) diameter lift fans, housed in pairs in two volutes, one on either side of the craft, outboard of the superstructure. The ducted propeller is designed for improved efficiency, noise reduction and to eliminate the risk of injury to anyone working alongside. An auxiliary power unit provides electrical supplies when the main engine is stopped.

CONTROLS: Vertical and horizontal control surfaces are fitted aft of the propeller duct.

HULL: Built in marine aluminium alloys.

SKIRT: Loop and segment skirt system, similar to that of VT 2, providing a cushion depth of more than 1·5m (5ft). This ensures good seakeeping for a craft of this size and enables it to clear substantial obstacles when manoeuvring ashore.

ACCOMMODATION: The arrangement of the craft includes a central superstructure with engine bay, the auxiliary machinery room and the crew's accommodation with bunks and galley. Above this is a control cabin, with pilot's and navigator's positions. The well deck forward provides space for the gun mounting and its

Impression of Vosper Thornycroft's 25-ton 18 metre patrol hovercraft. Maximum continuous speed is estimated at 60 knots in calm conditions, with a range of about 600n miles at a speed of 50 knots

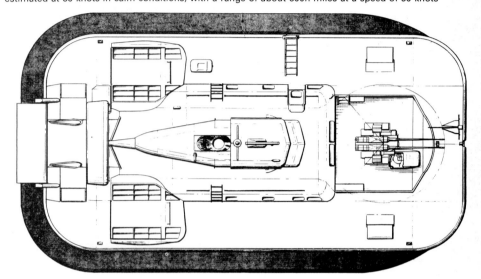

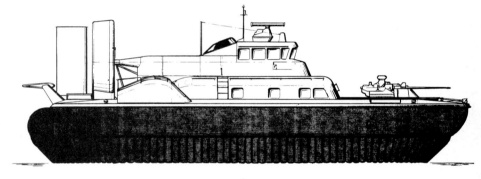

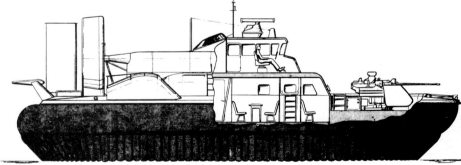

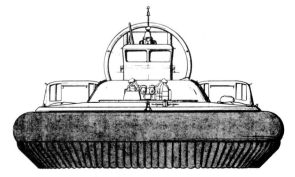

General arrangement of Vosper Thornycroft 18 metre hovercraft. Power for lift and thrust is supplied by a single Avco Lycoming Super TF25 gas turbine rated at 3,000shp maximum and 2,500shp continuous

operator, or, with suitable ramps, can be used to carry up to two Land Rovers or similar vehicles. Alternatively troops, in addition to the 35 who can be accommodated in the superstructure, can be transported in the well deck. Another option is a larger superstructure capable of accommodating more troops.

DIMENSIONS
Length overall: 18·4m (60ft 5in)
Width, hard structure: 9·3m (30ft 6in)
Height overall, on cushion: 6·2m (20ft 4in)

WEIGHTS
All-up weight: 25 tonnes
Disposable load, max: 9 tonnes

PERFORMANCE
Max continuous speed, calm conditions: 60 knots
Max range at 50 knots, calm conditions: 600n miles

VT 2

One of the largest military hovercraft yet built, VT 2 has an overall length of 30·1m (99ft) and an all-up weight of 100-110 tonnes, according to role.

A number of variants are available. In addition to a strike version, there is a logistic version for carrying troops, vehicles and guns; a multi-purpose configuration combining both weapons and a logistic capability and a mine counter-measures variant.

A VT 2 craft in a logistic support configuration is in service with the Royal Navy.

In both 1977 and 1978 the craft was employed in the Whisky Galore exercises to land troops and vehicles from ships in and around Loch Ewe and the Outer Hebrides. In 1977 VT 2 returned to the Solent by way of the north of Scotland and Pentland Firth, so completing a circumnavigation of Britain in a passage time of 60 hours.

To extend the VT 2's overall capabilities before participating in exercises in 1978, VT 2-001 was modified under Ministry of Defence contract to permit palleted cargo to be handled for transport from ship-to-shore. Modifications included the fitting of a loading hatch in the superstructure roof and laying roller tracking on the deck below.

In the spring of 1977 the VT2 was operated for six weeks in the Baltic based on the north coast of West Germany, and took part in trials and exercises with the West German and Danish Navies.

Subsequent activities are expected to include evaluation as a logistic support vessel to the Royal Navy's new Hunt-class mine counter-measure vessels and other roles related to mine warfare.

LIFT AND PROPULSION: Motive power for the integrated lift/propulsion system is supplied by two Rolls-Royce Proteus marine gas turbines, each rated at 4,250shp maximum. The two gas turbines are installed in port and starboard engine rooms amidships and each powers two drive shafts via a David Brown gearbox. One shaft transmits power to a bank of four centrifugal lift fans, which absorbs about one third of the output, the other drives a ducted propulsion fan via an inclined shaft.

The two variable-pitch fans, each 4·1m (13ft 6in) in diameter, have seven blades and each rotates in a duct of streamline section. The blades are of foam-filled glass-reinforced plastics. Manufactured by Dowty Rotol Limited, they are the largest propulsion fans yet made. In comparison with air propellers, ducted fans offer increased efficiency and substantial reductions in noise levels. The noise reduction results from the low fan tip speed of 150m/s (500ft/s). Other advantages offered are reduced diameter for a given thrust and power, and less danger to crew working in their vicinity. The variation in pitch provides differential thrust for manoeuvring. Downstream of the fan blades are stator blades, sixteen in each duct, ensuring uniformity of thrust and of the directional control provided by rudders mounted at the aft ends of the ducts.

The ducted fans are mounted with their shaft axes at an angle to the horizontal of about 13½ degrees, avoiding the need for right-angle

VT 2-001 returning to base after deployment in the Baltic

Royal Navy's VT 2 hovercraft (P234) undergoing one of a series of trials to examine the effect of underwater shock. This is the first such trial of a hovercraft which has a further ten years of guaranteed life and which carried a full crew on board at the time

VT 2 hovercraft (P234) operating overland

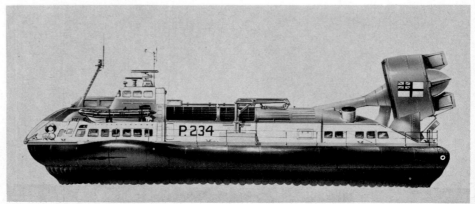

Profile of VT 2 (P234) as it will appear after modifications for the MCMV Support Role are completed

gearbox drives. This entails some slight loss in efficiency, but this is offset by savings in the losses in the right-angle boxes themselves and in the additional power for air cooling which would be needed for their lubricating oil.

Gas turbines, main gearboxes and lift fans are all housed in machinery spaces on either side of the craft outboard of the main longitudinal webs. The engines are mounted with their shaft axes parallel to those of the propulsion fans, so that normal gearing can be used for the 75% or so of the engine output which is transmitted to the propulsion fans. This arrangement also directs the turbine exhausts upwards, thereby simplifying the ductwork.

The remaining 25% of engine power is applied to the lift fans which are accommodated in separate compartments of the machinery spaces, two each side, with their axes horizontal. A vee-drive gear system effects the change in shaft axis at the output from the main gearbox to the lift fans. The fans draw air through grilled areas in the upper outboard part of the craft's superstructure amidships and discharge down to the cushion loop. A quantity of cushion air is diverted via a filtration system to remove salt and sand contamination to the Proteus gas turbine intakes, and a further quantity is ducted to bow thrusters for manoeuvring at low speeds.

CONTROLS: The pilot and engineer are accommodated atop the superstructure in a control cabin which has an all-round view. Rudder pedals provide steering via the control surfaces in the fan slipstream. Twin levers between pilot and engineer control fan pitch, and hence speed, and can be moved differentially to provide additional turning moments. To give close lateral control at low speeds side thrusters are fitted which utilise pressurised cushion air to provide side thrust. Hydraulically-actuated doors direct air from the ducts to port or starboard as required, in response to movement of a combined selector control at the pilot's position. Rapid trim adjustment is provided by elevators in the fan slipstream. A ballast control provides slow trim adjustment by pumping reserve fuel, totalling 3 tonnes, from one compartment to another. This is done electrically by means of a switch. Engine throttle levers are available to both pilot and engineer. Communications are normally operated by the pilot. Full navigational and machinery instrumentation is provided.

HULL: Construction is mainly in marine aluminium alloys with bolted or riveted joints. The main structural elements are the buoyancy raft, of egg-box form, providing 26 watertight compartments and a buoyancy reserve of more than 100%, and two deep vertical webs, forming fore-and-aft bulkheads enclosing the central bay of the craft. On the underside of the buoyancy raft are three pads on which the craft is supported when at rest on dry land. A lighter shell structure attached to the periphery of the raft and the main longitudinal webs encloses accommodation and machinery spaces and the central bay. In logistic support configuration a door with loading ramp is provided at the bow, extending across the full width of the central bay. A door can be incorporated aft if through loading is required. The design allows substantial flexibility in the choice of superstructure arrangement to suit a wide variety of roles.

SKIRT: A peripheral skirt contains a 1·58m (5ft 6in) deep air cushion at a pressure of about 31mb (65lb/ft²). The cushion is in the form of a single undivided cell. It provides a comfortable ride in rough seas, and enables the craft to clear obstacles overland up to 1·1m (3ft 7in) high.

The skirt is made of nylon-reinforced neoprene and consists of two main parts, loop and segments. The loop forms a continuous duct around the periphery of the craft, contained between inner and outer bands of skirt material attached to the raft structure. The lift fans deliver air to the loop through apertures in the raft plating. The segments are attached to the lower edges of the loop, and consist of 157 sets of inner and outer scoop-shaped pieces. The inner segments direct air flow outwards and downwards into the outer segments, and have holes which allow a

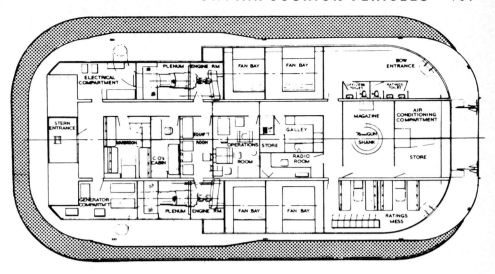

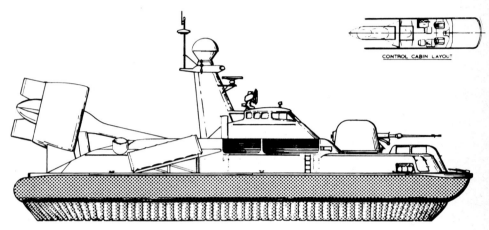

Outboard profile and deck plan of the VT 2 in fast missile hovercraft configuration. The craft illustrated is equipped with Otomat surface-to-surface missiles and a 76mm OTO Melara Compact gun

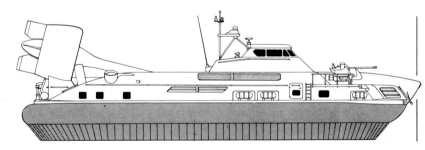

Outboard profile of multi-purpose variant of VT 2

controlled proportion of the air flow to pass directly into the main cushion under the craft. The outer segments turn the airflow from the inner segments downwards and inwards.

The whole flexible skirt assembly is stabilised by cables connecting every junction between adjacent pairs of segments and the inner loop to the raft structure. The outer segments are the only ones subject to wear and are attached with special fasteners so that they can be changed in a few minutes with hand tools, without having to lift the craft. Quite severe damage to the skirt, the loss of 30% of segments or 15% of the loop for example, can be accepted without seriously affecting the manoeuvrability of the craft.

SYSTEMS, ELECTRICAL AND HYDRAULIC: Auxiliary machinery includes diesel or gas turbine alternator sets for electrical supplies, a hydraulic system for the fan pitch control, loading ramp and door actuation, and side thruster doors.

DIMENSIONS (Typical)
Length overall: 30·17m (99ft)
Width overall: 13·3m (43ft 6in)
Cushion height: 1·58m (5ft 6in)
Cushion pressure: 31mb (65lb/ft²)
WEIGHTS
All-up weight: 100-110 tonnes, according to role
PERFORMANCE
The basic VT 2 hovercraft design provides a

vehicle which can carry a load of up to 32 tonnes for 550km (300n miles) at speeds of more than 60 knots (111km/h, 69mph) over sea, river shallows, shoals, mudflats, ice and snow. It can also travel over dry land reasonably free from obstructions. It is capable of operating in rough seas and accepting a substantial amount of damage.

VT 2—VARIANTS
LOGISTIC SUPPORT

Designed to carry a company of 130 fully-armed troops and their vehicles. The vehicle bay is approximately 21·33m (70ft) long, 5·02m (16ft 6in) wide and 2·89m (9ft 6in) high. It has a full-width bow ramp and door together with a 2·43m (8ft) wide stern ramp and door for the through loading and unloading of vehicles. The craft can carry payloads of 32 tons, together with fuel for five hours. Considerable overloading of the craft is acceptable at reduced performance so that with suitable deck and entrance ramp reinforcing a Chieftain battle tank could be carried. The vessel can be either shipped to a theatre of operations, or if required by a NATO country, it could be deployed to any point on the coastline of Europe or the Mediterranean under its own power. The longest "stage" would be from the United Kingdom to Gibraltar, a distance of approximately 1,100n miles. To allow an adequate reserve en route for rough seas the craft would carry additional fuel, starting out at an all-up weight of 115 tons.

WEIGHTS
Operating: 63 tons
Payload: 32 tons
Fuel: 15 tons
Starting all-up weight: 110 tons

MULTI-PURPOSE

This version is designed and equipped for the following role capabilities: light patrol, logistic support, firefighting, disaster relief and crash rescue. Normally these roles can be performed without adding to the basic equipment carried. The craft is also suitable for additional roles such as pollution control, radio interception and hydrographic survey. However these roles require extra equipment to be installed on board, in the form of palletised units which can be loaded into the centre bay. Although based on the VT 2, the multi-purpose craft differs from the logistic variant in several respects. The chief difference is in the design of the forward superstructure, where an extra deck level is provided, port and starboard, above the forward accommodation areas. This provides a location for a light gun to starboard (a 30mm twin Oerlikon mount is shown) and a fire-fighting monitor, hoses etc together with a Gemini inflatable to port. In addition, a new bow ramp is included which eliminates the need for an upward opening door and provides a clear field of fire for the gun. In the logistic role, trucks of up to about 4 tonnes may be carried and through loading is available for 1 tonne trucks. The rear door may also be used in such roles as crash rescue, pollution control and hydrographic survey when equipment must be deployed and recovered.

The control cabin is located amidships on the centreline for good all-round vision and is large enough to act as an operations centre. Lightweight machine gun mountings are provided aft of the cabin, also a Saab-Scania TV tracking system for gunfire control.

Internal accommodation includes space for 70 personnel, plus 86 folding seats in the centre bay. Galley equipment is located in the forward port compartment, while to starboard sick bay equipment, including four convertible berths, is fitted. Two chemical toilet facilities are located aft.

WEIGHTS
Operating (including fixed equipment): 70·5 tons
Disposable load: 34·5 tons
Starting all-up weight: 105 tons

FAST MISSILE HOVERCRAFT

This version is equipped with two Otomat surface-to-surface missiles and an OTO Melara 76mm Compact gun. Other armament of similar weight can be fitted to meet individual specifications. Armament and crew weight is 23½ tons, and with 10½ tons of fuel a typical endurance is five hours or 300n miles at 60 knots. An additional 10½ tons of fuel for the overload case (giving a half fuel weight of 100 tons) results in a range of 600n miles.

WEIGHTS
Operating: 66 tons
Armament and crew: 23·5 tons
Fuel: 10·5 tons
Starting all-up weight: 100 tons

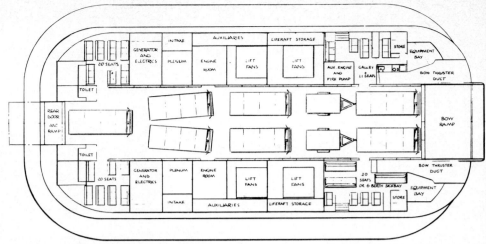

Deck plan of VT 2 multi-purpose craft. Employed in the logistics role, a typical payload would comprise seven one-ton Land Rovers and two trailers

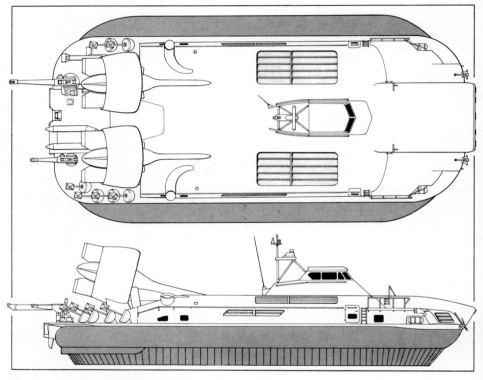

General arrangement of VT 2 mine countermeasures craft

MINE COUNTERMEASURES

Extended trials have been undertaken by the Naval Hovercraft Trials Unit, Lee-on-the-Solent, which is primarily concerned with the development of hovercraft for mine countermeasures duties. Interest in amphibious hovercraft for this application stems from its relative invulnerability to underwater explosions compared with displacement vessels, and their low magnetic and underwater noise signatures. The accompanying artist's impression shows one possible arrangement of a VT 2 for this particular role. As can be seen from the picture, the VT 2 is of suitable size for this work. The picture shows the sweepdeck space with sweepgear stowed. The gear illustrated is either in current use or readily available commercially.

The craft itself is a version of the multi-purpose design with an extended rear deck equipped with davits and MCM gear. The bow ramp is retained and this together with the use of containerised MCM equipment modules, allows some of the multi-role characteristics to be retained.

WEIGHTS
Operating: 69·3 tons
Disposable load: 35·7 tons
Starting all-up weight: 105 tons

Impression of a mine countermeasures craft based on the VT 2. Note the sweepgear on the rear deck extension

VT 2 preparing to tow. Note the protection to personnel afforded by the fan ducts and the ample deck space aft

UNITED STATES OF AMERICA

AEROJET LIQUID ROCKET COMPANY

(Subsidiary of Aerojet-General Corporation)
Corporate Office: PO Box 13222, Sacramento, California 95813, USA
Telephone: (916) 355 1000
Officials:
R I Ramseier, *President*
AALC Operations Office:
6906 West Highway 98, Panama City, Florida 32407, USA
Telephone: (904) 234 3378
Officials:
E F Davison, *Vice President and General Manager, AALC Programme*
F F Herman, *Operations Manager, AALC Programme*

Aerojet-General began research and development programmes on both rigid sidewall and skirted amphibious air cushion configurations in June 1966. The company's research and development programmes include lift system development, skirt and structural materials investigations and development, sub-scale and full-scale dynamic model testing, test laboratory development and full-scale vehicle operation. In addition, Aerojet has conducted government and company funded design and application studies on many rigid sidewall and skirted air cushion vehicle designs for military, non-military government and commercial roles. Work is at present concentrated on a US Navy contract for the development and testing of the AALC JEFF(A) amphibious assault landing craft.

AALC JEFF (A)

In 1970, Aerojet-General was awarded a contract by US Naval Ship Systems Command for the preliminary design of an experimental 160-ton 50-knot amphibious assault landing craft. This was followed in March 1971 by a further contract for the detail design, construction and test of the craft, which is designated AALC JEFF(A). Construction of the hull was initiated by Todd Shipyards Corporation, Seattle, Washington, in 1974. Hull construction was completed in November 1976, when the craft was moved to Aerojet's facility in Tacoma, Washington for final outfitting and contractor's tests. The craft first hovered on 15 April 1977. It was delivered to the US Navy's test facility in Panama City, Florida, in September 1977 for continuation of contractor tests and Navy trials.

Contractor sea trials were initiated in July 1978 and the craft was delivered to the US Navy

AALC Jeff (A) amphibious assault craft undergoing contractor's trials prior to delivery to the US Navy

on 22 June 1979. US Navy sea trials are now in progress.

The craft is designed to operate at a nominal speed of 50 knots in sea state 2 and carry up to 75 tons in palletised supplies and/or equipment. It is designed primarily for use by the US Marine Corps, and will carry tanks, trucks, half-tracks and other equipment from an LPD, LSD or LHA support ship to a point inland.

To ensure adequate world-wide operational capability, the specification calls for operation in temperatures from 0°—100°F.

LIFT AND PROPULSION: Cushion lift is provided by two 3,750hp Avco Lycoming TF40 gas turbines, one in each of the two sidestructures, driving two sets of four 1·21m (4ft) diameter fans through lightweight transmission and shafting connections.

Thrust is supplied by four 3,750hp Avco Lycoming TF40 gas turbines each driving a 2·26m (7ft 5in) diameter pylon-mounted shrouded propeller, located above the sidestructure, and outside the cargo deck area to provide free access and uninterrupted air flow. Each propeller pylon rotates to provide both propulsion and directional control.

HULL: Constructed in marine aluminium with maximum use of corrugated structures to minimise total craft weight. The main hull is formed by a buoyancy raft with port and starboard side structures. Each sidestructure contains three Avco Lycoming gas turbines with associated air intakes, exhausts, shrouded propellers, lift fans, transmissions and auxiliary power systems.

The bottom and deck structures of the hull are joined by longitudinal and transverse bulkheads to form a number of watertight flotation compartments. The cargo deck area is 211·82m² (2,280ft²); the bow ramp opening width is 6·55m (21ft 6in) and the aft ramp width is 8·33m (27ft 4in).

SKIRT: 1·52m (5ft) deep "Pericell" loop and cell type.

ACCOMMODATION: Two air-conditioned and sound-insulated compartments, each seating three crew members or observers. Access to each compartment is via the cargo deck.

DIMENSIONS
Length overall, on cushion: 29·3m (96ft 1in)
  on landing pads: 28·04m (92ft)
Beam overall, on cushion: 14·63m (48ft)
  on landing pads: 13·41m (44ft)
Height overall, on cushion: 7·03m (23ft 1in)
  on landing pads: 5·77m (18ft 11in)
Bow ramp opening width: 6·55m (21ft 6in)
Stern ramp opening width: 8·33m (27ft 4in)
Cargo deck area: 211·82m² (2,280ft²)

WEIGHTS
Gross: 156,991kg (340,000lb)
Empty: 81,697kg (180,000lb)
Fuel: 18,144kg (40,000lb)
Design payload: 54,431kg (120,000lb)
Design overload: 68,038kg (150,000lb)

PERFORMANCE
Design speed with design payload: 50 knots
Range at 50 knots: 200n miles
Max gradient, standing start: 11½%
Nominal obstacle clearance: 1·21m (4ft)

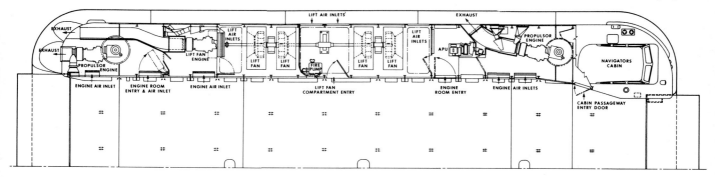

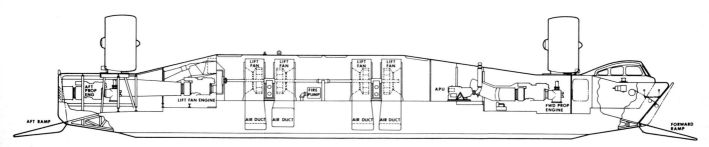

Inboard profile and plan view of AALC Jeff (A)

AIRCUSHION BOAT COMPANY INC

401 Alexander Avenue, Building 391, Tacoma, Washington 98421, USA
Telephone: (206) 272 3600
Officials:
W W Buckley, *President*
F C Gunter, *Vice President*

The Aircushion Boat Company is responsible for the development of the Airboat—a concept described by the company as an air-cushion-assisted catamaran. Vessels of this series of sidewall craft are based on conventional fibreglass hulls and employ water propeller or waterjet propulsion. Lift is supplied by an independent engine/fan system and flexible skirts are fitted fore and aft to contain the air cushion.

The company states that the cushion supports 75% of the loaded weight of the Airboats, and that as a result of the reduced drag the prototype uses 20% less fuel per mile. Another advantage is that when travelling at high speed, the air cushion softens the ride by preventing heavy slamming. Vessels of this type are being marketed by the company for a variety of applications including fast crew boats, water taxis, patrol boats, survey and sports fishing craft.

42FT AIRBOAT

The 12·8m (42ft) long Airboat is a high speed passenger ferry/freighter capable of operating in 1·37m (4ft 6in) waves. In passenger configuration seating is provided for 21 plus a crew of two.

A feature of the design is the extension of the bow well ahead of the air cushion. When rough water forces the bow down at speed the broad area forward of the cushion planes and raises the bow without slamming.

With the lift fan system off, the craft operates as a conventional displacement catamaran and has a top speed of 15 knots. With the lift system on, acceleration to the cruising speed of 30 knots is easily attained in ten boat lengths. In 2·4-3·04m (8-10ft) following seas a stable, near horizontal attitude is maintained while contouring swells and no tendency to broach or lose directional control is experienced.

LIFT AND PROPULSION: Motive power is supplied by three diesels, one for lift and two for propulsion. The lift engine drives a large low rpm centrifugal fan contained in a reinforced box which is an integral part of the hull structure. Power is transmitted via a clutch and Spicer shaft to a heavy duty, lightweight right-angle gearbox. Power delivered to the fan at cruise condition pressure and airflow is 180hp. Each of the propulsion engines is turbocharged and drives a waterjet. The standard fuel tank capacity is 300 gallons, providing a cruising range of more than 250 miles at 30 knots.

Marine propellers can be fitted to the vessel instead of waterjets if required. The powerplant remains the same, but the propulsion engines supply power through reversing gearboxes to shafts and marine propellers. Hydraulically operated twin rudders are mounted on the transom of each of the hulls. The propeller-driven version is capable of the same top speed, with slightly improved fuel economy.

HULL: Robust, fire-retardant foam and fibreglass sandwich structure, with unitised beam tying the catamaran hulls. High freeboard, wide buoyant hull and low profile for seaworthiness in rough seas and gale force winds.

ACCOMMODATION: In passenger/crew boat configuration, accommodation is provided for 21 seated passengers and a crew of two. The passenger saloon is completely enclosed with 1·98m (6ft 6in) high headroom throughout. The cabin contains a galley, head and large storage area. The bridge is elevated for 360 degree view and is located slightly aft of the bow. A sliding hard top provides upward visibility if required.

DIMENSIONS
Length: 12·8m (42ft)
Beam: 5·18m (17ft)
PERFORMANCE
Service speed: 30 knots

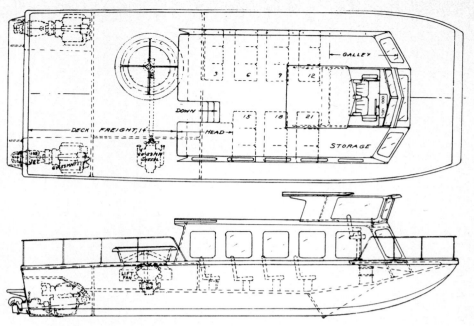

General arrangement of waterjet-propelled 42ft Airboat

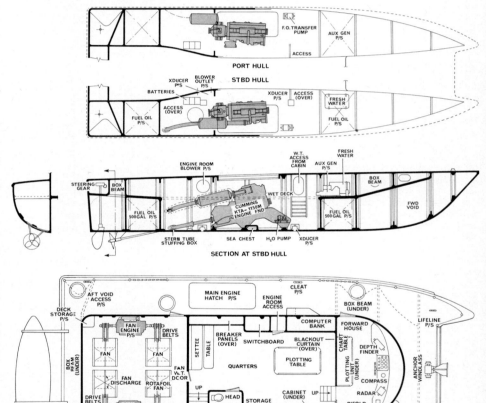

Inboard profile and deck plans of Airboat IV

Max speed: in excess of 33 knots
Max speed, displacement condition: 15 knots
Fuel consumption at 30 knots: 154·56 litres/h (34 gallons/h)
Cruising range at 30 knots: over 402km (250 miles)

AIRBOAT IV

Work on this addition to the Airboat range began in the summer of 1976. Like the Airboat III, the new vessel, a 16·7m (55ft) survey craft, is based on the concept of an air-cushion assisted catamaran hull on which a cabin and pilothouse have been built to suit customer requirements.

In the case of the Airboat IV, the cabin can be adapted to seat up to 40 passengers.

Maximum speed of the craft, which will be propelled by water screws driven by two 550hp Cummins KTA 1150 diesels, will be about 35 knots.

LIFT AND PROPULSION: Cushion lift is provided by two 275hp Volvo Penta TAM D70CS, each driving twin 0·6m (2ft) diameter double-entry, centrifugal fans. Fan air is discharged directly through the wet deck, between the catamaran hulls, into the cushion. Motive power for the propulsion system is provided by either two 550hp Cummins KTA 1150 diesels or twin 800hp MTU 8V331 diesels. Each engine drives a 0·66m (2ft 2in) diameter Michigan bronze propeller via a reversing gearbox and an inclined

shaft. Waterjets can be fitted to the vessel instead of marine propellers if required. Fuel is carried in four 2,272 litre (500 gallon) capacity integral fibreglass tanks, two in each hull. Refuelling points are located on the weatherdeck, two on each hull. Recommended fuel is grade 2 diesel.

CONTROLS: Hydraulically-operated twin rudders control craft heading on the propeller-driven variants. On models equipped with waterjets, craft direction is controlled by jet flow deflection.

HULL: Fabricated in Airex core, fibreglass sandwich laminate. Decks and top of pilothouse in balsa cored fibreglass. Bow shell plate designed to withstand slamming loads of up to 20 psi.

SKIRT: Patented inflated double-cylinder bags at bow and stern.

ACCOMMODATION: Operating crew comprising captain, navigator and deckhand are accommodated in a raised pilothouse forward. Up to 40 passengers can be accommodated in the main cabin, which is heated and ventilated. Air conditioning is optional. Passenger seats are of lightweight aircraft-type, with a central aisle between the seat rows. Entry doors are at the side of the deckhouse, one port, one starboard.

SYSTEMS, ELECTRICAL: 110V ac from diesel auxiliary generator. Shore power adaptor, plus 24V dc supply for engine starting, and 12V dc for navigation lights, etc.

APU: Onan diesel.

DIMENSIONS

EXTERNAL

Length overall, power off: 16·7m (55ft)
  on cushion: 16·7m (55ft)
Beam overall, power off: 7·62m (25ft)
  on cushion: 7·62m (25ft)
Height overall, displacement condition excluding mast: 3·65m (12ft)
  on cushion: 3·9-4·2m (13-14ft)
Draft afloat, propellers: 1·82m (6ft)
  waterjets: 1·06m (3ft 6in)

INTERNAL

Passenger cabin
Length: 12·19m (40ft)
Max width: 4·57m (15ft)
Max height: 1·98m (6ft 6in)
Floor area: 55·74m² (600ft²)
Baggage holds: In cabin, plus weatherdeck storage locker

WEIGHTS

Normal empty: 21,681·7kg (47,800lb)
Normal all-up weight: 29,483·48kg (65,000lb)
Normal payload: 2,177·2kg (4,800lb)
Max payload: 4,082kg (9,000lb)

PERFORMANCE

Max speed, calm water: 35 knots

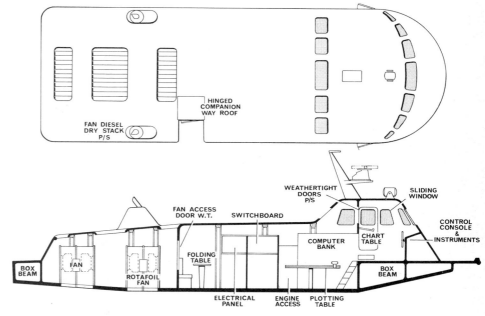

Profiles and deck plan of Airboat IV

Max speed, calm water, max continuous power: 30 knots
Cruising speed, calm water: 30 knots
Turning circle diameter at 30 knots: 3 boat lengths
Water speed in 4ft waves and 15 knot headwind: 30 knots
Max wave capability on scheduled runs: 1·82m (6ft)

Max survival sea state: 5
Still air range and endurance at cruising speed: 650n miles

PRICE: Approx price of c1•.ft, fob Tacoma USA—US$575,000. Base engines extra, depending on choice.

TERMS: Partial payment on signing contract, plus progress instalments.

AIR CUSHION SYSTEMS

25975 SW 182nd Avenue, Homestead, Florida 33030, USA

Telephone: (305) 248 4795

Officers:

John Van Veldhuizen

Air Cushion Systems has been building air cushion vehicles since 1960. The craft employ an air bearing system invented by Mr Van Veldhuizen. The object of the system is to provide improved stability and control and also to reduce cushion pressure. Beneath the hardstructure are up to five longitudinal trunks which divide the air cushion into four separate chambers. Air is fed into each chamber via multiple feeding holes running the length of each chamber. Flexible seals are fitted at the bow and stern. Features of the designs can be seen in the accompanying photographs.

7·92m (26ft) air bearing ACV operating in the Florida Keys area in 1965

5·64m (18ft 6in) air bearing ACV designed by John Van Veldhuizen in 1968. Power is furnished by a 500in³ Cadillac engine

Beneath the hardstructure of Air Cushion Systems' ACVs are up to five longitudinal trunks which divide the air cushion into four separate chambers. Air is fed into each chamber via multiple feeding holes running the full length of each one. Flexible skirts seal the ends of the chambers at the bow and stern

AIR CUSHION SYSTEMS

Ensign, Raymond Enterprises, PO Box 2160, Rancho Palos Verdes, California 90274, USA
Telephone: (213) 377 8750
Officials:
Col Jacksel M Broughton USAF (Retd)

First craft to be introduced by this ACV manufacturer is the AC-5 Beaver, an amphibious utility vehicle powered by three Avco Lycoming piston engines, and designed to carry payloads weighing up to 2,268kg (5,000lb) on its 19·5m² (210ft²) cargo deck. In the design stage is an enlarged version, the AC-44, powered by three 900hp lightweight diesels. The AC-44 is intended primarily as a heavy lift freighter or amphibious barge for the trans-shipment of loads in the 20-ton range.

AC-5 BEAVER

This new ACV "workhorse" has been designed to accomplish a wide variety of tasks requiring the movement of people and equipment in environments and weather conditions where wheeled vehicles, boats and helicopters cannot work effectively or efficiently. To ensure low maintenance costs and ease servicing in remote areas the craft is powered by three Avco Lycoming 10-360 engines which are identical to those employed in thousands of fixed-wing aircraft and helicopters used throughout the world. The three-bladed reversible-pitch thrust propellers are also standard items, with spares readily available "off-the-shelf".

A wide range of equipment and superstructure modules can be accommodated on the Beaver's flatbed hull which incorporates a number of tie-down points. An optional self-powered rotating extension boom crane can be fitted for loading and unloading. The deck height and open side areas simplify self-loading from trucks or by fork lift.

One of the major features of the craft is the simplicity with which it can be transported from one work site to another. It can be shipped over long distances by air or sea in a 12·19m (40ft) container after minor disassembly of its modular components, or it can be converted into a trailer by two men, ready for trailing behind a pick-up truck.
LIFT AND PROPULSION: A single Lycoming 10-360 AIB aero-engine drives a 1·52m (5ft) diameter six-bladed axial fan mounted in a vertical duct aft of the control cabin for lift. Thrust is furnished by two pylon-mounted Lycoming 10-360 aero-engines aft, each driving a ducted 1·57m (5ft 2in) diameter Hartzell Propeller

AC-5 Beaver amphibious ACV. Motive power is supplied by three Avco Lycoming 10-360 aero-engines, one for lift, two for propulsion. The Beaver can carry loads of up to 2,267kg (5,000lb). Maximum speed over calm water is 55 knots

Company three-bladed reversible-pitch aluminium propeller.
CONTROLS: Directional control is provided by six vertical vanes hinged to the rear of each propeller duct. At low speeds craft heading is controlled by a retractable nose wheel.
HULL: Welded aluminium space frame construction with riveted aluminium skin and plywood decking. Integral wash water and fuel tanks. Two outer 0·6m (2ft) wide sponsons running the full length of the craft each side, hinge upwards to reduce the overall width to 2·4m (8ft) for stowing into containers or towing by road.
SKIRT: Bag type skirt, with roll stabilisation subdivision, provides 0·6m (2ft) hard structure clearance.
ACCOMMODATION: Fully enclosed cabin forward for driver. Optional extras include passenger modules with 12 and 16 seats.
DIMENSIONS
Length overall: 10·58m (34ft 9in)
Width overall: 4·21m (13ft 10in)
Hull width: 3·6m (11ft 10in)
Height overall, on cushion: 3·53m (11ft 7in)
  on landing pads: 2·89m (9ft 6in)
Main load space, deck level: 3·55 × 4·01m (11ft 8in × 13ft 2in)
Main load area: 14·21m² (153ft²)
Side deck area: 4·64m² (50ft²)
WEIGHTS
Max gross: 5,125kg (11,300lb)
Empty: 2,540kg (5,600lb)
Max deck load: 2,267kg (5,000lb)

PERFORMANCE
Max operating speed, over smooth water at max gross weight: 55 knots
  over rough water: 32 knots
  over smooth ground and paved areas: 45 knots
  over rough/rocky ground: 20 knots
Turning radius, tracking gear extended, over land: 3·65m (12ft) at 5 knots
  4·57m (15ft) at 10 knots
Turning radius, tracking gear up, land and water:
  6·09m (20ft) at 5 knots
  12·19m (40ft) at 10 knots
  24·38m (80ft) at 20 knots
  60·96m (200ft) at 40 knots
Stopping distance, on cushion, hard ground from 40 knots: 48·76m (160ft)
  smooth water: 36·57m (120ft)
Hard structure clearance height: 0·6m (2ft)
Max gradient, at sustained speed of 5 knots at 5,125kg (11,300lb) gross weight: 17%

AC-44

Currently in the design stage, the AC-44 is an enlarged version of the AC-5 with a load capacity of 20 tons. It will accept a 12·19 × 3 × 2·43m (40 × 10 × 8ft) cargo container directly from a ship and carry it across combinations of water and land to designated storage or delivery areas. Heavy cargo handling equipment will be carried on the craft.

The hull structure and skirt system will be similar to those of the AC-5, but because of the mass of the AC-44 and its payload, it will be fitted with

a separate lateral control augmentation system which will take the form of a bow-mounted steering fan driven by the lift engine.
LIFT AND PROPULSION: Lift will be supplied by a single 900hp lightweight diesel driving two eight-bladed axial fans. Two 900hp diesels driving two 2·9m (9ft 6in) diameter three-bladed reversible-pitch propellers will provide thrust.

DIMENSIONS
Length overall: 26·21m (86ft)
Width overall: 8·23m (27ft)
Hull depth: 1·06m (3ft 6in)
Height, off cushion: 4·26m (14ft)
Skirt depth: 0·9m (3ft)
WEIGHTS
Empty: 14,061kg (31,000lb)

Payload and fuel: 20,865kg (46,000lb)
Gross: 34,926kg (77,000lb)
PERFORMANCE
Max operating speed, over land: 96·5km/h (60mph)
over water: 64·37km/h (40mph)
Fuel consumption: 306·61 litres/h (81 US gallons/h)

ALASKA HOVERCRAFT INC

5740 B Street, Anchorage Industrial Center, Anchorage, Alaska 99502, USA
Telephone: (907) 277 5686
Officials:
Harry G Saylor Jr, *President, Sales Director*
Mike E Proctor, *Vice President, Operations Director*
Marvin F Proctor, *Secretary, Treasurer, General Manager*
David Aigner, *Plant Manager*

Latest addition to the Alaska Hovercraft design range is the 27ft Contender, the prototype of which was completed in June 1980. The craft is now in production and the first three units have been sold.

TIGER SHARK

This fully amphibious four-seater has been designed for a variety of light transport and leisure applications in Alaska. The basic craft has an open cockpit but a canopy is available if required. More than thirty have been sold.
LIFT AND PROPULSION: Integrated system employing a single 85hp Volkswagen industrial engine which drives a single 711·2mm (2ft 4in) diameter centrifugal fan for lift and a single 1·62m (5ft 4in) diameter wooden propeller for thrust. Regular grade automotive fuel is used and the fuel consumption is 11·35 litres/h (3 gallons/h).
CONTROLS: Twin aerodynamic rudders hinged to the rear of the propeller guard provide directional control.
HULL: High impact glass fibre structure. Internal framework of aluminium. Aluminium and steel engine mounting.
SKIRT: Extended loop type with truncated bow. Fabricated in 22oz shelterite material coated to withstand Alaskan temperature ranges.
ACCOMMODATION: Seats are provided for a driver and up to three passengers. Seats can be removed to permit light freight to be carried. Either a canvas or a glass fibre canopy are available together with an optional heating system.
SYSTEMS, ELECTRICAL: 12V negative earth system, generator charged.
RADIO: Various transmitter/receivers available. Recommended equipment for Alaskan bush.
DIMENSIONS
Length overall, power off: 5·18m (17ft)
Beam overall, power off: 2·43m (8ft)
Height overall, power off: 2·59m (8ft 6in)
WEIGHTS
Normal empty: 498·92kg (1,100lb)
Normal payload: 453·57kg (1,000lb)
Normal gross: 952·50kg (2,100lb)
Max payload: 544·28kg (1,200lb)
PERFORMANCE
Max speed across calm water: 72·42km/h (45mph)
Cruising speed, calm water: 48·28-56·32km/h (30-35mph)
Max headwind: 32·18km/h (20mph)
Still air range, standard tanks: 225km (140 miles)
with optional fuel tank: 338km (210 miles)
Max vertical obstacle clearance: 304mm (12in)
PRICE: Approximate cost of craft, fob Anchorage, Alaska is $10,000

CONTENDER

Latest addition to Alaska Hovercraft Inc's range is the Contender, an 8·23m (27ft) fully amphibious thirteen-seater intended as a fast, economical means of transporting passengers and freight throughout the year in Alaska.
LIFT AND PROPULSION: Motive power for

Tiger Shark, utility four-seater built in Anchorage, Alaska by Alaska Hovercraft

Cockpit of the Tiger Shark can be enclosed by either a canvas or glass fibre canopy and a heating system can be provided

Alaska Hovercraft Inc's new 8·23m Contender, a fully-amphibious passenger/freight hovercraft designed for a range of applications in Alaska

the lift system is provided by a single 115hp V6 engine. This drives a pair of matched 889mm (2ft 11in) centrifugal lift fans located to the rear of the control cabin. The fans are designed and man-

ufactured by Alaska Hovercraft. Thrust is supplied by a single 350hp engine driving a 1·82m (6ft) diameter two-bladed propeller via a Gillmore belt drive. Fuel for both engines is carried in two 182 litre (40 gallon) tanks. Fuel is sufficient for an endurance of 6 hours.

CONTROLS: Heading is controlled by twin rudders. An elevator, mounted between the twin fins, provides longitudinal trim.

HULL: Hull and sidebodies are built in marine grade aluminium. These are sealed and filled with foam for greater strength and reserve buoyancy. The two sidebodies fold upwards to facilitate trailering and loading into transport aircraft. By disconnecting the skirt at four positions, the craft can be prepared for transporting within 20 minutes.

ACCOMMODATION: Enclosed control cabin with seats for driver and co-driver with an additional jump-seat between for one person. Separated from the control cabin is a passenger cabin seating ten. Canopy of the passenger cabin and seats are easily removed for freight applications. Removal of the canopy provides a 2·43 × 2·13m (8 × 7ft) well for cargo. With a flat deck added to the well deck the total cargo deck area is increased to 4·26 × 2·43m (14 × 8ft).
SKIRT: Loop and segment type, fabricated in shelterite material and coated to withstand Alaskan temperature changes.
SYSTEMS, ELECTRICAL: Two independent

systems, one on each engine. 12V, negative earth, alternator charged.
DIMENSIONS
Length overall, power off: 8·43m (27ft 4in)
Beam overall, power off: 4·26m (14ft)
Height, power off: 2·74m (9ft)
Transport width: 2·43m (8ft)
WEIGHTS
Empty: 2,494kg (5,500lb)
Max payload: 1,700kg (3,750lb)
Gross: 4,195kg (9,250lb)
PERFORMANCE
Max speed, calm water: 73km/h (45mph)
Vertical obstacle clearance: 571mm (1ft 10½in)

BELL AEROSPACE TEXTRON

Division of Textron Inc
New Orleans Operations: PO Box 29307, New Orleans, Louisiana 70189, USA
Telephone: (504) 255 3311
Officials:
John J Kelly, *Vice President*
John B Chaplin, *Director of Engineering*
Roland Decrevel, *Project Manager*
Clarence L Forrest, *Director, Full-Scale Test and Project Manager, LC JEFF(B)*
Donald E Kenney, *Director of Administration*
Robert S Postle, *LCAC Project Manager*

Bell Aerospace began its air cushion vehicle development programme in 1958. Craft built by the company range in size from the 18ft XHS3 to the 160-ton JEFF(B) which is undergoing sea trials.

The company has rights to manufacture and sell in the USA machines employing the hovercraft principle through a licensing arrangement with the British Hovercraft Corporation and Hovercraft Development Ltd.

In addition to importing seven BHC SR.N5s, three of which were employed by the US Navy and later by the US Coast Guard for use and evaluation, Bell built three SK-5 Model 7255s—the company's first production ACVs—to a US Army specification. The craft were airlifted to Viet-Nam, where they performed a variety of missions, including high speed troop/cargo transportation and patrol.

In January 1969 the US Surface Effect Ships Project Office awarded Bell a contract for the detailed design of a 100-ton surface effect ship test craft. Construction began in September 1969 and the preparation of the craft for trials began early in 1971. An extensive test and evaluation programme began in February 1972 on Lake Pontchartrain, Louisiana.

In May 1973 the SES-100B was transferred to the Naval Coastal Systems Laboratory at Panama City, Florida, for deep water and high sea state testing in the Gulf of Mexico. In January 1974 the company announced that the SES-100B had successfully completed the testing necessary to confirm and expand the technology necessary for the design of a 2,000-ton ocean-going surface effect ship.

In March 1971 the company was awarded a Phase II contract by the US Navy authorising it to start work on a programme covering the detail design, construction and test of an experimental 160-ton AALC (amphibious assault landing craft), designated LC JEFF(B).

Built at the NASA Michoud Assembly Facility, New Orleans, the craft was transferred to the Naval Coastal Systems Center, Panama City, Florida, in early April 1977. A period of checking all systems was followed by contractor's tests in the Panama City area. The craft was then delivered to the US Navy's Experimental Trials Unit at Panama City for crew training and operational trials.

In July 1974 Bell was awarded a US $36 million contract to conduct an advanced development programme for a 2,000-ton, high-speed ocean-going, operational warship—the 2KSES. The 18-month contract awarded by the Naval Material Command covered the design, development and testing of full-scale subsystems and components including transmission, waterjet systems, lift fans and skirts, as well as a method of

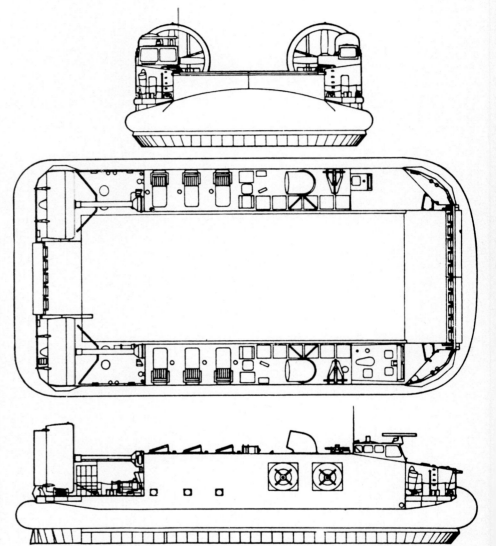

General arrangement of Bell's Amphibious Assault Landing Craft (AALC) JEFF(B). Power is supplied by six 2,800hp Avco Lycoming gas turbines driving four centrifugal impellers for lift and two four-bladed ducted propellers for thrust

controlling the vessel's ride characteristics in a variety of sea states. In addition, the company continues to support surface effect ship development through studies in advanced systems in lift and propulsion.

In October 1977, it was announced that Bell had linked with Halter Marine, the New Orleans-based shipbuilders in a joint venture to develop and build a range of commercial surface effect ships.

On 28 September 1979, Bell signed a US$21 million contract with the US Army Mobility Equipment R & D Command (MERADCOM) for the first four of twelve LACV-30s (Lighter, Amphibious Air Cushion Vehicles — 30-ton payload) with the first deliveries due in 1981. Production is in hand at Bell's Niagara Frontier Operations, Wheatfield, New York.

Bell Aerospace Canada (see Canadian section) has built several prototypes of the Bell Model 7380 Voyageur heavy haul ACV, the second of

which has been purchased by the Canadian Ministry of Transport for use by the Canadian Coast Guard. Production of additional Voyageurs is in hand. Two Voyageurs, designated 001 and 003, were transferred to the ACV/SES Test and Training Center, Panama City, in late 1975 for use in a training programme for US Army personnel.

The company also initiated a programme for the US Air Force that covers the design, development, installation and test of an air cushion landing system aboard a de Havilland XC-8A Buffalo transport aircraft. The first ACLS landing of the XC-8A took place at Wright-Patterson Air Force Base, Dayton, Ohio on 11 April 1975.

The corporation's current ACV activities are divided amongst its plants and associate companies as follows:
Bell Aerospace Textron: LACV-30
Niagara Frontier Operations
Buffalo, New York

Bell Aerospace Canada Textron: Voyageur and
AL-30
Grand Bend, Ontario, Canada

Bell Aerospace Textron
New Orleans Operations: JEFF(B) and SES-
100B
New Orleans, Louisiana

Bell Halter Inc: Bell Halter SES and Rodolf
New Orleans, Louisiana

SK-5 MODEL 7255

Details of the SK-5 Model 7255 and its predecessor, the Model 7232, will be found in *Jane's
Surface Skimmers 1972-73* and earlier editions.

AALC JEFF(B)

In March 1971 US Naval Ship Systems Command awarded Bell's New Orleans Operations a
contract for the detail design, construction and
testing of an experimental 160-ton, 50-knot air
cushion assault landing craft.

Two companies are developing ACV test craft
to the 68,038kg (150,000lb) payload, 50-knot
specification—Bell and Aerojet-General. The
Bell project is designated LC JEFF(B). Both
craft will operate from the well-decks of landing
ships and also alongside cargo ships.

The Bell contract involves mathematical and
scale model investigations, interface and support
system design, subsystem and component testing
and design and systems analysis.

The 160-ton Amphibious Assault Landing
Craft LC JEFF(B) was completed in March
1977. It was transferred on 1 April 1977 to the
US Naval Coastal Systems Center, Panama City,
Florida, for builder's trials. Full-scale testing
began with static hovering trials on 29 October
1977. First overwater operation was on 16
December 1977. Completion of contractor trials
and handing over of the craft to the Navy took
place on 28 July 1978. Naval evaluation of the
JEFF(B) began with a series of system trials.
Initial mating trials with the Landing Ship Dock
USS *Spiegel Grove* (LSD 32) were conducted in
November 1978. By May 1980, the LC JEFF(B)
had accumulated more than 251 hours of underway testing, a large part at full payload gross
weight, and was being prepared for operational
demonstrations. These demonstrations will play
a key role in the Navy's acquisition plan for the
Landing Craft Air Cushion (LCAC), the operational version of the JEFF craft. During 1978 and
1979, the JEFF(B):

operated consistently at full gross weight;
demonstrated operations at maximum overload weight;
operated at full weight with two of its six
engines shut down;
exceeded 75 knots;
operated in the Gulf in sea state 3;
repeatedly transitioned from water to land
over various beaches in the area and operated
over adjacent sand dunes.

LC JEFF(B) is designed to operate at a nominal speed of 50 knots in sea state 2, and accommodate 60 to 75 tons in palletised supplies and/or
equipment. In simulated beach attacks JEFF(B)
has carried ashore to a drop point a 60-ton main
battle tank, a jeep and a detachment of US
Marines. To ensure adequate world-wide operational capability, the specification calls for operation in temperatures from 0°-100°F and requires
that the performance criteria can be met with a 25
knots headwind on a 100°F day.

LIFT AND PROPULSION: Motive power is
supplied by six 2,800hp Avco Lycoming gas turbines, driving four 1·52m (5ft) diameter double-
entry centrifugal impellers for lift, and two four-
bladed 3·58m (11ft 9in) diameter, Hamilton-
Standard variable pitch, ducted propellers, for
thrust. Fuel capacity is 29,094 litres (6,400 gallons).

CONTROLS: Deflection of two aerodynamic
rudders hinged at the rear of the propeller duct
exits, differential propeller pitch, and the
deflection of bow thrusters atop the side structures provide steering control. All controls are
located in a raised bridge located well forward on
the starboard superstructure. The helmsman's

LC JEFF(B) has exceeded 75 knots during trials

JEFF(B) being moved into the well deck of the Landing Ship Dock USS *Spiegel Grove* (LSD-32) using the ship's
amphibious in-haul device (AID)

JEFF(B) positioned inside the *Spiegel Grove's* well deck. JEFF(B) is equipped with fore and aft loading ramps
for the rapid on and off loading of troops, equipment and vehicles including the 60-ton main battle tank

platform is raised to provide 360 degree vision for the two helmsmen, who have within easy reach all the necessary controls, navigation equipment and instruments. A third seat is provided at this level for another crew member or wave commander. On a lower level in the bridge is an engineer's station with monitoring instrumentation and a radar operator/navigator station. The crew will normally comprise four operating personnel and two deck supervisors.

HULL: Overall structural dimensions of the craft, 24·38 × 13·1 × 5·79m (80 × 43 × 19ft), have been dictated by the well deck dimensions of the US Navy's LSDs (Landing Ships Dock) and LPDs (Amphibious Transport Dock).

The main hull is formed by a 1·37m (4ft 6in) deep buoyancy raft with port and starboard side structures. The main deck between the side structures forms the cargo deck, which is 20·11m long by 8·02m wide (66ft by 26ft 4in), and provides an unobstructed cargo area of 161·46m² (1,738ft²). A full width ramp is provided at the bow and a narrower ramp, capable of taking the main battle tank, at the stern.

The bottom and deck structures of the hull are separated by longitudinal and transverse bulkheads to form a buoyancy raft with a number of watertight flotation compartments. The craft fuel tanks and bilge system are contained within these compartments.

Plating at the bottom and side of the hull is stiffened by aluminium extrusions, and the main cargo deck is in mechanically fastened hollow truss-type core extrusions. The transverse bulkheads consist of sheet webs of aluminium alloy integrally-stiffened extrusions, with upper and lower bulkhead caps, also of aluminium extrusions.

The basic framing of the sidestructures is aluminium back-to-back channels, which coincide with the transverse bulkheads and are spaced apart to straddle the hull bulkheads.

Each sidestructure contains three Avco Lycoming gas turbines, and their associated air intakes, exhausts, lift fans, transmissions and auxiliary power system.

SKIRT: Peripheral bag and finger type, with a 1·52m (5ft) high cushion compartmented by longitudinal and transverse keels. The upper seal bag attachment hinge line is raised high over the bow ramp area and the vertical diaphragm contains non-return valves similar to those fitted to the SR.N4.

DIMENSIONS
Length overall: 26·43m (86ft 9in)
   stowed: 24·38m (80ft)
Beam overall: 14·32m (47ft)
   stowed: 13·1m (43ft)
Height: 7·16m (23ft 6in)
Cargo area: 160·71m² (1,738ft²)
Bow ramp width: 8·53m (28ft)
Stern ramp width: 4·41m (14ft 6in)
WEIGHTS
Normal gross: 149,688kg (330,000lb)
Normal payload: 54,431kg (120,000lb)
Overload payload: 68,038kg (150,000lb)
PERFORMANCE
Design operational speed: 50 knots in sea state 2
Range: 200n miles
Max gradient continuous: 13%

SES-100B TEST CRAFT

SES-100B is the official designation for the 100-ton class sidehull surface effect ship (SES) test craft which has been built for the US Navy by Bell Aerospace at New Orleans.

It is part of a long-range programme by the US Navy to develop multi-thousand ton, ocean-going ships with speeds of 80 knots or higher.

This programme stems from research undertaken by the US Office of Naval Research in 1960, the US Navy Bureau of Ships (now the Naval Ship System Command) and the US Maritime Administration, which in 1961 sponsored the first programme for the development of a 100-ton SES, known as the Columbia.

Construction of the Bell SES began in August 1970. The vessel was launched on 22 July 1971 for hovering trials, and builder's trials, with the craft underway, began on 4 February 1972. A

JEFF(B) unloading a 60-ton main battle tank during a simulated beach attack

SES-100B set up a new world record speed of 91·9 knots (106mph) on 25 January 1980 across an instrumented test range on St Andrew Bay near Panama City

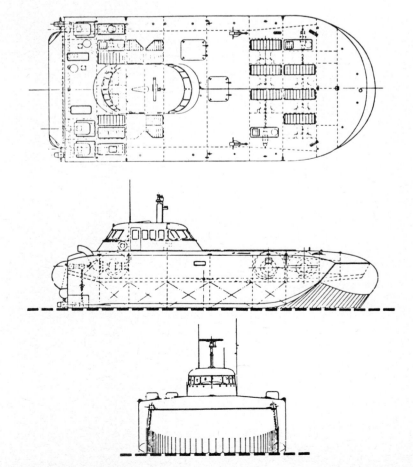

General arrangement of Bell SES-100B 105-ton test craft

test and evaluation programme encompassing performance trials, stability and seakeeping characteristics, structural load investigations, habitability and operational data, and other pertinent data necessary for the development of high speed surface effect ships, was conducted in the New Orleans area and in the Gulf of Mexico where a variety of sea conditions were experienced.

In January 1974, Bell Aerospace announced that the SES-100B had successfully completed the testing necessary to confirm and expand the technology necessary for the design of a 2,000-ton ocean-going SES.

On 25 January 1980, the SES-100B achieved a new world speed record of 91·9 knots (106mph) on St Andrew Bay near Panama City.

The craft has operated at sustained speeds of more than 50 knots in sea state 3 in the Gulf of Mexico, and has repeatedly demonstrated performance, stability, and habitability exceeding expectations.

It successfully launched an SM-1 (General Dynamics RIM 66B Standard MR) medium-range guided missile on 8 April 1976, while travelling at a speed of 60 knots (70mph) across the Gulf of Mexico. The solid rocket motor propelled the 16ft 6in missile straight upwards, it then pitched over in a westerly direction toward the target five nautical miles away. The missile's sensing device located the target and guided it to a hit.

The SES-100B completed its trials at the Naval Coastal Systems Center in December 1977 and is currently being tested by personnel of the Navy Surface Effect Ship Test Facility (SESTF) at Patuxent River, Maryland

Development of SES systems will result in the production of very high speed, multi-thousand ton ships for a variety of missions. Such development would make it possible for the US Navy to have a smaller but more effective fleet which would revolutionise naval warfare.

LIFT AND PROPULSION: Power is supplied to the lift system by three United Aircraft of Canada (UACL) ST6J-70 marine gas turbines. The engine/fan systems provide pressurised air to seals and cushion in both normal modes of operation and in the event of system failure. An important feature of the design has been to ensure the safety of ship and crew since the craft is designed to investigate the boundaries of ship operation at high speed in rough seas. The fans, constructed from marine aluminium, are of centrifugal design for ruggedness and stability of operation.

Power is supplied to the two marine propellers by three Pratt & Whitney FT 12A-6 marine gas turbines.

Auxiliary power for engine starting and emergency use is provided by a Solar T-62T-27 high speed turbine producing 100shp at 8,000rpm.

All engines are housed in engine rooms beneath the weather deck and take in air through appropriately placed demister screens to minimise sea water and spray ingestion.

The fuel system, which also serves as a ballast system, is integral with the sidehulls.

HULL: The SES-100B is a single, all-welded continuous structure, incorporating two catamaran-style sidehulls and is constructed from high-strength, corrosion-resistant marine aluminium alloy sheet and plate. The hull carries an integral deckhouse welded to the after portion of the weather deck. The deckhouse is so positioned to optimise the ride quality and habitability of the ship's complement of personnel while retaining good visibility from the command station.

The sidehulls, which virtually skim the surface of the water, provide basic stability to the craft and also seal the air cushion and prevent leakage along the port and starboard sides of the ship. The sealing of the air cushion is completed at the bow and stern by flexible fabric seals. The bow seal is of pressurised bag type with convoluted fingers. The stern seal is of Bell design and capable of providing the necessary trim to the craft.

ACCOMMODATION: The deckhouse houses all controls necessary for the operation of the craft and accommodation for four test crew and

SES-100B, 105-ton surface effect ship test craft seen at speed in sea state 3 in the Gulf of Mexico, off Panama City

Deckhouse of the SES-100B is at the aft end of the weatherdeck and accommodates a four-man crew and up to six observers. The engines—three FT12A-6s for propulsion and three ST6J-70s for lift—are located beneath the weatherdeck. Air is drawn through demister screens to minimise seawater and spray ingestion

An SM-1 medium-range guided missile was successfully launched from the SES-100B while travelling at a speed of 60 knots across the Gulf of Mexico on 8 April 1976. Twenty seconds later the SM-1 hit its target, a surplus vessel positioned 10 miles off the Florida coast, on the test range of the Armament Development and Test Centre, Eglin Air Force Base, Florida

six observers. It is capable of sustaining the crew and observers for greater than 24 hour missions in life support functions. Navigation and communication equipment for all-weather operation is included in the crew subsystem and housed in the deckhouse.

SYSTEMS, EMERGENCY: Safety equipment in the form of fire detection and extinguishing equipment, life rafts, warning lights, etc, meet the requirements of the US Coast Guard Rules of the Road, both International and Inland.

The characteristics of the SES-100B are as follows:

DIMENSIONS
Length overall: 23·68m (77ft 8½in)
Beam: 10·67m (35ft)
Height (top of radar): 8·2m (26ft 11in)
WEIGHTS
Normal gross: 105 tons
Normal payload: 10 tons
POWER PLANTS
Propulsion: 3 Pratt & Whitney FT 12A-6 marine gas turbines
Lift: 3 UACL ST6J-70 marine gas turbines
PERFORMANCE
Speed greater than 80 knots on calm water
PERSONNEL
Crew (test mission): 4
Observers: 6
MATERIALS
Hull and appendages: Marine aluminium and titanium
Seals: Nitrile PVC Nylon

BELL AEROSPACE TEXTRON
Division of Textron Inc
Head Office and Works: PO Box 1, Buffalo, New York 14240, USA
Telephone: (716) 297 1000
TWX: 710-524-1663
Telex: 91-302
Officials:
Norton C Willcox, *President*
Robert A Norling, *Vice President (Operations) (Niagara Frontier Operations)*
Dr Clifford F Berninger, *Vice President (Research and Engineering)*
John R Clark Jr, *Vice President (Eastern Region)*
Robert W Hussa, *Vice President (Manufacturing)*
John J Kelly, *Vice President (New Orleans Operations)*
Joseph R Piselli, *Vice President (ACV Programs)*
Donald F Bonhardt, *Vice President (Product Assurance)*
John W McKinney, *Vice President (Finance)*
John H Pamperin, *Vice President (President, Dalmo Victor Operations)*

LACV-30-1 with bow-mounted swing crane which gives the craft a self-discharge capability in areas where materials handling equipment is not available

MODEL 7467 LACV-30

This stretched version of the Voyageur has been designed to meet the US Army's requirements for a high-speed amphibious vehicle for LOTS (Lighter-Over-The-Shore) operations.

In the autumn of 1979 Bell signed a US $40 million contract with the US Army Mobility Equipment R & D Command (MERADCOM) for the first eight of twelve LACV-30s (lighter, amphibious air cushion vehicles — 30-ton payload). Production has begun at Bell's Niagara Frontier plant and the first deliveries will be made in 1981. Two LACV-30 off-the-shelf prototypes were built under a US $4·9 million contract in 1975.

The chief modifications are a 3·35m (11ft) lengthening of the deck ahead of the raised control cabin to facilitate the carriage of additional Milvan containers; the siting of a swing crane at the bow, also the provision of a surf fence and a bow loading ramp.

The LACV-30 is intended to replace conventional vessels of the LARC-5 and the LARC-15 types. It will provide the US Army with a rapid lift capability enabling it to move cargo and equipment over water, beaches, ice, snow and marginal areas. A range of military cargoes can be carried, from containers, wheeled and tracked vehicles, to engineering equipment, pallets, packs and barrels.

Endurance at cruising speed depends on the configuration/role in which the craft is used. For the drive-on cargo and Milvan cargo roles the craft can carry payloads of 30 tons with an endurance of two hours. In the self-unload Milvan cargo role the payload is reduced to 26·5 tons for the same endurance. Other configurations give endurance figures of between 5 hours and 9 hours 6 minutes with varying payloads.

Although intended primarily for use as a lighter in support of LOTS operations, the craft is also suitable for a number of secondary roles such as coastal, harbour and inland water inspection; patrol, search-and-rescue missions and medical evacuation.

LIFT AND PROPULSION: Integrated system, powered by two Pratt and Whitney ST6T Twin-Pac gas turbines mounted aft, one at each side of the raised control cabin. Each engine is rated at 1,800shp maximum and 1,400shp at normal output. The output of each is absorbed by a three-bladed Hamilton Standard 43D50-363 reversible-pitch propeller and a 2·13m (7ft) diameter, twelve-bladed, fixed-pitch light aluminium alloy, centrifugal lift fan.

FUEL: Recommended fuel is standard aviation kerosene-Jet A-1, JP4, JP5 or light diesel fuel oil. Main usable fuel capacity is 9,419 litres (2,272 gallons). Fuel ballast/emergency fuel capacity 6,960 litres (1,531 gallons).

SYSTEMS, ELECTRICAL: Starter generators: four gearbox-driven, brushless, 28V dc, 200A each. Batteries: two nickel cadmium, 28A dc, 40Ah each.

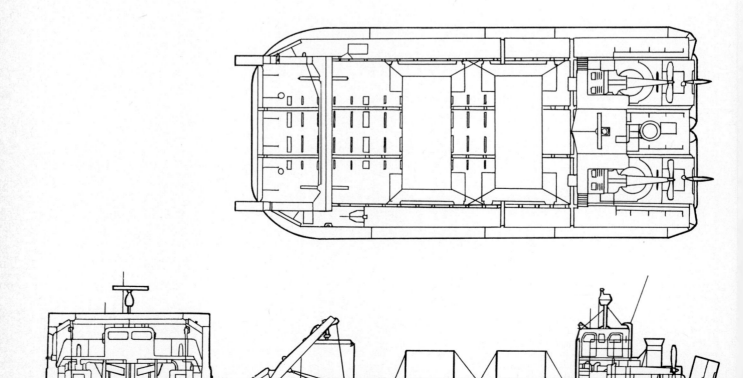

General arrangement of Bell Model 7467 LACV-30, an amphibious lighter with a 30 ton payload

DIMENSIONS
Length overall, on cushion: 23·3m (76ft 6in)
Beam overall, on cushion: 11·2m (36ft 8in)
Height overall, on cushion: 8·83m (29ft)
  off cushion: 7·86m (25ft 9in)
Skirt height, nominal: 1·21m (4ft)
Height, cargo deck, off cushion: 1·16m (3ft 10in)
Cargo deck: 15·69 × 9·9m (51ft 6in × 32ft 6in)
WEIGHTS
Design gross: 52,163kg (115,000lb)
PERFORMANCE (estimated)
Standard day, zero wind, calm water, at gross
  weight of 52,163kg (115,000lb):
  Normal rating: 74km/h (46mph)
  Max rating: 90km/h (56mph)
Estimated fuel consumption at cruising speed:
  1,159 litres/h (255 gallons/h)

LACV-30-2 during tests conducted by the US Army at Fort Story, Virginia. For the drive-on cargo and Milvan container cargo roles the craft can carry a payload of 30 tons, with an endurance of two hours

BELL HALTER INC

6800 Plaza Drive, New Orleans, Louisiana
70127, USA
Telephone: (504) 245 6699
Telex: Halmar/58-4200
Officials:
John J Kelly, *President*
John B Chaplin, *Vice President, Engineering*
Bernard Heaps, *Vice President, Manufacturing*
John W Hedges, *Secretary*
Donald E Kenney, *Treasurer*
John W McKinney, *Vice President*
John K Lyons, *Assistant Treasurer*

Bell Halter Inc designs and builds surface
effect ships. The corporation replaces a joint venture established in 1977 and is owned by Bell
Aerospace Textron Division of Textron and Halter Marine Inc. Bell Halter combines Bell's
technical background in surface effect ships with
Halter's 20 years experience as boatbuilders.
Halter Marine is the world's largest builder of
offshore supply vessels, more than 800 of which
have been supplied for American and overseas
use. Their hulls have been constructed in
aluminium, steel and fibreglass. Halter has also
built a large number of fast patrol boats for navies
in the Middle East, South America and Far East.

Bell Halter currently offers a range of sidewall
ACVs (SES configuration) capable of speeds up
to 60 knots and with overall lengths of up to
60·96m (200ft). Larger vessels, up to 121·92m
(400ft) long and with speeds in excess of 70 knots
will be available in future.

In early 1980 Bell Halter sold four 110ft SES
offshore supply vessels, marking the first commercial sale of an SES in the United States. These
boats, currently under construction, are based on
the highly successful diesel-powered 110ft
demonstration SES launched in late 1977. A 48ft
SES hydrographic survey boat, built for the Portland (Oregon) District of the US Army Corps of
Engineers, passed acceptance trials in 1979 and
was delivered in early 1980.

BELL HALTER 48 HYDROGRAPHIC SURVEY BOAT (RODOLF)

The Bell Halter 48 operates as a displacement
catamaran at low speeds and as an air-cushion-
assisted planing catamaran at high speeds. With
the lift system shut down, speeds in excess of
24km/h (15mph) are possible, with the sidehulls
supporting 100% of the weight through a combination of buoyancy and planing forces. The lift
system can be employed at any speed to support
part of the weight of the boat. At high speeds, up
to 85% of the weight can be supported by the air
cushion, with a resulting increase of lift-to-drag
ratio from 5 to approximately 11. The maximum
speed is thereby increased to 56·32km/h
(35mph). Over the complete speed range, from
24 to 56km/h (15 to 35mph) approximately, total
power requirements, and hence fuel consumption, can be reduced by selecting the appropriate
lift fan rpm settings.

The first of these 14·63m (48ft) hydrographic
survey craft has been delivered to the US Army
Corps of Engineers.

Bell Halter 48ft Hydrographic Survey Craft, Rodolf

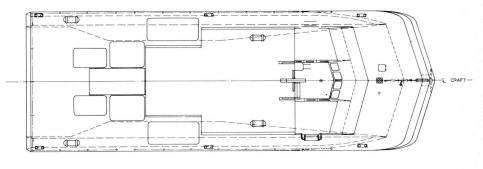

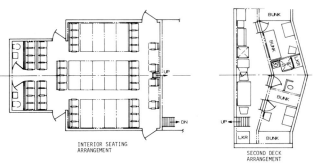

INTERIOR SEATING
ARRANGEMENT

SECOND DECK
ARRANGEMENT

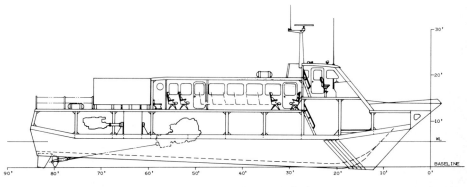

Bell Halter 85ft passenger and crew boat, inboard profile and deck plans

LIFT AND PROPULSION: The lift system is powered by a single Detroit Diesel 4-53N rated at 105shp at 2,600rpm (85°F and 152m (500ft)). Propulsive thrust is supplied by twin Detroit Diesel Allison 8V92N marine diesels, each driving a propeller via a standard Allison M reduction gear with a ratio of 1·52:1. Fuel is carried in four tanks, each with a capacity of 1,325 litres (350 US gallons).

CONTROLS: Directional control is provided by twin water rudders aft, one on each sidehull, in addition to the differential use of propeller thrust for slow speed manoeuvring.

HULL: The hull primary structure is built throughout in welded marine aluminium alloy 5086. The structure is of catamaran configuration and consists of two sidehulls, separated by decks and the cabin structure. The sidehull shell plating varies between ⅛ and ¼ in thick, depending on local pressures, and is stiffened by T-section longitudinals. Sidehull is maintained by frames and bulkheads that are spaced generally by 0·91-1·52m (3-5ft) and support the hull longitudinals.

Three watertight bulkheads are used in each sidehull and also across the centre section between the hulls. Two of these are located at the forward and aft ends of the cabin, and one is forward of the helmsman's platform. The latter also forms a collision bulkhead. The bulkheads provide transverse bending and torsional continuity to the hull structure. There are also longitudinal watertight bulkheads running the full length of the craft aft of the collision bulkhead.

SKIRT: Flexible skirts are provided at the bow and stern. The bow seal consists of eight fingers, each approximately 3·96m (13ft) long, 0·6m (2ft) wide and 1·95m (6ft 6in) high. All fingers are identical.

The stern seal has a constant cross-section and consists of two inflated lobes of coated-fabric material, with horizontal diaphragms to sustain pressure loads. End caps, which bear partly on the sidehulls, contain the air at the ends of the seal. Five vertical diaphragms are set at intervals across the seal to maintain a flat lower surface in order to minimise water contact and drag. Principal dimensions of the stern seal are: length 2·13m (7ft) and height 1·21m (4ft). Each of the lobes has a radius of approximately 304mm (1ft).

ACCOMMODATION: The deckhouse structure contains the pilothouse, cabin and lift system housing. The pilothouse is located in the forward portion with the pilothouse deck slightly higher than the weather deck elevation. The main cabin deck is recessed below the weather deck between the sidehulls. Similarly, the main cabin profile is lower than the pilothouse to allow visibility directly aft through rear-facing pilothouse windows. Two interior stairways lead from the main cabin deck level; one to the pilothouse level and the other to the aft section of the weather deck. Provision has been made for a total complement of seven crew members and/or observers.

DIMENSIONS
EXTERNAL
Length overall: 14·63m (48ft)
Beam overall: 7·31m (24ft)
Height overall: 4·72m (15ft 6in)
Draft, max static: 1·6m (5ft 3in)
Skirt depth, bow: 1·82m (6ft)
         stern: 1·21m (4ft)
Cushion area: 62·92m² (677ft²)
INTERNAL
Length: 7·01m (23ft)
Max width: 3·65m (12ft)
Max height: 2·13m (7ft)
Floor area: 25·64m² (276ft²)
WEIGHTS
Normal empty: 16·7 tons
Normal all-up weight: 18·7 tons
Normal gross: 22·3 tons
Normal payload: 2 tons
Max payload: 5·6 tons
PERFORMANCE
Max speed over calm water, max continuous power: 33 knots (29°C (85°F))
Cruising speed, calm water: 23 knots
Water speed in 1·22m (4ft) waves and 15 knot headwind: 24 knots

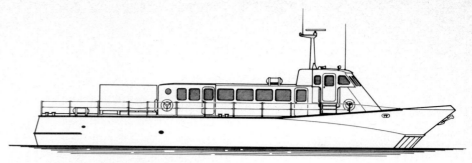
Bell Halter 85ft high-speed passenger and crew boat

Bell Halter 85ft, 188-seat passenger ferry

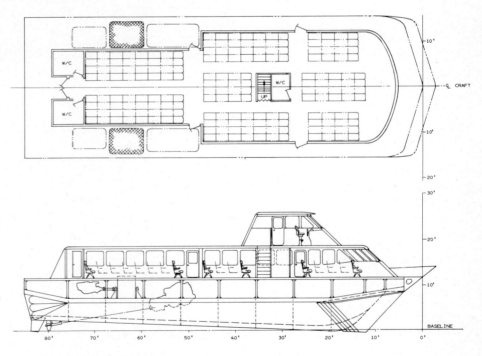
Inboard profile and deck plan, Bell Halter 85ft passenger ferry

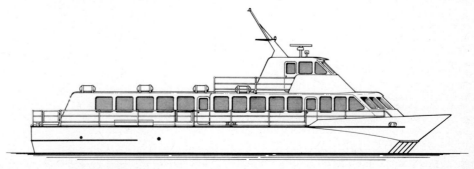
Outboard profile, Bell Halter 85ft 188-seat passenger ferry

Still air range and endurance at cruising speed: 1,090n miles and 50 hours
Max speed, over calm water, hullborne at 18·7 long tons displacement: 17 knots
PRICE AND TERMS: On request

BELL HALTER 85 (HIGH-SPEED PASSENGER AND CREW BOAT)

This 85ft long diesel-powered, high-speed ferry is available in two configurations, 25-100 seat crew boat or 188-seat passenger ferry. The hull and machinery are identical in each case, the main difference being an increase in the length of the passenger cabin of the latter.

LIFT AND PROPULSION: Two Detroit Diesel Allison 8V92N diesels (or similar) each rated at 350hp supply power for the lift fans and electrical generators and two Detroit Diesel Allison 16V92TA diesels, rated at 860hp each, are installed for propulsion. Each lift engine drives a 36·5in diameter lift fan to provide airflow to the cushion and seals. Two fan air inlets are located in the aft section of the weatherdeck. Air is blown through two longitudinal ducts leading to the bow and stern seals. Intermediate openings are provided for cushion pressurisation. Cushion pressure is 341·77kg/m² (70lb/ft²).

The two propulsion engines drive two 838mm (33in) diameter Michigan Wheel fixed-pitch, subcavitating propellers. Fuel is carried in four integral tanks built into the sidehulls. Total fuel capacity is 4,050 litres (1,070 US gallons). The lubricating system is an integral unit of the lift and propulsion engines and transmission systems. Fuel recommended is standard marine diesel. Refuelling points are located on the main deck on the port and starboard side of the deckhouse.

CONTROLS: Craft direction is controlled by twin rudders aft, one on each sidehull. Differential propeller thrust is employed for slow speed manoeuvring. The steering system is two-station hydraulic, operating with a rotary control valve which acts in conjunction with the steering wheel. Primary control is the hydraulic control system with a 762mm (30in) aluminium steering wheel located on the centre-line in the pilothouse. A second steering station is located on the upper deck, aft of the pilothouse. Mathers pneumatic engine controls are installed in the pilothouse and the upper deck stations.

HULL: The hull primary structure is built in welded marine aluminium alloy 5086.

SKIRT: The bow seal consists of eight fingers, each of which is approximately 7·31m (24ft) long, 914mm (3ft) wide and 3·65m (12ft) high. All fingers are identical. The stern seal, which has a constant cross section, consists of two inflated lobes of coated-fabric material, with horizontal diaphragms to sustain pressure loads. End caps, which bear partly on the side-hulls, contain the air at the ends of the seal. Five vertical diaphragms are set at intervals across the seal to maintain a reasonably flat lower surface in order to minimise water contact and drag. Principal dimensions are a fore and aft length of 2·74m (9ft) and a height of 1·22m (4ft). Each of the lobes has a radius of approximately 304mm (1ft).

ACCOMMODATION: Operating crew comprises a captain, first officer and four seamen. The crew boat version seats 25 to 100 passengers and the passenger ferry seats 188.

DIMENSIONS

EXTERNAL

Length overall: 25·99m (85ft)
Beam overall: 9·44m (31ft)
Height overall: 6·7m (22ft)
Cushion area: 155·6m² (1,675ft²)
Skirt depth, bow: 1·56m (5ft)
    stern: 1·21m (4ft)
Depth, moulded: 3·65m (12ft)
Draft, operational: 1·21m (4ft)
Draft, off cushion: 1·82m (6ft)

WEIGHTS

Normal empty: 54 tons
Normal gross: 67 tons
Normal payload: 13 tons

PERFORMANCE

Cruise speed, calm water: 33knots (29°C (85°F))
Cruise speed, 1·37m (4ft 6in) waves: 30 knots (29°C (85°F))
Range and endurance in 1·22m (4ft) waves, 15 knot headwind: 280n miles and 9 hours

PRICE AND TERMS: Upon request

BELL HALTER 110 DEMONSTRATION SES

Launched in late 1979, the BH 110 demonstration boat has undergone extensive successful testing by both commercial operators and the US Coast Guard. The basic hull and machinery layout permits modification of the deckhouse and

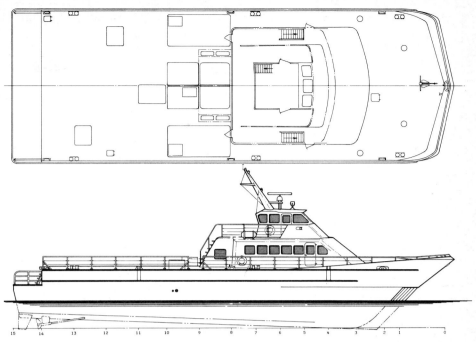

Outboard profile and plan of Bell Halter 110ft demonstration SES

Bell Halter 110ft demonstration SES

arrangement of the deck space to suit a number of alternative applications, from crew boat and 275-seat passenger ferry to fast patrol boat.

LIFT AND PROPULSION: Cushion lift is provided by two 445hp Detroit Diesel Allison 8V92TI diesels each driving identical high-pressure fans constructed in aluminium. Fan air inlets are located in a housing aft of the deckhouse. Cushion air is discharged into two longitudinal ducts between the second deck and wet deck. Half is released into the cushion for pressurisation, the remainder is programmed between the bow and stern seals.

Motive power for the propulsion system is supplied by two Detroit Diesel Allison 16V149TI diesels, each rated at 1,335hp at 1,900rpm for the crew boat version. Alternatively, SACM 195V12 engines can be fitted to provide increased speed. Each engine drives a 1·07m (42in) diameter Gawn-Burrill propeller via a Reintjes marine reduction gearbox. One right-hand and one left-hand rotating propeller are used. Four integral fuel tanks within the sidehulls provide a total capacity of 11,735 litres (3,100 US gallons). Refuelling is accomplished through fillers in the main deck and on the port and starboard sides. Oil is integral with the engines and gearboxes.

CONTROLS: Craft direction is controlled by twin rudders, one aft on each sidehull. Differential propeller thrust is employed for slow-speed manoeuvring. The steering system is activated hydraulically from the helm unit in the pilothouse.

HULL: The hull primary structure is built in welded marine aluminium alloy 5086. The structure is of catamaran configuration and consists of

two sidehulls that are separated by decks and transverse bulkheads. The sidehull shell plating varies between ¼ and ½in depending on local pressures, and is stiffened by T-section longitudinals. The spacing of the longitudinals is 178mm (7in) on the bottom plating and 304mm (12in) on the side plating. Sidehull shape is maintained by bulkheads spaced generally at 2·44m (8ft) which provide support for the hull longitudinals. Bulkheads have ⅛in webs with T-section and flat bar stiffening and flat bar caps sized appropriately for each bulkhead.

Four of the bulkheads in each sidehull and also across the centre section between the hulls are watertight. Two are located at the forward and aft ends of the cushion, and one is forward of the deckhouse. The latter also forms a collision bulkhead. The bulkheads provide the transverse bending and torsional continuity to the hull structure.

The cabin superstructure consists of T-section frames fabricated from flat bars and spaced the same as the frames on the hull. T-stiffened plate is welded to the framing.

SKIRT: The bow seal consists of eight fingers, each of which is attached to the underside of the centre hull. All fingers are identical. The stern seal, which has a constant cross section, consists of three inflated lobes of coated-fabric material. Horizontal diaphragms sustain pressure loads acting on the lobes. End caps, which bear partly on the sidehulls, contain the air at the ends of the seal.

ACCOMMODATION: The deckhouse structure contains a pilothouse on the 01 level and passenger cabin on the main deck. The pilothouse contains the controls, navigation and communications systems. The main cabin arrangement provides lounge-type seating. Toilet facilities are located aft.

The second deck contains staterooms for the crew, lounge seating for passengers, a galley, messroom and toilet facilities.

SYSTEMS, ELECTRICAL: AC and dc electrical systems provide electrical power. The prime system is a Detroit Diesel Allison diesel/generator set. The prime mover is rated at 86hp at 1,800rpm. The electrical output is 60Hz at 1,800rpm. The voltage is 208/240 three-phase with a 55kW rating.

DIMENSIONS
EXTERNAL
Length overall: 33·52m (110ft)
Beam overall: 11·88m (39ft)
Height, on cushion: 8·53m (28ft)
    off cushion: 6·87m (22ft 7in)
Draft, on cushion: 1·37m (4ft 6in)
    off cushion: 2·36m (7ft 9in)
Skirt depth, bow: 2·28m (7ft 6in)
    stern: 1·52m (5ft)
INTERNAL
Control cabin
Length: 4·57m (15ft)
Max width: 3·35m (11ft)
Max height: 2·13m (7ft)
Passenger cabin
Length: 8·53m (28ft)
Max width: 9·14m (30ft)
Max height: 2·13m (7ft)
Floor area: 78·04m² (840ft²)
WEIGHTS
Normal empty: 80 tons
Normal all-up weight: 107 tons
Max weight: 138 tons
Normal payload: 18 tons
Max payload: 49 tons
PERFORMANCE (16V194TI engines)

	sea state 0	sea state 3
Cruising speed,		
on cushion:	40 knots	33 knots
off cushion:	19 knots	15 knots

Range: 500n miles in sea state 3
PRICES AND TERMS: On request

BELL HALTER 110 DASHBOAT

In May 1980 it was announced that four BH 110 Dashboats had been ordered by Command Marine Inc, Lafayette, Louisiana, for transporting personnel and priority cargo between operating bases and oil drilling sites in the Gulf of Mexico.

The Dashboat is able to carry up to 120 passengers or 40 tons of cargo at 32 knots in calm seas and 28 knots in sea and weather conditions in which conventional forms of marine transportation cannot operate.

In overall design the Dashboats will be very similar to the Bell Halter 110 prototype. The first vessel was due to be delivered in the autumn of 1980, with the remaining three following at two-monthly intervals thereafter.

LIFT AND PROPULSION: Cushion lift is provided by two Detroit Diesel Allison 8V92N marine diesels, each driving a double-inlet centrifugal lift fan. Motive power for the propulsion system is furnished by two SACM 12V175 RVR marine diesels each rated at 1,330hp at 1,500rpm. Each drives a fixed-pitch propeller. Maximum fuel load is 7,500 gallons.

CONTROLS, HULL AND SKIRT: As for Bell Halter 110 prototype.

ACCOMMODATION: Deckhouse superstructure contains a pilothouse, beneath which is a passenger cabin on the main deck. The main cabin arrangement provides seating for 120 passengers.

DIMENSIONS: As for BH 110 prototype.
WEIGHTS
Max displacement: 150 long tons
Normal displacement: 126 long tons
Light ship displacement: 92 long tons
Max deck load: 40 long tons
RANGE
Sea state 0: 2,088 nautical miles
Sea state 3: 1,830 nautical miles

Bell Halter 110ft demonstration SES

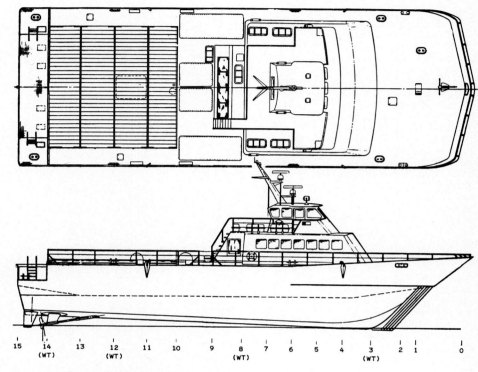

Outboard profile and plan of Bell Halter 110 Dashboat

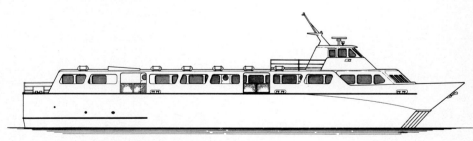

Outboard profile, Bell Halter 133ft passenger ferry

PERFORMANCE (based on max load)

Sea state	0 (calm)	3
		(waveheight to 4·6ft)
Speed,		
cushionborne:	32 knots	28 knots
off cushion:	19 knots	15 knots

BELL HALTER 133 PASSENGER FERRY

A proposed "stretched" version of the 110ft demonstration craft, the Bell Halter 133 is designed to carry 629 passengers or a payload of 45 tons. The propulsion engines are four Detroit Diesel Allison 16V149TI marine diesels rated at 1,335hp each, and driving two fixed-pitch, fully submerged propellers. The cruising speed is estimated at 40 knots in sea state 0 and 32 knots in sea state 3.

BELL HALTER 157

The Bell Halter 157 is a 157ft, 320-ton, 50-knot, 2,000n mile-range vessel with a hull form and structure identical to that of the Bell Halter

110ft demonstration boat. It is powered by two 20-cylinder MTU diesels, each driving a controllable pitch, fully submerged, supercavitating propeller. The lift system consists of two 12-cylinder MTU diesels each driving a double-width, double-inlet centrifugal fan. It can accommodate a wide variety of military payloads, depending upon the mission role selected.

LIFT AND PROPULSION: Cushion air is provided by two 1·42m (56in) double-entry fans, driven by two MTU 12V-331TC92 marine diesels. The lift fan assembly is located outboard on either side of the vessel. Fan air enters through intakes located on the 01 level of the superstructure. The fan output is fed forward to the bow seal and aft to the stern seal through ducts in the decking. A direct feed to the cushion is located below each fan outlet.

Two MTU 20V-956TB92 diesel engines provide power for propulsion through marine reduction gearboxes. The two propellers used are controllable pitch, fully submerged, supercavitating, with inclined shafts. Larger marine diesel engines, such as the SACM 240V20, can be

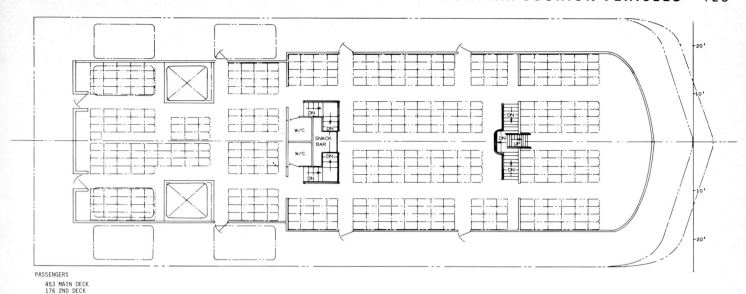

PASSENGERS
453 MAIN DECK
176 2ND DECK

Inboard profile and deck plan, Bell Halter 133ft passenger ferry

installed to provide higher speed. Gas turbine engine options are also available.

The four integrally built-in fuel tanks are within sidehulls. Maximum fuel capacity is 120 long tons. Oil is integral with engines and gearboxes.

CONTROLS: Two rudders located aft on the sidehulls and propeller pitch control are used for steering and manoeuvring.

HULL: The hull and superstructure are of all-welded marine-grade aluminium. The structure consists of two sidehulls in catamaran configuration separated by decks and transverse bulkheads. Longitudinal stiffeners are extruded T-sections, except where deep stiffeners are used at the wet deck. Transverse bulkheads, with vertical T-section stiffeners and heavy-plate cap members, extend down into the sidehulls.

Four watertight bulkheads are provided, each with watertight access doors, plus non-watertight bulkheads with openings as necessary. Hatches are provided in the main deck for engine and lift fan installation and removal, and for positioning payload below decks. All deck openings are reinforced and are generally aligned to minimise structural discontinuities.

SKIRT: The bow seal consists of eight fingers each of which are attached to the underside of the centre hull. All fingers are identical.

The stern seal has a constant cross section across the craft and consists of three lobes of coated-fabric material closed at each end with flat end caps.

ACCOMMODATION: The main deck contains space for a helicopter pad, spaces for weapons, a telescoping helicopter hangar, and the communications equipment room.

The second deck forward contains crew quar-

Bell Halter 157, 320-ton, 50-knot SES patrol boat

ters for 24 enlisted men, 4 chief petty officers, and 8 officers including galley, messroom, and toilet facilities; ship systems; and equipment rooms. All machinery spaces are located aft and away from living areas. Four ladders provide access to the main deck.

The 01 level contains the combat information centre (CIC), communications room, and helicopter control station.

The bridge is on the 02 level. Two wing bridges, also on the 02 level, house control stations for use during close quarter manoeuvring and/or station-keeping.

SYSTEMS, ELECTRICAL: AC and dc electri-

cal power. For basic ship power, two diesel generator sets are provided.

DIMENSIONS
EXTERNAL
Length overall: 47·85m (157ft)
Beam overall: 16·45m (54ft)
Cushion length: 35·35m (116ft)
Cushion beam: 12·9m (42ft 5in)
WEIGHTS
Normal gross weight: 320 tons
Capacity gross weight: 380 tons

PERFORMANCE
Range at 50 knots: 2,000n miles

BERTELSEN, INC

Head Office: 10526 West Cermak Road, Westchester, Illinois 60153, USA
Telephone: (312) 562 6170
Works: 113 Commercial Street, Neponset, Illinois 61345, USA
Officials:
William R Bertelsen, *Chairman of the Board, Vice-President and Director of Research*
William C Stein, *President and Treasurer*
Charles A Brady, *Secretary*

Dr William R Bertelsen, a general practitioner and talented engineer, was one of the first to build and drive an air cushion vehicle.

His interest was largely inspired by the difficulties he faced when trying to visit patients by car over icy roads. Having discovered that a helicopter would be too expensive to be a practical solution, he set to work to develop a vehicle that could be lifted free of the ground by air pumped beneath its base. Dr Bertelsen designed his first Aeromobile air cushion vehicle in 1950, and has since built and tested fourteen full-scale vehicles, ranging from simple plenum craft to ram-wings. One, the 18ft long Aeromobile 200-2, was a star exhibit at the US Government's Trade Fairs in Tokyo, Turin, Zagreb and New Delhi in 1961. Descriptions of the Aeromobile 14 and 15 can be found in *Jane's Surface Skimmers 1980* and earlier editions. An Aeromobile system of rapid transit, based on the Aeromobile 13, is described in the section devoted to Tracked Skimmers in this edition.

AEROMOBILE 16

Interest in this 7·82m (25ft 8in) long utility vehicle, the biggest to be constructed by Bertelsen so far, is being shown by potential customers throughout the United States and Canada. It employs a lift, propulsion and control system similar to that of the earlier Aeromobile 15. At the time of going to press the craft was being retrofitted with 1·01m (40in) diameter spun aluminium ducted fans powered by two 125hp Mercury outboard engines for increased thrust and efficiency. The ice-breaking capabilities of the A-16 were demonstrated during the winter of 1978-79. The craft can operate on cushion with one engine only, the other being employed for full propulsion and steering. It is one of the few air cushion vehicles capable of sidehill operation.

LIFT AND PROPULSION: Power is supplied by two duct-mounted, 125hp, two-cycle Mercury outboard engines, each driving a 1·01m (40in) diameter axial fan fabricated in spun aluminium. Each duct is spherical and gimbal-mounted at its centre so that it can be tilted and rotated in any direction. When the fan shaft is vertical the total airflow is discharged into the cushion. By tilting the gimbal the operator allows air from the fan to escape across the stern to provide propulsive thrust.

Bertelsen Aeromobile 16 undergoing hovering tests. The 7·82m long craft is the company's biggest to date. Payload capacity is 680kg (1,500lb)

The thrust force is instantly available throughout 360 degrees, and metered finely by degree of tilt, provides propulsion, braking or yaw torque. The maximum available force is equal to 100% of the propulsion force.

Fuel is carried in two 90 litre (24 US gallon) tanks, one behind the forward engine and one forward of the aft engine. Type of fuel recommended is regular automobile petrol. Fuelling points are located on deck above tanks.

HULL: Basic structure built in mild steel tubing. Designed to carry 680kg (1,500lb) payload. Total buoyancy 5,563kg (12,266lb).

ACCOMMODATION: Enclosed cabin with driver's seat forward and midship and rear bench seats behind, each seating three-four passengers. Access is via two entry doors, one each side. Seats are removable should the craft be required to undertake light utility roles. The cabin may be heated or air conditioned if required.

SYSTEMS, ELECTRICAL: Two 12V alternators and two 12V storage batteries.

DIMENSIONS
EXTERNAL
Length overall, power off: 7·44m (24ft 5in)
  skirt inflated: 7·82m (25ft 8in)
Beam overall, power off: 4·31m (14ft 2in)
  skirt inflated: 5·48m (18ft)

Structure width, power off, folded: 2·28m (7ft 6in)
Height overall, on landing pads: 1·72m (5ft 8in)
  skirt inflated: 2·13m (7ft)
Cushion area: 24·15m² (260ft²)
Skirt depth: 406mm (1ft 4in)
INTERNAL
Cargo bay
Length: 3·35m (11ft)
Max width: 1·82m (6ft)
Max depth: 0·68m (2ft 3in)
Deck area total: 27·78m² (299ft²)

WEIGHTS
Normal empty: 1,587kg (3,500lb)
Normal all-up weight: 2,267·96kg (5,000lb)
Normal payload: 680kg (1,500lb)

PERFORMANCE
Max speed, calm water, max power: 96·56km/h (60mph)
Cruising speed, calm water: 80·46km/h (50mph)
Turning circle diameter at 30 knots: 152·4m (500ft) estimated
Max wave capability: 1·21m (4ft)
Max survival sea state: 1·82m (6ft) waves
Still air endurance at cruising speed: 8 hours
Max gradient, static conditions: 10 degrees
Vertical obstacle clearance: 406mm (1ft 4in)

DEPARTMENT OF THE NAVY, NAVAL SEA SYSTEMS COMMAND (NAVSEA)

Headquarters: Washington DC 20362, USA
Office Address: US Naval Sea Systems Command, Advanced Technology Systems Code 03R12, National Center Building 2, Room 5E08, Washington DC 20362, USA

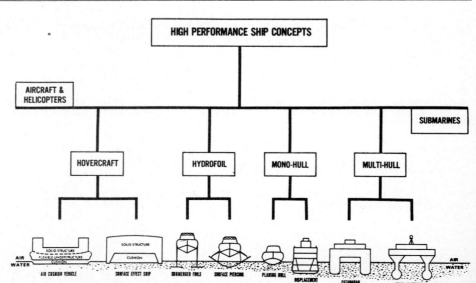

High performance ship concepts under development by US Naval Sea Systems Command

Officials:

James L Schuler, *Advanced Ship Development Manager*

The Naval Sea Systems Command (NAVSEA) is a primary technical sponsor for all US Navy hydrofoil and hovercraft programmes. The programme manager responsible for the development of all types of high performance ship concepts is

James L Schuler (Code 03R12).

Technical manager of the US Navy Advanced Hydrofoil Systems Development Programme is Robert Johnston of the David W Taylor Naval Ship Research and Development Center. The Amphibious Assault Landing Craft (AALC) Programme is being managed by J Benson (NAVSEA PMS 377J). The AALC Programme

includes the construction of two air cushion vehicles of about 160 tons design all-up weight. The craft are the JEFF(A), built by the Aerojet General Corporation, and the JEFF(B), developed by the Bell Aerosystems Corporation. Contracts for design of the production version of these craft were recently awarded to Bell Aerosystems Co and Rohr Marine Systems Co.

DOBSON PRODUCTS CO

2241 South Ritchey, Santa Ana, California 92705, USA

Telephone: (714) 557 2987

Officials:

Franklin A Dobson, *Director*

Dobson Products Co was formed by Franklin A Dobson in 1963 to develop and market small ACVs either in complete, factory built form, or as kits for private use. His first model, the Dobson Air Dart, won the first ACV race in Canberra in 1964. The company's Model F two-seater, has been described and illustrated in *Jane's Surface Skimmers 1973-74* and earlier editions.

The first Dobson craft designed for quantity production is the Model H, the latest test development of which is described here. Since good results have been obtained with the Dobson six-bladed variable-pitch propeller, and more positive control is desirable at low and negative speeds, a new model is under development using two side-by-side thrust units. This is expected to give powerful yaw control at all speeds in addition to a very considerable increase in positive as well as negative thrust. Other changes will be fairly minor.

DOBSON AIR CAR, MODEL H

This is a simplified and slightly larger machine than the original Model H. It has more efficient lift and thrust systems together with simplified controls and a slightly lower structural weight. Originally this model had a fan and propeller mounted on the same shaft, but in its latest configuration the engine drives the fan through a separate shaft and gearbox. This arrangement allows a much lower cg as well as improved streamlining.

LIFT AND PROPULSION: Integrated system powered by a single JLO engine rated at 18hp at 5,500rpm. The lift fan is a Multiwing 24-9-32, driven by a long shaft and a Dobson right-angle gearbox with a 2:1 reduction. The thrust unit is a Dobson six-bladed variable-pitch propeller driven at about 2,000rpm via a single vee-belt. The propeller is mounted in a specially designed abbreviated duct and produces more than 40·8kg (90lb) static thrust or 13·6kg (30lb) reverse thrust from 13hp, since 5hp is used by the fan. As the fan is driven separately only 13hp is carried by the vee-belt. A centrifugal clutch is used on the engine.

CONTROLS: Lateral motion of a control stick operates twin rudders, while fore-and-aft motion controls the propeller pitch, forward for thrust, aft for braking. The control stick also incorporates a motorcycle type twist-grip throttle.

HULL AND SKIRT: Hinged floats are used for buoyancy and these also support a flexible skirt which gives about a 203mm (8in) obstacle clearance. With the floats hinged upwards or removed, the overall width is less than 1·21m (4ft).

DIMENSIONS

Length: 3·35m (11ft)

Width: 2·28m (7ft 6in)

Height: 1·29m (4ft 3in)

Folded width: 1·14m (3ft 8in)

Obstacle clearance: 203mm (8in)

Cushion area: 5·11m² (55ft²)

WEIGHTS

Empty: 104·32kg (230lb)

Tools and miscellaneous: 4·52kg (10lb)

Fuel (6¾ US gallons): 18·14kg (40lb)

Pilot: 72·57kg (160lb)

Passenger: 72·57kg (160lb)

Max gross: 272·14kg (600lb)

Dobson Air Car Model H

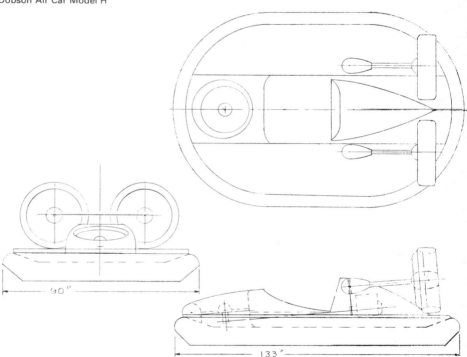

General arrangement of Air Car Model K

Rear view of Dobson Model K showing twin variable-pitch ducted propulsion fans

AIR CAR MODEL K

Franklin Dobson's latest Air Car design is among the first light hovercraft to employ variable-pitch ducted fans for thrust, braking and control. Plans are being made for limited production.

LIFT AND PROPULSION: Integrated system powered by a single Briggs & Stratton four-stroke opposed twin, of 688cm³ (42in³) displacement, rated at 18hp at 3,600rpm. This particular engine is much quieter than the two-stroke engines formerly used, in addition to which it incorporates a governor, an important safety feature. Power is transmitted to two 0·63m (25in) diameter thrust fans by vee-belts. The 0·56m (22in) diameter lift fan, mounted in a recessed duct ahead of the open cockpit, is driven via a shaft and right-angle gearbox. Thrust is about 36·3kg (80lb), with a noise level below 80dB.

CONTROLS: Because the engine is governed at a constant speed only a single control is required. Forward-and-aft movement of the control stick gives thrust or braking from the two variable-pitch thrust fans, while lateral movement produces differential thrust for steering.

SKIRT: Segmented type.

ACCOMMODATION: Open cockpit seating two side-by-side.

DIMENSIONS
Length overall: 3·68m (12ft 1in)
Beam overall: 2·28m (7ft 6in)

WEIGHTS
Gross: 272kg (600lb)
Empty: 118kg (260lb)

PERFORMANCE: Details not received

Two variable-pitch fans are employed on this new Dobson design for thrust braking and control. Because the Model K's engine is governed at constant speed, only a single stick control is needed. Fore-and-aft movement provides thrust or braking while lateral movement produces differential thrust for steering

LANDING CRAFT AIR CUSHION (LCAC) ACQUISITION PROGRAMME

US Naval Sea Systems Command, Washington DC 22202, USA
Telephone: (202) 692 8513
Officials:
Capt Charles H Piersall, Jr, *Project Manager*
Jeffrey L Benson, *Programme Manager*
Richard W Kenefick, *Deputy Programme Manager*
Cdr W Gene Wilder, *Design Manager*
Melvin W Brown, *Technology Manager*
Cdr Jon K Elliott, *ILS Manager*
Philip J Schneider, *Programme Engineer*
Edward Cowley, *Programme Engineer*
Paul Scheurich, *Programme Engineer*
Fannie M Thomas, *Programme Assistant*
Lcdr Kenneth W Shafer, *OIC, AALC, ETU*
Frank P Higgins, *Senior Trials Engineer, AALC, ETU*
Brian C Swanson, *TRW Support Contract Team Leader*

The US Navy has recently initiated a programme to acquire an advanced landing craft based on proven air cushion vehicle principles. Designated the Landing Craft, Air Cushion (LCAC) Acquisition Programme, the overall objective is to acquire, for the mid-1980s to 1990s, a high speed, over-the-beach, ship-to-shore amphibious assault craft able to lift all equipment required by the ground elements of a Marine Amphibious Force.

The programme is structured to build upon the proven technology that has been demonstrated and documented by the Navy's advanced research and development effort under the Amphibious Assault Landing Craft (AALC) Programme. Current emphasis is on the design, construction, test and trials of two 160-ton air cushion landing craft, designated Jeff(A) and Jeff(B), and a shipboard handling system, Amphibious In-Haul Device (AID). As an advanced research and development effort, the AALC Programme focuses on hardware for test or experimentation purposes, as opposed to hardware designed and engineered for eventual Fleet use. As such, the objective of the Jeff craft is to demonstrate the technical feasibility and military utility of air cushion vehicles in amphibious operations, so providing a firm foundation for the later acquisition of LCACs for the Fleet.

The Jeff craft are full-scale prototypes. In the early 1970s when they were designed, much of the technology surrounding air cushion vehicles was beginning to be well understood. However, the dimensional constraints of the Jeff craft, as they had to be compatible with the well decks of amphibious ships, coupled with the 60-ton payload requirement, led to the use of relatively high cushion densities (and cushion pressure-to-length ratios) when compared with commercial

Jeff(B) entering well deck of LSD-32 during an operational demonstration

craft. This is portrayed graphically in the accompanying diagram.

The specification of the Jeff craft called for operation in sea state 2, with a 25-knot headwind and 100°F ambient temperature. For airscrew propulsion, the 25-knot headwind, when added to the 50-knot overwater requirement, resulted in a propulsion system designed for 75 knots of relative wind. A 7m (23ft) height restriction further compounded the problem, virtually eliminating large free propellers and making the craft designers optimise the efficiency of their clipped propellers through the use of ducts. The 100°F temperature, most unlikely in sea state 2 or with a 25-knot wind, imposed even further limitations on gas-turbine engine performance.

The apparent over-specification of Jeff craft requirements was intentional, as they were developed to demonstrate advanced technology. Successful testing of these craft would assure that the design of any follow-on Fleet craft, now identified as the LCAC, would be based on known technological capabilities.

The Jeff(A) was designed and built by the Aerojet-General Corporation, a subsidiary of the General Tire and Rubber Company, Aerojet Liquid Rocket Company, Sacramento, California. Jeff(B) was designed and built by Bell Aerospace Textron, a division of Textron Inc, New Orleans Operations. The programme is managed by the Naval Sea Systems Command, Amphibious Ship Acquisition Project (NAVSEA PMS-377) as a part of the Advanced Landing Craft Programme. Overall technical administration of the design and construction of

both craft was provided by the AALC Programme Office of the Systems Development Department, David W Taylor Naval Ship Research and Development Center, Carderock, Maryland.

Jeff(B) was accepted by the Navy in July 1978, with the Jeff(A) following in June 1979. Both Jeff craft are currently undergoing Navy systems trials at the Naval Coastal Systems Center (NCSC), Panama City, Florida. Craft operations and maintenance are being conducted by US Navy personnel assigned to the AALC Experimental Trials Unit (ETU), a field detachment of the David W Taylor Naval Ship Research and Development Center.

In August 1979 the first of a series of Operational Demonstrations were completed. These were periods set aside for the Navy's Operational Test and Evaluation Force (OPTEVFOR) to independently assess the military utility of employing air cushion vehicles in amphibious operations. During the first three-week Operational Demonstration, both over-water and overland trials were conducted under a variety of conditions and payloads. Typical Marine Corps hardware was loaded and off-loaded to determine cycle times and to identify any interface problems. Various items of equipment up to and including the M60 tank were carried, on-cushion, at design speeds. Well deck entries and exits were conducted, under both wet and dry well conditions, with the Landing Ship Dock USS *Spiegel Grove* (LSD-32) at anchor and underway.

The first Operational Demonstration was an outstanding success and the positive results have provided the confidence needed to initiate a successful follow-on acquisition programme, that will be in harmony and full compliance with key acquisition directives.

LCAC Programme Acquisition Approach

In response to recent Government procurement guidance an LCAC acquisition approach was developed which requires extensive industry participation and encourages competition through the development phase of a programme. The aim of the guidance is to allow industry to contribute innovative solutions to system design, effectiveness and support.

Acquisition is guided by the following objectives:

1. The emerging LCAC design must represent a minimum technical risk. Research and development funds have been committed to the AALC Jeff craft for some time, and it is now time to proceed to production. The LCAC must be based upon the existing technology proven by the Jeff craft and by other appropriate sources. In areas requiring upgraded technology, the changes will be tested and demonstrated, possibly on the Jeff craft, prior to their use on the LCAC.

2. The lead craft must establish a minimum cost and schedule risk position for follow-on production. This means that not only must the lead craft be relatively easy to produce, it must also be a low technical risk. It must be able to make the transition from the soft tooling, as was used to build the "one-of-a-kind" Jeff craft, to hard tooling and full production techniques. Cost and schedule risks for follow-on craft procurement will be minimised by proving both tooling and production methods through the lead production of (nominally) six craft, and by maintaining the continuity of the production line through Initial Operational Test and Evaluation (IOT&E) of the lead production craft and until a follow-on production decision can be approved.

3. The earliest possible Fleet introduction of a true Initial Operating Capability (IOC) must be provided. One craft does not provide a true IOC. However, the six lead production craft provide a sufficient lift capability for the equipment normally deployed with a Marine Amphibious Unit (MAU), and thus provide a meaningful amphibious assault capability.

A Top Level Requirements (TLR) document was developed which is the basis for developing more detailed specifications as the design process continues. The TLR identifies minimum performance requirements for the LCAC terms of essential performance requirements, mission-oriented tasks, an assault mission scenario, and certain key minimum performance levels.

The essential performance requirements of the LCAC include a capability for: rapid on-loading/off-loading of cargo; vehicle drive-through; entering/exiting a dry well deck while the ship is underway; operating in formation with similar assault craft; manoeuvring under positive control of a Task Group Commander; detecting and avoiding other craft and obstacles; operating over land under Beach Master control; and mooring alongside amphibious task force ships and docks.

The mission-oriented tasks for the LCAC identified in the TLR include the ability to: land and be loaded/unloaded on a typical beach or littoral surface; accommodate the widest Marine Corps assault echelon vehicle; have a deck wide enough to allow three lanes of vehicles; have a deck space adequate to carry specified serials; and accept palletised cargo.

The assault mission scenario for the LCAC describes the functions that generally establish time and fuel requirements. These basic functions include: launch from a dry well with the ship underway; transit at best speed; traverse surf zone, inward-bound; proceed inland, alight and unload, lift off and leave area; traverse surf zone, outward-bound; transit to ship area; enter well deck, dry well, with the ship underway; and repeat the operation.

Jeff(B) in foreground and Jeff(A) in background

Jeff(A) during rough water tests

Jeff(B) carrying a US Marine Corp Tank and two howitzers onto a beach

The key minimum performance levels identified in the TLR are generally classified and relate to the required craft capabilities in various modes of operation in various sea states and associated winds, temperatures, and other external conditions.

An unusual feature of the LCAC TLR is the identification of enhancing characteristics. While the specifics associated with most of the enhancing characteristics are classified, in general they represent desirable craft capabilities, beyond those identified as essential performance levels and requirements, that will generally lead to a more capable craft. It may be possible, through innovation and careful design, to incorporate some enhancing characteristics into the minimum craft design without incurring additional craft cost or complexity, though not perhaps others. This incorporation must reflect a balance between craft capability and other factors such as unit cost, life cycle cost, and risk.

LCAC Design and Lead Production

The System Design/Specification (SD/S) competition, the first phase of LCAC acquisition, is already underway. The two competing contractors are Bell Aerospace Textron, New Orleans Operations and Rohr Marine Inc. Parallel competitive contracts were let in June 1980, with technical proposals due in January 1981 and management/cost proposals due in March 1981.

The system design effort is directed toward low risk and low cost objectives. At the same time, it allows for production innovations and, where justifiable, technology upgrading. While a performance specification-type contract provides for contractor flexibility, the system design evaluation will stress, and therefore minimise, risk and cost. To emphasise this direction, the competing contractors have been provided with Jeff craft detail design drawings and data from the Navy Systems Trials and Operational Demonstrations conducted with the Jeff craft. For changes proposed to existing Jeff craft technology, contractors will be required to incorporate test article fabrication and testing costs (and schedules) in their proposals. Contractor cost and schedule risk will be reduced by the award of an incentivised cost-reimbursable contract for sub-system design and lead production.

Various contract provisions will be structured to support the basic programme objectives. Cost control mechanisms have been incorporated in the system design contracts. While the basic designs will centre on the achievement of minimum performance requirements, excursions will be required to show capabilities resulting from the inclusion of certain enhancing characteristics. The incentive to obtain the lead production contract will reinforce the low-risk and low-cost programme objectives.

The results of the SD/S phase will be presented

to a Defense System Acquisition Review Council (DSARC) to support a request for permission to initiate LCAC SubSystem Design and Lead Production (SSD&LP). Since the system designs will be developed by contractors qualified to accomplish lead production, credible contractor-developed production cost estimates, derived from the individual contractor's system designs, will be produced. These estimates will be available for evaluation prior to the DSARC.

Sub-system design and lead production will result in the construction of six LCACs. The first LCACs off the lead production line will undergo an Operational Evaluation (OPEVAL), after which another DSARC decision will be requested to authorise follow-on production. The six craft built during the lead production will be delivered to the Fleet to provide a true initial operating capability of advanced amphibious assault landing craft. A six-craft production lot also justifies the use of hard tooling and production techniques. Since this approach allows for Initial Operational Testing & Evaluation (IOT&E) and DSARC before completion of the lead production phase, a hot production line will be available for initiation of follow-on production.

LCAC Programme — Jeff Craft Support

The sub-system design and lead production contract award will also include provisions for the

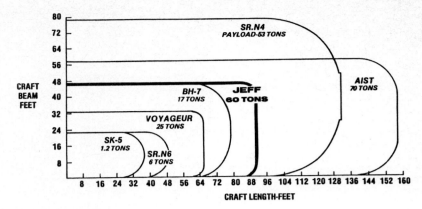

Comparison of planforms and payloads

selected contractor to support the operation of the Jeff craft. Navy systems trials are planned to continue to support the LCAC programme. The use of the Jeff craft to test and prove design improvements will allow the early and rapid introduction of design refinements. It will also assist in primary and alternative mission planning before the transfer of LCAC capability to the Fleet by unburdening the demands placed on the production craft.

The Jeff craft will also see service as the LCAC

trainer for initial operating and maintenance personnel. The trainer concept will provide hands-on experience which will be easily transferred to the LCAC, with an accompanying acceleration in the LCAC schedule. Retention of the Jeff craft, combined with a lead production schedule for six craft, allows comprehensive testing to minimise technological risk. Schedules can also be compressed through the use of the Jeff craft to prove upgraded technological concepts prior to their introduction into the production craft.

LOCKHEED-GEORGIA COMPANY
(Division of Lockheed Aircraft Corporation)

86 South Cobb Drive, Marietta, Georgia 30063, USA

Telephone: (404) 424 9411

PAR/WIG PROJECT

Lockheed's PAR/WIG (power-augmented ram-wing/wing-in-ground-effect) is a design study for a logistics vehicle for the US Navy with a cruising speed of Mach 0·40 and a range of 4,000n miles. It would cruise at an average height of 1·16m (3ft 9in) in sea state 3, increasing to 1·62m (5ft 4in) in sea state 4.

Characteristics of the craft include PAR lift augmentation for take-off and landing and all payload contained in the wing, thus obviating the need for a hull. Maximum payload capability of the craft would be 200,038kg (441,000lb), based on carrying four M60A3 main battle tanks, and 300,051kg (661,500lb) with six M60A3s with the necessary shoring and restraint hardware.

A design constraint imposed on the study was a span limitation of 32·91m (108ft) to allow the use of facilities designed for the majority of contemporary naval vessels.

LIFT AND PROPULSION: Power is supplied by four turbofan engines, each delivering 95,600lb st maximum at sea level. The engines would be similar to the STF477 turbofan designed by Pratt & Whitney Aircraft as a low energy consumption turbofan for the 1990s. The selected engine thermodynamic cycle is assumed to be similar to a low rotor modification of the STF477. The high-pressure compressor, the combustor and the high-pressure turbine characteristics of the basic STF477 core would be retained while the low-pressure spool is modified to meet the selected bypass and fan pressure ratios. The resulting engine configuration is assumed scaleable to the design point maximum thrust level of 95,600lb.

A dual rotor configuration is assumed with a variable-pitch, single-stage 1·15 pressure ratio fan and booster compressor stages gear-coupled to a low-pressure turbine and a high-pressure compressor driven by an air-cooled turbine. Performance and geometry characteristics of the variable-pitch fan would be similar to those available from an advanced Hamilton Standard 'Q-Fan'. A low emissions two-stage vortex-burning and mixing combustor will provide 1,430°C (2,600°F) maximum average combustor exit temperature. The engines are mounted on

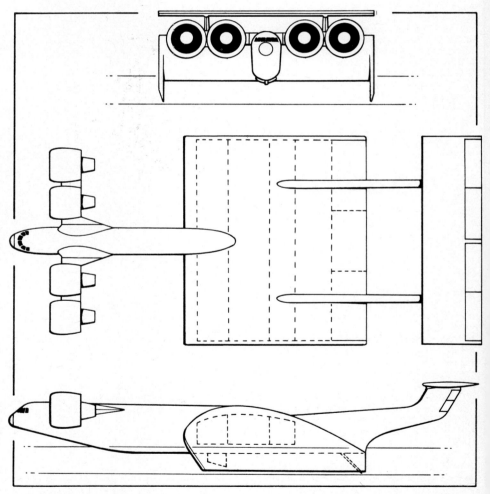

Lockheed-Georgia PAR/WIG spanloader concept. The thrust vector system allows the entire engine/nacelle/pylon installation to rotate as a unit to provide the powered ram for take-off and landing and the thrust vectoring for low-speed pitch control

the forward fuselage. A continuous torque box spans the fuselage width and supports all four engines. Engine rotation is accomplished by actuating the torque box which rotates all engines as a single unit.

The PAR/WIG thrust vector permits the entire engine/nacelle/pylon system to rotate to provide the powered ram for take-off and landing and the thrust vectoring for low-speed craft pitch control.

CONTROLS: PAR lift augmentation is employed during take-off and landing. The engines are rotated so that the primary propulsion efflux is directed towards the cavity beneath the wing formed by the wing undersurface, endplates, trailing edge flaps and the water surface. Use of this technique provides lift of up to six times the installed thrust, while still recovering 70% of the thrust for acceleration. Twin vertical fins, the wing flaps, ailerons and a variable-incidence tail-plane provide aerodynamic control. A hydrofoil provides hydrodynamic lift and drag during landing. Flying in ground effect close to the water surface prevents the aircraft from banking into a turn, obstacle avoidance therefore has to be undertaken by sideslipping.

WING AND FUSELAGE: Because PAR lift would be employed during take-off and landing the contact speed between the water and the primary structure is reduced to about 60%. Consequently there is no need for a conventional hulled undersurface and the structural weight of the aircraft can be reduced. The basic structural components are the very low aspect ratio wing, fuselage protruding ahead of the wing, twin boom and twin fins and single high-set tailplane aft of the wing, four rotatable pylon-mounted engines forward on the fuselage and the hydrofoil. The basic wing includes wing endplates and flaps and the static flotation structure.

In order to meet the requirements for an efficient low subsonic cruising speed, a spacious cargo compartment for spanwise loading and a flat undersurface for PAR lift augmentation, a modified Clark Y aerofoil design is employed. Wing flaps are of hinged split-surface type and are employed as both control surfaces and as hydrodynamic drag surfaces when landing. A load relief system is incorporated into the flap system to prevent excessive loads should the maximum allowable water contact speed be exceeded during landing. The outer panels also act as ailerons.

The hydrodynamic and structural configuration of the wing endplate is integral to the feasibility of the craft since it is the only structure required to impact the water at cruising speed. It is 27·73m (91ft) long, 2·77m (9ft 1in) high and has a beam width of 0·76m (2ft). The leading edge, which is wedge-shaped, has a sweepback angle of 30 degrees. The endplate design was determined from the results of analysis of endplate loads due to drag and side force at a speed of $M = 0·4$, using towing tank data.

Static buoyancy is provided by the displacement volume located beneath the wing cargo compartment floor and the forward fuselage crew compartment floor. Both buoyancy compartments are divided into watertight subdivisions to ensure that the craft remains afloat should the wing or fuselage lower surface suffer impact damage from floating debris.

A hydrofoil located beneath the centre of the fuselage provides both lift and drag during landing. Lift and drag co-efficients are 0·3 and 0·1 respectively. When landing, the engine vector angle is rotated to 30 degrees, flaps are set at 40 degrees and the power setting is reduced to 70%. This provides sufficient lift from the PAR system.

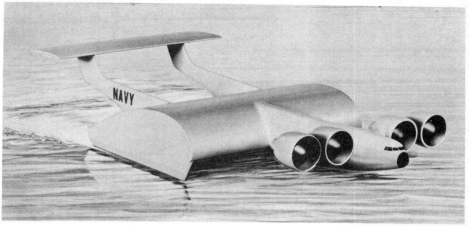

Primary mission for this WIG concept is over-water logistics, operating over sea state 3 for a range of 4,000 nautical miles. Take-off and landing is made from the ocean surface, cruising altitude is established in ground-effect and the craft proceeds to its destination at a speed of Mach 0·4

However, the horizontal thrust available is more than sufficient to maintain a speed of 89 knots and it becomes necessary to increase drag by use of the hydrofoil. At speeds of less than 37 knots, the wing endplates and flaps are allowed to touch the water and provide additional drag. Not until the speed has been reduced to 16 knots is the primary structure, wing or fuselage lower surface allowed to impact the water. The hydrofoil is constructed in titanium plate supported by heavy reinforcement structure.

A major proportion of the PAR/WIG structure will be in graphite epoxy composites in primary structural components. The remainder of the craft is in aluminium and steel alloys with the exception of those which have to be in contact with the water, such as the endplates and hydrofoil, which are constructed entirely in titanium for strength and corrosion resistance.

CARGO COMPARTMENT: The dimensions of the cargo compartment are designed to accommodate either of two alternative payloads. The first is to transport standard commercial sea/land containers 2·44m (8ft) wide, 2·9m (9ft 6in) high and 6·1 or 12·2m (20 or 40ft) in length at a gross payload density goal of 160kg/m³ (101lb/ft³). The second payload requirement includes the transport of standard vehicles for the US Army or US Marine Corps. A compartment height of 4·11m (13ft 6in) is required to accommodate a launcher with bridge, the maximum height of the tallest vehicle to be carried. The maximum payload capability of 200,000kg (441,000lb) and 300,000kg (661,500lb) is based on the requirement to transport either four or six M60A3 main battle tanks.

The span of 32·91m (108ft) is of sufficient length (spanwise) to accept five 6·1m (20ft) containers and the width of the aerofoil is sufficient to accommodate six rows, thus providing the contained volume necessary for thirty 6·1m (20ft) containers.

DIMENSIONS
Span: 32·91m (108ft)
Length: 72·6m (238ft 6in)
Height, wing undersurface to
   tip of tail: 10·36m (34ft)
Wing area: 913·05m² (9,828ft²)
Endplate, length: 27·73m (91ft)
   width: 0·61m (2ft)
   height: 2·74m (9ft)
Geometric aspect ratio: 1·19
Effective aspect ratio: 5·70
WEIGHTS
Operating: 162,340kg (357,900lb)
Fuel: 255,420kg (563,100lb)
Payload: 200,000kg (441,000lb)
Gross: 617,850kg (1,362,000lb)
Wing loading: 678kg/m² (139lb/ft²)
Thrust/weight: 0·2808
PERFORMANCE
Cruising speed: Mach 0·4
Cruising height: sea level
Note: Cruising height is based upon clearing the one-tenth highest wave crest and impacting the one-thousandth wave crest to a depth of 206mm (0·63ft) and 459mm (1·4ft) for sea state 3 and 4 respectively. A minimum clearance of 0·91m (3ft) is maintained between the one-thousandth wave crest and the wing lower surface primary structure during cruise operations in either sea state.

MARITIME DYNAMICS INC

PO Box 465, Tacoma, Washington 98401, USA
Telephone: (206) 759 1709; (206) 922 5233
Officials:
William C House, *President*

Maritime Dynamics is at present undertaking SEV data reduction, performance analysis and model testing for the US Navy. It is also developing a number of new ACV concepts, including the ART-1 arctic roller transport described below.

ART-1

The ART-1 arctic roller transport has been designed for use as a school bus and also for carrying mail and freight in south-western Alaska. Basically, it is an air-cushion supported truck employing low pressure tyres or rollers for propulsion. When traversing solid surfaces, including ice, it is supported and propelled solely by its rollers. But when the bearing strength of the surface is insufficient to support the footprint pressure of the rollers, or for operation over water, the skirts are dropped and air cushion assistance is provided. Propulsion is still provided by the rollers and, if required, additional thrust

ART-1 arctic roller transport

can be provided by selective venting of the cushion air.

Advantages claimed for the roller transport concept over air-propelled vehicles are a reduction in noise and improved propulsive efficiency. When the lift system is not required, fuel consumption is greatly reduced. Additionally, since the rollers are in constant contact with the surface, directional control of the craft is good, including in strong crosswinds and when negotiating side gradients.

The design incorporates as many developed components as possible and is capable of carrying a useful load of 1 tonne. Modular construction is employed enabling the vehicle to be dismantled into easily handled units for transporting by air in the C-130 Hercules.

A number of studies of the arctic roller transporter air cushion vehicle have been undertaken in sizes ranging from 1 ton to 100 tons payload. Initially, studies were concentrated on 10 to 40-ton payload vehicles in the belief that they were the more practical sizes for freight operations and would be more cost-effective when the anticipated freight market opened up.

More recently the company's attention has been drawn to the great need in Alaska for a school bus-type air cushion vehicle which could be employed to transport mail or freight when not in use as a school bus.

A study was conducted based on a small army vehicle which could easily be converted to a 17-student bus configuration. By removing the seats, as required, the vehicle could be used in off-duty hours as a truck.

The basic vehicle can be used to tow a second 25-passenger ART-1 trailer across reasonably level ground. The trailer would have a lift engine and fans for air cushion support but would not have a propulsion engine.

LIFT AND PROPULSION: Lift is supplied by a single 65hp Volkswagen air-cooled automotive engine driving via a right-angle bevel gearbox two centrifugal fans. Fan air is ducted fore and aft into a loop and pericell skirt system similar to that designed for Jeff(A). The entire lift system is located aft in order to simplify centre of gravity movement for widely varying loads. The propulsion system comprises a second Volkswagen engine of the same type and output driving four Rolligon-type low-pressure tyres mounted on standard Volkswagen differentials with shortened axles. This size of vehicle can be fitted with 1·21m (4ft) diameter rollers and could therefore be capable of clearing 609mm (2ft) obstacles.

CONTROLS: Craft direction is controlled by the differential application of brakes and power to the four wheels. The cushion pressure can be reduced to allow a proportion of the air to be borne by the rollers. The percentage borne by the rollers will depend upon the strength of the supporting surface and the amount of traction needed. In this way, the operator can vary the craft operating mode to suit the nature of the terrain.

HULL: All-welded marine aluminium structure.

SKIRT: Pericell type, comprising a loop (the upper semi-circular duct) and peripheral cells. Loop and cells are fabricated in rubber-coated fabric. Fingered bag skirt can be employed as an alternative. Transverse and longitudinal dividers are not required.

DIMENSIONS
EXTERNAL
Length, power off: 6·09m (20ft)
  skirt inflated: 7·92m (26ft)
Beam, power off: 3·04m (10ft)
  skirt inflated: 4·87m (16ft)
Height, power off: 1·93m (6ft 4in)
  skirt inflated: 2·89m (9ft 6in)
Hard structure draft in water: 228mm (9in)
INTERNAL
Load space: 3·04 × 2·74m (10 × 9ft)

WEIGHT (Tractor)
Gross: 3,822kg (8,425lb)
Payload: 907·18kg (2,000lb)
Fuel: 409 litres (90 gallons)
Empty: 2,268kg (5,000lb)

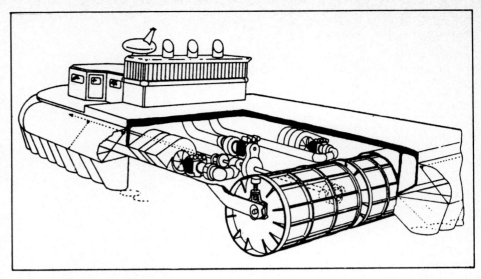

Lift and propulsion arrangements on ART-1 arctic roller transport

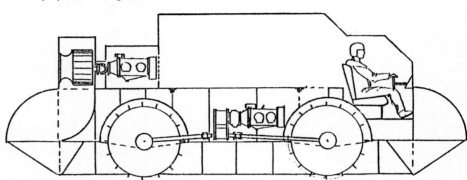

Inboard profile of an arctic roller transporter

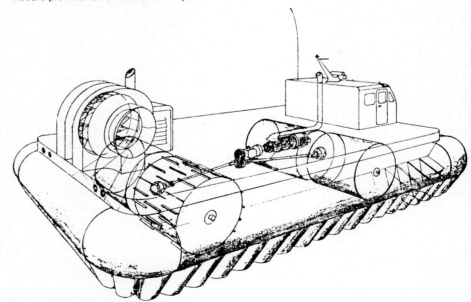

Machinery arrangement on ART-10 arctic roller transport

PERFORMANCE
Max speed across firm terrain: 40 knots
  with trailer: 25 knots
Max water speed, on cushion: 35 knots
  with trailer: 20 knots
Max range, hard ground or ice, off cushion:
  800km (500 miles)
  with trailer: 482km (300 miles)
Water, on cushion: 362km (225 miles)
  with trailer: 161km (100 miles)
Obstacle clearance: 609mm (2ft)

ART-10

This is an enlarged version of the ART-1. At the behest of the Alaska State Board of Education, it was considered for possible use as a school bus as well as a freighter. Since school bus operation alone would not offset the amortization costs, it was decided to design a removable school bus module to fit the truck bed space of the vehicle. The module measures 6·09 × 6·09m (20 × 20ft) and provides seating for 90 to 100 students. Assuming that the freight portion of the ART-10's application would contribute, together with the school bus role, an annual utilisation of 3,600 hours per year, then the cost per seat mile as a school bus would be of the order of 8 cents for a 100 per cent load factor. An operation having to depend on only a 50 per cent load factor would, of course, double the cost.

LIFT AND PROPULSION: The lift system comprises a single ST6 gas-turbine engine driving via a right-angle bevel gearbox two centrifugal fans. Fan air is ducted fore and aft into a loop and pericell skirt system similar to that designed for the Jeff(A) AALC (amphibious assault landing craft). The propulsion system comprises a second ST6 gas turbine driving via a reduction gearbox four Rolligon-type low pressure tyres mounted on standard truck tandem differentials with shortened axles. This size of craft could accommodate 1·82m (6ft) diameter rollers and thus would be capable of clearing 0·91m (3ft) obstacles.

CONTROLS, HULL, SKIRT: As for ART-1.

ACCOMMODATION: The ART-10 will carry a crew of two, an operator and an observer, who will alternate their duties. The crew cab will be a modified transport truck cab with basic bunking, toilet and messing facilities.

DIMENSIONS
Hard structure,
   length: 12·19m (40ft)
   beam: 6·09m (20ft)
   height, including gearbox: 2·59m (8ft 6in)
Air cushion duct and skirt,
   length: 14·02m (46ft)
   beam: 7·92m (26ft)
   height, on rollers or skirt: 3·65m (12ft)
Load area: 6·09 × 6·09m (20 × 20ft)
WEIGHTS
Gross: 20,411kg (45,000lb)
Payload: 9,071kg (20,000lb)
Fuel (300 US gallons): 907·18kg (2,000lb)
Empty: 10,432kg (23,000lb)
PERFORMANCE
Range, overland, at 40 knots
   into a 20-knot wind: 290n miles
   overwater (calm) at 37 knots: 120n miles
   overwater (rough) at 32 knots: 90n miles

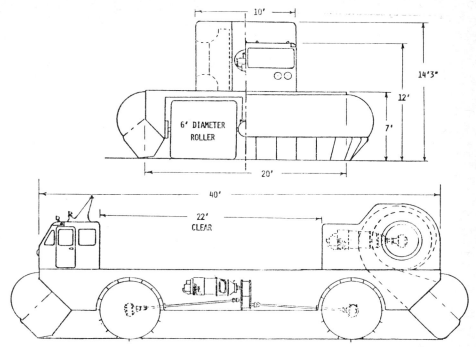

General arrangement of ART-10

NEOTERIC—USA— INCORPORATED

Fort Harrison Industrial Park, Terre Haute, Indiana 47804, USA
Telephone: (812) 466 2303
Officials:
Chris Fitzgerald, *President*
Donald Brown, *Secretary*

Neoteric—USA—Incorporated was formed in 1975 by three of the founders of Neoteric Engineering Affiliates Pty Ltd, of Melbourne, Australia (see separate entry). The Neova range of two-seat ACVs, which is now being manufactured and marketed by Neoteric USA, was first introduced by the Australian associate. The Neova, which is fully amphibious, is available in kit or ready-built form. The company welcomes enquiries from businesses wishing to manufacture the Neova range under licence.

NEOVA II

A highly-manoeuvrable light ACV, the Neova is an amphibious two-seater, intended primarily for recreational use. Neova II is supplied in kit form in five individual modules—base, machinery, ducts and controls, skirt and body. Individual components are also supplied, enabling the home builder to assemble any part of the complete vehicle. The purchaser can therefore buy what is needed and make the rest himself to keep costs as low as possible.

The overall dimensions of the machine—2·13 × 4·27m (7 × 14ft)—allow it to be transported by road on a flat trailer.

LIFT AND PROPULSION: Integrated system powered by a single 46hp Volkswagen engine. The company has developed a new turning belt drive transmission which is now offered as the standard kit, module 2. The new drive features a centrifugal clutch and an all-aluminium pod structure. Maintenance is reduced substantially and the life of the drive is increased. In addition assembly time is further reduced. Assembly time of the complete kit is now 350 hours as opposed to 700 hours for the original design with a wooden structure. Airflow is ducted into the plenum for lift and two outlets aft for thrust. The power module, comprising engine, transmission and axial-flow fans is mounted on a rubber-seated frame, secured to the main hull by three bolts. It is totally enclosed and when operating is impossible to touch. A large hatch provides ready access to the engine and all components.

CONTROLS: Back and forward movement of a dual stick control column operates two thrust

Latest version of the Neova II two-seater sports craft and runabout. Both the front cowl ahead of the cockpit and the protective grille above the engine and fans can be raised or removed to simplify access to the controls, battery and machinery

Forward and aft movement of a dual stick control column operates two thrust buckets which vary the power and direction of the thrust

buckets which vary the power and the direction of the thrust. The column is pulled back for reverse thrust and moved ahead for forward thrust. Differential use of the two columns, with one stick forward and the other back, is used for changing craft direction. The aerodynamic rudders at the rear of the propulsion ducts are normally used only for small corrections in heading at cruising speeds.

HULL: Home-built models are of ply construction, with steel attachments at lifting and towing points. A two-seat fibreglass body assembly is available as module 5. Skid pads on the underside protect the structure from damage by abrasion. An integral siphon system prevents the collection of excessive water within the hull. Buoyancy is 150%. The skirt module is removable as two single units.

ACCOMMODATION: Side-by-side seating for two.

DIMENSIONS

Length overall: 4·27m (14ft)

Beam overall: 2·13m (7ft)

Height overall, skirt inflated: 1·54m (5ft)

WEIGHTS

Normal all-up weight: 454kg (1,000lb)

Payload, maximum: 196kg (430lb)

PERFORMANCE

Cruising speed (at 75% power setting): 56km/h (35mph)

Max gradient from standing start: 1 : 10

Vertical obstacle clearance: 203mm (8in)

Endurance on full power: 3 hours with 34 litre tank

PRICE

Neova II

Information pack US$10, plus $2 air mail overseas

Deluxe plan pack US$50, plus $4 air mail overseas, (free with complete kit purchase)

Complete kit, less engine under US$5,000

Fully assembled Neova II, US$8,000. Payment in either Australian or US dollars

Individual components and material sets available from either Melbourne, Australia or Terre Haute, USA.

Neova II is fitted with a timing belt drive transmission, a centrifugal clutch and an aluminium pod structure

NORTH AMERICAN HOVERCRAFT CORPORATION

One World Trade Center, New York, NY 10048, USA

Telephone: (212) 775 1415

Officials:

George Dagher, *President*

North American Hovercraft Co is building the UK-designed AV Tiger in the United States under licence. Negotiations between the company and Air Vehicles Ltd of Cowes, Isle of Wight, were completed early in 1978. Air Vehi-

cles Ltd supplies a number of components for the craft.

Future production craft are likely to differ in certain aspects including the fitting of a US-built engine.

POWER BREEZE

8139 Matilija, Panorama City, California 91402, USA

Telephone: (213) 785 0197

Officials:

Dan W Henderson Jr, *President/Designer*

Power Breeze Air Cushion Vehicle Systems was founded originally to stimulate public interest in ACVs, and is currently selling plans to home builders for a small, easily assembled amphibious single-seater.

A set of plans costs US$5 and a ready made skirt costs US$35.

Total cost of construction in the USA, including ply for the hull, skirt material, metal tubing, propeller and engine is about US$400. Weight of the craft is 113kg (250lb) and the maximum speed is approximately 40·23km/h (25mph). The latest model of this circular platform single-seater folds to a width of 1·21m (4ft) to simplify storage and to permit it to be carried by a light truck or pick-up van.

A number of craft have been built to this design in the United States and Australia.

In addition to selling plans, the company is engaged in the sales of second-hand ACVs, and specialises in finding craft to meet the individual needs of its clients.

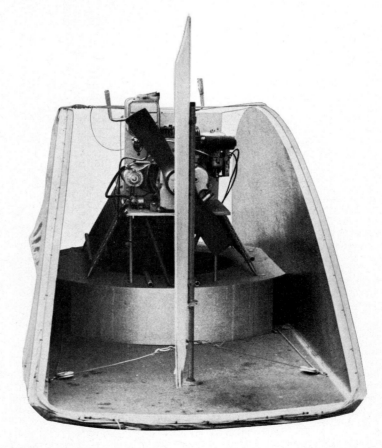

Power Breeze is marketing plans for this light, easily assembled amphibious single-seater, shown here folded for storage

ROHR INDUSTRIES, INC

Head Office: Foot of H Street, PO Box 878, Chula Vista, California 92012, USA
Telephone: (714) 575 4111
TWX: (910) 322 1870
Officials:
Carl L Sadler, *Chairman of the Board and Chief Executive Officer*
Harry W Tood, *President*

ROHR MARINE, INC

(A Subsidiary of Rohr Industries, Inc)
Head Office: Foot of H Street, PO Box 2300, Chula Vista, California 92012, USA
Telephone: (714) 575 4100
TWX: (910) 322 1870
Officials:
Wilfred J Eggington, *President*
F Patrick Burke, *Vice President, Development and Programme Management*
Darrell L Reed, *Vice President, Finance and Administration*
Bob Cramb, *Manager, Technical Services Development*
Edward J Renner Jr, *Director, Contracts and Materiel*
George Luedeke Jr, *Manager, Programme Development*
Irv Abel, *Programme Manager, LCAC*
Jack Edwards, *Manager, Advanced Design*
Larry Lorden, *Manager, Marine Business Development*
Haley Rogers, *Manager, International Programmes*
Jacqueline S Jenerette, *Manager, Public Relations*
Washington Office: 1/30 N Lynn Street, Suite 400, Arlington, Virginia 22209, USA
Telephone: (703) 525 9835
Telex: 892793
Officials:
Ted Harmon, *Washington Area Manager*

One of the world's leading producers of aircraft power packages and structures for three decades, Rohr Industries is a leading designer of aerospace and marine systems. Founded in 1940, the company is based in Chula Vista, California.

The company has nearly 40 years of experience as a major subcontractor to the aerospace industry, supplying engine pods and other specialised structural components for commercial and military aircraft. Its main plant occupies 130 acres of land, more than 2 million square feet of which comprises covered accommodation. Manufacturing facilities include machines, tooling, and precision welding equipment, which has been used extensively in the production of welded aluminium marine structures. Rohr currently has approximately 9,000 employees.

Rohr's research into high performance watercraft was initiated in 1962 when the company began tests on advanced hull concepts. Early test programmes included work on wing-in-ground-effect machines and hydro-ski tests for aerodynamically supported vehicles.

Rohr's entry into the surface effect ship area began in 1970 when it provided assistance with the operation of the XR-1 SES research craft under a US Navy contract.

In 1972 Rohr joined Litton Industries to begin work on preliminary design studies of a US Navy 2,000-ton Surface Effect Ship (SES) with ocean-going capability. A contract for the advanced development for the 2,000-ton concept was awarded to Rohr by the US Navy in July 1974.

The successful completion of the 2KSES preliminary design and advanced development phases in 1976 enabled the restructuring of the SES programme to encompass a larger 3,000-ton ship, the 3KSES. To implement the 3KSES and related programmes, Rohr Marine, Inc (RMI) was formed in October 1976 as a wholly-owned subsidiary of Rohr Industries, Inc.

Today, RMI is established as a leader in the development of large, ocean-going SES technology. In part, this is based on the company's innovations in key 3KSES components, such as durable planing seals, fixed waterjet inlets, low

XR-1, seen in D configuration, has a refined waterjet propulsion system with a variable-geometry water inlet similar to that on the SES-100A

SES-100A surface effect ship. Test planning, engineering services and data handling are among the services provided by Rohr under US Navy contract in support of the SES-100A test programme

drag hull forms and advanced lift fan-ride control sub-systems. Due to budgetary cutbacks, the 3KSES programme has been terminated. However, RMI continues advanced design work on other SES configurations utilising knowledge derived from the 3KSES programme. RMI is currently developing several surface effect ship designs, ranging from a small multi-purpose SES to a large logistics SES.

In June 1980, RMI won a US Navy contract for design work on the Landing Craft Air Cushion (LCAC) which is to transport equipment required by today's US Marine amphibious force operations.

XR-1 TESTCRAFT

Rohr's first contract in SES work, awarded in 1970, was for the modification and testing of the XR-1B SES testcraft. The craft has undergone further modification since then. Each time Rohr has incorporated advanced design features, many of them crucial to the success of the US Navy's SES.

The experiments undertaken led to the introduction of the planing seal, ride control system, and improved waterjet inlet designs, all of which have been to support the development of the 3KSES.

Many of these operations can be found on the 15·3m (50ft), 22-ton XR-1D. Since 1970, Rohr, and later RMI, have provided support services to the Navy for testing the XR-1D at San Diego and at the Navy's Surface Effect Ship Test Facility at Patuxent River, Maryland. Further details of the XR-1 can be found in *Jane's Surface Skimmers 1980* and earlier editions.

DIMENSIONS
Length overall: 15·3m (50ft)
Max beam: 5·8m (19ft)
WEIGHTS
Full load displacement: 23 tons

Light displacement: 21 tons
Payload (instrumentation and cargo): 0·6 tons
PERFORMANCE
Speed (½ fuel load, sea state 0, standard day): 43 knots

SES-100A

RMI, under contract to the US Navy, provided craft maintenance, logistics, engineering, test planning and data handling support for the Navy's SES-100A test programme. The SES-100A was designed and developed by Aerojet General Corporation under the sponsorship of the US Navy Surface Effect Ship Project Office. It was a waterjet-propelled 100-ton craft incorporating an integrated lift and propulsion system driven by four Avco Lycoming TF35 925 marinised gas turbines.

RMI began support activities on the SES-100A in December 1974, when the craft was moved from the builder's facility in Tacoma, Washington, to the Surface Effect Ship Test Facility (SESTF) at the Naval Air Station, Patuxent River, Maryland. The initial technical objective of the test programme was the thorough evaluation of the propulsion system following the replacement of the original strut-pod waterjet inlets with variable area flush inlets. This investigation resulted in the installation of sidehull "fences" to reduce air ingestion into the inlets. Craft performance in various sea states and ride quality characteristics were also investigated during this period.

During 1977 at the request of the Navy, RMI, as a part of the US Navy 3KSES contract, performed extensive modifications to the craft. Incorporation of 3KSES-type bow and stern seals were an important feature of this activity. During 1978 and 1979, design and performance tests of several configurations of these seals were performed in low-to-moderate sea states, and the calm water acoustic characteristics of the craft were investigated. In late 1979, testing of the SES-100A was discontinued, and in early 1980, the machinery was removed for use on other craft. Further details of the craft can be found in *Jane's Surface Skimmers 1980* and earlier editions.

DIMENSIONS
Length overall: 24·38m (80ft)
Max beam: 12·8m (42ft)
WEIGHTS
Full load displacement: 100 tons
Light displacement: 86 tons
Payload (instruments and cargo): 6·5 tons
PERFORMANCE
Speed (½ fuel load, sea state 0,
    standard day): 74 knots

SES-100B

RMI provided operational and maintenance support for the US Navy's SES-100B. In June 1978, at the request of the US Navy, RMI SESTF operations group participated in re-activation of the SES-100B which had been in storage at that facility. The craft was refurbished by a joint RMI-Navy maintenance crew and the first mission was run at SESTF in September 1978. The SES-100B was returned to storage at SESTF in February 1980.

3KSES

Rohr Marine was awarded a contract in late 1976 for the detail design, sub-system verification testing, planning and construction, and procurement of long-lead equipment for the construction phase of the 3,000-ton Surface Effect Ship (3KSES). The contract included an option for Rohr Marine for the construction of the ship. Work on this contract continued in San Diego until December 1979. The initial contract design requirements were complete and ship construction was scheduled to begin when the programme was terminated due to the withdrawal of funds.

In the 3KSES design, four 36,500hp marine gas turbines are employed to power waterjets which propel the ship at speeds in excess of 80 knots. Features of the design include full-length rigid sidehulls with advanced planing-type bow and stern seals made from elastomeric and composite materials. Critical to a high-speed, ocean-going SES, these seals are designed for better wear, reliability, and performance than their predecessors. Six mixed-flow fans connected in banks of three, each of which is driven by two 22,500hp marine gas turbines, comprise the lift system.

The ride control system (which reduces wave-induced motion by modulating air flow through mixed-flow fans) is another advance. Significant waterjet inlet design improvements have resulted in the development of fixed and flush low drag design with high efficiency and reliability.

The ship was designed to operate with other US Navy ships, craft, shore commands and aircraft during test evaluation deployment. It was designed to use existing Navy logistic support. Provision was made for vertical replenishment (VERTREP) underway, with the capability for rapid strike down of stores, provisions, and parts. It was also designed for underway alongside fuel connected replenishment (CONREP) and helicopter-inflight-refuelling (HIFR). Full maintenance support of embarked ASW helicopters was provided together with provision for the hangarage and fuelling of a V/STOL aircraft.

DIMENSIONS
Length overall: 81·07m (266ft)
Max beam: 32·3m (106ft)
WEIGHTS
Full load displacement: 3,047 tons
Light displacement: 1,836 tons
PERFORMANCE
Speed (½ fuel load, standard day),
    sea state 0: 94 knots
    sea state 3: 88 knots
    sea state 5: 72 knots
Range with payload (sea state 3): 3,107n miles
Payload (combat systems aircraft): 176 short tons
Crew (berthing): 125

Impression of Rohr 3KSES. The planing surface at lower extremity of the bow cushion seal is expected virtually to eliminate flagellation damage and minimise hydrodynamic drag

Rohr Advanced Naval Vehicle Concept Evaluation Study (ANVCE) SES3, based on 3KSES design

Rohr Light Multi-Purpose SES (LMSES) in patrol boat configuration

US NAVY ADVANCED NAVAL VEHICLE CONCEPT EVALUATION STUDY SES3 DESIGN (ANVCE)

In 1976, RMI developed a point design for a medium size air-capable SES warship. The 3,600-ton SES, or SES3, as it was called, is based on the 3KSES design.

The main purpose of the ANVCE project was to identify areas for marine vehicle technology development in the period 1995-2000. This allowed candidate ANVCE ship point designs to be divorced from any current programme for near-term mission needs and allowed them to meet common mission requirements with a common technical base.

Externally, several differences can be seen in the RMI SES3 and the RMI 3KSES. The differences in the combat suite are clearly visible with the SES3 incorporating a more extensive military payload for AAW, ASW, and SSW. Less obvious differences are internal modifications to the

3KSES. These include the use of 50,000hp marine gas turbines, an improved passive or indirectly-fed planing stern seal system, and other sub-system differences such as the use of armour and increased crew accommodation.

It represents a projection of technology from the 3KSES testship of the 1980s to an operational, frigate-sized warship of the 1990s. Many of the improvements in the waterjet propulsion system projected for the SES3 design later were adopted for the 3KSES project and only the passive stern seal design awaits continued development.

DIMENSIONS
Length overall: 81·07m (266ft)
Max beam: 32·3m (108ft)
WEIGHTS
Full load displacement: 3,600 long tons
Light displacement: 2,064 long tons
Payload (combat systems aircraft): 406 short tons

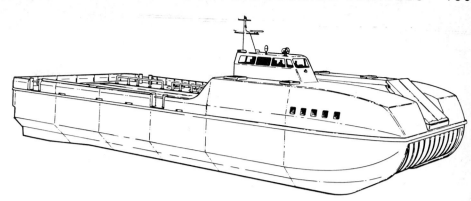

Rohr 350-ton LMSES workboat

PERFORMANCE
Speed (½ full load, standard day)
    sea state 0: 106 knots
    sea state 3: 100 knots
    sea state 5: 90 knots
Range with payload (sea state 3): 3,200n miles
Operating crew: 140

US NAVY LCAC PROGRAMME

In June 1980, Rohr Marine, Inc was awarded a US Navy contract for the system design and specification phase of the Landing Craft Air Cushion (LCAC) acquisition programme. The next phase (to be awarded in early 1981) includes sub-system design and production of six lead craft. The first LCAC will be in operation in 1985 and as many as 79 are scheduled for construction. The 50-knot LCAC allows assault ships to stand off beyond a hostile beach yet remain able to deliver troops and equipment at the required build-up rates. The LCAC rides over underwater obstacles, can operate through plunging surf 2·43m (8ft) high, and can discharge its 60-ton payload, for example a tank, or three lanes of trucks and equipment onto firm ground beyond soft beaches or marsh areas where they can quickly join troops flown in by helicopter. LCACs, when in operation, will open to assault four to five times the coastal sites now available, vastly compounding an enemy's defence problems.

Two US Navy prototype air cushion landing craft, Jeff(A) and Jeff(B), have been built in a programme initiated in 1971. These craft have been in operation since 1977.

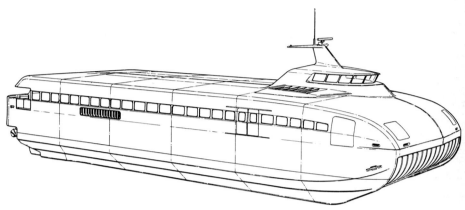

LMSES 130-ton commuter ferry

LIGHT MULTI-PURPOSE SES (LMSES)

Another RMI advanced marine vehicle is the light multi-purpose SES (LMSES). The LMSES has been designed to provide to full advantage the speed, stability, and economy of the SES concept and is based on readily producible common design features for hull and machinery. It provides a basic platform powered to meet a wide variety of commercial and military uses within economic operating levels. Variations of LMSESs are accomplished by the addition of individually built structures above the main deck. This can reduce acquisition cost through decreased engineering, the use of common production tooling, and the benefit of multiple production runs.

Typical applications of the RMI LMSES common platform include:

COMMUTER FERRY. This is a low cost and easily maintained fast passenger/vehicle ferry. By reducing travel time and offering a far more comfortable ride it will provide distinct advantages over current conventional ferry services.

Highly manoeuvrable, and safe to operate in busy inland waterways, it will have a service speed in excess of 60 knots in calm seas. More than 350 single class passengers will be accommodated on a single deck fitted with 28-inch aircraft type seats. In addition, there is a lounge and a food preparation space for providing snacks and meals en route.

CAR FERRY. The car ferry LMSES design features single class seating for 270 passengers and space for 27 standard-sized cars. It will accommodate a variety of vehicles ranging from cars, vans, trucks, semi-trailer rigs to buses. Bow and stern ramps are provided for straight-through vehicle loading.

OFFSHORE UTILITY BOAT. This provides an economical, reliable and fast all-weather service for the transport of personnel or cargo necessary for offshore oil operations, salvage or other over-water commercial work boat uses. It is configured to transport a substantial load of cargo and personnel. The open deck cargo area can accommodate large or awkwardly shaped payloads and outsize equipment. Passenger seating forward is sufficient for up to 75 personnel. With 45 to 55 knot speeds, it can provide rapid shuttle services to offshore oil rigs or salvage sites. Its shallow draft facilitates inshore salvage operations, and its high-speed, rapid reaction potential is particularly useful for fire-fighting applications.

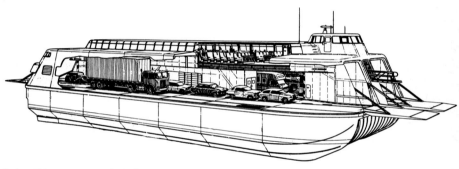

Rohr 158ft passenger/vehicle ferry

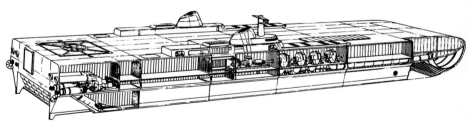

Rohr 11,500-ton Logistics Surface Effect Ship (LSES). Machinery layout

The utility LMSES can also serve as a general coastal transport where rapid delivery is required for perishable items or goods with high inventory costs.

PATROL BOAT. In this role the LMSES offers rapid response for surveillance, surface engagements and rescue and assistance missions. Its speed and sea-keeping surpasses that of conventional patrol craft.

The box-like hull structure of the LMSES patrol boat is adaptable for a variety of high volume, low density military payloads including multiple helicopters. Its 40 to 50-knot speed offers tactical advantages over slower conventional ships and permits rapid reaction from a state of readiness when in port. Its high speed and minimal hull immersion on cushion reduce vulnerability to submarine torpedoes and mines. Vulnerability to battle damage is reduced by protecting vital ship areas, personnel and machinery with armour plating. Redundancy and dispersal of the machinery within the craft further decrease its vulnerability.

LMSES COMMUTER FERRY CHARACTERISTICS
DIMENSIONS
Length overall: 42·06m (138ft)
Max beam: 16·05m (53ft)
Draft, off-cushion: 2·89m (8ft 6in)
    on-cushion: 457mm (1ft 6in)
Baggage storage forward: 2,800ft³ (containerised)
Cargo storage forward: 900ft³ (bulk)
WEIGHTS
Displacement full load: 285 long tons
Displacement light ship: 247 long tons
Payload, passengers (one class): 350
    baggage and cargo: 22 short tons
    operating crew: 3
    cabin attendants: 12
PERFORMANCE
Speed (½ fuel load, standard day),
    sea state 0: 62 knots
    sea state 2: 58 knots
    sea state 4: 50 knots
Range with payload (sea state 3): 1,150n miles

LOGISTICS SURFACE EFFECT SHIP (LSES)

The Logistics Surface Effect Ship, or LSES, is a roll-on roll-off transport capable of rapid, world-wide delivery of large quantities of vital military equipment and supplies, tanks, trucks, artillery, munitions and fuel or premium commercial cargo. Ocean passage will be swift: 3½ days in the case of an Atlantic crossing compared to 7 days for a conventional ship. Port time will also be brief: less than 12 hours to load or unload. Generous deck areas and cargo spaces are well suited for military or commercial cargo. The LSES design provides a stowage capacity normally found on conventional merchant ships many times larger in displacement.

DIMENSIONS
Length overall: 191·11m (627ft)
Max beam: 38·4m (126ft)
Gross vehicle/cargo space,
    weather deck: 4,700m² (50,670ft²)
    under deck: 6,200m² (66,780ft²) or 54,000m³
    (1,905,768ft³)
WEIGHTS
Full load displacement: 11,500 long tons
Light ship displacement: 4,798 long tons
Payload, vehicles/cargo: 3,600 short tons
Operating crew: 34
PERFORMANCE
Speed (½ fuel load, sea state 3,
    standard day): 50 knots
Range with payload, sea state 3: 3,000n miles

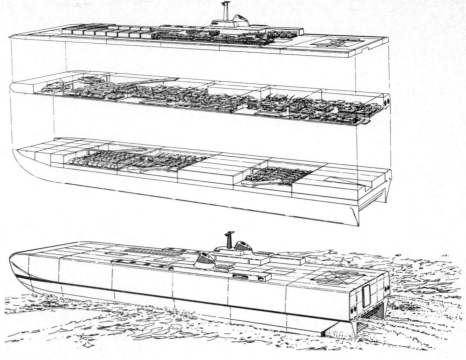

LSES deck layouts

SURFACE EFFECT SHIP ACQUISITION PROJECT

PO Box 34401, Bethesda, Maryland 20034, USA
Cables: SESPO c/o Naval Ship Research and Development Center, Bethesda, Maryland, USA
Officials:
Captain Carl C Drenkard, USN, *Project Manager*
Commander Charles A Vinroot, USN, *Deputy Project Manager*

In the past the US Navy has studied the role of the large displacement SES (5,000 to 10,000 tons). The primary aim of the programme was to provide data for the design of an SES which would combine high speed with a large payload, long range and economy in a single multi-purpose hull. It is now reconstructing its SES programme with an emphasis on a lower cost approach. Under this new programme, it will study close-term mission requirements and also maintain a development potential for future requirements.

Approximately $419 million has been spent on the SES programme in the United States in the seventeen years up to the summer of 1980, with a further $4·1 million of fiscal year 1979 funds deferred pending further studies.

The programme was not funded in fiscal year 1980 and it is likely that the deferred funds will be employed to assist the Navy in capitalising on past SES development and to take advantage of current low-cost, low-risk technology by exploring the close-term military effectiveness of a relatively small SES of less than 1,000 tonnes displacement.

It is considered that such a craft will have potential as an escort or could be the forerunner of a large SES design suitable for logistics roles.

During the autumn of 1980 it was disclosed that the US Navy, at a cost of $4·1 million had acquired the Bell Halter BH 110 demonstrator with the intention of lengthening the craft by up to 15·24m (50ft). The US Coast Guard will, it seems, be the prime user of the craft and will assess its suitability for performing patrol and interception duties along the Eastern seaboard. This is particularly relevant in view of the extension of US territorial waters and will also assist in controlling the flow of illegal immigrants from islands in the Caribbean.

This evaluation of a commercially available SES should provide the US Navy with a valuable input for its study of low-cost, low-risk SES concepts.

US Navy's two 100-ton test craft cruise in formation at 65 knots

One of the foremost advocates of the SES for the US Navy during the 1970s was Admiral Elmo R Zumwalt, then Chief of Naval Operations. He has been advising the incoming Reagan administration on the defence postures which should be adopted during the next four years and there are strong indications that he has advised the resumption of SES and ACV funding as a method of maintaining both a technological lead and in some areas parity with Soviet developments in these areas.

The US Navy Surface Effect Ship Acquisition Project, through design construction and operation of several test craft and a comprehensive technology programme is providing large high-speed ships capable of performing combat and support missions. In 1976 the US Navy selected Rohr Marine, Inc to design and build a 3,000-ton SES (3KSES) capable of high speed operations in the open ocean, but the programme was terminated in December 1979 after the withdrawal of funds.

Test craft activities have been directed primarily towards 3KSES type systems and subsystems. SES-100A1 and XR-1D have numerous systems representative of 3KSES installations and are used to bridge the gap between studies, analyses, model tests and full scale equipment. Midshipmen and officers have the opportunity of studying and participating in SES technology and operation, making use of the XR-5 at the US Naval Academy, Annapolis, Maryland, and the XR-3 at the Postgraduate School, Monterey, California.

The propeller-driven SES-100B, formerly based at Panama City, Florida, is now in storage at the Surface Effect Ship Test Facility. The SES-100B and the SES-100A1 operated together for the first time in October 1978, manoeuvring in formation at 65 knots, then separating to make opposing passes with closing speeds above 120 knots. The SES-100B has been used to demonstrate the operational effectiveness of semi-submerged supercavitating propeller systems.

XR-1D STRUCTURAL LOADS TESTS

The structural loads test programme provides two categories of structural design information: slamming load pressures on the forward sloped "wet deck" (underside of the central hull) in the off-cushion condition. Particular emphasis was placed on a comparison between maximum localised point pressures and area pressures in the fore-and-aft direction, and on hull girder bending loads and shear reactions resulting from wave slamming. This programme was characterized by four outstanding features:

a. The fully instrumented craft operated hull-borne in very high sea states.
b. Pressure panels were used to measure design (distributed) rather than peak pressures.
c. Correlation was established between slamming loads and slamming pressure time histories.
d. Tests were of sufficient duration to measure design limit values without need for statistical extrapolation.

In early 1978 the most severe tests took place when the XR-1D operated off-cushion at low speed, 2-3 knots, at various headings into waves up to 8ft high and wind gusts to 65 knots, corresponding to sea state 7 for the 3KSES. A year later the XR-1D embarked upon a series of partial cushion missions into wind and wave conditions only slightly less severe than encountered during the previous series. Slamming was again encountered, but somewhat different to that experienced during the off-cushion missions. The crew reported that the heaviest impacts occurred further aft, on the wet deck near the centre of the craft. It was also found that the bow seal was subjected to extremely severe loads, greatly exceeding those encountered during any preceding operations. Information and experience from XR-1D off-cushion and partial cushion operation in heavy seas has been used in the 3KSES programme to ensure that this ship would be able to survive the most adverse conditions.

XR-1D RIDE CONTROL SYSTEM TEST PROGRAMME

A ride control system (RCS) was designed for the 3KSES to reduce vertical accelerations to acceptable habitability limits by appropriate control of air flow into the air cushion. This is accomplished by use of controllable vent valves, by variable geometry fans (controllable inlet blockage) or by combination of the two methods. An effective RCS significantly increases the crew's ability to perform throughout the range of speed and sea state for which the ship is designed. However RCS power demands affect range, payload and endurance and therefore must be minimised, commensurate with habitability requirements.

The XR-1D programme to develop and demonstrate an efficient RCS is based on use of feedback sensors and electronic controls activating vent valves and variable lift fans to control the ship's vertical accelerations while maintaining adequate thrust from the waterjet propulsion system. Precise measurement of immersion is a key element: accordingly a nuclear immersion sensor will be used during the test programme. The sensor consists of a shielded radioactive gamma ray source mounted in the "fence" beneath the starboard side wall and outboard of the waterjet inlet, and detector electronics within the hull. The source will emit a collimated beam of gamma photons, and the rate at which they reach the detector is translated into depth of side wall immersion. This value is used for feedback in the air ingestion control loop. The RCS test programme has five objectives:

a. Develop stable operation at full airflow modulation capability for simple control laws (pressure or acceleration).
b. Systematically evaluate RCS effectiveness in terms of ride quality improvement and power demands for various sea/speed conditions.
c. Correlate test results with model data and theory.
d. Evaluate effectiveness of other control laws under consideration for the 3KSES RCS.
e. Apply significant results to the 3KSES.

XR-3

The 2,727kg (6,000lb) XR-3 is the Navy's smallest manned test craft. It is 7·09m (26ft) long and 3·66m (12ft) wide. This two-seater has been operated at Monterey for several years, enabling graduate students to acquire knowledge of SES technology. Interest is presently concentrated on the effects of seal design and characteristics upon seal loads and craft performance, since the XR-3's two-dimensional stay-stiffened seals resemble those of the SES-100A1 and the system contemplated for the 3KSES. The XR-3 seals have been instrumented to measure seal position and attitude as well as lift and drag forces. Data taken at various speeds, seal positions, craft longitudinal centre of gravity locations, and craft heel angle in turns are being used for correlation with model and other testcraft seal loads experimental data. The information enhances the understanding of seal drag, its effect

Structural loads tests of the XR-1D in high seas were completed in early 1979. Evaluation of the ride control system were to continue into 1980

Severity of conditions in which XR-1D operated is evident above

XR-3 continues as a much-used research vehicle at the US Navy Postgraduate School

on hump traverse, and provides design guidelines for future seal systems.

The XR-3 continues to provide data each year for several theses. A sampling of subjects indicate the thoroughness with which every aspect of that craft has been studied: validation of nonlinear six degree of freedom mathematical model in calm water, effects of seal shape variations on craft performance, survey of pressure distribution in plenum chamber, static pressure effects on stern seal lift and drag, and a study of pitch and roll transients using the XR-3 computer programme.

XR-5

The latest testcraft, XR-5, displaces 3,420kg (7,500lb). Its length of 14·3m (46ft 9in) and

beam of 2·51m (8ft 3in) give it a greater length to beam ratio than any earlier Navy SES. It is used by midshipmen at the US Naval Academy, Annapolis as a research vehicle for continued development of high length to beam ratio SES as well as a training craft for advanced ship concepts. Test and evaluation programmes are providing a broad data base for correlating test craft data with experimental model data. Variations in displacement, longitudinal centre of gravity location, air-flow rate and seal position are parameters being examined to evaluate their effect on performance, manoeuvring and motions in seas. The XR-5 trials are taking place on the Severn River and on the Chesapeake Bay. Direction and support is being provided by the Academy faculty and the Aviation and Surface Effects Department of the David W Taylor Naval Ship R & D Center.

The test craft and test equipment provide midshipmen with experience in conducting research with an experimental vehicle as well as an introduction to the SES concept. Future programmes for the XR-5 will include modifications to the sidewalls, seals, and steering methods to assess their effect on craft operation and handling. Other programmes will involve instrumentation of the craft to measure wave-induced slamming loads.

SES-100A

Seals characterised by light weight "planers" contacting the water surface have been designed originally to equip the 3KSES. The planers are joined at their edges by flexible joints to form a compliant seal, able to adapt to wave contours. In combination with full length side hulls, the seals ensure positive pitch stability at all speeds and sea states. Drag characteristics are considered equal to or better than earlier configurations. Most significantly, environmental testing demonstrated that planers are extremely resistant to water erosion and damage due to high speed operation.

The SES-100A1 was reconfigured to accept 3KSES-type bow and stern seals which are suitable for use throughout the 100A1 operational envelope. The sidewalls reflect 3KSES geometry and extend further forward than the original structure. Individual lift fans and ducts supply air to the bow seal, cushion, and stern seal.

The SES-100A1 in its most recent configuration became operational in March 1978 and within a few missions had attained 65 knots with significantly less propulsion power than required for equivalent speed prior to the extensive modifications. A speed of 74 knots was reached during envelope expansion tests.

The primary objective of the test programme was verification of functional performance and structural integrity of the 3KSES-type seal. Basic tests and static seal system tests, accomplished during 1978-79, provided valuable geometry and static loads information used to refine and verify 3KSES seal system analytic computer programmes contributing to detail design and associated manufacturing procedures. During the same period extensive underway tests in 3KSES-scaled speed and sea state conditions indicated areas where specific components of the bow seal system required re-evaluation and modification. These tests also provided additional seal wear design information, contributed to development of seal maintenance and repair concepts and provided extensive dynamic environmental type seal loads data for verification of detail design analytical tools. The test programme was expanded to include evaluation of new bow seal components (ie interplanar joints) developed from new designs and manufacturing processes. A heavily instrumented metallic planar was tested in high sea states and provided large-scale planar loads data for verification of design tools.

RCS tests were performed simultaneously to check and adjust the RCS which underwent extensive modifications incidental to the reconfiguration, including re-arranged vent valves, modified air distribution ducting and new control circuitry. Later tests were planned to cover higher sea states, first to the boundaries of the scaled 3KSES speed/sea state spectrum and ultimately to the limits of the 100A.

SURFACE EFFECT SHIP TEST FACILITY

The test facility built specifically as a base for the SES-100A1, SES-100B and other test craft is located on the Naval Air Station, Patuxent River,

Future naval officers are introduced to SES technology both in the classroom and by use of the XR-5

SES-100A entering the U-dock which supports the syncrolift platform

Maryland. Temperate climate, deep water and ready access to rough water provide an ideal environment for small and moderate size SES. Specialised SESTF shops and the excellent facilities of the Naval Air Test Center provide support to the various testcraft.

Prefabricated buildings provide space for a boathouse which accommodates the 100A, 100B, XR-1D and one or two smaller craft on their cradles, seal and maintenance shops, warehouse and administration area.

A syncrolift drydock and transfer system is the principal feature of this facility. It is basically an elevator-type drydock consisting of four hoisting units, each connected to a corner of a 50ft by 100ft platform. The platform is lowered to the required depth; the craft is floated over the submerged platform and cradle which is then raised to bring the craft, cradle and platform completely above water level. The unit has adequate capacity (200 tons) to lift the craft, even if severely damaged with several compartments flooded. The lift-

ing platform is equipped with tracks to receive the transfer cradles specifically designed to accommodate each SES. When the lifting platform is elevated so that the track is level with the track on the transfer car, the SES may be moved from the platform to the transfer car and thence moved into the boat house. Berthing facilities immediately adjacent to the syncrolift provide fuelling, defuelling, electric power, potable water and sewage.

ADVANCED DESIGN

The project's ultimate objective is development of SES technology to a high level of confidence and assist the introduction into the Navy of a class of SES escort ships of approximately 3,000 tons displacement, to be followed by design and construction of larger ships for additional missions. The designs of both escort class and larger ships will be closely related and synchronised with the development, test and evaluation of the 3KSES and succeeding designs.

SKIMMERS INCORPORATED

PO Box 855, Severna Park, Maryland 21146, USA

Telephone: (301) 647 0526

Officials:
M W Beardsley, *President and General Manager*
H L Beardsley
W D Preston

Overseas Representative: United Kingdom: Airhover Ltd (see UK section)

Skimmers Inc was formed in April 1966 to produce plans for use by homebuilders in constructing the Fan-Jet Skimmer sport ACV. It is affiliated with the Beardsley Air Car Co.

Recently the company has designed a small two-seat ACV and an experimental prototype is under construction.

FAN-JET SKIMMER

Fan-Jet Skimmer was designed by Col Melville Beardsley, a former USAF technical officer, and one of the pioneers in ACV development in the USA, to be the simplest and cheapest one-man ACV that could be devised. More than 40 craft of this type have been built to date.

LIFT AND PROPULSION: Power for the integrated lift/propulsion system is provided by a

Chrysler two-cycle 6hp engine, driving a 457mm (18in) axial flow fan. The fan has a marine plywood hub with nine sheet metal formed blades. The primary air flow, used for direct thrust, is ejected through a propulsive slot control flap located aft of the fan duct. The area of the slot can be varied by a hinged flap controlled by a lever. This and the throttle lever and ignition switch are the only controls. The secondary air flow, for cushion lift, passes into a rearward plenum chamber.

CONTROLS: The craft is steered by kinesthetic control (body movement) which the designer feels is the ideal method of control for a craft of this size.

HULL: The main structural component is a tractor inner tube, giving 217·5kg (700lb) of buoyancy, around which is an aluminium framework of square tube, and L girders. The topside bow profile is in plywood. The structure is decked in vinyl-coated nylon fabric which is also used for the self-extending skirt system.

DIMENSIONS
Length overall: 2·9m (9ft 8in)
Beam overall: 1·8m (6ft 2in)
Height overall on landing pads: 0·9m (36in)
Skirt depth: 0·2m (9in)
Draft afloat: 0·12m (5in)
Cushion area: 4m² (44ft²)

WEIGHTS
Normal all-up weight: 113kg (250lb)
Normal payload (operating): 68kg (150lb)
Max payload: 81·6kg (180lb) approx

PERFORMANCE
Max speed, calm water: 29km/h (18mph)
Cruising speed, calm water: 29km/h (18mph)
Max wave capability: approx 153mm (6in)
Still air range: approx 56km (35 miles)
Max gradient, static conditions: 5 degrees approx
Vertical obstacle clearance: 127mm (5in)

For full over-the-hump performance with an operator weighing more than 79·4kg (175lb) the installation of two power plants is recommended each identical with the standard single power unit. With an operator weighing up to 102kg

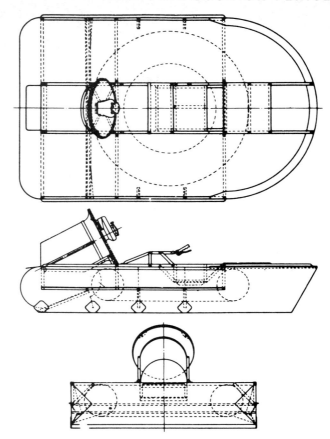

Fan-Jet Skimmer, designed by Melville Beardsley

(225lb) the speed of the twin is approximately 20% greater than the standard single engine.

With the overall length of the twin-engine model increased to 3·4m (11ft 2in), it will carry a useful load of 160kg (350lb) at maximum speeds of approximately 56·33km/h (35mph) over smooth land and 35·4km/h (22mph) over calm water.

UNITED STATES HOVERCRAFT MANUFACTURING CO INC

Box 1191, Lynwood, Washington 98036, USA
Telephone: (206) 466 4533
Cables: Hoverco, Box 1191, USA 98036
Officials:
Gerald W Crisman, *President*
E Wood Peabody Jr, *Vice President*
Sharron E Crisman, *Secretary*
Henry A Roche, *Financial Adviser*

Formed originally in 1961 as Gemco Incorporated, United States Hovercraft Manufacturing Co has built a number of light and ultra-light craft, including the first hovercraft to cross the Mississippi. The company is at present concentrating on the production of a two-seater, the 6300 Hoverbird, a six-seater—the Model 5501 Eagle—and a light utility variant, the Model 5502 Crane. In the planning stage are two larger vehicles, the Alaskan, an amphibious utility craft with a payload capacity of 10-12 tons and the Pioneer, a 30-seat passenger ferry. In 1979 the company was appointed as a representative for Space Hovercraft Ltd of Ottawa, Canada. It is also marketing and selling the Odyssey 700 four-seater, designed by Space Hovercraft, in the Seattle area.

MODEL 5501 EAGLE

The prototype of this glass fibre-hulled six-seater completed its trials in 1974. Hulls for both the Eagle and a light utility version, the Model 5502 Crane, are being built by the Tacoma Boatbuilding Co, of Tacoma, Washington, in conjunction with Rienell Boats.

LIFT AND PROPULSION: Integrated system employing a single Ford 429 automobile engine which drives a stainless multibladed fan for lift and a Hartzell variable and reversible-pitch propeller for propulsion. Total fuel capacity is 151·5 litres (40 US gallons).

Eagle, glass fibre-hulled six-seater

Multi-purpose variant of the Eagle, the Crane with a well deck aft of a three-seat cabin

CONTROLS: Deflection of triple rudder vanes mounted at the aft end of the propeller duct, together with thrust ports, forward and aft, provide heading control. Reverse propeller pitch employed for braking.

HULL: Moulded fibreglass structure with honeycomb aluminium reinforcement at stress points. Buoyancy boxes filled with expanded polyurethane.

SKIRT: Simple bag type in Hypalon material.

ACCOMMODATION: Fully enclosed cabin for driver and five passengers. Access is via two centrally-placed gull-wing doors, one port, one starboard. Air-conditioning optional.

SYSTEMS, ELECTRICAL: 12V for starting and services.

DIMENSIONS

Length overall: 6·4m (21ft)
Beam overall: 3·35m (11ft)
Height overall, on cushion: 2·74m (9ft)
    off cushion: 2·13m (7ft)
Cabin: 2·13 × 1·83m (7 × 6ft)

WEIGHTS

Empty: 635kg (1,400lb)
All-up weight: 1,125kg (2,700lb)
Disposable load: 499kg (1,100lb)

PERFORMANCE

Max speed: in excess of 60 knots
Endurance: 4 hours
Normal range: 386km (240 miles)
Stopping distance: 106·68m (350ft)
Obstacle clearance: 609mm (2ft)
Max wave capability: 0·914-1·22m (3-4ft)

MODEL 5502 CRANE

This multi-duty version is almost identical to the Model 5501 Eagle apart from the provision of a well deck immediately aft of its cabin. The Crane's cabin measures 1·22 × 1·83m (4 × 6ft) and seats three, with the driver in the central position. Access to the cabin is via a gull-wing door at the rear, leading from the well deck.

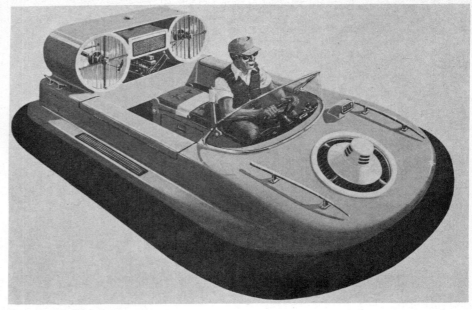

Hoverbird amphibious two-seater

Machinery arrangement, dimensions, weight and performance are similar to those of the Eagle.

MODEL 6300 HOVERBIRD

The Hoverbird is a fibreglass-hulled utility two-seater with twin ducted thrust fans. The company reports that forty have been ordered for use in Alaska and fifty-five in the rest of the USA. Price per craft "ready-to-fly" is slightly below US $4,000.

LIFT AND PROPULSION: Cushion air is supplied by a 28hp Kohler engine mounted ahead of the cockpit and driving a multibladed fan. Thrust is furnished by a single 46hp Volkswagen automotive engine driving via a belt transmission two ducted fans aft.

HULL: Moulded fibreglass structure.

SKIRT: A simple bag skirt is standard. A segmented skirt can be supplied if required.

ACCOMMODATION: Open cockpit with tandem seating for driver and one passenger. Fold-down seat backs provided for comfort and safety.

DIMENSIONS

Length overall: 3·65m (12ft)
Width: 2·13m (7ft)
Height, on cushion: 1·49m (4ft 11in)
    on landing pads: 1·21m (4ft)

UNIVERSAL HOVERCRAFT

1204 3rd Street, Box 281, Cordova, Illinois 61242, USA
Telephone: (309) 654 2588
Officials:
R J Windt, *Director*

Formed in 1969, this company has designed and built 30 different sports and utility ACV prototypes, ranging from an ultra-light single-seater to a seven-seater powered by a 200hp automotive engine. Plans for some of these designs are available to home builders. It has recently developed three new single-engined amphibious craft—a 3·65m (12ft) two-seater, a 3·96m (13ft) four-seater and a 5·48m (18ft) six-seater.

Work has also been undertaken on air cushion vehicles propelled by waterjets, outboard motors and sails.

Descriptions of the UH-10C, UH-11S and UH-11T will be found in *Jane's Surface Skimmers 1980* and earlier editions.

UH-12S

This lightweight two-seater is capable of carrying two adults and their camping or fishing equipment at up to 56·32km/h (35mph) over water.

LIFT AND PROPULSION: A single JLO 340 or 440 engine drives the lift fan and the thrust propeller via a V-belt system. The 0·61m (2ft) diameter fan turns at a maximum of 3,500rpm, while the 1·21m (4ft) diameter thrust propeller turns at 2,200rpm at full throttle.

CONTROLS: Three aerodynamic rudders behind the propeller provide directional control.

HULL: Construction is of fir ribs and stringers and ⅛in plywood covering. Fibreglass applied to all joints and edges.

ACCOMMODATION: Tandem arrangement with passenger seated behind driver on a sliding seat.

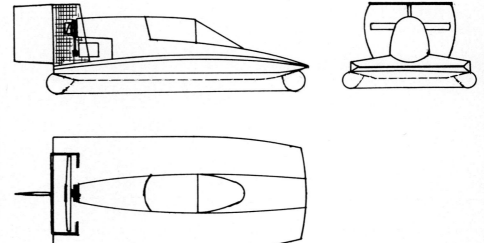

UH-12S lightweight two-seater for two adults and their camping or fishing equipment

UH-12S 72·5km/h (45mph) amphibious two-seater, powered by a single 440cc JLO two-cycle petrol engine

DIMENSIONS
Length: 3·91m (12ft 10in)
Width: 1·82m (6ft)
Height: 1·52m (5ft)
WEIGHTS
Empty: 147kg (325lb)
Normal payload: 158·75kg (350lb)
Max payload: 204·1kg (450lb)
PERFORMANCE
Max speed, over land: 72·42km/h (45mph)
    over water: 56·32km/h (35mph)
Gradient at 450lb gross weight: 23%
PRICE: Plans US$15.

UH-12T

This amphibious two-seater is based on the company's original prototype which was built early in 1969. The new hull is easier to build and provides automatic pitch control. As thrust is increased, the aerofoil-shaped hull generates more lift, offsetting the pitching moment caused by thrust. The height of the centre of thrust has also been reduced.
LIFT AND PROPULSION: Motive power for the lift system is provided by a 133cc Chrysler two-cycle petrol engine which drives a 0·66m (2ft 2in) diameter four-bladed fan at 4,500rpm. About five per cent of the cushion air is employed to inflate the bag-type skirt. Thrust is provided by a 25hp JLO 395 two-cycle engine driving a 0·914m (3ft) diameter two-bladed propeller.
CONTROLS: Directional control is provided by a single aerodynamic rudder.
HULL: Mixed wood and fibreglass construction. Structure comprises fir ribs and stringers covered with ⅛in plywood. Cockpit floor and other highly stressed areas strengthened with fibreglass.
ACCOMMODATION: Single bench seat for driver and one passenger. Cockpit canopy can be fitted for use in cold weather.
DIMENSIONS
Length overall: 3·81m (12ft 6in)
Beam overall: 1·82m (6ft)
WEIGHTS
Empty: 124·73kg (275lb)
All-up weight: 272·14kg (600lb)
PERFORMANCE
Max speed, over land: 72·5km/h (45mph)
    over water: 64·37km/h (40mph)
Max gradient: 26%
PRICE: Plans US$15 per set.

UH-12T2

The latest two-three seater to be designed by Universal Hovercraft for the homebuilder, this easily constructed craft is powered by standard lawnmower engines. The low rpm of these engines ensures quiet operation and a long engine life. Construction costs range from US$200 - US$500, depending on the quality of the engines and the materials used.
LIFT AND PROPULSION: Lift is supplied by a 5hp Briggs and Stratton engine driving a 0·6m (24in) diameter, 14in pitch four-bladed wooden fan at 3,000rpm. Maximum cushion pressure is 11lb/ft². Thrust is provided by a 10hp Briggs and Stratton engine driving a 1·06m (42in) diameter, 40cm (16in) pitch two-bladed propeller aft. Total fuel capacity is 6·15 litres (1½ US gallons).
CONTROLS: Triple rudders hinged to the rear of the propeller guard control craft handling.
HULL: Wooden structure built from pine ribs and struts and covered with ⅛in plywood skin. The structure is designed to survive a 64km/h (40mph) plough-in in choppy water.
SKIRT: 177mm (7in) deep, 304mm (12in) diameter bag skirt, fabricated in 16oz/yd² neoprene-coated nylon.
ACCOMMODATION: Enclosed cabin seating driver and up to two passengers on a movable tandem seat.
DIMENSIONS
EXTERNAL
Length overall, power off: 3·93m (12ft 11in)
Beam overall, power off: 1·82m (6ft)
    skirt inflated: 2·03m (6ft 8in)
Cushion area: 6·03m² (65ft²)
Skirt depth: 177mm (7in)

UH-12T2 2-3 seater for homebuilders, employing two standard lawnmower engines for lift and propulsion

INTERNAL
Cabin length: 1·21m (4ft)
Max width: 0·6m (2ft)
WEIGHTS
Normal empty: 136·07kg (300lb)
Normal gross: 272·14kg (600lb)
Normal payload: 136·07kg (300lb)
Max payload: 181·44kg (400lb)
PERFORMANCE
Max speed, calm water: 56·32km/h (35mph)
Max wave capacity: 304mm (12in) chop
Max gradient, static conditions: 12 degrees at 600lb
Vertical obstacle clearance: 152mm (6in)
PRICE: Plans US$15

UH-13SA

The prototype of this craft was built in 1974 from 25mm (1in) thick urethane foam fibreglass laminate. This type of construction proved too difficult for the home builder and so the craft was redesigned for wooden construction. An integrated lift/propulsion system is employed. Once engine speed is above idling the correct amount of lift is automatically maintained throughout the entire engine speed range by a patented system.
LIFT AND PROPULSION: Motive power is provided by a single JLO 440 driving a 0·63m (2ft 1in) diameter four-bladed lift fan and a 1·21m (4ft) diameter propeller via a V-belt reduction drive.
CONTROLS: Craft heading is controlled by twin rudders behind the propeller.

HULL: Construction is similar to that of UH-12T.
ACCOMMODATION: Two adults and two children can be carried in two bench-type seats.
DIMENSIONS
Length: 4·21m (13ft 10in)
Width: 1·98m (6ft 6in)
WEIGHTS
Empty: 181·42kg (400lb)
Normal payload: 181·42kg (400lb)
Max payload: 272·14kg (600lb)
PERFORMANCE
Max speed, over land, snow, ice: 96·56km/h (60mph)
    over water: 80·46km/h (50mph)
Max gradient: 26%
PRICE: Complete plans, US$9. Full-scale outline US$3 extra

UH-13T

This new derivative of the UH-13 employs the same basic hull as the UH-13S, but exchanges its automatic lift system for a separate lift engine.
The 13T can carry 136-181kg (300-400lb) even when powered by 10 to 16hp four-cycle lawnmower engines.
LIFT AND PROPULSION: Recommended engines: Lift, 8hp four-cycle vertical shaft mower engine or equivalent. Thrust, two-cycle 20-55hp (295-760cc) or 10-16hp four-cycle engine weighing under 45kg (100lb).
DIMENSIONS
Length: 4·21m (13ft 10in)
Beam: 1·98m (6ft 6in)

Structure of UH-13SA is built in fir or pine ribs and stringers, covered with ⅛in plywood. Top speed over land is 96·56km/h (60mph)

WEIGHTS
Payload: 317kg (700lb)
Empty: 192-215kg (425-475lb)
PERFORMANCE
Max speed over water: 64-96km/h (40-60mph)
  land, ice and snow: 72-112km/h (45-70mph)
Hover height: 203mm (8in)
Max gradient: 15-33%

UH-14B

An amphibious four-seater, the UH-14B has a maximum payload capacity of over 362·85kg (800lb). Employment of a large slow-turning propeller for thrust permits high-speed cruising while generating very little noise.
LIFT AND PROPULSION: A JLO 230 two-cycle engine turns a four-bladed fan for lift. Alternatively, an 8hp vertical shaft lawnmower engine may be used for lift. Thrust is supplied by a JLO 440 two-cycle engine driving a 1·21m (4ft) diameter propeller through a V-belt speed reduction system.
CONTROLS: Heading is controlled by multiple aerodynamic rudders aft of the propeller.
HULL: Construction is of fir or pine ribs and stringers, which are covered with ⅛in plywood.
DIMENSIONS
Length: 4·52m (14ft 10in)
Width: 2·13m (7ft)
Height off cushion: 1·52m (5ft)
WEIGHTS
Empty: 204kg (450lb)
Normal payload: 226·78kg (500lb)
Max payload: 362·85kg (800lb)
PERFORMANCE
Max speed, over land, snow, ice: 96·56km/h (60 mph)
  over water: 88·51km/h (55mph)
Max gradient at 650lb gross weight: 28%
PRICE: Complete plans US$14. Full-scale outline US$5.

UH-14T

The UH-14T is a utility two-seater with a cargo hold aft of its bench-type seat. This space may also be used for a rearward facing seat. Total payload capacity is 317·5kg (700lb).
LIFT AND PROPULSION: Lift air is supplied by an 8hp lawnmower engine or a JLO 230cc engine driving a four-bladed 0·66m (2ft 2in) diameter fan. A JLO 440 engine driving a 0·914m (3ft) diameter two-bladed propeller provides thrust.
CONTROLS: Large aerodynamic rudder at rear of propellers controls craft heading.
HULL: Construction is similar to that of the UH-12T.
DIMENSIONS
Length: 4·26m (14ft)
Width: 1·98m (6ft 6in)
Height off cushion: 1·22m (4ft)
WEIGHTS
Empty: 181·42kg (400lb)
Normal payload: 226·78kg (500lb)
Max payload: 317·5kg (700lb)
PERFORMANCE
Max speed, over land, snow, ice: 88·51km/h (55mph)
  over water: 72·42km/h (45mph)
Max gradient at 272·14kg (600lb) gross weight: 22%
PRICE: Complete plans, US$14. Full-scale outline, $4.

UH-16S

Introduced in 1980, the UH-16S seats five-six and has a maximum speed over land, snow and ice of 104km/h (65mph).
LIFT AND PROPULSION: Integrated system, employing the same type of automatic lift control as fitted to the 13S, 18S and 26S. Motive power is furnished by a 1,500cc or larger Volkswagen, Corvair or any other four-cylinder water-cooled automotive engine weighing less than 150kg (350lb). Thrust, 68-158kg (150-350lb).
CONTROLS: Heading is controlled by multiple aerodynamic rudders aft of the propeller.

UH-13T three-to-four seat utility hovercraft

UH-14B four-seater with maximum payload capacity of 362·85kg (800lb)

UH-14T utility two-seater with total payload capacity of 317·5kg (700lb)

ACCOMMODATION: Enclosed cabin seating five-six.
DIMENSIONS
Length: 5·15m (16ft 11in)
Width: 2·28m (7ft 6in)
WEIGHTS
Empty: 340-453kg (750-1,000lb)
Payload: 340kg (750lb) with 1,500cc VW engine and over 454kg (1,000lb) with 2,300cc four-cylinder Ford engine

PERFORMANCE
Speed over water: 88·51km/h (55mph)
  land, snow and ice: 104km/h (65mph)
Clearance height: 177-304mm (7-12in)
Gradient: 15-25%

UH-17S

Construction of the prototype UH-17S, which has an integrated lift/propulsion system powered by either a Volkswagen or Corvair engine of 50-140hp, was completed in May 1970. The craft, which seats a driver and up to three passengers, is said to be extremely quiet and control is precise. It is capable of towing water or snow skier, sleds or ski boards.

LIFT AND PROPULSION: A single 75hp Corvair automobile engine drives a 1·06m (3ft 6in) diameter centrifugal fan mounted vertically on a shaft inside a transverse duct. Air is drawn by the fan from each end of the duct. Propulsion air is expelled through outlets at the stern and lift air is ducted into a plenum below. The fan feeds air into the cushion at 240ft³/s and provides 150lb thrust.

ACCOMMODATION: Enclosed cabin seating driver and up to three passengers on two bench-type seats.

DIMENSIONS
Length: 5·43m (17ft 10in)
Beam: 2·41m (7ft 11in)
WEIGHTS
Empty: 430·89kg (950lb)
Normal loaded: 725·71kg (1,600lb)
Max loaded: 861·78kg (1,900lb)
PERFORMANCE
Max speed, over land: 67·59km/h (42mph)
    over water: 56-64km/h (35-40mph)
Continuous gradient at 1,200lb: 12%

UH-18S

This was the first hovercraft to complete the journey from Los Angeles to San Diego, a distance of 169·98km (105 miles) across open seas. It accommodates up to seven persons on three bench-type seats. Normal payload is 1,200lb. An automatic lift system similar to that used on the UH-13S is employed to simplify driving, improve reliability and decrease maintenance costs.

LIFT AND PROPULSION: Motive power is supplied by a single Corvair automotive engine, rated at 90hp at 3,600rpm, driving a 0·914m (3ft) diameter four-bladed fan for lift via the automatic lift system, and a 1·87m (6ft 2in) diameter two-bladed propeller through a V-belt speed reduction system. The lift fan turns at a constant 2,400rpm while the propeller turns 1,700rpm at full throttle.

Range of engines which can be used on this craft includes any air-cooled engine from 60-150hp and any four to six cylinder water cooled unit weighing under 181·42kg (400lb).

CONTROLS: Heading is controlled by triple aerodynamic rudders located behind the propeller.

HULL: Construction is similar to that of the UH-18T.

DIMENSIONS
Length: 5·63m (18ft 6in)
Width: 2·43m (8ft)
Height: 1·82m (6ft)
WEIGHTS
Empty: 498·92kg (1,100lb)
Normal payload: 544·28kg (1,200lb)
Max payload: 635kg (1,400lb)
PERFORMANCE
Max speed, over land, snow, ice: 104·6km/h (65mph)
    over water: 88·51km/h (55mph)
Max gradient: 30%
PRICE: Complete plans, US$21. Full-scale outline $5.

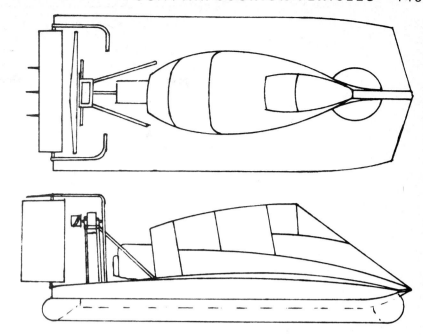

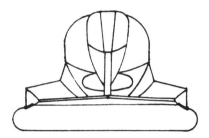

UH-16S, 5-6 seat utility and leisure craft

UH-17S features an integrated lift/propulsion system powered by a 75hp Corvair automobile engine

Universal Hovercraft's UH-18S is capable of operating in the surf zone

UH-18S towing two water-skiers at a time

UH-18T light utility ACV

UH-18S seven-seat ACV

UH-18T

The prototype of this amphibious six-seater was built in 1971 and has accumulated over 400 operating hours, mainly on open seas.

It was the first hovercraft to visit Catalina island, 41·84km (26 miles) off the coast of California. It has also been employed extensively for water and snow skiing.

The aerofoil shaped hull is similar to that of the UH-12T and UH-14T.

LIFT AND PROPULSION: Lift is provided by a 25hp JLO 395 two-cycle engine driving a 762mm (2ft 6in) diameter four-bladed fan at 3,200rpm. About 5% of the air is employed to inflate the bag skirt. Propulsive thrust is supplied by an 85hp Corvair automobile engine driving a 1·52m (5ft) diameter two-bladed propeller at up to 2,800rpm.

CONTROLS: Craft heading is controlled by a single rudder operating in the propeller slipstream and two auxiliary rudders hinged to the rear of twin fins, one each side of the propeller guard. All three rudders are operated by a steering wheel. Separate throttles provided for lift and thrust engines.

HULL: Mixed wood and grp construction. Hull frame is built from fir ribs and stringers and covered with ¼in plywood. Highly stressed areas covered with glass fibre.

SKIRT: 0·46m (1ft 6in) diameter bag skirt, providing 0·304m (1ft) vertical clearance.

ACCOMMODATION: Driver and up to five passengers seated on two three-place bench seats. Cabin can be enclosed by canopy in cold weather.

DIMENSIONS
Length: 5·56m (18ft 3in)
Beam: 2·43m (8ft)
Height, off cushion: 1·82m (6ft)
on cushion: 2·13m (7ft)
WEIGHTS
Empty: 453·57kg (1,000lb)
Normal loaded: 907·14kg (2,000lb)
Max loaded: 1,088kg (2,400lb)
PERFORMANCE
Max speed, over land: 104·6km/h (65mph)
over water: 88·5km/h (55mph)
Max gradient: 30%
PRICE: Complete set of plans for homebuilding, US$25, including full-scale outline.

UH-26S

This 15-seat craft completed its trials in May 1979. Ribs and stringers are in fir and pine and covered with a ¼in plywood skin. The driver's seat is placed high and forward for good visibility.

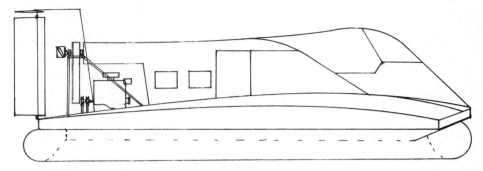

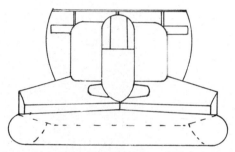

Outboard profile and head-on view of UH-26S

UH-26S amphibious 15-seater during trials

The passenger compartment can seat up to 15 or eight plus 1,200lb of cargo. The craft may also be equipped for touring with sleeping space for four to seven persons.

LIFT AND PROPULSION: Integrated system. Power supplied by a standard V-8 283-400in³ automobile engine driving a 1·06m (3ft 6in) diameter, four-bladed fan for lift and a 2·43m (8ft) diameter two-bladed propeller for thrust.

DIMENSIONS
Length: 7·92m (26ft)

Width: 3·65m (12ft)
WEIGHTS
Empty: 1,133·92kg (2,500lb)
Payload: 1,133·92kg (2,500lb)
PERFORMANCE
Max speed, over land: 104·6km/h (65mph)
over water: 88·5km/h (55mph)
Hover height: 355mm (14in)
Max gradient: 25%
PRICE: Complete set of plans available US$45.
Full size rib outline $10.

VENTURE AERO-MARINE

Box 5273, Akron, Ohio 44313, USA
Telephone: (216) 836 8794
Officials:
Paul W Esterle, *Proprietor*

Venture Aero-Marine is a major supplier of kits for homebuilt hovercraft in the United States. It will also supply partially or fully assembled hovercraft, custom built, to order and offers a wide range of components from engine mountings and fan ducts to skirts and steering systems.

In response to a demand from young enthusiasts who cannot afford full-scale craft, the company offers a line of five radio-controlled and free flight model hovercraft kits.

In addition the company publishes 'The Hoverlog', a comprehensive annual catalogue of sports hovercraft and accessories, currently in its sixth edition.

Universal Hovercraft UH-18SF built for a client by Venture Aero-Marine

WATER RESEARCH COMPANY

3003 North Central Avenue, Suite 600, Phoenix, Arizona 85012, USA
Telephone: (602) 265 7722

Officials:
Richard R Greer, *President*

The Water Research Company was formed in 1972 to consolidate activities surrounding the patents held or applied for by Richard R Greer relating to various aspects of water-borne vehicles. The company has subsequently prepared conceptual studies on a class of winged surface effect vessels (WSEV) intended to fill a variety of US Navy and commercial freight applications.

The conclusions of this study were published in *Naval Engineer's Journal*, April 1974, and further comprehensive conclusions also setting forth energy savings and use of alternate fuels were published in *Jane's Surface Skimmers 1975-76*. Present efforts are directed to providing assistance in related research activities and further research studies.

WINDCRAFT M & M INC

1526 Laskey Road, Toledo, Ohio 43612, USA
Officials:
Mike Clare, *President*
Don Collier, *Production Manager, Chief Test Driver*

Windcraft M & M Inc, is one of the few companies in North America involved in the quantity production of "ready-to-fly" sports hovercraft. Production is at present concentrated on the Hurricane, a one-two seat amphibious craft powered by a modified snowmobile engine and capable of 56·32km/h (35mph) over sand and snow. Hurricane is registered by the US Coast Guard as a Class A boat.

HURRICANE

In 1970 one of these moulded fibreglass sportscraft was the winner of the first national hovercraft race to be staged in the United States. Easy to operate, it is intended primarily to familiarise enthusiasts with the concept of air riding and is one of the fastest-selling, ready-built sports hovercraft in the world.
LIFT AND PROPULSION: Integrated system powered by a single 52hp Xenoah G44BW two-cylinder two-stroke liquid-cooled engine. The engine drives via a toothed belt a 76cm (30in) diameter Windcraft 30 axial lift/thrust fan. Airflow is ducted into the plenum for lift and via two outlets aft for thrust. Maximum static thrust is 34·47kg (76lb) at 3,900rpm.
CONTROLS: Heading is controlled by a single aerodynamic rudder at the base of the fin aft and operated by a handlebar.
HULL: Moulded fibreglass structure comprising top and bottom shells bonded together.
SKIRT: Bag type.
ACCOMMODATION: Open cockpit for up to two seated in tandem.
DIMENSIONS
Length overall: 3·6m (11ft 10in)
Width: 1·75m (5ft 9in)
Height: 1·7m (5ft 7in)
WEIGHTS
Basic: 165·55kg (365lb)
Gross: 360·58kg (795lb)
PERFORMANCE
Max speed, over ice: 80·46km/h (50mph)
   short grass: 48·2km/h (30mph)
   snow/sand: 56·32km/h (35mph)
   water: 48·28km/h (30mph)

Windcraft Hurricane light sports ACV

ACV OPERATORS

ABU DHABI
MARINE TRANSPORT SERVICES CO

This organisation operates a Tropimere SH2-4 which was delivered in September 1977.

AUSTRALIA
AUSTRALIAN LIGHT HOVERCRAFT SERVICES

1 Leon Street, Thorneside, Queensland 4158, Australia

An aquatic and terrestrial weed control service is offered with the aid of modified Scarab II light hovercraft.

BAHRAIN
MINISTRY OF THE INTERIOR

A Tropimere Dash 6 craft has been employed in Bahrain since 1978 as a quick response rescue hovercraft for the Bahrain Coast Guard. A second Dash 6 is expected to join the Coast Guard for similar duties.

BELGIUM
MINISTRY OF WORKS

Antwerp, Belgium

A Hovermarine 216 *Kallo* is employed as a River Scheldt survey craft.

CRAFT OPERATED
HM.2-315 *Kallo*

BRAZIL
AEROBARCOS DO BRASIL TRANSTOR

This company operates three Hovermarine 216 type sidewall hovercraft on a 3n mile route between communities and business areas in the Bay of Guanabara, Rio de Janeiro.

CRAFT OPERATED
HM.2 321 *Gavea*
HM.2 322 *Gragoata*
HM.2 323 *Guarativa*

CANADA
BRITISH COLUMBIA GOVERNMENT

In 1979 a Canadian-built wire-guided hoverferry entered service on the river crossing at Fort Nelson in British Columbia. The HL-105 hoverferry takes 5 minutes for the 609m (2,000ft) single crossing and can carry a payload of 50 tons. It is operated by the BC Highways & Public Works Department.

CANADIAN ARMED FORCES

One AV Tiger is based at Cold Lake, Alberta for overland evaluation.

CANADIAN COAST GUARD HOVERCRAFT UNITS

Headquarters: Transport Canada, Canadian Coast Guard, Fleet Systems Branch, Tower A, Place de Ville, Ottawa, Ontario K1A ON5, Canada
Unit Addresses: Canadian Coast Guard Hovercraft Unit, PO Box 23068, AMF Int'l Airport, Vancouver, British Columbia V7N 1T9, Canada
Telephone: (604) 273-2556
Canadian Coast Guard ACV Laurentian Region, ACV Unit, 850 Nuns Island Boulevard, Nuns Island, Montreal, Quebec H3E 1H2, Canada
Telephone: (514) 283-7882
Administration: Vancouver Unit: Regional Director, Canadian Coast Guard, PO Box 10060, Pacific Centre, 700 West Georgia Street, Vancouver, British Columbia V7Y 1E1, Canada
Montreal Unit: Director, Canadian Coast Guard, 2 Place Quebec, Room 212, Quebec, Quebec G1R 205, Canada

The Canadian Coast Guard Hovercraft Unit in Vancouver was formed on 5 August 1968, to evaluate the use of hovercraft in search and rescue and other Coast Guard duties.

CCG Odyssey at Prescott, Ontario

Canadian Coast Guard Voyageur providing logistic support during the construction of a lighthouse in St Lawrence River

In May 1977, the unit took delivery of a new SR.N6 hovercraft, serial No 039 to boost the search and rescue capabilities.

OPERATIONS: The normal area of patrol is the Straits of Georgia and Gulf Islands — an area of approximately 500 square miles. The unit is often called upon outside this area on search and rescue missions.

The average patrol distance is 80 miles.

Since 1 April 1969, the unit has carried out well over 3,000 SAR missions, directly involving some 5,500 persons. These include marine, aircraft distress and mercy missions. The unit is now manned on a 24-hour basis in order to respond to the large number of incidents occurring in the area.

It is anticipated that in 1981 the unit will be directed by the Rescue Coordination Centre to respond to more than 1,000 distress calls.

Other operations included the checking, servicing and repairing of marine navigational aids within the patrol area, transporting men and materials for aids construction and the laying of underground cables in marshy terrain; aircraft accident inspection; water pollution investigation; carriage of Inspectors for spot safety checks of tugs; working with police departments; exercises with the Canadian Armed Forces vessels; training and familiarisation of selected Government personnel, and experimental work with other Government agencies.

EQUIPMENT: One SR.N5 serial No 021, and one SR.N6 No 039, modified to Coast Guard requirements.

Equipment includes navigation and communications equipment, such as radar, HF and VHF direction finder, HF/MF, VHF/FM and VHF/AM radiotelephone, two Nightsun 65 million candle power searchlights, 2 × 6 man inflatable liferafts, 2 × 100 gallon auxiliary fuel tanks (extending endurance to 9 hours at maximum power), stretchers, first aid kit, fire-fighting equipment, towing gear and other SAR equipment.

In January 1974, the CCG took delivery of a refurbished Voyageur 002. This forms the equipment of her Development and Evaluation Unit, whose current task is to evaluate the vehicle in various CCG roles. For five years the Unit was based in Montreal. In April 1980, the Evaluation and Development Unit was disbanded and the Unit was reformed as the Laurentian Region ACV Unit, thus becoming an integral part of the CCG's operational fleet. The Unit's duties encompass the whole spectrum of CCG operational roles. The ACV has proven to be particularly suited to operations requiring high response speed, operations across water/land interface, and in shoal conditions. Specific roles include: navigation aids servicing, re-supply of light stations, construction support, pollution control, inshore icebreaking, search and rescue, and regulation enforcement.

The Unit is equipped with one Bell Aerospace Voyageur Serial No 002, registration CH-CGA, fitted with all navigation and communications equipment required for safe operations in the area of work. This craft can carry a portable crew module to enable the crew to stay aboard for extended periods, if necessary.

In March 1980 CCG took delivery of a Space Hovercraft Odyssey 700 four-seat utility craft to be used as transportation for lighthouse keepers at Long Point, Lake Erie, Ontario and for navigation aids servicing.

CANADIAN HOVERWAYS

CRAFT OPERATED
North American Tiger based at Moosonee, Ontario for charter.

DEPARTMENT OF ENVIRONMENT AND NATIONAL RESEARCH COUNCIL

CRAFT OPERATED
Towed trailers and air cushion assist transporters undergoing evaluation in logging and heavy transport.

RIVTOW, VANCOUVER, BRITISH COLUMBIA

CRAFT OPERATED
PSL 003 Angevinière, three-seat utility craft

Lebed, the Soviet Navy's new 90-ton initial amphibious assault landing craft

CHINA (PEOPLE'S REPUBLIC)

ACVs are required in China for a variety of military and civil applications, including the operation of fast passenger ferry services over river networks with route distances of up to 240-320km (150-200 miles). A number of test craft have been built, one of which is being operated from Chungking on a passenger ferry service. Largest hovercraft to be built in China so far is a 70-ton multi-duty design, which can be used as an amphibious assault craft or high speed passenger/vehicle ferry. The craft, which was launched at Tianjin in August 1979, resembles a scaled-down SR.N4. The prototype is undergoing evaluation.

EGYPT
EGYPTIAN NAVY

Alexandria, Egypt

In 1975 the Egyptian Navy purchased three refurbished SR.N6 hovercraft for coastal defence patrols along the Egyptian coastline. Negotiations for three BH.7 hovercraft for similar duties are in progress with BHC.
CRAFT OPERATED
SR.N6 016
SR.N6 032
SR.N6 034

FINLAND
BOARD OF ROADS AND WATERWAYS

A 22-ton payload capacity passenger/vehicle ferry has been ordered by the Finnish Board of Roads and Waterways from the Wärtsilä Helsinki Shipyard for delivery in 1981. The vehicle, which will carry either 16 cars or two buses, plus up to 50 passengers, will be operated in the

Finnish archipelago, particularly in winter conditions. Details of the craft, designated PUC 22-2500SP, will be found in the Addenda.

PINTALIITÄJÄPALVELU (HOVERCRAFT SERVICE)

Paattistentie 141, SF-20360 Turku 36, Finland

CRAFT OPERATED
Amficat 4, M/S Pinturi
Route(s): Year-round taxi service to islands in the Turku archipelago. Licensed by Finnish Board of Navigation for passenger services. 11,000km (6,214 miles) completed by early summer 1978 in 1,300 operations.

FRANCE
FRENCH NAVY

Toulon, France

The French Defence Ministry has undertaken studies of fully amphibious and sidewall types of hovercraft including projects with SEDAM. Although it is not clear whether there will be any requirement announced by the French Government in the near future, there are signs that the French Navy is interested in the anti-submarine warfare and mine countermeasure potential of SES and ACV craft.

FRENCH RAILWAYS (SNCF)

Operating in conjunction with British Rail Hovercraft Ltd, SNCF began operating the N 500-02 Ingénieur Jean Bertin under the Seaspeed banner on 5 July 1978. SNCF also holds an option on a second craft. N 500-02 operates on both the Boulogne-Dover and Calais-Dover services.

LANGUEDOC-ROUSSILLON REGIONAL DEVELOPMENT BOARD

Montpellier and Perpignan, France

CRAFT OPERATED
2 × N 102

HONG KONG
HONG KONG AND YAUMATI FERRY CO LTD

This company, which is the biggest operator of passenger ferry hovercraft in the world, has a fleet of 16 Hovermarine 216 and 218 craft.

CRAFT OPERATED
HM.2-326 (Type 216) (HYF-101)
      327 (Type 216) (HYF-102)
      328 (Type 216) (HYF-103)
      329 (Type 216) (HYF-104)
HM.2-435 (Type 218) (HYF-105)
      443 (Type 218) (HYF-106)
      445 (Type 218) (HYF-107)
      446 (Type 218) (HYF-108)
      447 (Type 218) (HYF-109)
      448 (Type 218) (HYF-110)
      457 (Type 218) (HYF-111)
      458 (Type 218) (HYF-112)
      459 (Type 218) (HYF-113)
      462 (Type 218) (HYF-114)
      463 (Type 218) (HYF-115)
      464 (Type 218) (HYF-116)

On 17 November 1978 a service was opened between Hong Kong and Canton (PRC) using two Hovermarine 218 craft. It is anticipated that up to five of the 218 craft will be employed on this route. The company has received a licence to operate this service for up to five years.

Biggest ACV to be built in the Chinese People's Republic, is this 70-ton multi-duty craft. The prototype is currently being evaluated in the amphibious initial assault role, but other variants are expected

NAVAL HOVERCRAFT TRIALS UNIT

Two SR.N6 hovercraft from this unit are currently based in Hong Kong performing patrol duties relating to the control of illegal immigrants from South-east Asian countries.

IRAN
IRANIAN NAVY

Hovercraft base: Khosrowabad, Iran

Eight BHC Winchesters are retained by the Iranian Navy on logistics duties and coastal patrol.

Also in service with the IN are six BH.7 hovercraft. The first two craft, BH.7 Mk 4s, are operated in the logistic support role. The remaining four are Mk 5s. The Mk 5 is a multi-role craft and is designed to carry surface-to-surface, surface-to-air missiles on its side decks.

CRAFT OPERATED:
SR.N6 040 (IN 01) Mk 4
SR.N6 041 (IN 02) Mk 4
SR.N6 042 (IN 03) Mk 3
SR.N6 043 (IN 04) Mk 3
SR.N6 044 (IN 05) Mk 4
SR.N6 045 (IN 06) Mk 4
SR.N6 046 (IN 07) Mk 4
SR.N6 047 (IN 08) Mk 4
BH.7 002 (IN 101) Mk 4
BH.7 003 (IN 102) Mk 4
BH.7 004 (IN 103) Mk 5
BH.7 005 (IN 104) Mk 5
BH.7 006 (IN 105) Mk 5
BH.7 007 (IN 106) Mk 5

IRAQ
IRAQI NAVY

It is understood that expansion of the Iraqi Navy is planned and both British and Soviet amphibious hovercraft have been identified as being possible additions to the Navy, to carry out coastal and river patrol duties and provide support for any logistic duties which might occur within the Arabian Gulf. The British Hovercraft Corporation's SR.N6 design, in a modified form, seems likely to be selected.

ISRAEL
ISRAELI NAVY

The Israeli Navy has two SH.2 Mk 5 nineseater hovercraft for use as support craft.

ITALY
ITALIAN INTERFORCE UNIT

Ancona, Italy
CRAFT OPERATED
SR.N6 036 (HC 9801)

JAPAN
BIWAKO KISEN CO LTD

CRAFT OPERATED
HM.2 Mk III 63P
Route(s): Hamaohotsu-Biwako Ohohashi (15km)

JAPANESE NATIONAL RAILWAYS

Kokutetsu Building, 6—5 Marunouchi 1-chome, Chiyoda-ku, Tokyo 100, Japan

A service between Uno in Okayama Prefecture and Takamatsu in Kagawa Prefecture was inaugurated in November 1972, using MV-PP5-07, named *Kamome* (Sea Gull). Since April 1980, MV-PP5-18 named *Tobiuo* (Flying Fish) has been in use. Route distance is 22km; journey time 23 minutes. *Kamome* has an annual utilisation of 2,200 hours.

KYUSHU YUSEN CO LTD

CRAFT OPERATED
HM.2 Mk IV 93P
Route(s): Hakata-Iki Island (73km). Opened July 1978.

Two of the four Mitsui MV-PP5 hovercraft operated by Oita Hoverferry Co Ltd between Oita Airport, Oita and Beppu cities

MEITETSU KAIJO KANKOSEN CO

18-1 Sanbonmatsu-cho, Atsuta-ku, Nagoya, Japan

Began regular services across the Mikawa and Ise Bays between Gamagori and Toba in September 1969 with an intermediate stop at Nishiura and Irako. The craft employed is MV-PP5 14, *Angel 3*. Craft operates three routes: Gamagoori to Nishiura 11·5km (15mins); Nishiura to Irako, 33·6km (30mins), Irako to Toba, 23·2km (20mins). Annual utilisation, 400 hours for two months (July and August) only each year.

NIPPON KAI KANKO FERRY CO LTD

This company began operating two PP15s, PP15-01 *Cygnus* and PP15-02 *Cygnus No 1*, in April 1978. These craft, one of which is used as a reserve, operate for six months each year (April to October) with an annual utilisation of about 1,500 hours per craft.
Route(s): Manao-Ogi, 150km (2 hours 15 mins); Ogi Suzu, 105km (1 hour 25 mins); Suzu-Manao, 60km (50 mins).

OITA HOVERFERRY CO LTD

1-14-1 Nishi-shinchi, Oita, Japan

Oita operates four MV-PP5s, 03, 04, 06 and 10 named *Hakucho 3*, *Hobby 1* and *3*, and *Angel 2*. Two craft are normally operated with two in reserve.
Route(s): Oita Airport to Oita City, 29km (24 mins), Oita Airport to Beppu City, 31km (26 mins), Oita City to Beppu City, 12km (10 mins). Annual utilisation, about 1,500 hours per craft.

YAEYAMA KANKO FERRY K K

No 1 Aza-ohkawa, Ishigaki, Okinawa, Japan

Delivered to her owners in the spring of 1972, MV-PP5 08 *Koryu* operates a service linking Ishigaki with Taketomi, 6·5km (5 mins); Ishigaki to Obama, 19km (15 mins); Ishigaki to Kuroshima, 18·5km (20 mins); Ohara to Obama, 28km (20 mins); Ohara to Kuroshima, 14·5km (10 mins). Annual utilisation, about 1,800 hours.

JORDAN
JORDAN VALLEY AUTHORITY

Amman, Jordan

CRAFT OPERATED
HM.218 460 *Princess Bedia*
HM.218 461 *Princess Sumaya*
Route(s): 50km route along Dead Sea. Each craft seats 70 passengers. Luggage panniers on cabin roof.

NETHERLANDS
ROTTERDAM PORT AUTHORITY

In April 1978 the Rotterdam Port Authority ordered four Hovermarine 218 Port Patrol Craft in a contract valued at approximately Fl 11 million (£1·7 million). The craft, which have the serial numbers 449, 450, 451 and 452, are based on the standard 18m (60ft) long 218 hull, with provision for port monitoring and emergency services in two separate superstructure modules.

NEW ZEALAND
DEPARTMENT OF CIVIL AVIATION

The New Zealand Department of Civil Aviation has one SR.N6 Winchester for crash rescue services at Mangere Airport, Auckland.
CRAFT OPERATED
SR.N6 014 *Whakatopa*

NORTH SHORE FERRIES

HM.2 319, *Whakatere*, is operated by this company between Waiheke Island and Auckland, North Island. Service began in March 1978.

NIGERIA
PIPELINE CONTRACTORS INCORPORATED

CRAFT OPERATED
Sealand SH.2 007. The operator of this craft is an oil exploration company and the craft assists in this activity.

FEDERAL MINISTRY OF TRANSPORT (IND)

19th Floor, Western House, Broad Street, Lagos, Nigeria

This company operates a high-frequency passenger ferry service between Calabar and Oron, across the Calabar river, from 7 am to 7 pm daily. Distance, 15n miles. Load factor, 73-90%.
CRAFT OPERATED
Two HM.2 Mk IVs

PGH

Lagos, Nigeria

This construction company operates one HM.2 Mk 4 441 on a shuttle service between Lagos and a major construction site outside the city.

PAKISTAN
PAKISTAN COAST GUARD AUTHORITY

The Pakistan Coast Guard Authority has two SH.2 six-seat craft for patrol and interception duties.
CRAFT OPERATED
SH.2 009
SH.2 010

PHILIPPINES
BATAAN-MANILA FERRY SERVICES CO

Manila, Philippines

This company, which also owns a Raketa hydrofoil, has two HM.2 Mk III sidewall hovercraft

for passenger ferry service between central Manila and the Island of Corregidor. Services to other parts of Manila Bay are also offered.
CRAFT OPERATED
HM.2-332 *Sea Express 102*
336 *Sea Express 103*

PORTUGAL
SOCIEDADE TURISTICA PONTA DO ADOXE SARL

Avenida Casal Ribeiro 46-6, Lisbon, Portugal
CRAFT OPERATED
HM.2 Mk III 308 *Soltroia*
HM.2 Mk III 318 *Troiano*
Route(s): Setubal-Troia/Sesimbra

SAUDI ARABIA
SAUDI ARABIAN COASTAL AND FRONTIER GUARD

Ministry of the Interior, Airport Road, Riyadh, Saudi Arabia

The Saudi Arabian Coastal and Frontier Guard operates a number of SR.N6 Winchesters on patrol, contraband control, search and rescue and liaison duties. The craft are attached to bases at Jeddah and Aziziyah on the east and west coasts. Negotiations are in progress for the supply of craft of larger capacity than the existing SR.N6s.
CRAFT OPERATED
SR.N6 038
SR.N6 048
SR.N6 049
SR.N6 050
SR.N6 051
SR.N6 052
SR.N6 053
SR.N6 054

UNION OF SOVIET SOCIALIST REPUBLICS
MINISTRY OF THE RIVER FLEET

The 50-seat Sormovich ACV has been operating experimental services on the Volga and Oka rivers and a derivative is expected to go into production. The most widely used commercial ACV at present is the 48-50 seat Zarnitsa sidewall craft, one hundred of which have been introduced into service since 1970. This is being followed into production by the enlarged, 80-seat Orion and the Rassvet, thirty of which are being built at Sosnovska for the Black Sea Shipping Line.

Well over one hundred Zarya air-lubricated hull craft have been completed and many of these are in service on shallow rivers in the eastern areas of the Soviet Union. Wing-in-ground-effect machines are being developed for high-speed ferry services along the main rivers. These are described as being capable of travelling within several metres of the river surface at speeds of some 250km/h (155mph).

SOVIET ARMY

Gus, a military version of the Skate 50-seat fast ferry, is in service with the Soviet Army.

SOVIET NAVY

Several experimental ACVs are being evaluated by the Soviet Navy, and a military version of the Skate which bears the Nato codename "Gus", is in service with the Soviet naval infantry as an assault landing craft. Recently it has been joined in service by the 90-ton Lebed initial amphibious assault landing craft. It will operate from the well docks of LSDs and will carry vehicles up to the size of a battle tank. Largest air cushion vehicle in service is the 220-ton "Aist", similar in many respects to the SR.N4 Mountbatten and employed to carry tanks and mechanised infantry. Some ten are in service in the eastern Baltic and the Black Sea areas.

Soviet Navy Aist during an amphibious assault landing exercise in the Baltic

British Rail's new hovercraft terminal, at Western Docks, Dover

UNITED KINGDOM
BRITISH RAIL HOVERCRAFT LIMITED
(Seaspeed Hovercraft)

Head Office: 50 Liverpool Street, London EC2P 2BQ, England
Telephone: 01-247 7600
Telex: 883339
Representation Overseas: SNCF, Armement Naval, 3 rue Ambroise Paré, 75010 Paris, France
Dover Route Headquarters: Seaspeed International Hoverport, Dover CT17 9TG, England
Telephone: 0304 208013
Telex: 965915
Reservations: Maybrook House, Queens Gardens, Dover CT17 9UQ, England
Telephone: 01-606 3681 and (Dover) 0304 208288, (Birmingham) 021 236 0701 and (Manchester) 061 228 2041
Telex: 96153
Officials:
J M Bosworth, CBE, *Chairman*
J M Lefeaux, *Managing Director*
D D Kirby, *Director*
M J H P Southgate, *Director*
M E A Keeling, *Director*
A J Tame, *Marketing Director*
P A Yerbury, *Technical Director*
D H C Sumner, *Finance Manager*
Captain D Meredith, *Operations Manager*
R F Harris, *Personnel Manager*

British Rail Hovercraft Ltd, a wholly-owned subsidiary of British Railways Board, was formed in March 1966 and launched its first commercial service in July 1966, between Southampton and Cowes. The cross-Channel service for passengers and cars between specially constructed hovercraft terminals at Dover and Boulogne began in August 1968 using an SR.N4 *The Princess Margaret*. A year later the service was augmented by the introduction of a sister craft, *The Princess Anne* and in October 1970 a service was initiated between Dover and Calais.

During 1978 the first of the two stretched SR.N4 Mk III craft came into operation. *The Princess Anne*, formerly a Mk 1 craft, had a 55ft midships section inserted at the British Hovercraft Corporation's factory at Cowes, Isle of Wight. Now the largest hovercraft in the world, it is driven by four uprated Marine Proteus gas turbine engines of 3,800shp, each driving a fan unit and a 6·4m (21ft) propeller. Craft motion is considerably less than that experienced on the standard N4, and operating limitations have been extended to cope with waves up to 3½ metres high. Passenger comfort has also been improved by incorporating the car deck cabins into large, outward facing passenger decks. The finish and trim in these widened compartments has been completely re-designed, with new overhead ventilation, underseat heating, improved hand luggage storage and lighting. A new and improved skirt design with lower pressure ratio featuring deeper fingers and increased air cushion depth at the bow has improved passenger comfort and resulted in faster crossing times in adverse weather. Seaspeed's second N4, *The Princess Margaret*, rejoined the Seaspeed fleet on 10 May 1979, after being 'stretched'.

A new era in cross-Channel hovercraft operations began in July 1978 when Seaspeed took delivery of the French-built SEDAM N 500-02. The craft, operated by SNCF (French Railways) flies under the Seaspeed banner. With three jumbo hovercraft, two 'stretched' SR.N4s, known as 'Super 4s' and the French-built SEDAM N 500 craft, Seaspeed can provide an annual total carrying capacity for 3·3 million passengers and 470,000 vehicles. To accommodate this increased traffic a new purpose built terminal complex was opened at Dover in 1978, situated on 15 acres of reclaimed land between the Prince of Wales Pier and the North Pier in Western Docks. Completely independent of the conventional ferry operations it contains its own passport control and immigration services. Designed on an airport style principle, passengers arrive via a landscaped terminal approach and enter a spacious arrival concourse. Facilities include duty and tax free shops, licensed bars, a cafeteria, snack bar, bureau de change and a nursing mothers room. Motorists check into a multi-lane arrival area with space for 178 cars.

In 1977 the Boulogne Chamber of Commerce and Industry, who control the port installations for ships and hovercraft in the area, decided to go ahead on the first phase of work for the reception of the giant machines. This stage included widening the ramp and extending the hoverpad to take three hovercraft at the same time; the enlargement of the car parking area; the provision of a visitors' car park, building a maintenance block for servicing the N 500 craft, which is based at Boulogne and also a repair area.

In 1978, work started on the second phase — the building of a new passenger terminal complex. It has two distinct buildings. One, an hexagonal tower which houses the administrative offices and the control tower, the other a single storey building for passenger traffic. A footbridge connects the two buildings.

The reception lounge is equipped with a ticket counter, ticket office, bureau de change, cafeteria for 150 people, newsagent's shop, automobile and car hire desks and other passenger amenities including public telephones and toilets. Beyond the customs, immigration and ticket control points, passengers enter a large departure lounge which has a licensed bar and a duty-free shop.

Outgoing and incoming routes for motorists pass under the hexagonal block where ticket inspections etc are made under cover.

The new hoverport complex at Boulogne was opened to the public on 30 May 1979.

In 1980, a new railway platform was built adjacent to the reception lounge at Boulogne Hoverport for trains to and from Paris all the year round. Seaspeed carried a record 315,000 passengers between London and Paris, via Boulogne Hoverport, in 1979.

DEPARTMENT OF INDUSTRY NATIONAL MARITIME INSTITUTE

St Johns Street, Hythe, Hampshire SO4 6YS, England

Operated by the National Maritime Institute as a support craft for marine trials and operations. The HM.2 is based on the Lymington River.

CRAFT OPERATED
HM.2 Mk III 310 (GH 2051)

HOVERLLOYD LIMITED

Ramsgate Office: International Hoverport, Pegwell Bay, Ramsgate, Kent, England
Telephone: 0843 54881
Reservations: 0843 55555 or 01-499 9481
Telex: 96323
Registered and Head Office: Board of Chief Executive, Sales Administration, 49 Charles Street, London W1X 8AE, England
Telephone: 01-493 5525

British Rail Seaspeed's 300-ton Super 4, *The Princess Anne*. During 1980 the company's two Super 4s and the French-built SEDAM N 500-02 were expected to carry a total of 1½ million passengers on the Dover-Boulogne, Dover-Calais services

The Princess Margaret, Seaspeed's second SR.N4 Mk 3 "Super 4", rejoined the Seaspeed fleet on 10 May 1979. It carries up to 416 passengers and 55 vehicles

Dubigeon-Normandie/SEDAM N 500 *Ingénieur Jean Bertin* joined the Seaspeed fleet in July 1978, operating on the Boulogne-Dover (crossing time 35 minutes) and Calais-Dover (30 minutes) routes. It carries up to 400 passengers and 65 vehicles

Sir Christopher, one of four BHC SR.N4 Mk II widened Mountbattens operated by Hoverlloyd between Ramsgate and Calais

Telex: 262374
Officials:
James A Hodgson, *Chairman and Managing Director*
Bengt-G Nilson, *(Swedish), Director*
James W Clement, *Director*
Howard V Archdeacon, *Associate Director*
Robert H Harvey, *Associate Director*
Emrys Jones, *Associate Director*
Andrew Ramsay, *Associate Director*
David Wise, *Associate Director*

Hoverlloyd Ltd is a British registered company, part of the Broström group whose head office is in Gothenburg, Sweden. It was formed in 1969 to operate a cross-Channel car and passenger ferry service between Ramsgate and Calais. The company operates four BHC SR.N4 Mk II hovercraft.

The crossing between Ramsgate and Calais takes 40 minutes and there are up to twenty-seven return trips a day in summer and a minimum of four a day in winter. On 1 May 1969, the company opened coach/hovercraft/coach services between London and Paris. This service takes eight hours. There are up to five daily departures during summer and two during winter.

On 1 April 1974, Hoverlloyd opened coach/hovercraft/coach services between London and Brussels, via Kontrijk or Mons. The service takes seven hours to Brussels. There are up to four daily services in the summer peak and a daily departure is maintained year-round.

Another coach/hovercraft/coach service, linking London with Amsterdam, began on 6 April 1979, and takes 9½ hours. During the summer this service will offer daily departures with twice weekly trips during the remainder of the year.

Hoverlloyd inaugurated two new coach services in May and June 1980 respectively to the Pyrenees and the French Riviera, both with up to two departures and returns a week. The Lourdes route serves Bordeaux, Bayenne (for Biarritz), Pau and Tarbes, and the Nice route, Aix-en-Provence, Ste Maxime, St Raphael and Cannes.

Passengers are able to buy tickets from travel agents, or by making a booking direct from Hoverlloyd ticket office, 8 Berkeley Square, London W1, or by ringing reservations at Ramsgate (0843 55555 or 01-499 9481) and at any Hoverlloyd terminal. Those travelling with a car pay only for their car, according to its length. The car charge covers the driver and up to four passengers. For vehicles there are four tariffs; 'A', 'B', 'C' and 'D'. 'A' tariff is more expensive and is applied in peak hours during summer, in either direction, according to a detailed traffic analysis, 'B' and 'C' tariffs are cheaper and account for the balance of the departures listed for the summer. The 'D' tariff applies throughout the year on selected flights.

The tariffs have been designed to encourage a balance in the origin of cross-Channel traffic, and to spread the daily peaks of traffic.

Covering at present an area of 23 acres at the northern end of Pegwell Bay, Hoverlloyd International Hoverport is located on a site raised 2·4m (8ft) above the level of the beach, so that operations are unaffected by tides. The hoverport consists of a group of long low buildings which contain customs and immigration, Hoverlloyd administrative departments and a large engineering section, as well as a wide range of modern passenger facilities, including a visitors observation platform. There is a large car-parking area alongside the main building. In front of the hoverport, facing the sea, is a large concrete apron on which the hovercraft land and load/unload. Large ramps give access to the apron from the beach. Between the buildings and the cliffs nearby is the car park and car reception area which is joined to the main road which in turn connects with the Thanet Way and the M2 motorway to London.

CRAFT OPERATED
SR.N4 002 GH 2004 *Swift*
SR.N4 003 GH 2005 *Sure*
SR.N4 005 GH 2008 *Sir Christopher*
SR.N4 006 GH 2054 *Prince of Wales*

HOVERTRAVEL LIMITED

Head Office: 12 Lind Street, Ryde, Isle of Wight, England
Telephone: 0983 65181
Telex: 86513-Hoverwork
Terminal Offices: Quay Road, Ryde, Isle of Wight (Tel: 0983 65241); Clarence Pier, Southsea (Tel: 29988)
Officials
C D J Bland, *Chairman and Managing Director*
E W H Gifford, *Director*
D R Robertson, *Director*
J Gaggero, *Director*
J J M Youens, *Director*
A C Smith, *Director*
R G Clarke, *Director and General Manager*
G W Black
J E Benneyworth
G M Palin, *Company Secretary*

Hovertravel Limited is a £200,000 company which was formed in 1965 to operate two SR.N6 Winchester hovercraft across the Solent between Ryde, Isle of Wight and Southsea and Gosport. The Gosport route was discontinued some years ago but the company has assumed responsibility for the operation of the Cowes to Southampton hovercraft ferry service under the name Solent Seaspeed.

Journey time is approximately 7 minutes on the Ryde to Southsea route and 20 minutes between Cowes and Southampton. Approximately 650,000 passengers are carried each year on both routes together with many tons of parcel packages. By September 1979 the total number of passengers carried exceeded 5·5 million.

The combined fleet operated by Hovertravel, Hoverwork and Solent Seaspeed, which during 1979 completed an estimated 8,000 hours of operation, includes:

3 SR.N6 Winchester Class Mk1S hovercraft GH2035, GH2014, GH2015; 2 SR.N6 Winchester Class Mk1 hovercraft GH2010, GH2012; 1 SR.N6 Winchester Class Mk1 freighter GH2011.

HOVERWORK LIMITED

(Wholly owned subsidiary of Hovertravel Limited)

12 Lind Street, Ryde, Isle of Wight, England
Telephone: 0983 65181
Telex: 86513
Officials:
C D J Bland, *Managing Director*
D R Robertson, *Director*
E W H Gifford, *Director*
A C Smith, *Director*
R G Clarke, *Director*
G M Palin, *Secretary*

SOME TYPICAL HOVERWORK OPERATIONS

Year	Location	Type of Operation	Type of Terrain
1969	Netherlands—the Waddenzee	Seismic survey	Shallow water, tidal area with large expanses of sand banks at low water
1969-70	Abu Dhabi	Seismic survey	Very shallow water combined with coral reefs
1970	Bahrain	Gravity survey	Shallow water and operations over coral reefs
1970	Netherlands—the Waddenzee	Seismic survey	Shallow water, tidal area with large expanses of sand banks at low water
1970	Tunisia—Sfax	Seismic survey	Very shallow water
1970	Algiers	Passengers	Transport from Algiers Port to Fair site including half a mile down a specially prepared road
1971	Bahrain	Seismic survey	Shallow water and operations over coral reefs
1971	Saudi Arabia —Red Sea	Seismic survey	Very shallow water combined with coral reefs
1971	Netherlands—the Waddenzee	Seismic survey	Shallow water, tidal area with large expanses of sand banks at low water
1971	Netherlands—Dollard Bay	Service drilling rig	Shallow water, tidal area. 3 miles of sand to cross at low water
1971	Arctic Circle	Logistics	In leads of pack ice over shallow water including plateau of rock with depths from 0·5 to 6 feet
1971	England—North Sea Haisbro & Leman Banks	Seismic survey	Very shallow water in places, moving sand banks with various tidal streams. Total area strewn with wrecks rendering it unsafe and impractical to use boats
1972	Tunisia—Sfax	Seismic survey	Very shallow water and shoreline land work
1972	North West Territories, Canada	Seismic survey	Shallow water, ice
1972	UK—The Wash	Logistics	Mud, shallow water
1973	UK—Maplin Sands	Geological survey for London's third airport	Tidal sands, shallow water
1974 through '75 to '76	Saudi Arabia	Seismic survey	Shallow water, reefs, uncharted areas
1975	Australia—Thursday Island	Casualty evacuation and general transport	Shallow water and reefs. No conventional docking facilities
1975	UK—The Wash	Transportation of men and materials	Tidal areas half mud half water
1976	UK	Seismic survey	Tidal area of Liverpool Bay and Blackpool
1976	Algiers	Passengers	Transport from Algiers Port to Fair Site including half a mile down a specially prepared road
1977-80	United Arab Emirates	Seismic surveys	Very shallow water combined with coral reefs and sand bars

Hoverwork Limited is a subsidiary of Hovertravel Limited and was formed in 1966. The company provides crew training and charter facilities for all available types of ACVs, thus bridging the gap between the operators and manufacturers.

The company has trained over 50 hovercraft captains and has received some 40 charter contracts, including film sequences and the operation of the SR.N6 craft for mineral surveys all over the world. The company operated the hovercraft passenger service during Expo' 67 at Montreal and a service at the 1970 and 1976 Algiers Expositions.

Hoverwork is the largest international operator of hovercraft, having access to Hovertravel's 56 and 38-seater SR.N6s. Hoverwork has undertaken operations in areas from the Arctic to the equator. These have included logistics operations in the northern part of Svalbard and in equatorial parts of South America. To date Hoverwork has operated in the following areas: Canada, South America, Mexico, Brunei, Netherlands, Bahrain, Kuwait, the United Arab Emirates, Saudi Arabia, Algeria, Tunisia, English North Sea, Spitzbergen and Australia.

INTERNATIONAL HOVERSERVICES LIMITED

Head Office: 138 Rownhams Lane, North Baddesley, Southampton, Hampshire SO5 9LT, England
Registered Office: 6 Rockstone Place, Southampton, Hampshire SO1 2EP, England
Operating Base: No 28 Berth, Eastern Docks, Southampton SO1 1JH, England
Telephone: 0703 23068
Officials:
Lieutenant-Commander M D Dawson, RN MNI, *Chairman & Joint Managing Director*
G W Black, *Director*
Mrs E Hands, *Secretary*

International Hoverservices Limited began operations in July 1970, between Bournemouth and Swanage, and since then has operated various scheduled and charter services in the Solent and Poole Bay areas. The company has also provided a craft on charter for operations between Gorey (Jersey) and Cartaret (France), and in the Seine Estuary.

The company can provide craft for charter and a consultancy and training service for prospective operators.
CRAFT OPERATED
HM.2 Mark III, GH2018, GH2019 and GH2024

NAVAL HOVERCRAFT TRIALS UNIT

HMS Daedalus, Lee-on-the-Solent, Hampshire PO13 9NY, England
Telephone: 0705 550143
Commanding Officer: Commander P B Reynolds, OBE, RN

The Naval Hovercraft Trials Unit has been evaluating hovercraft in naval roles since 1975. The trials have been concerned mainly with mine countermeasures, amphibious assault and logistics. An additional task is patrolling for illegal immigrants in the Hong Kong area.

The Royal Navy currently owns five hovercraft for evaluation purposes: one VT 2, one BH.7, and three SR.N6s. Two of the SR.N6s are currently deployed to Hong Kong.

Evaluation has shown the hovercraft to have great potential as a mine countermeasures (MCM) vessel, and towards this goal the 100-ton Vosper Thornycroft VT 2 is presently being modified for a role as a MCM logistic support craft. In this role the craft will be used to re-supply MCM vessels at sea, thereby improving their effective time on task.
CRAFT OPERATED
SR.N6 XV 859   Fitted with dual
SR.N6 XV 615   controls and radar
SR.N6 XV 617   for training
BH.7 XW 255—modified to Mk IV version embodying bow door and Sea Rider with davit.
VT 2-001 P234

VT 2-001 of the Naval Hovercraft Trials Unit accompanied by the Unit's BH.7 and one of its three SR.N6s

First of four Bell Halter 110ft SESs for Command Marine Inc being launched at Chalmette, Louisiana. The new craft will be able to carry up to 120 passengers or 40 tons of cargo at 32 knots in calm seas and at 28 knots in sea state 3

UNITED STATES OF AMERICA
CITY OF TACOMA

The first of two Hovermarine 221 multi-role harbour service craft was scheduled for delivery to the City of Tacoma, Washington State in 1981. Based on a Hovermarine 200 series hull, it will be equipped with a wide range of firefighting, rescue, navigational and communications equipment. It is designed to cope with both ship and harbour installation fires.

COMMAND MARINE, INC

Lafayette, Louisiana, USA

Command Marine has ordered four Bell Halter 110ft surface effect ships to service offshore rigs and platforms in the Gulf of Mexico. The first was due to be delivered by the autumn of 1980 with the other three vessels following at two-monthly intervals.

US ARMY CORPS OF ENGINEERS

First of the Bell Halter 48 hydrographic survey boats was delivered to the US Army Corps of Engineers in early 1980. It has been named Rodolf.

US ARMY MOBILITY EQUIPMENT R & D COMMAND (MERADCOM)

On 28 September 1979, a US$40 million contract was placed with Bell Aerospace Textron by MERADCOM for the first eight of twelve LACV-30s (Lighter, Amphibious Air Cushion Vehicle-30 ton payload) with the first deliveries due in 1981.

US NAVY LCAC ACQUISITION PROGRAMME

Competitive contracts for the LCAC system design were awarded on 5 June 1980 to both Bell Aerospace Textron and Rohr Marine Inc. Pilot production proposals are due in January 1981. A contract to build six LCACs will be awarded to the winning contractor in 1981.

By the mid-1980s, the first LCAC will be introduced to the US Fleet giving the US Navy/Marine Corps team full amphibious landing capability. Full production is expected to be underway by 1984.

US NAVY/US COAST GUARD

Bell Halter's 110ft SES demonstrator has been purchased by the US Navy. After being stretched by 50ft, the craft is to be employed by the US Coast Guard. Value of the contract, including US Coast Guard modifications and stretching, is $4·1 million.

VENEZUELA
MARAVEN SA

Three Hovermarine 218 crewboats are operated by Maraven SA in support of offshore rigs on Lake Maracaibo.

TURISMO MARGARITA CA

This operator has a fleet of three HM.2 hovercraft which are used on services between the Isla de Margarita and Puerto la Cruz on the Venezuelan mainland. The HM.2 takes two hours for the 55 mile long journey.
CRAFT OPERATED
HM.2 325 *Kenndy*
HM.2 330 *Kenna*
HM.2 331 *Kelly*

ZAIRE
SOCIETE MINIERE DE BAKWANGA

Mbujimayi, R C Lulubourg 10,424, Zaire
CRAFT OPERATED
CC.7 002

ACV TRAILERS
AND
HEAVY LIFT SYSTEMS

AUSTRALIA

TAYLORCRAFT TRANSPORT PTY LTD

Airport, Parafield, South Australia 5106, Australia
Telephone: (08) 258 4787
Telex: AA 88777

Taylorcraft Transport Pty Ltd has been active in ACV research and development since 1966. It ceased operations in 1980, but R V Taylor, the company's founder and managing director, is available as a consultant on ACV matters and may be contacted at the above address, or telephone and telex numbers.

Drawings and design information for the range of ACVs developed by the company may be made available at cost to anyone interested in manufacturing the craft.

Details of the range of ACVs, Trailaire hover-trailers and the Taylorcraft Liftaire industrial skirt system will be found in *Jane's Surface Skimmers 1980* and earlier editions.

CANADA

HOVERLIFT SYSTEMS LTD

6814U—6th Street SE, Calgary, Alberta T2H 2K4, Canada
Telephone: (403) 253 5239
Telex: 03-821682
Officials:
D M Simmons, P Eng
R F Mamini, *Vice President, Engineering*
L G Cuthbert, *Vice President, Operations*
Associated companies:
Hanseatic Industries Pte Ltd
1st Floor, M & G Centre, Clemenceau Avenue, Singapore 9
Telephone: 324424
Telex: 25566
Simmons Technik GmbH
Postfach 1807, D-5400 Koblenz, Federal Republic of Germany
Telephone: (02 61) 34341
Telex: 862806

Hoverlift Systems Ltd is a member of the Simmons Group of Companies. The group's main interest is the exploitation of mineral resources, and its entry into the field of industrial air cushion vehicles was through a requirement to increase the mobility of oil drilling equipment. The company has diversified its product line to include heavy load amphibious transporters, both towed and self-propelled, icebreakers, and the conversion of awkward loads to an air cushion transportation mode. The company has also developed a range of modular construction transporters under the name Hoverflex. Using a series of common structural, power plant and skirt modules, transporters can be assembled at remote sites in sizes up to several hundred tonnes load capacity.

HOVERLIFT HL-101

HL-101 is a fully amphibious air cushion ferry or ship-to-shore lighter designed and built by oilfield personnel for operation in the Canadian North. The hull is an exceptionally rugged all-metal structure of welded steel construction.

Payload capacity is 20,000lb (9 tons) with 30% reserve buoyancy over water and 30,000lb (13·5 tons) over land at a maximum of 58mb (0·85psi) ground pressure.

For ease of transport the vehicle's side decks fold to permit loading on one live-roll oilfield trailer without crane. It can also be loaded on the C-130 Hercules, one of the transport aircraft engaged in regular supply operations in the Canadian North and other remote regions.
LIFT: Motive power is supplied by a single 197hp Caterpillar 3208, or equivalent Detroit diesel engine, driving a Joy Industrial steel fan, or equivalent, through a direct coupling.

Hoverlift HL-104 La Crete hoverferry, Pioneer 1, operated by Alberta Transportation on the Peace River, Northern Alberta

HL-105 hover transporter capable of carrying loads up to 75 tonnes

PROPULSION: Cable and on-board winch or towed by tractor.
HULL: Welded steel structure.
SKIRT: 229mm (9in) pitch segmented skirt in hot-bonded natural rubber/nylon material. Spray skirt in neoprene nylon material. Skirt segments capable of routine operation across newly broken ice ledges; may be replaced individually from deck if necessary.
DIMENSIONS
Length overall: 12m (39ft 4in)
Width overall: 5·7m (18ft 10in)
Load deck length, centre deck: 8·5m (28ft)
    side decks: 11m (36ft)
Load deck width: 5·5m (18ft 2in)
PERFORMANCE: Speeds and gradients within winch or tractor capability.

HOVERLIFT HL-104

The HL-104 was designed and built as a 40-ton capacity year-round cable ferry across the Peace River in Northern Alberta. It closely follows the design concepts of HL-101. The hull of the ferry is constructed in road transportable sections which are pin-jointed together on site. This feature provides a convenient method of transport to the operational location, and the potential for removal to another site if traffic requirements change.

Another feature of the craft is its mode of operation. Due to a number of local conditions, including ice in the river, fast currents and steep banks on either side, the ferry moves in a broadside mode and climbs out of the river on both sides for loading and unloading from approach roads parallel to the river banks.

This feature allows shallower gradients on the approach roads, and a run-off escape route at the other end of the load deck in case of vehicle brake failure or iced-up decks. It also ensures that, during the break-up period when a considerable quantity of broken ice is coming down the river, there is no build-up of broken ice on the upstream side of the ferry during unloading or when waiting for traffic.

The ferry is winch propelled, using two bull-wheel winches hydraulically driven through variable displacement pumps mounted on the front end of the crankshaft of the lift engines.

The ferry is capable of continuing operation at lower speeds in the event of single engine failure. It has already demonstrated its capability of maintaining a ferry service when no other means of crossing was available, over both thin ice and rotting ice, and considerable water level changes.
LIFT: Motive power is provided by two Caterpillar 3408 diesel engines, each driving a fan and a variable displacement hydraulic pump. New York Blower Series 40 centrifugal fans are provided, driven through automatic centrifugal clutches.
PROPULSION: Two Timberland Equipment bull-wheel winches provide a variable speed drive along 1in diameter cables. The winches are driven by Sunstrand hydraulic motors.
HULL: The hull is an all welded steel fabrication constructed in three sections which are pin-jointed together. Separate buoyancy compartments are provided to give a buoyancy reserve of 50% under fully loaded conditions.
SUPERSTRUCTURE: The control cabin and engine rooms are of fibreglass construction, and the general layout has been designed so the ferry can be operated by one man if necessary.
SKIRT: Segmented skirt in natural rubber/nylon material fabricated by hot-bonding. Segment depth from underside of hull, 0·91m (3ft). Each segment is individually mounted on light alloy bars for ease of changing.
DIMENSIONS
Length overall: 20·19m (66ft 3in)
Width overall: 11m (36ft 1in)
Load deck length: 20·02m (65ft 8in)
Load deck width: 4·88m (16ft)
Depth of hull: 1·37m (4ft 6in)
Trucking width of sections: 3·76m (12ft 4in)
PERFORMANCE
Payload: 45 tonnes (100,000lb)
Max speed over water: 2·68m/s (8·8ft/s)
Max gradient capability: 8–10% (1:12–1:10)

Hoverlift HL-301 air cushion icebreaker secured to the bow of a small harbour tug. Its hinged side sections permit it to be transported by road from one operating site to the next

HL-115 Salamander may be propelled by four Terra-Tired wheels or flexible paddle wheels

ALTERNATIVES: To accommodate various customer requirements the configuration of the craft may easily be "stretched" by the addition of appropriate structural and skirt sections.

HOVERLIFT HL-105

HL-105, a stretched version of the HL-104, was built by adding a second identical centre section to the HL-104 design. It was test hovered in November 1978 and delivered to the British Columbia Ministry of Transportation, Communications and Highways in January 1979. It is presently operating on-site, crossing the Fort Nelson River.

The HL-105 ferry has a year-round capability. The Fort Nelson route is a mixture of water and marsh in the warmer months and ice in the winter. On this crossing, the ferry travels in the normal fore-and-aft direction, and vehicles are loaded and unloaded from approach roads which are parallel to the route across the river.
SPECIFICATION
Generally as for HL-104, with the following modifications:
Engines: Two General Motors Detroit Diesel 12V71
Width overall: 14·82m (48ft 7in)
Load deck width: 8·67m (28ft 6in)
Payload: 75 tonnes (165,300lb)

HOVERLIFT HL-115 SALAMANDER

Salamander is a 10-tonne amphibious truck, which basically consists of an industrial air cushion platform fitted with four large Terra-Tired wheels. For primarily marine use, the wheels can be easily replaced by flexible paddle wheels. The function of these wheels is to provide amphibious traction (the large Terra-Tire treads give 8-9·7km/h (5-6mph) in water) and steering, and they do not support the vehicle weight. With both wheel units steerable independently, control is excellent. Overland speeds of up to 40km/h (25mph) are possible.

The wheel units can be hydraulically raised and lowered to give the best traction in varying terrains. HL-115-R Salamander has been derived from HL-101 which had undergone considerable testing while fitted with both Terra-Tires and paddle wheels. HL-115-R is capable of transportation by rail, road or air.

SPECIFICATION
Lift: One Deutz BF10L413 Diesel, one centrifugal fan.
Propulsion: Hydraulic power take-off from lift engine to wheel motors.
Hull: Welded steel structure, folds in three sections for transport.
Skirt: Segmented skirt in natural rubber/nylon material.

DIMENSIONS
Hull length: 10·9m (35ft 10in)
Hull width: 6·14m (20ft 2in)
Load deck lengths, centre deck: 7m (23ft)
    side decks: 10m (33ft)
Load deck width: 6m (20ft)

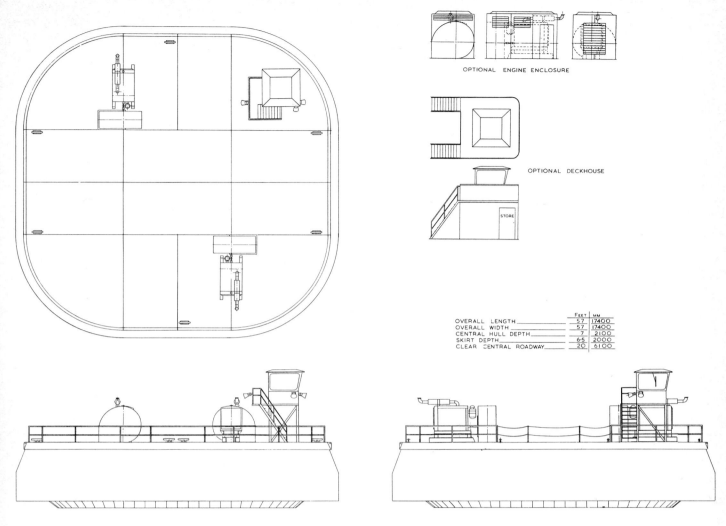

OPTIONAL ENGINE ENCLOSURE

OPTIONAL DECKHOUSE

STORE

	FEET	MM
OVERALL LENGTH	57	17400
OVERALL WIDTH	57	17400
CENTRAL HULL DEPTH	7	2100
SKIRT DEPTH	6·5	2000
CLEAR CENTRAL ROADWAY	20	6100

Outboard elevations and plan of Hoverflex 400 amphibious barge with 43-tonne load capacity

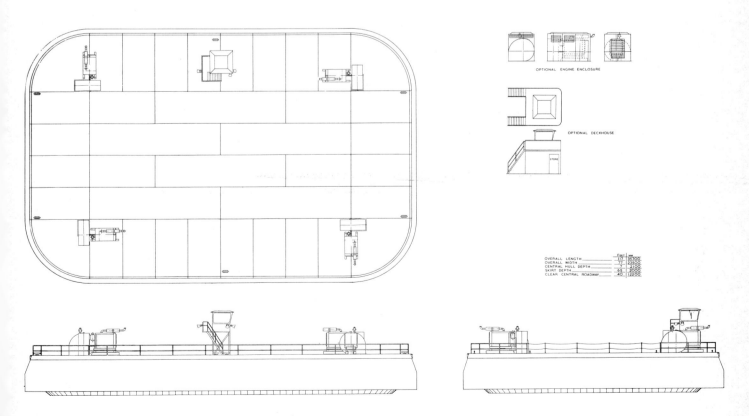

OPTIONAL ENGINE ENCLOSURE

OPTIONAL DECKHOUSE

STORE

	FEET	MM
OVERALL LENGTH	117	35700
OVERALL WIDTH	77	23500
CENTRAL HULL DEPTH	7	2100
SKIRT DEPTH	6·5	2000
CLEAR CENTRAL ROADWAY	40	12200

Largest member of Hoverflex 400 series is this 200-tonne capacity modular transporter design

HOVERLIFT HL-301

Based on HL-101, the HL-301 has a heavier hull and increased power to adapt it for icebreaking duties. The hinged side sections are retained to enable the craft to be transported rapidly from one operational site to another by road when required.

In operation, the platform is designed to be winched to ice anchors or to be secured to the bow of a smaller harbour tug or similar craft.

It is intended for icebreaking in harbours and other congested areas where manoeuvring space is limited. The first production platform is in operation with St Lawrence Seaway Authority, where it has been used on the bow of a 20m (65ft) tug, breaking ice up to 0·6m (24in) thick.
SPECIFICATION

Generally as for HL-101, with the following modifications:
Engine: General Motors Detroit Diesel type 8V71.
Fan: New York Blower Series 40 centrifugal.

HOVERFLEX AMPHIBIOUS BARGES

The Hoverflex concept has been developed to meet the growing industrial need for amphibious transporters, in a wide range of sizes, which can be easily transported to site and put into service quickly.

Based on the use of welded steel hull modules, they are assembled from appropriate groupings of standardised hull sections, lift power packs and skirt segments. All modules are easily transported by road or rail, so that on-site assembly is possible for all sizes. Assembled Hoverflex transporters can be increased or decreased in size to suit changing needs.

There are three series in the Hoverflex range, 200, 400 and 500. All models in each series are powered by two, three or four standard power packs consisting of a diesel engine driving a fan and hydraulic pump. Any model may be fitted with bolt-on propulsion equipment consisting of winches and/or wheels and/or marine propellers. In each of these categories, three standard propulsion units are available.

HOVERLIFT HL-533 ICEBREAKER BOW

A design contract was awarded to Hoverlift Systems Ltd by the Canadian Coast Guard in April 1977 for an icebreaking air cushion bow. The design was completed and designated HL-302. HL-302 was cancelled in favour of the cheaper modular HL-533 design (see Hoverflex 500 series). A contract to build the HL-533 was awarded to Hoverlift Systems Ltd in February 1979, to be in operation for the 1980-81 ice season.

As with the HL-302 design, the platform is capable of hovering independently of the parent ship and when attached to the bow of the ship the cushion is sealed to the bow.
SPECIFICATION
Lift packs: Three General Motors 16V71T Diesels; three Howden Canada centrifugal fans.
Hull: All steel, modular construction.
Skirt: Segmented skirt in natural rubber/nylon material.

Hoverflex Standard Series

	Payload range (tonnes)	Deck sizes (m)	Moulded depth (m)	Hover height (m)
200 Series	13-170	15 × 10 to 28 × 23	1·5	1·2
400 Series	42-200	15 × 15 to 34 × 21	2·1	1·6
500 Series	43-422	21 × 15 to 36 × 30	2·5	1·8

DIMENSIONS
Length: 21m (70ft)
Beam: 21m (70ft)
Hull depth: 2·5m (8ft 2in)
WEIGHTS
Design operating weight: 271 tonnes (59,700lb)

SKIRT MANUFACTURE AND DEVELOPMENT

The company has built a hot bonding assembly facility for making a very wide range of skirt sizes. Development work has been undertaken on conventional segments, special units for icebreaker bow seals, special "add-on" skirt systems for converting various structures to an air cushion transportation mode, and spray suppressing skirts. Very efficient spray skirts have been developed for the company's product range, and an effective spray skirt has been supplied for one Voyageur hovercraft. The company is able to undertake design, development and manufacture of skirt systems and associated devices.

CONSULTANCY

In addition to the product range mentioned above, Hoverlift Systems Ltd can offer an all-Canadian Consultancy Service on all aspects of the industrial application of the air cushion principle.

FRANCE

DUBIGEON-NORMANDIE/ SEDAM

152 avenue Malakoff, 75116 Paris, France
Officials:
See ACV section

SEDAM is developing a range of amphibious barges to offload cargo ships in ports which, because of the vast growth of sea transport, have become almost permanently congested.

This congestion is forcing large numbers of vessels to queue up to be unloaded, and sometimes necessitates a wait of 30-100 days. Such delays, because of the high cost of demurrage and insurance, frequently lead to an increase of 50% to 100% in freighting charges.

SEDAM is proposing the use of its Amphibarges to unload the vessels and carry their cargo to warehouses close to the port, but clear of the main areas of congestion. Their amphibious capability would enable them to make the transition from water to land and carry their loads up to the warehouses where conventional fork lift trucks, mobile cranes and other freight handling equipment would be employed for offloading.

The manufacture of components for the Amphibarges could take place in the countries in which they are to be used. This would not only permit the customer to make considerable savings in transport costs, but also create a source of local employment.

AMPHIBARGES

LIFT: Four marinised diesel-engines, mounted one each side of the load deck, forward and aft, each drive a single centrifugal fan to feed air to the multiple skirt system. The skirts, made of terylene based material, are secured in position by quick-fasteners to facilitate repair and replacement. Skirt life is about 1,000 hours.

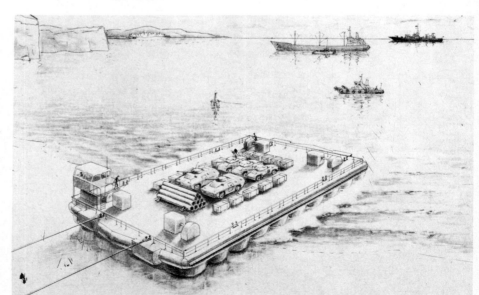

100-ton capacity Amphibarge for both commercial and military use

DIMENSIONS	A50	A100	A200
Length	22m	39·6m	39·6m
Width	12m	18m	19m
Loading deck area	220m²	500m²	500m²
Height on rest	2m	2m	2·5m
Max load	1·8 tonnes/m²	1·8 tonnes/m²	1·8 tonnes/m²
Floatability volume	220m²	500m²	735m²
Weight when empty	55 tonnes	130 tonnes	155 tonnes
POWER			
Lift	4 × 300hp	4 × 500hp	4 × 500hp
Propulsion	2 × 100hp	2 × 200hp	2 × 300hp
Generator	20kVA	20kVA	20kVA

HULL: Modular craft structure comprising a number of cylindrical buoyancy tanks laid side-by-side longitudinally. Surmounting the buoyancy tanks are supports for the deck and below it are fastenings for the multiple skirt system and landing pads. At the bow and stern half-cylinders are employed as strengtheners against impacts incurred during towing or pushing. Surface of the deck is in diamond head plating. In the loading area the deck is strengthened by longitudinal and transverse girders. Railings are optional.

PROPULSION OVER WATER: Among alternative methods of over water propulsion are tugs and outboard motors. Points for the installation of two outboard engines are provided aft. Speed with outboard engines of suitable output will be about 5 knots.

OVER LAND: Drag overland is approximately 1% of the total weight when operating over a flat surface with no wind. Towing can be by a wheeled vehicle or a tractor with caterpillar tracks. Alternatively, one or more winches can be installed aboard, enabling the craft to pull itself overland to a fixed point by a cable.

CONTROLS: The operator's position and all necessary controls are in a raised bridge above the engine compartment on the starboard side. Crew would normally comprise an operator, engineer and seaman.

CARGO HANDLING: Optional roller track can be fitted for handling heavy vehicles. Express rollers are available for loading and positioning containers. Removable tank can be provided for handling bulk goods.

OPERATING PROCEDURE:
1 Cargo is off-loaded directly into the amphibarge by the ship's derricks (20 to 60 tons/h according to cargo);
2 the self-propelled amphibarge reaches the shore;
3 the amphibarge is lifted and pulled to the warehouse by minimal towing force (winch or tractor);

4 goods are unloaded by local means (cranes, forklifts, etc).

Particulars of the A50, A100 and A200

PERFORMANCES	A50	A100	A200
Payload	50 tonnes	100 tonnes	200 tonnes
Tolerable overload	10 tonnes	20 tonnes	none
Max wave height	1m	1m	1m
Speed (calm water)	5 knots	5 knots	5 knots
Recommended max gradient	3%	3%	3%
Land speed	5km/h	5km/h	5km/h
Fuel consumption			
Lift	250kg/h	401kg/h	442kg/h
Propulsion	35kg/h	61kg/h	102kg/h

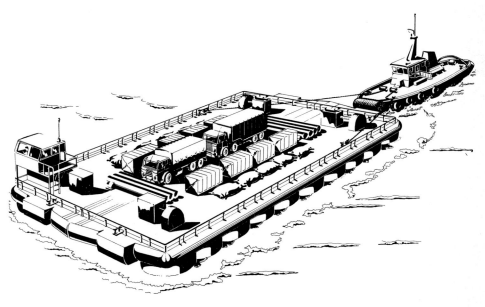

Tugs and outboard motors can be used to propel the Amphibarge

Amphibarges, with payloads capacities of 50, 100 and 200 tonnes, respectively, are given in this entry.

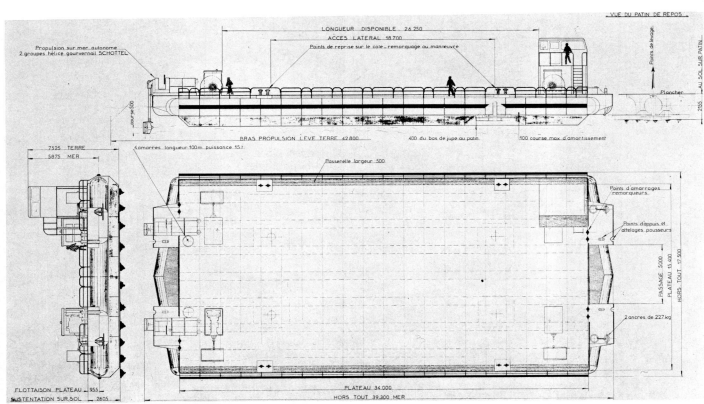

General arrangement of a Sedam 100-ton capacity Amphibarge. Power for the lift fans could be supplied by four 500hp marinised diesels. Two 200hp diesels driving water-propellers through Schottel drives give a water speed of 5 knots. The outboard propellers are raised at the point where the land towing system takes over

JAPAN

MITSUI ENGINEERING & SHIPBUILDING CO LTD

6-4, Tsukiji 5-chome, Chuo-ku, Tokyo 104, Japan

Officials:

See ACV section

Mitsui has designed a 310-ton hoverbarge for use in either deep or shallow waters. A feature of the craft, designated SEP-1, is the provision of jack-up legs, similar to those employed on some offshore oil rigs. This facility enables the craft to be located above test or survey sites in shallow waters or in areas of marsh or tundra.

310-ton Mitsui SEP-1 hoverbarge

UNION OF SOVIET SOCIALIST REPUBLICS

ALL-UNION OIL MACHINERY RESEARCH INSTITUTE, WEST SIBERIA (VNII neftmash)

Tyumen, USSR

Officials:

A V Vladimirskii, *Director*

V A Shibanov, *Head of Air Cushion Vehicle Department*

Air cushion platforms with load capacities of up to 200 tons have been under development in the West Siberian lowlands since 1965. Some 80% of the gas and petroleum sites in this area are located amidst almost impassable swamps, salt marshes, taiga and stretches of water.

In the Tyumensk area, where deep wells are being drilled, more than 200 tons of support equipment are required at each site in addition to between 130-180 tons of drilling gear. In 1965, a group of ACV engineers and designers headed by V A Shibanov left the Urals for Tyumen to apply their efforts to the design of a hoverplatform capable of carrying a complete oil rig across tundra and taiga, and also to the design and construction of an all-terrain vehicle capable of towing the drilling rig, on hover, to the drilling sites.

Small scale models were employed by the group during the development stages, and several attempts were made before a completely satisfactory design was conceived.

The most successful arrangement—the BU-75-VP—is illustrated. It comprises a rectangular, all-metal buoyancy raft (the load carrying member), with side structures to carry a bag-type skirt. A derrick, derived from a standard BU-75 drilling rig, was mounted on the central raft, and the drilling pump, generally delivered to sites separately, was also installed on board. Apart

BU-75-VP oil rig, the first in the world to be mounted on an air cushion platform

Diagram of a typical Soviet-designed ACV oil rig platform

1. flexible bag skirt
2. air cushion
3. fan
4. drilling rig engines (employed to drive fans during moves)
5. derrick
6. drilling rig base
7. tractor
h air gap
H hard structure clearance

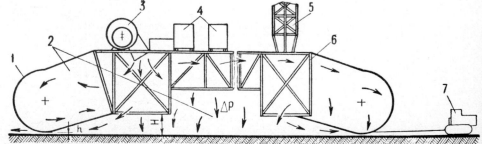

from specialist items of oil drilling gear, the platform is equipped with lift fans and drilling engines which serve a dual purpose by driving the lift fans when the platform is changing location.

Two tractors are normally required to tow the platform in a fully loaded condition.

Transport and routeing problems are now greatly simplified as the need to detour virtually impassable lakes, marshes, and snow or water-filled ravines no longer arises. The rig has been employed in oilfields at Shaimskoye, Urai and Samotlor.

Two more multi-ton cargo-carrying ACV platforms have been completed at the Tyumen Ship Repair yard. One platform, which was put into service in 1974, has a load capacity of 200 tons.

A more recent design has been undergoing tests at the Strezhevoye workings at Alexandrov field in the Tomsk region. Large ACV rigs with a capacity of several thousand tons are under development.

BU-75-VP

DIMENSIONS
Length: 30m (98ft 5in)
Width: 20m (65ft 7in)
WEIGHT: All-up: 170 tonnes
PERFORMANCE: Speed (depending on towing vehicle): about 9·65km/h (6mph)

ACV TRAILERS

Three ACV trailers are being developed by the organisation—a 6-ton platform; the PVP-40 with a cargo capacity of 40 tonnes and a larger derivative with a capacity of 60 tonnes. The PVP-40 has been undergoing state acceptance trials in Surgut and the Soviet far north and if put into production will be employed in the construction of oil installations and pipelines, by geological surveys and on drainage and irrigation schemes.

The PVP-40 is powered by a single diesel engine driving two centrifugal fans. Its 60-ton counterpart is powered by a single gas turbine driving twin axial-flow fans. Discs or wheels fitted to swinging arms at the rear provide directional control when reversing. "Trains" of ACV trailers can be employed to carry heavy loads and a further development is an articulated trailer, several times the length of platforms like the PVP-40, with one tractor forward and another at the rear.

ACV TRACTORS

Towing requirements for the rigs and ACV trailers built in Tyumen were met at first by conventional GTT amphibious crawler tractors. Since these were unable to cope with very soft terrain, development of a true multi-terrain tractor was undertaken, and this led to the construction of the Tyumen I. This was the first of a completely new ACV type with combined crawler propulsion and air cushion lift. The first model, now relegated to Tyumen's ACV museum, carried a 2-tonne load at speeds up to 40km/h (25mph) in off-road conditions. It is described as a broad, squat vehicle on long narrow caterpillar tracks, with a flexible skirt bet-

PVP-40 air cushion trailer undergoing field tests. The trailer, which has a load capacity of 40 tons, is designed for carrying heavy, single-piece cargoes and machines, drilling and oil-production equipment in the difficult and marshy terrain of the Soviet Union's northern regions

Rear view of the PVP-40 air cushion trailer showing the unusual arrangement of varied length segments of the bag skirt

A 6-ton capacity air cushion trailer towed by a 5-ton capacity MVP-3 combined ACV/crawler tractor. Both vehicles have been developed by the West Siberian Branch of the All-Union Oil Machinery Research Institute

ween its crawlers. The second was the MVP-2 which was upgraded soon afterwards to the MVP-3 5-tonne capacity model. The MVP-3 uses extremely narrow crawler tracks for propulsion, steering and support on hard surfaces. As with the Bertin Terraplane series of wheel-assisted ACVs, the weight transfer to the crawler track is variable according to the nature of the terrain being crossed and the gradient. It is said to be capable of 80·46km/h (50mph) over swamps with 1·01m (40in) high hummocks and cruises at 48·28km/h (30mph). At the time of its first

demonstration to the Soviet press in July 1974, it had completed 96·56km/h (60 miles) over Siberian swamps.

Operation of the vehicle appears to be relatively simple. Main controls are an accelerator for the single engine, which has an automatic clutch, and two standard tracked vehicle steering levers which skid-steer through the differential use of the tracks.

The policy at Tyumen is to standardise on composite crawler ACV systems rather than air propeller or endless-screw type propulsion.

MINISTRY OF THE MERCHANT MARINE, LENINGRAD CENTRAL DESIGN BUREAU

HOVERBARGES

The Leningrad Central Design Bureau has designed a self-propelled amphibious hoverbarge, the prototype of which has been built at the Layskiy ship repair yard. It is intended for use from a new class of ships which can work in arctic and other conditions. The hoverbarges would be employed to discharge the cargoes onto shores which do not have port facilities.

The ships will moor between 10-20 nautical miles offshore, launch the platforms from their decks onto the sea, and then load them with cargo.

Soviet 50-ton payload self-propelled amphibious hoverbarge prototype

Only one platform of this type has been built so far and this can carry loads of up to 50 tons. According to Vadim M Perov, Head of Administration for Ordering and Supervising the Construction of New Vessels for the Soviet Ministry of the Merchant Marine, thought is being given to the building of a series of special icebreaker transport vessels or arctic supply ships on which ACV platforms of this type and capacity would be standard equipment.

The ACV platform prototype is said to have 'proved itself well' and it is understood that the special supply ships to carry hoverbarges of this type will be built during the next five to eight years.

UNITED KINGDOM

AIR CUSHION EQUIPMENT (1976) LTD

15-35 Randolph Street, Shirley, Southampton, Hampshire SO1 3HD, England
Telephone: 0703 776468
Telex: 477537
Officials:
J D Hake, *Chairman*
L A Hopkins, *Director*
R C Gilbert, *General Manager*
R R Henvest, *Works Manager*

Air Cushion Equipment (1976) Ltd is involved in the design, development and manufacture of air and water cushion systems. Main products are skirt systems for hovercraft and industrial applications, special skirt systems for use with water as a cushion fluid, the "Water Skate" heavy load carrying module system, low pressure air pallets, lifting bags and flexible drinking water containers.

A service offered on a world-wide basis is the movement of heavy loads using either air or water cushions. The best known of the services offered by this company is the design and production of equipment used for moving oil storage tanks, of which 121 had been moved by the autumn of 1979.

The technology and skirt types developed by the company are based on the original work carried out by Hovercraft Development Ltd and developed to suit the special requirement and specification of the client.

Much research and development has been undertaken into the behaviour of skirt systems under widely varying operating conditions and the company has skirt systems for use in tropical and Arctic conditions.

Cushion pressures investigations range from the low pressure amphibious hovercraft requirement through to 225psi achieved during the development of the "Water Skate" system.

The company accepts contracts for all aspects of air cushion engineering and manufacturing.

LOW PRESSURE AIR SYSTEMS

Design services are offered in the application of the hover principle utilising low-pressure air (2psi and below) for the movement of heavy and awkward loads over unprepared ground. This embraces air cushion systems engineering and the design and manufacture of skirts.

"WATER SKATE" LOAD-CARRYING PALLET AND HIGH PRESSURE WATER SYSTEMS

The "Water Skate" load-carrying pallet uses water as the cushion fluid and has been tested up to 225psi. Modular in application the total system can be used in multiples of the required number of three sizes of pallet of 5, 35 and 100 tonnes capacity. The equipment uses normal contractors' pumps to give water at the required pressure and flow. One pump can feed several modules via a control manifold and console. The manifold can be used to vary the pressures to each module thus eliminating the necessity to present equipment symmetrically about the centre of gravity. The pressure gauges can be calibrated in weight giving the operator the ability to weigh a bulky structure and to identify the centre of gravity to verify practical readings against calculation.

The areas of use for this product are diverse but include the movement of oil rig jacket structures and deck modules, concrete caissons, transformers, ship sections and hulls, plant and machinery, bridge sections and the launching of structures, ships and boats.

The high pressure water cushion system is offered to those companies who require a low

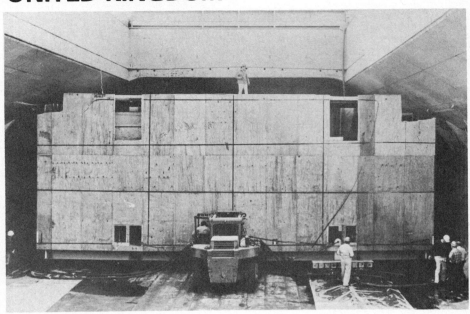

Moving a 113-tonne gas compressor module into a ship's hold using three Type AA Water Skate Modules

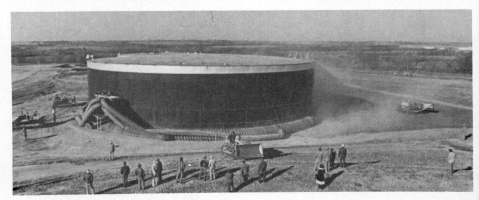

With a mobile blower unit suspended from the tank inflating the skirt, Hover Systems Inc moved this storage tank to a prepared site

cost system of dense and large load movement. The principle is similar to that of the modular skirt system and tank moving system but uses a water feed system similar to that used for the "Water Skate" modules.

Note: *the word "Water Skate" is a trade mark of ACE Ltd.*

TANK MOVING

Tank moving, using an air cushion for support, has now become a well established procedure. The method offers many advantages over the older conventional forms of movement such as water flotation, mechanical skidding, cranes or bogies. Route preparation is kept to a minimum and it is seldom necessary to reinforce the tank. A tank move can usually be completed in about seven to ten days, depending on the size of the tank and the distance to be moved. Once the skirt has been assembled on the tank and the tank has been lifted from its foundation, the distance that it can be moved is infinite and only requires the provision of an appropriate means of propulsion and a clearway of adequate width. With all other methods movement is normally limited to comparatively short distances, or the time for the move becomes very extended.

As air is ducted from the fan to the cushion area it percolates through the tank foundation until sufficient pressure is built up to lift the tank. No jacking is required. Once on cushion the tank can be towed or winched to its new location. The air cushion system allows omnidirectional mobility, hence to change direction or rotate the tank about its vertical axis requires only the application of towing forces in the appropriate direction. Location to dimensional tolerances of ± 2in can easily be obtained. The towing force required is usually in the order of 1% of the weight of the tank.

Tanks of all types can be moved on air including those with floating, fixed and column supported roofs and welded or riveted construction. A 700-tonne floating roof tank moved in Pauillac for Shell France was the largest tank moved on air to date and on this occasion an added innovation was used, floating the roof on a second cushion of air during the move. This not only reduces the possibility of damage to the roof but also reduces the pressure differential developed across the bottom of the tank.

Tank moving on air cushion is undertaken by licensed contractors as follows:

UK, Western Europe and Arabian Gulf (part)—Mears Construction Ltd
Canada and USA—Hover Systems Inc
Southern Africa—National Process Industries Pty
Japan—Nippon Kensan Co

AVON INDUSTRIAL POLYMERS (MELKSHAM) LIMITED

Melksham, Wiltshire, England
Telephone: 0225 703101
Telex: 44142
Flexible Fabrications Division:
Bumpers Way, Bristol Road, Chippenham, Wiltshire SN14 6NF, England
Telephone: 0249 56242
Telex: 444557
Officials:
B Stacey, *Managing Director*
D Gale, *Director*
D Wisely, *Director*
B Rowley, *Director*
R Wilmott, *Director*
D Bedford, *Director*
D Wisely, *Business Manager, Flexible Fabrications*
E F Lane, *Sales Manager, Flexible Fabrications*

The Flexible Fabrications Division of Avon Industrial Polymers (Melksham), is part of the Avon Rubber Group. Within the one factory complex Avon produces its full range of hovercraft skirt components, a newly-introduced range of liquid-containing pillow tanks, and various lightweight fabrications such as a flexible curtain for refrigerated container vehicles, a range of naval and commercial dry diving suits, and aircraft jet engine intake plugs.

Long-established as the major supplier of hovercraft skirt components in the UK (all the cross-Channel craft use Avon skirt materials), the company has now been appointed as the prime supplier of skirt components to the Bell-Halter consortium, which is developing a range of surface effect ships in the United States. The company also provides skirt components and systems for giant hoverbarges operating on major construction and civil engineering projects in such differing climates as Arabia and the Arctic.

For Bell-Halter, Avon has completed five sets of the world's largest hovercraft skirt components. The Bell-Halter 110 has a bow seal consisting of eight fingers each 25ft wide, 15ft high and weighing 100kg (224lb). Its stern seal is 30ft wide, 10ft long and 6ft 6in high, and weighs one ton. The craft can be used as a supply and workboat for the offshore oil industry, but can be easily modified to become a crew boat, a 275-seat passenger ferry, a fast patrol boat, or a military vessel carrying a sophisticated range of weapons including guided missiles.

Sea Pearl, the largest hover transporter in the world, lifting off at Abu Dhabi. The craft, 180 × 80ft wide and fitted with Avon skirts, was used to carry LNG plant to Das Island, 110 miles away

Mackace hover platform fitted with Avon hovercraft skirts, in operation in the Dead Sea where a search for deposits of potash is underway

In Britain both British Rail Hovercraft and Hoverlloyd, the cross-Channel operators, have long used Avon skirt components for the SR.N4 craft in its original and stretched form.

Avon has been awarded a substantial research and development contract by the UK Department of Trade and Industry. Avon is expecting to considerably improve the durability and performance of hovercraft skirt materials on behalf of the hovercraft industry as a whole.

BRITISH HOVERCRAFT CORPORATION

Osborne, East Cowes, Isle of Wight, England
Officials:
See ACV section

AIR CUSHION HEAVY LOAD TRANSPORTER (AIR CUSHION EQUIPMENT SERIES I)

Transformer units now in service weigh between 155 and 250 tons and 400-ton units are in prospect. On occasion the CEGB has been involved in the heavy expense of strengthening and even rebuilding bridges to accept these loads when no alternative route has been available.

The use of air cushion equipment, however, provides a practical and economic alternative. By providing an air cushion under the centre section of an existing transporter it is possible to support a high proportion of its gross weight. Distributing the gross load over the whole length of the transporter reduces the bending moments and sheer force imposed on bridges so that these heavy transformers can be transported without risk over existing bridges.

The transporter illustrated has a length of 27·4m (90ft) and a maximum width of 5·13m (16ft 10in). The payload is normally supported between two bogies each of which may have up to 48 wheels.

The skirt containing the air cushion is an easily handled unit which is fitted under the load and side beams of the trailer. Any spaces between the load and trailer frame are 'timbered-in' to take the upward thrust.

This type of skirt system can be built to suit any size of transporter and the one illustrated measures 9·57 × 4·26m (32 × 14ft). It is constructed largely of nylon/neoprene sheet extending across the underside of the load platform and formed into a bellows around its periphery. To the bottom of the bellows is attached a series of plates, each about 0·3m (1ft) long, which make contact with the road surface. Thus the only escape route for air from the cushion is through the small gap formed between the plates and the ground by the roughness of the surface.

Any general unevenness of the surface, such as the camber of a road or the hump of a bridge, causes the bellows of the 'skirt' to flex so that the plates can remain in contact with the road.

The cushion was designed for a 155-ton lift, when the cushion pressure reaches 5·4psi. At this pressure, when moving over the roughest road surfaces, the volume of air escaping from underneath the shoes is approximately 373·5m³/min (13,200ft³/min) (free air volume flow).

In the Series I equipment, the power to maintain the air cushion is provided by four Rolls-Royce B81SV petrol engines delivering 235hp (gross) at 4,000rpm. Each engine drives, through a gearbox, its own centrifugal compressor, with engine, gearbox and compressor mounted together on a steel underbed as a complete working unit. The four units supplying the power are built onto a road vehicle chassis. This vehicle, which also contains stowage space for the folded cushion container, is attached to the rear of the transporter train whenever it is required for a bridge crossing. It is connected to the air cushion through four 1ft diameter air ducts, each connected to a power unit. The ducts are connected by sections of flexible hose to allow for relative movement between the vehicles.

The first commercial load carried by the transporter was a 155-ton transformer for delivery to the Central Electricity Generating Board's substation at Legacy, near Wrexham, from the AEI Transformer Division Works at Wythenshawe, Manchester. The route involved crossing the Felin Puleston Bridge which, under normal circumstances, was incapable of withstanding the combined weight of the transporter and the transformer. By using the air cushion to relieve the load on the transporter's wheels the stress on the bridge was reduced by about 70 tons.

Had a conventional transporter been used the bridge would have had to be strengthened at a cost equal to about half the cost of developing and equipping the transporter.

Optimum relief is obtained by taking up about one-third of the gross load in the skirt and transferring this proportion from the bogies to a position under the piece being carried. Current

Four 200hp Noel Penny gas turbines are mounted together as a module on the swan neck of the heavy load trailer

requirements are for re-distribution of between 85 tons and 125 tons of the gross load in this manner and to date over 870 bridges have been crossed using the air cushion with savings in bridge strengthening costs estimated to be well in excess of £4 million.

Future movements of larger plants are likely to call for relief up to 200 tons. Recognising this potential requirement and also the fact that the existing equipment has already had a considerable part of its operating life the Board decided in 1973 to order a second set of equipment, designated Series II, which would cover all present and anticipated future requirements whilst allowing the Series I equipment to be held for back up and stand by duties. The latter has become particularly important in view of the substantial increase in air cushion assisted movements recently.

Series II equipment incorporates new features and design improvements made in the light of operating experience with the original system; main differences being centred around the air supply units.

Air is supplied by four 200hp gas turbines running on diesel fuel and each directly coupled to an axial compressor to give an output potential up to

7·3psi with a 20% increase in air capability. The gas turbines, supplied by Noel Penny Turbines Ltd are mounted together on a module on the swan necks of the heavy load trailer. The swan necks also carry the control cabin, fuel tanks, batteries, and battery charger so that no separate air supply vehicle is required. The trailer can now operate as a single unit when the air cushion is in situ. The need for flexible air duct sections is avoided, also the loss of time in connecting or disconnecting flexible sections and replacing the rear tractor by the blower vehicle as is required for Series I equipment.

Since becoming operational the transporter has assisted in the movement of more than 40 pieces of heavy electrical plans to the CEGB's power stations and transmission sub-stations and in conjunction with the movement of plant destined for export. During these movements the equipment has been used to give loading relief at 1,000 bridges that would otherwise have needed to be strengthened or rebuilt at an estimated cost of more than £3 million.

The Series II equipment is now in full commercial service. Similar equipment is available on a world-wide hire basis to other users.

MACKACE HOVERSYSTEMS

Funtley Road, Funtley, Fareham, Hampshire PO17 5ED, England
Telephone: 0329 285541
Telex: 86518 MACHOV G
Officials:
M J Fripp, *Technical Director and General Manager*

Mackace Hoversystems, a Westland company, has specialised in the design and construction of air cushion supported platforms for use in many facets of industry. It has helped to build the world's first hover dredger, has built a range of modular platforms and has also built the world's largest hover transporter which has a payload capacity of 250 tons. In addition the company has constructed two 160-ton hover transporters to cross the River Yukon in Alaska.

It is now studying amphibious platforms of greater payload capacities capable of moving giant petrochemical modules.

The company has recently introduced a simple self-propulsion system for its hover platforms. It has also developed a new system for laying submarine cables which simplifies un-reeling the cable.

Mackace has moved to a site near Fareham where it has constructed a research and development centre. Regular demonstrations are held to permit visitors to see hover platforms operate over land and water.

250-TON ACT

Sea Pearl, the world's largest hover transporter, was launched during 1974 and now operates in the Persian Gulf.

It was used initially to carry pre-fabricated sections of a liquid natural gas plant for a distance of about 110 miles. It allowed components to be transported from the fabrication area across rocks and sand to the sea, and then across the sea and directly onto the selected site without having to change the mode of transport for each sector of the journey.

Sea Pearl can be towed by crawler tractors on land and by tug at sea.
LIFT SYSTEM: Cushion lift is supplied by two 890hp MWM TBD 602 V12 diesels, each driving a 1·39m (4ft 7in) diameter Alldays Peacock

1,400 BA DIDW centrifugal fan. Each fan delivers 3,823m³ (135,000ft³) of air per minute, giving a cushion pressure of 0·07kg/cm² (1psi).
SKIRT: 1·21m (4ft) deep, open segment type, with double segments aft and an anti-spray flap.
BALLAST: A seawater ballast system is fitted to permit the craft to be employed as a ship-to-shore transporter.
DECK EQUIPMENT: Two 10-ton hydraulic winches are fitted at the bow for loading plant components. Twin hydraulic capstans are located amidships for use during mooring, manoeuvring and anchoring.
ACCOMMODATION: Elevated bridge and quarters for a five-man crew.
DIMENSIONS
Length overall: 54·86m (180ft)
Beam overall: 24·38m (80ft)
Length, load deck: 48·16m (158ft)
Beam, load deck: 15·85m (52ft)
Height on cushion: 9·94m (32ft 8½in)
Height off cushion: 8·72m (28ft 8½in)
WEIGHTS
All-up: 750 tons
Payload: 250 tons

Sea Pearl, the world's biggest hover transporter, during operations in the Persian Gulf

Two 160-ton payload hoverplatforms employed as chain ferries to carry vehicles and equipment across the Yukon river

PERFORMANCE, FULLY LOADED: Calm water, towing force of 15 tons, 7 knots. In 2·74m (9ft) high by 76·2m (250ft) long waves, 3 knots.

160-TON AIR CUSHION FERRY

Following experiments conducted in November 1974, Mackace was awarded contracts to build two cable-drawn hoverferries, which operated across the River Yukon in Alaska. Named the Yukon Princess I and Yukon Princess II, the platforms were used to carry vehicles and equipment across the River Yukon whether frozen solid, breaking up, liquid or just covered with thin ice. During this contract it was observed that the hover ferries broke up ice up to one metre thick. The hover platforms were based on a modular float raft with special Mackace skirt frames attached to the periphery. The cushion system gave a hover height of 48in when fully laden. The two craft carried up to 2,000 tons of cargo across the Yukon daily.

LIFT SYSTEM: Two 700hp GM Detroit diesel engines designed to operate in temperatures of −57°C (−60°F). Each engine drives an Alldays Peacock 1,100 BA DIDW centrifugal fan, each of which delivers 2,605m³ (92,000ft³) of air per minute, giving a cushion pressure of 0·7kg/m² (1psi).

SKIRT: 5ft deep segmented skirt with spray skirt.

WINCHING SYSTEM: Two winches were employed to tow the craft backwards and forwards across the 1,500m (5,000ft) crossing.

ACCOMMODATION: Heated cabin for the crew and an elevated bridge.

YUKON PRINCESS I

DIMENSIONS
Length overall: 38·7m (127ft)
Beam overall: 25·7m (84ft 6in)
Length of load deck: 29·9m (98ft 3in)
Beam of load deck: 17m (56ft)
Height on cushion: 7·62m (25ft)
Height off cushion: 6·1m (20ft)
WEIGHTS
All-up: 375·9 tonnes (370 tons)
Payload: 162·6 tonnes (160 tons)

YUKON PRINCESS II

DIMENSIONS
Length overall: 38·5m (126ft 6in)
Beam overall: 24·8m (81ft 6in)
Length of load deck: 29·8m (97ft 9in)
Beam of load deck: 16·1m (53ft)
Height on cushion: 7·62m (25ft)
Height off cushion: 6·1m (20ft)
WEIGHTS
All-up: 418·6 tonnes (412 tons)
Payload: 162·6 tonnes (160 tons)

HOVER PLATFORMS

Mackace modular hover platforms range in payload capacity from 15 to 150 tons. Based on

Mackace self-propelled hover platform during an offshore application

30-ton Mackace hover platform for Jordan

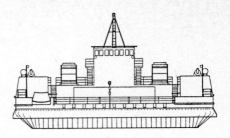

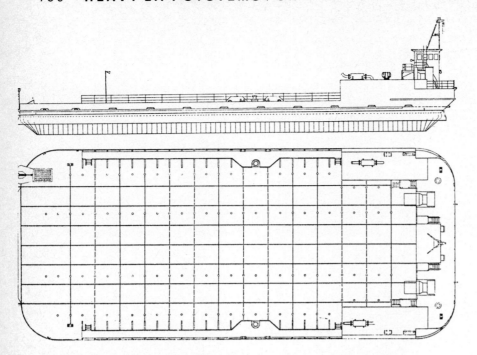

General arrangement of the 250-ton payload capacity Mackace hover transporter

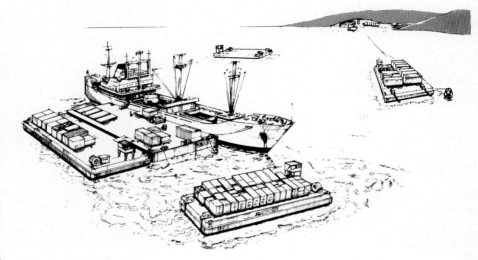

the standard Uniflote pontoon, each platform can be expanded or contracted to suit particular requirements.

Specially fabricated skirt frames are cantilevered off the sides of the Uniflote pontoons. The neoprene-coated nylon weave skirt is attached beneath the frames to protect it against accidental damage.

Each frame has its own skirt segment attached and is quickly replaced if damaged. The self-contained power packs driving the lift system are also mounted on the skirt frames, leaving the deck area clear. Contract labour can handle and assemble the platforms on site.

PROPULSION: The platforms can be self-propelled up to 150 tonnes; alternatively they can be winched or towed. Outboard motors can be employed for marine propulsion.

The overland self-propulsion system is based on hydraulically-operated driving wheels. Combined with the hover system, the driving wheels allow the hover platform complete freedom of movement over any terrain, independent of towing equipment.

CUSTOM-BUILT PLATFORMS

Purpose-built hover platforms can be designed and built from 15 to 1,000 tons, depending on the customer's requirements and proposed operating conditions. These can be built on-site or in nearby fabrication facilities using local labour and materials under supervision of Mackace engineers.

SPIN TANK

This was developed in response to a request for a simplified cable-laying system. The Mackace Spin Tank system of cable laying employs a cushion of low pressure water and simple skirt to support a cable drum on a vertical axis, thus eliminating problems with cable snatch, reel sagging and over-feed. The system has been tested at Mackace's test facilities.

HOVER MODULES FOR PETROCHEMICAL PLANT

In March 1977 Mackace Hoversystems announced that it is able to offer large hover modules of up to 5,000-ton capacity for petrochemical plants.

The concept is to build the petrochem modules on a giant 400 × 200ft modular steel grid. Once completed a Mackace hover system is attached to the periphery and the module is hovered from the fabrication bay into the sea where its air cushion carries it above a ballasted sea-going barge. The

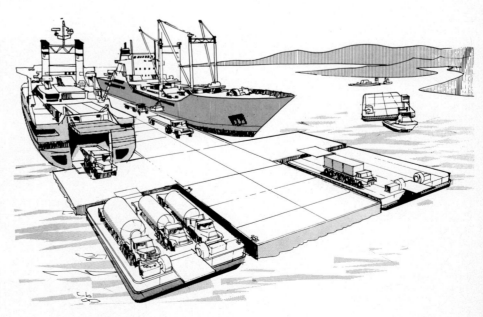

Two proposed ship-to-shore systems employing Mackace transporters

barge is deballasted, the module comes off hover and is made fast to the barge ready for a normal sea tow to the installation site.

On arrival the barge is ballasted to water level so that the module can hover off. It then hovers to the exact installation site (towed or winched by conventional means) where, once in position, the air power is switched off and the module sits on its prepared foundation. The Mackace hover system is removed for re-use and the grid (already with services fitted) is filled with concrete to make a permanent base.

This simple concept reduces the need for heavy lifting gear and site work is restricted to the assembly of modules to form the complete plant.

The key feature of this concept is its simplicity. A petrochem module can be assembled by usual contracting labour in an established fabrication facility and the self-contained skirt frames are fixed to the platform module by mechanical couplings which are re-usable. The actual number of skirt frames needed depends on the number of modules to be towed to site, the duration of the voyage and the rate of delivery required.

Mackace has been involved in the petrochem and construction industry for some years, supplying hover platforms and large hover transporters to overcome transportation and logistics problems in geographically hostile areas. The result of this experience is a range of hover transporters capable of operating with maximum reliability in any climate. Their independence from ports, docks, tides or ground and sea conditions make the hover transporters among the few machines which can work literally round-the-clock in any conditions.

ARCTIC DRILL BARGE SYSTEM

Hoverbarges are now a proven way of getting into difficult areas, having been used from Abu Dhabi in the Middle East to frozen areas of Alaska. They become more economical as their size increases and this leads to an ideal situation with the problem of drilling and supplying goods in the Arctic.

Mackace's main hover drill barge will weigh some 6,000 tons, and have an approximate size of 91·4 × 76·2m (300 × 250ft). With a cushion pressure of 1·5psi, and an average hover height of 1·83m (6ft) the barge will be capable of traversing difficult terrain. Fitted out as a self-contained unit for working long periods on site in low temperatures, it will be mainly enclosed. It is expected to be moved two to three times a year by winching to a new position. Anchors would be located in the ice for rigidity. Anchor positions would be laid out by a hover tender vehicle, which would also act as a secondary supply vessel, and in the case of emergencies, such as a blow-out, would be capable of drilling a relief hole. This secondary hover barge would be much smaller, probably with a payload of 160 tons, but will be self-propelled with air propellers, giving it a speed of 8 knots.

The main drill barge will not be completely dependent on this supply vessel, having its own helicopter pad and a tracked vehicle fleet for use in emergencies. It is expected that these vehicles will work within the 300m (1,000ft) contour line of the Beaufort Sea area once the new leases have been issued.

Because of the problems of vehicles being

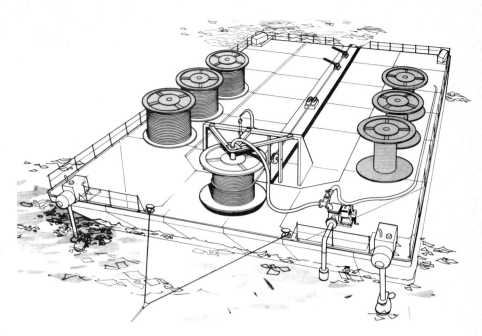

The spin tank system of cable laying, developed by Mackace, employs a cushion of low pressure water and a skirt to support a cable driven on a vertical axis, thereby eliminating problems of overfeed, reel sagging and cable snatch

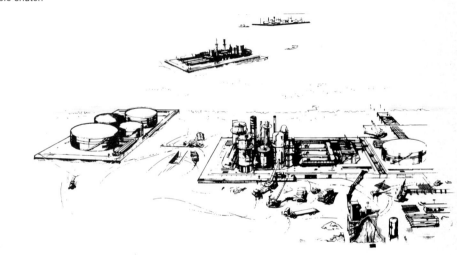

Impression of a Mackace petrochemical plant module. The module would be built on a 400 × 200ft modular steel grid. Once completed, a Mackace hover system would be attached to the periphery. The module would then be hovered from the fabrication bay into the sea where its air cushion would carry it onto the top of a ballasted sea-going barge

crushed by ice in the past, it is expected to maintain a moat around the barge during the winter months employing the waste heat of the system on board. The air cushion also has the ability to break ice of certain thicknesses, as demonstrated by Mackace on the Illinois River with the US Coast Guard during the trials programme of 1978. Because of the enormous drilling programme involved, and the content, Mackace is negotiating with a number of potential joint venture partners in the drilling business, of whom they hope to have an agreed partner soon so that a complete package can be offered to the oil companies.

MEARS CONTRACTORS LIMITED

Dorcan House, Dorcan Way, Swindon, Wiltshire SN3 3TS, England
Telephone: 0793 40111
Telex: 449824 (G)

Air Cushion Division:
Wallhouse Road, Slade Green, Erith, Kent DA8 2LB, England
Telephone: 03224 37266
Telex: 8953460

Officials:
R W Bale, BSc, CEng, FICE, *Managing Director*
D R Eales, *Associate Director*
D G Kinner, CEng, MIMechE, *Contracts Engineer*

Mears Contractors Limited holds the franchise for Air Cushion Equipment (1976) Ltd's system of tank moving throughout the United Kingdom and Western Europe.

Tanks moved by the company range in size between 48m diameter, 700 tonnes weight; 68m diameter, 530 tonnes weight and 6m diameter, 7

tonnes weight. A 700-tonne tank was relocated by Mears Contractors Ltd for Shell Française at their refinery near Bordeaux.

The equipment consists of a segmented skirt system, diesel-driven air supply fans and inter-connecting ducting, all of which can be readily shipped to any location in the above areas.

Site surveys are undertaken by a Mears engineer in conjunction with an appointed associate company, in countries outside the United Kingdom, which provide non-specialist plant and equipment for the move. Mears provide the lift equipment and specialist supervision.

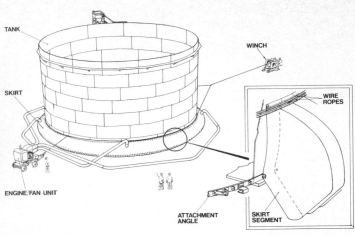

A 68m diameter tank, weighing 530 tonnes relocated for Stanic at the company's refinery in Livorno, Italy. The technique employed by Mears Contractors Limited is shown in the accompanying diagram

PINDAIR LIMITED

Quay Lane, Hardway, Gosport, Hampshire PO12 4LJ, England

Telephone: 070 17 87830
Telex: 86210 SKIMA G
See ACV section for officials and company background

Mike Pinder originally conceived and patented a process for moving oil tanks on air cushions while working in the oil industry in 1966 and has retained a keen interest in low speed applications of the air cushion principle. Although mainly involved in design, manufacture and marketing of small hovercraft, Pindair Limited is interested in designing small platforms, trailers, lighters and agricultural equipment embodying air cushions and various methods of propulsion.

Particular concepts under active study are as follows:

Agricultural air cushion platforms: Simple bolt-together air cushion platforms using lightweight diesel engines and centrifugal fans in various sizes up to ten tonnes payload, enabling equipment and crops to be transported over soft or wet ground. These platforms are conceived as having various optional bolt-on propulsion and guidance systems to suit the particular application.

Rigid amphibious air cushion platforms: Similar to the above, but incorporating buoyancy and suitably marinised. Particularly suitable for ship-to-shore lightering work where harbours are not available.

Inflatable amphibious air cushion platforms: Similar to the above but designed to be quickly packed into a smaller size for transport or storage. It is envisaged that a vehicle such as a Land Rover could be made fully amphibious by adding this equipment, giving it greater versatility in military and exploratory applications.

UNITED STATES OF AMERICA

GLOBAL MARINE DEVELOPMENT INC

PO Box 3010, Newport Beach, California 92663, USA
Telephone: (714) 752 5050
Telex: 69-2316
Officials:
R C Crooke, *President*
R B Thornburg, *Vice President*
S B Wetmore, *Vice President – Engineering*
Associated Companies:
Arctic Systems Ltd, Calgary, Alberta, Canada
Arctic Engineers and Constructors, Houston, Texas, USA
(Above are wholly owned subsidiaries)

Global Marine Development Inc (GMDI), a wholly owned subsidiary of Global Marine Inc of Los Angeles, California, is primarily concerned with the development and operation of marine related systems, generally those having a significant element of advanced or new technology. One of these systems involves the use of air cushion vehicles in conjunction with oil and gas exploration and production programmes in Arctic regions.

ACT-100

Construction of the prototype ACT-100 was completed in April 1971. The craft is essentially an ACV barge designed to transport 100-ton payloads throughout the year across Arctic tundra, muskeg and marsh without unduly disturbing the soil and vegetation. It will also traverse offshore ice and open water.

Five months of testing under arctic winter conditions on the Great Slave Lake at Yellowknife during 1971-72 demonstrated that the craft is able to operate in temperatures of −45·6°C (−50°F) without difficulty. It proved extremely stable and manoeuvrable when travelling over level terrain, slopes, water, and over varying thicknesses of ice. It also showed unusual ice-breaking ability in thicknesses up to 660mm

ACT-100 air cushion transporter

(26in) and had no difficulty in traversing broken ice.

The Canadian Ministry of Transport employed the ACT-100 under contract to investigate the feasibility of operating air cushion ferries in the Mackenzie River highway system. Initial trials were conducted at Tuktoyaktuk, NWT, in November 1972. The craft was towed 322km (200 miles) up the Mackenzie for final ferry trials at Arctic Red River in June 1973.

In December 1973 the ACT-100 was employed by Imperial Oil Ltd to transport drill rig supplies and equipment from Langley Island to Adgo Island. Adgo is an expendable artificial island constructed by Imperial in the Beaufort Sea to support an exploratory drilling operation. The ACT-100 carried loads of up to 99·8 tons over ice, broken ice, and water.

LIFT: Cushion air is supplied by two 640hp Caterpillar D-348 diesel engines driving two 1·37m (4ft 6¼in) diameter Joy 5425 NOL steel centrifugal fans. Air is fed directly into the cushion without ducting. Cushion pressure is 144lb/ft². Diesel is contained in a single 500 US gallon integral tank in the main hull amidships.

CONTROLS: Towing cables to pull vehicle and wheels beneath centre of hull. A liquid ballast is provided for trim.

HULL: Box-type hull in A537 low temperature alloy steel. Hull is designed to support a 100-ton payload.

SKIRT: 1·52m (5ft) deep fully segmented skirt in rubber-coated nylon.

CREW: Control cabin accommodates one operator and assistant. A third member of the operating crew is the towing vehicle operator.

ACCOMMODATION: A "habitat" unit, with complete camp facilities for 35-40 men and storage facilities, can be mounted on the hull.

SYSTEMS: 110/220V, 60Hz 30kW generator for lighting, control and pumping.

COMMUNICATIONS: None permanently installed.

DIMENSIONS
Length,
    power off: 23·71m (75ft 3⅜in)
    skirt inflated: 24·15m (79ft 3in)
Beam overall,
    power off: 17·38m (57ft 0⅜in)
    skirt inflated: 18·59m (61ft)
Height overall,
    power off: 1·98m (6ft 6in)
    skirt inflated: 3·2m (10ft 6in)
Draft afloat: 1·04m (3ft 5in)
Cushion area: 308·068m² (3,316ft²)
Skirt depth: 1·52m (5ft)
CONTROL CABIN
Length: 2·43m (8ft)
Max width: 2·74m (9ft)
Max height: 2·43m (8ft)
Floor area: 6·89m² (72ft²)
FREIGHT HOLDS: Open deck, with tankage available beneath.
WEIGHTS
Normal empty: 150 US tons
Normal all-up: 250 US tons
Normal payload: 100 US tons
Max payload: 130 US tons
PERFORMANCE (at normal operating weight):
Speed (dependent on tow vehicle): 9·65km/h (6mph) plus
Still air range and endurance at cruising speed: 12 hours at average speed of 9·65km/h (6mph) = 115·87km (72miles)
Vertical obstacle clearance: 1·21m (4ft)

ACDS

The latest design of an ACV drilling rig is the Air Cushion Drilling System (ACDS) which was initially designed for use in offshore arctic regions but also has been considered as a candidate for drilling in marshlands and swamp areas where its amphibious ability is equally useful.

The system offers two important advantages in its arctic configuration, the complete drilling system can be moved between locations at any time during the summer or winter, and the unit can remain over the wellhead even with moderate ice movement.

The ACDS is a two unit system consisting of an Air Cushion Drill Platform (ACDP) and an Air Cushion Support Platform (ACSP). Both units consist of identical hulls, 64 × 52·7 × 3m (210 × 173 × 10ft) overall, one of which contains the complete drilling equipment package and the other (ACSP) contains the accommodation, additional pipeline equipment and consumables.

ACT-100 air cushion transporter

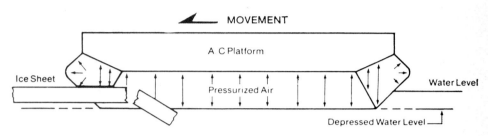
← MOVEMENT

A C Platform

Ice Sheet | Pressurized Air | Water Level

Depressed Water Level

Action of the air cushion platform when an ice sheet is encountered. On contact, the skirt rises above the ice, continuing to act as an air seal. The ice sheet then loses its flotation support from below as the water beneath it is depressed by the cushion of pressurised air within the skirt zone. The ice sheet then becomes a cantilevered ledge and on reaching its critical length breaks, and the overhang section falls off into the displaced water below. The arrows in the drawing above show the force vectors within the skirt

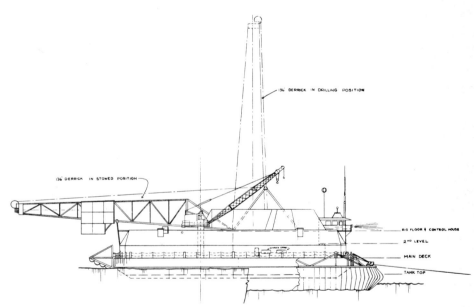
Smaller version of the ADS with a length of 46·93m (154ft). Height of the derrick in drilling position would be 41·45m (136ft) measured above the upper deck

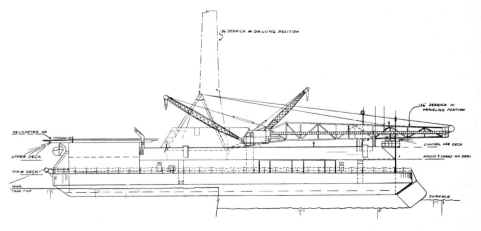
Profile of the 70·4m (231ft) long, 3,840-ton air cushion arctic offshore drilling system (ADS), showing the derrick in travelling and drilling position, the control house and helipad

The latter unit also serves as a backup- drill rig as the accommodations are portable, modular units which can be removed and a standard land rig installed on the main deck to allow a relief well to be drilled if required.

LIFT: A 3,500kW common-bus ac power generating system, with silicon-controlled rectifiers, supplies power to the drilling equipment and three of the four lift fan drive motors on the ACDP. The fourth lift fan is powered by 1,275hp direct drive diesel engine. All lift fans on the ACSP are similarly powered by diesel engines.

The fans deliver a maximum pressure of 1·5psi or an all-up weight of 3,100 tons. For normal rig moves the cushion pressure is 1·1psi providing a total lift of 2,300 short tons.

SKIRTS: 2·4m (8ft) hover height is provided by retractable, fully segmented HDL-type skirts of rubber coated nylon fabric (99oz/yd²).

PROPULSION: Moving the ACDS will be accomplished by use of two onboard traction winches and logistic support vehicles which will both handle the 31·8mm (1¼in) wire line and also act as dead men. Alternatively, the winch line can also be secured to ice anchors providing a maximum tractive effort of 72,700kg (160,000lb). The ACDS will have a minimum velocity of 6·4-8km/h (4-5mph).

LOGISTIC SUPPORT: Candidate vehicles include ice-breaking workboats; self-propelled, 50-ton hovercraft; conventional barges frozen-in near the drilling locations; fixed-wing aircraft; tracked vehicles and large rubber-tyred vehicles. The selection will be determined by specific condition, economics, availability and other operator requirements.

ACCOMMODATION: A totally enclosed and heated working environment will help maintain maximum crew efficiency, even during the coldest arctic weather. Modern crew quarters for 70 men are included.

A preliminary specification for the 3,100-ton ACDS is given below.

DIMENSIONS
Length: 64m (210ft)
Beam: 52·7m (173ft)
Depth of hull: 3m (10ft)
WEIGHTS AND CAPACITIES
Gross weight: 3,100 short tons
Casing: 210 short tons
5in drill pipe: 15,000ft
Liquid mud: 1,425bbl
Fuel oil: 1,700bbl
Max variable load, ACDP: 1,325 short tons
  ACSP: 1,675 short tons

ICEATER I

The icebreaking characteristics of the ACT-100 led to the development of a new vehicle designed specifically to aid the passage of a conventional ship through ice-bound waters.

The craft, known as the VIBAC (Vehicle, Ice-Breaking, Air Cushion) system, is attached to the bow of the ship as soon as it enters an ice-field. Close visual observation and films have revealed what happens when the air cushion platform approaches an ice sheet, and how the air cushion icebreaking phenomenon takes place.

On making contact with the ice sheet the skirt rises up over the ice while continuing to maintain its air seal. The ice sheet then penetrates the zone of pressurised air beneath the craft, where the water level within the skirt area is depressed to a lower level than the bottom of the ice layer. The ice has now become a cantilevered ledge without water support beneath. When the cantilevered section reaches its critical length, failure occurs and the overhanging section breaks off and falls into the depressed water below.

Under the sponsorship of Transport Canada, the ACT-100 was modified into an icebreaking system and named Iceater I. It was first demonstrated during the 1975-76 winter season at Thunder Bay, Ontario. Scoring an impressive first in the history of ice breaking and transiting, it maintained continuous headway through ice up to 0·812m (32in) thick at speeds up to 9 knots.

A 14ft-deep 'V' notch was cut into the stern of

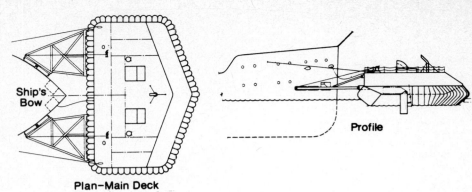

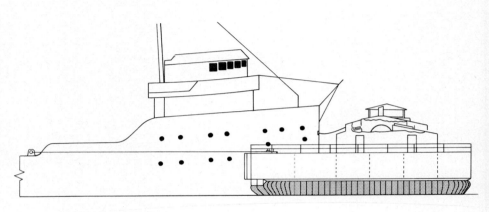

Early VIBAC air-cushion ice-breaker concept designed for attachment to conventional ships travelling through Arctic waters. The unit was an outcome of experience with the ACT-100 on the Great Slave Lake, where it continuously broke ice as thick as 0·685m (27in)

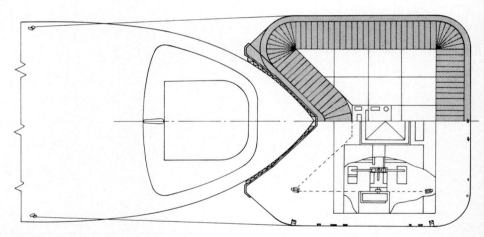

Iceater I—general arrangement

	Length	Beam	Displacement	Horsepower
ASL Iceater-1 has now operated with four different vessels:-				
Thunder Cape, harbour tug	32m (105ft)	8·11m (26ft 7in)	600 tons	1,440shp
CCGS Alexander Henry	57·91m (190ft)	13·2m (43ft 6in)	2,240 tons	3,550shp
CCGS Griffon	65·22m (214ft)	14·93m (49ft)	2,793 tons	4,250shp
MV Imperial St Clair	122·49m (415ft)	22·55m (74ft)	16,450 tons	6,500 shp

the ACT-100 to accommodate the bow of the *CCGS Alexander Henry.* The Thunder Bay tests began on 15 January 1976 in temperatures of –30°C. They continued for 3½ months, with the *Alexander Henry* and Iceater I coupled together as a single unit.

Maximum speed of the icebreaking operations undertaken so far has been 9 knots in 431mm

(17in) thick ice and the maximum thickness of ice broken continuously has been 0·812m (32in). Channel clearing has been significantly simplified and speeded-up by the system and it has been found that because of the method employed and its configuration, Iceater can work alongside locks, piers, docks and other vessels without fear of damage.

LIFT: Air pressure is generated by two Caterpillar D-348 diesels, each directly coupled to a 1·37m (4ft 6in) Joy A-1670 Airfoil centrifugal fan. Each engine develops 440hp at 1,850rpm. The fans develop 170,000ft³/min air flow within the plenum at a nominal pressure of about one psi, or 29in water pressure gauge. Consequently, water below the ice sheet is depressed by an equal amount 29in (0·73m).

HULL: Box type structure in ASTM A537 low temperature alloy steel.

SKIRT: 1·52m (5ft) deep fully segmented skirt in natural rubber coated on nylon fabric, 99oz/yd².

GENERATOR: Single Perkins/Bemac II, 30kW

BALLAST PUMP: 10hp Viking, 200 gallons/min

DIMENSIONS

Length: 23·77m (78ft)

Beam: 17·37m (57ft)

Height (on landing pads)
   to main deck: 1·21m (4ft)

WEIGHTS

Light: 190 tons

Gross: 270 tons

PACT-50

Subsequent to the successful operation of the ACT-100 over a number of years and under a wide variety of environmental conditions, a second generation air cushion transporter was designed with a ground drive and water propulsion system. The Self-propelled Air Cushion Transporter (PACT) was initially conceived to work in conjunction with the ACDS, though it can function equally effectively as an independent cargo/personnel carrier or as a lighter in remote areas.

The payload of the PACT is a direct function of its logistic support requirements and for ACDS operations under study, a 50-ton payload was optimum. However, should the need arise the payload can be increased by a factor of two to four without difficulty.

Power is provided by two Detroit 16V-149Tl diesel engines, each driving one lift fan (87,000ft³/min at approximately 1psi) and two hydraulic pumps (350hp each) which drive two hub-mounted hydraulic motors on each drive wheel.

A preliminary specification for the PACT-50 is given below.

DIMENSIONS

Length: 29·56m (97ft)

Beam: 21·34m (70ft)

Depth of hull: 1·83m (6ft)

Hoverheight: 1·83m (6ft)

WEIGHTS

Payload: 50 tons

Light weight: 165 tons

Gross weight (dry): 215 tons

A notch plug has been built to fit the 14ft-deep 'V' cutout in the stern of Iceater-I to accommodate a ship's bow. The purpose of the plug is threefold: to permit the Iceater to be pushed by a flat bow tug; to further break up ice cusps in the after end of the plenum, and to divert broken ice outboard as far and as quickly as possible. The plug was designed and built in the winter of 1977-78 and the two photos show it being raised from lowered to stowed position

Iceater-I coupled with the 16,450-ton *MV Imperial St Clair*. With the icebreaker platform attached, the cleared track is straighter and wider than that created by conventional ice-breaking techniques and the ship is more manoeuvrable

MARIDYNE

1169 East Ash Avenue, Fullerton, California
92631, USA
Telephone: (714) 992 1620

MARIDYNE ACV-4000 BACKHOE

The Backhoe is basically an air cushion platform equipped with a hydraulically-operated
backhoe. The prototype has been designed and
built for the mechanised harvesting of oyster beds
in the trial areas within Puget Sound, requiring
raking, light digging and lifting, but it can also be
employed for trenching, dredging or light
excavating on mudflats, marshes or shoreline
areas which cannot be reached by conventional
machines because the footing is too soft. On level
surfaces the craft, which is 5·5m (18ft) long and
weighs 1,814kg (4,000lb), can be moved without
difficulty by two men.

LIFT: Cushion air is supplied by a single Wisconsin petrol engine, developing 37hp at 2,400rpm,
driving a 60·96cm (24in) diameter Rotafoil centrifugal fan. Cushion pressure is 17lb/ft² and the
airflow is 12,000ft³/min. Fuel is carried in a single
72·7 litre (16 gallon) tank.

PROPULSION: Tests have shown that the
backhoe itself can be employed for locomotion.
Alternative methods of propulsion include one or
two persons pushing; the use of a winch or
hydraulically-driven capstan with a 2,000lb maximum line pull for steep slopes; hydraulically-
driven rear-mounted wheels fitted with soft tyres
and, for overwater use, a 50hp outboard motor
fitted on a retractable mounting bracket.

CONTROLS: All air cushion, propulsion and
backhoe controls at operation console.

HULL: Raft type structure in aluminium with
foam for additional bouyancy. The side sections
are of fibreglass construction and are removable
to reduce the overall width for transport by road.

SKIRT: Loop and segment type in neoprene or
nylon fabric. Hull clearance 305mm (12in). Total
of 120 peripheral fingers, all independently
replaceable.

DIMENSIONS
Length: 5·5m (18ft)
Width: 4·57m (15ft)
Height: 2·44m (8ft)
Reach from swing mast: 4·27m (14ft)
Digging depth (max): 2·13m (7ft)
Swing arc: 270 degrees
Transport width, side sections removed: 2·39m
 (7ft 10in)

Maridyne's ACV-4000 Backhoe, designed for trenching, dredging or light excavating on mudflats, marshes
or shoreline areas which cannot be reached by conventional machines

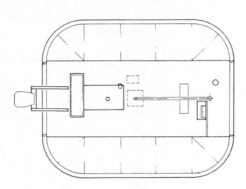

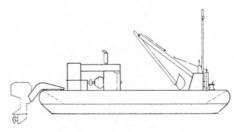

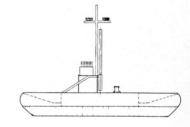

General arrangement Maridyne ACV-4000 Backhoe

PHOENIX HOVERCRAFT CORPORATION

Suite 223, 2077 South Gessner, Houston, Texas
77063, USA
Telephone: (713) 784 2420
Telex: 791 449 Phoenix
Officials:
Dan Turner, *President*
Ray Golding, *Vice President, Engineering*
UK office:
Phoenix Hovercraft Corporation, 5 Grosvenor
Square, Southampton, Hampshire, England
Telephone: 0703 36430

Phoenix Hovercraft Corporation and Phoenix
Hovercraft International were formed in Houston, Texas, in 1980 to design, construct and market throughout the world a range of hovercraft
products. One of the first ventures of Phoenix
Hovercraft Corporation is the construction of an
amphibious hoverbarge oil drilling rig, propelled
by paddle wheels. Known as the Wetlands
Drillbarge System (WDBS), the concept will be
marketed in areas where intertidal or swamp
conditions make the use of conventional drilling
equipment difficult or impossible. A range of

Models of the two Phoenix service barges locked onto the drill barge

hovercraft crewboats as well as two-seater leisure craft is also planned.

Phoenix Hovercraft Corporation and Phoenix Hovercraft International were formed by Phoenix Management Corporation which has already established itself, through Phoenix Seadrill, as a specialist in the field of shallow-water drilling with the Big Foot class of jack-up drilling platforms.

It was recognised by William R Hargrove, Phoenix Management Corporation's president, that the hovercraft principle, although well-established in Europe, had taken time to gain acceptance in the United States. The new companies have, therefore, drawn strongly on European management, as well as design and equipment manufacturing expertise, to launch the new venture.

Detailed design work of the WDBS is being undertaken by UK naval architects Burness Corlett and Partners. The skirts and fans are being supplied by British manufacturers and the barge is being constructed by Brown & Root in Houston.

Development of the WDBS is expected to open up many potentially rich hydrocarbon fields in the wetlands areas of the United States where exploration work is currently restricted due to the problems of transporting drilling equipment to the site. Access is often made difficult by the need to dredge canals or construct, fill and board roads. This takes time and limits operational flexibility.

However, the use of the WDBS overcomes these problems. By using the hovercraft principle, completely equipped drill rigs can be transported direct to the location, requiring no access by specially dredged waterways or built roads. They create little or no environmental or ecological disturbance: the barge hovers at a height of 1·22m (4ft) and exerts a ground pressure of only 1·5psi (by comparison, a man exerts a pressure of 5-10psi).

WETLANDS DRILLBARGE SYSTEM (WDBS)

The WDBS consists of three hovercraft and a

The two Wetlands service barges can act as cargo carrying units with payloads of 300 tons each. One is a bulk carrier, the other is designed to carry general equipment. Mud, pipes and equipment can be moved quickly to the rig site

	Drill barge	Service vessel A	Service vessel B
Length	54·9m (180ft)	54·9m (180ft)	54·9m (180ft)
Beam	16·8m (55ft)	16·26m (53ft 4½in)	16·26m (53ft 4½in)
Depth	3·66m (12ft)	3·05m (10ft)	3·05m (10ft)
Max variable load	3,000 tons	300 tons	300 tons
Fuel oil	2,930bbl	2,960bbl	2,960bbl
Water	6,500bbl	2,220bbl	2,220bbl
Bulk mud	53·24m³ (1,880ft³)	—	—
Active mud	870bbl	—	—
Reserve mud	830bbl	—	—
Bulk mat	—	113·3m³ (4,000ft³)	0
Slugging pitt	40bbl		
Sand trap	200bbl		
Sack mat	44·6m² (480ft²)		
Pipe rack area	12·2 ×17·07m (40 × 56ft)	11 × 9·45m (36 × 31ft)	0
Drive on deck area	—	8·23 × 16·15m (27 × 53ft)	40·54 × 9·45m (133 × 31ft)
Deck loading	—	350lb/ft²	350lb/ft²

DRILL MAST BEING HAULED INTO POSITION FOR DRILLING OPERATION

HELICOPTER LAUNCHING PAD

SEPARATE CREWS QUARTERS VESSEL

SV's CONTROL CABIN

BULK MATERIAL CONTAINERS

SEGMENTED SKIRT SYSTEM

BULK MATERIAL AND PIPE CARRYING SELF PROPELLED HOVER SV 'A'

FAN AND DIESEL POWER UNIT FOR HOVER LIFT

EQUIPMENT CARRYING HOVER SV 'B'

PADDLE WHEEL SELF PROPULSION

DRILL SLOT WITH SKIRTS REMOVED FOR OPERATION

REAR SKIRT SYSTEM FOR DB

Operation of Phoenix Hovercraft Corporation's Wetlands Drill Barge System (WDBS). The system, which enables drilling equipment to be moved into otherwise inaccessible marsh and swamplands at low cost, comprises two hover service vessels that lock onto a drill barge to form a complete hovering unit of 2,500 tons, exerting only 1·5psi on the surface. After delivery of the drill barge and crew to a particular location, the service vessels act as supply vessels, transporting materials and equipment. By basing the system on modules of a manageable size, maximum use can be made of inland waterways

conventional barge. The drilling barge is 54·9m (180ft) long with a beam of 16·8m (55ft) and depth of 3·66m (12ft). It carries standard equipment for drilling to a depth of 9,144m (30,000ft). The two service vessels are each 54·9m (180ft) long by 16·26m (53ft 4½in) wide and 3·05m (10ft) deep with a maximum variable load capacity of 300 tons.

Before operations start a service vessel fitted with an hydraulic dragline clears a path in the wetlands, removing over-size obstacles and placing route markers. Where slopes are too great for the WDBS self-propulsion system, ground anchors are sunk and the WDBS is assisted in climbing inclines by winching.

Transportation to the drilling site begins on inland waterways. Each service vessel is equipped with paddle wheels for self-propulsion: one pushes the drill barge which is on hover, the other moves the non-hovering quarters barge. No unit has a width greater than 17·07m (56ft) in order to permit passage through the maximum number of lock gates.

Once near the drilling site, the quarters barge is anchored in the waterway and the two service barges lock onto the drill barge to form a complete hoverbarge drill system using a specially designed Phoenix device to link the air system of all three barges together. The complete system is then hovered into the wetlands and onto the drill site.

Once the drilling barge is on site the service vessels return to the waterway to pick up the housing module which is carried as a dead weight between the two service vessels. The unit is placed a few feet from the drilling barge and connected by a personnel bridge. By now the drilling barge has come off hover and is anchored.

The service vessels now act as cargo-carrying units, each with a payload of 300 tons. One is a bulk carrier of fuel oil and water, the other acts as a general equipment carrier.

Lift power for the WDBS system is provided by standard industrial diesels coupled to high volume, low pressure centrifugal fans. The system's overall weight of 2,500 tons requires 3,500hp for cushion lift.

The skirt, which is fabricated in flexible fabric, is of the fully segmented type and is bolted round the periphery of the barges. Each segment can be replaced in ten minutes. Small tears can usually be repaired on site without removing the segment. The platform will, however, operate with up to ten per cent of the segments damaged.

Concurrently with the construction of the WDBS, Phoenix Hovercraft Corporation is also developing a range of six to twelve-seat hovercraft crew boats for offshore oil support and other general marine tasks, and a range of two-seat leisure craft aimed specifically at the US market.

The system is designed to accommodate the largest rig currently on the market. The substructure is designed to accommodate a G.N.C. 1,300,000lb conventional 43·28m (142ft) mast with 9·14m (30ft) base. The substructure is astride a 4·06 × 12·19m (13ft 4in × 40ft) slot. Four modules consisting of drill barge, two service vessels and crew's vessels complete the system.

TRACKED SKIMMERS

BRAZIL

FEI
FACULTY OF INDUSTRIAL ENGINEERING

Research Vehicle Department (DEPV), Faculty of Industrial Engineering, São Bernado do Campo, Avenido Oreste Romano 112, São Paulo, Brazil
Telephone: 443 1155
Officials:
Rigoberto Soler Gisbert, *Director of Vehicle Research*

The Vehicle Research Department of the FEI, founded in 1968, has designed a number of small air cushion vehicles, one of which is about to be put into production.

The Department's first and most ambitious project to date has been the design and construction of the TALAV tracked air cushion vehicle, development of which is being supported by the Ministry for Industry and Commerce through FUNAT—a government fund for sponsoring new technological developments.

The prototype, an all-metal vehicle propelled by twin Marboré VIs, and seating 20 passengers, displays several novel features, including the siting of the main passenger access door at the front. The whole of the front section moves forward telescopically to provide space for entry and exit. This arrangement facilitates the loading of freight when necessary, and should an emergency stop occur when carrying passengers on a narrow elevated guideway, walking out through the front will be far safer than through the sides, say the designers.

It is also stated that passenger handling will be simplified at termini, where the vehicles can be drawn up side-by-side without the need to devote valuable space for platforms.

The main application foreseen for vehicles of this type is that of city centre to suburbs or city centre to airport links.

To enable construction to be undertaken without difficulty in developing areas where manpower is available, the structure is based on easily-handled sub-assemblies and standard panels of aluminium honeycomb.

The design team is at present concentrating on the development of an efficient yet economical approach to the construction of guideways.
LIFT AND PROPULSION: Cushion air is delivered by fans powered by a 70hp engine. Cushion pressure, 195·3kg/m² (40lb/ft²), cushion area 301·93m² (3,250ft²). Two 900lb st Turboméca Marboré VI gas turbines supply propulsive thrust.
DIMENSIONS
EXTERNAL
Length: 15·54m (51ft)
Width: 2·26m (7ft 5in)
Height: 2·87m (9ft 5in)

Prototype of the FEI, 20-seat TALAV tracked air cushion vehicle. Designed to cruise at 321·86km/h (200mph), the vehicle is powered by twin Turboméca Marboré VI gas turbines

INTERNAL
Internal height, passenger saloon: 2·13m (7ft)
WEIGHTS
Empty: 2,948·35kg (6,500lb)
Loaded: 5,896·7kg (13,000lb)

PERFORMANCE
Cruising speed: 321·86km/h (200mph)

FRANCE

SOCIÉTÉ DE L'AÉROTRAIN

Tour Anjou, 33 quai National, 92806 Puteaux, France
Telephone: 776 43 34
Telex: 610385 Bertrin Putau
Officials:
Benjamin Salmon, *Chairman*

Originally named "Société d'Etudes de l'Aérotrain", this company was formed on 15 April 1965 to develop a high speed transportation system based on air cushion support and guidance principles conceived by Bertin & Cie.

Jean Bertin, Chairman of the company from 1971 until he died, prematurely, on 21 December 1975, was known as the father of the Aérotrain. His name will remain attached to a number of outstanding inventions in the air cushion field and in many others, including aeronautics.

The Aérotrain has completed its experimental phase as far as the air cushion technique is concerned. The 01 half-scale prototype, after nearly three years of test runs at speeds up to 346km/h (215mph), successfully attained its phased design requirements, namely the verification of dynamic behaviour, the development of integrated sus-

pension systems, and the accumulation of data for the design and costing of full-scale operational vehicles.

The 02 half-scale prototype has undergone similar tests in order to produce data for vehicles operating at speeds above 322km/h (200mph). A speed of 423·26km/h (263mph) was attained by the vehicle in January 1969.

There are three families of Aérotrain systems, Interurban, with speeds of 280-400km/h (175-250mph); Suburban, with speeds of 160-200km/h (100-125mph) and the new Tridim system, designed for speeds of up to 80km/h

(50mph) as the distance between suburban stations generally ranges between several hundred yards and one or two miles.

The speeds selected will be based on economic considerations. Suburban systems will cover a variety of routes from city centres to airports and city centres to satellite towns and suburban areas. The size, speed and control system of each vehicle will be decided according to the route.

Current studies are aimed primarily at developing associated techniques including propulsion modes for the various speeds and environments, controls, signals and stations.

A mathematical model has been developed in order to computerise the various parameters for both families of applications. This enables operating costs to be obtained, in an optimised form, for given traffic requirements.

Two full-scale vehicles, the 80-seat Orleans inter-city Aérotrain and the 40-44 seat suburban Aérotrain have undergone extensive trials. During trials between 1969 and 1971, the 80-seat I-80 "Orleans" Aérotrain completed more than 700 hours of operation on its 18km (11·2 mile) track north of Orleans, carrying more than 10,000 people at a speed of 260km/h (160mph). In January 1973, the vehicle was taken to the UTA maintenance facility at Le Bourget airport where it was equipped with a 15,000lb st JT8D-11 turbofan, permitting its speed to be studied in the 360-400km/h (220-250mph) range.

In November 1973, a speed of 400km/h (250mph) was attained and by May 1974, 150 hours of operation had been logged in this configuration, during which 2,000 professionally interested passengers had been carried.

All these programmes, completed or under way, represent a financial development effort of roughly US $22 million. The French Government extended its support at every stage by means of various loans, subsidies and orders.

In November 1969, the company formed a US subsidiary, Aérotrain Systems Inc, to build and market Aérotrains in the United States and Mexico. Initially this company was jointly held by Rohr Industries Inc, Bertin et Cie and Société de l'Aérotrain. Since 1976, it has been held by the two latter. A 60-seat, 140mph, LIM-propelled prototype was completed in December 1972 and was successfully tested in 1975-76 on an experimental line built at the US Department of Transport centre at Pueblo, California.

In 1971, another subsidiary was formed, Aérotrain Scandinavia AB, in which the Salén Group has a 50% interest. A third company, formed in Brazil with the support of four French banks, is Aérotrain Systemas de Transporte.

In December 1973 an agreement was signed between Bertin & Cie, Aérotrain, Spie-Batignolles, Jeumont-Schneider, SGTE MTE and Francorail-MTE to co-operate with the promotion and operation of Aérotrain systems and various aspects of production of French projects.

Since 1974, feasibility studies have been under way for the Marseilles metropolitan area including connections between the airport and Aix-en-Provence, for the EUROPOLE Project linking Brussels to Geneva (via Luxembourg, Metz, Nancy, Strasbourg, Basle, Berne and Lausanne) and for several projects in Argentina.

EXPERIMENTAL AEROTRAIN AEROTRAIN 01

An experimental, half-scale prototype, this vehicle was operated along a test track 6·7km (4·2 miles) long. The track has an inverted T cross section, the vertical portion being 55cm (1ft 10in) high and the horizontal base 1·8m (5ft 11in) wide. A turntable is fitted at each end.

The vehicle is of light alloy construction. The slender body has seats at the front for six people, and an engine compartment at the rear. Lift and guidance are provided by two centrifugal fans, driven by two 50hp Renault Gordini motor car engines, linked by a shaft. The fans supply air to the guidance and lift cushions at a pressure of about 25g/cm² (0·35lb/in²), the maximum airflow being 10m³/s (350ft³/s). Propulsion is provided

Impression of the latest Aérotrain variant, a 360km/h fan-jet propelled vehicle seating 144 passengers. It has been designed for the EUROPOLE project, which will link Brussels with Geneva, via Luxembourg, Metz, Nancy, Strasbourg, Basle, Berne and Lausanne

Aérotrain 01, a research vehicle built for tests up to and above 250mph on the No I track at Gometz

Turntables are installed at each end of the present Aérotrain test track, but they will not be used normally on operational lines. In service Aérotrains will be able to manoeuvre independently on the flat floor surfaces of stations

Aérotrain 02, a research vehicle built for tests up to and above 250mph on the No I track at Gometz

by a 260hp Continental aero-engine, mounted at the top of a 1·2m (3ft 11in) tail pylon and driving a reversible-pitch propeller, which is also used for normal braking. There are brake pads at the rear of the vehicle which grip the vertical track section like a disc brake.

The first test run on the track was made on 29 December 1965. The prototype was intended to evaluate and demonstrate the Aérotrain principle on a small scale, and was developed with the

active support of the French Government and French Railways.

Although the vehicle was designed for a maximum speed of 200km/h (125mph) tests have been undertaken at higher speeds with the help of booster rockets to supplement the propulsive airscrew. In December 1967, the vehicle reached the top speed of 345km/h (215mph) several times with a jet engine assisted by two booster rockets.

DIMENSIONS
Length, overall: 10m (32ft 10in)
Width, overall: 2m (6ft 7in)
Height, overall: 3·7m (12ft 2in)
Height to top of body: 1·6m (5ft 3in)
WEIGHTS
Basic: 2,500kg (5,500lb)
PERFORMANCE
Cruising speed: 200km/h (125mph)
Top speed: 303km/h (188mph)

EXPERIMENTAL AEROTRAIN 02

Aérotrain 02 is an experimental half-scale prototype designed for high speed tests on the track at Gometz used by the first prototype.

Due to the track's relatively short length, a more powerful thrust engine, a Pratt & Whitney JT 12, is installed in order to maintain high speeds over a distance of 2km (1·3 miles) for performance measurements.

During its first series of test runs, the Aérotrain 02 attained 378km/h (235mph). A booster rocket was then added, and a series of tests followed, culminating in a record speed of 422km/h (263mph) being attained. The average speed recorded over the 2-3 mile track was 411km/h (255mph).

The air cushions for lift and guidance are provided by fans driven by a Turboméca Palouste gas turbine. At high speed, the dynamic pressure is sufficient to feed the air cushions.

The internal space has been devoted in the main to test instrumentation. Seats are provided only for the pilot and a test engineer.

Aérotrains 01 and 02 were both equipped with

I-80HV Aérotrain with its turbofan thrust unit

propulsion engines which were readily available from the aviation market and capable of giving high speed on a short test track. Operational vehicles use quieter power arrangements.

FULL-SCALE AEROTRAIN I-80 ORLEANS INTERCITY PROJECT

This medium-range inter-city vehicle (the Orleans-Paris line will be 113km (70 miles) long) was designed originally with airscrew propulsion for speeds up to 300km/h (186·41mph), but has now been equipped with a silenced turbofan engine which has increased its speed to 400km/h (250mph). The vehicle carries 80 passengers, in airline comfort, in an air-conditioned and sound-proofed cabin.

The lift and guidance air cushions are fed by two axial fans driven by a 400hp Turboméca Astazou gas turbine. At high speeds, they will be fed by dynamic intake pressure.

On the original model thrust was supplied by a shrouded propeller, driven independently by two 1,300hp Turmo III gas turbines.

In January 1973, the vehicle was taken to the UTA maintenance facility at Le Bourget, where it was fitted with a 15,000lb thrust Pratt & Whitney JT8D-11 turbofan, which permitted the systematic study of the I-80 and its components at speeds in the 354-426km/h (220-250mph) range.

Hydraulically retractable tyred wheels are incorporated to help to achieve silent operation

Prefabricated concrete beams of the Orleans track have a minimum ground clearance of 4·87m (16ft). This allows the track to be constructed across roads and agricultural land without causing obstruction *(Photo: P M Lambermont)*

SIDE VIEW

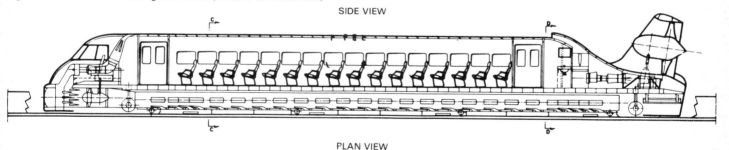

PLAN VIEW

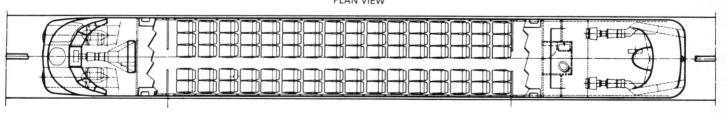

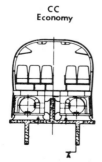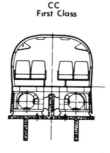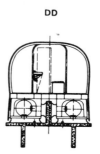

FRONT — CC Economy — CC First Class — DD — REAR

Aérotrain I-80—a typical Aérotrain configuration for medium-range inter-city traffic, carrying 80 passengers at a cruising speed of 180mph and a top speed of 190mph

near and in stations, and also to assist in manoeuvring and switching the vehicle on station
floors. The vertical rail of the inverted T track is
unnecessary at low speeds.

A very low empty-weight-to-payload ratio has
been possible because of the lack of concentrated
loads inherent in the vehicle. This permits the use
of lightweight supporting structures—tracks and
stations.

Vehicles will not be coupled, so that very high
frequency services can be maintained throughout
the day. With headways as low as one minute,
simple or articulated vehicles offer a range of
capacities which largely cope with the peaks of
traffic expected in known inter-city lines.

Two articulated cars with seats for up to 160
passengers and luxury models with a wider aisle
and reduced seating capacity are being considered in feasibility studies being undertaken for
several projected routes.

DIMENSIONS
Length, overall: 30·5m (101ft 8in)
Length, at track level: 27·75m (92ft 6in)
Width: 3·2m (10ft 8in)
Height at fan jet air intake: 5·1m (17ft)
WEIGHTS
Gross: 24 tonnes
PERFORMANCE
Test speed range: 354-426km/h (220-250mph)

THE GUIDEWAY

The first leg of the future Orleans to Paris
line—a track 18·5km (11·5 miles) long—was
completed in July 1969. It includes turntables at
both ends and a central platform for manoeuvring and switching.

In mid-1973 the French Government
confirmed that the line is to be completed in due
course, but did not announce details.

The track has been designed for a service speed
of 402km/h (250mph). It is mounted on pylons
along the entire route. The prefabricated concrete beams, of 20m (67ft) span, have a minimum
ground clearance of 4·9m (16ft). This allows the
track to be constructed across roads and culti-
vated land.

Due to the low stresses produced by the Aérotrain vehicles it has been possible to design a
lightweight elevated track structure, which is less
expensive than an equivalent ground track. Local
ground subsidence, which may occur during the
first years after erection, will be countered by
adjusting the pylon heads. This will be limited to
a simple jacking operation using built-in devices
in the pylon structure.

The radii of curves and gradient angles will
depend upon the accelerations admissible without causing discomfort to passengers. Banking
can be provided if necessary. Banking of 7% is in
fact incorporated in three curves in the Orleans
track. The radius requirements are therefore the
same as for other guided systems of transport for
similar speeds. The advantage of the Aérotrain
track is that there are no gradient limitations and
it can therefore be constructed with a much smaller number of curves.

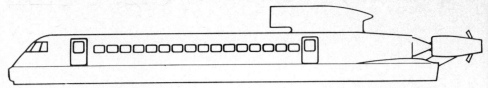

Side view showing the revised configuration of the I-80HV Aérotrain with its new turbofan thrust unit

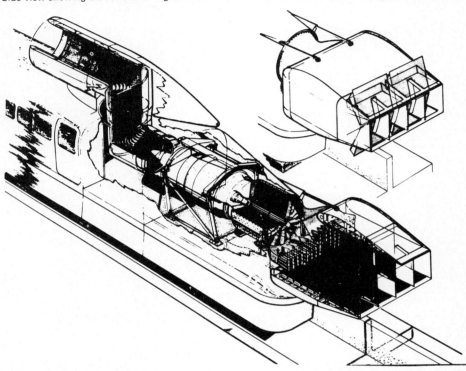

I-80HV Orleans Aérotrain after being fitted with a 15,000lb thrust Pratt & Whitney JT8D-11 turbofan, which
has permitted the behaviour of the vehicle's systems to be studied at speeds of 380-430km/h (236-270mph).
Considerable attention has been given to sound attenuation. As seen in the cutaway drawing, the air intake
has been designed for the maximum effectiveness, and a special high dilution ejection system suppresses
the noise of the exhaust gases

TESTS

Speed, acceleration and braking characteristics
have confirmed expectations, and the riding comfort has proved to be highly satisfactory. Under
all operating conditions, including propeller
reverse braking, negotiating curves and in cross
winds of 50km/h (31mph), the average accelerations were less than 0·6m/s² at all times, with
values of 0·3 to 0·5m/s² during normal cruising
conditions.

Since the interior noise level in the passenger
compartment is between 75 and 78 dBA, it is
possible to converse in normal tones. A level of
70-72 dBA will be reached on series production
vehicles.

External noise, 90-95 dBA at 60m (65yds)
compares favourably to that of a modern electric
train, with a much shorter duration.

During the 850 hours of operation there was
no breakdown which caused the vehicle to stop
on the guideway, with the exception of a single
incident involving hydraulic circuits to the propeller, which were repaired in less than an hour.
Only three items, other than the air cushions,
have necessitated a major repair since the vehicle
was put on the guideway. The air cushions have
been completely trouble-free.

The third phase of the test programme con-
sisted of an endurance, or accelerated service test
involving 200 hours of running time. Thirty-six
operating days were utilised and a daily average
of six hours continuous operation were completed. The cruising speed established was
250km/h (154·33mph). Since this involved
acceleration and deceleration between 0 and
250km/h (154·33mph) every six minutes, a
commercial operation of 1,000-2,000 hours or
200,000-400,000km in terms of wear on the vehicle was simulated. The rate of air cushion lip
wear experienced indicates a useful lip life of
40,000 to 50,000km and a practically negligible
cost factor of 0·001 to 0·002 francs per pas-
senger/kilometre.

It is to be noted that cultivation has been
resumed around and underneath the guideway
which, in sharp contrast with the high permanent
way maintenance costs experienced by the railways, has required no maintenance whatsoever
since it was built.

HIGH SPEED I-80 HV "ORLEANS" AEROTRAIN

In November 1973, the I-80 "Orleans" Aérotrain began a series of tests with a new propulsion
system. The two Turmo III gas turbines, which
powered a shrouded propeller, were replaced by
a 15,000lb thrust Pratt & Whitney JT8D-11 turbofan, fitted with a sound suppressor system
designed by Bertin & Cie. The ride characteristics remained outstanding at speeds up to
416km/h (260mph) in spite of the size of the new
propulsion unit which resulted in the vehicle
being 4 tons over weight.

The compressors and air feeders remained
unchanged.

On 5 March 1974, the vehicle attained
430km/h (270mph), with an average speed (in
each direction) of 418km/h (263mph) over a distance of 1·86 miles. The sound insulation has
been extremely effective, resulting in a noise
level 2dBA lower than the original propulsion
system.

In 1976, the Orleans vehicle was still in use for
demonstrations. By May 1976 it had completed
925 hours of operation including 212 hours with
its JT8D-11 turbofan. During this time it has
carried 13,500 passengers, 3,280 of whom have
been carried at speeds in excess of 400km/h
(250mph).

SUBURBAN AEROTRAIN AEROTRAIN S-44

The prototype 40-44 passenger suburban vehicle is equipped with a linear induction motor.
The vehicle underwent trials at Gometz between
1969 and 1972, where its 3km (1·9 mile) test

Aérotrain guideway track beams can be adjusted at
the pylon heads in the event of ground subsidence

Prototype of the 40-44 seat suburban Aérotrain seen on its 3km (1·9 miles) test track at Gometz

track runs parallel to that used by the Aérotrain 01 and 02 experimental vehicles. During its test programme the vehicle was operated at speeds up to 170km/h (105mph). The S-44 is currently undergoing modification as part of the company's development programme for the new 24km (15 mile) La Défense—Cergy line.

The power for the two axial lift fans is provided by a 525hp GM Chevrolet V8 car engine. Practically silent operation is achieved since there is no noise of rolling wheels. No vibration is communicated to the track structure which can therefore be erected in urban areas without fear of any noise disturbing local communities, even if steel is used for the longer spans of the guideway.

This vehicle is equipped with an electrical linear motor developed by the Société Le Moteur Linéaire (Merlin & Gerin Group). It provides a thrust of 18,000N at 137km/h (85mph) and has been currently operated at speeds above 160km/h (100mph).

Electric current is collected from the threephase 1,000V power line set alongside the track.

Braking performance is particularly efficient. During normal operation braking is obtained either by dephasing the linear motor supply (or in the case of failure of this supply by feeding it with dc current from the battery), or by a hydraulic braking system equipped with friction pads which grip the vertical portion of the track.

The passenger cabin is divided into four ten-seat compartments, each provided with two doors. An additional half-compartment forward can accommodate four passengers seated on folding seats.

Automatic doors are provided on both sides of each passenger compartment which will help to reduce stopping time. The coupling of several of these vehicles will be possible, but this should only be necessary at peak hours for heavy commuter traffic.

The seating arrangement is optional; each of the various layouts is optimised to provide the maximum possible space for passengers.

DIMENSIONS
Length: 14·4m (47ft)
Beam: 2·75m (9ft 4in)
Height: 3·1m (10ft 2in)
WEIGHTS
Loaded, linear motor: 11,500kg (25,000lb)
  automotive version: 10,000kg (22,000lb)
PERFORMANCE
Cruising speed: 180km/h (113mph)

A lower speed system is being designed for urban lines with stations only ½ mile apart.

THE GUIDEWAY

In this programme the track is at ground level. The horizontal support is an asphalt carpet and

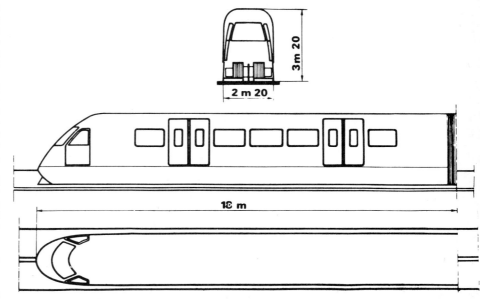

Unit of the suburban Aérotrain. Two of these 80-seat units are coupled to form a vehicle, and on the Cergy-Défense line, two vehicles will be coupled to form each train—providing a total seating capacity per train of 320 passengers

the upright is an aluminium beam which is used for both guiding the vehicle and as an induction rail for the linear motor. A 3km (1·9 mile) long track has been constructed at the company's base at Gometz.

Operational suburban lines will generally be supported on pylons in order to leave the ground free. The use of an elevated track will reduce the construction time and avoid costly tunnelling on many sections of urban/suburban projects.

PROJECT STUDIES

Société de l'Aérotrain has conducted detailed studies of a dozen projects. The technical and operational characteristics of the vehicles may substantially differ from those of the two prototypes, particularly as regards capacity and cruising speed.

The mathematical model, which has enabled the company to examine technico-economical optimisation procedures, an approach to operations, station design, and baggage handling has produced data based on a number of projected situations. The two major fields which are being investigated are inter-city services and suburban links, mainly between city centres and airports.

Suburban links require, in some cases, a higher capacity than the one provided by the Gometz-type vehicle. Capacity can be increased by widening the vehicles, or coupling them, to provide an

Three-phase powerline alongside the track at ground level provides electric current for the linear motor

hourly capacity of around 10,000 passengers each way.

Projects of an almost urban nature are also being investigated with the Tridim version.

CERGY-PONTOISE—LA DEFENSE SUBURBAN AEROTRAIN

A decision was taken by the French government in July 1971 to build an Aérotrain rapid transit line from the new business centre of La Défense, just outside Paris, to the new town of Cergy-Pontoise. The line was due to be opened early in 1979. Although the contract for its construction was signed on 21 June 1974, it was cancelled the following month by a new French government which introduced sweeping cutbacks in public expenditure to counter inflation.

The travel time between Cergy-Pontoise and

La Défense with this system would have been less than ten minutes. The line was intended to connect with the new express metro linking La Défense with Etoile, and the Opéra, the journey times being four and seven minutes respectively.

Cergy-Pontoise had a population of 200,000 in 1975 and will have between 350,000 and 400,000 by the year 2000. A satellite town of the capital, it is about 30km west of Paris.

TRACK: The length of the route is 24km (15 miles).

The track will be elevated for most of the distance, providing a clearance of 5m (16ft) above ground. Supporting pylons will be 20-25m (66-83ft) apart. The track itself will be 5·3m (17ft 8in) wide and will be double. Each side will have an aluminium alloy vertical centre rail providing both guidance for the vehicles and the secondary, or induction element, for the linear motor. Electric power is supplied by wayside rails carrying 1,500V dc.

The horizontal radii of curves are kept above 1,200m to allow a high cruising speed. The steepest slope is 6% and occurs when climbing a cliff after a crossing of the Seine.

The Aérotrain vehicle to be used on this service will be supported and guided by air cushions, and propelled by a linear induction motor.

The vehicles will each comprise two units, and on the Cergy-Défense line a train will consist of two coupled vehicles.

SUPPORT AND GUIDANCE: Each unit has its own air cushion guidance and support systems, air for which is put under pressure by electrically driven fans.

PROPULSION: Each unit will be equipped with a linear induction motor of variable voltage and frequency which will be regulated by on-board power-control equipment.

BRAKING: Two systems will be employed.

Another line for the first commercial operation is being selected. One possibility is in the Marseilles area, with a section linking the suburbs of the city with Marignane airport and Aix-en-Provence, and extensions to the industrial complexes and new cities under construction around Etang de Berre.

TRIDIM URBAN TRANSPORTATION SYSTEM

The Tridim system has been designed to solve the transportation problem in urban areas or suburbs where the distance between stations ranges from a few kilometres down to several hundred metres.

It is believed that the solution to this problem lies in an overhead transportation system adapted to passenger flows ranging from a few thousand to 10-15,000 per hour and offering appreciable comfort, speed and frequency. To transport 6,000 passengers per hour, trains of three vehicles of 50 seats each every 90 seconds will be sufficient. If a larger module is adopted, 20,000 passengers can be carried hourly.

The Tridim system is designed to meet these requirements through the use of an air cushion for suspension and a flexible rack-and-pinion system, rubber-tyred traction-wheels, or linear induction motor for propulsion.

It consists of small-size self-powered air cushion vehicles moving on a lightweight overhead track.

The capacity of each vehicle can be between four and 100 seats according to customer requirements. The required capacity can be obtained by varying the width and the length of the vehicles or grouping any number of vehicles to form a train. Since June 1973, a four to six seat prototype vehicle has been under test at a research centre of the French National Electricity Company (EDF) located at Les Renardières, near Fontainebleau, on a 305m (1,000ft) track which includes a straight section, grades, curves and points.

Characteristics of this vehicle are as follows:
Loaded weight: 1·2 tons
Nominal propulsion power: 15kW
Lifting power: 4kW
Max speed: 50km/h (31mph)
Max slope: 20%

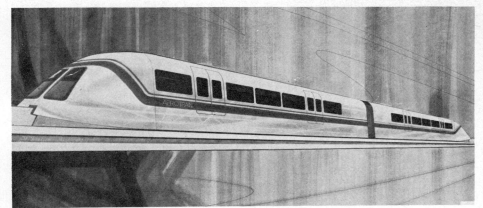

Artist's impression of the Cergy-Défense suburban Aérotrain

Rohr-built Aérotrain, constructed under a US Department of Transportation contract. The vehicle, which is 94ft long, with 60 seats, is designed to LS specification. In May 1976 it attained a speed of 230km/h (144mph) a world record for a LIM-propelled, all-electric TACV

Four-seat Tridim urban transport vehicle on its "switchback" test track

Power supply: cc 160V
Number of air cushions: 8
Air pressure: 900kg/m² (184·33lb/ft²)

The Tridim vehicle is built on a modular basis, with additional modules being added as required to provide the desired capacity.

In the case of the type VM 1 (designed for a specific client), the passengers are transported in modules measuring approximately 10ft by 6ft and equipped with nine seats placed along the longitudinal walls. There is also room for a maximum of four standing passengers, which brings the rush-hour capacity to 13 passengers for each module, ie 52 per vehicle, 36 of whom are seated (the vehicle consists of four modules).

Propulsion and lift are obtained from electric energy collected from a "third" rail (direct-current power supply).

The vehicle is guided by a low metal rail fixed on the track in line with the vehicle axis. This is the inverted-T track fundamental to the Aéro-train technique. Besides its guidance function, this rail carries the propulsion rack and keeps the vehicle retained on the track, which makes overturning impossible in the event of incident or abnormal operating conditions.

LIFT: The basic advantages of employing the air-cushion principle are:

suspension of concentrated loads and shocks, hence possibility of a lightweight vehicle structure on the one hand, and of the overhead track on the other; the absence of rolling noise and vibration; vehicle maintenance drastically reduced, and virtually non-existent for the track; and finally low total cost of the transportation system due to the simplicity and the light weight of the track.

The air cushion system requires a power supply of only 4 to 5hp per supported metric ton. This is expected to be reduced to the order of 2hp per metric ton. The air cushion supply is operated by sound-insulated electric fans.

PROPULSION: In the case of the VM 1 the vehicle is propelled by a patented rack-and-pinion system. But alternative methods include rubber-tyred traction wheels acting on the centre guidance rail or linear induction motor, according to requirements. The former consists of a dual rack fixed on the guiding rail and two pinions carried by the vehicles and driven by electric propulsion motors. It allows operation on tracks with steep slopes and maintains acceleration and braking performance in any weather including conditions of snow and ice.

The ability to climb steep slopes enables the stations to be built at street level or at the level of

Aérotrain Tridim urban transport vehicle

another transportation system for ease of transfer.

OVERHEAD TRACK: The system is intended primarily for an overhead track but it can also be used at ground level or as an underground system. In the case of an overhead track, the viaduct can be made of metal or of reinforced concrete, the choice between the two materials being dictated mainly by the line layout.

This consists of pylons supporting beams of 20-30m (66-100ft) span carrying the guideway which has a width of about 2·23m (7ft 4in) for single track or 4·72m (15ft 6in) for dual track in the case of the VM 1 system. The track itself consists mainly of the guiding rail with its rack.

The absence of concentrated loads, either static or dynamic, allows the use of a light viaduct, which leads to less cost.

As an example, with metal construction, a dual track viaduct weighs approximately 590kg/m (1,300lb/m) (VM 1).

VM 1 SPECIFICATION

The system can be adapted to client specification.

Capacity of the VM 1 is 52 passengers, 36 of whom are seated.

DIMENSIONS
Length: 16·26m (53ft 4in)
Width: 1·93m (6ft 4in)
Height: 2·59m (8ft 6in)
WEIGHTS
Empty: 5,900kg (13,000lb)
Loaded: 9,900kg (21,800lb)
PERFORMANCE
Nominal speed: 64-80km/h (40-50mph)
Max speed: 80-104km/h (50-65mph)
Average acceleration between 0 and 40mph: 0·12g
Emergency deceleration: 0·2g
Allowable slope at 40mph: 3%
Max allowable slope at reduced speed: 15% to 25%
Minimum turning radius: 24·4m (80ft) approx
MOTOR POWER
for propulsion: 150kW approx
for cushion: 35kW
OVERHEAD TRACK
Span: 20-30m (66-100ft) for normal span
Height above ground: 4·88m (16ft) on average
Width of track, single track: 2·23m (7ft 4in)
    dual track: 4·72m (15ft 4in)
Electrical power supply by conductor rail

URBA

Compagnie d'Energetique Linéaire mb

5 rue Monge, 92000 Vanves, France

Telephone: 644 33 22

Officials:

J Rechou, *Manager, Marketing and Licensing*

The URBA mass transport system, invented in 1966 by Maurice Barthalon, aims at providing a means of urban transport which combines absence of noise, vibration and atmospheric pollution with low capital and maintenance costs and a high degree of flexibility of installation and operation. The vehicle, which may operate singly or in trains, is suspended from its track by an air lift system in which the pressure is subatmospheric, and propulsion is by electric linear induction motors. The cabin of the vehicle is suspended from a number of Dynavac air bogies which run within an elevated track, the section of which is like a flattened, inverted U, with inward facing flanges on the bottom edges of the sides, on which the air bogies sit when at rest. The air bogies house the lift fans which draw air from the space between the track and the top of the bogie, so producing a pressure difference which causes the air bogie to lift off the track flanges.

Special sealing arrangements provide a controlled leak into the lift chamber which decreases as the weight of the vehicle increases, so increasing the pressure difference. The air bogies therefore remain in a stable, floating condition without being in contact with the track.

Lateral guidance is provided by similar but smaller Dynavac cushions between the sides of the bogie and the sides of the track. The air bogies also house the linear induction motors which

URBA 4 prototype seats 6-12 passengers and has a cruising speed of 80km/h (50mph)

URBA 20, a light urban transport vehicle with a service speed of 72km/h (45mph) and seating 20 passengers

react with a reactor rail projecting downwards from the centre of the track. This effectively divides the lift chamber into two independent halves, thus providing a degree of roll control. The suspension between the cabin and the air bogie acts as a secondary suspension system (the air cushion being the primary) and provides for articulation of the air bogies so that the vehicle can take curves of small radius.

In order to carry the development of URBA from a vehicle to a fully integrated public transport system, the Société d'Etudes de l'URBA (SETURBA) has been formed by the Caisse des Dépôts et Consignation, the Entreprise

Bouygues and the Gazocéan-Technigaz Group.

The registered office of the Society is at 4 place Raoul Dautry, Paris 15, France.

SETURBA has accelerated the application of URBA by confirming, technically and economically, the best means of applying this new method of transport and has prepared the constitution of a new company charged with the industrial and commercial development of the URBA system.

A technical and financial appraisal of URBA, undertaken by the SETURBA study group, proved favourable, and this has led to the establishment of Société de l'URBA (SU), supported by former associates of SETURBA.

URBA has been specially designed to satisfy the transport needs of medium-size towns of 200,000 to 1,000,000 inhabitants, and the suburbs of large cities.

The prototype URBA 4, and later two URBA 8s coupled together, were demonstrated at Lyon during 1968. The prototype has been in daily use for several years at the Ecole Centrale of Lyon, where research and development has been supported by DGRST, DATAR, ANVAR and the Ministry of Transport. The computer analysis of its dynamic behaviour has confirmed its stability, its comfort and its ability to take small radius curves.

Several international assessments, including a searching study by Eurofinance, consider URBA as one of the most promising of the new means of transport for the years 1970 to 1990. A certain number of towns in France and abroad, including Rouen, Bordeaux and Montpellier, and three different lines located on the outskirts of Paris, have been studied. A special study has also been undertaken for the new business centre of La Défense, on the western side of Paris. These bring out the favourable capital and operating costs which should place the price per passenger per kilometre of URBA at a level comparable with that of the bus today.

URBA 8

A prototype urban and suburban monorail, URBA 8 is an improved version of the URBA 4, with three linear motors instead of two, and seats for eight passengers. Two URBA 8s were demonstrated at Lyon on 4 December 1968, on a 79m (87yd) track. They operated singly and coupled, with acceleration and deceleration in the range 0·25 to 0·35g (with 0·5g deceleration in an emergency) and at speeds up to 48·28km/h (30mph). It consists of a rectangular-framed cabin seating up to eight passengers and suspended from three Dynavac air bogies running in an experimental 80m (260ft) track.

PROPULSION: Propulsion and normal braking is by three linear motors of 25kW, weighing 80kg (176lb) and providing a thrust of 100kg (220lb) at starting, 30kg (66lb) at normal service speed. Supply is from 380V, three-phase, 50Hz mains.

Impression of a single-track URBA 30 line, with supporting columns located in the centre of a highway

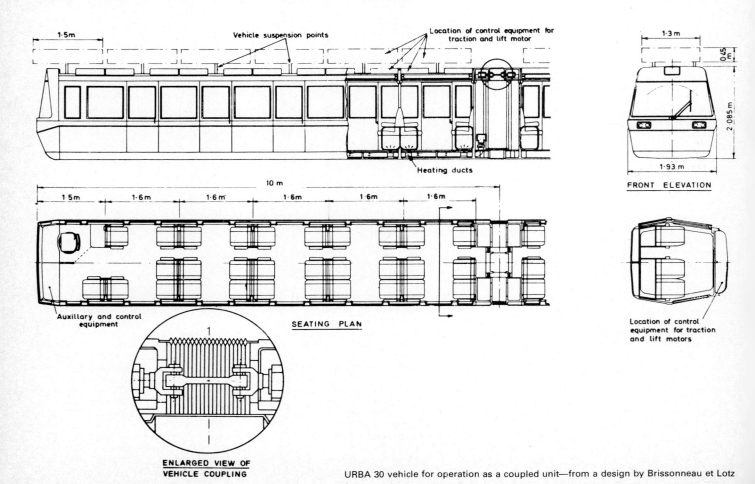

Vehicle suspension points

Location of control equipment for traction and lift motor

Heating ducts

1·5m

10 m

1·5m 1·6m 1·6m 1·6m 1·6m 1·6m

Auxiliary and control equipment

SEATING PLAN

1·3 m

2·085 m

1·93 m

FRONT ELEVATION

Location of control equipment for traction and lift motors

1

ENLARGED VIEW OF VEHICLE COUPLING

URBA 30 vehicle for operation as a coupled unit—from a design by Brissonneau et Lotz

The motor is the first to be designed as an industrial unit for vehicle propulsion.

CABIN: The cabin is rectangular and measures 4·5m (14ft 10in) long, 1·6m (5ft 3in) wide and 1·2m (4ft) high. It is built from 4cm square section tube and diecast corners of a type normally used for the framework of holiday bungalows.

The floor is of light alloy and the sides are perspex. Suspension between the cabin and the three air bogies is by rubber cord springs and hydraulic automobile shock absorbers.

Tests have demonstrated that the air bogie

concept is suitable for sharp curves, can climb steep slopes and provides good acceleration and braking. It cannot be derailed.

URBA 20

An enlarged version of the URBA 4, this model will seat 20 passengers in a cylindrical cabin and have a top speed of 72km/h (45mph). More efficient lift fans will be employed on this model which will require a total of 12kW for lift power. All-up weight will be 4,750kg (10,470lb).

URBA 30

This is the first model designed to go into service as a public transport system and will seat 30 passengers in rows, three abreast. The initial design will have five special, lightweight automatic doors on one side. Overall dimensions of the cabin will be: length 9m (29ft 6in), width 1·9m (6ft 3in), height 2m (6ft 7in) overall, loaded weight 5·3 tons. Propulsion will be by linear motors.

GERMANY, FEDERAL REPUBLIC

TRANSRAPID-EMS

Gesellschaft für elektromagnetische Schnellverkehrssysteme (Joint Venture Group Krauss-Maffei and MBB)

Steinsdorfstr 13, D-8000 Munich 22, Federal Republic of Germany
Telephone: (089) 22 66 94/22 73 40
Telex: 529463 trmue

In April 1974 it was announced that Krauss-Maffei (KM) and Messerschmitt-Bölkow-Blohm (MBB) were to develop jointly a high-speed transportation system.

As agreed with the Federal Minister of Research and Technology, the corporate managements of both companies decided to conduct their future development activities for a track-guided high-speed transportation system—started in the late sixties—on a joint basis.

In 1971 both companies presented to the public the world's first large-scale test vehicles supported, guided, and driven by magnetic fields. In the meantime extensive testing performed on test rigs and test tracks at München-Allach and Ottobrunn has demonstrated that contact-free magnetic suspension using controlled electromagnets can be achieved and is practical for high-speed ground transportation systems.

Both companies, using different approaches, arrived at very similar research results.

The chief objective of the joint venture group is to develop a uniform high-speed transportation system for Europe for economic long-haul passenger and freight transportation.

Research work is being financed by the Federal Minister of Research and Technology as well as by funds from the two companies.

On 19 February 1976, 401·3km/h (249mph) was attained by the Komet research vehicle, a world record for Maglev vehicles.

All electromagnetic levitation system activities within the Federal Republic of Germany are now concentrated within two groups—the Magnetbahn Transrapid consortium and the Projectgruppe Magnetschwebebahn. The former is responsible for the construction of the new Emsland 30km (18·64-mile) test track between the towns of Lathen and Dörpen, while the latter is responsible for the propulsion of the TR.06, a 200-seat, 400km/h (250mph) test vehicle, which is due to begin trials on the test track in 1982.

The Magnetbahn Transrapid consortium comprises the following companies: AEG-Telefunken; Brown, Boveri & Cie; Dyckerhoff & Widmann; Krauss-Maffei AG; Messerschmitt-Bölkow-Blohm GmbH; Siemens AG and Thyssen-Industrie.

Projektgruppe Magnetschwebebahn (project group for the magnetic levitation system) comprises AEG-Telefunken, Brown, Boveri & Cie and Siemens. Its project leader is C P Parsh, Projektgruppe Magnetschwebebahn, E41Pm, in Fa, Siemens AG, Postfach 3240, 8520 Erlangen.

Co-ordination of the entire project is the responsibility of Messerschmitt-Bölkow-Blohm. The project leader is Mr Eitlhuber, Konsortium Magnetbahn Transrapid, Steinsdorfstrasse 13, 8000 Munich 22.

TRACK

The track for a rapid transit system based on the principle of magnetic suspension and guidance would consist of the supporting concrete

Rotary test track to study the operational behaviour of synchronous linear machines (SLIM)

First full-scale test vehicle to employ magnetic suspension guidance and propulsion was MBB's basic experimental craft. Weighing 5·6 tonnes and 7m (23ft) in length, it has reached 100km/h (62mph) on a 700m (760yd) track

pylons and beams, the ferromagnetic support and guidance rails, the secondary part of the linear motor, and the power rails.

In order to ensure the safe operation of a rapid transit system on the one hand, and not to endanger the environment by its operation on the other, the track will be supported on pylons spaced approximately 24m (78ft) apart with the elevation (clearance) of the track being at least 4·5m (14ft 9in). This eliminates to a large extent the need for special structures at intersections with roads, rail tracks, etc.

A fast and reliable switching system for traffic diverging from and merging with the main line is necessary for smooth and safe operation of a rapid transit system.

Experiments with an electromagnetic switch with no moving parts revealed that special

devices were needed on board which added weight and increased aerodynamic drag. Currently, a mechanical switch is being developed.

PRINCIPLE OF MAGNETIC LEVITATION

In the selected principle of magnetic attraction, the vehicles are supported and guided by controlled electromagnets along armature rails fastened to the guideway. Sensors continuously measure the air gap between the vehicle magnets and the armature rails (10-20mm). The data measured is transmitted to control units which control the attractive forces of the magnets and thus keep the vehicle in a hovering condition.

In addition to the development of the magnetic levitation and guidance system, vehicle development also includes other components, such as linear motor propulsion energy transfer, vehicle frame, braking, emergency gliding and safety systems. The design of cost-saving, elevated guideways and planning of the necessary stationary facilities, such as stations, power supply, etc are of equal significance for the overall system.

Knowledge and experience gained and substantiated through extensive testing on various test stands formed the basis for the construction of experimental vehicles and test tracks in Ottobrunn, München-Allach and Manching.

TEST STANDS

Static, dynamic and rotating magnet test stands were built for the purpose of defining and optimising magnets for the levitation and guidance system and various control techniques. Support force losses and braking forces on magnets as a result of eddy current effects at high speeds can be measured and power transmission methods tested on rotation test stands. Switching tests with magnetically levitated vehicles are performed on switch test stands. Linear motor test stands are used to determine thrust and lateral forces on single- and double-sided linear motors and to measure temperature, current and voltage.

BASIC VEHICLE

MBB began work on the vehicle and the test track in July 1970. On 4 February 1971, the first suspension tests of the experimental vehicle took place in the test laboratory. On 2 April 1971, the first test runs were made on MBB's special test track.

On 5 May 1971, the experimental vehicle was presented to the public for the first time in the presence of the Federal Minister for Educational Science and the Federal Minister for Transportation.

It demonstrated the feasibility of magnetic suspension and guidance with linear motor propulsion, and provides information on those parameters not covered during simulation of the system, and development of the components.

Weighing 5·6 tonnes and with a length of 7m (23ft), it has an asynchronous linear motor with 200kW nominal power which is capable of accelerating the vehicle on the 700m (766yd) test track to a speed of 100km/h (62mph).

Four controlled suspension magnets and two guidance magnets on each side of the vehicle lift it and guide it during operation with a nominal air gap of 14mm (½in) between the magnets and the rails.

TRANSRAPID 02 RESEARCH VEHICLE

In October 1971 Krauss-Maffei started operating an experimental 12m (39ft 4in) long vehicle on a 930m (1,017yd) test track. It reached a maximum speed of 164km/h (101·9mph). A novel power pick-up system ensures troublefree transmission of electric energy at high speeds. A secondary suspension system with pneumatic shock absorbers and and vibration dampers constitutes the link between the vehicle superstructure and the hovering chassis.

Guideway and vehicle concepts provide realistic test data. The test results obtained so far have revealed that the system requirements can be fulfilled without difficulty.

TRACK
Length: 930m (1,017yds)
Radius of curvature: 800m (875yds)
EXPERIMENTAL VEHICLE
Length: 11·7m (38ft 4½in)
Width: 2·9m (9ft 6in)
Height above track surface: 2·05m (6ft 8¾in)
Number of seats: 10
Weight: approx 11,000kg (24,250lb)
Payload: 2,000kg (4,409lb)
Design speed of vehicle: approx 350km/h (220mph)
PROPULSION BY LINEAR INDUCTION MOTOR
Thrust (transient): approx 32kN
Present vehicle speed (due to short track length): approx 160km/h (100mph)
Synchronous speed LIM at 50Hz: approx 180km/h (112mph)

SERVICE BRAKES
Brake retardation by LIM: approx 2·5m/s²
  by jaw brake: approx 8·5m/s²
  by friction brake: approx 8m/s²
ELECTROMAGNETIC SUPPORT AND GUIDANCE SYSTEM
Air gap: 10-25mm (½-1in)
POWER SUPPLY
Support and guidance system: Voltage 380V three-phase current, 50Hz
Power: 32kW

TRANSRAPID 03 RESEARCH VEHICLE

In October 1971, the company started operating a dual-purpose test facility which allows a comprehensive system comparison between magnetic cushion and air cushion techniques using the same vehicle specifications and the same track with completely identical operating conditions. Vehicles and track have been designed for a maximum speed of approximately 140km/h (87mph). The track length is 930m (1,017yds) allowing the attainment of a speed of about 160km/h (100mph), which has already been reached with the magnetic cushion vehicle. This experimental system provides realistic information since it subjects the support, guid-

ance and propulsion system to extreme loads both during straight runs and cornering.

Transrapid 03 is the basic Transrapid 8-ton research vehicle adapted for tests as a tracked air cushion vehicle. The payload of two tons and overall dimensions are identical to those of the vehicle in its earlier configuration. The programme, which is supported by the Federal Ministry of Research and Technology, is enabling the TACV and Maglev concepts to be compared under identical conditions for the first time.

Tests with air cushion support began at the end of 1972 and finished in 1973.

As a TACV, the vehicle is supported and guided by a total of 14 air cushion pads. Six, each with a cushion area of 3m² (32·29ft²), support the vehicle on its elevated concrete guideway, and eight, mounted in pairs, each of about 1m² (10·76ft²) cushion area, provide lateral guidance along the LIM reaction rail. The air cushion lift system is of plenum type and each pad has a rubber skirt. Cushion air is supplied by a two-stage compressor.

The vehicle is propelled by a French-made LIM system, which accelerates the vehicle to 145km/h (90mph) on its 930m (1,017yd) guideway.

Krauss-Maffei's Transrapid research vehicle in 02 configuration, with magnetic support, guidance and propulsion systems

Transrapid's 03 research craft permitted a full systems comparison between magnetic and air cushion techniques, using the same vehicle specifications and the same track under completely identical operating conditions

Comparisons covered the following areas: vehicle dynamics; weight; load tolerances; vertical air gap tolerances; specific power requirements for support and guidance; effects on the environment (noise level); reliability; life; reaction to weather influences; maximum speed; aerodynamic drag; investment, operating and maintenance costs.

Results of the comparison showed that magnetic levitation technology is superior.

TRACK
Length: 930m (1,017yds)
Radius of curvature: 800m (875yds)
EXPERIMENTAL VEHICLE
Length: 11·7m (38ft 4½in)
Width: 2·9m (9ft 6in)
Height above track surface: 2·05m (6ft 8½in)
Number of seats: 10
Weight: 9,600kg (21,200lb)
Design speed of vehicle: approx 140km/h (87mph)
PROPULSION BY LINEAR INDUCTION MOTOR
Thrust (transient): approx 2·9 Mp
Vehicle speed (due to short track length): approx 160km/h (100mph)
Synchronous speed LIM at 50Hz: approx 180km/h (112mph)
SERVICE BRAKES
Brake retardation by LIM: approx 2·3m/s²
　by jaw brake: approx 8·5m/s²
　by friction brake: approx 8m/s²
POWER SUPPLY
Support and guidance system: 380V three-phase current, 50Hz
Power: 235kW
LIM: Voltage 1·7 kV three-phase current, 50 Hz
Output: 3MVA

MAGNET TEST VEHICLE

Operation of the magnet test vehicle started on the Ottobrunn test track in 1972. The vehicle consists of a platform supported and guided by wheels and accelerated by a hot water rocket.

It was used to test magnets and acceleration sensors at different speed levels up to 225km/h (140mph). The components were tested in conjunction with an instrumented test rail mounted in the guideway.
TECHNICAL DATA
Vehicle length: 3·6m (11ft 9¾in)

KOMET COMPONENT TEST VEHICLE

The Komet is an unmanned, magnetically levitated and guided vehicle with a mounting rack for testing components at speeds up to 400 km/h. This mounting rack allows the installation of magnets, linear motors and power pick-ups of various designs, which can be tested in combination with instrumented rails, which can also be easily replaced. The test data is transmitted to a fixed receiving station via a telemetry system. The Komet is accelerated by means of a thrust sled equipped with up to six hot-water rockets in order to achieve the desired high speeds on only 1,300m length of test track.
TECHNICAL DATA
Component test vehicle:
　length: 8·5m (27ft 11in)
　width: 2·5m (8ft 2½in)
　height: 1·7m (5ft 7in)
　weight (without instrumented components): 8,800kg (19,400lb)
　max speed: 400km/h (250mph)
Thrust sled:
　length: 5m (16ft 5in)
　width: 2·5m (8ft 2½in)
　height: 1·5m (4ft 11in)
　starting weight: 7,500kg (16,534lb)
Guideway:
　track gauge: 2·2m (7ft 2½in)
　length: 1,300m (1,422yds)
　　including acceleration section: 300m (328yds)
　　test section: 300m (328yds)
　　deceleration and safety section: 700m (766yds)

TRANSRAPID 04

The Transrapid 04 is one of the largest

MBB hot-water rocket-driven test carrier on its track at Ottobrunn

Komet, an unmanned magnetically-guided and levitated component test vehicle established a world record for Maglev vehicles on 19 February 1976 when it attained 401·3km/h on its 1,300m guideway

Transrapid 04, employing magnetic levitation and a linear induction motor for propulsion

passenger-carrying magnetically levitated and LIM-propelled experimental vehicles to date.

The elevated guideway, with curves of different radii, represents a further development on the way to future applications. Different design principles and materials, such as concrete and steel, were used in order to test various alternatives. For the first time, a LIM reaction rail was mounted horizontally on the guideway beam.

The 2,400m (1½mile) test track allows the testing of different system components under realistic conditions and at higher speeds. The results of the test programme will be the basis for the definition of future test vehicles and large-scale test facilities.
TECHNICAL DATA
Vehicle, length: 15m (49ft 2½in)
　width: 3·4m (11ft 2in)
　height: 2·8m (9ft 2in)
　weight: 16,500kg (36,376lb)
　max speed: 250km/h (155mph)
　propulsion: asynchronous linear motor
　max thrust: 50,000N
Guideway:
　track gauge: 3·2m (10ft 6in)
　length: 2,400m (1½ miles)
　radii of curvature: 800-3,100m (875-3,390yds)
　span: 17-20m (55ft 8in-65ft 7in)
　max guideway inclination: ±11 degrees

TRANSRAPID 05

Transrapid-EMS (Krauss-Maffei and Messerschmitt-Bölkow-Blohm) was awarded a contract from the German Federal Ministry of Research and Technology to build together with Thyssen Henschel Company a demonstration facility for a magnetically levitated transportation system. Site of this demonstration project was the International Transportation Exposition, IVA 79, in Hamburg.

Transrapid-EMS had the responsibility for building the 26m long, two-section vehicle which has seats for 68 passengers. This is the fifth maglev vehicle to be constructed by the Krauss-Maffei, MBB, and Transrapid-EMS consortium. The levitation and guidance system has four bogies with individually spring-suspended electromagnets using a decentral, hierarchical control system.

A synchronous, iron-backed linear long stator motor serves as propulsion unit. With this version of a linear motor the primary coils are mounted in the track while the levitation magnets serve as its secondary.

Within the joint programme, Thyssen Henschel and the Braunschweig Technical University are responsible for the guideway (length approximately 1,000m), the track-mounted primary of the motor and other stationary installations. Sponsored and financed by the Federal

Ministry of Research and Technology, the chief aim of the project is to demonstrate to a broad public the advanced state of development of the high-speed maglev system in West Germany.

TECHNICAL DATA
Train: 2 sections
Length: 26m (85ft 3in)
Width: 3·1m (10ft 2in)
Height: 2·7m (8ft 10in)
Capacity: 68 passengers
Total weight: 36 tonnes
Max speed: 80km/h (50mph)
Propulsion: Synchronous linear long stator motor

TRANSRAPID 06

The Federal Ministry of Research and Technology has agreed to build a 31km (19¼ mile) test track in the Emsland district in northern Germany. The facility will be constructed in several steps, tests with the Transrapid 06 commencing in 1980-81. The train will consist of two sections and will be designed for speeds up to 400km/h (250mph).

Development and construction of the vehicle and the test facility will be a joint effort by the West German companies already engaged in research and development in the maglev field.

TECHNICAL DATA
Train: 2 sections
Total length: 54m (176ft 5in)
Width: 3·7m (12ft)
Height: 3·8m (12ft 6in)
Capacity (total): 200 seats
Total weight: 122 tonnes
Max speed: 400km/h (250mph)
Propulsion: Synchronous long-stator linear motor

TRANSRAPID 07

A concept for a high speed, short haul, maglev system has been developed for connecting two cities or an airport to a city (airport link).

TECHNICAL DATA
Train: 2 or 4 sections
Length, per section: 32m (105ft)
  the first 2 sections: 64m (210ft)
  the second 2 sections: 124m (407ft)
Width: 3·6m (11ft 8½in)
Height: 3·85-4·15m (12ft 8in-13ft 7in)
Weight per section: 80 tonnes
Total weight: 320 tonnes
Max speed: 250-350km/h (155-220mph)
Propulsion: Synchronous/asynchronous linear motor

TRANSRAPID 08

This is a concept for a 400km/h prototype train for 240 passengers. The first section of the train will be tested at the government operated test facility for transport technology near Augsburg from 1980 onwards. Vehicles of similar design will first be applied to less densely populated areas or to connect them with major airports.

TECHNICAL DATA
Train: 2 sections
Length: 64m (210ft)
Width: 4·2m (13ft 9in)
Height: 4m (13ft 1in)
Capacity: 240 passengers
Payload: 24 tonnes
Weight of train: 170 tonnes
Max speed: 400km/h (250mph)
Propulsion: asynchronous linear motor

Transrapid 05 maglev train on display at the IVA '79 International Transportation Exhibition in Hamburg

Transrapid 06 400km/h (250mph) maglev train which is to be tested at the test track at Emsland

JAPAN

JAPAN AIR LINES

HSST Development Department, Engineering and Maintenance, Japan Air Lines Maintenance Center Building, 9-1 Haneda Kuko 1 Chome, Ohta-ku, Tokyo 144, Japan
Telephone: Tokyo (03) 747-2295
Officials:
Toshio Fukui, *General Manager, HSST Development Department Engineering and Maintenance*

Japan Air Lines has completed a number of successful test runs with manned and unmanned test vehicles which are levitated by electromagnetic force and powered by linear induction motors. The vehicle, known as the High Speed Surface Transport (HSST), is being developed to provide air travellers with rapid ground transportation between cities and airports.

HSST DEVELOPMENT

Stage 1 (1973-75): Basic studies and bench

JAL's HSST test vehicle undergoing high-speed tests on a 1,600m test track at Higashi-Ogishima, Kawasaki

tests of components for HSST-01 test vehicle.

Stage 2 (1976): Low speed tests initiated on 189m track to obtain information on linear induction motors and electromagnets.

Stage 3 (1977-79): Testing of electromagnets and linear induction motors at higher speeds on 1,300m track.

Stage 4 (1977-79): Completion of HSST-02 and start of tests with this vehicle.

The test track was then extended to 1,600m in length and two curved tracks were added (radii 280m and 2,000m). High speed runs were repeated up and down the track and were performed without any problems. The preliminary design of a prototype test vehicle and major components has begun and introduction into commercial operations is expected to be in the 1980s.

HSST LEVITATION AND PROPULSION

The HSST uses the principle of electromagnetic levitation with onboard magnets which are prevented from coming into contact with the track by an electronic sensing device that maintains the gap between the magnet and the rail at 10mm.

Loss of wayside power is overcome by the use of onboard batteries which in an emergency would provide levitation for several minutes while the vehicle gradually touched down on the rails on its emergency sliding shoes.

Propulsion is furnished by a linear induction motor that produces a propelling force without any form of link between the rails and the vehicle. No totally new technology is required in the development of the HSST since all the components in the system have been proved in principle.

HSST-01

The HSST-01 test vehicle is the first test vehicle of its kind to be designed and built by JAL engineers. Built at the company's engineering centre at Haneda airport, Tokyo, it is currently undergoing tests at a special site at Higashi-Ogishima, Kawasaki. Modifications undertaken during its development include the fitting of wings to increase its aerodynamic stability at high speeds.

Although operating on a relatively short track only 1·3km (now extended to 1·6km) in length, the vehicle has achieved a speed of 307·8km/h (191·25mph) with the assistance of booster rockets. Highest speed attained without rocket assistance is 220·6km/h (137mph). On tracks sufficiently long to enable the craft to be braked safely, speeds of around 300km/h (186mph) should be attainable without booster rockets. Total distance recorded on test runs amounted to 1,050km (652 miles) (HSST-01) and 2,869km (1,782 miles) (HSST-02) by the end of March 1980.

LEVITATION SYSTEM: Eight electromagnets, four on each side, attached to the "wrap around" sections of the bodywork. 150V dc for levitation is supplied by onboard batteries.

PROPULSION SYSTEM: Asynchronous single-sided, short stator linear induction motor onboard and a horizontal aluminium reaction plate in the middle of the track. Power from the motor is picked up from each of three power rails (which run alongside the track) by carbon shoes on the vehicle's power collector.

Maximum thrust: 340kg (750lb)

Power source: 3-phase variable voltage and variable frequency

Maximum power: 200kVA

Voltage: 0-600V

Frequency: 0-350Hz

DIMENSIONS

Length overall: 4·2m (13ft 9in)

Width: 2·6m (8ft 6in)

Height: 1·1m (3ft 7in)

WEIGHTS

Empty: 1,000kg (2,204lb)

PERFORMANCE

300km/h (186mph) on a 1·3km (1,421 yard) track

HSST-02

JAL's second test vehicle was designed to operate at speeds up to 100km/h (62mph) on a 1·6km (1,750yd) track. Its primary uses are to

Japan's first four-car HSST (High Speed Surface Transport) is likely to appear like this when it enters commercial operation. It will carry 400 passengers plus their baggage the 60km (40 miles) between Tokyo and the Tokyo International Airport at Narita in 14 minutes

HSST track as it would appear running above an existing highway. The system uses a linear induction motor to produce speeds of up to 300km/h (186mph). The track is designed to avoid the deep shadow normally associated with the areas below a conventional road or railway

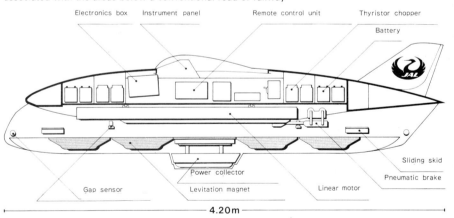
General arrangement of HSST-01 test vehicle

Seating eight passengers and an operator, the HSST-02 is designed for speeds of up to 100km/h on a 1·6km test track. The vehicle, which has been operating since May 1978, has already carried more than 2,500 passengers

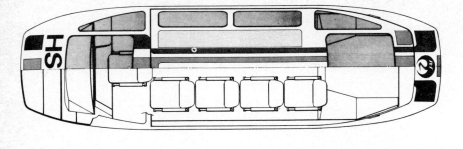

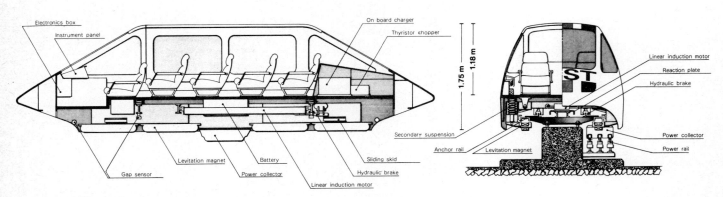

External and seating arrangements of HSST-02 test vehicle

gather design data and assess the ride quality of vehicles of this type. Seats are provided for up to eight passengers. The body is of semi-monocoque light alloy construction. Secondary suspension is provided between the body shell and the electromagnets of the levitation system.
LEVITATION SYSTEM: Basically the same as that for the HSST-01. Ac electric power supply for the linear induction motor is rectified to 120V dc for levitation by inboard rectifier. The power rails and power collectors are basically the same as those for HSST-01.
PROPULSION SYSTEM: A single-sided short stator linear induction motor is installed.
Maximum thrust: 300kg (661lb)

Power source: 3-phase variable voltage and variable frequency
Maximum power: 200kVA
Voltage: 0-600V
Frequency: 0-120Hz

COMMERCIAL HSST

JAL's proposed commercial HSST will have a body similar in shape to the Douglas DC-8 jet airliner with similar interior styling. The minimum size train would comprise two stream-lined end vehicles, each seating 112 passengers. Standard "mid-train" or middle vehicles, each seating 120 passengers, would be added according to passenger load demand.

Cruising speed would be about 300km/h (186mph) and the standard acceleration 0·1g, approximately the same as a standard electric train. Power used at cruising speed would be in the region of 5kW per passenger. Levitation and propulsion arrangements would be the same as those for the HSST-01.
DIMENSIONS
Length, streamlined end vehicle: 21·8m (71ft 6in)
    standard middle vehicle: 18·2m (59ft 9in)
Width: 3·8m (12ft 6in)
Height: 3·2m (10ft 6in)
Seats, streamlined end vehicle: 112
    standard middle vehicle: 120

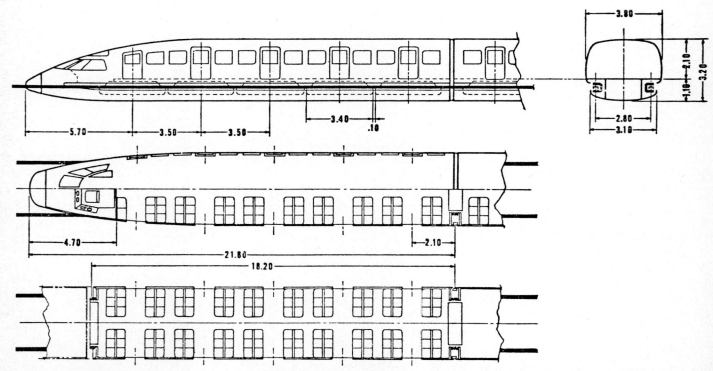

Commercial HSST concept prepared by Japan Air Lines to provide air travellers with fast ground transportation between cities and outlying airports. The streamlined end vehicles and the standard middle vehicles have a seating configuration resembling that of a commercial jet airliner. Two end vehicles linked comprises a minimum train; other sections are added to meet seat demand

UNION OF SOVIET SOCIALIST REPUBLICS

INSTITUTE OF DIESEL LOCOMOTIVE ENGINEERING, MOSCOW

The design of tracked skimmers started in Moscow during the five-year plan period 1971-75. Professor Alexander Zolotarsky announced in May 1972 that the technical and economic assessment of TACV systems was being undertaken at the Institute of Diesel Locomotive Engineering at its research establishment near Moscow.

It appeared from his statement that the first vehicles were to be powered by gas turbines and would operate on concrete tracks. Construction of prototype vehicles capable of speeds in excess of 300km/h (186mph) was due to start "in the nearest future". Professor Zolotarsky foresaw the use of TACVs to link densely populated industrial centres and resort areas where conventional railways are usually overloaded. They could also be operated successfully in the marshy areas of Siberia and in the North, as well as in permafrost areas.

Research undertaken jointly by the VNII Wagonbuilders, the Design Bureau for Aviation Research of AS Yakovlev and the Kalinin Wagon Factory led to the construction of a high-speed, jet-propelled research locomotive, the VNIIVOS-KOROST, preliminary details of which were released in 1971.

Thrust for the vehicle, which was designed to travel on wheels on a conventional track at speeds up to 250km/h (155mph) was provided by two Ivchenko AI-25 turbofans of the type employed on the Yak-40 airliner, and normally rated at 1,500kg (3,300lb st). These are sited above the cabin of the locomotive.

Data gathered from the Korost was employed in the design of primary and secondary suspensions systems, magnetic rail disc and air brakes and other features.

Full scale facilities for research into trains powered by linear induction motors have also been provided at a new transport research centre, a few miles from Kiev, capital of the Ukraine. It is intended to make a thorough investigation of the possibilities opened up by modern technology, including propulsion systems and original methods of suspension including air and magnetic cushions.

In 1978 it was announced in Moscow that construction of a track for the world's first operational magnetically levitated vehicles would begin at Alma Ata in 1979. The new system is designed to lift the vehicles a few centimetres above the track and drive them by linear motors.

The first phase of the construction will be a 13km (8 mile) commuter section within the city, to be followed later by a 65km (40 mile) extension outside the city, providing fast access to a recreation complex at Kapchagai.

One of the aims of the Soviet railway authority is to provide maglev trains capable of speeds of 300-500km/h (186-310mph) suitable for the rapid transportation of long-distance, commuter and airport services.

In "Young Technician", March 1979, reference was made to the Soviet maglev system as follows.

The magnetic suspension arrangement is relatively simple. The track is laid with magnetic slats. Permanent magnets of the same polarity are also fixed to the base of the carriage. The repellent faces of the line magnets keep the carriage in suspension, creating a gap between it and the slats of about 1 to 1·5cm. The motor in this new transport system is also unusual.

A traditional electric alternating motor has a stator—a steel ring with windings. In this case it is effectively cut in half and unwound, with the stator conductors laid out on the bottom of the carriage. The rotor is an aluminium slat placed along the axis of the track. The name "rotor" is in this instance a matter of convention; it does not move. It is generally called the "reactive rail". The working principle of a linear electric motor is

Prototype of the Soviet Union's first maglev vehicle

Impression of Soviet maglev vehicle showing the overhead guideway

essentially the same as in a traditional one: an electric current taken up by a special "shoe" with three contact conductor wires parallel to the track supplies energy to the stator. A magnetic wave begins to run along the conductors, bringing vertical currents to the reactive rail. The complementary action of the rotor and stator induce magnetic forces which impel the carriage along the track. Electrical energy is directly converted into translational movement. The magnetic suspension and linear motor system is simple, reliable and silent in operation because there are no moving parts. Nevertheless, wheels are fitted to the prototype.

This is because the permanent magnetic suspension system does not have a lateral carriage stabilisation system. At bends in the track or in high cross-winds the coach lacks directional control. For this reason the first experimental model has rollers which transfer lateral forces into channels in the track. The rollers only fulfil an auxiliary function and do not limit the speed (up to 100km/h). The permanent magnets with which

the complete track must be "paved" are suitable for laboratory conditions. In the case of the Alma-Ata track the suspension principle is a little different, being electro-magnetic.

An operational passenger-carrying track will be mounted on pylons, which will allow the track to be constructed across roads without impeding road traffic. On both sides of the supports will be skegs which will run along the complete length of the track. Two strips of steel will be attached to the skegs. The carriage itself will carry a powerful electro-magnetic suspension system. The desired air gap and carriage stabilisation both in the vertical and horizontal planes will be provided by automatic current regulators supplying the electromagnets.

The attraction forces to the steel strips will be generated in the same manner. Movement along the track will be effected by a linear electric motor.

The first section of the Soviet maglev railway will come into operation during the next five year plan, which begins in 1980.

NOVOCHERKASSK LOCOMOTIVE TECHNICAL INSTITUTE

During 1980 a conference on high-speed land transport systems was held in Novocherkassk. The choice of Novocherkassk as the venue was determined by the fact that the city's Locomotive Technical Institute is one of the main centres for the design of high speed ground transport systems.

A model of a maglev system has been constructed in a large hangar to provide a 30m (99ft) track. A 40kW motor propels a model magnetically-levitated and propelled train at speeds in excess of 48·3km/h (30mph). The model is automatically held at a constant gap of 15mm ($^{19}/_{32}$in) above the track.

On the basis of the tests now being made, it is hoped to scale up the results to provide data for the design of a 40-ton train, carrying 100 passengers at speeds between 402 and 483km/h (250-300mph).

UNITED STATES OF AMERICA

BERTELSEN INC

Head Office: 9999 Roosevelt Road, Westchester, Illinois 60153, USA
Telephone: (312) 681 5606
Works: 113 Commercial Street, Neponset, Illinois 61345, USA

Dr William R Bertelsen, Director of Research, Bertelsen Inc, has proposed the use of a vehicle based on the twin-gimbal Aeromobile 13 for a tracked skimmer system. It is described in US Patent No 3,845,716 issued on 5 November 1974.

Dr Bertelsen suggests that the system, based on the use of ACVs in simple, graded earth grooves, would be ideal for mass transportation in developing countries where no large investments have been made in roads, railways or airlines. The fuel can be petroleum in oil-rich areas or hydrogen in depleted or polluted areas. Whereas in densely populated countries new rights of way will inevitably be elevated or underground, there should be little difficulty in obtaining rights for the guideways in developing countries. In large countries with relatively empty interiors, the low-cost surface groove will be ideal.

Current or abandoned railway rights-of-way can be used for the Bertelsen Aeromobile-Aeroduct system, since rail gradients are acceptable to the Aeromobile. Hills can be climbed by the use of steps on which the vehicle is on the level or slightly inclined uphill most of the time. It climbs simply by lifting its mass in ground effect up each step, each of which would be slightly lower than its skirt height. Relatively low propulsive power is neccessary to climb a hill in this manner and no increase in lift power is necessary.

The Aeromobile vehicles employed for the system would be fully automated. Journey data would be fed into an onboard mini-computer and the vehicles would follow the route through

Impression of a tracked air cushion vehicle, based on the Bertelsen Aeromobile 13, in its guideway system

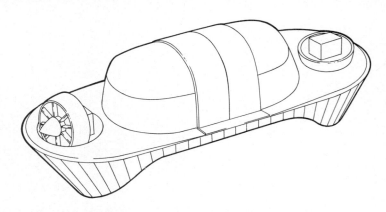

Impression of a tracked air cushion vehicle based on the Bertelsen Aeromobile 13

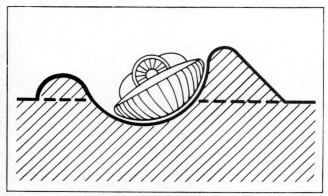

Aeromobile shown in graded groove at speed in left curve

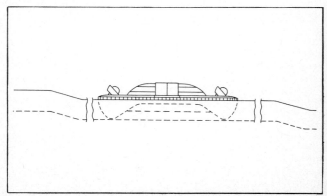

Side view, stepped aeroduct for grade climb and descent

signals emitted at junction points. A tape could guide the car across the country with a sleeping or reading driver. Dr Bertelsen states that the car would move from low to high-speed lanes automatically and remain in high-speed lanes until the signals at junctions told it to move down into a slower lane before turning off. This process would be repeated automatically until the car left the automatic guideway system.

THE AERODUCT SYSTEM

The air cushion vehicle, so unquestionably superior for off-road and amphibious transport of heavy loads, can also carry loads just as trucks and trains do, on rights-of-way. However, the right-of-way for the ACV will be different. It should be wider due to modern loads and because the length and width of the base of the vehicle determines the lift area and the total ACV hauling capacity. The ACV right-of-way should be semi-circular in cross section or a cylindrical tube to provide guidance and yaw stabilisation of the frictionless craft. There should be steps up and down grades to facilitate grade climbing and descent by frictionless but massive craft.

The system has the attributes of being frictionless; it has a high speed; provides a very soft, shockless, self-damped ride; offers a heavy load carrying capacity; and a low ground pressure which renders it amphibious.

Because the ACV is frictionless, a cylindrical groove provides perfect guidance for high speed translation longitudinally down the track. It also allows the craft to centrifugate up the wall on a curve, which obviates side forces on passengers or loads.

The low ground pressure makes the right-of-way very inexpensive to build and maintain. Whether of sodded or lightly paved earth, ploughed, ice-coated snow or in the form of a sheet metal tube or groove, all are far less expensive than the high pressure of conventional roads or railways (30 to 100psi in tyres, up to 10,000psi on rails).

The groove (or tube) can be located on, along, next to, above, or below existing roads or rails, requiring no further acquisition, and will not interfere with existing road drainage. The new ACV modality can be compatible with all existing surface transport. It will cost far less per mile to build and maintain than its conventional counterpart.

Adaptation of ACVs and Aeroducts to massive loads of 100,000lb or more per vehicle is easily possible, and adaptation of the vehicle beds to flat surface for loading, unloading, storing, staging, servicing, etc, is also possible. The loaded "trailers" may be moved singly or in trains down the hollow path at high speed. Tractors or pushers for these loads would have similar adaptability to flat or semi-cylindrical surfaces. The tractors would probably be powered by turbine-driven gimbal fans, capable of full manoeuvrability with 100% of propulsive force available for forward thrust, braking, lateral force, or for steering torque. Only a gimbal type of handling vehicle or 'tug' could manage the 100,000lb ACVs on 'flat' surfaces and against winds and gusts. Crawlers or tyre wheel tractors could attempt the flat surface handling of the massive carriers, but experience shows that paving becomes necessary for repeated traverse of ground by any land vehicle. However, grass is often adequate for ACVs. The air cushion 'tug' will be irreplaceable in the sodded or otherwise lightly prepared mileages of grooves between important shipping centres, with, for example, grain elevators, mines, stockyards, factories, cities, forests, oil and gas fields.

The system is designed to be all-inclusive, providing every type of transport need, from personal transit, 'mass' transit, taxis, police, fire and emergency service, mail, freight, parcel, grocery and milk delivery to refuse pickup.

AIR CUSHION APPLICATORS, CONVEYORS AND PALLETS

AUSTRALIA

FLOMAT (AUST) PTY LTD
18 Rowe Street, Eastwood 2122, New South Wales, Australia

Flomat (Aust) Pty is a licensee of Jetstream Systems Co of Hayward, California. Details of the conveyor system built by the company can be found under the entry for Jetstream Systems Company, USA.

FRANCE

SOCIÉTÉ BERTIN & CIE
Head Office and Works: BP 3, 78370 Plaisir, France
Telephone: 056 25 00
Telex: 69 62 31 F
Officials:
Fernand Chanrion, *President Director General*
Michel Perineau, *Director General*
Georges Mordchelles-Regnier, *Director General*
M Croix-Marie, *Head of Air Cushion Department*

Research on ground effect and air cushion principle applications has been undertaken by Bertin et Cie since 1956. The company developed the original technique of separately fed plenum chambers surrounded by flexible skirts—see entries for Dubigeon-Normandie Shipyards/SEDAM (ACVs) and Société de l'Aérotrain (Tracked Skimmers). The same basic technology is being applied extensively to industrial materials handling.

In the past, developments in this field have mainly covered special applications. A stage has now been reached where standard equipment can be made available for a large number of handling applications.

Bertin has now made available standard components and, according to the type of problem to be solved, offers clients 'do-it-yourself-kits', plus advice, technological assistance or full design services.

Standard do-it-yourself kits
These are available in the following configurations:

Circular Cushions
These form the basis of the handling platforms. Their positioning and number is determined by function, the weight and nature of the loads (height, position of centre of gravity etc).

Three cushions at least must be employed to ensure stability.

The cushions can be fitted on to a chassis with spring fastenings.

The flexible lips will not suffer wear under normal conditions but are interchangeable in cases of accidental damage.

Circular cushions are produced as standard units in three sizes: Ø 300, Ø 450, Ø 600.

General characteristics are given in the accompanying table.

Standard Modules
Standard modules, complete with chassis, and based on one of the four types of standard circular cushions available (see table) are available in two models:
—quick assembly modules which can be assembled at will to form platforms in a variety of sizes
—independent pads ready to be inserted beneath loads which have a rigid, flat underside.

Lifting capacity of these modules is comparable to that of the corresponding circular cushion.

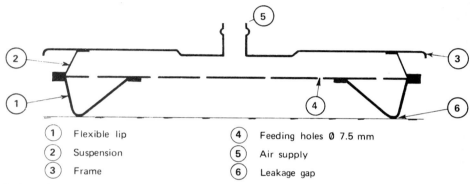

1. Flexible lip
2. Suspension
3. Frame
4. Feeding holes Ø 7.5 mm
5. Air supply
6. Leakage gap

Basic configuration and components of a Bertin circular cushion

Standard Bertin circular cushion

Bertin metal air cushion skids for use over very even surfaces

Honeycomb Cushions
Honeycomb cushions are available in three standard sizes. Fully stable, these cushions allow full use of the load-bearing surface for lift. In addition they are very thin but can bear very heavy loads when at rest.

These cushions employ inflatable joints to seal off adjacent square cells which are fed separately through vents from a single plenum. The plenum itself is fed from any suitable compressed air source.

Rigid Air Cushions

Metal air cushion skids are available in the range of Bertin industrial materials handling equipment. These can be used across even surfaces and operate without surface contact on an air film a few hundredths of a millimetre deep. Applications include a 3,000kg payload platform for feeding a press mounted on seven 200mm diameter skids. This unit can withstand a pressure of 26,000kg when at rest beneath the press.

Water Cushions

Circular water cushions are available for very heavy loads. Power required for lift with water cushions is 20 to 30 times less than with standard air cushions.

Soft Air Pads

Small square air pads 100 × 100 × 25mm with a 150kg load capacity. These pads are designed especially for moving tools on press tables.

Machinery handling in factories

Major applications of Bertin air cushions to solve machinery and material handling problems within factories, listed in past issues of *Jane's Surface Skimmers*, include:
air film cushion sheer tables (1966);
air cushion platforms to install 40,000lb machinery units within factory buildings (1966);
air cushion chassis for moving machinery (1968);

Circular Cushions

Type	Ø 300	Ø 450R	Ø 600	Ø 600R
Overall diameter	0·364m	0·54m	0·68m	0·68m
Height (at rest)	0·035m	0·05m	0·05m	0·05m
(under pressure)	0·045m	0·07m	0·075m	0·075m
	±5mm	±5mm	±5mm	±5mm
Weight	5·5kg	8·5kg	14kg	15kg
Lift area	0·07m²	0·16m²	0·28m²	0·28m²
Load capacity	500kg	1,200kg	2,500kg	4,000kg

Special cushions are available for higher load capacities

air cushion conveyors adapted to specific loads (1969);
air film conveyors for the transfer of soft or tacky sheet material (1970);
loading platform for lorries (1970);
cast mould press feeding platform on air cushions (1971);
transfer of 12-ton spinning mills on air cushions (1972);
permanent air cushion platforms for the transfer of 5-ton diesel engine cooling units from the assembly line to the dispatching area (1972);
air cushion platforms for precise positioning of metal blanks under a magnetic unstacking unit (1973);
permanent air cushion platforms fitted under 30-ton profiling machines facilitating the use of alternative machines along a production line (1973);
50-ton capacity platform to introduce loads within an X-ray control room through staggered protection walls (1974);

air cushion turntable for 50-ton loads of glassware (1974);
space-saving air cushion system to rotate railway trucks along their assembly line (1975);
shipyard air cushion platforms to facilitate positioning of large hull sections (1976);
metal sheet handling platforms and two-tier mobile lifting table for transfers in stores (1976);
positioning heavy parts for assembly in the motor car industry (1977);
moving ceiling structures on building sites (1979).

The most recent applications are mainly in the field of assembly lines. Bertin air cushions are now extensively used to move machinery and assembled units.

Since the first air cushion system was supplied in 1975 to rotate railway trucks, several similar systems have been manufactured. In 1978 a full size swivel bridge traversing table on air cushions with a load capacity of 150 tons was designed and supplied.

Bertin standard module in the form of an independent pad, ready to be inserted beneath a load with a rigid, flat, underside

Bertin honeycomb cushion for heavy loads

ETABLISSEMENTS NEU

Division B, Sac Postal 2028, 59013 Lille Cedex, France

Etablissements NEU is a licensee of Jetstream Systems Co of Hayward, California, USA. Details of the conveyor system built by the company can be found under the entry for Jetstream Systems Company, USA.

GERMANY, FEDERAL REPUBLIC

HELMUT FRANK BLECHVERARBEITUNG

Laufdorferstrasse, D-6331 Bonbaden, Federal Republic of Germany

This company is a licensee of Jetstream Systems Company of Hayward, California, USA. Details of the conveyor system built by the company can be found under the entry for Jetstream Systems Company, USA.

TRINIDAD

COELACANTH GEMCO LTD

1 Richardson Street, Point Fortin, Trinidad
Officials:
Nigel Seale, *Director*
Kelvin Corbie, *Director*
R Varma, *Secretary*

Coelacanth Gemco Ltd, the first company to specialise in the design and construction of air cushion vehicles in the West Indies, has developed a hover conveyor system and a hover pallet.

The pallet, measuring 0·91×1·22m (3×4ft), is

capable of lifting and moving 453·59kg (1,000lb) while operated by one man and great potential is seen for the use of these units within Trinidad factories.

The hover-conveyor system is designed in modules of 3·05m and 4·57m (10ft and 15ft), enabling a system of any length to be devised to suit changing production line requirements.

Coelacanth Gemco is also working on a self-contained unit, powered by a 100hp diesel engine driving a 0·91m (36in) eight-blade axial fan at 2,500rpm to produce 849·5m³ (30,000ft³) of air per minute at 6in wg pressure.

This will be used in the movement of oil company tanks between various locations. Multiples of this unit will enable tanks of any size to be moved after attaching the skirt system.

Coelacanth hoverpallet employed in a workshop to move air-conditioning equipment. This particular model lifts loads up to 453·592kg (1,000lb). Other models, operating on factory air supplies of 5·62kg/cm² (80psi), will carry loads of up to 15·24 tonnes (15 tons). The model seen above operates on either 115 or 230V ac

UNION OF SOVIET SOCIALIST REPUBLICS

LENINGRAD INSTITUTE OF ENGINEERING AND CONSTRUCTION

Leningrad, USSR

An air cushion vibrating platform designed to improve the rate of setting and uniformity of concrete has been designed and built by the Leningrad Institute of Engineering and Construction. It oscillates vertically, horizontally and diagonally.

The idea of employing an air cushion in constructing vibrating platforms for the production of prefabricated reinforced concrete was proposed and introduced by technologists in the Byelorussian Ministry of Construction.

Conventional vibrating platforms require considerable quantities of metal in their construction and costly foundations, the weight of which can be 18-20 times the load capacity of the platform. The concentrated dynamic loads frequently lead to the breakdown of the platform's framework, and during operation the vibration and noise cause severe discomfort to plant personnel.

The operating principle of vibrating platforms using air cushions is as follows. Beneath the vibrating platform, which is a framework with a metal bottom, air is fed by a fan to form an air cushion between the foundation and the bottom of the vibrating platform. As a result, the vibrating platform (along with a form filled with mixed concrete) is lifted into the air. The vibrating system is then switched on and the mixture is allowed to set under the influence of vertical oscillations with an amplitude of 0·3–1mm. To limit power expenditure, the cushion forms a closed system with an elastic apron. The pressure in the air cushion is 600-800kg/m² with a lift of 6-10 tons.

These platforms have a load capacity of 2–3 tons. They do not require special concrete foundations and are mounted on a sandy base 100–150mm thick. The power consumption of existing mass-produced platforms with load capacities of 4, 6 and 8 tons are 14, 20 and 40 kW,

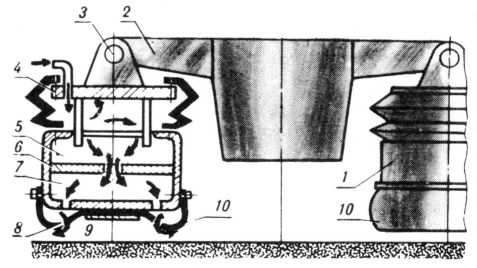

Diagram showing operation of the Novocherkassk Polytechnic air pads and handling platform

respectively, in contrast to 10, 14 and 28 kW for air cushion vibrating platforms. Use is made of the ability of an air cushion to distribute pressure evenly over the entire reaction surface, and of its outstanding shock absorbing qualities.

NOVOCHERKASSK POLYTECHNIC

The Novocherkassk Polytechnic has developed a series of air pads and platforms capable of supporting loads of up to 12·5 tonnes. The air supply is from a compressor or the factory air supply.

A platform with a load capacity of 40–80 tonnes is in the design stage and a feature is an automatic load relief should the air supply be cut off.

A diagram showing the system evolved at the Polytechnic accompanies this entry. It comprises two or more compressed air pads (1) which are generally rectangular in shape, and two connecting supports for the load or load platform (2). The supports are connected to the air pads by articulated joints (3) and rest on compressed air jacks (4). Air is fed into the pads through a regulator and enters the chamber of the compressed air jack (5). It then passes through the baffle plates (6) which ensure a constant differential in pressure between the cushion air plenums and the compressed air jack chamber. Cushion air enters the plenum (7) and then escapes through the discharge nozzle (8) into the recess (9) between the flexible seals and the supporting surface.

The system has undergone extensive tests and it is thought likely that it will have wide application in Soviet industry, particularly in the movement of machines and material stocks in warehouses.

UNITED KINGDOM

AIRMATIC ENGINEERING (UK) LTD

King Street, Sileby, Loughborough, Leicester-shire LE12 7LJ, England
Telephone: 050 981 2816
Officials:
R D Owen, *Managing Director*
P Lucas, *Commercial Manager*

This company is manufacturing and marketing the Pneu-Move air bearing systems for manual movement of loads of up to approximately 10 tonnes.

TURNTABLES AND WORK TRANSFER SYSTEMS

Both turntables and linear systems can be stopped and effectively locked in any position by turning off the compressed air supply. At this point the metal bearing pads settle onto their tracks, resulting in a firm, robust working surface, sturdy enough for high precision work, as in the optics industry, for example.

Another advantage of Pneu-Move systems is that they are self-cleaning, exhaust air being constantly expelled onto the bearing track. They are also extremely adaptable: the control valves may be automatic, remote, foot or hand operated, to meet individual requirements.

Turntables are available in a range of sizes, either free-standing or flush floor fitted, with a machined surface, checker plate, 'T' slots or other arrangements by request. Linear systems are normally designed to suit the particular applications.

INSPECTION ROTARY AIR TABLE

A recent addition to the Pneu-Move air bearing range is the inspection rotary air table. Four sizes of inspection table are available and these are supplied in two grades of accuracy, according to application. Optional features for the table top include 'T' slots, drilled and tapped holes and jig-bored location holes. The basic table may be supplied with indexing by shot-pin location and also a lock and fine angular adjustment as well as a digital readout system.

The table can be used while supported on an inspection surface plate or granite table top and a linear translation facility of the air flotation type for these surfaces.

The table consists of a base casting onto which are fixed air bearing pads. The rotating top is supported on these pads each of which is connected to the common air supply through the control console. When no air is supplied to the lift bearings the table top sits firmly on the base casting which has been machined to fine limits, thus the base acts as a reference spacer between the top and the surface it stands on.

Inspection rotary air table

Pneu-Move Work Transfer System uses air flotation to provide rapid movement of heavy work-pieces between three drilling machines, saving time and reducing operator fatigue

TRI-GLIDE

TRI-GLIDE is a three-pad air bearing system for moving loads over any precision surface, eg a surface plate or a machine tool table. Where these surfaces have holes, or T-slots, TRI-GLIDE will pass over them, but with a slightly reduced load capacity. TRI-GLIDE is virtually frictionless, floating heavy work-pieces or measuring equipment over expensive precision surfaces without damage or wear.

Where accurate work is to be performed, eg marking out or measuring, TRI-GLIDE can be supplied optionally with the top surface of the three pads precision ground to equal height within ±0·005mm (±0·0002in).

TRI-GLIDE three-pad air bearing system

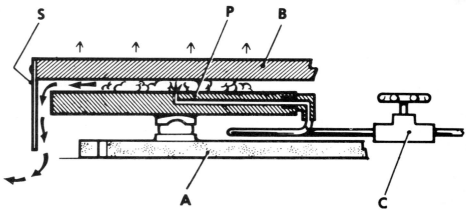

Method of turntable operation. Air supply valve 'C' is opened to allow compressed air to pass through the flotation pads 'P'. The pressure lifts turntable top 'B' on a cushion of compressed air to permit rotation. Exhaust air is expelled sideways, thus preventing any ingress of dirt. When the new position is reached, the air supply is closed, allowing the table top to settle onto bearing pads 'P'
Pneu-Move turntables consist of a base plate 'A' with fixed air-flotation bearing pads 'P' (usually three), on which rests the rotating table top 'B'. The latter has a protective skirt 'S'. Each pad is connected to a common air-line supply through operating valve 'C'

AIR CUSHION EQUIPMENT (1976) LTD

15-35 Randolph Street, Shirley, Southampton, Hampshire S01 3HD, England
Telephone: 0703 776468
Telex: 477537
Officials:
J D Hake, *Chairman*
L A Hopkins, *Director*
R C Gilbert, *General Manager*
R R Henvest, *Works Manager*

Close-up of a Water Skate load-carrying pallet in position below a ship section

Water Skate system being employed to move a French-built locomotive aboard a roll-on, roll-off cargo vessel for shipment to the USA

ACE "WATER SKATE" LOAD-CARRYING PALLET

Two sizes of pallet are available: Module A, with 35-tonne maximum capacity at 6 bar and Module AA, with 100-tonne maximum capacity at 6 bar. Both have a rise height of 75mm and use water as the cushion fluid.

Due to the modular concept of the system, loads of many thousands of tonnes can be moved by the selection of the numbers of pallets used. A simple flexible skirt system retains water under pressure while still allowing sufficient water to escape to lubricate the surface between the skirt and the ground. For movement of heavy loads on sloping surfaces a restraining line is recommended.

The type of flexible seal used in the pallet facilitates the lifting and movement of a load without the use of complex hydraulic jacking systems or heavy cranes. The equipment will operate over any surface from rough concrete to compacted soil with the minimum of ground preparation and the use of supplementary sheeting.

Water is usually provided via water pumps and distributed through normal flexible hoses. Each pallet is controlled by a standard gate valve.

When the valve is opened water is supplied to the pallet and the lift of 75mm is achieved.

The load is normally moved by towing, winching or a combination of both. The drag coefficient, which is very low, especially when using a running sheet, is generally between 2-3% of the total weight.

The heaviest load movement to date using the AA modules was a 10,000-tonne capacity barge destined for operation in the North Sea, weighing 1,800 tonnes. Twenty-one AA modules were arranged in five lines and operated along five temporary tracks over a beach to the low water line. Water was supplied in two stages via two delivery pumps feeding a four pump system giving the required operating pressure of 6 bar.

One of the most difficult moves attempted to date was the loading of a railway locomotive into a roll-on, roll-off cargo vessel. The lack of head room in the ship and the requirement for a single load moving system to move the locomotive from the rail track into the ship, then from the ship to the new location and rail track, presented problems with equipment specification. The Water Skate system, however, gave the solution enabling the locomotive to be jacked from and onto the trackway while maintaining a low profile for entry between decks.

Another unusual marine loading took place when a 320-tonne Link Span Bridge, destined for a cross-Channel ferry service, was loaded onto a sea-going barge which carried it to Boulogne. Other marine associated work included the slipway launching of a 240-tonne grain barge and a 180-tonne trawler.

On land, Water Skate operations have ranged from moving six oil production modules of 400 tonnes average weight destined for the North Sea, to the transfer of a dockside crane from one rail track to another.

The Water Skate is operated under licence from Air Cushion Equipment Limited by Lifting Services International, a division of Taylor Woodrow Construction Limited, except in North America, where Hover Systems Inc, of Media, Philadelphia, is the agent.

The equipment is normally hired by the client, who is also given technical assistance, although contract movements are also undertaken. Companies also have the option of purchasing Water Skate equipment for operation by their own personnel.

MINI WATER SKATE

To meet a growing demand from industrial users with heavy or dense 'problem' loads, Lifting Services International have introduced a Mini "Water Skate" load-bearing module. Working at a water pressure of 6 bar each module will lift 10 tonnes and on smooth concrete will use 100 litres of water per minute.

The skates can be used in multiples of three or more to form a load movement system to suit individual applications and, because they are omni-directional, heavy loads can be manoeuvred in confined spaces. Force needed to move a load is approximately 2 to 5% of the deadweight.

Type AA pallets were used to launch this 300-tonne diving platform

Module size

`A`   `AA`

1·2

1·2

inlet pipe   BSP inlet pipes

Inflated 235mm
Deflated 160mm

Weight 104 kg   2·44   Weight 185 kg

Lift pressure ratio

Maximum working pressure 6 Bar (87 psi)

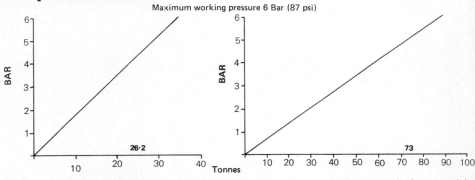

BAR   BAR   Tonnes

26·2   73

The Skate is a low cost lifting and manoeuvring pad using water under pressure from a standard commercial water pump. The two types shown here have a maximum lift of 35 tonnes and 100 tonnes respectively, and can be employed in a multi-modular system to suit individual requirements

System to lift 40 metric tons
Surface finish and condition allowing use at 6 Bar (88psi)
Number of modules required   4
Pump capacity required (4x100)   400 litres/min (88 gpm)
Pump Head pressure recommended 8 Bar

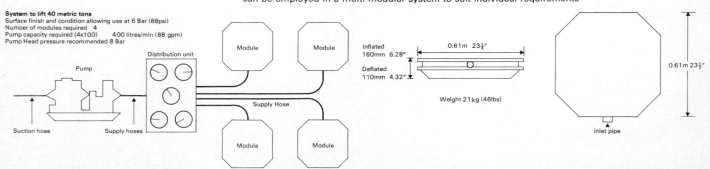

Pump   Distribution unit   Module   Module   Inflated 160mm 6.28"   0.61m 23½"   0.61m 23½"

Deflated 110mm 4.32"

Suction hose   Supply hoses   Supply Hose   Module   Module   Weight 21 kg (46lbs)   inlet pipe

Six type A pallets were employed to move and locate ship sections weighing 65-110 tonnes in a French dry dock

BRITISH HOVERCRAFT CORPORATION

East Cowes, Isle of Wight, England
Officials:
See ACV section

HOVERPADS

BHC Hoverpads are simply fitted beneath a load carrying platform and connected by air-line via a control valve to the factory mains. Two sizes of hoverpad are currently available, 38cm and 66cm diameter (15in and 26in). These can be used in multiples to move loads in the range of 0·5-5 tons per pad. Air consumption is dependent on the load and the smoothness of the floor surface. Typically, a 1,000kg (1 ton) load can be floated with 1m³/min (40ft³/min) air supply from a 6 bar (80psi) compressed air line.

Westland Gazelle helicopter being moved across the flight shed at Yeovil with the help of BHC hoverpads

Manoeuvring a 2½ ton diesel engine at Leyland Vehicles' plant using BHC hoverpads in conjunction with a scissor lift table

LIGHT HOVERCRAFT COMPANY

Felbridge Hotel & Investment Co Ltd, London Road, East Grinstead, Sussex, England
Telephone: 0342 24424
Officials:
Lindsay H F Gatward, *Proprietor*

This company markets a pedestrian-controlled hoverpallet which has a payload capacity of 152kg (336lb).

Lift power is provided by an 8hp Briggs & Stratton petrol engine which drives a plastic/alloy axial fan mounted beneath a close mesh safety guard. Since the power unit is of the lawn mower type, the general noise level is low.

The pallet which is built in glass fibre can be used over a wide range of unprepared surfaces including snow, ice, mud, water, grass, swamp and sand. Ploughed fields with ridges of up to 152mm (6in) can be traversed with a reduced payload. The over-water and swamp applications are restricted by the amount the operator is prepared to become immersed, or the degree by which his ability to control the vehicle is impaired. Machines can be winched across areas of deep water. Working under these conditions, however, applications such as wildfowling, reed collection, slurry control and insect spraying in swamp areas are possible.

Two directional wheels are fitted and these can be adjusted or removed according to the degree of directional control or ground contact pressure required.

A clip-on spraying unit, manufactured by E Allman & Co Ltd, Birdham Road, Chichester, Sussex, has been developed for use in conjunction with the pallet.

Skirt is of HDL segmented type in nylon-coated polyurethane. Depth is 127mm (5in).

SPECIFICATIONS
Length (with handle): 2·89m (9ft 6in)
Width: 1·21m (4ft)
Height (with handle): 0·91m (3ft)
Weight (approx): 72·57kg (160lb)
Skirt depth: 127mm (5in)
Fuel capacity: 3·4 litres (6 pints)
Engine: 4-cycle (319cc)
Endurance (approx): 2 h/gallon
Payload: 152kg (336lb)
Payload area: 2·6m² (28ft²)

Light Hovercraft Co's hoverpallets can be used over a wide variety of unprepared surfaces including agricultural land. A clip-on attachment can be supplied for crop-spraying

Assembled hoverpallets ready for despatch. The plastic/alloy axial lift fan is mounted beneath a close mesh safety guard

One of the applications for which the hoverpallet has proved ideal is that of snow removal. Its payload capacity is 152kg (336lb)

LING SYSTEMS LTD

Little End Road, Eaton Socon, St Neots, Huntingdon, Cambridgeshire PE19 3JH, England

Ling Systems Ltd is the exclusive licensee in the United Kingdom, Ireland, and the Netherlands for the Jetstream air cushion conveyor system. Equipment is in use to handle a wide range

of scrap materials—metal, paper, board and plastic, also many types of unit loads—boxes, both full and empty; plastic bottles; cap closures; can ends and pressed and moulded parts.

ROLAIR SYSTEMS LTD

Ampere Road, London Road Industrial Estate, Newbury, Berkshire RG13 2AE, England
Telephone: 0635 49525
Telex: 847015 ROLAIR G
Officials:
B H Wright, RD, BSc, BCom, CEng, MIEE, *Chairman and Managing Director*
D L Campbell, MC, *Director*
M F Dowding, CBE, MA, CEng, MIMechE, *Director*
N F Haycock, CEng, MIEE, *Director*
R H Lacey, CEng, MIMechE, *Director*

Lord Macpherson of Drumochter, JP, *Director*
A A A Stammers, MIMechE, *Director*

Rolair Systems Ltd has an exclusive licence from Rolair Systems Inc, of Santa Barbara, California, USA, for the manufacture and sale of air film equipment for the transport of heavy industrial loads. Their range of equipment working off the shop air supply includes Air Skates which may be used in sets of four or more (individual Skate capacities range from ½ ton to 26½ tons); standard steel transporters incorporating four or six bearings with capacities from 1 ton to 240 tons which may be used separately or in

combination for heavier loads. Also available are battery operated steel transporters with in-built air blowers which may be used where no air supply is available or in controlled environments where outside air cannot be used. A standard range of air film turntables with capacities up to 250 tons is available. Vehicle turntables are also manufactured.

Existing applications of Rolair equipment in the United Kingdom range from unit loads of less than one ton to over one thousand tons. Applications include generator and transformer movements, ship section transporters, omni-mobile cranes on air bearings and standard transporters for interbay movement, steel ladle transfer cars, turntables incorporated into machine tools or used in paint booths and fettling shops, movements of machine tools, oil rig modules, printing machinery, heavy diesel engines. Rolair transporters can also be used to form a production line for heavy equipment.

United Kingdom customers include BP Chemicals, Brush Electrical, CEGB, GEC, Hawker Siddeley Group, IBM, ICI, Kodak, Rolls-Royce, Short Brothers & Harland, Sunderland Shipbuilders, Westland Helicopters and many others.

Two Rolair 12-tonne transporters move £1 million RB211 engines in the engine overhaul shop at Heathrow. Powered by pneumatic motors the transporters pick up the pallet mounted engines and move them on a thin film of compressed air

Part of a 600-tonne Rolair movement system supplied to GEC Power Transformers, Stafford, for transformer handling

UNITED STATES OF AMERICA

AERO-GO, INC

5800 Corson Avenue South, Seattle, Washington 98108, USA
Telephone: (206) 763 9380
Telex: 320058
Officials:
Kurt Kosty, *President*
William A Shannon, *Vice President*

Associated companies:
Aero-Go Luft-Und Wasserkissentechnik GmbH
Nuelehweg 3, Postfach 1241, D-5340 Bad Honnef, Federal Republic of Germany
Goran Fredriksson, *General Manager*

Aero-Go Scandinavia AB
Energigatan 3A, S-721 38 Västerås, Sweden
Åke Hedman, *General Manager*

Aero-Go (UK) Ltd
Chiddingstone Causeway, Penshurst, Kent, England
M Fitzcharles, *Managing Director*

Avio-Diepen BV
Vliegeld Ypenburg, ZH 2109 Rijswijk, Netherlands
R de Rooij, *Director*

M Claessens
Kloosterstraat 107, B-2070 Ekeren, Belgium
R Metzelaar, *Sales Manager*

Dr Hans Kraus Ges mbH & Co KG
A-9210 Portschach, Austria
G Sandhofer, *Sales Manager*

International Marketing Services
22 rue de Vintmille, 75009 Paris, France
M Pioline, *Manager*

Pfingstweid AG
Box 761, Pfingstweidstrasse 31A, CH-8022 Zurich, Switzerland
B Maechler, *Director*

Aero-Go Italia, SRL
Via Statuto 1B, 21021 Milan, Italy
Leonardo Desenzani, *Manager*

Aero-Go, Inc manufactures fluid film load movement equipment and systems for general industrial applications. It provides a broad range of standard equipment complemented by the capability to supply complete complex materials handling systems based on fluid film technology. Founded in 1967 to market new developments in dual chamber air film bearings pioneered by the Boeing Company, Aero-Go today holds exclusive rights to extensive developments in the industry.

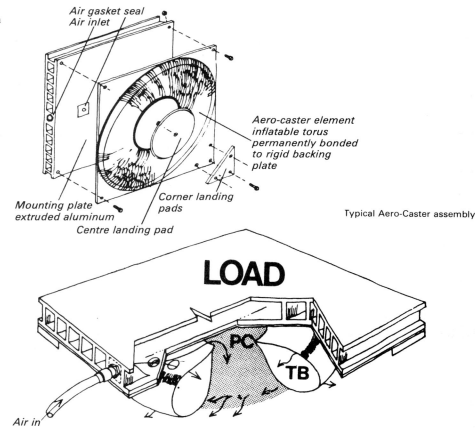

Air gasket seal
Air inlet

Aero-caster element
inflatable torus
permanently bonded
to rigid backing
plate

Corner landing
pads

Mounting plate
extruded aluminum

Centre landing pad

Typical Aero-Caster assembly

LOAD

PC

TB

Air in

Aero-Caster Load Module Assembly

Deflated: the load is supported solidly on the Aero-Caster centre and corner landing pads.
Inflating: when air enters the Aero-Caster, the central plenum chamber (PC) fills and the hollow torus bag (TB) inflates, sealing its lower circular edge against the underlying surface.
Floating: when air pressure within the chamber equals the load's weight above it, it must escape downward against the surface. The load gently lifts and the captured air bubble (PC) escapes to circulate under the flexible bottom face. The 0.005-inch film is now floating the load

The basic principle of all Aero-Go Fluid Film Systems is shown in the cut-away illustration. Supporting heavy loads and simultaneously providing nearly zero friction and omni-directional movement is inherent in these systems. This results in low initial cost and low operating cost as the source of compressed air is normally the existing factory air system.

AERO-CASTER LOAD MODULES

The air film Aero-Caster is manufactured in eight sizes ranging from 30·5cm (12in) diameter, with a 454kg (1,000lb) lift capacity, to 121·9cm (48in) diameter with a 36,300kg (80,000lb) capacity. Individual load modules are used in sets of three or more of one size, and are normally slipped beneath a load in a triangular or square pattern with the centre of gravity of the load placed over the pattern's geometric centre.

Within the rated limit of each caster's lift capacity, a load is lifted in direct proportion to the air pressure applied. A 53·3cm (21in) unit with a face area of 1,808cm² (280in²) will lift 3,182kg (7,000lb) maximum at 1·76kg/cm² (25psi). Four model K21Ns will therefore float loads up to 12,700kg (28,000lb) maximum at an air pressure of 1·76kg/cm² (25psi).

Load module systems are available complete with interconnecting hose manifolds, air-regulation control console and fittings as required by a customer. They are a popular rigging tool for the movement of loads between crane bays, into tight storage areas, or installing new machinery into a plant.

The heaviest load was moved on air film in September 1977 at Beynes near Paris, France. A new 2,000-tonne concrete boxbridge was moved 34m (112ft) into a precise location under an overhead railway line in half an hour. Two truck winches pulled the load floating on 54 units of the 121·9cm (48in) load module size. The National French Railways (SNCF) has been using them to install bridges throughout France since March 1976.

AERO-PALLETS

Load-moving platforms can be supplied with built-in Aero-Casters. Lightweight aluminium extrusion or structural steel construction is employed when loads are over 18,150kg (40,000lb). Accessories include internal or detachable air motor drives to simplify large load movement and guidance by a single operator.

AERO-PLANKS

When the loads to be carried are long or are likely to vary in weight, as do the industrial air-conditioners at Trane Co's plant in Wisconsin, a set of two or more planks are placed beneath their base, spaced to meet the requirements of the changing load.

The company also manufactures air-driven platform trucks, Aero-Trucks, Aero-Turntables and machine-tool holding bedplates movable on air film.

"WATER FILM" AERO-CASTERS

In 1971 Aero-Go introduced "Water Film" casters which convey high-tonnage loads on water film. A number are in use at several major shipyards and offshore oil-drilling platform docks. To date, the largest ship constructed with the use of Aero-Caster load modules is a 3,400-ton ferry, built by Vancouver Shipyards Co, Canada.

The largest and heaviest single load yet moved on a water film system is a new 4,000-ton grand-stand section added to the outdoor sports stadium in Denver, Colorado in spring 1977.

Seating 23,000 people, the three-tiered section is 163m (535ft) long by 60m (200ft) deep by 42m (135ft) high. It will be moved backwards or forwards 44m (145ft) several times per year to change the central playing field area for football, baseball, soccer and other outdoor events.

A total of 163 Model 48NHDW water film Aero-Casters are located in clusters of from two to four units each, under the section's support framing at 47 different lift points. The casters move over fourteen 2m (6ft) wide sealed-concrete runways with built-in drains. Water recirculates to the system from a 60,000-gallon storage tank. The thrust of hydraulic rams employed to push the grandstand into position is approximately 3,628kg (8,000lb).

MOBILE MACHINE BEDPLATES

Aero-Go introduced the mobile machining bedplate concept in 1978. This air film product line enables greatly increased efficiency in using large machine tools. The mobility of an air film pallet is mated with the accuracy and precise positioning required for locating parts in front of large machine tools. Two of these special pallets, working in sequence, enable the time consuming "set-up" of parts to be done at the same time

Aero-Caster load modules are employed to move transformers weighing up to 100 tons at the Westinghouse Electric Corporation plant in Seattle, Washington

A single operator can move rolls of paper weighing up to 1,041kg (4,500lb) on a Rollmaster air pallet at the Mead Packaging plant in California. Rolls are lifted, moved and precisely positioned for loading on machine roll stands

In late 1974 Brown & Root activated a fluid film transport system capable of lifting and floating 2,000-ton drill rig platform structures. This water film system incorporates water elevators that evenly distribute loads between the multiple legs of platform structures as these structures are moved from land to barges. Moves are powered and controlled by rubber tyred vehicles. Sixteen water film transporters incorporating 32 heavy duty water Aero-Casters lift and float loads up to 2,000 tons. A 100hp diesel driven water pump takes 3,030 litres (800 gallons) of water per minute to work this system.

machining is underway. Typical efficiency improvements of 30% in machine time utilization is achieved. Aero-Go is now supplying complete systems including the accurate positioning components for a variety of customers.

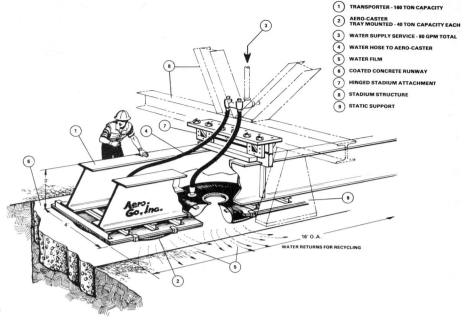

1. TRANSPORTER - 160 TON CAPACITY
2. AERO-CASTER TRAY MOUNTED - 40 TON CAPACITY EACH
3. WATER SUPPLY SERVICE - 80 GPM TOTAL
4. WATER HOSE TO AERO-CASTER
5. WATER FILM
6. COATED CONCRETE RUNWAY
7. HINGED STADIUM ATTACHMENT
8. STADIUM STRUCTURE
9. STATIC SUPPORT

16' O.A.
WATER RETURNS FOR RECYCLING

Typical lifting point beneath the grandstand at Denver

JETSTREAM SYSTEMS COMPANY

3486 Investment Boulevard, PO Box 4177, Hayward, California 94540, USA

Telephone: (415) 785 9360

Officials:
Stanley Lenox, *President*
Warren P Landon, *Vice President, Marketing*
Eugene S Batter, *Vice President, Operations*

Jetstream Systems Company holds the world-wide rights for Jetstream air film conveyors and processing equipment.

Jetstream uses low-pressure air delivered to a plenum by a fan or fans and introduced to the conveyor surface through various types of orifices along the full length of the conveyor to maintain a film of air flowing close to the conveyor surface. This air film both lifts and moves the objects being conveyed. It conveys packages of various types; small items which must be kept properly oriented; scrap metal, plastic, and paper; and granular materials.

The air can be heated or cooled to condition the product while it is being conveyed. A rectangular fluid bed utilising the air film principle is available where longer retention times are required.

The system provides constant controlled power around curves and up inclines including vertical faces. Entry points and spurs, inputs and outputs, can be added easily anywhere along the conveyor. Maintenance and wear are greatly reduced because no moving parts are in contact with the product. Objects can be accumulated on the conveyor with very low back-pressure since they are riding on an air film and no belts or chains are dragged across the bottom.

POWER SUPPLY: Pressure of air necessary: $1/10$in water gauge to $1/2$psi. Air ducting and centrifugal fans are generally fitted as an integral part of the conveyor.

CONVEYOR SYSTEM: Units are designed to suit product. The length can run to 1,000ft or more and the width from 1in to 10ft or more as necessary.

ROLAIR SYSTEMS, INC

PO Box 30363, Santa Barbara, California 93105, USA

Telephone: (805) 968 1536
Telex: 658 433

Officials:
S L Morley, *President*
R E Burdick, *Vice President/Secretary*
H W Huthsing, *Vice President*
C A Bunton, *Director*
R E Burdick, *Director*
V L Cunningham, *Director*
H A Fritzche, *Director*
J F Pendexter, *Director*
W W Watling, *Director*

Licensees:
Rolair Systems Ltd, United Kingdom
Marubeni Corporation, Japan

Rolair Systems Inc manufactures a range of equipment making use of compliant air bearings for moving heavy or large loads. Key personnel with the company were engaged in the same field with General Motors between 1962 and 1968. The company was incorporated in 1968 as Transocean Air Systems Corporation. In 1971 its name was changed to Rolair Systems Inc.

The company's products include standard catalogue items and unlimited custom-engineered systems. Government, military and industrial use of Rolair air film systems is world-wide. Systems now operating range in weight handling capacities up to 14 million pounds.

The basic compliant air bearing device comprises a membrane holding compressed air which conforms to the floor. Controlled escape of this air in a thin layer between membrane and floor forms a frictionless air film which 'floats' the load, enabling it to be moved in any horizontal direction by a force only one-thousandth of the weight

Complete Rolair-assisted turntable assembly for offloading containerised cargo. In this photograph the turntable pier/platform is being rotated by two men

of the load. Air pressure is self-regulating according to the bearing size and its load. Typically a 2ft diameter bearing will lift 4,000lb; four 2ft bearings will carry a truck.

Several typical applications are described below.

PORTABLE PIERS FOR OFFLOADING CONTAINERISED CARGO

The Civil Engineering Laboratory, Naval Construction Battalion Center, Port Hueneme, California, USA has successfully designed a transportable pier/platform for over-the-shore offloading of containerised barge-ships and roll-on, roll-off supply vessels for the US Department of Defense. The pier/platform had to be able to accommodate two-way traffic comprised initially of 35 by 8ft trucks and with the capability to cope with 40 by 8ft trucks. In addition, in order to keep pier width to a minimum, it was necessary to install turntables for truck turn-around. Turntables would permit piers to be kept to two-lane widths rather than eight-lane widths which would be necessary if truck backing was required in turnaround.

All requirements have been fully satisfied by the development of a totally portable, two-lane, modular causeway. Each module measures 90 by 21ft. Truck turnaround is accomplished utilising Rolair air film components under a specially designed turntable.

Turntables are made up of 12 to 34in diameter Rolair ST Bearings. The bearings are mounted to deck beams in an inverted position and operate against the steel plate underside of the turntable rotating platen. This allows the load to be lifted and rotated while the bearings remain in a fixed position. The turntable structure is 48ft long, weighs 16 tons and can support a load of 22 tons. Two men can easily rotate fully loaded turntables manually, or one man can rotate it using a power drive conversion.

Causeways utilising Rolair turntables have been fully tested and accepted by the Navy as the solution to the problem of developing portable, quick-erection, over-the-shore piers for container offloading.

AIR BEARINGS AID SHIP STORAGE

A programme for reverse ship storage and upkeep for the US Navy has resulted in over $1 million savings in both money and man hours.

The US Navy's ship repairing facility on Guam operates a reserve craft branch, responsible for the security, maintenance and upkeep of out-of-service-in-reserve Navy vessels. The problem was to store effectively and protect ten 300-ton YFUs, a landing-craft type vessel, against Guam's hostile tropical environmental elements, including typhoons.

In this first application of its kind the problem was solved by utilising four Rolair air film transporters. The 120-ton capacity transporters, each equipped with four air bearings, enabled the craft to be floated on dry land to a "high and dry" area, safe from the problems inherent in water storage.

Experiments had been made previously, using heavy equipment and grease on steel plate, but it took four days and 714 man hours to store one YFU. With air film transporters, two a day can be positioned, requiring 76 man hours each, using very little in the way of equipment.

Manoeuvrability was another problem solved with air film transporters. The air film transporters allowed the manoeuvring of the craft in any direction with little difficulty.

The air film transporters, topped with interfacing keel or bilge blocks, are positioned under the YFU after the craft is lifted onto the dock from the water by two floating cranes. A 100 × 400ft steel-trowelled concrete slab is provided at the dockside for storage. Two lift trucks are used to tow and manoeuvre the craft to their storage position.

After trying both compressed air and water as the fluid for the air bearings, water was determined to be the best fluid for this particular operation. Rolair supplied transporters with both air and water inlets so either could be used.

To remove the air film transporters, a second set of keel or bilge blocks, 6½ft high was built-up between the concrete slab and the hull. Then, using wedges, the hull was raised a few inches so that the transporters could be simply moved. The 6½ft block height was chosen to permit personnel and vehicle access under the hulls for periodic hull inspection.

Securely-anchored, protected bay storage is the normal storage procedure practised by the Navy for other than small boats. It was recognised that there are a number of economic disadvantages with this method. For example, there is the need for cathodic hull protection; periodic dry-docking for barnacle removal; expensive electronic flooding alarm surveillance as well as regular visual waterline checks by each watch. In addition costly anchors ($3,000 each) are lost from time to time during the typhoon season.

It is estimated that the ten YFUs stored at SRF Guam by the "high and dry" method have saved the Navy $100,000 per craft to date, an amount

After rotation the container truck faces out over the water at the end of the causeway ready to drive aboard a containerised bargeship or roll-on, roll-off ferry. The turntables also permit piers to be kept to two-lane width rather than eight-lane width which would be necessary if truck backing was required in a turnaround

Rolair air film transporters with keel or bilge blocks being "floated" beneath a crane-supported YFU

Fully "floated" 300-ton YFU landing craft being moved to its storage location on Rolair transporters by two low-horsepower forklift trucks

continually increasing due to the reduced inspection necessary.

VARIABLE-PLAN SPORTS STADIUM

Rolair air bearings will be used to vary the seating configurations of a new 28,000-seat

stadium under construction in Honolulu.

The stadium comprises four 7,000-seat sections and the air bearings will be employed to rotate each through a 45 degree arc to provide ideal seating patterns for either football or baseball games.

Located under each of the four stadium sections will be 26 Rolair transporters, each incorporating four air-bearings. These will be inflated by three main air compressors, each with a capacity of 1,250cfm. The sections will be moved by a system of lightweight hydraulic jacks. A rail guideline will prevent the sections drifting when 20-knot Pacific tradewinds are blowing. Each stadium section has a fixed pivot point and it is estimated that only 20 minutes will be required to move each one through its 45 degree arc—a total distance of 53·34m (173ft).

In baseball configuration the stadium will have an open double "horseshoe" look. For football the four sideline sections will be moved inward to form straight sidelines with the spectators on the 50 yard line only 12·19m (40ft) from the sideline, and only 7·62m (25ft) away from the goal line.

Ramps connecting the stadium sections extend and retract on air film with each move.

AUTOMATIC MODULAR HOME PRODUCTION LINE

Rolair has designed and installed a fully-automated air film walking beam conveyor system which moves factory built home modules simultaneously through eighteen assembly stations several times an hour.

The system can handle modules with lengths of up to 18·28m (60ft) and widths up to 4·26m (14ft).

ASSEMBLY LINE FOR CRAWLER TRACTORS

One of the most advanced air film systems in operation today is in use at the Caterpillar Tractor plant at Gosselies, Belgium, where an automatic assembly line has been installed by Rolair for Model 225 Excavators.

The first line for these vehicles was installed at the company's plant at Aurora, Illinois, USA. Experience with the Aurora plant has led to certain improvements on the Gosselies plant. For example, air tools are used throughout the line, allowing the air-powered transporters to serve as the air supply for the tools. This enables assemblers to connect their tools at the start of the assembly and leave them connected throughout the line.

The assembly operation begins on a 175ft-long section of track immediately preceding the air pallet area. There, drive assemblies are built on manually-propelled transfer carts.

First, the tractor's two planetary gears are aligned on a stationary fixture. A housing is then lifted into position by an overhead crane. After the housing has been connected to the axles, the unit is lifted onto a transfer cart. Small components are then added to the housing as the cart is moved to the end of the track. The sub-assembly and cart now weighs about 18,000lb and requires two men to push it. At this point the sub-assembly is lifted by the overhead crane and positioned on one of the air pallets. Now one man can easily move the 9-ton load.

Components are brought to the air pallet line on flat-bed trucks and lifted by crane onto the pallets. Workers climb portable step ladders to perform the necessary welding and bolting operations. The same air source that supplies the pallets is used to power air-articulated assembly tools.

Each transporter has a 45ft hose mounted on a retractable reel. Air hose connectors are installed below the surface every 25ft along the assembly line. This allows the transporter 90ft of travel before changing air connectors.

When air is fed into the system, each bearing diaphragm inflates, traps a shallow bubble of air and lifts the load slightly off the floor. Controlled leakage around the edge of the bearings creates a lubricating layer of air between the transporter and floor. Friction is practically eliminated and the transporter can be moved with a minimum of force.

A master clock controls the complete assembly line. Magnetic sensors are located on the bottom of the transporters, and utilising a series of electromagnets embedded every 10ft along the

Air film is used to rearrange four massive 7,000-seat stadium sections at the Aloha Stadium, on the island of Oahau, Hawaii, about 3 miles from Honolulu. The movable grandstands enable the basic stadium shape to be changed easily to provide the best accommodation for both those taking part in the events and the spectators. Built and installed by Rolair Systems Inc, the air film system swings four of the 147ft high stadium sections a distance of some 200ft through a 40 degree arc to provide ideal seating patterns for football, baseball, soccer and special events. Moving time for each section takes less than 30 minutes. The three photographs above show the three main configurations: **Top:** oval configuration for football; **Centre:** double horseshoe for baseball; **Bottom:** open configuration for special events

assembly line floor, the transporter can be directed to move from station to station. The electromagnets are normally energised. When the control clock de-energises a specific electromagnet, the sensor on the transporter opens, providing an air supply to the air bearing, causing the transporter to advance toward the next energised electromagnet. Since each electromagnet is individually controlled, the air transporter can be moved any distance along the line.

At the same time as the air system is activated, two guide wheels automatically lock onto a V-type floor rail and guide the transporter down the assembly line. As a safety factor a 25-second delay is provided between air activation and initial machine movement, allowing ample time for assemblers to move from the path of the transporter.

Although the major portion of the line is automatic, some manual movement remains. At the end of the line, where the assembly floor is wide enough for two machines on transporters to operate side-by-side, excavators undergo flushing and computer testing of the hydraulic system. Advancing from the assembly line, the transporter's guide wheels are retracted and two men simply 'float' the 20-ton load into the test area.

With the air film transporter system, Caterpillar feels that the assembly line can be easily altered. It can be lengthened over a weekend simply by laying more concrete. A turn can be added the same way, and if the line has to be shortened, the section no longer required is simply abandoned. A relocation can be effected by simply picking up the whole system and setting it down on a new strip of concrete.

AIRCRAFT GROUND TESTING INSTALLATION

An air flotation system has been installed by Vought to allow quicker positioning of each plane for testing operational equipment. The system uses an air film and replaces hand-operated tripod-type jacks. It has provided not only a saving in time, but a safer environment for testing. Twelve Corsair II light attack aircraft can be closely positioned within a single hangar.

Three air bearings, connected directly to a T-shaped dolly, make up the casters for each of six "sets" of bearings in use in the hangar. Their design is such that they easily handle the 19,000lb aircraft. On-off air valves for the bearings are operated quickly by a single employee. The bearings have their own stabilising chamber, eliminating any throttling of incoming air. Inlet air pressure is supplied at 75psi from standard 1in plant lines.

MOVING STEEL PRESSURE VESSELS

Pressure vessels for refineries, nuclear generators and the chemical industry represent one of the most difficult types of material handling problems for their manufacturers. The vessels are massive, bulky and hard to handle.

At Kobe Steel's plant in Takasago, Japan, the problem of transporting 1,000-ton pressure vessels from the assembly floor to the X-ray facility for weld examination was solved by the use of four 250-ton capacity air transporters. The transporters, based on designs by Rolair Systems are manufactured by its Japanese licensee, Marubeni Corporation.

In the Kobe Steel plant, overhead cranes are used for loading and unloading the 1,000ft long pressure vessel fabrication line. The task of transporting the vessels between the fabrication line and the weld X-ray building, some hundreds of feet away for safety reasons, had been assigned to multi-axle, heavy-duty flatbed trucks at a round-trip cost of approximately $10,000 and a frequency of as much as twice a day. The new system, while representing a six-figure investment, provided Kobe Steel with an economical solution that was expected to pay for itself within the first year with ease.

The Rolair transporters are completely air-operated, using existing shop air supplies. Located underneath each 10in-high structural steel transporter are eight disc-like air bearings

A gantry-type Omni-Mobile crane delivering a 1,814·37kg (4,000lb) load from the production line onto a flatbed truck

An Omni-Mobile crane of the travelling bridge type. Because of its omnidirectional movement, the crane can be moved around obstacles

which are specially compounded elastomeric compliant diaphragms.

When air is applied to the system through flexible hoses connected to the shop air supply, the bearings inflate. Controlled leakage creates a lubricating layer of air between the bearings and the floor. Friction is completely eliminated and the transporter can easily be moved in any horizontal direction by means of a built-in air motor drive system.

Each 250-ton capacity transporter contains four air motor drives mounted in tandem on opposite axes. By selective activation of the drives, the load can be moved as the operator wishes, including a full 360 degree turn around the load's vertical axis.

Wall-mounted retractable hoses permit easy movement between the fabrication line and the X-ray building at slow walking speeds. The system is designed for one-man operation for loads up to 500 tons. Two operators, one for each pair of transporters, are required for heavier loads, with maximum system capacity at 1,000 tons.

Once in position, the load is lowered gently to the floor by simply shutting off the air supply. With this ability of frictionless movement, a 1 : 1,000 force : load ratio results which means

simple lightweight air motors can move the unwieldy pressure vessels very easily and to precise positioning.

SPACE SHUTTLE SOLID ROCKET BOOSTERS

The use of air film movement systems in the production and operation of the solid rocket boosters (SRB) for the US Space Shuttle Programme represents an unmatched in-depth integration of air film into production. Air film equipment is used from the first phase of production to recovery and remanufacture.

Primary solid rocket booster elements are the motor, which includes the case, propellant, igniter and nozzle; forward and aft structures; and separation, recovery, electrical and thrust vector control sub-systems. Each booster is 45·41m (149ft) long and 3·65m (12ft) in diameter, weighs approximately 1,293,000lb and produces 2,900,000lb static thrust.

The solid rocket motor, the primary component of the booster, contains 1,100,000lb of solid propellant. The motor is built in four casting segments: a forward segment, two centre segments, and the aft segment. To these segments the nozzle assembly is added. Each of the casting segments is manufactured independently and transported, together with the nozzle exit cone assembly, to the launch site, where they are assembled.

For the first time rocket motors will be routinely recovered and re-used. When the spent boosters are separated from the shuttle vehicle external tank they will descend to the ocean by parachutes. Towed back to the Kennedy Space Center (or later to Vandenberg Air Force Base), the boosters are disassembled and the motors returned to the manufacturer, Thiokol Corporation. Residue is washed from the case segments, which are then refurbished, re-insulated and again loaded with propellant. Each case segment is designed to be used 20 times over. Some parts of the nozzle, igniter hardware, and the safe and arming devices will also be refurbished and re-used.

Rolair Systems, Inc, designed and built the air film equipment for Thiokol Corporation.

Production cycle: Use of air film begins at sub-contractor level and spans through the production steps at Thiokol's Utah-based Wasatch Division to NASA's operations at Marshal Space Flight Centre and Kennedy Space Centre.

For example, Standard Tool and Die Company uses Rolair bearings to position 22-ton mandrels during machining operations. The mandrels are used in casting the solid rocket fuel into the proper shape within the casting segment. What is unique about Standard Tool and Die's application of air film is that the air bearings remain with air-on for over 24 hours continuously to provide friction-free precision alignment during machining.

Utility handling equipment: Air film utility handling equipment is used throughout Thiokol. Examples include a standard air film transporter for handling such parts as nozzle flexible bearings to specially designed dollies to handle case segments weighing up to 11,000lb throughout the plant with ease.

Shot blast turntable: New segments are grit-blasted at one of Thiokol's sub-contractors, Rohr. As a part of the refurbishment after recovery, expended case segments are processed through grit blasting before painting and reprocessing. Rolair provided an air film turntable for this operation. The turntable rotates on inverted air bearings and has a low height and very few moving parts for high reliability. The turntable drive system is synchronised with the automatic grit-blasting equipment to avoid damage to the case segments.

Painting turntable: 32ft long casting segments are lowered into a pit by crane onto an air film turntable for automatic painting inside and out. Since the painting equipment moves only up and down, the rotational drive system of the Rolair turntable is designed for highly accurate and repeatable control to ensure uniform application of paint. The drives are hydraulic with a digital readout to indicate speed accurately.

Empty case handling and rotation: When the case segments are joined into casting segments the innovation of the air film system becomes pronounced. At this stage 3·65m (12ft) diameter cylinders, 9·75m (32ft) long and weighing up to approximately 25 tons must be manoeuvred throughout the plant. But, more important, they must be rotated around the horizontal axis of the cylinder as insulation and other components are added to the evolution of the solid rocket booster.

For movement over the floor in confined quarters Rolair designed a drive system with umbilical operator control. The operator first selects the mode of movement by a dial selector on the control. Then the left thumb depresses a dead-man protected button to actuate the air bearings, and the right thumb causes the drive mode selected to be activated. The release of either thumb causes movement to cease automatically.

As insulation and other components are added to the casting segments horizontal rotation is necessary. To accomplish this curved air bearings were perfected which conform to the perimeter of the 3·65m (12ft) diameter casting segments.

1,000-ton pressure vessel at the Kobe Steel Works, Takasago, Japan, being transported from the assembly floor to the company's weld X-ray facility on four 250-ton capacity Rolair air bearings

US space shuttle with boosters

For rotation the same umbilical control selector switch is positioned to either clockwise, counter-clockwise, or free float. The same thumb-operated actuators implement the desired motion.

Air-bearing usage in the case processing areas has provided for very efficient usage of the existing floor space and enables these large space shuttle segments to be moved between work stations with minimum effort. The ability to rotate these large hardware items during various process operations without additional tooling has enabled a very streamlined process to be established.

180-ton loaded case handling and rotation:
Before incorporation of the solid rocket fuel itself the empty casting segment weighs about 70,000lb. It is then moved horizontally to the casting pits on a special designed trailer, installed vertically into the casting pits and cast with approximately 290,000lb of solid fuel.

A tractor-trailer transporter 139ft long, 14ft wide and with a capacity of 200 tons arrives at the casting pit. On arrival the centre deck of the trailer is lowered to the ground by built-in jacks and the 58-wheeled front and rear wheeled jeep dollies are unhitched from the centre deck and moved away. The centre deck weighs 55,000lb and moves over the ground on twelve air bearings. In addition, thirty curved air bearings are shaped to support the solid rocket motor segments when loaded with propellant.

Using a similar but higher capacity drive and control system than the unloaded case dollies, the centre deck and empty casting segment are floated across a temporarily covered crane rail and into a 200-ton capacity breakover fixture. The breakdown raises the empty centre deck in preparation to receive a loaded socket motor segment.

A vertical loaded segment lifting beam attached to a 200-ton capacity gantry crane removes the loaded segment from the casting pit and places it onto the breakover fixture. The breakover process is reversed, the air bearings float the total system weighing approximately 200 tons back across the temporary crane rail covers and into position to hook to the tractor-trailer transporter.

When the loaded case segment and centre deck are re-united with the 58-wheeled trailer they are moved by road to the next manufacturing operation. At each location, the centre deck is again lowered and over-the-ground and rotation motion is accomplished using air film.

Air bearings have simplified the entire handling of loaded segments. The tractor-trailer transporter length prohibited it from being positioned between the casting pits, where the segment could be handled with the 200-ton gantry crane. Other methods considered for moving the segment to the crane, such as a rail system, exceeded the allotted budget for facility modification and re-arrangement. Air bearings require only a level concrete pad thick enough to withstand the total load and bridges for crossing over the gantry rails.

At other assembly buildings where crane capacity is limited to that required for tooling there was no other way to handle the segments short of expensive building modifications to provide drive through capabilities. Now, it is simply a matter of driving straight to the front of the building, lowering and disconnecting the air bearing dolly from the transporter, and floating it into the building.

Static test firing: Some of the completed motor segments are joined into a solid rocket motor (SRM) for test firing at Thiokol. An SRM consists of four segments, incorporates 1,100,000lb of solid propellant and produces 2,900,000lb st at sea level.

Rolair equipment is used to join the four segments horizontally to install the SRM into a massive static test stand for horizontal firing. Using a combination of hydraulics and air film the Rolair equipment permits adjustment on six axes to a tolerance of ±1/64in. The space shuttle joining equipment is a modification of earlier equipment built to join the Saturn V moon rocket which first put US astronauts on the Moon.

Rolair is working with NASA, United Technologies Corporation and other contractors "downstream" of the actual SRM production. At the launch area at Kennedy Space Center air film turntables, dollies, disassembly fixtures and other systems will be used to set up the SRBs for flight as well as recover and refurbish them after flight.

This Rolair air film system dolly enables an operator to position 3·65m wide casting segments for the space shuttle solid rocket motor with a remote control device. A casting segment, one of which is seen in the background, can also be rotated horizontally on curved air bearings that cradle the segment on the dolly

Centre deck of this tractor-trailer transporter moves across the ground on 12 air bearings. A vertical loaded segment lifting beam attached to a 200-ton capacity gantry removes the loaded segment from the casting pit and places it onto the breakover fixture

Rolair equipment is used to join the four segments of a solid rocket motor horizontally before installing it in a huge static test stand for horizontal firing

A pair of Rolair Air Beams can handle weights up to 240,000lb

MOVEMENT OF GAS COMPRESSION MODULES

Southwest Industries Division of Ingersoll-Rand Co had the problem of moving a pair of gas compression modules in preparation for barge loading at Port Iberia, Louisiana. Each module measured 40×60ft× 3 storeys high. Module No 1 weighed 370 tons and Module No 2 300 tons. An additional problem was an uneven surface over which the modules had to be moved.

The problem was solved utilising Rolair air bearings positioned under the modules after they had been jacked up. "Flooring" surface was made passable using sheet metal overlays. When air was introduced to the bearings, the modules were floated on a thin cushion of air allowing a small tractor to turn the massive loads 90 degrees and move them to the water's edge.

The use of Rolair air bearings, in addition to allowing relatively easy positioning of these massive units, also resulted in an estimated saving of 1½ weeks of time over conventional moving methods since the total time to accomplish two separate moves along the same path was three days. Actual movement of modules with the air film system took three to four hours.

Gas compression modules are used to conserve natural gas and eliminate the air pollution that results from flaring unused gas. The modules extract natural gas from a well, scrub (ie, clean) it, compress it and force the compressed gas back down the hole to maintain well pressure.

AIR BEAMS

A new, simple and low-cost material handling tool is the Rolair Air Beam which uses workshop air piped into compliant air bearings housed within tubular steel beams. Designed primarily for in-plant rigging and frequent large load movement assignments, Air Beams are available with lifting capacities from 4 to 120 tons. Cost comparisons against conventional moving methods show that Air Beams are lower in initial investment and operating costs.

LIGHTWEIGHT AIR BEARINGS

Named "LT" Air Bearings, these are primarily designed for medium duty and for circumstances under which one man might have to position bearings under load and move an entire load by himself. This has been accomplished by constructing the air bearing housing in structural aluminium which offers the additional benefit of

370-ton gas compression module being moved in preparation for barge loading at Port Iberia, Louisiana

Rolair LT lightweight air bearing with the air bearing housing built in structural aluminium

reducing the cost of the complete bearing since aluminium is less expensive than structural steel.

Weight capabilities of a single bearing unit range from 500 to 2,000kg (1,000 to 4,000lb).

HYDROFOILS

BOLIVIA

HELMUT KOCK

PO Box 491, Lome Linda, California 92354, USA

Helmut Kock, designer of the Honald Albatross hydrofoil, which operated New York's first commercial hydrofoil service, and former chief engineer of International Hydrolines Inc, has designed and built a 47ft hydrofoil ferry for Crillon Tours of La Paz, Bolivia. The craft, the Bolivia Arrow, was built during 1976 at Huatajata, on the shore of Lake Titicaca (12,000ft) and entered service in February 1977.

All materials, equipment, engines, tools and machinery were imported from the United States. The entire craft is of welded aluminium and was built by Helmut Kock with the aid of a few Bolivian Indians who, in order to undertake the work, were first taught how to use modern hand and electric tools and automatic welding techniques.

Helmut Kock is currently negotiating for the construction of a 65ft hydrofoil for use by one operator in California and one on the Eastern seaboard of the United States. Interest is also being displayed in a 113ft design.

BOLIVIA ARROW

Crillon Tours Ltd, La Paz, Bolivia, has operated four of Helmut Kock's 20-seat Albatross craft on tourist routes across Lake Titicaca since the late 1960s. The need to cope with increasing tourist traffic and to provide a craft capable of crossing the full length of the lake led to a decision by Darius Morgan, Crillon's chief executive, to build a craft tailored to the company's requirements on the shore of the lake. Construction of the Bolivia Arrow began on 1 December 1975 and it was launched in September 1976. Very little adjustment was required before the craft entered service in February 1977. The craft is designed for medium range fast ferry services on rivers, bays, lakes and sounds.
FOILS: Surface-piercing trapeze foil system with W configuration pitch stability subfoil. Welded aluminium construction designed by Helmut Kock, US patent no 3, 651, 775.
POWER PLANT: Twin Cummins VT8-370 diesels, each developing 350shp at sea level and oversize to compensate for loss of power due to altitude. Each engine drives its own propeller via an inclined shaft. Engine room is amidships, after the third row of seats.
ACCOMMODATION: Crew comprises a captain, deckhand and a tourist guide. The captain is accommodated forward in a raised wheelhouse. His seat is on the hull centreline with the wheel, engine controls and main instrumentation in

Bolivia Arrow cruising at 32 knots across Lake Titicaca, Bolivia

Bolivia Arrow, showing the new foil system designed by Helmut Kock

front. Passengers are accommodated in a single saloon equipped with seats for 40. Seats are arranged in ten rows of two abreast, separated by a central aisle. A washbasin/WC unit is provided and also a luggage compartment. All void spaces are filled with polyurethane foam.
DIMENSIONS
Length overall: 15·24m (50ft)

Hull beam: 3·55m (11ft 8in)
Width across foils: 4·87m (16ft)
Draft, hullborne: 2·28m (7ft 6in)

WEIGHTS
Displacement fully loaded: 14 tons

PERFORMANCE
Cruising speed: 32 knots

CANADA

DE HAVILLAND AIRCRAFT OF CANADA, LIMITED

Garratt Blvd, Downsview, Ontario M3K 1Y5, Canada
Telephone: (416) 633 7310
Telex: 06-22128
Officials:
D N Kendall, *Chairman*
J W Sandford, *President and Chief Executive Officer*
P Genest, *Director*
D G A McLean, *Director*
J W McLoughlan, *Director*
G F Osbaldeston, *Director*
A M Guérin, *Director*
H W Grant, *Director*
J M Pierce *Director*
M A Cohen, *Director*

D B Annan, *Senior Vice President*
W T Heaslip, *Vice President, NFA Program*
R D Hiscocks, *Vice President, Engineering*
F A Johnson, *Vice President, Customer Support*
S B Kerr, *Vice President, Finance and Administration*
J A Timmins, *Vice President, Marketing and Sales*
W J Easdale, *Vice President, Personnel and Industrial Relations*
R G McCall, *Vice President, Operations*
S Morita, *Hydrofoil Project Manager*

In early 1961 the Canadian Department of Defense contracted de Havilland Aircraft of Canada Ltd for a feasibility and engineering study based on the NRE ASW hydrofoil report. The company's recommendations were approved in April 1963 and led to the construction of the FHE-400 fast hydrofoil escort warship. The

programme had two fundamental objectives: (a) to establish in practice the feasibility of an ocean-going hydrofoil of the proposed size and characteristics, and (b) to evaluate the prototype as an ASW system.

FHE-400 was commissioned as HMCS *Bras d'Or* in Halifax and was tested in brief displacement mode trials in September 1968. The foilborne transmission was fitted during the winter of 1968 and the first foilborne trial took place on 9 April 1969. The craft attained a speed of 63 knots during calm water trials in July 1969. Rough water trials during the winter of 1971 culminated in a 2,500 mile "shake down" cruise from Halifax to Bermuda and Norfolk, Virginia.

Foilborne trials were conducted in 3·04–4·57m (10–15ft) waves (sea state 5) at speeds in excess of 40 knots. Hullborne trials were conducted in higher sea states.

While objective (a), to confirm operations feasibility in open ocean conditions, was met, objective (b), ASW system operation, was suspended because of a change in Canadian defence priorities, requiring priority attention to territorial and coastal surveillance. The craft was therefore put into store, although research in this field continued. Reports suggest that the craft is to be reactivated. In the meantime the company reports that wide interest is being shown in a smaller and similar design—the DHC-MP (Maritime Patrol) 100 which will have the same seakeeping capability. Possible civil applications include oil-rig resupply, coastguard work and fisheries patrol.

Details of the FHE-400 will be found in *Jane's Surface Skimmers 1980* and earlier editions.

DHC-MP-100

De Havilland Canada's latest hydrofoil design is the DHC-MP-100, a multi-duty vessel of 104 tons displacement and a maximum speed of 50 knots. Twin gas turbines power the foilborne propulsion system instead of the single turbine employed in the FHE-400, the foil system has been simplified, and although the craft is smaller than its predecessor the same outstanding seakeeping performance is maintained.

A worldwide market survey has been undertaken to determine the needs of potential customers outside Canada and reports indicate that considerable interest is being shown in the craft particularly for the following applications: oil rig re-supply, coastguard patrol, search and rescue, customs and excise, gunboat, missilecraft and ASW patrol.

In general the configuration and construction follows that of the FHE-400.
FOILS: Canard, surface-piercing configuration with approximately 90% of the weight carried by the main foil and 10% by the bow foil. The bow foil is of diamond shape and acts as the rudder for both foilborne and hullborne operations. The main foil, of trapeze configuration combines a fully submerged central section with dihedral surfaces outboard.
POWER PLANT, FOILBORNE: Foilborne propulsion is supplied by two 3,100shp gas tur-

DHC-MP-100 equipped as a fast patrol boat or convoy escort, with a 57mm Bofors automatic gun mounted on the foredeck and, for self-defence, a Vulcan gun package mounted on the afterdeck

bines each driving a fixed-pitch supercavitating three-bladed propeller. Power is transmitted via dual shafts through each of the two inner foil struts to gearboxes at the intersections of the struts and foils.

Among the engines likely to be specified are the Rolls Royce Marine Proteus, the Marine Tyne and the Avco Lycoming TF 40.
POWER PLANT, HULLBORNE: Hullborne propulsion is supplied by two 400hp diesels driving two two-bladed propellers through outdrive units.

Data for the basic craft and the main variants are given below.

DHC-MP-100 GENERAL PURPOSE

In this configuration, the craft can be equipped for coastguard, search and rescue, fisheries and environmental patrol, customs and excise duties and oil rig re-supply.
DIMENSIONS
EXTERNAL
Length: 36m (118ft 1in)
Beam: 6·4m (21ft)
Width across main foil: 15·5m (50ft 9¾in)
Draft hullborne: 5·33m (17ft 5⅞in)
Freeboard, hullborne: 2·44m (8ft)
WEIGHTS
Crew and supplies: 2,930kg (6,460lb)
Role equipment and fuel: 26,800kg (59,084lb)
Total payload: 29,730kg (65,540lb)
Basic: 75,740kg (167,000lb)
Displacement: 105,470kg (104 tons)
PERFORMANCE
Max speed, estimated: 90km/h (50 knots)
Range, 18,000kg fuel capacity
　at 18·5km/h (10 knots): 3,500km (1,910n miles)
　at 74km/h (40 knots): 1,180km (642n miles)
27,000kg fuel capacity

at 18·5km/h (10 knots): 5,250km (2,865n miles)
at 74km/h (40 knots): 1,770km (963n miles)

GUNBOAT

For coastal patrol, interdiction or for escorting larger ships or convoys, a 57mm Bofors gun can be fitted. For self-defence a Vulcan gun is mounted on the afterdeck. Other armament installations can be fitted within weight and centre of gravity limits.

Overload fuel will extend the range in displacement condition to a maximum of 4,600km (2,500n miles). In the maximum overload condition take-off may be restricted to moderate sea states.

The foil system stabilises the vessel and gives it the seakeeping characteristics of a ship of 1,000-1,500 tons, thus improving accuracy of shot and crew performance for a craft of this size.
DIMENSIONS
As for basic craft
WEIGHTS
Crew and supplies: 2,930kg (6,460lb)
Bofors gun and ammunition: 7,140kg (15,740lb)
Vulcan gun system: 1,540kg (3,395lb)
Fuel: 18,150kg (40,000lb)
Total payload: 29,760kg (65,600lb)
Basic: 75,740kg (167,000lb)
Displacement: 105,500kg (104 tons)
PERFORMANCE
Range at 18·5km/h: 3,500km (1,910n miles)
Range at 74km/h: 1,180km (642n miles)

MISSILECRAFT

To complement the gunboat role, the MP-100 may be fitted with missiles like the Harpoon and Exocet. The fire control system is located in the large operations room.

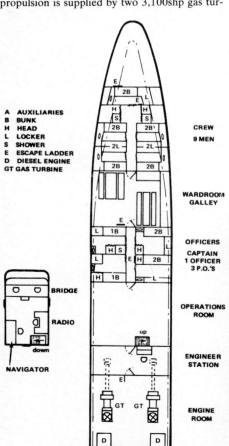

A AUXILIARIES
B BUNK
H HEAD
L LOCKER
S SHOWER
E ESCAPE LADDER
D DIESEL ENGINE
GT GAS TURBINE

CREW
9 MEN

WARDROOM
GALLEY

OFFICERS
CAPTAIN
1 OFFICER
3 P.O.'S

OPERATIONS
ROOM

BRIDGE

RADIO

NAVIGATOR

ENGINEER
STATION

ENGINE
ROOM

Typical accommodation arrangement on a patrol escort version of the MP-100 hydrofoil

Operated as a missile equipped patrol craft, the MP-100 would carry two launchers aft—Harpoon and Exocet missiles are two choices—and for self-defence, a Vulcan gun pack is mounted aft between the missiles. An alternative arrangement would be to mount the gun on the foredeck and its detection gear above the bridge

For self-defence a Vulcan gun system is mounted aft between the missile containers. An alternative arrangement is the mounting of the gun on the foredeck and its detection system above the bridge.

DIMENSIONS
As for basic craft
WEIGHTS
Crew and supplies: 2,930kg (6,460lb)
Missile system: 4,530kg (10,000lb)
Vulcan gun system: 1,540kg (3,395lb)
Fuel: 20,400kg (44,974lb)
Total payload: 29,400kg (64,816lb)
Basic: 75,740kg (167,000lb)
Displacement: 105,140kg (103·5 tons)
PERFORMANCE
Range at 18·5km/h: 3,960km (2,150n miles)
Range at 74km/h: 1,340km (723n miles)

ASW PATROL CRAFT

The craft can cruise at convoy speed on its displacement propulsion units while using variable-depth sonar to search for submarines. On making contact it can attack at high speed.

Lightweight VDS gear is installed. This has a low-drag body and cable and can be towed at over 55km/h (30 knots). The system is of modular construction and can be quickly installed or removed. Torpedoes can be mounted in multiple tubes. Sonar and fire-control systems are fitted in the operations room. A Vulcan gun can be mounted on the foredeck with sensors above the bridge.

An ASW version equipped with lightweight VDS gear and torpedoes mounted in multiple tubes. Full sonar and fire-control systems are provided in the operations room

DIMENSIONS
As for basic craft
WEIGHTS
Crew and supplies: 2,930kg (6,460lb)
VDS gear: 5,080kg (11,200lb)
Torpedoes: 3,035kg (6,700lb)
Vulcan gun: 1,540kg (3,395lb)
Fire control: 4,080kg (9,000lb)

Fuel: 15,860kg (35,000lb)
Total payload: 32,525kg (71,700lb)
Basic: 75,740kg (167,000lb)
Displacement: 108,265kg (106·8 tons)
PERFORMANCE
Range at 18·5km/h: 3,150km (1,710n miles)
Range at 74km/h: 1,040km (565n miles)

WATER SPYDER MARINE LTD

157 Richard Clark Drive, Downsview, Ontario M3M 1V6, Canada
Telephone: (416) 244 5404
Officials:
J F Lstiburek, *President*
G A Leask, *Secretary/Treasurer*
A Lstiburek, *Vice President*
L Civiera, *Sales Manager*
J F Lstiburek, *Designer*

Water Spyder Marine Ltd is a wholly-owned Canadian company operating under charter issued by the Government of the Province of Ontario. It produces three fibreglass-hulled sports hydrofoils which are available either ready-built or in kit form.

WATER SPYDER 1-A

The Water Spyder 1-A is a single-seat sports hydrofoil powered by a long-shaft outboard of 10-25hp.
FOILS: The foil system comprises a split W-type surface-piercing main foil supporting 98% of the load, and an adjustable outrigged trim tab which supports the remaining 2%.
HULL: Two-piece fibreglass reinforced plastic construction, foam-filled for flotation. Standard fittings and regulation running lights.
ACCOMMODATION: Single fibreglass seat.
POWER PLANT: Any suitable outboard engine of 10–25hp (Mercury, Evinrude or Chrysler) with long shaft.

CONTROLS: Controls include joy-stick and rudder pedals.
DIMENSIONS
Length overall, hull: 1·828m (6ft)
Beam overall, foils retracted: 1·219m (4ft)
    foils extended: 2·133m (7ft)
WEIGHTS
Empty: 36·24kg (80lb)
PERFORMANCE
Max speed: 64·37km/h (40mph)
Max permissible wave height in foilborne condition: 457·2mm (1ft 6in)
Turning radius at cruising speed: approx 3·04m (10ft)
PRICE: Standard craft and terms of payment, US$1,400; terms, cash. Delivery, three weeks approximately from date of order, fob Toronto.

WATER SPYDER 2-B

The Water Spyder 2-B is a two-seat sports hydrofoil powered by a long-shaft outboard of 20-35hp.
FOILS: The foil system comprises a split W-type surface-piercing main foil supporting 98% of the load and an adjustable outrigged trim tab which supports the remaining 2%.
HULL: This is a two-piece (deck and hull) moulded fibreglass structure and incorporates buoyancy chambers. Standard fittings include a curved Perspex windshield and regulation running lights, fore and aft.
ACCOMMODATION: The craft seats two in comfortably upholstered seats. The trim tab

assembly is adjustable from inside the cockpit.
POWER PLANT: Any suitable outboard engine of 20-35hp (Mercury 200L or 350L Chrysler Evinrude) with long-shaft extension.
CONTROLS: Controls include steering wheel with adjustable friction damper and trim tab control.
DIMENSIONS
Length overall, hull: 3·6m (12ft)
Beam overall, foils retracted: 1·6m (5ft 4in)
    foils extended: 2·2m (7ft 4in)
WEIGHTS
Empty: 99·7kg (220lb)
PERFORMANCE
Max speed: up to 64km/h (40mph)
Max permissible wave height in foilborne mode: 457·2mm (1ft 6in)
Turning radius at cruising speed: 3m (10ft) approximately
PRICE: Standard craft and terms of payment, US$2,500; terms, cash. Delivery, three weeks from date of order, fob Toronto.

WATER SPYDER 6-A

An enlarged version of the Water Spyder 2. Model 6-A is a six-seat family pleasure hydrofoil boat, with a two-piece moulded fibreglass hull.

The seats, located immediately over the main foil, are arranged in two rows of three abreast, one row facing forward, the other aft.

Power is supplied by a long-shaft outboard motor of 60-115hp.

Water Spyder 6-A is a six-seat hydrofoil. The main foil, trim-tab support and engine fold upward so the craft can be floated on and off a trailer

DIMENSIONS
Length overall, hull: 5·79m (19ft)
Beam overall, foils retracted: 2·5m (8ft 3in)
  foils extended: 3·96m (13ft)
Height overall, foils retracted: 1·37m (4ft 6in)
Floor area: 2·78m² (30ft²)

WEIGHTS
Gross tonnage: 1 ton approx
Empty: 444kg (980lb)
PERFORMANCE
Max speed: 56-64km/h (35-40mph)
Cruising speed: 51km/h (32mph)

Max permissible wave height in foilborne mode:
  0·76m (2ft 6in)
Turning radius at cruising speed: 6·09m (20ft)
PRICE: Standard craft and terms of payment,
US$4,500; terms, cash. Delivery, three weeks
from date of order, fob Toronto.

CHINA (People's Republic)

HUTANG SHIPYARD
Shanghai, People's Republic of China

Hydrofoil torpedo boats of the Hu Chwan (White Swan) Class have been under construction at the Hutang Shipyard since about 1966. Some 140 are in service with the navy of the People's Republic of China and another 32 have been lent or leased to the Albanian navy, four to Pakistan, four to Tanzania and three to Romania.

Seven others, of a slightly modified design, have been built in Romania since 1973.

HU CHWAN (WHITE SWAN)
FOILS: The foil system comprises a bow subfoil to facilitate take-off and a main foil of trapeze or shallow V configuration set back approximately one-third of the hull length from the bow. At high speed in relatively calm conditions the greater part of the hull is raised clear of the water. The main foil and struts retract upwards when the craft is required to cruise in displacement condition.
HULL: High speed V-bottom hull in seawater resistant light alloy.
POWER PLANT: Three 1,100hp M-50 type water-cooled, supercharged 12-cylinder V-type diesels, each driving their own inclined propeller shaft.
ARMAMENT: Two 21in torpedo tubes, plus four 12·7mm machine guns in two twin mountings.
DIMENSIONS (approx)
Length overall: 21·38m (71ft 6½in)
Beam overall: 5·02m (16ft 6in)
Hull beam: 3·96m (13ft)
Draft hullborne: 1m (3ft 3in)
WEIGHTS
Displacement full load: 40 tons
PERFORMANCE
Max speed foilborne calm conditions: 55 knots
Range: 500n miles approx

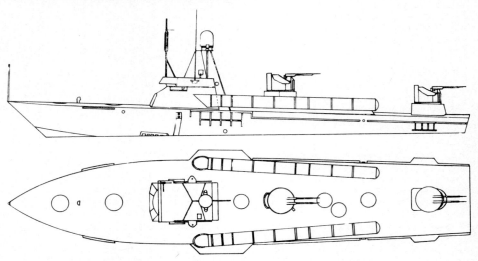

General arrangement of Hu Chwan torpedo/fast attack hydrofoil of the Chinese Navy

One of four Hu Chwan-class torpedo/fast attack craft built by the Hutang Shipyard, Shanghai, and supplied to the Pakistan Navy

FRANCE

DTCN
DIRECTION TECHNIQUE DES CONSTRUCTIONS NAVALES

DTCN is undertaking many of the responsibilities previously assigned to the Délégue Général pour l'Armement (DGA), including ship design and construction and fleet training and modernisation. Concerned chiefly with shipbuilding, DTCN has four shipyards in operation and a total work force of 24,800. The shipyards are at Toulon, Brittany-Brest, Lorient and Cherbourg. Apart from building vessels for the French and foreign navies, the four yards undertake routine and special maintenance and perform complete refits.

DTCN also has a large design centre based in Paris, which employs more than one thousand naval architects and engineers. Although its primary responsibility is to prepare general criteria and outline specifications for vessels for the French Navy, it also directs initial studies and design undertaken by organisations under the direction of DTCN as well as those undertaken by privately owned companies working under French Navy contracts. The first hydrofoil design undertaken by DTCN is the 185-tonne Saphyr, a preliminary description of which appears below.

SAPHYR

The Saphyr is derived from the H.851, the designation given to a preliminary design study for a missile-equipped, 120-tonne hydrofoil, undertaken by Aérospatiale, STCAN and several branches of DTCN between 1966 and 1978. The design and research programme was assisted by the use of a 4·5-tonne submerged foil test craft, the H.890, designed by Aérospatiale.

Several variants of the Saphyr are envisaged, including a fast strike craft with four MM 40 Exocet ship-to-ship missiles and a fast patrol model suitable for fishery protection or for patrolling exclusive economic zones (EEZ).
FOILS: Fully submerged canard configuration with about 80% of the weight supported by the aft foils and 20% by the bow foil. The bow foil, which rotates for steering, retracts forwards and upwards ahead of the bow.
HULL: Constructed in marine corrosion-resistant aluminium alloys.
POWER PLANT: Foilborne propulsion is supplied by two 7,170shp Allison 570-KA two-shaft marine gas turbines, each driving a pod-mounted propeller mounted at the base of the two aft foil

struts. Power is transmitted to the propellers via mechanical right-angle drives. Hullborne propulsion is provided by two diesels driving two Schottel Z-drive propeller units which can be rotated through 360 degrees.
SYSTEMS, WEAPONS: Main armament comprises a single 76/62 OTO Melara gun forward and four MM 40 Exocet missiles in two twin mounts aft. Two chaff launchers are mounted on the roof of the deckhouse. Standard electronics fit for the missile strike craft variant comprises a Thomson-CSF TRS 3200 Castor II fire control radar, a surveillance radar and a Decca or SMA navigation radar.
DIMENSIONS
Length: 32·7m (107ft)
Draft, foilborne: 1·95m (6ft 5in)
  hullborne: 2·3m (7ft 6in)
WEIGHTS
Fully loaded: 185 tonnes
PERFORMANCE
Max speed, foilborne: 53 knots
  hullborne: 10 knots
Max range, foilborne: 740n miles at 40 knots
  hullborne: 2,400n miles at 10 knots

GEORGES HENNEBUTTE
Société d'Exploitation et de Développement des Brevets Georges Hennebutte
Head Office: 43 avenue Foch, 64200 Biarritz, France
Works: 23 impasse Labordotte, 64200 Biarritz, France
Telephone: 23 03 70
Telex: 22128
Officials:
G Hennebutte, *Managing Director*

Ets G Hennebutte was founded in 1955 to design and build inflatable dinghies. Its Espadon series of sports craft is employed by lifeguard patrols in France and elsewhere in the world and also by the French Navy.

Development of the Espadon to meet a range of special requirements led to the construction of a number of experimental craft, including one with an inflatable parasol delta wing and another with a Lippisch type wing for aerodynamic lift while operating in ground effect. Preliminary descriptions of these craft have appeared in *Jane's Surface Skimmers 1977-78* and earlier editions.

In another approach hydroskis have been fitted to the Etel 422 Swordfish, a winged version of which is currently under construction.

Hennebutte Etel 422 Swordfish equipped with hydroskis. A winged variant is under construction

ETEL 422 SWORDFISH

This new variant of the Etel 422 employs the same basic inflatable hull but is equipped with hydroskis, wings and a ducted fan. The Etel 422 is the only inflatable craft to have crossed the Etel barrier, a feat accomplished during a severe storm in 1967. The accompanying photograph shows an earlier experimental version of the Etel 422 equipped with hydroskis and a marine outboard engine driving a water propeller. A speed of 112km/h (70mph) was achieved during trials.
LIFT AND PROPULSION: Aerodynamic lift at cruising speed and above is provided by a wing. Thrust is supplied by an RFB SG85 fan-thrust pod, combining a 50hp Wankel air-cooled rotary engine with a three-bladed, ducted propeller.

HULL: Catamaran type hull with rigid central frame and inflatable, nylon-coated neoprene outer sections.

ACCOMMODATION: Open cockpit for driver.

DIMENSIONS
Length overall: 4·22m (13ft 10in)
Beam overall: 2·5m (8ft 2in)

SOCIETE NATIONALE INDUSTRIELLE AEROSPATIALE
Head Office: 36 boulevard de Montmorency, 75781 Paris (2) Cedex 16, France
Telephone: 524 43 21
Telex: AISPA 620 059F
Works: BP13, 13722 Marignane, France
Telephone: (91) 89 90 22

In 1966 the Direction des Recherches et Moyens d'Essais (Directorate of Research and Test Facilities) initiated a basic hydrofoil design and research programme with the object of building a prototype hydrofoil ferry with a displacement of 55 tons and a speed of 50 knots.

The companies and organisations co-operating in this programme are: Aérospatiale, project leader; STCAN, the hull test centre; several French government laboratories of the DTCN; Alsthom—Techniques des Fluides—and Constructions Mécaniques de Normandie.

The main headings of the programme are:
hydrodynamics (foils, struts and hull);
foil hydroelasticity data and flutter phenomenon;
automatic pilot;
material technology relative to foils, struts and hull.

The design and research programme is nearly complete and the results will be processed and refined using a 4-ton submerged foil test craft, the H.890, designed by Aérospatiale. The craft is employed in a comprehensive test programme which is under the control of Aérospatiale and DTCN, a French government agency.

In addition to the SA 800 55-ton hydrofoil ferry, preliminary designs have been completed for a missile-carrying 118-ton hydrofoil combat vessel, the H.851, and a commercial variant, intended for mixed-traffic ferry services. The latest project is a 174-tonne missilecraft with a speed of 54 knots and capable of operating in Force 5 weather at 50 knots. Armament would comprise four Exocet missiles and one rapid-fire automatic cannon.

H.890 4-ton submerged foil test vehicle employed by Aérospatiale to develop automatic control systems and gather data for the design of larger vessels. It has attained 52 knots during high-speed runs

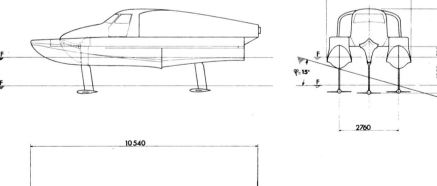
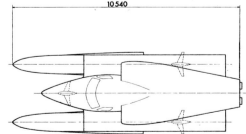

H.890 in canard configuration and renamed H.891

H.890

This 4·5-tonne seagoing test vehicle is being employed to gather data for foil systems and accelerate the development of autopilot systems for large hydrofoils.

The combination of catamaran hull and pure jet propulsion allows the foils to be arranged in either conventional configuration—two foils forward and one aft—or canard configuration, with one foil forward and two aft.

The vessel was developed and built under contract to the French government agency DTCN by Aérospatiale's Helicopter Division in conjunction with Constructions Mécaniques de Normandie and Alsthom—Techniques des Fluides—of Grenoble. It has been undergoing tests on the Etang de Berre since it was launched on 16 June 1972. A speed of 52 knots has been reached during trials.
FOILS: Fully submerged system with facilities for changing from conventional (aeroplane) to canard configuration as required. In aeroplane configuration about 70% of the weight is supported by the twin bow foils, which are attached to the port and starboard pontoons, and 30% by the single tail foil, mounted on the central hull section aft.

The stern foil rotates for steering and all three struts are fixed (non-retractable). Lift variation of the three foils is achieved by an autopilot system, developed by Aérospatiale and SFENA, which varies the incidence angles of all three foils.

During the first series of tests the foils were tested in conventional configuration. During the second series the canard configuration was adopted.

HULL: Catamaran type, constructed in corrosion-resistant light alloys. Central hull, which incorporates control cabin, engine bay and test instrumentation, is flanked by two stepped pontoons.

ACCOMMODATION: Seating is provided for two, pilot and test observer.

POWER PLANT: Twin 480 daN Turboméca Marboré VIc gas turbines, mounted in the central hull structure aft of the cabin, power the craft when foilborne. Hullborne propulsion is supplied by a 20hp Sachs 370 engine driving via a hydraulic transmission a folding-blade Maucour waterscrew located at the top of the aft foil strut. The waterscrew rotates through ±90 degrees for steering.

DIMENSIONS
Length, overall: 10·66m (34ft 11½in)
    waterline: 9·3m (30ft 6in)
Beam, overall: 3·9m (12ft 9½in)
Draft, afloat: 1·72m (5ft 8in)
    foilborne: 0·37m (1ft 3in)
WEIGHTS
Normal take-off: 4·5 tonnes
PERFORMANCE
Cruising speed, foilborne, calm conditions: 50 knots
    hullborne, calm conditions: 6 knots
Craft is designed to cross waves up to 0·8m (2ft 8in) high without contouring.

H.891

This modified version of the H.890 underwent its first trials programme in 1976. The hull is the same as that employed for the H.890 but the foils are arranged in canard configuration instead of the earlier conventional or "aeroplane" configuration.

Accommodation is provided for a pilot and two test engineers.

Power is provided by a single Turboméca Turmo IIIC₃ marinised gas turbine delivering 1,100kW. The power available is nearly five times that required by the H.890 to attain 50 knots. One of the primary reasons for providing the craft with an excess of power is to enable it to be employed as a test-bed for a variety of new types of propulsion, including Z-drives.

Modifications to the craft were undertaken by Aérospatiale under the direction of STCAN (Service Technique des Constructions et Armes Navales) which designed the experimental propulsion system.

WEIGHTS
Weight operational, with 2½ hours fuel: 4·7 tonnes approx
PERFORMANCE
Cruising speed foilborne, calm conditions: 54 knots
Speed over waves of up to 0·8m (2ft 8in) without contouring: 50 knots
Cruising speed, hullborne: 6 knots

SA 800

The SA 800 is a design study for a mixed-traffic hydrofoil powered by two Turmo IIIC turbines driving a waterjet propulsion unit. Conventional marine light alloy construction is employed and the craft will have incidence-controlled, fully-

In-canard configuration the H.891 is capable of 54 knots in calm conditions

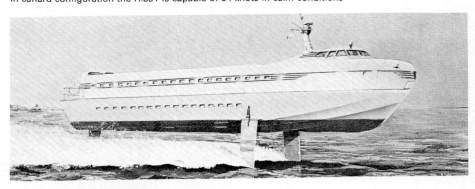

Artist's impression of SNIA SA 800 waterjet-propelled hydrofoil ferry

submerged foils operated by a sonic/electronic sensing system.

A number of variants of the basic design are being studied for alternative applications, including prospecting, marine research, coastal surveillance and naval patrol. Trials conducted with dynamic models have been successful and are continuing. Preliminary design studies are now complete.

FOILS: The foil system is fully submerged and of 'aeroplane' configuration. All three foil struts retract hydraulically completely clear of the water. An SNIAS sonic autopilot system controls the incidence angle of the two bow foils and adjustable control flaps on the rear foils.

HULL: The hull is of conventional marine corrosion-resistant aluminium alloys. Features include a deep V bow, designed to minimise structural loading due to wave impact, and a flat W section aft for good directional control when hullborne.

POWER PLANT: Foilborne propulsion is supplied by two 1,300shp Turboméca Turmo IIIC gas turbines driving a SOGREAH waterjet propulsion unit mounted at the base of the aft foil strut.

Output from the transmission shafts of the two turbines, which are mounted end-to-end, intakes outwards, athwart the stern, passes first to a main bevel drive gearbox, then to a drive shaft which extends downwards through the aft foil strut to a waterjet pump gearbox located in a nacelle beneath the aft foil. Air for the turbines is introduced through intakes at the top of the cabin aft. Filters are fitted to the intakes to prevent the ingestion of water or salt spray into the gas turbine. There is a separate hullborne propulsion system, with a 400hp diesel driving twin water propellers beneath the transom.

ACCOMMODATION: The elevated wheelhouse forward of the passenger compartment seats the captain and engineer. All instrumentation is located so that it can be easily monitored. Navigation and collision avoidance radar is fitted. Accommodation is on two decks, each arranged with three seats abreast on either side of a central aisle. As a passenger ferry the craft will seat 200—116 on the upper deck and 84 on the lower; and in mixed traffic configuration it will carry 8-10 cars on the upper deck with the lower deck seating capacity remaining at 84. Cars are loaded via rear door/ramps. Baggage holds are provided forward of both upper and lower saloons.

DIMENSIONS
Length overall: 26·88m (88ft)
Max beam, deck: 5·4m (18ft)
WEIGHTS
Displacement, fully loaded: 56 tonnes (55 tons)
Payload (200 passengers with luggage or 84 passengers with luggage and 8-10 cars): 18,300kg (40,300lb)
PERFORMANCE
Max speed, calm conditions: 55 knots
Cruising speed: 50 knots
Cruising speed, sea state 5: 48 knots
Range, at 50 knots, calm sea: 250n miles
    at 48 knots, sea state 5: 200n miles

Craft is designed to platform over 3m (10ft) high waves, crest to trough, and contour 4m (13ft) high waves.

ISRAEL

ISRAEL SHIPYARDS LIMITED

POB 1282, Haifa 31000, Israel
Telephone: 749111
Telex: 45132 YARD IL
Cables: Israyard
Officials:
D Yallon, *Company Secretary*

Israel has for some time been negotiating with the United States government for the purchase of two Flagstaff multi-duty naval hydrofoils from Grumman Aerospace Corporation, together with the acquisition of a licence for the series production of these craft in Israel. It is understood that once the immediate needs of the Israeli Navy have been met, Israeli-built craft would be made available for export.

In the early autumn of 1977 it was announced by the US government that agreement had been reached on the joint development of hydrofoils by the two countries and Grumman Aerospace Corporation stated it had "received its first order for the Flagstaff from an overseas client". Later the Corporation confirmed that the country concerned is Israel. In May 1979 it was reported that two 92-tonne Flagstaff IIs were under construction, one at Stuart, Florida, the other in Israel. The first craft to be completed will be that built in the United States. Trials are due to begin early in 1981.

Construction of the Israeli-built craft will almost certainly be undertaken by Israel Shipyards Limited, Haifa, which is currently building the 415-ton Reshef (Flash) missile boat for the Israeli and overseas navies. It is understood that up to fourteen may be built under licence.

Details of the Flagstaff will be found in this section in the entry for Grumman Aerospace Corporation, USA.

ITALY

CANTIERI NAVALI RIUNITI (CNR)
(Fincantieri Group)
Via Cipro 11, 16129 Genoa, Italy
Telephone: 59951
Telex: 270168 CANTGE 1
Officials:
Enrico Bocchini, *Chairman and Managing Director*
Antonio Fiori, *General Manager*
Sergio Castagnoli, *Commercial Director*
Pasquale Teodorani, *Project Director*
Francesco Cao, *Project Director*

Cantieri Navali Riuniti, SpA, has taken over the interests of Alinavi which was formed in 1964 to develop, manufacture and market advanced military marine systems.

Under the terms of a licensing agreement, CNR has access to Boeing technology in the field of military fully-submerged foil hydrofoil craft.

In October 1970, the company was awarded a contract by the Italian Navy for the design and construction of the P 420 Sparviero Class hydrofoil missilecraft. This is an improved version of the Boeing PGH-2 Tucumcari. The first vessel, given the design name Swordfish, was delivered to the Italian Navy in July 1974. An order for a further six of this type was placed by the Italian Navy in February 1976.

SWORDFISH
The Swordfish missile-launching hydrofoil gunboat displaces a maximum of 64 tonnes and is designed for both offensive and defensive missions. Its combination of speed, firepower, and all-weather capability is unique in a ship of this class.

The vessel has fully-submerged foils arranged in canard configuration and an automatic control system. A gas-turbine powered waterjet system provides foilborne propulsion and a diesel-driven propeller outdrive provides hullborne propulsion. A typical crew comprises two officers and eight enlisted men.

FOILS: Fully-submerged canard arrangement, with approximately one-third of the dynamic lift provided by the bow foil and two-thirds by the two aft foils. The aft foils retract sideways and the bow hydrofoil retracts forwards into a recess in the bow. Bow doors preserve the hull lines when the forward hydrofoil is either fully extended or retracted. Foils and struts are built in corrosion-resistant stainless steel.

Anhedral is incorporated in the aft foils to enhance the directional stability of the craft at shallow foil depths. In addition, the anhedral assures positive roll control by eliminating tip broaching during rough water manoeuvres.

CONTROLS: Automatic system incorporating two aircraft-type gyros, one to sense pitch and roll and the other to sense yaw, plus three accelerometers to sense vertical movements (heave) of the craft. An ultrasonic height sensor is used to detect and maintain flying height above the water surface. Information from the sensors is sent to a hermetically-sealed solid-state computer, which calculates movement of the control surfaces necessary to maintain boat stability, and/or pre-selected flying height, and sends appropriate commands to the servo-mechanisms that control flap movement.

Foilborne steering: Helm commanded automatic control system controls hydraulic servo-actuated hydrofoil flaps and steerable forward hydrofoil strut to produce coordinated (banked) turns in design sea conditions.

Hullborne steering: Helm commanded steerable outdrive unit. Helm-driven potentiometer sends signals to a servo-valve controlling steering hydraulic motor. Manual emergency hullborne steering is provided on the aft deck.

HULL: Both hull and superstructure are built entirely in corrosion-resistant aluminium, the hull being welded and the superstructure riveted and welded.

BERTHING: Two fixed berths in the compart-

Turning radius of the Swordfish at 40 knots is less than 125m (137yds)

Swordfish hullborne with foils retracted. Continuous speed, hullborne, is 8 knots

First of the Italian Navy's missile equipped hydrofoil gunboats during foilborne firing tests of its 76mm OTO Melara cannon. Given the design name Swordfish, the craft is the first of the P 420 Sparviero Class

ment under the bridge, plus eight folding berths in the forward crew space. One toilet and one sink. A folding table with benches in the forward crew space.

POWERPLANT, FOILBORNE: Power for the waterjet is supplied by one Rolls-Royce Proteus 15M/553 gas turbine. At the customer's option the craft may be fitted with the "sprint" model of this gas turbine, which incorporates water injection. The "sprint" model ("wet") develops 5,000shp maximum versus the 4,500shp of the normal ("dry") Proteus. Adoption of the "sprint" model permits take-off at higher displacements and therefore, more fuel and/or military payload to be carried. It also provides better craft performance in very high sea states,

particularly in conditions of high ambient temperatures. The respective performance characteristics of the Swordfish equipped with 'dry' and 'wet' models of the Proteus are shown in the accompanying performance table.

Engine output is transferred to a single double-volute, double-suction, two impeller centrifugal pump, rated at 28,000 US gallons/min at 1,560rpm and absorbing approximately 4,700shp (4,766 CV). Water is taken in through inlets on the nose of each aft foil at the foil/strut intersection and passes up through the hollow interiors of the struts to the hull, where it is ducted to the pump. From the pump, the water is discharged through twin, fixed-area nozzles located beneath the hull under the pump.

POWERPLANT, HULLBORNE: A General Motors 6V-53 diesel engine, rated at 160shp (162 CV) at 2,600rpm, powers a Schottel-Werft SRP-100 steerable propeller outdrive unit, which is mounted on the centreline of the transom. The unit is retractable and rotates through 360 degrees. Propeller is fixed-pitch. Power is delivered to the outdrive at about 1,700rpm.

FUEL: Fuel oil is NATO 76, carried in three tanks located amidships and integral with the hull, side keelson and platform deck. Total capacity is about 14,550 litres (3,850 gallons).

Fuel oil system: Two primary 208V 400Hz 26·5 litres/min (7 gallons/min) submerged pumps and two standby 28V dc 26·5 litres/min (7 gallons/min) external pumps. The dc pump is started automatically by a pressure switch in the fuel supply line if ac pump power is lost.

Craft may be refuelled through main deck connection at dock or at sea. The fuel tanks are equipped with fuel level indicators and vents.

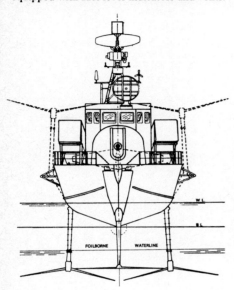

AUXILIARY SYSTEMS:

Hydraulics: Two independent systems: foilborne and ship service. Systems pressure, 3,000psi. Systems fluid, MIL-H-5606.

Foilborne system: normal and standby 21·8 gallons/min pumps serve hydraulic control system.

Ship service system: normal and standby 32·5 gallons/min pumps serve other uses including hydrofoil retracting and locking, bow door, hullborne outdrive retraction and steering, foilborne turbine starting, foilborne turbine exhaust door, cannon loading, and the fixed saltwater fire pump.

ELECTRICAL:

Turbine generator sets: At customer's option, either two or three identical sets, one installed in forward machinery space, the other(s) in the aft machinery space.

Each set consists of a Solar T-62 T-32 gas turbine engine capable of developing a maximum output of 150shp (152 CV) under standard conditions and driving a General Electric 208V 400Hz three-phase alternator rated at 75 kVA, a 30V dc starter-generator with 200A generating capacity, and one hydraulic pump for ship service and hullborne steering.

Starting battery sets: One 24V, 34Ah capacity starting battery is provided for the hullborne diesel engine and for each solar turbogenerator set.

Emergency battery set: Two additional 24V batteries in parallel provide 68Ah capacity to power in emergency conditions, radios, intercommunications system and navigation lights.

Shore power: Craft requires up to 30 kVA of 200V three-phase four wire 400Hz power.

Intercommunication system: The system consists of one station in each space and three external stations, allowing complete craft machinery and weapons coordination.

Every station is a control unit and has a reversible loudspeaker with press-to-talk switch.

Main station is equipped with radio operation access control.

Emergency announcements can be made to all stations simultaneously.

Selective communications are available between any two or more stations.

Navigation horn: One electrically operated horn mounted on forward top of deckhouse.

Signal searchlight: One portable incandescent signal searchlight mounted on the deckhouse canopy.

Depth sounder: Transducer on the hull bottom 152mm (6in) above the keel and a recorder at the navigation station measure and record water depth from echo soundings. Recorder may be set for sounding depths of 0-38·6, 38·6-86·9, 77·2-125·4, 0-115·8, 96·5-212, 193-309 metres (0-20, 20-45, 40-65, 0-60, 50-110, 100-160 fathoms). Recorder contains electronic circuits and a two-speed mechanism with a stylus which burns a black mark on moving chart paper. A white line mode of recorder operation eliminates false traces below the true bottom line on the chart and allows detection of small objects close to the bottom and an indication of hard or soft composition of the sea bottom.

Navigation set: The shipboard navigation system (ShipNav) automatically performs, independently of all external aids, precise dead reckoning navigation for both foilborne and hullborne operations. It continuously computes and displays the craft's current position, true heading, true course, and true speed. Actual position is displayed digitally on counters in latitude and longitude coordinates and pictorially on standard charts having local coordinate information. Indicators display true heading, course, and speed.

Speed log: Hull rodmeter, foil rodmeter, rodmeter selector switch and calibration unit, transmitter and remote indicator set measures craft hullborne or foilborne speed, computes the distance travelled and displays both at the navigation station and helm.

IFF system: The system consists of an IFF/ATC transponder (APX 72) and an IFF interrogator coupled to the radar.

Navigation and search radar: SMA Model 3RM7-250B radar performs navigation and search operations with master indicator, rayplot

1 Forward hydrofoil retracted
2 OTO Melara 76mm cannon
3 Fire control radar
4 Vertical ladder
5 Main mast
6 Anemometer
7 Antenna
8 Navigation and search radar
9 Antenna
10 Antenna
11 Surface-to-surface missile launchers (P/S)
12 Ensign staff
13 Turbine exhaust: foilborne propulsion

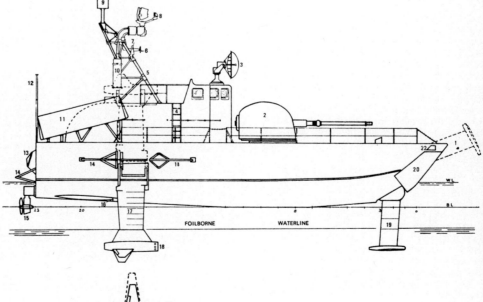

14 Guards
15 Propeller outdrive: hullborne propulsion
16 Waterjet nozzle (P/S)
17 Aft hydrofoil extended (P/S)
18 Water inlet (P/S): foilborne propulsion
19 Forward hydrofoil extended
20 Bow doors (P/S)
21 Watertight hatches
22 Height sensors: automatic control system (P/S)
23 Optical putter-on
24 Starboard gyrocompass readout
25 Port gyrocompass readout

with variable range marker (VRN) bearing control unit and remote indicator.

Set operates in "X" band and is tunable from 9,345 MHz to 9,405 MHz. Set has two different transmitters and it is possible to select the proper one by a RF switch unit. Peak power output is 7kW for navigation purposes and 250kW for search purposes.

Performance includes a minimum range less than 182m (200yds), range discrimination better than 10m (11yds), azimuth discrimination less than 1·2 degrees and maximum range of 40n miles.

HF-SSB radio system AN/ARC-102: The AN/ARC-102 uses the Collins 618T/3 HF single-sideband transceiver for long range voice, CW, data or compatible AM communication in the 2·000 through 29·999 MHz frequency range. It is automatically tuned in 28,000 1-kHz channel increments by means of an operator's remote control unit. The operating frequency is indicated directly in a digital-type presentation. Nominal transmit power is 400W pep. in SSB or 125W in compatible AM. The system is tuned through the antenna coupler Collins 490T-1 to a helical monoplane antenna.

UHF radio system AN/ARC-109: Two identical units are provided. The AN/ARC-109 transceiver has two separate receivers: a main tunable receiver and a guard receiver. Common circuit design is maintained in the two receivers. Each receiver uses a carrier-to-noise ratio squelch system. Receiver selectivity is ±22 kHz at —6 dB and ±45 kHz at —60 dB.

The 20-channel preset memory in the fre-

PARAMETER	Without water injection		With water injection	
	15°C/ 59°F	22°C/ 80°F	15°C/ 59°F	22°C/ 80°F
Displacement (tonnes)	62·5	60	64	64
Military payload (tonnes)	11·7	11·7	14	14
Fuel (tonnes)	9·4	6·9	9·4	9·4
Max foilborne intermittent speed in calm sea (knots)	50	48	50	48
continuous speed in calm sea (knots)	45	43	45	43
continuous speed in sea state 4 (knots)	41	39	41	39
Hullborne continuous speed (knots)	8	8	8	8
Foilborne range at max continuous speed (n miles)	400	300	400	400
Hullborne range (n miles)	1,050	920	1,150	1,050
Turning radius at 40 knots	less than 125m			
Foilborne stability: max vertical acceleration	0-25g (rms) in sea state 4			
Hullborne stability with foils up	stable in 50 knot wind			
with foils down	stable in 70 knot wind			
Endurance	5 days			

quency control utilises a magnetic core storage system with solid-state drivers and interrogators.

DAMAGE CONTROL:

Bilge pumps: Pumps are mounted in the bilge of each watertight compartment and controlled from the engineer's station.

Freon flooding systems: Two 24kg (53lb) freon

FE1301 (CBR F₃) storage cylinders are provided in the engineer's compartment. One 2·27kg (5lb) freon cylinder is piped to Proteus turbine shroud. Systems manually controlled by engineer.

Portable fire extinguishers: A 1kg (2lb) dry chemical extinguisher is mounted in each of the seven manned compartments.

1 Helm/main control console
2 Helm station (starboard)
  Conning station (port)
3 Combat Operations Centre (COC), door
4 Companionway ladders
5 COC electric power distribution panel
6 COC electronics (speed log, radios, etc)
7 Air intake forward machinery room
8 Demister panels for combustion air
9 Aft machinery room
10 Gas turbine engine: foilborne propulsion
11 Forward machinery room
12 Pump drive coupling
13 Waterjet pump
14 Waterjet nozzle (P/S)
15 Main electrical switchboard
16 Main electrical power distribution panel
17 Engineer's console
18 Engineer's station
19 Fuel oil tanks (3)
20 Void
21 Electric hot plate
22 Refrigerator

23 Cannon revolving feeding magazine
24 Folding mess table with benches (2)
25 Crew lockers (8)
26 Crew berths (8)
27 Rope locker (P/S)
28 Forward hydrofoil retraction well
29 Watertight doors
30 Galley stores locker
31 Lavatory
32 Sink
33 Officers' stateroom
34 Turbine generator set
35 Diesel engine: hullborne propulsion
36 Search and navigation radar electronics
37 Fire control radar components
38 Fire control radar computer
39 Gyrocompass and Stable element
40 Electronic equipment
41 Automatic control system
42 Electronic equipment bay (unmanned)
43 Water closet

1 Helm/main control console
2 Helm station
3 Conning station
4 Companionway ladders
5 Watertight doors (P/S)
6 Air-inlet plenums: forward machinery room (P/S)
7 Exhaust duct
8 Machinery combustion air inlets
9 Combat Operations Centre

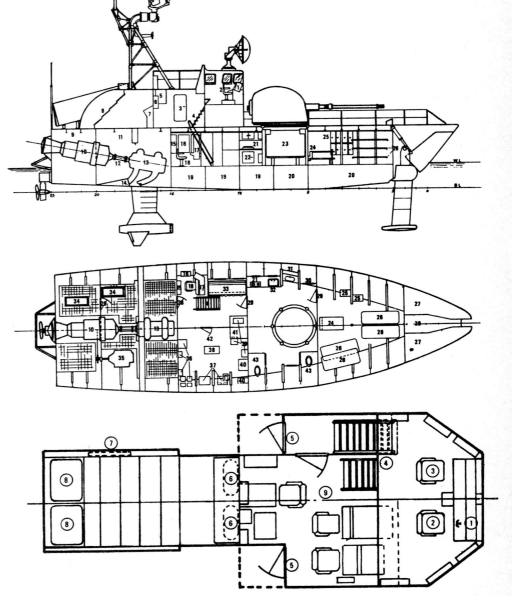

VENTILATION AND AIR CONDITIONING: Unit air conditioners (6 units) are distributed throughout the manned spaces to provide heating and cooling.

ARMAMENT: A typical military payload consists of:

one dual purpose 76mm automatic OTO Melara gun and ammunition

two fixed missile launchers and two ship-to-ship missiles, eg Sea Killers, Otomat or Exocet

gunfire and missile launch control system(s)

other military electronics, eg ECM

A variety of other payloads may be accommodated according to customer needs.

DIMENSIONS
Length overall: 22·95m (75ft 4in)
  foils retracted: 24·6m (80ft 7in)
Width across foils: 10·8m (35ft 4in)
Deck beam, max: 7m (23ft)
WEIGHTS
Max displacement: 64 tonnes
PERFORMANCE

Exact craft performance characteristics depend upon the choice of foilborne gas turbine by the customer and operating conditions which, in turn, can affect the quantity of fuel carried. Performance figures shown below, therefore, are representative:

Swordfish, first missile-launching hydrofoil vessel to be built for the Italian Navy

Foilborne intermittent speed in calm water: 50 knots
  continuous speed in calm water: 45 knots
  continuous speed in sea state 4: 38–40 knots
Hullborne continuous speed, foils down: 7·6 knots

Foilborne range at max continuous speed: up to 400n miles
Hullborne range: up to 1,150n miles
Turning radius at max foilborne continuous speed: less than 125m (410ft)
Endurance: 5 days

RODRIQUEZ CANTIERE NAVALE SpA

Via S Raineri 22, 98100 Messina, Italy
Telephone: (090) 774862
Telex: 980030 RODRIK I
Officials:
Cav Del Lavoro Carlo Rodriquez, *President*
Dott Ing Leopoldo Rodriquez, *General Manager*
Dott Ing Giovanni Falzea, *Technical Manager*

Rodriquez Cantiere Navale SpA, formerly known as Cantiere Navaltecnica SpA, and as Leopoldo Rodriquez Shipyard, was the first in the world to produce hydrofoils in series, and is now the biggest hydrofoil builder outside the Soviet Union. On the initiative of the company's president, Carlo Rodriquez, the Aliscafi Shipping Company was established in Sicily to operate the world's first scheduled seagoing hydrofoil service in August 1956 between Sicily and the Italian mainland.

The service was operated by the first Rodriquez-built Supramar PT 20, *Freccia del Sole*. Cutting down the port-to-port time from Messina to Reggio di Calabria to one-quarter of that of conventional ferry boats, and completing 22 daily crossings, the craft soon proved its commercial viability. With a seating capacity of 75 passengers the PT 20 has carried between 800-900 passengers a day and has conveyed a record number of some 31,000 in a single month.

The prototype PT 20, a 27-ton craft for 75 passengers, was built by Rodriquez in 1955 and the first PT 50, a 63-ton craft for 140 passengers, was completed by the yard in 1958.

By the end of July 1977, the company had built and delivered more than 130 hydrofoils. The new RHS models, the only craft now built by the company, are fitted on request with a Hamilton Standard electronic stability augmentation system.

At the time of going to press, the company had under construction three RHS 150s and four RHS 160s. Construction of the company's first RHS 200 began in 1978.

Apart from these standard designs, the company offers a number of variants, including the M 100, M 150 and M 200 fast patrol craft, the M 300 and 600 fast strike craft and the RHS Hydroil series of mixed passenger/freight hydrofoils, based on the RHS 70, 140 and 160, but adapted for servicing offshore drilling platforms.

RHS 70

This is a 32-ton coastal passenger ferry with seats for 71 passengers. Power is supplied by a single 1,430hp MTU diesel and the cruising speed is 32·4 knots.
FOILS: Surface-piercing type in partly hollow

Freccia delle Magnolie, a 71-seat Rodriquez RHS 70 hydrofoil passenger ferry operated by Ministero di Trasporti on Lake Maggiore

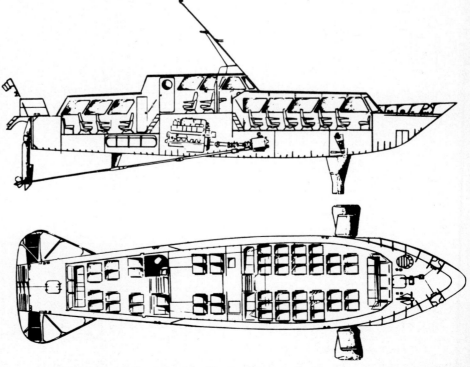

General arrangement of the RHS 70, 71-seat hydrofoil passenger ferry. Power is supplied by a single 1,430hp MTU 12V331 TC 82 diesel

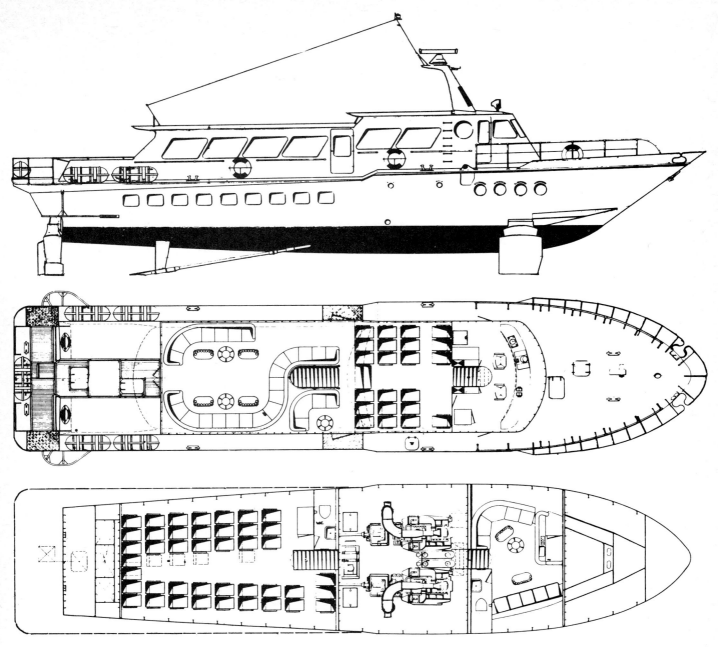

Outboard profile and deck plans of RHS 110 54-ton hydrofoil passenger ferry

welded steel. During operation the angle of the bow foil can be adjusted within narrow limits from the steering position by means of a hydraulic ram operating on a foil support across the hull.

HULL: V-bottom hull of riveted light metal alloy construction. Watertight compartments are provided below the passenger decks and in other parts of the hull.

POWER PLANT: A single MTU 12V331 TC 82 diesel, developing 1,430hp at 2,340rpm, drives a three-bladed bronze aluminium propeller through a Zahnradfabrik W 800 H 20 gearbox.

ACCOMMODATION: 44 passengers are accommodated in the forward cabin, 19 in the rear compartment and 8 aft of the pilot's position, above the engine room, in the elevated wheelhouse. A w/c washbasin unit is provided in the aft passenger compartments. Emergency exits are provided in each passenger compartment.

SYSTEMS, ELECTRICAL: 24V generator driven by the main engine; batteries with a capacity of 350Ah.

HYDRAULICS: 120kg/cm³ pressure hydraulic system for rudder and bow foil incidence control.

DIMENSIONS
Length overall: 22m (72ft 2in)
Width across foils: 7·4m (24ft 3in)
Draft hullborne: 2·7m (8ft 10in)
    foilborne: 1·15m (3ft 9in)

WEIGHTS
Displacement fully loaded: 31·5 tons
Useful load: 6 tons
PERFORMANCE
Cruising speed, half loaded: 32·4 knots
Max speed, half loaded: 36·5 knots

RHS 110

A 54-ton hydrofoil ferry, the RHS 110 is designed to carry a maximum of 110 passengers over routes of up to 485·7km (300 miles) at a cruising speed of 37 knots.

FOILS: Surface-piercing type, in partly hollow welded steel. Hydraulically operated flaps, attached to the trailing edges of the bow and rear foils, are adjusted automatically by a Hamilton Standard stability augmentation system for the damping of heave, pitch and roll motions. The rear foil is rigidly attached to the transom, its incidence angle being determined during tests.

HULL: V-bottom of high-tensile riveted light metal alloy construction, using Peraluman plates and Anticorrodal profiles. The upper deck plates are in 3·5mm (0·137in) thick Peraluman. Removable deck sections permit the lifting out and replacement of the main engines. The superstructure which has a removable roof is in 2mm (0·078in) thick Peraluman plates, with L and C profile sections. Watertight compartments are provided below the passenger decks and other parts of the hull.

POWER PLANT: Power is supplied by two 12-cylinder supercharged MTU MB 12V 493 Ty 71 diesels, each with a maximum output of 1,350hp at 1,500rpm. Engine output is transferred to two three-bladed bronze-aluminium propellers through Zahnradfabrik W 800 H20 gearboxes. Each propeller shaft is 90mm (3·5in) in diameter and supported at three points by seawater lubricated rubber bearings. Steel fuel tanks with a total capacity of 3,600 litres (792 gallons) are located aft of the engine room.

ACCOMMODATION: The wheelhouse/observation deck saloon seats 58, and the lower aft saloon seats 39. Additional passengers are accommodated in the lower forward saloon, which contains a bar.

In the wheelhouse, the pilot's position is on the port side, together with the radar screen. A second seat is provided for the chief engineer. Passenger seats are of lightweight aircraft type, floors are covered with woollen carpets and the walls and ceilings are clad in vinyl. Two toilets are provided, one in each of the lower saloons.

SYSTEMS, ELECTRICAL: Engine driven generators supply 220V, 50Hz, three-phase ac. Two groups of batteries for 24V dc circuit.

HYDRAULICS: Steering, variation of the foil flaps and the anchor windlass operation are all accomplished hydraulically from the wheelhouse. Plant comprises two Bosch pumps installed on the main engines and conveying oil from a 60 litre (13 gallon) tank under pressure to the control cylinders of the rudder, foil flaps and anchor windlass.

FIREFIGHTING: Fixed CO_2 plant for the main engine room, portable CO_2 and foam fire extinguishers of 3kg (7lb) and 10 litres (2 gallon) capacity in the saloons, and one water fire fighting plant.

DIMENSIONS

EXTERNAL

Length overall: 25·6m (84ft)
Width across foils: 9·2m (30ft 2¼in)
Deck beam, max: 5·95m (19ft 2in)
Draft hullborne: 3·3m (10ft 9⅞in)
  foilborne: 1·25m (4ft 1in)

WEIGHTS

Displacement, fully loaded: 54 tons

PERFORMANCE

Max speed: 40 knots
Cruising speed: 37 knots
Range: 485·7km (300 miles)

RHS 140

This 65-ton hydrofoil passenger ferry seats 125-140 passengers and has a cruising speed of 32·5 knots.

FOILS: Surface-piercing V foils of hollow welded steel construction. Lift of the bow foil can be modified by hydraulically-operated trailing-edge flaps.

HULL: Riveted light metal alloy design framed on longitudinal and transverse formers.

ACCOMMODATION: 125-140 passengers seated in three saloons. The belvedere saloon, on the main deck above the engine room, can be equipped with a bar. W/C washbasin units can be installed in the forward and aft saloons.

POWER PLANT: Power is provided by two MTU 12V 493 Ty 71 12-cylinder supercharged engines, each developing 1,350hp at 1,500 rpm. Engine output is transmitted to two, three-bladed 700mm diameter bronze propellers through Zahnradfabrik gearboxes.

SYSTEMS, ELECTRICAL: Two engine-driven generators supply 24V dc. Two battery sets each with 350Ah capacity.

RHS 110, a 110-seat passenger ferry equipped with a Hamilton Standard stability augmentation system

Fabricia, an RHS 140 operated by Toremar on a passenger service between Livorno/Porto Ferraio and Piombino

HYDRAULICS: Steering and variation of foil flap incidence is accomplished hydraulically from the wheelhouse. Plant comprises two Bosch pumps installed on the main engines and conveying oil from a 70 litre (15·4 gallon) tank under pressure to the control cylinders of the rudder and foil flaps.

FIREFIGHTING: Fixed CO_2 plant for the engine room; portable CO_2 and foam fire extinguishers in the saloons. Water intake connected to bilge pump for fire hose connection in emergency.

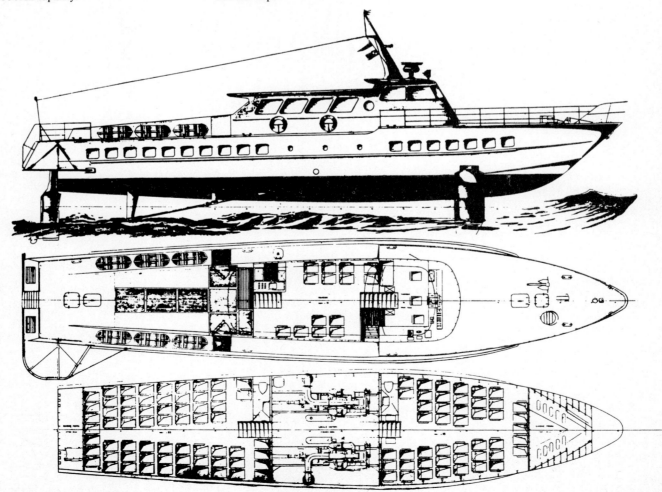

RHS 140, 125-140-seat passenger ferry

DIMENSIONS
Length overall: 28·7m (94ft 1½in)
Width across foils: 10·72m (35ft 2¼in)
Draft hullborne: 3·5m (11ft 5¾in)
  foilborne: 1·5m (4ft 11in)
WEIGHTS
Displacement, fully loaded: 65 tons
Carrying capacity, including 3 tons bunker, and 5
  tons fresh water, lubricating oil and hydraulic
  system oil: 12·5 tons
PERFORMANCE
Max speed, half load: 36 knots
Cruising speed: 32·5 knots
Range at cruising speed: 550km (340 miles)

Freccia Delle Valli, an RHS 150 variant built for services across the Italian lakes

RHS 150

Combining features of both the RHS 140 and the RHS 160 the RHS 150 hydrofoil passenger ferry is available in two versions: a seagoing model with seats for 150 and a variant specially developed for services across the Italian lakes, seating 180. Power is supplied by two 1,430hp MTU supercharged 4-stroke diesels which give the craft a cruising speed of 32·5 knots and a cruising range of 130n miles.
FOILS: Surface-piercing W foils of hollow welded steel construction. Lift of the bow foil can be modified by hydraulically-operated trailing edge flaps.
HULL: Riveted light metal alloy design framed on longitudinal and transverse formers.

ACCOMMODATION: The standard model seats a total of 150 in three saloons. High density model design originally for services on the Italian lakes seats 180—63 in the aft saloon, 45 in the forward saloon and 72 in the belvedere. The forward and stern saloons each have a toilet/WC unit.

POWER PLANT: Motive power is furnished by two supercharged MTU MB 12V 331 TC 82 4-stroke diesels each developing 1,430hp at 2,140rpm continuous. Engine output is transmitted to two bronze propellers via two Zahnradfabrik BW 255L gearboxes.

SYSTEMS, ELECTRICAL: Two 1,300W engine-driven generators supply 24V dc.

DIMENSIONS
Length overall: 28·7m (94ft 1½in)
Width across foils: 11·0m (36ft 1⅛in)
Draft hullborne: 3·1m (10ft 2in)
  foilborne: 1·4m (4ft 7⅛in)
WEIGHTS
Displacement, fully loaded: 65·5 tons
PERFORMANCE
Cruising speed, fully loaded: 32·5 knots
Cruising range: 240km (130n miles)

RHS 160

One of the latest additions to the Rodriquez range is the RHS 160, a 90-ton passenger ferry with seats for 160–200 passengers and a cruising speed of 36 knots.

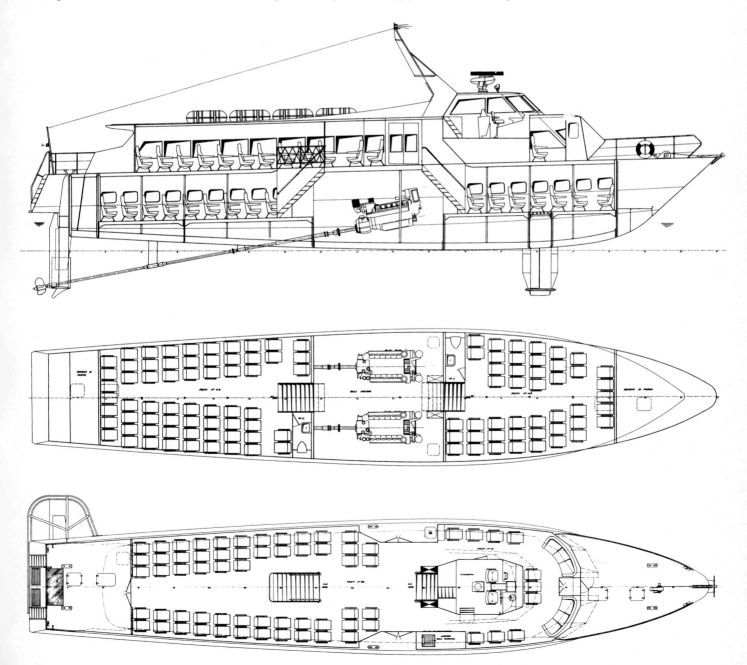

Inboard profile, lower and upper deck plans of RHS 150

FOILS: Surface-piercing W foils of hollow welded steel construction. Craft in this series feature a bow rudder for improved manoeuvrability in congested waters. The bow rudder works simultaneously with the aft rudders. Hydraulically-operated flaps, attached to the trailing edges of the bow and rear foils, are adjusted automatically by a Hamilton Standard electronic stability augmentation system, for the damping of heave, pitch and roll motions in heavy seas.

HULL: Riveted light metal alloy longitudinal structure, welded in parts using inert gas. The hull shape of the RHS 160 is similar to the RHS 140 series. In the manufacture of the hull, plates of aluminium and magnesium alloy of 4·4% are used whilst angle bars are of a high-resistant aluminium, magnesium and silicon alloy.

ACCOMMODATION: 160-200 passengers seated in three saloons. 57 passengers are accommodated in the forward cabin, 57 in the rear compartment and 46 in the belvedere. Forward and aft saloons and belvedere have a toilet, each provided with w/c washbasin units and the usual toilet accessories.

POWER PLANT: Power is provided by two supercharged MTU MB 12V 652 TB 71 4-stroke diesel engines each with a maximum output of 1,950hp at 1,460rpm under normal operating conditions. Engine starting is accomplished by compressed air starters. Engine output is transmitted to two, three-bladed bronze propellers through two Zahnradfabrik 900 HS 15 gearboxes.

SYSTEMS, ELECTRICAL: Two 35kVA generating sets, 220V, 60Hz, three-phase. Three insulated cables for ventilation, air-conditioning and power. Two insulated cables for lighting, sockets and other appliances, 24V dc for emergency lighting, auxiliary engine starting and servocontrol. A battery for radio telephone supply is installed on the upper deck. Provision for battery recharge from ac line foreseen.

HYDRAULICS: Steering is accomplished hydraulically from the wheelhouse. Plant comprises a Bosch pump installed on the main engines and conveying oil from a 45 litre (10 gallon) tank under pressure to the control cylinders of the

Botticelli, a 90-ton Rodriquez RHS 160 passenger ferry

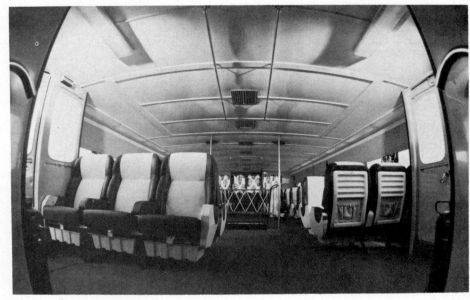

Interior of the 46-seat belvedere cabin on RHS 160

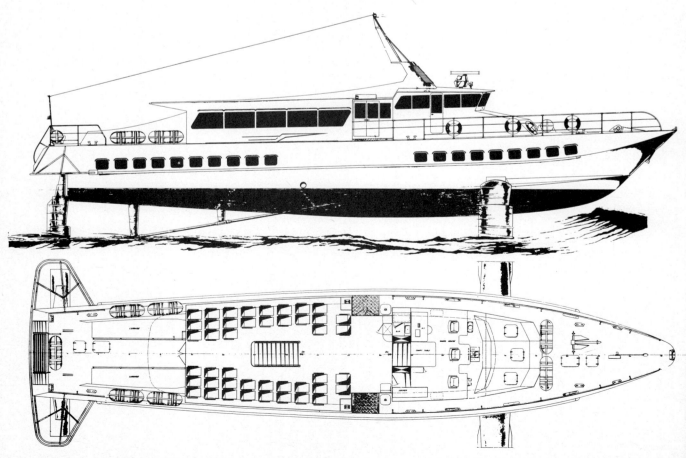

Outboard profile and upper deck plan of RHS 160

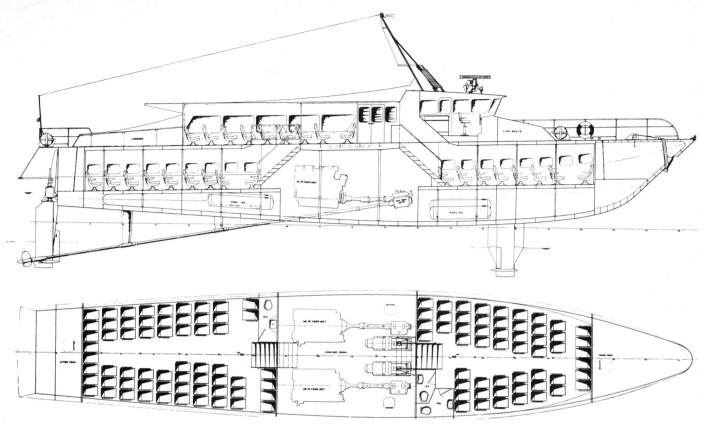

Inboard profile and lower deck plan of RHS 160

rudder and anchor windlass, whilst a second hydraulic pump, which is also installed on the main engines, conveys oil under pressure to the flap control cylinders.

FIREFIGHTING: Fixed CO_2 plant of four CO_2 bottles of about 20kg each for the engine room and fuel tank space; portable extinguishers in various parts of the craft. Water intake connected to fire pump for fire connection in emergency.

DIMENSIONS
Length overall: 30·95m (101ft 6in)
Width across foils: 12·6m (41ft 4in)
Draft hullborne: 3·7m (12ft 6in)
　foilborne: 1·35m (4ft 6in)

WEIGHTS
Displacement, fully loaded: 90 tons
Payload, passengers and luggage: 13·5 tons
PERFORMANCE
Max speed: 39 knots
Cruising speed: 36 knots
Cruising range: 483km (300 miles)

RHS 200

Construction of this 125-ton, 254–310 seat fast ferry began in 1978. Power will be provided by two supercharged MTU MB 16V 652 TB 71 4-stroke diesel engines. The designed cruising speed is 36 knots.

FOILS: Surface-piercing W foils of hollow welded steel construction. Craft in this series feature a bow rudder for improved manoeuvrability in congested waters. The bow rudder operates simultaneously with the aft rudders. An advantage of the W configuration bow foil is its relatively shallow draft requirement in relation to the vessel's overall size. Hydraulically-operated flaps are fitted to the trailing edge of the bow foil to balance out longitudinal load shifting, assist take-off and adjust the flying height. The craft can also be equipped with the Hamilton Standard electronic stability augmentation system, which employs sensors and servomechanisms to

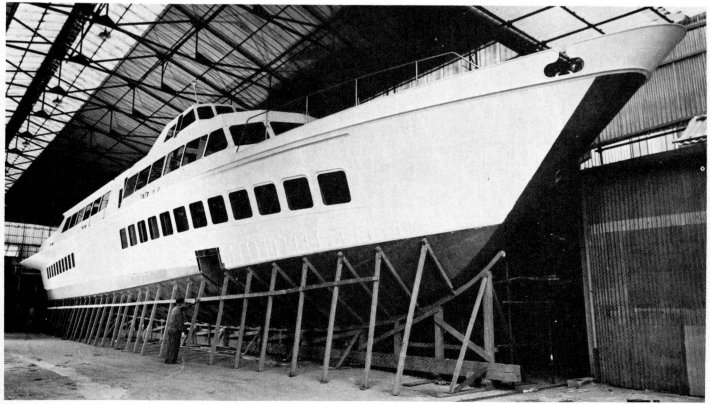

RHS 200 under construction at the Rodriquez shipyard, Messina, Sicily

automatically position flaps on the bow and stern foils for the damping of heave, pitch and roll motions in heavy seas.

HULL: V-bottom hull of high tensile riveted light metal alloy construction, employing Peraluman plates and Anticorrodal frames. The rake of the stem is in galvanised steel.

ACCOMMODATION: Seats can be provided for up to 310 passengers, according to the route served. There are three main passenger saloons and a bar. The standard seating arrangement allows for 127 in the main deck saloon, 55 in the aft lower saloon and 72 in the bow passenger saloon. Seating is normally four abreast in two lines with a central aisle. The bar, at the forward end of the wheelhouse belvedere superstructure, has either an eight-place sofa or 19 seats.

The wheelhouse, which is raised to provide a 360 degree view, is reached from the main deck belvedere saloon by a short companionway. Controls and instrumentation are attached to a panel on the forward bulkhead which extends the width of the wheelhouse. In the centre is the steering control and gyro-compass, on the starboard side are controls for the two engines, gearboxes and controllable-pitch propellers, and on the port side is the radar. Seats are provided for the captain, chief engineer and first mate. At the aft of the wheelhouse is a radio-telephone and a chart table.

POWER PLANT: Motive power is supplied by two supercharged MTU MB 16V 652 TB 71 4-stroke diesel engines, each with a maximum output of 2,530hp at 1,460rpm under normal operating conditions. Engine output is transferred to two supercavitating, controllable-pitch propellers.

SYSTEMS, ELECTRICAL: Two generating sets. One 220V, three-phase ac, for all consumer services, the second for charging 24V battery sets and operating fire-fighting and hydraulic pumps. Power distribution panel in wheelhouse for navigation light circuits, cabin lighting, radar, RDF, gyro compass and emergency circuits.

FIREFIGHTING: Fixed CO_2 self-contained automatic systems for power plant and fuel tank spaces, plus portable extinguishers for cabins and holds.

DIMENSIONS
Length overall: 35·8m (117ft 5in)
Width across foils: 14·5m (47ft 7in)
Draft hullborne: 4·55m (15ft 1¾in)
  foilborne: 2·05m (6ft 8⅓in)
WEIGHTS
Displacement fully loaded: 125 tons
PERFORMANCE
Cruising speed: 36 knots
Max speed: 41 knots
Cruising range: 200n miles

Impression of RHS 200 fast ferry

RHS ALIYACHT

A luxury hydrofoil yacht of light alloy construction, the RHS Aliyacht is derived from the RHS 110 passenger ferry. It is powered by two 1,350hp MTU MB 12V 493 Ty 71 diesel engines and has a cruising speed of 38 knots.

The craft is equipped with the Hamilton Standard electronic stability augmentation system, which is designed to provide a smoother ride in heavy seas. The system uses sensors and servo-mechanisms to position foil flaps automatically for the maximum damping of heave, pitch and roll motions.

FOILS: Bow and rear foils are of surface-piercing type, and constructed in partly hollow welded steel. Two hydraulically-operated flaps, attached to the trailing edges of the bow foil, are adjusted automatically by the stabilisation system for the damping of heave, pitch and roll motions. The rear foil is rigidly attached to the transom, its incidence angle being determined during tests.

HULL: The V-bottom hull is of high-tensile riveted light metal alloy construction, using Peraluman (aluminium and magnesium alloy) plates and Anticorrodal (aluminium, magnesium and silicon alloy) profiles. The rake of the stem is in 3·5mm (0·137in) thick galvanised steel. The superstructure is constructed in 2mm (0·078in) Peraluman plate, and the roof is detachable to facilitate the removal and replacement of the main engines.

ACCOMMODATION: Main deck accommodation comprises the wheelhouse and radio cabin, a comfortably furnished saloon and a galley. The saloon can be fitted with two four-seat sofas,

armchairs, tea-table, a metal table with four chairs, and a bar. Below deck, from aft peak forward, is a large cabin for the owner, with its own bathroom and small private drawing room; two double cabins for guests with adjacent WC/washbasin/shower units, and beyond the engines, a cabin for the captain and engineer, and two single cabins for guests.

The wheelhouse is reached via a companionway from the saloon and is connected by a door with the upper deck. The pilot's position, controls and instruments are on the port side, together with the radar screen.

POWER PLANT: Power is supplied by two supercharged 12-cylinder MTU MB 12V 439 Ty 71 diesels, each rated at 1,350hp at 1,500rpm. Engine output is transferred to two three-bladed bronze-aluminium propellers through Zahnradfabrik BW 800 H20 gearboxes.

SYSTEMS, ELECTRICAL: Two 10kW, 220V, three-phase Onan generating sets, coupled to batteries, provide 24V dc for engine starting, instruments, lighting, radio, etc.

DIMENSIONS
EXTERNAL
Length overall: 24·5m (78ft 9in)
Beam overall: 6·1m (20ft)
Hull beam: 5·85m (19ft 2¼in)
Draft hullborne: 2·95m (9ft 8⅛in)
  foilborne: 1·25m (4ft 1¼in)
WEIGHTS
Displacement, loaded: 52 tons
PERFORMANCE
Max speed: 41 knots
Cruising speed: 38 knots
Range: 644km (400 miles)

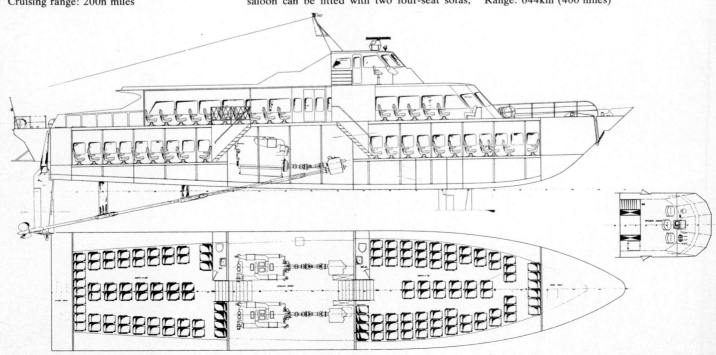

Inboard profile and lower deck arrangement of RHS 200

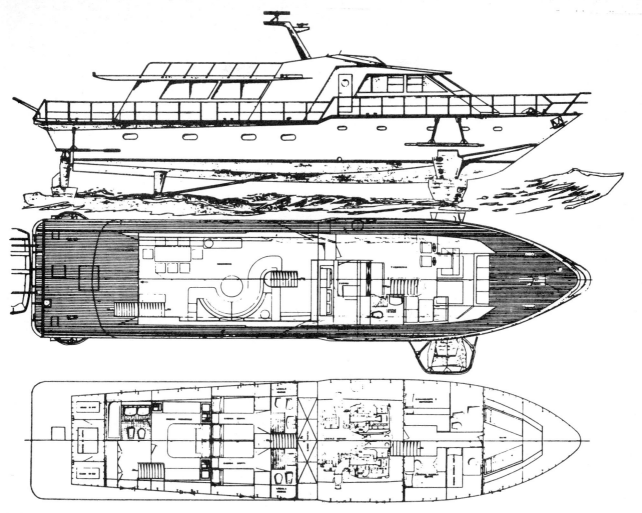

Rodriquez RHS Aliyacht

RHS HYDROILS

These are derivatives of RHS passenger-carrying hydrofoils, and are designed to ferry personnel, materials and equipment between offshore oil rigs and shore bases. Vessels in the series feature an open cargo deck aft of the bridge superstructure instead of an aft passenger saloon. The three main types are the RHS 70, the RHS 140, and the RHS 160 Hydroil.

RHS 70 HYDROIL

The first of the new series of RHS 70 Hydroil offshore drilling platform supply vessels has been built for ENI Oil Corporation, which is employing the craft in the Adriatic. A mixed passenger/cargo version of the RHS 70 passenger ferry, this variant has an open cargo deck aft of the bridge superstructure in place of the Caribe's main passenger cabin. Dimensions of the cargo deck are: length 7·5m (24ft 7in); width 3·5m (11ft 6in) and height 1·05m (3ft 5in).

FOILS: Bow and rear foils are of surface-piercing V configuration, with about 66% of the weight supported by the bow foil and 34% by the rear foil. Each foil, together with its struts and horizontal supporting tube, forms a rigid framework which facilitates the exchange of the foil structure. The foils are of hollow-ribbed construction and fabricated from medium Asera steel. The forward foil can be tilted within narrow limits by means of a hydraulic ram acting on the foil strut supporting tube. The angle of attack can therefore be adjusted during operation to assist take-off and counteract the effect of large variations in loading.

HULL: The hull is of riveted light metal alloy (Peraluman) and framed on a combination of longitudinal and transverse formers. Watertight compartments are provided in the bow and stern, and a double-bottom runs from immediately aft of the engine room, beneath the full length of the cargo deck, to the after peak. Contained within

the double-bottom are six cylindrical aluminium fuel tanks with a total capacity of 2,250 litres (495 gallons). Access to the fore and aft compartments is via removable deck hatches. The deck is of 5mm (0·196in) Peraluman, suitably reinforced to withstand heavily concentrated loads. Two 125mm (4·9in) diameter scuppers are provided aft for rapid drainage. Heavy rubber fenders are provided at the bow and stern.

ACCOMMODATION: The craft has a crew of two, and seats up to 12 passengers in a comfortably appointed saloon, immediately aft of the wheelhouse. Passengers have a choice of six armchairs and two, three-place settees, one of which converts into a bed for transporting sick or injured personnel. All seats are equipped with safety belts. Aft of the saloon is a fully equipped galley, with refrigerator, a gas cooker with two gas rings, cupboards, plate rack and sink unit. Two folding wooden tables permit up to eight passengers to take meals at one sitting. A

Rodriquez RHS Aliyacht, powered by two MTU diesels rated at 1,350hp. Cruising speed is 38 knots and range 400 miles

toilet/washbasin unit is provided opposite the galley on the port side. The engine room, wheelhouse and passenger saloon are fully heated and ventilated. A full range of safety equipment is carried including inflatable rafts and lifebelts for each passenger and crew member.

POWER PLANT: Power is supplied by a 12-cylinder supercharged MTU 12V 331 TC 82 with a maximum output of 1,430hp at 2,340rpm. Engine output is transferred to a three-bladed 700mm (27·5in) bronze-aluminium propeller through a Zahnradfabrik BW 800 H20 gearbox. The propeller shaft is 90mm (3·5in) in diameter, and supported at three points by seawater lubricated rubber bearings. In an emergency, hullborne propulsion is provided by a 105hp Mercedes OM 352 diesel with a Mercruiser Z-drive. The engine is installed in the aft peak and propels the craft at about 5 knots.

SYSTEMS, ELECTRICAL: 220V 50Hz three-phase ac, 24V dc; provision for 220V 50Hz three-phase shore supply. The dc supply is from a 24V generator driven by the main engine and feeding a 235Ah battery. AC supply is derived from a four-stroke Onan diesel generator set, located in the engine room.

HYDRAULICS: One Bosch Hy/ZFR 1/16 AR 101 for steering and bow foil incidence control.

COMMUNICATIONS AND NAVIGATION:
Radio: VHF radio-telephone to customers' requirements.
Radar: Decca, Raytheon etc, to customers' requirements.

DIMENSIONS
Length overall, hull: 20·95m (68ft 9in)
Hull beam: 5·06m (16ft 7in)
Width over foils: 7·4m (24ft 3in)
Draft hullborne: 2·7m (8ft 10in)
  foilborne: 1·14m (3ft 9in)
WEIGHTS
Max take-off displacement: 33·12 tons
Max load on open cargo deck: 3 tons
PERFORMANCE (with normal payload)
Cruising speed: 32 knots
Range: 480km (300 miles)

RHS 140 HYDROIL

The second in the Rodriquez Hydroil range is a mixed passenger/cargo version of the 65-ton RHS 140. As with the smaller RHS 70 Hydroil, the main passenger saloon is replaced by a large open cargo deck for loads up to 6 tons. The deck is 9·5m (31ft 2in) long, 4·8m (15ft 9in) wide and 1·19m (3ft 11in) high.

The craft will carry a crew of two and up to 14 passengers. Two variants are available, one equipped with seats for 23 passengers and with a cargo capacity of 5 tons and the other with seats for 60 passengers and a cargo capacity of 3 tons. Power will be supplied by two 12-cylinder supercharged MTU 12V 493 Ty 71 engines, each with a maximum output of 1,350hp.

DIMENSIONS
Length overall, hull: 28·5m (93ft 6in)
Hull beam: 6·1m (20ft)
Width over foils: 10·72m (35ft 2in)
Draft hullborne: 3·5m (11ft 6in)
  foilborne: 1·5m (4ft 11in)
WEIGHTS
Normal take-off displacement: 64 tons
PERFORMANCE
Cruising speed: 32-34 knots
Range at cruising speed: 480km (300 miles)

RHS 160 HYDROIL

Latest addition to Rodriquez's range of offshore oil rig support vessels, the RHS 160 features an open cargo deck aft of the bridge superstructure and additional fuel and water tanks in the place of the lower aft passenger saloons. The vessel carries a crew of 5 and 42 passengers, plus 10 tons of cargo, at a cruising speed of 35 knots.

FOILS: Surface-piercing W foils of hollow welded steel construction. Craft in this series feature bow and aft rudders, both of which operate simultaneously. Hydraulically-operated flaps, attached to the trailing edges of the bow and rear foils are adjusted automatically by a Hamilton Standard electronic stability augmentation system, for the damping of heave, pitch and roll motions in heavy seas.

HULL: V-bottom hull of high tensile riveted light metal alloy construction. In the manufacture of the hull, plates of aluminium and magnesium alloy of 4·4% are used, whilst angle bars are of a high resistant aluminium, magnesium and silicon alloy. Inert gas welding (Argon) is used for strengthening beams, web frames, keelsons and stringers. Steel and rubber fenders are fitted aft and in the sides of the main deck to protect the foils from damage when docking.

ACCOMMODATION: Passengers are accommodated in a forward saloon, seating 37, and the upper belvedere saloon, seating 5. The seats, designed for maximum comfort, have arms and each is provided with an ash tray and magazine holder. The toilet, finished in Formica or similar laminate, is provided with a w/c basin and normal accessories.

Crew members are accommodated in two

Porto Corsini, first of the RHS 70 Hydroil 33-ton offshore drilling platform supply vessels. The craft has been built for ENI, the Italian oil company and is seen operating from one of the company's drilling platforms. Loads of up to 3 tons can be carried on the open cargo deck aft of the bridge structure. Cruising speed with normal payload is 32 knots

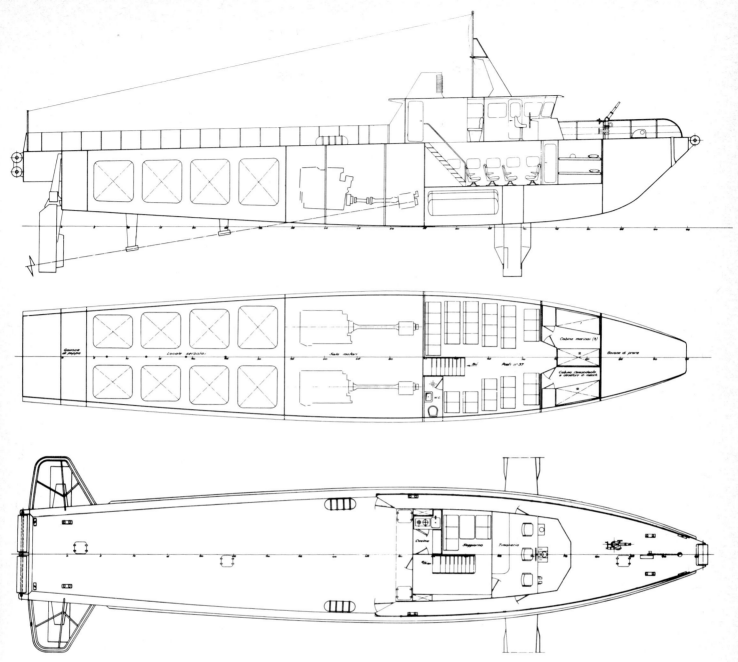

RHS 160 Hydroil

cabins forward, that on the starboard being provided with two berths and a locker, while the port cabin has three berths and lockers. The wheelhouse is located well forward and has seats for the master in the centre, chief engineer on the starboard side and radar operator on the port side. All steering and other controls are located in the wheelhouse, including a circuit control panel for the navigation lights, craft lighting, radar, gyro-compass and various other electrical consumer and emergency circuits.

POWER PLANT: Power is provided by two supercharged MTU MB 12V 652 TB 71 4-stroke diesel engines, each with a maximum output of 1,950hp at 1,460rpm. Engine starting is accomplished by compressed air starters. Output is transmitted to two three-bladed bronze propellers through two Zahnradfabrik 900 HS 15 gearboxes.

SYSTEMS, ELECTRICAL: Two 35kVA generating sets, 220V, 50Hz, three-phase for ventilation and air-conditioning; 220V, 50Hz, single-phase for lighting and other appliances; 24V dc for auxiliary lighting, engine starting and servocontrol.

HYDRAULICS: Steering is accomplished hydraulically from the wheelhouse. Plant comprises a Bosch pump installed on one of the main engines and conveying oil under pressure from a 45 litre (10 gallon) tank to the control cylinders of the rudder and anchor windlass, whilst a second hydraulic pump, which is installed on the other main engine, conveys oil under pressure to the flap control cylinders.

The two systems are interchangeable and equipped with safety valves, manometers and micronic filters.

FIREFIGHTING: Fixed CO_2 plant for engine room and fuel tank space; portable appliances include two 6kg powder extinguishers and one 5kg CO_2 extinguisher in the engine room; two 10 litre water extinguishers in the passenger saloons and one 6kg powder extinguisher in the wheelhouse.

Two water extinguishing systems are provided, one driven by the main engine and the other by a motor driven pump. The system can supply a monitor on the upper deck at the bow and two fire hose water outlets located amidships on the upper deck. A dual-purpose water/foam nozzle can be supplied on request.

DIMENSIONS
Length overall: 31·3m (103ft)
Moulded beam: 6·2m (20ft 4⅛in)
Width across foils: 12·6m (41ft 4in)
Draft hullborne: 3·7m (12ft 6in)
   foilborne: 1·35m (4ft 6in)
WEIGHTS
Displacement, fully loaded: 85 tons
PERFORMANCE
Cruising speed: 35 knots
Cruising range: 322km (200 miles)

M-RHS 150 SEARCH AND RESCUE CRAFT

This new variant of the well-known RHS 140 is a multi-purpose rescue craft equipped for a full range of S & R duties, including fire-fighting and wreck marking. It has a top speed of 36 knots and can operate in heavy seas at a considerable distance from its shore base. A Merryweather dual-purpose water/foam monitor is located on the foredeck and an 8·5m daughter boat is carried on the upper deck aft.

A sick bay is provided and can be fitted out to accommodate 30 to 40 survivors.

A feature of the design is the filling of the double bottom with expanded polystyrene to provide sufficient buoyancy to make it unsinkable, even with the watertight compartments flooded.

FOILS: Surface-piercing W foils of hollow welded steel construction. Foil lift is varied by flaps operated by an electronic/hydraulic system developed by Rodriquez in conjunction with Hamilton Standard. Under calm sea conditions, the flaps can be operated manually.

HULL: Riveted light metal alloy design framed on longitudinal and transverse formers. Areas of the attachment points of the bow and rear foils are reinforced with steel. Steel is also used for the rake of the stem, the stern tube for the propeller shaft and the propeller shaft attachment.

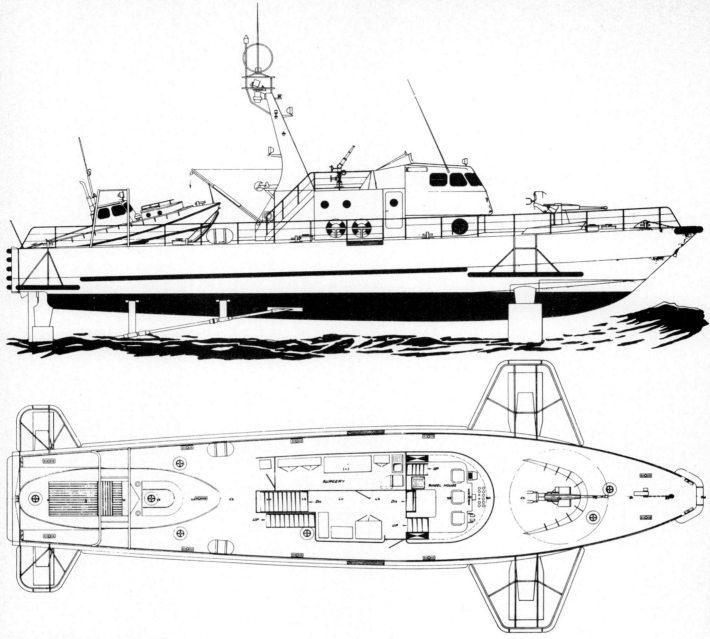

M-RHS 150 Search and Rescue craft

ACCOMMODATION: Berths, lockers and living accommodation provided for a crew of eleven, comprising the captain, two officers, two petty officers and six seamen. Seats are provided in the wheelhouse for an operating crew of three. A "flying bridge" with a duplicated set of instruments and controls, provides improved visibility during search operations. A ten-berth sick bay, complete with a small office for the doctor is provided aft. A large roof hatch is provided in the sick bay through which stretcher casualties can be lowered. If required, the sick bay can be fitted out to accommodate 30–40 survivors.

POWER PLANT: Power is provided by two MTU 12V 331 TC 82 12-cylinder supercharged diesel engines, each developing 1,430hp at 2,340rpm. Engine output is transmitted to two three-bladed, 700mm diameter bronze propellers through Zahnradfabrik gearboxes.

SYSTEMS, ELECTRICAL: Two engine-driven generators of 24V dc supply essential services and emergency lights. An ac system, powered by a generator set, supplies lighting and all other on board consumers. Two battery sets are provided for starting the main engines and generators.

HYDRAULICS: Steering and variation of foil flap incidence is accomplished hydraulically from the wheelhouse. Plant comprises two Bosch pumps installed on the main engines and conveying oil from a tank under pressure to the control cylinders of the rudder and foil flaps.

AIR CONDITIONING: Provided on request.
FIREFIGHTING: Fixed CO_2 plant for the engine room and fuel oil bays; portable CO_2 and foam fire extinguishers at various parts of the craft. One Merryweather dual purpose foam/water monitor.

DIMENSIONS
Length overall: 28·7m (94ft 1½in)
Width across foils: 10·9m (35ft 9in)
Draft hullborne: 3·15m (10ft 4in)
  foilborne: 1·2m (3ft 11in)
WEIGHTS
Displacement, fully loaded: 65 tonnes (64 tons)
PERFORMANCE
Max speed: 36 knots
Cruising speed: 32·5 knots
Endurance at cruising speed: 18 hours, 600 miles
  at low speed: 50 hours, 600 miles
Cruising range: 1,110km (600n miles)

M-RHS 150 PATROL CRAFT

The patrol variant of the M-RHS 150 is designed for fisheries law enforcement missions, patrolling and customs operations against ships offshore. It has a similar specification to the Search and Rescue variant but a fully loaded displacement of only 64 tonnes. Accommodation is provided for a crew of twelve, comprising the captain, three officers, four petty officers and four seamen.

M PATROL CRAFT

Derived from RHS passenger vessels, the M series craft are designed for coast guard and anti-contraband patrol. Suitably armed, they can undertake various naval duties, ranging from patrol to minelaying. The armament shown in the accompanying drawings can be augmented or substituted by surface-to-air and surface-to-surface missiles according to requirements.

M 100

The M 100 is similar in design and performance to the two PAT 20 patrol hydrofoils built by Rodriquez for the Philippine Navy.

FOILS: Bow and rear foils are surface-piercing V configuration and identical to those of the standard RHS 70. About 59% of the total weight is borne by the bow foil and 41% by the rear foil. The foils are of hollow ribbed construction and made from medium Asera steel.

Total foil area is 10·4m² (112ft²). The angle of incidence of the forward foil can be varied during flight by means of a hydraulic ram acting on the foil strut supporting tube.

HULL: The hull is of riveted light alloy construction with Peraluman (aluminium and magnesium alloy) plates and Anticorrodal (aluminium, magnesium and silicon alloy) profiles.

ACCOMMODATION: The crew comprises a captain, two officers and eight NCOs and ratings. The pilot's position is on the left of the

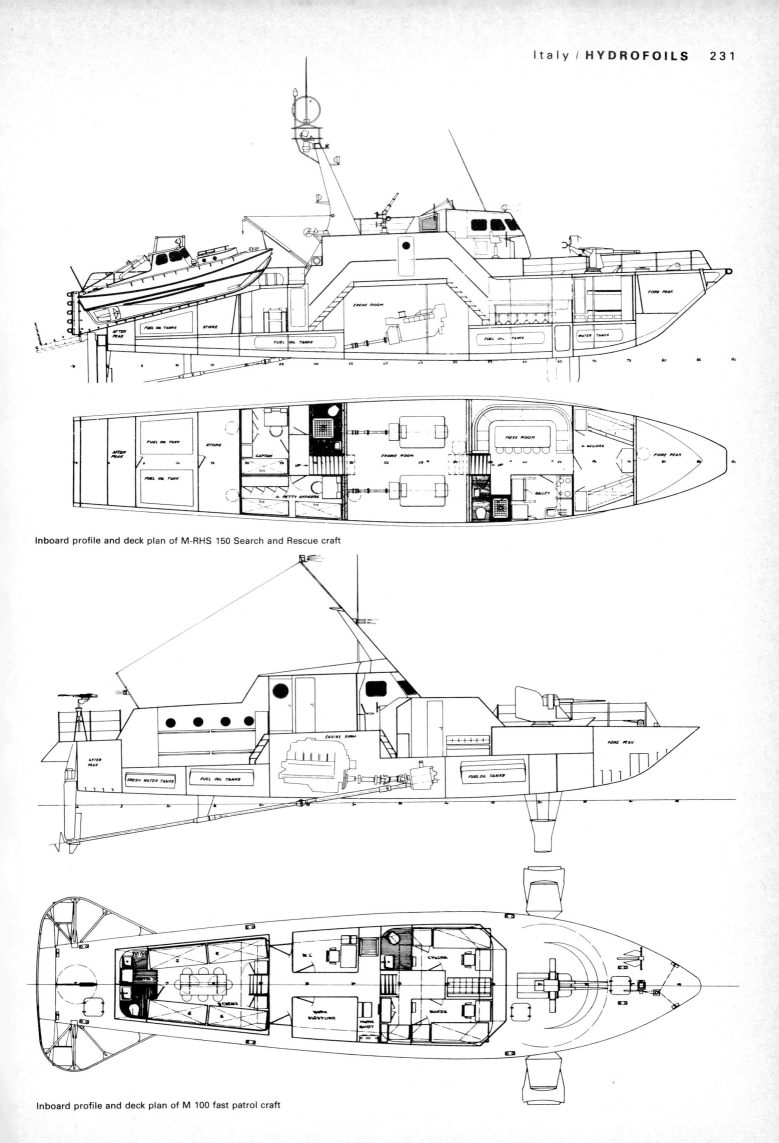

Inboard profile and deck plan of M-RHS 150 Search and Rescue craft

Inboard profile and deck plan of M 100 fast patrol craft

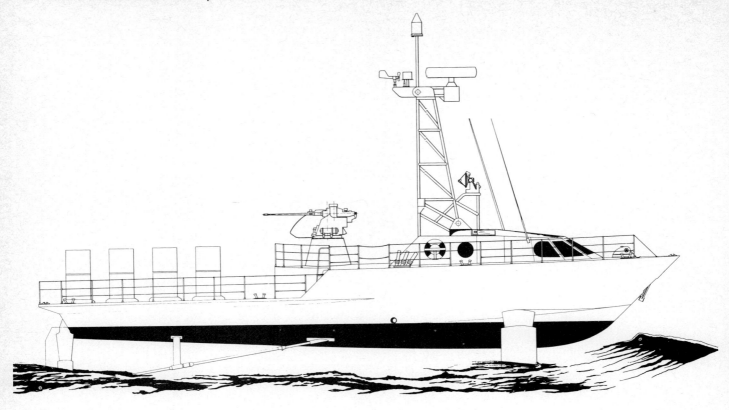

Outboard profile and deck views of M 150, fast patrol variant of RHS 110

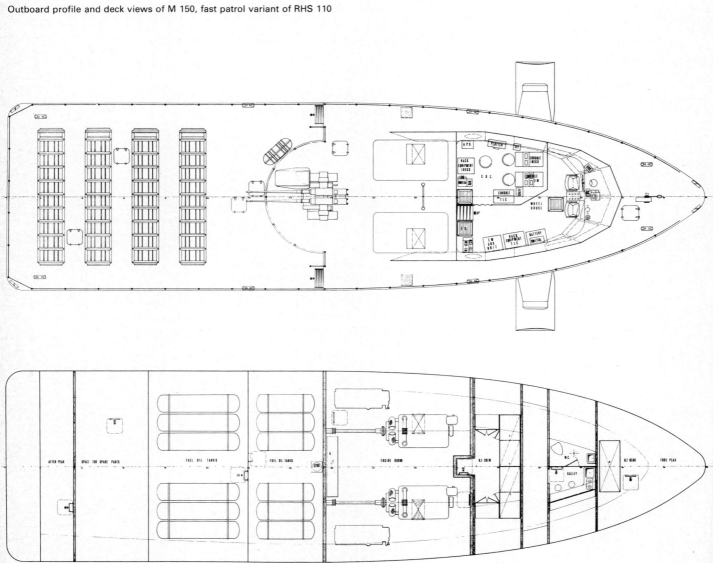

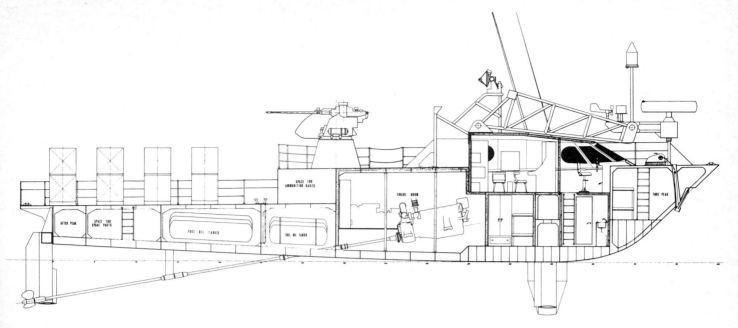

M 150, fast patrol boat variant of RHS 110 passenger ferry

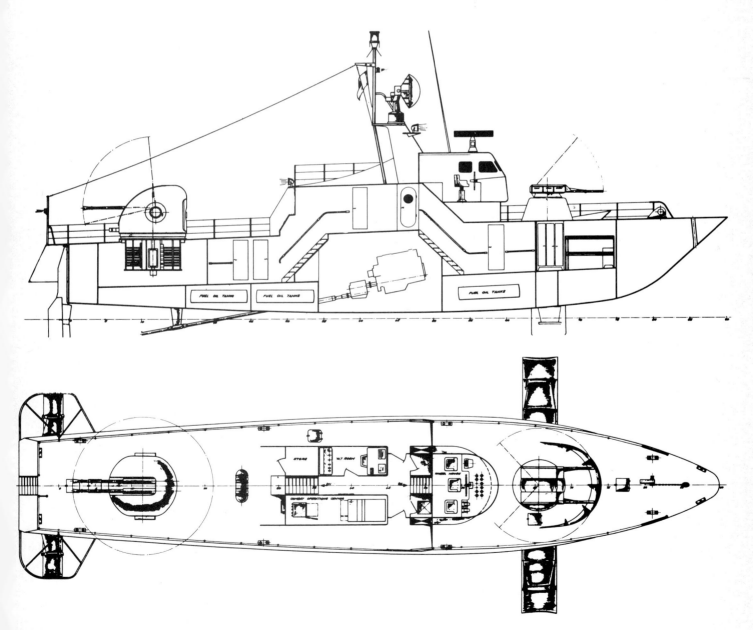

General arrangement of M 200

wheelhouse, with the principal instrumentation; and the radar operator sits on the right with the auxiliary instrumentation. The pilot is provided with an intercom system connecting him with the officers' cabin, engine room and crew cabin. The internal space has been divided as follows:

(a) the forward or bow room, subdivided into two cabins, one for the captain, the other for two officers, and including a w/c with washstand and a storeroom with a refrigerator.

(b) the stern room, with eight berths for the NCOs and ratings, a w/c with washstand and a galley equipped with a gas stove and an electric refrigerator.

(c) the deck room, aft of the wheelhouse, with tilting sofa and table for R/T equipment.

Air conditioning is installed in the captain's and officers' quarters.

POWER PLANT: Power is supplied by a supercharged 12-cylinder MTU 12V 331 TC 82 with a max continuous output of 1,430hp at 2,340rpm. Engine output is transferred to a three-bladed bronze aluminium propeller through a Zahnradfabrik BW 800/S reversible gear. Fuel (total capacity 2,800kg) is carried in ten cylindrical aluminium tanks located in the double bottom beneath the bow room and the stern room. Dynamic and reserve oil tanks in the engine room give a total oil capacity of 120kg. An auxiliary engine can be fitted in the stern for emergency operation.

ARMAMENT AND SEARCH EQUIPMENT: Single 12·7mm machine gun mounted above well position in bow, and two searchlights or one 8cm Oerlikon 3Z8DLa rocket launcher.

M 150, fast patrol boat variant of RHS 110 passenger ferry

SYSTEMS, ELECTRICAL: 220V, 10kW, diesel generator with batteries. Supplies instruments, radio and radar and external and internal lights, navigation lights and searchlights.

HYDRAULICS: 120kg/cm² pressure hydraulic system for steering and varying forward foil incidence angle.

APU: Onan engine for air conditioning when requested.

DIMENSIONS
Length overall, hull: 20·89m (68ft 6in)
Hull beam: 4·79m (15ft 8¾in)
Beam overall: 7·4m (24ft 4in)
Draft hullborne: 2·76m (9ft 1in)
    foilborne: 1·2m (4ft)
Height overall,
    hullborne: 6·44m (21ft)
    foilborne: 8m (26ft 3in)

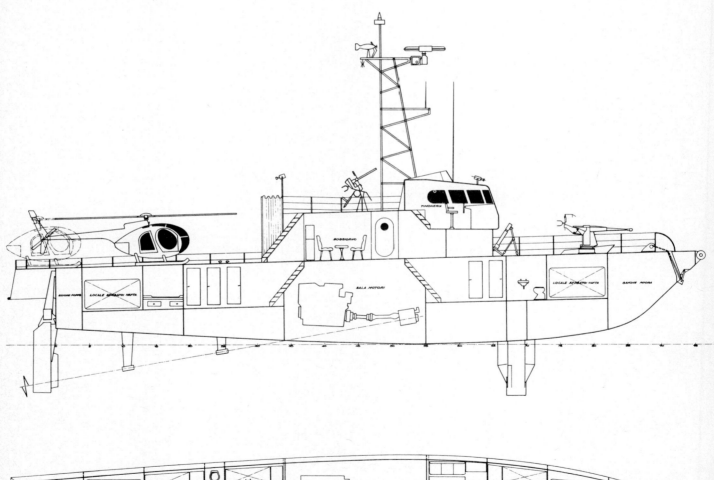

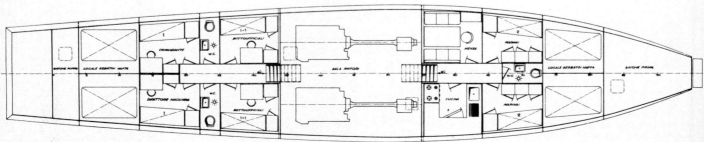

Inboard profile and deck plan of M 300

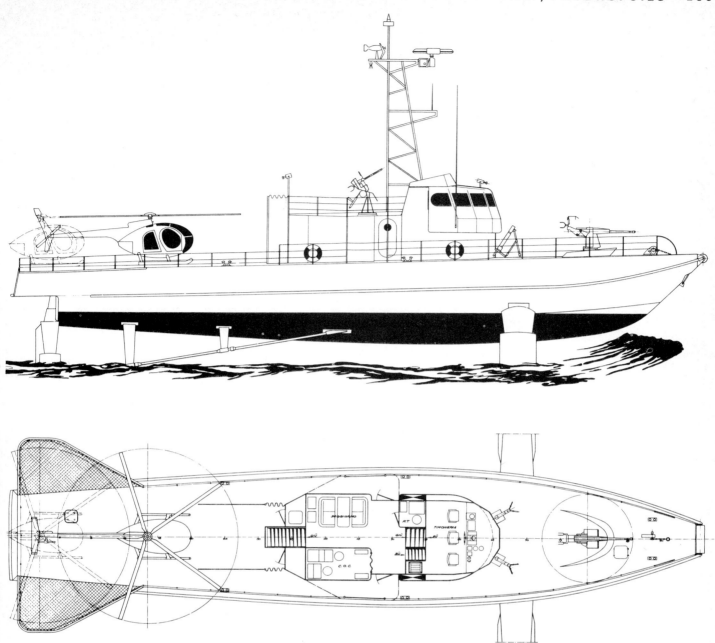

Outboard profile and deck plan of M 300

WEIGHTS
Net tonnage: 28 tons
Light displacement: 26 tons
Max take-off displacement: 32·5 tons
Useful load: 7·6 tons
Max useful load: 8·1 tons
PERFORMANCE
Max speed foilborne: 38 knots
 hullborne: 13 knots
Cruising speed foilborne: 34 knots
 hullborne: 12 knots
Max permissible sea state, foilborne: Force 4
Designed range at cruising speed: 869km (540 miles)
Number of seconds and distance to take-off: 20 seconds, 100m (328ft)
 to stop craft: 12 seconds, 50m (164ft)
Fuel consumption at cruising speed: 145kg/h (320lb/h)
 at max speed: 180kg/h (397lb/h)

M 150

This is the fast patrol boat version of the RHS 110 passenger ferry. Modifications include a revised cabin superstructure with an upper bridge; the installation of 8 Sistel Sea Killer medium-range missiles and a 20mm Hispano-Suiza twin-mounting, and the provision of fuel tanks of additional capacity increasing the operating range to 900km (560 miles).

Dynamic model of M 300

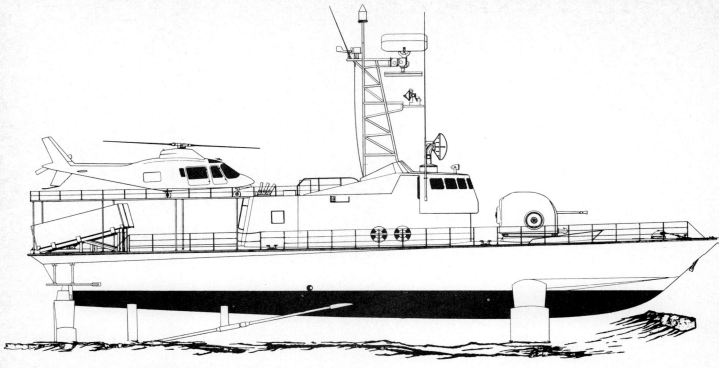

Outboard and inboard profile of M 600 fast strike missile craft

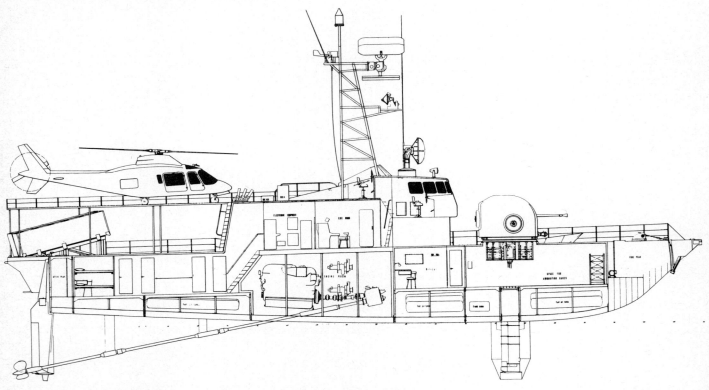

FOILS, HULL, POWERPLANT: Arrangements similar to those of the RHS 110.

ACCOMMODATION: Berths provided for eight officers and non-commissioned officers and eight ratings.

DIMENSIONS
Length overall: 25·4m (83ft 2in)
Beam overall: 8·4m (27ft 6¾in)
Height of hull structure: 2·85m (9ft 4in)
Draft foilborne: 1·25m (4ft 1in)
  hullborne, fully loaded: 3m (9ft 10in)
WEIGHTS
Displacement, empty: 36 tons
  loaded: 50 tons
PERFORMANCE
Max speed: 41 knots
Cruising speed: 38 knots
Cruising range: 900km (560 miles)

M 200

Derived from the RHS 140 passenger ferry this fast patrol variant can be armed with a 40mm Breda-Bofors twin naval mounting and one 8cm Oerlikon 2Z8DLa rocket launcher, and has a maximum speed of 37 knots. Above the wheelhouse is an open bridge with duplicate steering, engine controls and instrumentation.

WEIGHTS
Displacement loaded: 64 tons
  empty: 50 tons
PERFORMANCE
Max speed foilborne: 37 knots
Cruising speed: 34 knots
Minimum foilborne speed: 23·3 knots
Range: 1,127km (736 miles)

M 300 AND 600 FAST STRIKE CRAFT

The 90-ton M 300 and 125-ton M 600 are two hydrofoil missilecraft designed to augment the existing range of Rodriquez fast patrol boats.

Though differing in size, the two craft are almost identical in terms of overall design, construction and internal arrangements. Both are equipped with the SAS stability augmentation system, which stabilises the vessels in bad weather, and the Breda-Bofors twin 40mm/L 70 or similar rapid-fire cannon. In addition the M 300 will carry two Otomat or similar missile launchers and the M 600 will carry four.

Power for the M 300 is provided by two 1,950hp MTU 12V 652 TB 71 diesels, while the M 600 has two MTU 16V 652 TB 71 diesels each rated at 2,600hp. Maximum speed of both craft is in excess of 38 knots.

Dimensions, weights and performance figures are given at the end of the summary. The following characteristics apply to both designs.

FOILS: Surface-piercing W foils of hollow welded steel. Craft in this series have a bow rudder for improved manoeuvrability. The bow rudder works simultaneously with the aft rudders to provide fully co-ordinated turns. Hydraulically-operated flaps, attached to the trailing edges of the bow and rear foils are adjusted automatically by an SAS electronic stability augmentation system for the damping of heave, pitch and roll motions in heavy seas.

HULL AND SUPERSTRUCTURE: V-bottom hull of high tensile riveted light metal alloy construction. Argon gas welding employed on strengthened beams, web frames, keelsons and stringers. Basic hull structure is longitudinal; forepeak and after peak are transverse type structures. Steel is employed for the stern, fore and aft foil attachment points, propeller struts and foils. Cadmium plated rivets are used for jointing steel and light alloy components. Side plating ranges in thickness from 3·5–5mm; the upper deck varies from 3–4mm and plating on the stem and stern platforms is 2mm thick.

The superstructure is built on transverse frames with stanchions and beams every 300mm.

ACCOMMODATION: Berths, living and working accommodation and full w/c washroom facilities for total complement of 12, including commissioned and non-commissioned officers and ratings. The wheelhouse, all living spaces and fire control room are air-conditioned. Ventilation system provided for the engine room.

PROPULSION

M 300

Two MTU 12V 652 TB 71 4-stroke diesels, each delivering 1,950hp at 1,460rpm.

M 600

Two MTU 16V 652 TB 71 4-stroke diesels, each delivering 2,600hp at 1,460rpm.

On both designs engine output is transferred via a short intermediate shaft, universal joint and Zahnradfabrik 900 HS 15 gearboxes to two hollow, stainless steel propeller shafts operating two, three-bladed bronze-aluminium propellers. The drive shafts are supported by brackets and on the aft foils by rubber bearings lubricated by the water coolant system.

Stainless steel controllable-pitch propellers are available as an alternative to the fixed-pitch bronze-aluminium type.

FUEL OIL: Diesel fuel oil is carried in fibreglass-reinforced, welded aluminium tanks located in the double bottom. All tanks are connected to a service tank from which oil is delivered to the injection pumps. Each engine

has two suction and two engine pumps. Before reaching the injection pumps, fuel is fed through two filters in parallel, with replaceable filter elements, and water drain cocks. Injection excess fuel is piped back to the service tank.

Tanks are refuelled through necks on the main deck, each equipped with air vents and fuel level calibrated in kilograms and gallons.

SYSTEMS: Two systems are installed, each pressurised by a gear pump installed on one of the main engines. The first is used for the steering system and anchor winch, the second supplies the cylinder operating the lift control flaps and the bow rudder. The two systems are interchangeable and equipped with safety valves, manometers and micronic filters. Hydraulic pressure is also used for operating the weapons systems.

DRAINAGE AND FIRE CONTROL: Bilge pumps, operated by the main engines, can empty water from any compartment. Drain valves can be operated from both the engine room or from the deck. One pump can also supply water for fire hoses located on the amidship and aft sections of the vessels, port and starboard.

CO_2 system installed for fuel bays and engine room. Portable dry chemical and foam extinguishers also fitted.

ELECTRICAL: Two systems, dc and ac. 24V dc system operates navigation lights, radio and starts auxiliary engines. AC system, for all the other requirements, comprises two diesel generating sets delivering 70kVA, 220V, three-phase 50Hz. Meters for monitoring voltage, amperage. frequency and power of ac systems are on main switchboard, located in engine room, from which isolated or parallel operation of the two alternators is controlled. Also on board are circuit breaker and switches for the transformer when the craft is connected to shore power, and distributing panels for the power and lighting system.

SAFETY: The presence of smoke, fire and high temperatures in various parts of the craft, as well as the malfunctioning of machinery, auxiliary sys-

tems and hydraulics automatically sets off an electric alarm.

NAVIGATION AND COMMUNICATIONS: The craft are equipped with all navigation lights as well as an electrically operated horn and signal lights. Communications and navigation systems (radio, Decca Navigator and Flight Log etc) are fitted to the customers' requirements and are therefore considered optional equipment.

M 300

DIMENSIONS

Length, overall: 30·95m (101ft 6in)
 waterline: 26·25m (86ft 1in)
Beam, moulded: 6·2m (20ft 4in)
 across foils: 12·5m (41ft 4in)
Draft, hullborne: 3·7m (12ft 1in)
 foilborne: 1·4m (4ft 7in)
WEIGHTS
Displacement: 92 tonnes (90 tons)
Military payload: 15 tonnes (14·76 tons)
Liquids, fuel oil and water: 11·7 tonnes (11·52 tons)
PERFORMANCE
Max speed: in excess of 68·5km/h (37 knots)
Cruising speed: 66·5km/h (36 knots)
Cruising range: 925km (500n miles)

M 600

DIMENSIONS

Length, overall: 35m (114ft 9in)
 waterline: 30·1m (98ft 9in)
Beam, moulded: 7m (23ft)
 across foils: 14·4m (47ft 3in)
Draft, hullborne: 4·55m (14ft 11in)
 foilborne: 2·15m (7ft)
WEIGHTS
Displacement: 125 tonnes
Military payload: 21·45 tonnes
Liquids, fuel, oil and water: 16·3 tonnes
PERFORMANCE
Max speed: 70·5km/h (38 knots)
Cruising speed: 68·5km/h (37 knots)
Cruising range: 925km (500n miles)

Artist's impression of M 600 hydrofoil fast patrol boat

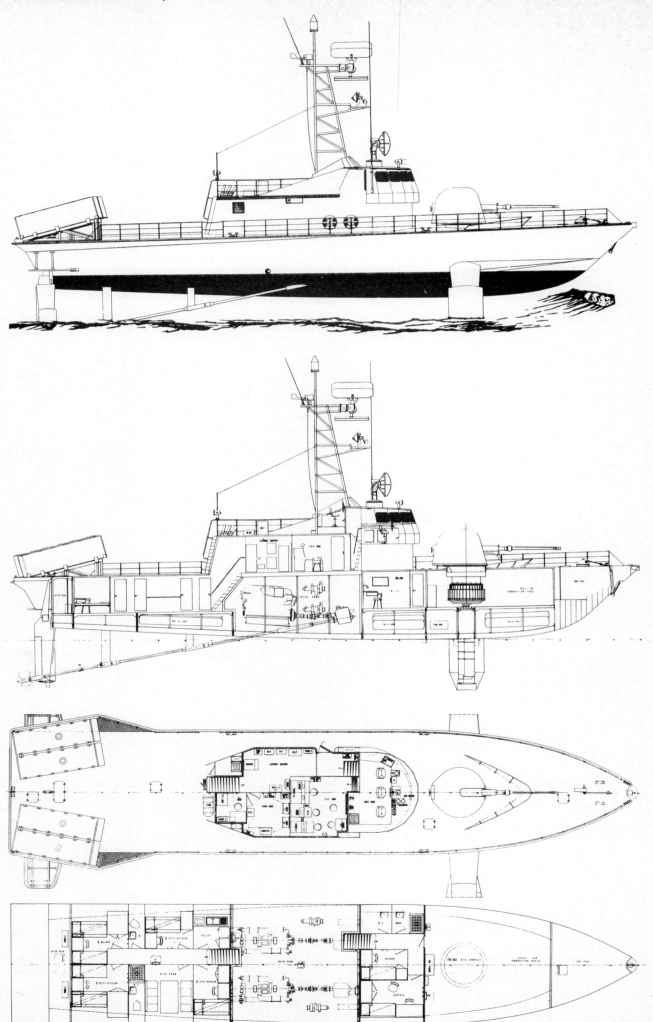

M 600 variant with four missiles and a single dual-purpose naval gun mount forward

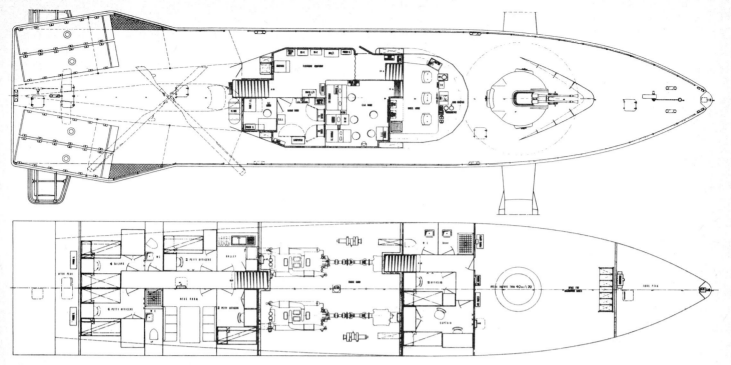

This version of the M 600 has a helicopter landing pad above the missile launchers aft. A Breda-Bofors twin 40mm/L70 or similar dual-purpose rapid-fire cannon is mounted forward

JAPAN

HITACHI SHIPBUILDING & ENGINEERING CO LTD

Head Office: 6-14 Edobori 1-chome, Nishi-ku, Osaka, Japan
Telephone: Osaka 443 8051
Telex: J 63376
Works: 4-1 Mizue-cho, Kawasaki-ku, Kawasaki, Kanagawa Pref, Japan
Telephone: Kawasaki 288 1111
Officials:
Takao Nagata, *Chairman of the Board of Directors*
Masao Kinoshita, *President*
Toshikazu Yuguchi, *Executive Vice President, General Manager of Ship Business Headquarters (Sales Director)*
Norimasa Ishii, *Manager of Kanagawa Works*

Hitachi, the Supramar licensee in Japan, has been building PT 3, PT 20 and PT 50 hydrofoils since 1961. The majority of these have been built for fast passenger ferry services across the Japanese Inland Sea, cutting across deep bays which road vehicles might take two to three hours to drive round, and out to offshore islands. Other PT 20s and 50s have been exported to Hong Kong, Australia and South Korea for ferry services.

Specifications of the PT 3 (*Jane's Surface Skimmers 1967-68*), PT 20 and PT 50 will be found under Supramar (Switzerland). The Hitachi-built craft are identical apart from minor items.

In the spring of 1974, the company completed

First PT 50 Mk II to be completed is the *Hikari 2*, built by Hitachi Shipbuilding & Engineering Co at its Kawasaki yard for Setonaikai Kisen Co Ltd. The vessel, which carries 123 passengers and a crew of seven, is employed on the route Hiroshima-Imabari

the first PT 50 Mk II to be built at its Kawasaki yard. The vessel *Hikari 2,* is powered by two licence-built MTU MB 820Db diesels, seats 123 passengers and cruises at 33 knots. It was delivered to its owner, Setonaikai Kisen Co Ltd, of Hiroshima City in March 1975.

Hitachi has constructed twenty-five PT 50s and fourteen PT 20s.

A special military hydrofoil, based on the Schertel-Sachsenburg foil system, and designated PT 32, has been designed by the company and two are in service with the Philippine Navy.

POLAND

GDANSK SHIP RESEARCH INSTITUTE

Technical University, Gdansk, Poland
Telephone: 414712

Research on problems connected with hydrofoil design and construction has been conducted by the Department of Theoretical Naval Architecture at Gdansk Technical University since 1956.

Experience with various dynamic test models led to the construction of the K-3 four-seat runabout which, powered by an FSC Lublin con-

verted auto-engine, has a top speed of 50km/h (27 knots).

In 1961 the Department was invited by the Central Board of Inland Navigation and United Inland Shipping and River Shipyards Gdansk, to design a hydrofoil passenger ferry for service in the Firth of Szczecin. Designated ZRYW-1 the craft seats 76 passengers and cruises at 35 knots. It was completed in 1965.

During 1966 the Ship Research Institute designed two hydrofoil sports craft, the WS-4 Amor and the WS-6 Eros. The prototypes were completed in 1967 and both types were put into

series production during 1972.

In 1971, a catamaran-hulled research hydrofoil, the Badacz II, was built for the Ship Hydrodynamics Division of the Institute. The vessel is employed to tow models of ACVs and hydrofoils in coastal waters and provide data and performance measurements. It is also being employed to test new propulsion systems.

The largest hydrofoil craft to be designed by the Institute is a 300-ton passenger/car ferry.

Details of the ZRYW-1, Amor, Eros and Badacz II can be found in *Jane's Surface Skimmers 1974-75* and earlier editions.

ROMANIA

The Romanian navy is operating between 15 and 20 Chinese-designed Hu Chwan (White Swan)-class hydrofoil torpedo boats. The first three were shipped from the Hutang Shipyard, Shanghai, complete, while the remaining craft have been constructed locally under a building programme started in 1973.

Although the Romanian craft are identical outwardly in most respects to the imported models, there are minor differences in defensive armament and superstructure design.

FOILS: System comprises a bow subfoil to stabilise pitch and facilitate take-off and a main foil of trapeze or shallow V configuration set back approximately one-third of the hull length from the bow. At high speed in relatively calm conditions the greater part of the forward hull is raised clear of the water. The mainfoil and struts retract upwards when the craft is required to cruise in displacement conditions.

HULL: High speed V-bottom hull in seawater resistant light alloy.

POWER PLANT: Three 1,100hp M50 or M401 watercooled, supercharged 12 cylinder, V-type diesels, each driving its own inclined propeller shaft.

ARMAMENT: Two 21in torpedo tubes, plus four 14·5mm cannon in two twin mounts.

Romanian-built hydrofoil torpedo boat of the Chinese designed Hu Chwan class *(Jane's Fighting Ships)*

DIMENSIONS (Approx)
Length overall: 21·8m (71ft 6½in)
Beam overall: 5·02m (16ft 6in)
Hull beam: 3·96m (13ft)
Draft, hullborne: 1m (3ft 3in)

WEIGHTS
Displacement full load: 45 tons
PERFORMANCE
Max speed foilborne, calm conditions: 55 knots
Range: 926km (500n miles) approx

SINGAPORE

VOSPER PRIVATE LIMITED

Mailing Address: PO Box 95, Singapore 1
Telephone: 4467144
Telex: RS 21219
Cables: Vosper Singapore
Administration/Works: 200 Tanjong Rhu, Singapore 1543
Officials:
A Gilchrist, *Managing Director*
C F Campbell, *Sales and Commercial Director*
C V Cripps, *Marketing Director, West Asia and East Africa*
R M W Oldfield, *Marketing Director, Middle East*
C J Dake, *Marketing Director, Far East*

Vosper Private Limited, the Singapore-based subsidiary of Vosper Limited, is the sole builder in South-east Asia of the Supramar range of hydrofoils. The company has a building licence agreement with Supramar Hydrofoils AG of Lucerne, Switzerland.

Vosper Private Limited is building PT 20s and PT 50s and marketing them in the Far East. This is the first time any Singapore shipyard has built hydrofoils.

Supramar PT 20B Mk II built by Vosper Private Ltd at its Singapore yard

The vessels under construction are mainly for export. They will be used for high speed passenger transport, logistic support and patrol duties. Details of the designs are given in this section under Supramar Hydrofoils AG, Switzerland.

SWITZERLAND

SUPRAMAR HYDROFOILS AG

Ausserfeld 5, CH-6362 Stansstad, Switzerland
Telephone: (041) 61 31 94
Telex: 78228 Supra CH
Officials:
Baron Hanns von Schertel, *President*
Dipl Ing Harry Trevisani, *General Manager*
Dipl Ing Eugen Schatté, *Research and Development*
Jürg Bally, *Board Member*
Ernst Schneider, *Board Member*

Supramar was founded in Switzerland in 1952 to develop on a commercial basis the hydrofoil system introduced by the Schertel-Sachsenberg Hydrofoil Syndicate and its licensee, the Gebruder Sachsenberg Shipyard. Supramar AG was reorganised in April 1980 under the name of Supramar Hydrofoils AG.

The co-operation between the companies started in 1937 and led to the development of the VS6, a 17-ton hydrofoil, which in 1941 attained 47·5 knots, and the VS8, an 80-ton supply hydrofoil completed in 1943 which attained 41 knots. The inherently stable, rigid V-foil system

Supramar PT 20 built by Hitachi Shipbuilding & Engineering Co Ltd

used on these and subsequent Supramar vessels, stems from experimental work undertaken by Baron Hanns von Schertel between 1927-1937.

In May 1953, a Supramar PT 10, 32-passenger hydrofoil began the world's first regular passenger hydrofoil service on Lake Maggiore, between Switzerland and Italy. In August 1956, the first Rodriquez-built Supramar PT 20 opened a service across the Straits of Messina and became the first hydrofoil to be licensed by a marine classification authority for carrying passengers at sea.

Supramar employs a staff of highly qualified scientists and engineers specialising in hydrodynamics, marine engineering, foil design, propulsion and shipyard production. In addition to building its own hydrofoils it licenses other shipyards to produce its hydrofoil designs.

Supramar hydrofoils being built by these companies are referred to elsewhere in this section under the respective company headings.

The latest Supramar design is the PTS 75 Mk III, a development of the PT 50 with increased engine power and full air stabilisation. The prototype was constructed by Vosper Thornycroft at the company's Portchester yard and delivered to Hong Kong in late 1974. The second vessel of this type was completed in early 1976 by Supramar's licensee in Hong Kong. The company has also completed designs for a modernised PT 50 which is available as the PT 50 Mk II. A new version of the PTS 150 Mk II has been operating between Miami and the Bahamas and is now operating between Toronto and Youngstown, New York, near Niagara Falls. This is the PTS 150 Mk III, a second generation craft with improved performance and greater passenger comfort.

The company is also developing a fully sub-merged foil system with air stabilisation. First craft to use this system is the Supramar ST 3A, a 4·9-ton experimental boat built under a US Navy contract. During tests in the Mediterranean it demonstrated promising stability and seakeeping qualities and reached a speed of 54·5 knots. Military and para-military versions of all Supramar commercial hydrofoils are now available. In addition Supramar has completed the design of a patrol boat hydrofoil which meets the tactical requirements of the NATO navies. The vessel, the MT 250G, has an operational displacement of 250 tons and a maximum intermittent speed of 60 knots.

Supramar's latest hydrofoil concept is the CT 70, a hydrofoil catamaran designed especially for use in shallow waters where draft limitations preclude the use of conventional hydrofoil craft.

PT 20 Mk II

The PT 20 Mk II, a 27-ton boat for 72 passengers, is considered by Supramar to be the smallest size hydrofoil suitable for passenger-carrying coastal services. The first of this very successful series was built by the Rodriquez shipyard at Messina in 1955 and since then nearly 70 PT 20s of various types have been built in Sicily, Japan, Netherlands and Norway. The design has been approved by almost every classification society. Fast patrol boat variants are also available.

FOILS: Foils are of standard Schertel-Sachsenberg, surface-piercing type, with 58% of the load supported by the bow foil and the remaining 42% by the rear foil. Submerged foil area in foilborne condition is 5·5m². Together with the struts and a horizontal guide, each foil forms a uniform framework which facilitates the exchange of the foil elements. The medium steel foils are of partly hollow, welded construction. The angle of incidence of the bow foil can be adjusted within narrow limits from the steering stand by means of a hydraulic ram operating on a foil support across the hull. To counteract the effects of large variations in passenger load and to ensure optimum behaviour in sea waves the angle of attack can be adjusted during operation.

HULL: The hull has a V-bottom with an externally added step riveted into place. Frames, bulkheads, foundations, superstructure and all internal construction is in corrosion-proof light alloy. Platings are of AlMg 5 and the frames, bars and other members are made in AlMgSi. Watertight compartments are provided below the passenger decks and in other parts of the hull.

POWER PLANT: Power is supplied by a supercharged, 12-cylinder MTU 12V 493 Ty 70 diesel with an exhaust turbo-compressor. Maximum continuous output is 1,100hp at 1,400rpm. A BW 800/HS 20 reversible gear, developed by Zahnradfabrik Friedrichshafen AG, is placed between the engine and the drive shaft.

ACCOMMODATION: The boat is controlled entirely from the bridge which is located above the engine room. Forty-six passengers are accommodated in the forward cabin, twenty in the rear compartment and six aft of the pilot's stand in the elevated wheelhouse. There is an emergency exit in each passenger compartment, and the craft is equipped with an inflatable life raft and life belts for each person. A crew of four is carried.

SYSTEMS, ELECTRICAL: 24V generator driven by the main engine: batteries with a capacity of approx 250Ah.

HYDRAULICS: 120kg/cm² pressure hydraulic system for rudder and bow foil incidence control.

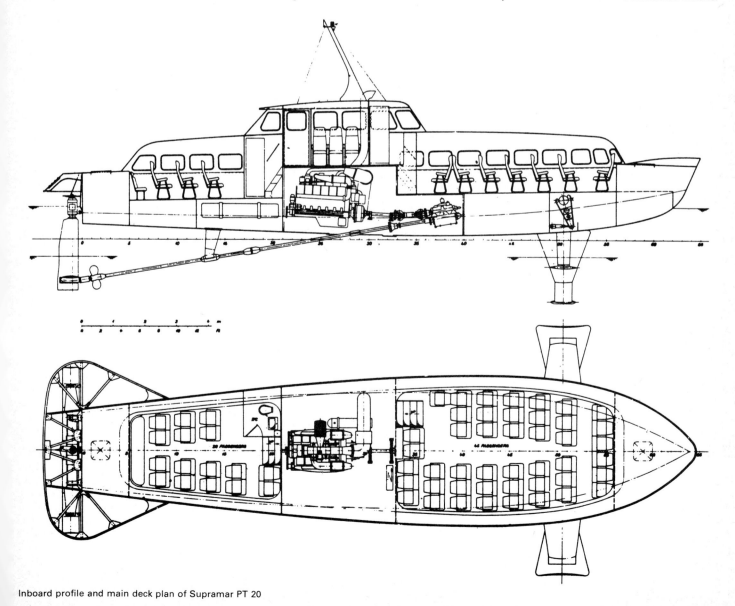

Inboard profile and main deck plan of Supramar PT 20

COMMUNICATIONS AND NAVIGATION: VHF ship-shore radio is supplied as standard equipment. Radar is optional.

DIMENSIONS

EXTERNAL

Length overall, hull: 20·75m (68ft 1in)
  over deck: 19·95m (65ft 6in)
Hull beam, max: 4·99m (16ft 4in)
Width across foils: 8·07m (26ft 5in)
Draft hullborne: 3·08m (10ft 1in)
  foilborne: 1·4m (4ft 7in)

INTERNAL

Aft cabin (including w/c): 13·5m² (145ft²)
Volume: 27m³ (954ft³)
Forward cabin: 26m² (280ft²)
Volume: 50m³ (1,766ft³)
Main deck level (including wheelhouse): 12m² (129ft²)
Volume: 24m³ (847ft³)

WEIGHTS

Gross tonnage: approx 56 tons
Max take-off displacement: 32 tons
Light displacement: 25 tons
Deadweight (including fuel, oil, water, passengers, baggage and crew): 7 tons
Payload: 5·4 tons

PERFORMANCE (with normal payload)
Cruising speed, foilborne: 63km/h (34 knots)
Max permissible wave height in foilborne mode: 1·29m (4ft 3in)
Designed range at cruising speed: 400km (216 miles)
Turning radius: 130m approx (427ft)
Take-off distance: 150m approx (493ft)
Take-off time: 25 seconds
Stopping distance: 70m (230ft)
Fuel consumption at cruising speed: 150kg/h (330lb/h)

SEA TEST: Prototype tests were undertaken in the Mediterranean in every kind of sea condition, and further tests have taken place off Japan. Acceleration measurements have shown maximum values below 0·5g when accelerometer had been fitted above the bow foil. Maximum lateral acceleration was 0·32g. Measurements were made in wave heights of approximately 1·2–1·5m. These are the maximum measurements obtained and subsequent tests have seldom equalled these figures.

PT 20B Mk II

In this model of the PT 20, the engine room and bridge are arranged in the foreship. This improves the pilot's vision in waters likely to have an influx of driftwood and provides a large main passenger cabin with seats for 55 and an upper deck cabin with seating for 16 passengers.

The layout of this craft has been based on experience gained with the Supramar PT 27 which was designed for servicing the offshore drilling platforms on Lake Maracaibo. This design has been slightly modified to meet the requirements of passenger services.

FOILS: The foil design is similar to that of the PT 20 Mk II. About 66% of the total weight is borne by the bow foil and 34% by the rear foil. Submerged foil area in foilborne condition is 6·2m². The forward foil can be tilted within narrow limits by means of a hydraulic ram acting on the foil strut supporting tube. The angle of attack can therefore be adjusted during operation to assist take-off and to counteract the effect of large variations in passenger loads.

HULL: This is of riveted light metal alloy design and framed on a combination of longitudinal and transverse formers. Watertight compartments are provided below the passenger decks and in other parts of the hull, and some are filled with foam-type plastic.

POWER PLANT: Power is supplied by a supercharged 12-cylinder MTU 12V 493 Ty 70 diesel with a maximum continuous output of 1,100hp at 1,400rpm. Average time between major overhauls is approximately 10,000 hours. Engine output is transferred to a three-bladed 700mm diameter bronze subcavitating propeller through a BW 800/H 20 reversible gear made by Zahnradfabrik. The propeller shaft is supported at three points by seawater lubricated rubber bearings.

Supramar PT 20B

ACCOMMODATION: The PT 20B Mk II has a crew of four and seats 71 passengers. The main passenger compartment seats 55, and the small cabin behind the pilot's stand seats a further 16. Access to the main compartment is through either of two doors, located port and starboard, to the rear of the wheelhouse. An emergency exit is provided at the rear of the main passenger compartment.

The PT 20B Mk II can also be delivered with fully integrated air conditioning equipment. The total passenger capacity will then be reduced to 69.

A full range of safety equipment is carried, including inflatable rafts and lifebelts for each passenger and crew member.

SYSTEMS, ELECTRICAL: 24V generator driven by the main engine, batteries with a capacity of approximately 250Ah.

HYDRAULICS: 120kg/cm² pressure hydraulic system for operating rudder and bow foil angle of incidence control.

COMMUNICATIONS AND NAVIGATION: A VHF ship-shore radio is supplied as standard equipment. Radar is an optional extra.

DIMENSIONS

EXTERNAL

Length overall, hull: 20·85m (68ft 5in)
  over deck: 19·5m (64ft)
Hull beam, max: 5·16m (16ft 11in)
Width over foils: 8·6m (28ft 3in)
Draft hullborne: 3m (9ft 10in)
  foilborne: 1·3m (4ft 3in)

INTERNAL

Main passenger compartment (including w/c):
  Length: 9·3m (30ft 7in)
  Width: 3·8m (12ft 6in)
  Height: 2m (6ft 7in)
  Floor area: 22·1m² (237ft²)
  Volume: 44m³ (1,553ft³)

WEIGHTS

Gross tonnage: 50 tons approx
Max take-off displacement: 32·5 tons
Light displacement: 25·4 tons
Deadweight (including fuel, oil, water, passengers, luggage, crew): 7·5 tons
Payload: 5·8 tons

PERFORMANCE (with normal payload)
Cruising speed: 63km/h (34 knots)
Max permissible wave height in foilborne mode: 1·29m (4ft 3in)
Turning radius: approx 130m (426ft)
Take-off distance: approx 150m (492ft)
Take-off time: approx 30 seconds
Stopping distance: approx 70m (231ft)
Stopping time: approx 10 seconds
Fuel consumption at cruising speed: 150kg/h (330lb/h)

PT 20 Mk IIs and PT 20B Mk IIs

These are high-speed versions of the PT 20 Mk II and PT 20B Mk II. Each is powered by a single supercharged MTU 12V 396 TB 83 diesel with a continuous output of 1,560hp at 1,845 rpm.

PERFORMANCE
Cruising speed: 72km/h (39 knots)

PTL 28

The PTL 28 is derived from the PT 27 utility and oil rig supply vessel, three of which have been in service for twenty years with the Shell Oil Company on Lake Maracaibo, Venezuela.

Features of the new craft include facilities for loading across the bow as well as the stern, twin rudders for improved manoeuvrability, and a variety of structural and mechanical modifications to simplify and reduce maintenance. The Schottel drive now has only two bevel gears, the hull is of welded construction, and the foil and propeller mounting arrangements have been redesigned to facilitate servicing. All components of a non-essential nature have been omitted.

Normally seats are provided for 54, but the number of passengers can be increased if the range is reduced. The weather deck above the engine room is available for cargo; heavy loads are compensated by a reduction in passenger capacity. A cargo compartment can be made available at the rear of the passenger cabin (up to frame 17), a typical load being 1,825kg (4,023lb) of cargo combined with 33 passengers.

FOILS: Schertel-Sachsenberg surface-piercing

Supramar PTL 28, employed by Shell for servicing offshore oil platforms on Lake Maracaibo, Venezuela

system similar to that of the PT 20 Mk II. Bow foil of hollow welded stainless steel. Foil, vertical struts, inclined fins and horizontal supporting tube form a framed structure which can easily be detached when necessary. The complete assembly divides into two to facilitate transport. Once the angle of incidence is adjusted no further alteration is necessary.

The rear foil is similar to the bow foil in type and construction. The complete system is mounted on its bearings at the transom by four bolts.

HULL: Constructed in seawater-resistant light metal alloy, the V-bottomed hull is of hard chine type and framed longitudinally. All joints are welded. Hoist fittings are provided to facilitate maintenance.

POWER PLANT: Power is supplied by a 12-cylinder MTU 12V493 Ty 70 diesel, rated at 1,000hp at 1,400rpm continuous and 1,350hp at 1,500rpm maximum.

Engine output is transferred to a three-bladed bronze propeller through a Zahnradfabrik BW 800 H20 reverse gearbox. Hullborne propulsion is provided by a 150hp diesel engine directly coupled to a Schottel Z-drive unit which can be rotated through 360 degrees. During take-off and when foilborne, the lower bevel gear and hullborne propeller are retracted hydraulically into a recess in the hull bottom.

ACCOMMODATION: The PTL 28 has a crew of three and seats 54 passengers in a single saloon aft of the engine room. The bridge is located forward and provides a 360 degree view. The captain's seat, together with the operating controls and instrumentation, is located on the hull centreline.

DIMENSIONS
EXTERNAL
Length overall, hull: 20·75m (68ft 1in)
  over deck: 19·95m (67ft 6in)
Hull beam, max: 4·99m (16ft 4in)

Width over foils: 8m (26ft 3in)
Draft hullborne: 2·95m (9ft 8in)
  foilborne: 1·5m (4ft 11in)
WEIGHTS
Displacement fully loaded: 28 tonnes (27·56 tons)
Disposable load: 5·6 tonnes (5·51 tons)
Light displacement: 22·4 tonnes (22·05 tons)
PERFORMANCE
Max speed: 72km/h (39 knots)
Cruising speed: 65km/h (35 knots)
Range: 260km (140n miles) approx

PT 50 Mk II

The successful and profitable operation of the PT 20 led to the development of the PT 50, a 63-ton hydrofoil passenger ferry designed for offshore and inter-island services. The prototype was completed early in 1958, and more than 30 are operating regular passenger services in areas ranging from the Baltic and Mediterranean to the Japanese Inland Sea.

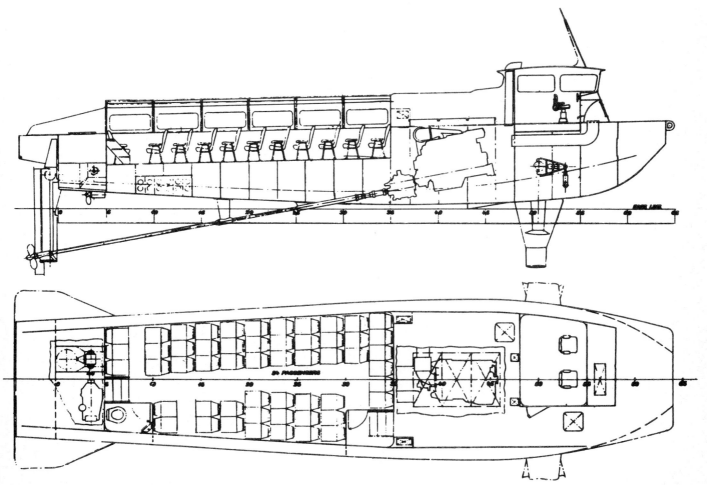

Inboard profile and passenger deck plan of Supramar PTL 28 utility craft and supply vessel

The craft has been approved by almost every Classification Society including Registro Italiano Navale, Germanischer Lloyd, Det norske Veritas, American Bureau of Shipping and the Japanese Ministry of Transport. The requirements of the SOLAS 1960 convention for international traffic can be met by the type if required.

FOILS: Both rear and forward foils are rigidly attached to the hull but the lift of the forward foil can be modified by hydraulically operated flaps, which are fitted to assist take-off and turning, and for making slight course corrections and adjustment of the flying height. The foils are of hollow construction using fine grain and MSt 52-3 steel throughout. Foils in stainless steel construction are optional.

The bow foil comprises the following elements:

two fins, forming connecting links between the foil and the supporting structure which is riveted to the hull;

the hydrofoil, which (according to its foil section characteristics) generates the lift and, with the stern foil, provides transverse stability in foilborne conditions;

two struts, which transmit the main lift loads to the supporting structure.

The rear foil system comprises the following elements:

the hydrofoil, which generates the lift;

two side struts;

a single rudder which transmits the lift to the supporting structure.

For improved passenger comfort the PT 50 Mk II can be provided with a roll stabiliser on the bow foil. The system, including the motion sensing device, has been developed by Supramar.

HULL: Of hard chine construction, the hull is of partly riveted, partly welded light metal alloy design and framed on longitudinal and transverse formers. Steel is used only for highly stressed parts such as the foil fittings, and the shaft brackets and exits.

ACCOMMODATION: The PT 50 Mk II is available in three interior configurations:

1. For 111 passengers including bar and catering facilities.
2. Standard version, with seats for 122 passengers.
3. Commuter version, seating 136 passengers.

The crew varies from 6-8 members, depending mainly on local regulations.

Passenger seats are of lightweight aircraft type and the centre aisle between the seat rows has a clear width of 76cm (30in). Ceilings are covered with lightweight plastic material and the walls, including web frames, are clad in luxury plywood or artificial wood. Toilets are provided in the rear and forward passenger spaces. Floors in the passenger compartments are provided with thick carpets. Each passenger compartment has an emergency exit. Inflatable life rafts and lifebelts are provided for 110% of the passenger and crew capacity.

POWER PLANT: The craft is powered by two MTU 12V 331 TC 71 turbocharged diesels, each developing 1,100hp at 2,140rpm continuous. Engine output is transmitted to two three-bladed 700mm diameter bronze propellers through two inclined stainless steel propeller shafts, each supported at four points by seawater lubricated runner bearings. Reverse and reduction gear with built-in thrust is manufactured by Zahnradfabrik Friedrichshafen, West Germany. The reverse clutches are solenoid-operated from the bridge.

Eight cylindrical fuel tanks with a total capacity of 3,650 litres are located in the aft peak and below the tank deck. Oil capacity is 320 litres.

SYSTEMS, ELECTRICAL: Engine driven generator; 24V battery set.

HYDRAULICS: 120kg/cm² pressure hydraulic system for operating twin rudders and front foil flaps.

AIR CONDITIONING: Air conditioning can be provided as optional equipment.

COMMUNICATIONS AND NAVIGATION: Standard equipment includes UHF and VHF radio telephone. Radar and Decca Navigator is optional.

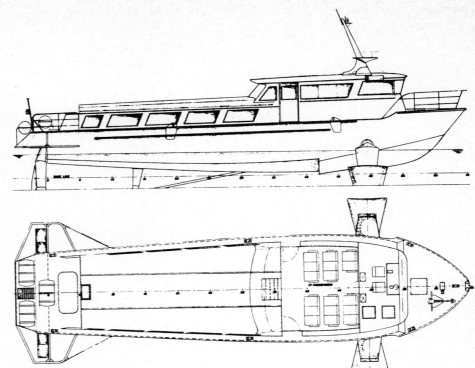

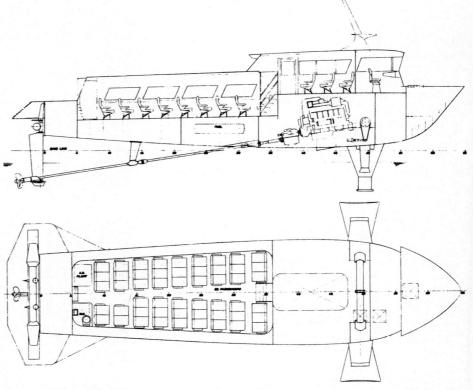

Outboard profile and plan and inboard profile and passenger deck of Supramar PT 20B Mk II

Guia, a Hitachi-built PT 50, which has been in regular service with Far East Hydrofoil Co Ltd on the 36km Hong Kong-Macao route for more than 10 years

DIMENSIONS

EXTERNAL

Length overall: 27·75m (91ft)
   over deck: 26·4m (86ft 7in)
Hull beam max: 5·84m (19ft 2in)
Beam over deck: 5·46m (17ft 11in)
Width over foils: 10·8m (35ft 5in)
Draft hullborne: 3·55m (11ft 8in)
   foilborne: 1·55m (5ft 1in)

INTERNAL

Aft passenger compartment (including w/c):
   Length: 9m (29ft 7in)
   Width: 4·9m (16ft)
   Height: 2m (6ft 7in)
   Floor area: 44·1m² (474ft²)
   Volume: 88m³ (3,108ft³)
Forward passenger compartment (including w/c):
   Length: 7·1m (23ft 3½in)
   Width: 5·4m (17ft 9in)
   Height: 2m (6ft 7in)
   Floor area: 37·3m² (412ft²)
   Volume: 67·6m³ (2,703ft³)
Main deck foyer:
   Length: 3·9m (12ft 9½in)
   Width: 4m (13ft 1½in)
   Height: 2m (6ft 7in)
   Floor area: 15m² (161ft²)
   Volume: 57·6m³ (2,030ft³)

WEIGHTS

Max take-off displacement: 63·3 tons
Light displacement: 49·3 tons
Deadweight (including fuel, oil, water, passengers, baggage and crew): 14 tons
Payload: 9·5 tons

PERFORMANCE (with normal payload)

Max speed foilborne: 67·5km/h (36·5 knots)
Cruising speed foilborne: 63km/h (34 knots)
Range: 600km (325n miles)
Turning radius: 470m (1,542ft)
Take-off distance: 250m (819ft)
Take-off time: 35 seconds
Stopping distance: 80m (264ft)
Time to stop craft: 10 seconds
Fuel consumption at cruising speed: 300kg/h (710lb/h)

PT 50 Mk IIs

This is a high speed version of the PT 50 Mk II, powered by two MTU 12V 396 TB 83 diesels, each developing 1,560hp at 1,845rpm.

PERFORMANCE

Cruising speed: 72km/h (39 knots)

PTS 75 Mk III

The Supramar PTS 75 Mk III is an advanced derivative of the PT 50. It seats up to 160 passengers and is designed for higher speed, improved seaworthiness and greater riding comfort. By increasing the specific PT 50 engine power of 43hp/ton to 50hp/ton a top speed of about 38 knots is obtained with the vessel fully loaded, and sufficient power is provided for operation in tropical waters.

An improved Schertel-Supramar air stabilisation system is fitted, and this, combined with a new W-foil configuration, considerably reduces rolling, pitching and vertical accelerations. The vessel can operate foilborne in waves up to 1·82m (6ft) in height with full power.

The prototype was completed at the Vosper Thornycroft, Paulsgrove, Portsmouth yard in May 1974. The second craft of this type was completed in early 1976 by Supramar's licensee in Hong Kong, Supramar Pacific Shipbuilding Co Ltd.

FOILS: The foil configuration is surface-piercing and incorporates the Schertel-Supramar air stabilisation system. The bow foil assembly forms a rigid framework which facilitates the exchange of the foil structure. The foil is of hollow steel construction. It has three supporting struts, one on the centre line and one on either side. These are bolted to welded steel suspension points on the keel and chine respectively. Hydraulically operated flaps are fitted to the trailing edges to assist take-off, facilitate course corrections and provide automatic stabilisation when low frequency disturbances are encountered.

The rear foil is of surface-piercing Schertel-Supramar type and attached to the transom.

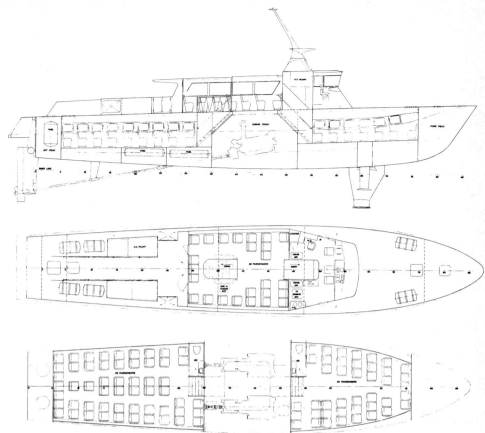

Inboard and outboard profiles and deck plans of Supramar PT 50 Mk II

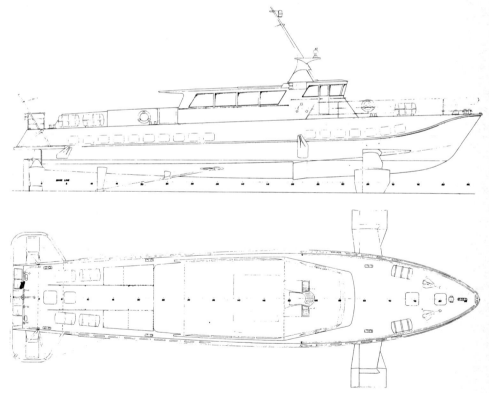

Method of construction is the same as that employed for the bow foil. The complete assembly—foil, rudder sternpost, rudder, and two inclined struts—forms a rigid frame unit which is attached or detached as necessary. The aftermost propeller bearings are attached to the foil, the propellers being sited aft of the foil.

HULL: Hard chine type, constructed in partly riveted, partly welded corrosion resistant light metal alloy. A longitudinal frame system is employed, with transverse frames 900mm apart. Steel is used only for highly stressed parts such as the foil fittings and shaft exits. A new hull construction method is being employed for this design. The hull is built in the inverted position and turned upright after the plating is completed.

HULL: Hard chine type, constructed in partly riveted, partly welded corrosion resistant light metal alloy. A longitudinal frame system is employed, with transverse frames 900mm apart. Steel is used only for highly stressed parts such as the foil fittings and shaft exits. A new hull construction method is being employed for this design. The hull is built in the inverted position and turned upright after the plating is completed.

ACCOMMODATION: Depending on operating requirements, between 130 and 160 passengers can be accommodated in three saloons. In the standard version airliner type seats are provided for 135 passengers, 19 in the upper aft saloon, 61 in the lower aft saloon and 55 in the lower forward saloon.

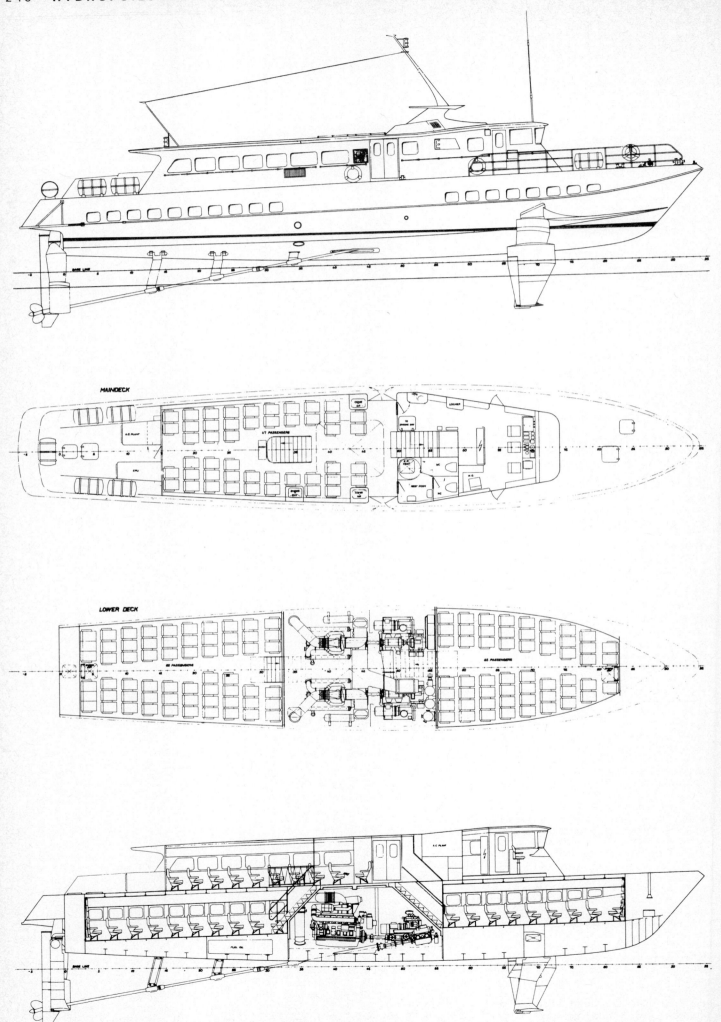

Inboard and outboard profiles and deck views of Supramar PTS 75 Mk III

Ceilings are covered with lightweight plastic material, walls including web frames, are clad in luxury ply or artificial wood, and the floors are provided with thick carpets.

Three toilets are installed on the upper deck, within easy reach of all three saloons.

Passengers board the craft through wide side doors on the upper deck opening to a central foyer from which companionways lead to the lower passenger saloons. A promenade deck is available aft of the upper saloon and can be reached by passengers from the lower saloons via the foyer. Sufficient space for luggage is provided in the foyer. The upper aft saloon can be modified into a small dining room, if required, reducing the passenger capacity by 19.

All passenger saloons have emergency exits. A lifebelt is stowed beneath each seat and most of the inflatable life rafts are stowed aft and on the forward main deck.

POWER PLANT: Power is supplied by two 12-cylinder, MTU MB12V 652 SB70 super-charged diesels, each with a normal continuous output of 1,650hp at 1,380rpm, and 1,950hp at 1,460rpm maximum. Under tropical conditions normal continuous rating is 1,590hp at 1,380rpm and 1,810hp at 1,460rpm maximum. Engine output is transferred to two 950mm (3ft 1⅜in) diameter three-bladed bronze propellers through a Zahnradfabrik BW 900 HS 15 reversible gearbox, which is hydraulically operated and remotely controlled from the wheelhouse. The propeller shafts are in stainless steel and

Second Supramar PTS 75 Mk III to be ordered by Far East Hydrofoil Co for the Hong Kong-Macao service, built in Hong Kong by Supramar Pacific Shipbuilding Co Ltd

supported at four points by seawater lubricated rubber bearings. Fuel is carried in integral tanks beneath the lower deck in the bottom compartments.

SYSTEMS, ELECTRICAL: Two 37kVA water-cooled 60Hz diesel-driven 380V generators

installed in the engine room. An emergency generator of similar capacity is provided at main deck level.

HYDRAULICS: 120kg/cm² pressure hydraulic system for operating all hydraulic driven consumers.

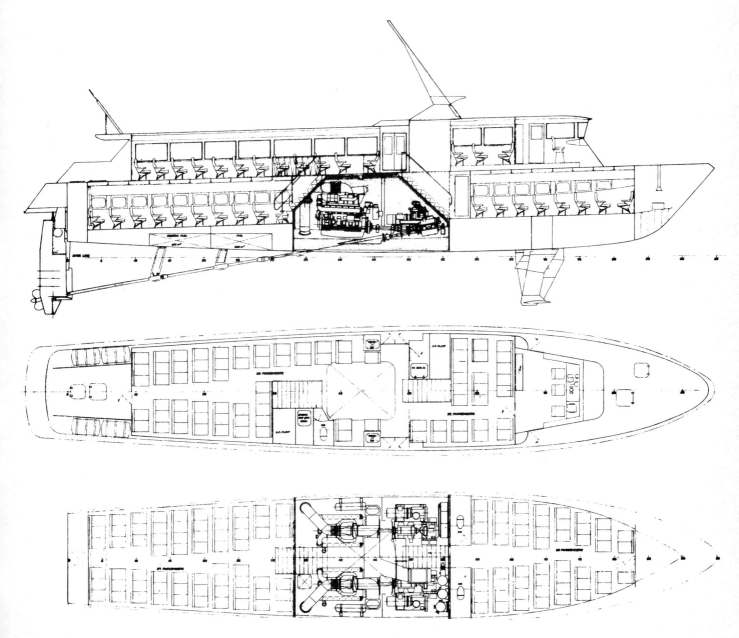

Inboard profile and deck plans of Supramar PT 100, short-haul commuter version of PTS 75 Mk III, accommodating 200 passengers

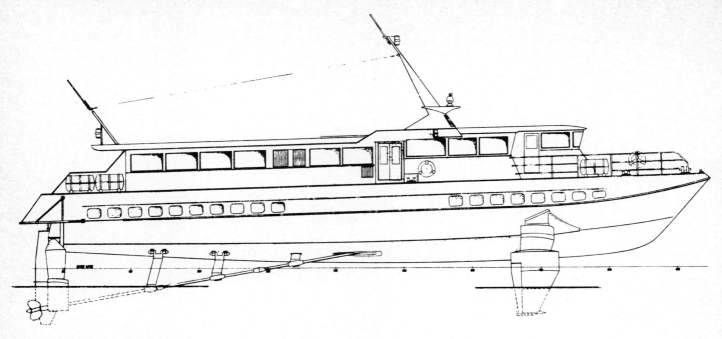

Outboard profile of Supramar PT 100

AIR CONDITIONING: An air conditioning system is provided. Capacity is sufficient for adequate temperature and humidity conditions in all passenger saloons and on the bridge when operating the craft in tropical conditions.

COMMUNICATIONS AND NAVIGATION: UHF radio, VHF radio-telephone and magnetic compass are standard. Radar, Decca Navigator and gyro compass to customer's requirements.

DIMENSIONS

EXTERNAL

Length overall, hull: 30m (98ft 6in)
   deck: 29·2m (96ft)
Hull beam max: 5·8m (19ft 1in)
Width across foils: 11·6m (38ft 1in)
Draft hullborne: 4m (13ft 1in)
   foilborne: 1·96m (6ft)

INTERNAL (standard version)

Aft lower saloon
   Length: 9m (29ft 6in)
   Width: 4·6m (15ft 1in)
   Height: 2·15m (7ft 1in)
   Floor area: 42m² (452ft²)
   Volume: 92m³ (3,249ft³)

Forward lower saloon
   Length: 8·1m (26ft 7in)
   Width: 4·7m (15ft 5in)
   Height: 2·15m (7ft 1in)
   Floor area: 37m² (398ft²)
   Volume: 82m³ (2,896ft³)

Upper aft saloon
   Length: 4·5m (14ft 9in)
   Width: 4·2m (13ft 9in)
   Height: 2·1m (6ft 11in)
   Floor area: 18m² (193ft²)
   Volume: 38m³ (1,342ft³)

Foyer
   Length: 5·1m (16ft 9in)
   Width: 4·2m (13ft 9in)
   Height: 2·1m (6ft 11in)
   Floor area: 20m² (215ft²)
   Volume: 42m³ (1,483ft³)

WEIGHTS

Max take-off displacement: 85 tons
Light displacement: 68·5 tons
Disposable load (including fuel, oil, water, passengers, luggage and crew): 16·5 tons

PERFORMANCE (with normal payload)

Cruising speed: 66·5km/h (36 knots)
Max speed: 72·5km/h (39 knots)
Range: 333km (180n miles)
Turning radius approx: 700m (2,350ft)
Take-off distance approx: 500m (1,600ft)
Take-off time approx: 50 seconds
Stopping distance approx: 100m (330ft)
Time to stop craft approx: 20 seconds
Fuel consumption at cruising speed: approx 600kg/h (1,323lb/h)

SUPRAMAR PT 100

A variant of the PTS 75 Mk III is the PT 100, designed especially for short-haul commuter routes and accommodating 200 passengers.

Main dimensions and characteristics are identical to those of the PTS 75 Mk III. The layout is shown in the accompanying general arrangement drawing.

PTS 150 Mk III

Supramar PTS 150 Mk III is an improved version of PTS 150 Mk II, the first of which was built in 1968 under the supervision of Norske Veritas and fulfils Solas requirements. Two of these vessels went into service in December 1970 between Las Palmas and Tenerife in the Canary Islands and in 1971 they operated between Palma, Majorca and Ibiza. Finally they were put into operation between Copenhagen and Malmö. A third vessel was added and all three PTS 150 Mk IIs have been in service between Florida and the Bahamas.

On the Mk III the speed has been increased to 40 knots, the most economic cruising speed for a craft of this size. In comparison with the Mk II the response to wave motions is further reduced as a result of the increased effectiveness of the stabilisation system.

FOILS: Combined surface-piercing and submerged system. Compared with the Mk II, the new configuration reduces the hydrodynamic resistance by about 20%. The forward foil is placed at frame 85 and the rear foil at the transom. The bow foil carries approximately 62% of the weight of the craft. In foilborne condition the boat is inherently stable.

The foil units are adjusted in such a way that the distance between baseline (keel without step) and water level at service speed amounts to 1·35m (4ft 5in). An additional adjustment of the flying height when travelling foilborne is possible by means of the hydraulically operated flaps of the forward foil and rear foil. These adjustments are remotely controlled from the bridge.

The lift generating foils are made of high-strength structural steel of fine grained type. All other parts, such as struts and rudders, are constructed of structural steel in accordance with German Standard MSt 52-3.

The W-shaped forward foil unit comprises the lift generating foil and the supporting elements, ie two side struts and one centre strut. Port and starboard side of the foil are detachably connected at the lower foil point. The foil unit is connected to the hullside foil fittings by means of steel bolts. The foil fittings themselves are made of steel, and form a part of the hull and are riveted to the light metal alloy hull part.

Similar to the forward foil unit the rear foil unit is of a closed frame structure formed by the pipe girder, two struts, one hydraulically operated rudder and the lift producing foil. The rudder transmits the main part of the lift of the rear foil through the pipe girder into the hull. The whole rear foil can easily be removed by dismounting four bolt connections. The aftmost propeller bearings are attached to the rear foil. The propellers are located behind the rear foil.

STABILISATION SYSTEM: The vessel is provided with an improved Supramar stabilisation system which enhances the seakeeping qualities and enables the boat to cope foilborne with waves up to 3m (10ft) at full power and up to 3·6m (12ft) at reduced speed.

Apart from the augmentation of effectiveness of the stabilisation resulting from speed increase, the new system generates higher motion reducing moments than obtained by the existing PTS 150s. This is particularly true for the pitch stabilisation and the avoidance of hull-wave contact in a following sea. A similar system has been paved on the PTS 75. The roll-stabilisation is similar to the system employed on the PTS 75 Mk III but is more effective. The bow centre strut produces stability augmentation and roll motion damping side forces with aid of alternate air-feeding to either side. These forces also counteract the transverse forces caused by the bow foil in a heeled position in a seaway, thus reducing lateral accelerations and greatly enhancing passenger comfort.

HULL AND SUPERSTRUCTURE: Partly riveted and partly welded construction employing a system of longitudinal and transverse frames. It has high deadrise and hard chine sections for performance as a planing hull and for structural impacts in a seaway while foilborne. A step is provided to facilitate take-off. While the main or structure deck is continuous from bow to stern, the lower deck is interrupted by the engine room, sited amidships. The superstructure, which is also longitudinally and transversally framed, is not included in the load bearing structure. Several expansion joints have therefore been provided.

The subdivision of the hull can be seen on the general arrangement drawing. The hull is subdivided by four watertight bulkheads (continuous from bottom to main deck) into five watertight main compartments. The double bottom frame 8 to frame 44 and from frame 71 to frame 102 is further subdivided separately by four watertight floor frames into six double bottom cells. The superstructure extends from frames 8 to 102 and is subdivided by transverse walls at frames 45 to 78 into three main compartments. The aft main

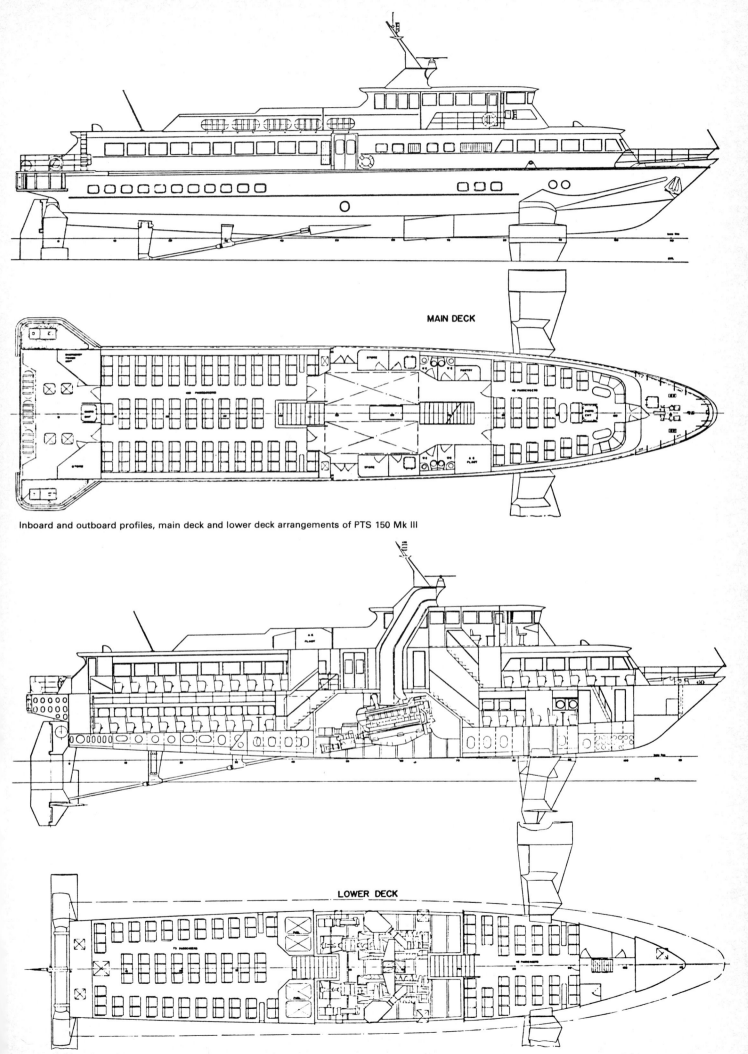

MAIN DECK

Inboard and outboard profiles, main deck and lower deck arrangements of PTS 150 Mk III

LOWER DECK

deck forms a partly roofed open air deck for the passengers' convenience.

ACCOMMODATION: The PTS 150 Mk III carries 270 passengers in four saloons, two on the main deck and two on the lower deck. The forward compartment main deck seats 46, and the aft compartment 105. On the lower deck the forward compartment seats 46 and the aft compartment 73.

Passengers board the craft through double doors to the single centralised foyer, from which doors and companion ladders lead to the respective passenger saloons on the upper and lower decks.

Provision is made for all passengers to be served in their seats with cold meals and drinks.

Passenger seats are of lightweight aircraft type. Floors and ceilings are covered with lightweight plastic materials and the walls are clad in luxury plywood. Each passenger saloon has fitted carpets. Each room has an independent ventilation unit. Four toilets are provided.

The bridge, which is on a separate level above the main deck, slightly forward of midships, is reached by a companion ladder at the aft of the forward passenger compartment. All passenger saloons have emergency exits.

The craft carries 13 inflatable RFD liferafts (for 110% of the classified number of passengers and crew) which are stowed along both sides of the superstructure deck, and on the aft maindeck. Lifejackets are arranged beneath the seats.

POWER PLANT: Power is supplied by two 16-cylinder four-stroke MTU MD 16V 956 TB82 supercharged diesels with a maximum continuous output of 2,800kW (3,800hp) at 1,500rpm. To improve torque characteristics during take-off two engine-mounted Maybach torque converters are provided.

Reverse and reduction gears are of the lightweight Zahnradfabrik BW 1500 HS 22 hydraulically-operated type, and incorporate the propeller thrust bearings. The gears are pneumatically remote controlled from the wheelhouse. The propeller shafts are made of a heat-treated stainless steel and each supported by five seawater lubricated rubber bearings. Two three-bladed propellers of approximately 1·3m are placed behind the rear foil.

SYSTEMS, ELECTRICAL: The following main systems are used:

For power, permanently installed heating and cooking apparatus: 380V rotary current, 50Hz three-wires, insulated from the ship's structure.

For light sockets and instrumentation: 220V ac, 50Hz two-wires, insulated from the ship's structure.

For remote control and monitoring: 24V dc, two-wires, insulated from the ship's structure.

Two shore connections are provided, both on the superstructure deck. The main shore connection is for the supply of the bus bar of the main switchboard. The second shore connection is exclusively for the heating of the boat and preheating of the main engine.

HYDRAULICS: Steering, variation of the front foil flap angle and the angle of the rear foil flap are all operated hydraulically. Each system has its own circuit which is monitored by a pressure controlled pilot lamp.

CONTROLS: Starting, manoeuvring and operation of the craft is controlled from the bridge, but in cases of emergency the main engines may be controlled from the engine room.

The two main engines are each controlled by an operating lever designed for singlehanded control. Propeller reversal is also by means of these levers, the reverse gear being actuated by pneumatic remote control between bridge and main engines.

To start the boat both operating levers must be put in the "full ahead" position simultaneously. Foilborne speed can be regulated by fine adjusting of the operating levers. No other control devices are necessary for the main engines.

Levers for variation of the front foil flap angle

Interior of the PT 150 DC showing the forward saloon on the upper deck

Aft saloon on the upper deck of the PT 150 DC seen from the rear

A PT 150D operating in the Baltic

and the angle of the rear foil flap are actuated only before and after starting. During foilborne operation these can be used for trim compensation. All instrumentation and monitoring equipment is installed on the bridge.

AIR CONDITIONING: The vessel is equipped with air conditioning and heating plant which guarantees a room temperature of between 20 and 25°C, dependent on the relative humidity. Air rate is 25m³/h/person.

COMMUNICATION AND NAVIGATION: Standard navigation equipment includes a gyro master compass with transformers, rectifiers and one multiple steering repeater positioned ahead of the helmsman, Loran or Decca Navigator and radar.

Communications equipment includes radio telephone equipment for normal and emergency use.

DIMENSIONS
EXTERNAL
Length overall, hull: 37·9m (124ft 3in)
    deck: 37·1m (121ft 10in)
Hull beam, max: 7·5m (24ft 7in)
Deck beam, max: 7·4m (24ft 3in)
Width across foils: 16m (52ft 5in)
Draft hullborne: 5·6m (18ft 4in)
    foilborne: 2·4m (7ft 9in)
WEIGHTS
Displacement, fully loaded: 175 tons
Disposable load (payload plus consumable stores): 35 tons
Passenger capacity: 270
PERFORMANCE
Cruising speed at 6,880hp: 74km/h (40 knots)
Range: 460km (250n miles)
Max permissible wave height in foilborne mode at full power (head seas) for passenger acceptability: 3m (10ft)

ST 3A FULLY SUBMERGED FOIL RESEARCH CRAFT

In 1965 the US Navy awarded Supramar a contract for the construction and testing of a five-ton research craft with fully submerged air stabilised foils. The objectives of the tests were the investigation of the effectiveness and reliability of the Schertel-Supramar air stabilisation system under a variety of wave conditions.

FOIL SYSTEM: The craft was fitted with two fully-submerged bow foils and one fully-submerged rear foil. The load distribution was 62% on the bow foils and 38% on rear foil. A rudder flap was attached to the end of the rear foil strut.

AIR FEED SYSTEM: Lift variation was achieved without movable foil parts. Each foil has two air ducts with outlets on the suction side. Air was drawn through these apertures from the free atmosphere via the foil suspension tube and the hollow struts. Air valves, controlled by sensors, governed the quantity of air admitted to the respective ducts.

CONTROLS: The signals of a depth sensor, a rate gyro and damped pendulum were added and amplified. The pneumatic follow-up amplifier drew its propulsion power from the subpressure which was produced at a suction opening at the strut near the foil. The amplifier output was connected with the air valve. The depth sensor probed the submergence depth digitally by means of suction orifices at the front struts. No motor-driven power source was required for the control system which, as well as the air feed system for lift variation of the foils, was designed for simplicity and reliability.

HULL: The hull, of hard chine construction, was basically that of a standard Supramar ST 3, modified to accommodate the new foil system, gas turbine and test equipment. To facilitate take-off, a step was provided and a ram wedge was fastened to the stern bottom. The hull clearance (tip of step to water surface) of only 36cm (1ft 2½in) was due to the requirement that an existing ST 3 hull, with an inclined propeller shaft, was to be used for the tests.

POWER PLANT: The craft was powered by a single 1,000hp GE 7 LM100 PG 102 gas turbine. Engine output was transferred to a 0·38m (1ft 3in) diameter S-C bronze propeller through a reduction gear, a V-drive and an inclined stainless steel shaft. A 35hp Mercury outboard was installed on the port side of the transom to provide auxiliary propulsion. To feed the stabilisation gyros a 6hp gasoline engine was installed in the forepeak and coupled to a three-phase ac generator.

DIMENSIONS
Length overall, hull: 10·32m (33ft 10in)
Width over foils: 3·6m (11ft 10in)
  over hull: 2·7m (8ft 10in)
Draft hullborne: 1·55m (5ft 1in)
  foilborne (front foil): 0·5m (1ft 7½in)
Hull clearance: 0·36m (1ft 2½in)

WEIGHTS
Displacement: 4·9 tons

PERFORMANCE
Max measured test speed: 101km/h (54·5 knots)
Max speed (design): 104km/h (56 knots)
Take-off time: 14·5 seconds
Stopping distance: 50-5 knots: 120m (390ft)
Turning radius at 40 knots: 230m (750ft)
SEA TEST: Sea trials along the Mediterranean coast revealed that the craft, despite a small hull clearance, was capable of taking waves 0·9–1·2m (3–4ft) high, and with a minimum length of about 30·4–36·4m (100–120ft), at 45 knots in all courses from head to beam seas, partially contouring. In waves over 1·2m (4ft) the hull periodically touched wave crests, which was accompanied by a marked speed reduction (very high Froude number) during water contacting. In a following sea, and in all courses up to about 60 degrees to a following sea, foilborne operation was limited to 0·76m (2ft 6in) waves due to the control system, which at that time had no heave sensor. At a wave height of 0·91m (3ft) (a tenth of boat length), vertical accelerations of only 0·08g had been measured, which compares very

Supramar ST 3A

favourably with the sea test results of other craft with fully submerged foils.

NAVAL HYDROFOILS

Derived from Supramar's range of commercial vessels, this new range of military hydrofoils is designed for naval defence duties, coast guard and anti-contraband patrol.

SUPRAMAR PAT 20

This military version of the Supramar PT 20B Mk II is in service with several navies for patrolling coastal and sheltered waters. It has good seakeeping capabilities for a craft of this size.

FOILS: Schertel-Sachsenberg surface-piercing type in structural steel.

POWER PLANT: The main propulsion engine is an MTU Type 331 12-cylinder, four-stroke diesel, developing 1,430hp maximum intermittent and 1,300hp continuous. Engine output is transferred to a three-bladed propeller via an inclined shaft.

HULL: Riveted seawater-resistant light metal alloy structure.

ARMAMENT: Two 40mm Bofors L/70 automatic guns, one forward, one aft. Ammunition stored in compartments beneath.

DIMENSIONS
Length overall: 21·75m (71ft 4in)
Width over foils: 8·6m (28ft 2in)
Draft hullborne: 3·1m (10ft 2in)
  foilborne: 1·4m (4ft 7in)

WEIGHTS
Displacement loaded: 31 tons
Disposable load (fuel, consumable stores, crew, provisions, armament and ammunition): 6·3 tons

PERFORMANCE
Cruising speed: 35 knots
Range: 536km (300n miles)

PAT 70

The PAT 70 is similar in design and construction to the PT 50 Mk II.

FOILS: Bow and rear foils are of surface-piercing V configuration and fabricated in structural steel.

HULL: Riveted light alloy construction.

POWER PLANT: Power is provided by two MTU MB 12V 652 12-cylinder four-stroke diesels, each rated at 1,725hp continuous and 1,950hp maximum intermittent. Engine output is transferred to two three-bladed propellers via twin inclined propeller shafts.

ARMAMENT: A typical weapon fit would comprise two 40mm Bofors L/70 automatic mounts, one forward, one aft.

DIMENSIONS
Length overall: 29·5m (96ft 9in)
Width over foils: 10·7m (35ft 1in)
Draft hullborne: 3·8m (12ft 6in)
  foilborne: 1·7m (5ft 7in)

WEIGHTS
Displacement loaded: 69 tons

Disposable load (fuel, consumable stores, crew, provisions, armament and ammunition): 14 tons

PERFORMANCE
Cruising speed: 39 knots
Range: 536km (300n miles)
Max permissible wave height foilborne: 1·8m (6ft) wave

NAT 85

Derived from the PTS 75 Mk III passenger ferry, this fast patrol boat variant is armed with a 40mm Breda Bofors twin naval mounting and Otomat guided missiles.

FOILS: Surface-piercing configuration, incorporating the Schertel-Supramar air stabilisation system.

HULL: Hard chine type, constructed in partly riveted, partly welded corrosion resistant light alloy.

POWER PLANT: Power is supplied by two MTU MB 16V 652 16-cylinder 4-stroke diesels, each rated at 2,300hp continuous and 2,610hp maximum. Engine output is transferred to two three-bladed propellers through a Zahnradfabrik reversible gearbox.

ARMAMENT: Anti-Ship Missiles: Two Otomat Mk I missile launchers aft. Guns: 40mm Breda Bofors L/70 twin naval mounting on the foredeck, ahead of the superstructure.

ELECTRONICS: Thomson-CSF Canopus C fire control system.

DIMENSIONS
Length overall: 30·4m (99ft 9in)
Width over foils: 12m (39ft 4in)
Draft hullborne: 4·3m (14ft 1in)
  foilborne: 2·3m (7ft 6in)

WEIGHTS
Displacement loaded: 85 tons
Disposable load (fuel, consumable stores, crew, provisions, armament and ammunition): 16 tons

PERFORMANCE
Cruising speed: 42 knots
Range: 741km (400n miles)
Max permissible wave height: 2·3m (7ft 6in) waves

NAT 90

Based on the PTS 75 Mk III, this alternative fast strike missilecraft variant has waterjet propulsion and fully retracting foils. It is intended for operations in areas where the hullborne draft would be too deep for satisfactory navigation, particularly in sheltered waters. The foils are retracted hydraulically above the waterline.

FOILS: Surface-piercing V configuration. Bow foil is "split" to permit the two halves to swivel upwards hydraulically. The aft foil assembly is built as a single unit and comprises the foils, a central rudder/water strut, to which the rudder flap is attached, and two side struts.

HULL: Hull and superstructure in combined riveted and welded seawater resistant light metal.

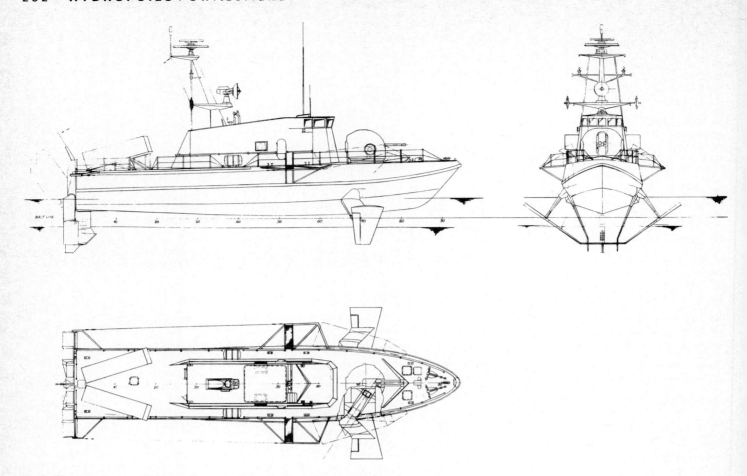

Outboard elevations and weatherdeck plan of Supramar NAT 90 fast strike missile craft

All compartments are air-conditioned, including the bridge.

POWER PLANT: Power for the waterjet propulsion system is supplied by two MTU MB 16V 652 16-cylinder, four-stroke diesels, each rated at 2,300hp continuous and 2,610hp maximum intermittent. Each is connected to a Rocketdyne Powerjet 18 single-stage, axial-flow waterjet. During foilborne operation water enters through an inlet located at the forward lower end of the aft centre foil strut. When the craft is operating in hullborne mode, with foils retracted, water enters the propulsion system through an inlet located in the bottom of the hull. Hullborne speed (foils retracted), with a single Powerjet 18 in use is 15 knots, with both Powerjets in use, 25 knots.

ARMAMENT: A typical weapons fit would be one Breda/Bofors L/70 twin 40mm mounting forward of the superstructure and two Exocet missile launchers aft.

DIMENSIONS

Length overall: 29·9m (98ft 1in)
Width across foils: 11·8m (38ft 8in)
Draft hullborne: 4·1m (13ft 5in)
   foils retracted: 1·3m (4ft 3in)
   foilborne: 1·9m (6ft 3in)

WEIGHTS

Displacement loaded: 85 tons
Disposable load (fuel, consumable stores, crew, provisions, armament and ammunition): 15 tons

PERFORMANCE

Max cruising speed: 39 knots
Range: 741km (400n miles)
Max permissible wave height: 2·3m (7ft 6in) waves

NAT 190

NAT 190 is the designation given to the military version of the Supramar PTS 150 Mk III. As a fast strike craft its main armament would comprise two 40mm Bofors L/70 automatic twin mounts and three Exocet MM 38 missile launchers.

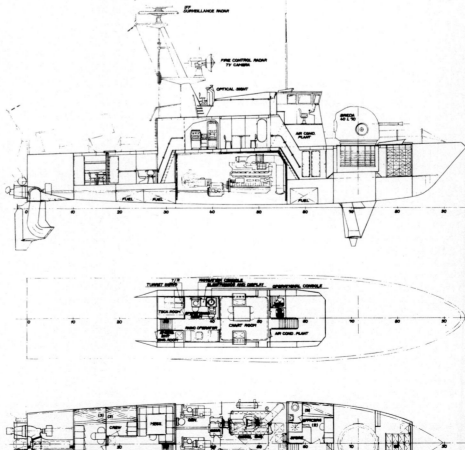

Inboard profile and deck plans of Supramar NAT 90, with waterjet propulsion and retracting foils

FOILS: Fixed surface-piercing foils of Schertel-Supramar air stabilised type. In the event of the air stabilisation system failing, the craft is able to continue operating in foilborne mode although foil submergence would be increased moderately.

POWER PLANT: Foilborne propulsion is supplied by two MTU 16V 956 TB 82 16-cylinder diesels each driving a three-bladed propeller via an inclined shaft. Each engine is rated at 3,800hp continuous at 27°C.

ARMAMENT: Typical weapons fit would comprise two 40mm Bofors L/70 automatic dual purpose guns, one forward and one aft and three Exocet MM 38 anti-ship missile launchers.

ELECTRONICS: Thomson-CSF Vega-Pollux tactical information unit and fire control system.

DIMENSIONS
Length overall: 37·9m (124ft 4in)
Width over foils: 16·6m (54ft 6in)
Draft hullborne: 5m (16ft 5in)
   foilborne: 2·1m (6ft 11in)
WEIGHTS
Displacement loaded: 180 tons
Disposable load (fuel, consumable stores, crew, provisions, armament and ammunition): 40 tons
PERFORMANCE
Cruising speed: 39 knots
Foilborne range: 1,072km (600n miles) at 36 knots
Hullborne range: 1,850km (1,000n miles) at 10 knots
Endurance at sea: 3-5 days
Max permissible wave height: 2·8m (9ft) waves at reduced speed: 3·5m (11ft 6in) waves

SUPRAMAR MT 250

This is a design concept for a 250-tonne patrol boat hydrofoil which meets the tactical requirements established by the West German and other NATO navies. It conforms to the fast patrol boat standards of the West German Navy and has a maximum intermittent speed of 60 knots.

Main dimensions of the vessel are similar to those of the Swedish Spica class, Vosper Tenacity, Israeli Sa'ar class and the West German Type 148. It is designed for all-weather operation in the western Baltic, the Skagerrak and other areas with similar operational conditions.

Foilborne propulsion is supplied by gas-turbine powered waterjets. The foil system is of fully-submerged type employing the Schertel-Supramar air stabilisation system.

As a significant part of the total operating time will be in the hullborne mode, a separate hullborne propulsion plant is provided which guarantees adequate speed in the two hullborne modes: foils retracted and foils extended.

FOILS: Canard system with a single fully-submerged bow foil and two fully-submerged rear foils. The foils are of welded hollow shell construction in stainless steel. All three are retracted clear of the waterline hydraulically. The design avoids the use of hinged doors or panels to raise the bow foil.

CONTROLS: The stabilisation system is a combined automatic control process employing flaps for damping low frequency motions and air-control for high frequency motions. Roll stabilisation is effected by air control of the outer rear foil and the rear foil struts, also by the operation of flaps on the outer rear foil.

Pitch and heave are controlled by flaps on the bow foil and flaps in the centre section of the aft foil.

The stabilisation system consists of four units: the sensors, a computer (for automatic flight control), a command unit and the transactuators.

HULL: Hull and superstructure is of partly riveted, partly welded seawater-resistant light metal alloy. There are seven watertight transverse bulkheads.

INTERNAL LAYOUT/ACCOMMODATION: Accommodation and operations rooms are located almost entirely below deck leaving a relatively large free deck area. Crew would normally comprise twenty one, officers and ratings. Operating and control rooms are all fully air-conditioned. Minelaying equipment, conforming

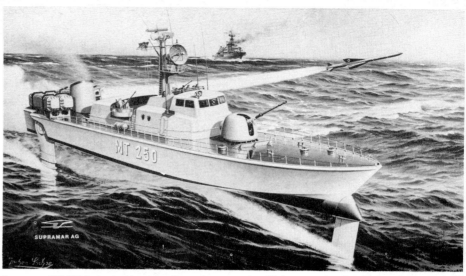

Supramar MT 250 fast patrol boat for all-weather operation. Main powerplant is a Marine Olympus TM3

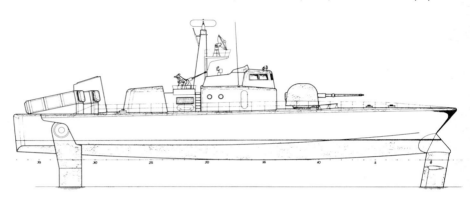

to NATO standards, can be installed as an alternative to missile launchers. Stand-by space is available for a substantial number of Mk 55 mines. There are three officers' cabins and two crew rooms, two toilets with wash basins, one pantry, store rooms, operating and control rooms for ship and machinery. The control and operations rooms have direct access to the bridge and the radio room. All facilities are provided for an intended sea endurance of three to five days.

POWER PLANT, FOILBORNE: The main propulsion plant consists of a slightly modified version of the Rolls-Royce Marine Olympus TM 3, with the following ratings:
   performance: 25,350ps
   power turbine speed: 5,450rpm
   spec fuel consumption: 0·219kg/PSh
   ambient air temperature: 15°C
This comprises an Olympus gas-generator and a single-stage long-life power unit mounted on a common base. The forward end of the gas-generator mates with the air-intake plenum chamber, which has a cascaded bend to give an undisturbed airflow to the engine intake. Flexible joints are applied to the faces of the air-intake and exhaust system to allow relative movement between the module and the ship's uptakes and downtakes. At the engine ratings given, estimated time between overhaul for the gas-generator is 2,000 hours.

A Metastream M 4000 elastic coupling of approximately 1,500mm length connects the power turbine output shaft with an Allen epicycle gear box. The latter is flanged directly to a Rocketdyne Powerjet 46 pump. The Allen gear box has a reduction ratio of approx 1:5·5.

The Rocketdyne Powerjet 46 pump has twin side water intakes and is rigidly mounted to the ship's structure. It transmits thrust via three points.

AUXILIARY PROPULSION PLANT: The auxiliary propulsion plant comprises two 8-cylinder MTU 8V 331 TC 71 diesel engines driving via REINTJES WAV 500 A reverse and reduction gears and inclined propeller shafts two variable-pitch KAMEWA propellers. The propellers are arranged in a duct at the transom.

The MTU 8V 331 TC 71 diesel has the following ratings and characteristics:
   output continuous: 750 PS at 2,055rpm
   output intermittent: 815 PS at 2,120rpm
   number of cylinders: 8 in V form
ARMAMENT: Optional, but can comprise surface-to-surface missiles of Exocet, Otomat or similar types or OTO Compact gun mount and additional 20mm anti-aircraft guns. Provision has been made for various types of combat systems including Vega II-53 or Mini-Combat-System WM 28.
DIMENSIONS
Length overall, foils extended: 43·7m (143ft 4in)
Beam max over deck: 9·4m (30ft 9in)
Max width over foils: 15·8m (51ft 11in)
Draft foilborne: 3·35m (11ft)
Draft hullborne,
   foils extended: 6·95m (22ft 9in)
   foils retracted: 2·2m (7ft 2in)
WEIGHTS
Operational displacement: 250 tonnes
PERFORMANCE
Speed max continuous,
   foilborne: 55 knots
   hullborne, foils retracted: 13 knots
   hullborne, foils extended: 9·5 knots
Range,
at max continuous speed foilborne: 741km (400n miles)
at max continuous speed hullborne, foils extended: 3,340km (1,800n miles)
at max continuous speed hullborne, foils down: 2,400km (1,300n miles)
Max permissible sea state, foilborne: 3·6m (12ft) waves

SUPRAMAR MT 80

The MT 80 is designed for operation in coastal waters. A fully submerged retractable foil system enables it to operate under adverse weather conditions. It can be equipped with a variety of weapons and control systems.

The hull and superstructure are of combined riveted and welded light metal alloy construction. The foils are of high tensile structural steel. The main propulsion system consists of one Rolls-

Royce Proteus gas turbine driving either a water-jet pump, or a propeller via a double bevel gear arrangement. The armament and weapon control system is optional.

DIMENSIONS
Length overall: 29m (95ft 2in)
Beam max: 5·8m (19ft)
Width over foils: 8·9m (29ft 2in)
Draft hullborne, foils extended: 4·4m (15ft 5in)
    foils retracted: 1·5m (4ft 11in)
    foilborne: 2·1m (6ft 10in)
WEIGHTS
Displacement: 85 tons
PERFORMANCE
Speed: 53 knots
Range: 741km (400n miles)
Crew: 8–12
Sea endurance: 3 days
Max permissible sea state, foilborne: 2·7m (9ft)
    waves

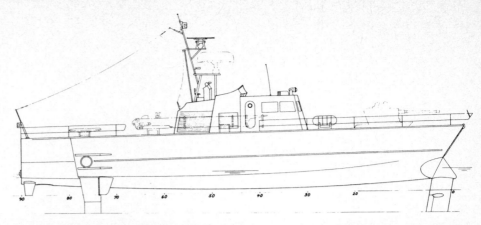

Outboard profile of the Supramar MT 80, 80-tonne hydrofoil for patrol duties in coastal waters. The foilborne propulsion system comprises a single Rolls-Royce Marine Proteus driving a waterjet pump or a propeller via a double-bevel drive

SUPRAMAR 500-SEAT PASSENGER FERRY

In August 1972, Supramar revealed that it is undertaking studies for the design of a 500-seat passenger ferry.

SUPRAMAR CT 70 CATAMARAN HYDROFOIL

The Supramar hydrofoil catamaran has been designed especially for operation in shallow and sheltered waters, where draft limitations preclude the use of conventional hydrofoil craft. Berthing is possible at any existing pontoon or quay facility without adaption, as the foils are well within the hull beam and thereby fully protected against damage while drawing alongside.

One of the major applications foreseen for this new class of hydrofoil is that of fast water bus on urban passenger services. Other likely roles include those of oil-rig support vessel, leisure craft and water sports, especially fishing.

About 80-90% of the lift is produced by the foils, and the remainder by the partly immersed hull planing surfaces forward, which also provides stability. The arrangement permits the plac-

ing of the foils below the water surface at a depth generally free of floating debris.

In the case of partial foil ventilation, the planing surfaces prevent high angles of list and also impede deep immersion in the waves of a following sea. In cases where retractable foils are required a simple method of retraction can be incorporated.

Because of the uncomplicated nature of the concept and the ease of foil retraction, it is felt that it could be successfully applied to outboard craft.

FOILS: System comprises two Supramar type foils arranged in tandem. The bow foil is located at frame 60 and the rear foil at frame 6.

When foilborne 65% of the weight is supported by the bow foil and the side keels while the remaining 35% is supported by the rear foil. Flying height is adjusted by hydraulically-operated flaps on the bow foil. Foils are in St 52-3 high tensile structural steel.

HULL: The hull, which is of hard chine construction, comprises two side hulls and one central

hull. Its design is based on experience gained from the construction of a wide variety of hydrofoil craft.

All members included in the longitudinal strength of the vessel, such as longitudinals, shell and deck plating, are of riveted construction. Transverse members, including web frames and bulkheads, are welded, but the connections with main deck, side and bottom shell, are riveted.

POWER PLANT: Motive power is provided by two MTU 331 type 12-cylinder four-stroke diesel engines, each rated at 1,100ps continuous and 1,300ps maximum intermittent. Each drives a propeller via an inclined shaft. The engines are rated for 45°C air intake temperature and 32°C seawater temperature.

ACCOMMODATION: Total seating capacity is for 159 to 166 passengers. There is one large saloon only. Major obstructions, like staircases, have been avoided. Windows are in safety glass and tinted anti-sun grey. On the standard version passenger seats are each fitted with arm rests, an ashtray and a number plate. Four toilets are

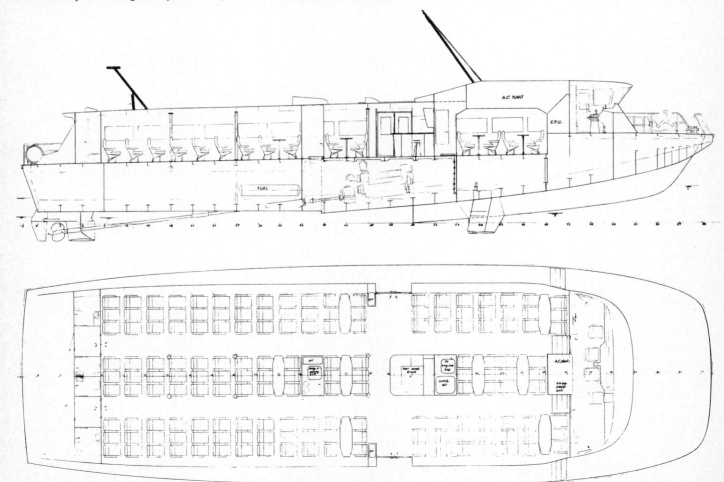

General arrangement of Supramar CT 70 hydrofoil catamaran

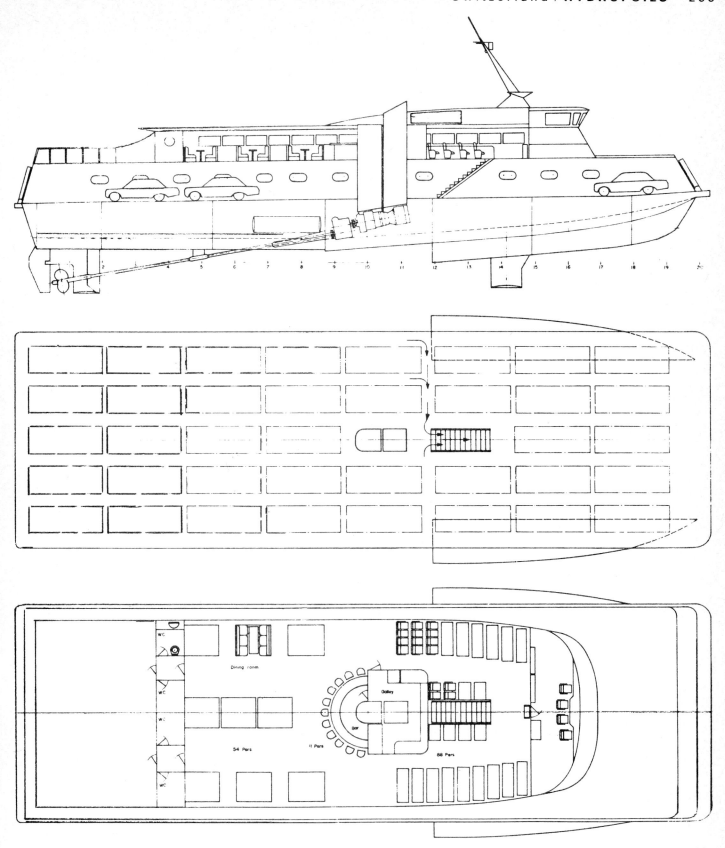

Supramar 200T hydrofoil catamaran car ferry designed to carry 38 cars and 153 passengers

located in the aft of the saloon each fully-equipped with WCs, washbasins, mirrors and towels.

On the short-haul model the passenger seats are more simple and only two toilets are provided. There are three luggage compartments, one adjacent to the embarkation doors leading to the passenger saloon, and two at the aft of the saloon.

DIMENSIONS
Length overall: 28m (91ft 10in)
Beam, max moulded: 9·3m (30ft 6in)
Draft hullborne: 1·8m (5ft 11in)
   foilborne: 1m (3ft 3in)

WEIGHTS
Displacement, fully loaded: 68·5 tonnes (67·45 tons)
   unloaded: 51·7 tonnes (50·9 tons)
Disposable load: 16·8 tonnes (16·56 tons)
Payload: 13·6 tonnes (13·4 tons)
Driving fuel and crew: 3·2 tonnes (3·15 tons)
Number of seated passengers: between 159 and 166

PERFORMANCE
Max speed, foilborne: about 61·5km/h (33 knots)
Cruising speed, foilborne: about 57·5km/h (31 knots)

200T HYDROFOIL CATAMARAN CAR FERRY
This projected mixed-traffic ferry is intended mainly for services across larger lakes with cities or industrial centres on opposite sides. It has twice the speed of conventional displacement ferries and a very economical performance.
HULL: Lightweight design using partly riveted and partly welded seawater-resistant aluminium alloys. Highly stressed parts such as fittings for the foils, shaft, struts etc are in steel.
FOILS: Tandem arrangement. The fully-submerged front foil is well protected by the partly immersed planing surfaces, from floating

debris. Electrohydraulically actuated flaps are fitted for adjusting the flying height. Rear foil is fully submerged.

POWER PLANT: Propulsive power is provided by two marinised gas turbines each rated at 3,700kW (5,000hp) continuous at 27°C air intake temperature. The propellers are placed behind the rear foil and are driven via reverse and reduction gears and two inclined shafts.

ACCOMMODATION: The lower deck carries 38 cars. Large stern and bow doors provide roll-on/roll-off facilities.

Passengers are accommodated on the upper deck which has adequate space to seat 260. A companion stair connects the passenger compartment directly with the car deck. Four toilets and/or luggage rooms are located in the aft part. The accompanying plan shows a configuration for long distance services with a passenger compartment for 88, a bar for 11 and a cafeteria for 54 persons. Total seating is for 153 persons. Food is prepared in a centrally located galley.

DIMENSIONS
Length overall: 42m (137ft 10in)

Width over hull: 15·6m (51ft 2⅝in)
Draft hullborne: 3·6m (11ft 9¾in)
    foilborne: 2·5m (8ft 2in)

WEIGHTS
Displacement loaded: 200 tons
Disposable load: 83 tons
Passenger capacity: 153-260
Car capacity: 38

PERFORMANCE
Cruising speed: 40 knots
Range: 425km (264 miles)

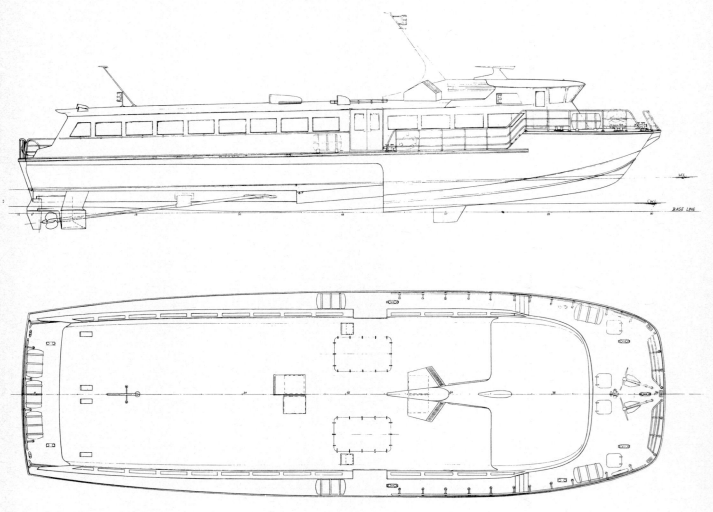

Supramar CT 70 hydrofoil catamaran

UNION OF SOVIET SOCIALIST REPUBLICS

KRASNOYE SORMOVO SHIPYARD

Head Office and Works: Gorki, USSR
Officials:
M Yuriev, *Shipyard Director*
Dr Rostilav Yergenievich Alexeyev, *Head of the Central Design Bureau for Hydrofoil Vessels*
Ivan Yerlykin, *Chief Hydrofoil Designer*
Export Enquiries: V/O Sudoimport, 5 UI. Kalyaevskaya, Moscow K-6, USSR
Telephone: 251-60-37, 251-05-05, 251-03-85
Telex: 272
UK Representative: Umo Plant Ltd, Blackhorse Road, Letchworth, Hertfordshire SG6 1HR, England
Telephone: 046 26 71411/6
Telex: 825247

Krasnoye Sormovo is one of the oldest established shipyards in the Soviet Union. In addition to building displacement craft of many kinds for the Soviet River Fleet, the yard constructs the world's widest range of passenger hydrofoils, many of which are equipped with the Alexeyev shallow draft submerged foil system. Dr Alex-

eyev started work at the end of 1945 on the design of his foil system which had to be suitable for operation on smooth, but open and shallow rivers and canals. He succeeded in making use of the immersion depth effect, or surface effect, for stabilising the foil immersion in calm waters by the use of small lift coefficients.

The system comprises two main horizontal lifting surfaces, one forward and one aft, with little or no dihedral, each carrying approximately half the weight of the vessel. A submerged foil loses lift gradually as it approaches the surface from a submergence of about one chord. This effect prevents the submerged foils from rising completely to the surface. Means therefore had to be provided to assist take-off and prevent the vessel from sinking back to the displacement condition. The answer lay in the provision of planing subfoils of small aspect ratio in the vicinity of the forward struts arranged so that when they are touching the water surface the main foils are submerged approximately to a depth of one chord.

The approach embodies characteristics of the Grunberg principle of inherent angle of attack

variation, comprising a "wing" and a stabiliser system. When the Alexeyev foils drop below the shallow draft zone, the craft converts momentarily to the Grunberg mode of operation, duplicating its configuration. The otherwise inactive sub-foils, coming into contact with the water surface, become the Grunberg stabilisers and cause the foils to climb up into the shallow draft zone where they resume normal operation in the Alexeyev mode.

The foils have good riding characteristics on inland waters and in sheltered waters.

The system was first tested on a small launch powered by a 77bhp converted car engine. Three more small craft were built to prove the idea, then work began on the yard's first multi-seat passenger craft, the Raketa, the first of which was launched in June 1957.

The yard also co-operates with the Leningrad Water Transport Institute in the development of seagoing craft with fully submerged V-type and trapeze-type surface-piercing foils, similar in configuration to those of the Schertel-Sachsenberg system. Craft employing V or trapeze foils are generally described as being of

Largest operational hydrofoil warship in the world is this new 400-ton Soviet fast patrol craft which has been given the NATO codename Babochka (Butterfly). Babochka is thought to be powered by three NK-12 gas turbines, each delivering between 12-15,000shp. Armament comprises two 30mm Gatling-type guns and eight 18in ASW torpedoes in two quadruple mounts

the Strela-type, Strela being the first operational Soviet design to use trapeze foils. Seating 92 passengers, the vessel is powered by two M-50 diesels and, visually speaking, is a cross between the PT 20 and the PT 50, though smaller than the latter. A military derivative, the Pchela (Bee) is currently employed by the Soviet frontier police for coastal patrol in the Baltic, Black Sea, Caspian and other sea areas.

The first hydrofoil vessels to enter service with the Soviet Navy were the 75-ton P 8-class, wooden-hulled torpedo boats which were equipped with bow foils and gas-turbine boost. These have now been retired.

Included in this entry is an illustration of the latest Soviet hydrofoil to enter production, the 230-ton Matka, which has been designed to replace the 20-year-old Osa missilecraft. Like the Turya fast attack torpedo craft, which is also based on an Osa hull, Matka has a bow foil only. Powered by three 5,000hp radial-type diesels it has a top speed of 40-45 knots under calm conditions. Further military hydrofoil designs under development are a 330-tonne fast strike craft, known to NATO by the code name Sarancha and a 400-tonne fast patrol boat known as Babochka. The Sarancha, armed with four SS-N-9 missiles and capable of speeds in excess of 50 knots, is currently undergoing trials with the Soviet Navy in the Baltic.

With an overall length of 50m (164ft) and an all-up weight of 400 tonnes, Babochka is the biggest military hydrofoil in operational service anywhere in the world today.

Among new Soviet passenger hydrofoils either in production or being prepared for series production at yards on the Baltic and Black Sea, are the Voskhod, a 71-seat Raketa replacement; the Kolkhida, a Kometa derivative with seats for 126 passengers, stability augmentation and a speed in excess of 36 knots, and the waterjet-propelled, 250-seat, 45-50 knot, Cyclone. A smaller hydrofoil is also in production. This is the Polesye, a 50-seat passenger ferry which is in production at the river craft shipyard at Gomel.

Substantial numbers of Soviet hydrofoils—especially Kometas, Meteors, Raketas, Voskhods and Volgas—are being exported. Countries in which they are being operated include Austria, Bulgaria, Czechoslovakia, Finland, Yugoslavia, Italy, Iran, France, Cyprus, Greece, East Germany, Morocco, Spain, West Germany, Poland, Romania, the United Kingdom and the Philippines.

Plans are being prepared to build a new generation of hydrofoil passenger ferries with a loaded displacement of 500-600 tons. Mixed passenger/cargo hydrofoils of up to 1,000 tons are also envisaged. These will be operated on routes of up to 1,250 miles and would successfully compete with conventional ships.

Soviet commentators state that although today's hydrofoils attain top speeds of 40-45

Outboard profile of Babochka showing the defensive armament, radar and electronic array. The foil system appears to be of conventional type with surface-piercing bow foils and a fully submerged foil aft

Stern view of Babochka showing the three angled turbine exhaust ducts aft and the large air intakes at the aft end of the deckhouse. Note the top of the strut for what appears to be a fixed surface-piercing bow foil

knots, this figure will rise to 65-75 knots in the near future. Although this will call for considerably more powerful engines, experimental vessels of adequate power to attain these speeds already exist.

BABOCHKA

The world's biggest and most powerful operational hydrofoil warship, this unexpected addition to Soviet sea power is designed for anti-submarine warfare. Motive power for its foil-borne propulsion system appears to comprise three NK-12 marinised aircraft gas turbines, each delivering between 12-15,000shp.

It is thought that this class is intended as a replacement for the 19-year-old Poti coastal anti-submarine vessel, now approaching the end of its service life.

Combustion air for the three gas turbines appears to be fed through a large inlet occupying the aft end of the deckhouse. Exhaust discharge to atmosphere is via three angled funnels on the aft deck. Judging from its size, the craft is almost certainly intended for operation on the open seas. If propeller driven, either vee or Z-drives are likely to have been employed so as to provide as great a clearance height as possible.

FOILS: Thought to be of conventional configuration, with a surface-piercing bow foil and fully-submerged rear foil, with an automatic sonic/electronic control system operating trailing edge flaps on each foil.

ARMAMENT: Two six-barrelled 30mm Gatling-type guns for AA defence, activated by a Bass Tilt fire control radar, and ASW torpedoes in two quadruple mounts located immediately ahead of the superstructure between the deckhouse and the forward 30mm mount. Electronic equipment includes High Pole B IFF, Square Head and Peel Cone radar.

DIMENSIONS
Length overall: 50m (164ft)
WEIGHTS
Normal take-off displacement: about 400 tons
PERFORMANCE
Max speed foilborne: 50 knots plus

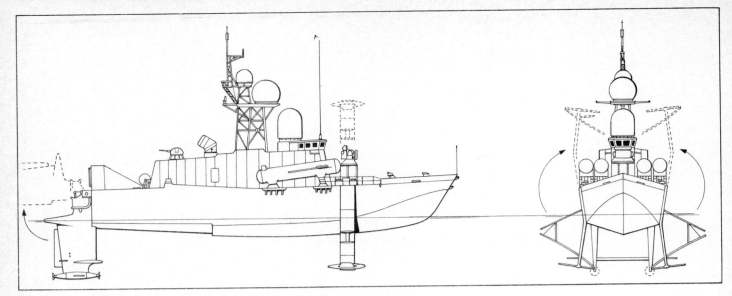

Provisional elevation and bow-on view of 330-tonne Sarancha missile-armed fast attack craft

SARANCHA

The forerunner of a new class of extremely formidable fast strike missile craft, the 330-tonne Sarancha is one of the world's biggest naval hydrofoils. Designed and built in Leningrad, the craft is armed with four SS-N-9 anti-ship missiles, an SA-N-4 ship-to-air missile system and a 30mm Gatling-type rapid-fire cannon. The foil system is fully retractable to simplify slipping and docking. Autostabilisation equipment is fitted as well as an autopilot and the latest navigation, target detection and fire control systems.

Operational evaluation trials with the Soviet Navy began in the Eastern Baltic in mid 1977. Sarancha is the NATO Code Name for the vessel.

FOILS: Combined surface-piercing and submerged system. The bow foil, which provides the necessary transverse stability is of split-V surface-piercing type and carries about 60% of the load and the single fully submerged rear foil supports the remaining 40%. The rear foil is supported by two vertical struts, each of which carries a twin propeller pod assembly at its base. The struts also carry the vertical shafts and second bevel gears of the Z-drive systems which transmit power from the gas turbines in the hull to the propellers. A sonic/electronic autopilot system controls lift by operating trailing edge flaps on the aft foil. Single rudders, which act individually for port or starboard turns, are fitted to the trailing edges of the aft foil struts. All three foil/strut units retract completely clear of the water, the two elements of the 'split V' bow foil sideways and the aft foil rearwards and upwards.

POWER PLANT: Foilborne power is believed to be provided by two NK-12 marinised gas turbines, each delivering 12-15,000hp. Power is transmitted to the two propellers at the base of each strut through two sets of bevel gears and two vertical shafts to the nacelle. The central compartment of this contains the lower reduction gear which transmits power from the vertical shafts to the propeller shafts. The power transmission system is thought to have been derived from that employed on the Typhoon commercial hydrofoil, also built in Leningrad.

ARMAMENT: Four SS-N-9 anti-ship missiles on four lightweight launchers amidship, one twin SA-N-4 surface-to-air missile launcher on forward deck and one 30mm Gatling-type rapid fire AA cannon aft. The SS-N-9s are activated by a Band Stand radar, the SA-N-4 launcher is controlled by a Pop Group radar and the 30mm cannon has a Bass Tilt fire control. The craft also carries a Band Stand radar for air search, a High Pole aerial for the IFF installation, ECM/ECCM equipment and Square Head naval radar.

DIMENSIONS
Length overall: 45m (147ft 8in)
Width, foils extended: 23m (75ft 6in)
Hull beam: 10m (32ft 9½in)
Draft hullborne, foils retracted: 2m (6ft 7in)

Sarancha, 330-tonne missile-armed fast attack craft *(DpA)*

WEIGHTS
Estimated normal take-off displacement: 330 tonnes
PERFORMANCE
Max speed foilborne: 50 knots plus

VOSKHOD-2

Designers of the Voskhod, which is gradually replacing craft of the ageing Raketa series, have drawn on engineering experience gained with the Raketa, and also the more sophisticated Meteor and Kometa.

Among the basic requirements were that the Raketa's general characteristics should be preserved; foilborne operation should be possible in 1m (3ft 3in) high waves, with a 3% safety factor; accommodation should be acceptable from health and safety viewpoints; noise levels should be significantly reduced, and that the maximum use should be made of standard mechanical, electrical and other components and fittings proven on the Raketa.

In fact, the end product bears little resemblance to its predecessor. In the visual sense, the Voskhod is more akin to a scaled-down Kometa with its engine room aft, replacing the rear passenger saloon.

Among the many design improvements to attract operators in the Soviet bloc countries and elsewhere are the following:

1. Employment of a vee-drive transmission, giving greater mean calm water clearance height aft, thereby reducing hydrodynamic drag under certain load conditions.

2. Provision of alternative embarkation points to facilitate passenger handling. Bow embarkation platforms are incorporated for loading from low level pontoons, and a stern embarkation area is located above the engine room, for loading from high landing stages.

3. Raising the number of seated passengers from 64 to 71 for more profitable operation on medium distance services.

4. Generous additional soundproofing, including cowlings on the engine and reduction gear, and the provision of sound absorbing material in the engine room on the deckhead, sides and forward bulkhead.

5. Provision for the future replacement of the M 401A diesel by a 2,000shp M 415 diesel.

6. Fitting of a variable-pitch, six-bladed propeller for improved handling and operating characteristics.

In June 1974, Voskhod 2-01 was put into service on the route Gorki-Kineshma, across the vast Gorki reservoir which cannot be navigated by the Raketa because of its limited seaworthiness. It continued in service until the end of the 1974 navigation season. During this time it was demonstrated that its operating and technical performance was significantly superior to that of the Raketa.

Experience accumulated during this experimental service indicated the need for a number of minor modifications which have been incorporated in the first series of production craft.

Voskhod 14 was launched in June 1980 and delivered to the Amur Line for summer services along the Amur river.

At the time of its inception, it was announced that the Voskhod would be available in a number of versions to suit a variety of local navigation and traffic requirements. Voskhod 3 will be powered by a gas turbine.

The vessel is designed for high-speed passenger ferry services during daylight hours on rivers, reservoirs, lakes and sheltered waters. It meets the requirements of Soviet River Register Class 'O' with the following wave restrictions (3% safety margin): foilborne, 1·3m (4ft 3in), hullborne, 2m (6ft 7in).

The passenger saloons are heated and provided with natural and induced ventilation. Full air-conditioning can be installed in craft required for service in tropical conditions. The crew comprises a captain, engineer, motorman and barman.

FOILS: Fixed foil system, comprising one bow foil with a pitch stability sub-foil immediately behind, one aft foil, plus an amidship foil to facilitate take-off. Bow and amidship foils appear to be of shallow V configuration and each has four vertical struts. The fully submerged stern foil has two side struts and is supported in the centre by the end bracket of the propeller shaft. The surface and lower parts of the foil struts and stabiliser are in Cr18Ni9Ti stainless steel, while the upper parts of the struts and stabiliser and also the amidship foil are in AlMg-61 plate alloy.

HULL: Similar in shape to that of the Kometa and earlier models of the Sormovo hydrofoil series, with a wedge-shaped bow, raked stem and spoon-shaped stern. A single step is provided to facilitate take-off. In fabricating the basic structure, which is largely in AlMg-61 aluminium magnesium alloy, extensive use has been made of arc and spot welding. The hull is framed on longitudinal and transverse formers. Below the deck it is divided into eight watertight compartments by transverse bulkheads. It will remain afloat with any one compartment or the machinery space flooded. Access to the forepeak, which houses the anchor capstan, is via the forward passenger saloon, and then through a rectangular hatch on the forecastle. Aft of the main passenger

Voskhod, the latest hydrofoil passenger ferry to enter service on Soviet inland waterways

saloon is an area split into three compartments by two longitudinal bulkheads. The lower central space contains the reduction gear and vee-drive, the starboard compartment contains the sanitary tank and the port compartment forms part of the double-bottom. Entrance to the engine compartment is via a door on the port side of the main deck. An emergency exit is provided on the starboard aft.

POWER PLANT: Power is supplied by a single M-401A four-stroke water-cooled, supercharged 12-cylinder V-type diesel, delivering a normal service output of 1,000hp at 1,550rpm. The engine which has a variable-speed governor and a reversing clutch, is sited aft with its shaft inclined at 9 degrees. Output is transferred via a flexible coupling to a single six-bladed variable-pitch propeller via an R-21 vee-drive gearbox.

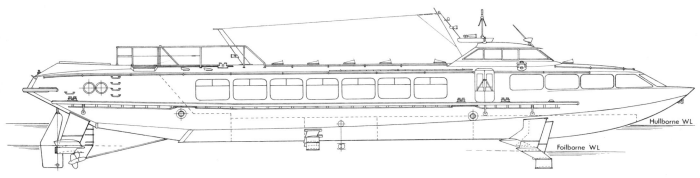

Voskhod-2, outboard profile

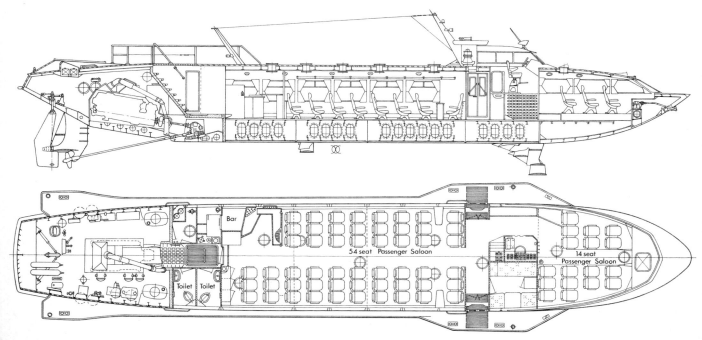

Voskhod-2, inboard profile and deck plan

Guaranteed service life of the engine before the first overhaul is 3,000 hours. The engine room is insulated with fire-retardent, heat and sound-insulating materials. Perforated aluminium alloy sheet is laid over the insulating materials.

CONTROLS: Single semi-balanced rudder in AlMg plate provides directional control. Operation of the engine, rudder, reverse gear and fuel supply is effected hydraulically from the wheelhouse.

ACCOMMODATION: Voskhod-2 carries a three-man operating crew, comprising captain, engineer and motorman plus a barman. Embarkation platforms sited immediately below the wheelhouse provide access for both passengers and crew. Passengers can be embarked from both sides and from the stern.

The captain and engineer are accommodated in a raised wheelhouse located between the forward and main saloon. Main engine controls are located in both the wheelhouse and the engine room.

Passengers are accommodated in two saloons, a forward compartment seating 17 and a main saloon seating 54. The main saloon has three exits, two forward, leading to the embarkation platforms and one aft leading to the stern embarkation area. Between the two saloons, on the starboard side, is a crew rest cabin. The saloons are fitted with upholstered seats, racks for small hand-luggage and pegs for coats. Spacing between seats is 900mm and the central aisle is 800mm wide.

At the rear of the main saloon is a small buffet and bar, and aft of the main saloon, at the foot of the rear embarkation steps are two WC/washbasin units.

SYSTEMS, ELECTRICAL: Power supply is 24-27V dc. A 3kW generator is attached to the engine and supplies 27·5V while the craft is operating. Four 12V storage batteries, each of 180Ah capacity and connected in series-parallel to form a single bank, supply power during short stops. An auxiliary circuit can be connected to shore systems for 220V, single-phase, 50Hz ac supply.

FIREFIGHTING: Four carbon dioxide and four foam fire extinguishers for the passenger saloons and wheelhouse. Remote-controlled system employing "3·5" compound in the engine room.

HEATING AND VENTILATION: Heating in the saloons is provided by pipes circulating water from the internal cooling circuit of the engine. Ventilation is both natural, using the dynamic pressure of the approaching air flow, and induced, by means of electric fans.

During the spring and autumn, the temperature of the ventilating air can be heated up to 21°C.

DRINKING WATER: Hot and cold water supplies. An electric boiler supplies hot water for washbasins and the small kitchen behind the snackbar. Drinking water tank has a capacity of 138 litres.

BILGE WATER: System designed for bilge water removal by shore-based facilities or service vessels.

ANCHOR: Matrosov system, weighing 35kg (77lb), attached to an anchor cable 8·4mm (⅓in) in diameter and 80m (262ft) long, and operated by hand winch in the forepeak.

DIMENSIONS
EXTERNAL
Length overall: 27·6m (90ft 7in)
Hull length: 26·3m (86ft 3½in)
Beam overall: 6·2m (20ft 4in)
Height above mean water level, foilborne, including mast: 5·7m (18ft 8in)
Draft hullborne: 2m (6ft 6¾in)
    foilborne: 1·1m (3ft 7¼in)
INTERNAL
Deck area: 105m² (1,130ft²)
    per passenger: 1·48m² (15·35ft²)
WEIGHTS
Displacement, fully loaded: 28 tonnes
Light displacement: 20 tonnes
Passengers per displacement tonne: 2·55
Payload, passengers and buffet/bar equipment: 5·9 tonnes

Turya foilborne. This 230-ton hydrofoil-assisted fast patrol craft is in production at more than one yard in Western Russia and one in the Soviet Far East

'Sprint' speed of the Turya, the primary duty of which appears to be anti-submarine patrol, is about 40-45 knots

Payload/displacement ratio: 21·2%
PERFORMANCE
Max speed, calm water, wind not in excess of force 3,
    at 1,550rpm (1,000hp): 70km/h (43·49mph)
    at 1,450rpm: 60km/h (37·28mph)
Turning circle diameter
    hullborne: 106m (348ft)
    foilborne: 380m (1,246ft)
Range, based on normal fuel supply of 1,400kg: 500km (310·68 miles)
Max wave height, with 3% safety margin
    hullborne: 2m (6ft 7in)
    foilborne: 1·3m (4ft 3in)

TURYA

Latest hydrofoil to enter service in numbers with the Soviet Navy is a diesel-powered torpedo-boat with a displacement of 230 tons. The vessel, which is based on the well-proven Osa missile-firing FPB hull, is equipped with a fixed, surface-piercing V or trapeze foil set back approximately one-third of the hull length from the bow. At 25 knots in relatively calm conditions, the foil system generates sufficient lift to raise the forward hull clear of the water, providing a "sprint" speed of 40-45 knots.

In addition to improving the maximum speed, the foils reduce the vessel's wave impact response, thus enhancing its performance as a weapon platform.

The installation of a pocket-size, variable-depth sonar on the transom suggests that the primary duty of Turya is anti-submarine patrol. The main armament appears to comprise four 21in single AS torpedo tubes similar to those mounted on the Shershen class fast attack craft, a forward 25mm twin mount and a twin 57mm AA mount aft.

The craft entered service in 1973 and a series production programme is under way, involving more than one yard in Western Russia and one in the Soviet Far East. Output is estimated at between four and five units per year and about thirty

are in service. Three have been supplied to the Cuban Navy.

Latest version of Turya is reported to be equipped with semi-retractable foils permitting the overall width to be reduced, thus enabling craft to be taken alongside conventional berthing facilities.

FOILS: Single main foil of trapeze configuration set back one-third of hull length from bow. Raises greater part of hull bottom clear of the water in calm conditions at speed of about 25 knots depending on sea conditions and loading. Similar system employed earlier on Soviet P 8 class, now retired, and on the highly successful Chinese Hu Chwan class.

HULL: Standard Osa hull, welded steel construction.

POWER PLANT: Three M-504 high performance radial-type diesels, each developing 5,000hp and driving variable-pitch propellers through inclined shafts.

SYSTEMS, RADAR: Pot Drum and Drum Tilt.

DIMENSIONS
Length: 39·3m (128ft 11in)
Beam: 7·7m (25ft 1in)
Draft: 1·8m (5ft 11in)
WEIGHTS
Max loaded displacement: 230 tons
Normal displacement: 200 tons
PERFORMANCE
Max speed foilborne: 40-45 knots

TYPHOON

The Typhoon, a gas-turbine powered fast ferry for 98-105 passengers, is the first production craft with automatically controlled fully-submerged foils to be built in the Soviet Union.

The prototype, constructed in Leningrad, was launched after preliminary fitting out on 12 December 1969. It is designed to operate at a service speed of 40-42 knots under calm conditions and 38 knots in sea state 4. The craft is at present undergoing trials. Phase 1 of the test

The Typhoon, first gas turbine powered passenger craft with fully-submerged foils to be built in the Soviet Union. Designed to operate at 36-45 knots, it seats 98-105 passengers. **Top left:** The basic similarity of the Typhoon's spoon shaped hull to that of the Kometa-M and other Sormovo designs is apparent. **Top right:** Typhoon during take off. Glass doors lead from the saloon into the vestibule and onto the promenade deck visible in this photo. **Bottom left:** View aft from the air-conditioned passenger saloon which can be equipped with 98-105 airliner-type seats. From the vestibule at the far end there are entrances to the baggage compartment, wheelhouse and WC/washbasin units. **Bottom right:** Captain B V Gromov, centre, at the helm, who has been responsible for handling the Typhoon during her trials programme with his engineer, G V Shikhurin

programme covered the foil system, the gas-turbine power plant, hull design and mechanical and other systems and during Phase 2, which was undertaken during 1972 and 1973, the vessel was put into passenger service to permit technical assessments to be made under commercial operating conditions.

It is stated that in waves of up to 2m (6ft 6in) high, not more than 10% of the 40-42 knot service speed is lost. Under these conditions, the Typhoon can complete the journey from Leningrad to Tallinn, the Estonian capital, in 4½ hours.

Ten new inventions have found application in the design and the prototype has been awarded a certificate by the State Inventions and Discoveries Committee.

Late in 1975, it was announced that the Typhoon was to enter production at a shipyard on the Baltic as part of the shipbuilding programme for the period 1976-1980.

FOILS: Fully submerged system of conventional configuration with 77% of the weight borne by the bow foil and 23% by the stern foil. The bow foil is supported by four vertical struts which are tapered from top to bottom. The two outboard struts are supported by auxiliary fins which provide additional stability during the transition from displacement to foilborne mode. Twin rudders are fitted at the trailing edges of the aft foil struts. The foils are built in OCr17Ni7Al high strength stainless steel. A sonic/electronic autopilot system controls four flaps on the bow foil and two on the stern foil. The total weight of the autopilot system, including all electronic components, assemblies, drive mechanisms and cables is less than 600kg (1,320lb). The system stabilises the craft from take-off to touchdown in heave and all three axes—pitch, roll and yaw. It is programmed to govern the angle of trim, the c of g position in relation to speed and see that the craft makes coordinated banked turns according to speed and sea state. Overriding manual control can be introduced if necessary.

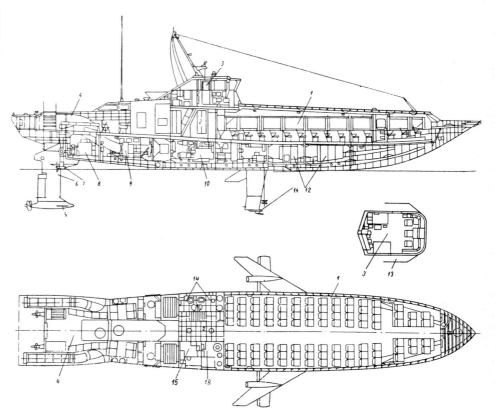

Inboard profile and passenger deck plan of the Typhoon:
1, passenger saloon; 2, vestibule; 3, wheelhouse; 4, promenade deck; 5, stern foil; 6, Z-drive foilborne transmission; 7, Z-drive hullborne transmission; 8, 165hp diesel; 9, Al-23C-I gas turbines; 10, diesel generators; 11, bow foil; 12, fuel tanks; 13, bridge; 14, lavatories; 15, bar; 16, baggage compartment

Two independent electro-hydraulic-drive systems are installed to actuate the flaps. Each has two pumps, one connected to the reduction gear of the main engine, the other to its turbo-compressor. Fluid reaches the actuating mechanisms under a pressure of 150kg/cm². Should one of the mains leading to the actuating mechanisms become unserviceable the second is connected. The failure of one bow or one stern flap in conditions up to sea state 4 does not reduce the stability of the vessel.

HULL: Similar in shape to that of the Kometa and earlier models in the Sormovo hydrofoil series, with a wedge-shaped bow, raked stem and spoon-shaped stern. There are two steps beneath the hull to facilitate take-off. The hull is of riveted construction and built in high strength aluminium magnesium alloy V-48TL. Longitudinal and transverse framing is employed with a spacing of 500mm (19·68in) in the hull and 1,000mm (39·37in) in the superstructure. By locating the wheelhouse aft of amidships, it has been possible to reduce the length of the control system cables while preserving good all-round vision.

Beneath the passenger saloon superstructure the hull is divided by transverse bulkheads into nine watertight compartments in which are accommodated the fuel tanks, diesel generators, gas turbines and diesel for hullborne propulsion. A watertight door is installed in the bulkhead separating the diesel generator and gas turbine compartment. The craft is designed to remain afloat should any two adjacent compartments become flooded.

POWER PLANT: Foilborne power is supplied by two 1,750hp Ivchenko AI-23C-1 marine gas turbines, each driving a single 0·68m (2ft 3in) diameter three-bladed propeller at 2,200rpm cruising. The gas turbines are started by starter generators from batteries and exhaust gases are expelled through an extension aft of the transom to prevent the craft from becoming covered with smoke or fumes.

Power from the main engines is transmitted to each propeller via a K-1700 Z-drive column, which is bolted to the transom. The drive shaft of each turbine is connected to the shaft of the upper reduction gear of the Z-drive. Power is transmitted via two sets of bevel gears and two vertical shafts to a nacelle which is divided into three compartments. The central compartment contains the lower reduction gear which transmits power from the two vertical shafts to the propeller shaft.

The stern foil is welded to the casing of the nacelle's bow compartment which contains the stern foil flap actuating mechanism.

Hullborne propulsion is supplied by a 165hp 6ChSP13/14 low-speed diesel driving two four-bladed propellers through KP-150 right angle drives, which rotate for steering and retract upwards when the craft is foilborne. The columns are steered either from the central control console in the wheelhouse or from a portable control panel which can be operated from any part of the vessel.

ACCOMMODATION: The vessel carries an operating crew of four—captain, engineer, radio operator/electrician and a seaman. Passengers are accommodated in an air-conditioned saloon equipped with 98-105 airliner-type seats. Glass doors lead from the saloon into the vestibule and onto the promenade deck. From the vestibule there is an entrance to the baggage compartment, wheelhouse and WC/wash basin units. The panels along the sides of the saloon are covered in non-inflammable laminated plastic and above with Pavinol imitation leather glued onto plywood. The deckhead is covered with Pavinol on a wooden frame. A special vibration-absorbing covering has been applied to the bulkhead facing the turbine compartment.

Rafts type PSN-10 are stored in containers along the sides of the vessel. These can be launched onto the water either by manual or automatic control from the wheelhouse. Lifebelts and lifejackets are carried aboard the vessel.

SYSTEMS, ELECTRICAL: Two 22kW generators and eight batteries type 6STK-180. Main electrical equipment operates on 400Hz ac current. Shore supply is effected through a transformer.

NAVIGATOR: Gyro course indicator, magnetic compass, hydraulic log and anti-collision radar.

COMMUNICATION: Ship-ship, ship-shore transceiver operating on R/T and W/T, also emergency radio.

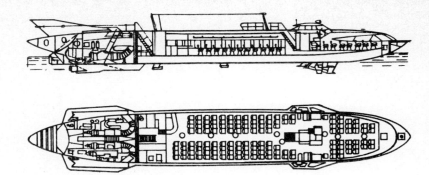

Inboard profile and deck view of the waterjet-propelled Burevestnik, powered by two 2,700hp Ivchenko AI-20 gas turbines

Burevestnik prototype during trials on the Volga

DIMENSIONS
Length overall: 31·4m (103ft 2¼in)
Width across foils: 10m (32ft 9¾in)
Hull beam: 5·6m (18ft 4½in)
Hull draft, displacement mode: 1·3m (4ft 3⅛in)
Draft, hullborne, including foils: 4·1m (13ft 5⅜in)
Mean draft foilborne: 1·1-1·3m (3ft 7in-4ft 3in)
Distance of bow foil below hull base line: 2·8m (9ft 2in)
WEIGHTS
Normal loaded displacement: 65 tons
PERFORMANCE
Max speed: 45 knots
Service speed: 40-42 knots
Hullborne speed: 5 knots
Max permissible sea state: designed to maintain a cruising speed of 38 knots in sea state 4

SEA TESTS

In sea state 4, vertical acceleration measured in the bows was reported to be at all times less than 0·5g. At the same time it was stated that angles of pitch and roll are around 0·75 degrees. In sea state 4, one bow flap and one stern flap out of action have not adversely affected stability.

BUREVESTNIK

First Soviet gas turbine hydrofoil to be designed for series production, the Burevestnik has two 2,700hp marinised aircraft gas turbines driving two two-stage waterjets. The prototype was launched in April 1964 and it was intended to build two models; one for medium-range, non-stop inter-city services, seats 130 passengers, the other, for suburban services, seats 150.

There is a four-man crew, comprising captain, engineer, motorman and a seaman.

After extensive trials and modifications, the prototype Burevestnik began operating on the Gorki-Kuibyshev route, about 700km (435 miles), on 26 April 1968. It is understood that the vessel has not yet entered production.

FOILS: There are two main foils and a midship stabiliser foil, all built in titanium alloy. Each is square-tipped and slightly wedge-shaped in planform. The foils are secured to the hull by struts and brackets. Each foil strut is welded to the upper surface of the foils, then bolted to the brackets. Upper and lower ends of the struts are connected by flanges. As with other craft employing the Alexeyev system, the foil incidence can be adjusted when necessary by the insertion of wedges between the flanges and the foils when the craft is in dock.

HULL: Hull and superstructure are built in aluminium-magnesium alloy. The hull is of all-welded construction and framed on longitudinal and transverse formers.

ACCOMMODATION: The prototype has two air-conditioned saloons with airliner-style seating for a total of 150 passengers. The well-glazed forward saloon seats 38, and the aft saloon 112. The saloons are decorated with pastel shade panels and soundproofed with glass fibre insulation. The engine room is at the stern and separated from the saloon by a sound-proof double bulkhead.

POWER PLANT: Motive power is supplied by two 2,700shp Ivchenko marinised gas turbines, adapted from those of the Il-18 airliner. These operate on either kerosene or light diesel fuel and

Burevestnik prototype during trials

have a consumption of 300 gallons per hour. Sufficient fuel can be carried to operate non-stop over a range of 500km (270n miles). The shaft of each of the two double suction centrifugal pumps for the waterjets is connected with the shaft of one of the turbines by means of a flexible coupling, via a reduction gear.

Auxiliary power is supplied by two 100hp turbo-generators, used for starting the main engines and generating the electrical supply when the craft is operating.

CONTROLS: Four rudders adjacent to the waterjet streams provide directional control. Reversing is achieved by applying deflectors to reverse the waterflow. The waterjets themselves are fixed and cannot be rotated.

Operation of the turbines, waterjets, rudders and deflectors is all effected from the wheelhouse by electro-hydraulic control.

SYSTEMS, ELECTRICAL: Two 12kW 28·5V generators mounted on each of the main engines supply power when the craft is operating. Two 14kW 28·5V generators driven by the auxiliary turbines supply power when the craft is at rest or when the 12kW generators are inoperative. Eight acid storage batteries are connected in series to give 24V supply power during short stops.

HYDRAULICS: 170kg/cm² pressure hydraulic system for operating rudders, hydro-reversal unit and anchor.

COMMUNICATIONS: A radio transmitter/receiver with r/t and w/t facilities is installed in the wheelhouse for ship-shore and inter-ship communications on SW and MW bands. A public announcement system is fitted in the passenger saloons and a two-way crew communications system is installed in the wheelhouse, engine room, anchor, gear compartment and mooring stations.

DIMENSIONS
Overall length: 43·3m (142ft)
Hull beam: 6m (19ft 8¼in)
Width across foils: 7·4m (24ft 3½in)
Draft hullborne: 2m (6ft 7in)
   foilborne: 0·4m (1ft 4in)
WEIGHTS
Light displacement: 41 tons
Full load displacement (max): 67 tons
Max fuel load: 11·5 tons
PERFORMANCE
Cruising speed: 93km/h (50 knots)
Range: 500km (310 miles)
Max wave height at reduced speed: 1-1·2m (3ft 3in-4ft)
Max wave height at full speed: 0·6m (2ft)
Speed astern: 6-9km/h (4-6mph)
Stop to full speed and distance: 95-100 seconds, 1,100m (1,203yds)
Stopping time from full speed and distance: 25 seconds, 360m (394yds)

BYELORUS

This craft was developed from the Raketa via the Chaika for fast passenger services on winding rivers less than 1m (3ft) deep and too shallow for vessels of the standard type.

In 1965 it was put into series production at the river shipyard at Gomel, in Byelorussia.

FOILS: The shallow draft submerged foil system consists of one bow foil and one rear foil.

HULL: Hull and superstructure are built in aluminium magnesium alloy. The hull is of all-welded construction and the superstructure is both riveted and welded.

ACCOMMODATION: The craft seats 40 passengers in aircraft-type seats, although the prototype seated only 30.

POWER PLANT: Power is supplied by an M-50 F-3 or M-400 diesel rated at 950hp maximum and with a normal service output of 600hp. The wheelhouse is fitted with an electro hydraulic remote control system for the engine and fuel supply.

DIMENSIONS
Length overall: 18·55m (60ft 6in)
Hull beam: 4·64m (15ft 2in)
Height overall: 4·23m (13ft 11in)
Draft foilborne: 0·3m (1ft)
   hullborne: 0·9m (2ft 11in)

A Raketa, left, and a Byelorus, right, pass one another on the River Lena

Byelorus, a 30-45 seat hydrofoil for fast ferry services on shallow waters, seen on the Karakum Canal, Turkmenia. Powered by a 735hp M-50 diesel driving a waterjet, the craft cruises at 60km/h (34 knots)

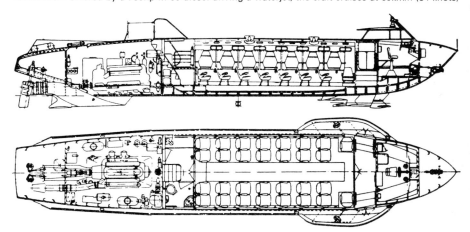

Profile and deck plan of the waterjet-propelled Byelorus, a ferry for fast passenger services on winding rivers less than 3ft 3in deep

Chaika, an experimental 30-passenger craft powered by a diesel-driven waterjet

WEIGHTS
Light displacement: 9·6 tons
Take-off displacement: 14·5 tons

PERFORMANCE
Cruising speed: 60km/h (34 knots)

CHAIKA

An experimental 30-passenger craft, Chaika is used as a test bed for the development of diesel-operated waterjet systems. It was designed initially as a 30-passenger waterbus for shallow rivers but was found to be unsuitable for negotiating sharp river bends at high speed. However, craft of this type are reported as being in limited service on the Danube.

In June 1971 it was announced that the craft had been employed in the development of super-ventilated V and trapeze foils for a speed range exceeding 50-80 knots.

HULL: Hull and superstructure are built in aluminium magnesium alloy.

POWER PLANT: An M-50 diesel, developing 1,200hp, drives a two-stage waterjet.

CONTROLS: Rudders adjacent to the water stream govern the flow of the ejected water for directional control.

DIMENSIONS
Length overall: 26·3m (86ft 3in)
Hull beam: 3·8m (12ft 6in)
Draft hullborne: 1·2m (3ft 10in)
   foilborne: 0·3m (1ft)
WEIGHTS
Displacement loaded: 14·3 tons
PERFORMANCE
Cruising speed, foilborne: 86km/h (46·5 knots)

Outboard profile of the 140-tonne Cyclone, a waterjet-propelled 250-seat hydrofoil ferry with accommodation on two decks. Design cruising speed is 42 knots

CYCLONE

An enlarged, double-deck derivative of the Kometa, the Cyclone seats 250 passengers and is propelled by waterjets driven by two 5,000hp gas turbines, making it the most powerful Soviet commercial hydrofoil to date. Maximum speed is 45-50 knots and the cruising speed is 42 knots.

It was announced in 1976 that, on completion of trials, the vessel will be put into series production at the Poti shipyard, on the Black Sea. Export models are planned. It is probable that these will be fitted with imported gas turbines and waterjet systems.

The craft complies with the requirements of Class KM 2MA2 of the USSR Passenger Register. It also meets fully all the specified conditions of the Stability Specifications, USSR Shipping Register. It is designed to operate foilborne in waves up to 3m (9ft 10in) high regardless of wave direction, and can operate hullborne in conditions up to sea state 5. Foilborne range, fully-loaded, is 300n miles.

FOILS: Surface-piercing system of conventional configuration comprising two main foils, one at the bow and one at the stern; an amidship foil to assist take-off, a pitch stability sub-foil immediately aft of the bow foil, and the associated struts by which the foils are attached to the hull. A sonic/electronic autopilot system controls lift by operating trailing edge flaps on the central section of the bow foil and at both ends of the stern foil. Flap angles are variable in flight and provide a variation in the lift generated by the bow foil of ±35% and ±85% by the stern foil. The foil flaps are adjusted automatically to dampen heave, pitch, roll and yaw motions in heavy seas. A rudder is fitted to the central bow foil strut for improved manoeuvrability in congested waters. Main and stability foils are of welded construction. Bow and stern foil surfaces, flap tie-rods, the lower ends of the bow and stern foil struts, and the central bow foil strut are built in steel alloy. The amidship foil and struts, pitch stability foil and the upper sections of the bow and stern foil struts are in aluminium-magnesium alloy.

HULL: Twin-deck structure. All-welded construction, similar to that employed on Kometa series. Extensive use is made of pressed panels and rolled aluminium-magnesium alloy strip. Hull is framed on longitudinal and transverse formers. Below the main deck the hull is subdivided by 11 watertight bulkheads into 12 compartments. The craft will remain afloat with any two adjacent compartments flooded up to a total length of 9m—or 21 per cent of the craft's overall length. To retard corrosion below the waterline, magnesium protectors are provided.

POWER PLANT: Power for the waterjet propulsion system is supplied by two marinised gas turbines, each rated at 5,000hp maximum and 4,500hp continuous. Each unit has a gas-discharge device and the reduction gear rate of rotation at the power take-off shaft is 950rpm. The shafts of both gas turbines are each connected via flange couplings to the reduction gear of an axial-flow waterjet pump, each of the two

pumps receiving water from a common intake. Fuel consumption per horsepower at continuous rating is 225g/h. Oil consumption of each gas turbine is 1·5kg/h and that of the reduction gear is 0·5kg/h. The service life of each gas turbine is 10,000 hours before the first overhaul.

ACCOMMODATION: Standard model is designed to carry a crew of 6 and 250 seated passengers. Three saloons are provided on the main deck—a 46-seat bow saloon, a 66-seat amidships saloon and a 74-seat aft saloon—and a further 64 are seated in an upper saloon on the top deck. A separate cabin is provided for the crew. Facilities include a luggage locker, a three-sided refreshment bar, a smaller bar and a promenade deck. Passenger saloons are fully air-conditioned and equipped with airliner-type seats arranged three abreast (32) and two abreast (77). Extensive use is made of heat, sound and vibration absorbing and insulation materials. Decks and serving spaces are overlaid with deep pile carpets. Captain and navigator are accommodated in a raised wheelhouse providing a 360 degree view. A remote control console in the wheelhouse is equipped with the necessary controls and instrumentation for the main and auxiliary engines, the autopilot system, manual steering and fire-fighting.

SYSTEMS, ELECTRICAL: APU drives two 14kW turbogenerators for 28·5V dc service and a 75kW diesel-generator set supplies alternating current at 230V and 50Hz. Two-wire, group-bus type distribution system.

HYDRAULICS: Three separate systems, the first for control of reversing gear, rudder and anchor winch; the second for control of the main engines and water jet nozzles and the third for flap control.

COMMUNICATIONS: R/T simplex/duplex single-band transceiver operating on 18 pre-selected frequencies in the 1·6-8·8 mHz band and transmitting distress signals on 2,182 kHz and 3,023·5 kHz; VHF R/T transceiver operating on seven channels in the 156·3-156·8 mHz band; portable lifeboat type radio, and a PA system.

NAVIGATION: Navigational radar, course indicating system with a steering repeater which automatically provides the course to be steered and transmits data to the repeater, magnetic compass, a log and an automatic steering and stabilisation system.

SAFETY EQUIPMENT: Ten 26-seat inflatable life rafts with provision for the automatic release of five (one side) at a time.

DIMENSIONS
Length overall: 49·9m (163ft 9in)
Width across foils: 13·2m (43ft 6in)
Hull beam: 8m (26ft 3in)
Height above water,
    foilborne (with folded mast): 9m (29ft 7in)
    hullborne: 6·4m (21ft)
Draft foilborne: 1·9m (6ft 3in)
    hullborne: 4·5m (14ft 9in)

WEIGHTS
Loaded displacement: 140 tonnes
Light displacement: 96·4 tonnes
Deadweight: 43·6 tonnes

PERFORMANCE
Max speed, foilborne: 45-50 knots
Cruising speed, foilborne: 42 knots
Endurance: 8 hours
Max wave height,
    foilborne: 3m (9ft 10in)
    hullborne: sea state 5
Range: 300n miles

KOLKHIDA

Kolkhida appears to be the official name given to the Kometa's replacement. The keel for the first one was laid at the Ordzhonikidze yard, Poti, at a ceremony attended by the First Secretary of the Georgian Communist Party's Central Committee on 28 May 1980. The occasion also marked the entry of the craft into series production.

Kolkhida, at one time known as the Albatros, will be powered by two newly-designed 1,500 hp diesels which will give the craft a top speed in excess of 36 knots. It will seat 120-126 passengers.

Among the various innovations introduced by the Central Hydrofoil Design Bureau are a new foil system with automatic lift control, the use of new materials in the hull structure, and a more rational cabin layout allowing the seating capacity to be increased substantially. The engine room is reported to be located aft, as on the Voskhod.

Overall dimensions are almost identical to those of the Kometa-M.

A feature of the craft is its exceptional stability. First vessels of the new class are expected to enter service in 1981. Production is due to continue until 1985.

KOMETA

Derived from the earlier Meteor, the Kometa is the first seagoing hydrofoil to be built in the Soviet Union. The prototype, seating 100 passengers, made its maiden voyage on the Black Sea in the summer of 1961, after which it was employed on various passenger routes on an experimental basis. Operating experience accumulated on these services led to the introduction of various modifications before the craft was put into series production.

Kometas are built mainly at Gorki and Poti, one of the Black Sea yards.

Kometa operators outside the Soviet Union include Inex-Nautical Touring, Split, Yugoslavia; Empresa Nacional de Cabotage, Cuba; Achille Onorato, Naples, Italy; and Transportes Touristiques Intercontinentaux, Morocco. Other vessels of this type have been supplied to Iran, Romania, Poland, Turkey, Greece, Bulgaria and the German Democratic Republic. Export orders totalled 52 by early 1978.

Export orders have mainly been for the Kometa-ME, designed for service in countries with a moderate climate, which was introduced in 1968. Two distinguishing features of this model are the employment of new diesel engines, with increased operating hours between overhauls, and a completely revised surface-piercing foil system, with a trapeze bow foil instead of the former Alexeyev shallow draft submerged type.

A fully tropicalised and air-conditioned version is now in production and this is designated Kometa-MT.

The present standard production Kometa-ME seats 116-120. Because of the additional weight of the Kometa-MT's air-conditioning system and other refinements, the seating capacity is reduced in the interest of passenger comfort to 102.

Official designation of the Kometa in the USSR is Hydrofoil Type 342. The craft meets the requirements of the Rules of the Register of Shipping of the USSR and is constructed to Hydrofoil Class KM ★ 2 11 Passenger Class under the Register's technical supervision. IMCO recommendations on fire safety are now being taken into account and non-flammable basalt fibres are being employed for sound and heat insulation and the engine room is clad with titanium plating. The craft is designed to operate during daylight hours on coastal routes up to 81km (50 miles) from ports of refuge under moderate climate conditions.

The standard craft has proved to be exceptionally robust and has a good, all-round performance. On one charter, a Kometa-ME covered 5,310km (3,300 miles) by sea and river in 127 hours. It can operate foilborne in waves up to 1·7m (5ft 7in) high and travel hullborne in waves up to 3·6m (11ft 10in).

One of the features of the latest models is the relocation of the engine room aft to reduce the noise in the passenger saloons and the employment of a vee-drive instead of the existing inclined shaft. The arrangement is expected to be similar to that on the Voskhod-2. The revised deck configuration allows more seats to be fitted. These modifications are also incorporated in the recently announced Kometa derivative, the Kolkhida, which will be fitted with two 1,500hp engines. In future, development of the Kometa and Kolkhida is likely to continue in parallel.

FOILS: Employment of a surface-piercing trapeze-type bow foil provides the Kometa-ME with improved seakeeping capability in waves. The foil system comprises a bow foil, aft foil, and two auxiliaries, one (termed "stabiliser") located above the bow foil for pitch stability, the other sited amidships near the longitudinal centre of gravity to assist take-off. The foils are connected to the hull by struts and brackets. Middle and side struts of the bow foil are of the split type. The lower and upper components of each strut are connected by flanges and bolts. The upper sections are connected to the hull by the same means.

The bow and stern foils are of hollow welded stainless steel construction. The midship and pitch stability foils and the upper components of the foil struts are in aluminium-magnesium alloy.

HULL: Similar in shape to that of the earlier Meteor, the hull has a wedge-shaped bow, raked stem and a spoon-shaped stern. Hull and superstructure are built in AlMg-61 and AlM-6g alloys. Hull and superstructure are of all-welded construction using contact and argon arc welding. The hull is framed on longitudinal and transverse formers, the spacing throughout the length of the hull is 500mm and in the superstructure 1,000mm.

Below the freeboard deck, the hull is divided by watertight bulkheads into thirteen compartments, which include the engine room, fuel compartments, and those containing the firefighting system, tiller gear and fuel transfer pump.

ACCOMMODATION: The Kometa-MT seats 102 passengers. It carries a six-man operating crew, comprising captain, engineer, motorman, radio-operator, seaman, and one barman. Embarkation platforms sited immediately below the wheelhouse provide access for both passengers and crew.

The captain and engineer are accommodated in a raised wheelhouse located between the forward and main saloons, and equipped with two seats, a folding stool, chart table, sun shield and a locker for signal flags. The wheelhouse also contains a radar display and radio communications equipment.

Kometas under construction at the Ordzhonikidze shipyard, Poti, in May 1980

Main engine controls are installed in both the wheelhouse and engine room.

Passengers are accommodated in three compartments, a forward saloon seating 22, and central and aft saloons seating 54 and 26 respectively. The central saloon has three exits, two forward, leading to the embarkation platforms and one aft, leading to the promenade deck. This is located in the space above the engine room and is partially covered with a removable metallic awning.

In the current production model of the Kometa-ME, the forward saloon seats 24, the central saloon seats 56 and the aft saloon 36.

To the starboard side is a crew's off-duty cabin, hydraulic system pump room, bar store and bar, and to the port are two toilets, boiler room, battery room and fire extinguishing equipment.

The aft saloon has two exits, one forward leading to the promenade deck, the other aft, leading to the weather deck, which is used for embarking and disembarking when the vessel is moored by the stern.

Floors of the passenger saloons, crew's cabins, bar and wheelhouse are covered in coloured linoleum and the deckhead in the passenger saloons, as well as bulkheads and the sides above the lower edge of the windows, are finished in light coloured pavinol. Panels of the saloons beneath the windows are covered with plastic.

Passenger saloons are fitted with upholstered chairs, racks for small hand luggage and pegs for clothing. The middle and aft saloons have niches for hand luggage and the former is fitted with cradles for babies. The bar is fully equipped with glass washers, an ice safe, an automatic Freon compressor, electric stove, etc.

SAFETY EQUIPMENT: A full range of lifesaving equipment is carried including five inflatable life rafts, each for 25 persons, 135 life jackets, and four circular life belts with life lines and self-igniting buoyant lights. Life rafts are located two on the forward sponsons and two on the aft sponsons . When thrown into the water the life rafts inflate automatically. Life jackets are stowed under the seats in all saloons, and the circular life belts are stowed on the embarkation and promenade platforms. Kometas for export are provided with life jackets on the basis of 25 persons per raft.

FIREFIGHTING EQUIPMENT: An independent fluid fire fighting system is provided for the engine room and fuel bay. An automatic light and sound system signals a fire outbreak. The fire fighting system is put into operation manually from the control deck above the engine room

door. Boat spaces are equipped with hand-operated foam and CO_2 fire extinguishers, felt cloths and fire axes.

POWER PLANT: Power is supplied by two M-401A water-cooled, supercharged 12-cylinder V-type diesels, each with a normal service output of 1,000hp at 1,550rpm and a maximum output of 1,100hp at 1,600rpm. Guaranteed service life of each engine before first overhaul is 2,500 hours. Each engine drives via a reverse gear its own inclined shaft and the twin propellers are contra-rotating. The shafts are of steel and are parallel to the craft. Guaranteed service life of the M-401A before each overhaul is 2,500 hours.

The propellers are of three-bladed design and made of brass.

Main engine controls and gauges are installed in both the wheelhouse and the engine room. A diesel-generator-compressor-pump unit is provided for charging starter air bottles; supplying electric power when at rest; warming the main engines in cold weather and pumping warm air beneath the deck to dry the bilges.

Diesel oil tanks with a total capacity of 3,000kg (6,612lb) for the main engines and the auxiliary unit are located in the afterpeak. Two lubricating oil service tanks and one storage tank located at the fore bulkhead of the engine room have a total capacity of 250kg (551lb). Diesel and lubricating oil capacity is sufficient to ensure a range of 370km (230 miles).

CONTROLS: The wheelhouse is equipped with an electro hydraulic remote control system for the engine reverse gear and fuel supply, fuel monitoring equipment, including electric speed counters, pressure gauges, lubricating and fuel oil gauges. The boat is equipped with a single, solid aluminium magnesium alloy balanced rudder, which is controlled through a hydraulic steering system or a hand-operated hydraulic drive. In an emergency, the rudder may be operated by a hand tiller. Maximum rudder angle is 35 degrees in hullborne conditions and 5·6 degrees foilborne. In the event of the steering gear failing the craft can be manoeuvred by differential use of the main engines, the rudder being locked on the centre line. The vessel can be pinwheeled in hullborne condition by setting one engine slow ahead, the other slow astern and turning the rudder hard over.

SYSTEMS, ELECTRICAL: Power supply is 24V dc. A 1kW dc generator is attached to each of the two engines and these supply power while the craft is operating. A 5·6kW generator is included in the auxiliary unit and supplies power when the craft is at rest. It can also be used when under way for supplying the heating plant or when the 1kW generators are inoperative. Four 12V acid storage batteries, each of 180Ah capacity and connected in series to provide 24V, supply power during short stops.

HYDRAULICS: The hydraulic system for controlling the main engines and reverse gear consists of control cylinders located in the wheelhouse, power cylinders located on the engines, a filler tank, pipe lines and fittings.

ANCHORS: The craft is equipped with two Matrosov anchors—a main anchor weighing 75kg (165lb) and a spare anchor weighing 50kg (110lb). The main anchor is raised by means of an electric winch located in the forepeak. The cable of the spare anchor can be heaved in manually and is wound over a drum fitted with a hand brake.

COMMUNICATIONS: A radio transmitter/receiver with r/t and w/t facilities is installed in the wheelhouse for ship-shore and inter-ship communications on SW and MW bands. A portable emergency radio and automatic distress signal transmitter are also installed in the wheelhouse. A broadcast system is fitted in the passenger saloons and a two-way crew communications system is installed in the wheelhouse, engine room, anchor gear compartment and mooring stations.

NAVIGATION: The following navigation aids are standard: a gyro compass, magnetic compass (reserve) and log.

KOMETA-ME
DIMENSIONS
Length overall: 35·1m (115ft 2in)
Beam overall: 11m (36ft 1in)
Height, foilborne from waterline to tip of mast: 9·6m (31ft 6in)
Draft, hullborne: 3·6m (11ft 9¾in)
  foilborne: 1·7m (5ft 6⅞in)
WEIGHTS
Light displacement: 44·5 tonnes
Fully loaded displacement: 60 tonnes
Gross register tonnage: 142·1 gross tonnes
PERFORMANCE
Max speed, intermittent: 66·8km/h (36 knots)
Cruising speed: 58km/h (32 knots)
Fuel consumption: 172g/hp/h
Oil consumption: 5g/hp/h

Kometa-M undergoing manufacturers' trials off Poti in May 1980

A Kometa-ME of Inex-Nautical Touring, Split, Yugoslavia. The vessel, which has a service speed of 32 knots, operates a coastal service on the Adriatic between Krila, Zadar and Split

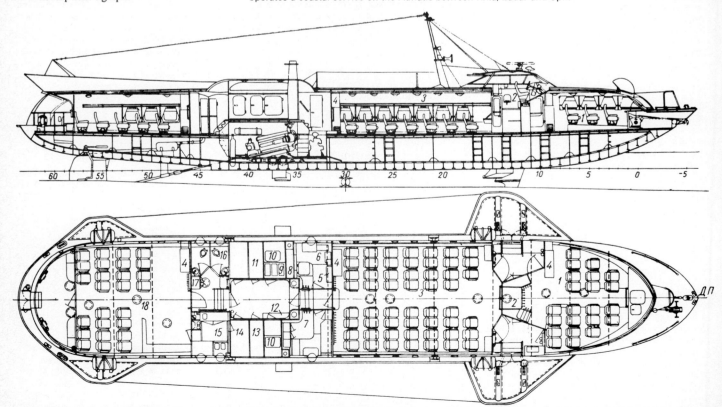

Internal arrangement of the Kometa-MT, designed for tropical operation. 1, 22-seat forward passenger saloon; 2, wheelhouse; 3, 54-seat main passenger saloon; 6, control position; 7, duty cabin; 8, liquid fire extinguisher bay; 9, battery room; 10, engine room; 11, boiler room; 12, installation point for portable radio; 13, store; 14, provision store; 15, bar; 16, WC/washbasin units; 17, boatswain's store; 18, 26-seat aft passenger saloon

Max sea state: Speed of the Kometa-M at full load displacement in sea states 0-2 and wind conditions up to force 3 is 32 knots. Under the worst permissible conditions under which the craft is able to navigate (sea state 5, wind force 6) it will operate hullborne at 10-12 knots. Sea states up to 4 and wind conditions up to force 5 are considered normal for Kometa operation.

KOMETA-MT

DIMENSIONS
Length overall: 35·1m (115ft 2in)
Beam: 11m (36ft 1in)
Height, foilborne, waterline to tip of mast: 9·2m (30ft 2¼in)
Draft, hullborne: 3·6m (11ft 9¾in)
    foilborne: 1·7m (5ft 6⅞in)
WEIGHTS
Light displacement: 45 tonnes
Fully loaded displacement: 58·9 tonnes
PERFORMANCE
Max speed: 61km/h (34 knots)
Service speed: 58km/h (32 knots)
Fuel consumption: 182g/hp/h
Oil consumption: 5·0g/hp/h
Range: 240km

Development of the Kometa is continuing. Current research is aimed at the introduction of a stability augmentation system employing either control flaps on the bow foil or air stabilisation on the stern foil and struts; the reduction of labour involved in construction; the introduction of design improvements through the use of grp and sandwich construction; noise reduction in the saloons and the extension of the cruising range.

MATKA

Latest of the Soviet Navy's hydrofoils to go into production is the Matka, a missile-equipped fast strike craft built at the Izhora Yard, Leningrad. Matka is designed to replace the 20-year-old Osa fast patrol boat and is based on the standard 39·3m Osa steel hull. A fixed surface-piercing trapeze foil is fitted at the bow to increase its speed in the lower sea states and reduce its wave impact response thereby improving its performance as a weapon platform. At between 24-28 knots, depending on sea conditions and loading, the bow foil generates sufficient lift to raise a substantial part of the forward hull clear of the water thus reducing hydrodynamic drag and providing a 'sprint' speed of 40-45 knots.

Matka is believed to have entered production in the spring of 1978. At least eight are in service.
FOILS: Single main foil of trapeze configuration set back one-quarter of hull length from bow. Raises much of the hull clear of the water in relatively calm conditions at speed of 24-28 knots depending on sea conditions and loading. Similar to system proven on Chinese Hu Chwan class and Soviet Turya. Latest version of Turya is reported to be equipped with semi-retractable foils permitting the overall width to be reduced, thus enabling craft to be taken alongside conventional jetties, piers and other vessels without damaging the foil tips. Matka is likely to employ similar foil arrangement.
HULL: Standard Osa hull, welded steel construction.
POWER PLANT: Three 5,000hp M-503 radial-type high-performance diesels, each driving a variable-pitch propeller through an inclined shaft.
ACCOMMODATION: Living, messing and berthing spaces for crew of 33.
ARMAMENT: Two SS-N-2C surface-to-surface missiles; one 76mm dual-purpose cannon and one six-barrelled Gatling-type 30mm cannon for close-in AA defence. Also chaff launcher.
RADAR: Fire control, Bass Tilt; IFF, High Pole and Square Head.
DIMENSIONS
Length: 39·3m (128ft 11in)
Hull beam: 7·7m (25ft 3in)
Draft: 3·9m (12ft 9½in)
WEIGHTS
Max loaded displacement: 220 tons
PERFORMANCE
Max speed foilborne: 40-45 knots

Matka fast strike craft on patrol in the Baltic (*Royal Swedish Air Force*)

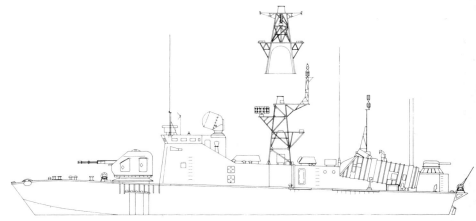

Outboard profile of the 220-ton, 40-45 knot Matka missile-equipped fast strike craft

METEOR

Dr Alexeyev's Meteor made its maiden voyage from Gorki to Moscow in the summer of 1960, bringing high performance and unprecedented comfort to the river boat scene, and setting the pattern for a family of later designs.

The craft is intended for use in daylight hours on local and medium-range routes of up to 600km (373 miles) in length. It meets the requirements of Class O, experimental type, on the Register of River Shipping in the USSR.

Accommodation is provided for a crew of five and 116 passengers. Cruising speed at the full load displacement of 54·3 tonnes across calm water and in winds of up to Beaufort force 3 is about 65km/h (35 knots).

Outside the Soviet Union Meteors are operated today in Bulgaria, Yugoslavia, Hungary and Poland.
FOILS: The foil arrangement comprises a bow foil and a stern foil, with the struts of the bow system carrying two additional planing subfoils.

Meteor is powered by two 12-cylinder M-50 diesels, each with a normal service output of 908hp. Ahead of the central fin is a removable metallic awning above the promenade deck

Meteor operated on the Danube by Mahart Magyar Hajozasi

Meteor. General Arrangement
A. Inboard profile; B. main deck plan. I. waterline hullborne; II. hull base line; III. waterline foilborne; IV. longitudinal centreline. 1. wheelhouse; 2. anchor compartment; 3. forward passenger saloon, 26 seats; 4. luggage compartment; 5. embarkation companionway; 6. crew duty room; 7. midship passenger saloon, 42 seats; 8. bar; 9. refrigeration unit; 10. engine room; 11. pantry; 12. boatswain's store; 13. calorifier; 14. fire fighting equipment; 15. promenade deck; 16. WCs; 17. tank; 18. aft passenger saloon, 44 seats; 19. tiller gear; 20. four-seat passenger cabin; 21. storage batteries; 22. hydraulic units; 23. main switchboard

The foils are attached to the struts, which are of split type, by flanges and bolts. The foils are in stainless steel, and the subfoils in aluminium magnesium alloy. The foil incidence can be adjusted when necessary by the insertion of wedges between the flanges and the foils when the vessel is in dock.

HULL: With the exception of the small exposed areas fore and aft, the Meteor's hull and superstructure are built as an integral unit. The hull is framed on longitudinal and transverse formers and both hull and superstructure are of riveted duralumin construction with welded steel members. Below the main deck the hull is sub-divided longitudinally into eight compartments by seven bulkheads. Access to the compartments is via hatches in the main deck. The craft will remain afloat in the event of any two adjacent compartments forward of amidship flooding or any one compartment aft of midship. Frame spacing in the hull is about 500mm while that in the superstructure is 1,000mm.

POWER PLANT: Power is supplied by two M-50 12-cylinder, four-stroke, supercharged, water-cooled diesels with reversing clutches. Each engine has a normal service output of 1,000hp at 1,700rpm and a maximum output of 1,100hp at 1,800rpm. Specific consumption at rated output g/bhp/h is not more than 193, and oil, not more than 6. Guaranteed overhaul life is 1,000 hours. Each engine drives its own inclined propeller shaft through a reverse clutch. Propeller shafts are in steel and the propellers, which are five-bladed, are in brass. The drives are contra-rotating.

Refuelling is effected via filler necks on each side of the hull. Fuel is carried in six tanks located in the engine room. Total fuel capacity is 3,200kg. Lubricating oil, total capacity 370 litres, is carried in two service tanks and a storage tank located on the forward bulkhead in the engine room. Fuel and lubricating oil is sufficient for a cruising range, foilborne, of not less than 600km (373 miles).

AUXILIARY UNIT: 12hp diesel for generating electrical power when the craft is at its moorings, warming the main engines in cold weather and operating drainage pump.

CONTROLS: Control of the engines, reverse gear and fuel supply is effected remotely from the wheelhouse with the aid of a hydraulic system comprising transmitter cylinders in the wheelhouse, and actuators on the engine. The engines can also be controlled from the engine room.

Craft heading is controlled by two balanced rudders, the blades of which are in solid aluminium magnesium alloy. The rudders are operated hydraulically from the wheelhouse, the rudder angle being checked by an electric indicator in the wheelhouse. In an emergency, with the craft in hullborne conditions, the rudder is put over with the aid of a detachable hand tiller fitted to the rudder stock.

At low speed the craft is capable of turning in its own length by pinwheeling—employing both engines with equal power in opposite directions—one ahead, the other astern.

Minimum diameter of the turning circle is approximately 250m (819ft) with the engines running at low speed (700-750rpm) and with the rudder put through an angle of 35 degrees. Turning circle diameter when operating foilborne with the rudder at an angle of 10 degrees is approximately 750m (2,460ft).

The vessel takes-off for foilborne flight in 120-140 seconds, ie within a distance of 25-28 lengths of her hull.

Landing run, with engines reversed, ranges from 1·5 to 2 hull lengths, while the braking distance without reversing the engines is within 3-4 lengths of the hull.

ACCOMMODATION: Passengers are accommodated in three compartments, a forward saloon seating 26, and central and aft saloons seating 46 and 44 passengers respectively. The central saloon has three exits, two forward leading to the embarkation platforms and one aft leading to the promenade deck above the engine room. On the port side of the central saloon, aft, is a small buffet/bar. Beneath the wheelhouse is a duty crew room and a luggage compartment which opens into the forward saloon.

The aft saloon has two exits, one leading to the promenade deck above the engine room and one to the weather deck aft. Forward and aft on both

sides of the craft are sponsons to protect the foil systems during mooring. The forward pair are used as embarkation and disembarkation platforms.

SYSTEMS, ELECTRICAL: 24-28·5V dc from the vessel's power supply or 220V ac, 50Hz, from shore-to-ship supply sources.

RADIO: Ship-to-shore radio telephone operating on any of ten pre-selected fixed frequencies. Also passenger announcement system and crew intercom.

NAVIGATION: Magnetic compass.

COMPRESSED AIR: System comprises two air storage bottles, each of 40-litre capacity, used for starting the main engines, operating emergency stop mechanism, closing feed cocks of the fuel tanks, recharging the hydraulic system accumulator and the ship's siren.

FIREFIGHTING: Remote system for fighting outbreak in engine room, with automatic light and sound indicator operating in wheelhouse. Hand-operated foam and CO_2 extinguishers provided in passenger saloons and wheelhouse.

DIMENSIONS
Length overall: 34·5m (112ft 2¼in)
Beam overall: 9·5m (31ft 2in)
Height foilborne above water surface: 6·8m (22ft 3¾in)
Draft hullborne: 2·4m (7ft 10½in)
   foilborne: 1·2m (3ft 11¼in)
WEIGHTS
Light displacement: 37·2 tonnes
Fully loaded: 54·3 tonnes
PERFORMANCE
Cruising speed, calm water: 65km/h (35 knots)
Limiting sea states,
   foilborne: Beaufort Force 3
   hullborne: Beaufort Force 4

MOLNIA

This popular six-seat hydrofoil sports runabout was derived from Alexeyev's original test craft. Many hundreds are available for hire on Russian lakes and rivers. In slightly modified form, and renamed Volga, the type is being exported to 44 different countries. The craft is navigable in protected off-shore water up to 2 miles from the land

and has particular appeal for water-taxi and joy-ride operators.

Molnia is no longer in production, having been replaced by the Volga. Details of the Molnia can be found in *Jane's Surface Skimmers 1976-77* and earlier editions.

NEVKA

This light passenger ferry and sightseeing craft is in series production at a Leningrad shipyard and the first units have been supplied to Yalta for coastal services on the Black Sea. A multi-purpose runabout, it is intended to cope with a variety of duties including scheduled passenger services, sightseeing, VIP transport and crew-boat. The standard version seats a driver and 14 passengers.

An export model was expected to be available from the spring of 1981 onwards.

The craft, which is designed to operate in waves up to 1m (3ft) high, is the first small hydrofoil in the Soviet Union to employ surface-piercing V foils, and also the first to employ a diesel engine in conjunction with a Z-drive.

In December 1971 a waterjet-propelled variant made its first cruise along the Crimean coast. The 16-mile trip from Yalta to Alushta was made in half an hour.

FOILS: Bow and stern foils are of fixed V surface-piercing configuration and made of solid aluminium magnesium alloy.

HULL: Glass fibre reinforced plastic structure assembled in four basic sections. The outer hull is assembled with the transom, the deck with the rib of the windscreen, the cabin/cockpit with the engine air intakes and afterpeak, and the inner hull with the companionway at the aft of the cabin.

The lower hull is subdivided by watertight bulkheads into four compartments.

The hull contours are designed to facilitate easy transition from hull to foilborne mode and minimise structural loadings due to wave impact. Two transverse steps are incorporated.

ACCOMMODATION: The craft can be supplied with an open cockpit and folding canopy, as a cabin cruiser with a solid top or as a sightseeing

This particular model of the Nevka is fitted with trapeze foils instead of the V-foils which appear to be standard on the export model. Power is supplied by a 235hp 3D20 diesel which drives a three-bladed propeller via a Z-drive

craft with a transparent cabin roof. As a cabin cruiser, the craft is equipped with bunks, a galley and toilet. The driver's stand can be located either at the forward end of the cabin or in a raised position amidships.

POWER PLANT: Power is supplied by a single 3D20 four-cycle, six-cylinder diesel, developing 235hp at 2,200rpm. The engine, located aft, drives a three-bladed propeller via a DK-300 Z-drive.

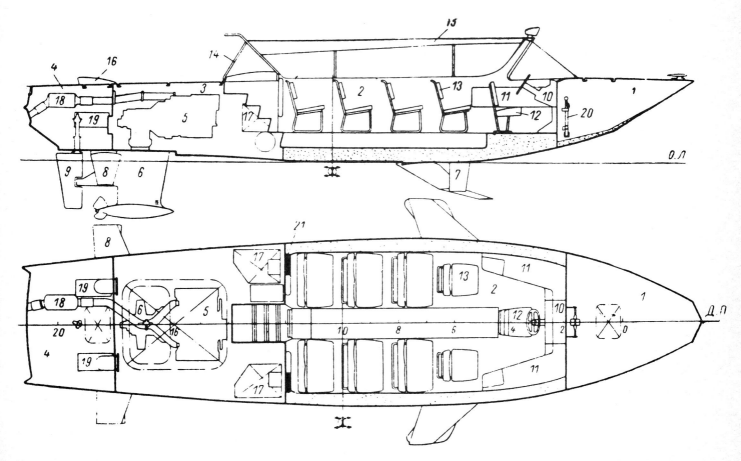

Internal arrangements of the standard Nevka, seating a driver and 14 passengers, (a) inboard profile; (b) deck plan. 1. forepeak; 2. passenger cabin; 3. engine bay; 4. afterpeak; 5. 235hp 3D20 four-cycle six-cylinder diesel; 6. DK-300 Z-drive; 7. bow foil; 8. rear foil; 9. rudder; 10. control panel; 11. lockers; 12. driver's seat; 13. passenger seat; 14. guard rail; 15. detachable awning; 16. engine air intakes; 17. fuel tank; 18. silencer; 19. storage batteries; 20. anchor; 21. lifebelt

CONTROLS: Craft heading is controlled by a single balanced rudder in solid aluminium alloy mounted aft of the rear foil main strut and operated by a steering wheel via a mechanical linkage. Other controls include a footpedal to control engine speed, and a reverse lever.

SYSTEMS, ELECTRICAL: Power is 24V dc. A 1kW engine-mounted generator supplies power while the craft is operating. Two 12V acid storage batteries, each of 180Ah capacity and connected in series to give 24V, supply power during stops.

FIREFIGHTING: An independent fluid fire fighting system of aircraft type is installed in the engine bay and is operated remotely from the driving seat.

DIMENSIONS
Length overall: 10·9m (35ft 11in)
Hull beam: 2·7m (8ft 11in)
Beam overall: 4m (13ft 2in)
Draft, hullborne: 1·7m (5ft 3in)
    foilborne: 0·9m (2ft 9in)

WEIGHTS
Max take-off displacement: 5·9 tons
Displacement unloaded: 4·1 tons
Payload: 1·05 tons

PERFORMANCE
Cruising speed: 30 knots
Normal cruising range: 160 miles
Diameter of turn at max speed: 109m (357ft)
Take-off time: approx 30 seconds
Max permissible wave height in foilborne mode: 1m (3ft 3in)
Fuel and lube oil endurance: 6 hours
Fuel consumption per hp at cruising rating: 178g/h

PCHELA (BEE)

This military derivative of the Strela is in service with the KGB for frontier patrol duties in the Baltic, Black Sea, Caspian and various other sea areas. The craft is equipped with a full range of search and navigation radar and is reported to have a speed of about 35 knots. Twenty-five were built between 1965-1972. The craft carry depth charges and two twin machine gun mounts.

RAKETA

The prototype Raketa was launched in 1957 and was the first multi-seat passenger hydrofoil to employ the Alexeyev shallow draft submerged foil system. Several hundred are now in service on all the major rivers of the USSR.

In January 1973 it was announced that more than three hundred Raketas were being operated on rivers and lakes in the Soviet Union, including sixty-six in service with the Volga United River Shipping Agency.

Variants include the standard non-tropicalised Raketa M seating 64 passengers; the current export model, the 58-seat Raketa T, which is both tropicalised and air-conditioned, and finally the Raketa TA, modified in London by Airavia Ltd, and licensed by the UK Department of Trade to carry up to 100 passengers (58 seated) on high density commuter and tourist routes on sheltered waters such as Westminster—Greenwich.

A substantial number of Raketas have been exported. Examples are currently in service in Romania, Hungary, Finland, Czechoslovakia, Yugoslavia, Austria, Bulgaria and the Federal Republic of Germany.

Production of the Raketa has now stopped and yards previously involved in their fabrication and assembly are building Voskhod and other designs.

The description that follows applies to the Raketa T, the standard export variant, powered by an M-401A diesel and with a cruising speed of about 58km/h (32 knots).

The vessel is designed for high-speed passenger ferry services during daylight hours on rivers, reservoirs and sheltered waters in tropical climates. It meets the requirements of the Soviet River Register Class 'O' with operation restricted to 0·8m (2ft 7in) waves when foilborne and up to 1·5m (4ft 11in) when hullborne.

The passenger saloon is provided with natural and induced ventilation and seats 58. The crew comprises a captain, engineer, deckhand and barman.

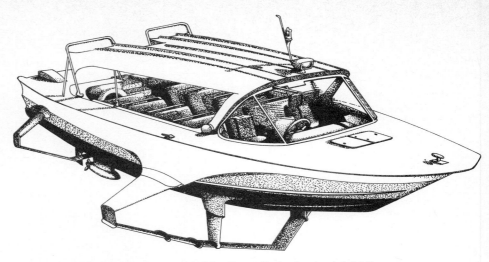

Perspective drawing of the export model of the 15-seat Nevka showing foil details

In service in growing numbers as a light passenger ferry and sightseeing craft, the Nevka is about to be offered on the export market. The standard model seats a driver and up to 14 passengers

Pchela fast patrol boat of the KGB frontier guard. Note the surface-piercing trapeze foils

FOILS: The foil system comprises one bow foil, one aft foil and two dart-like planing sub-foils, the tips of which are attached to the trailing edges of the outer bow foil struts. Foils, sub-foils and struts are in welded stainless steel. The bow foil, which incorporates sweepback, and the straight aft foil, are both supported by three vertical struts.

The base of the centre strut aft provides the end bearing for the propeller which is located beneath the foil.

HULL: The hull is framed on longitudinal and transverse formers and all the main elements—plating, deck, partitions, bulkheads, platforms and wheelhouse—are in riveted duralumin. The stem is fabricated in interwelded steel strips. Below the freeboard deck the hull is divided into six watertight compartments employing web framing.

ACCOMMODATION: The passenger saloon seats 58 in aircraft-type, adjustable seats. At the aft end of the saloon is a bar. The saloon has one exit on each side leading to the promenade deck and one forward, leading to the forecastle. Aft of the saloon is the engine room, promenade deck with additional seats, two toilets, a storeroom and a companionway leading up to the wheelhouse.

The craft carries a full range of life-saving and fire fighting equipment. There are 62 life jackets stowed in the passenger saloon and four for the crew in the wheelhouse and under the embarkation companionway. Two lifebelts are provided on the embarkation platform and two on the promenade deck. Fire fighting equipment includes four foam and four CO_2 fire extinguishers, two fire axes, two fire buckets and two felt cloths.

POWER PLANT: Power is supplied by a single M-401A water-cooled, supercharged 12-cylinder V-type diesel, with a normal service output of 900hp. The engine drives via a reverse gear and inclined stainless steel propeller shaft a three-bladed cast bronze propeller. The fuel system comprises two fuel tanks with a total capacity of 1,400kg, a fuel priming unit, and a hand fuel booster pump. A compressed air system, comprising a propeller shaft-driven air compressor and two 40-litre compressed air bottles is provided for main engine starting, emergency stopping, operating the foghorn and scavenging the water intake.

The diesel generator unit comprises a Perkins P3.152 diesel engine employed in conjunction with a Stamford C20 alternator.

CONTROLS: The wheelhouse is equipped with a hydraulic remote control system for the engine, reverse gear and fuel supply. The balanced rudder, made in aluminium-magnesium alloy, is controlled hydraulically by turning the wheel. A hand tiller is employed in an emergency. Employment of gas exhaust as a side-thruster to assist mooring is permitted at 850rpm.

SYSTEMS, ELECTRICAL: A 3kW generator, rated at 27·5V and coupled to the main engine is the main source of power while the vessel is under way. A 50Hz, 230V, 1,500rpm three-phase alternator supplies ac power. Four 12V acid storage batteries, each with a 132Ah capacity and connected in series to give 24V, supply power during short stops.

HYDRAULICS: The hydraulic system for controlling the main engine, reverse gear and fuel supply, consists of control levers located in the wheelhouse and on the main engine, power cylinders located on the engine, a filler tank, pipelines and fittings.

HEATING AND VENTILATION: Passenger saloon and wheelhouse are provided with natural ventilation, using ram inflow when the boat is in motion. Norris warming air-conditioning is fitted for use in hot weather. One conditioner is installed in the wheelhouse and eight are installed in the passenger saloon and bar. The cooled air is distributed throughout the saloon by electric fans installed on the ceiling. One is provided in the wheelhouse. A radio-telephone with a range of about 30km (19 miles) is installed for ship-to-shore and ship-to-ship communication. The vessel also has a public address system and intercom speakers linking the engine room, wheelhouse and forecastle.

DIMENSIONS
Length overall: 26·96m (88ft 5in)
Beam amidships: 5m (16ft 5in)
Freeboard: 0·8m (2ft 7½in)
Height overall (excluding mast): 4·46m (14ft 8in)
Draft, hullborne: 1·8m (5ft 11in)
  foilborne: 1·1m (3ft 7¼in)
WEIGHTS
Displacement, fully loaded: 27·09 tonnes
  light: 20·31 tonnes
PERFORMANCE
Service speed: about 58km/h (32 knots)
Max wave height, foilborne: 0·8m (2ft 8in)
  hullborne: 1·5m (4ft 11in)
Turning diameter, hullborne: 3-4 boat lengths
  foilborne: 15-16 boat lengths

SPUTNIK

The 100-ton Sputnik was the first of the Soviet Union's large hydrofoils. On its maiden voyage in

Raketa M operated on the Rhine by the Köln-Düsseldorfer Shipping Company between Cologne and Koblenz

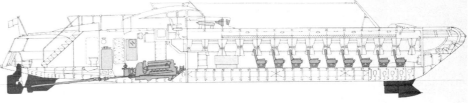

Inboard profile and plan view of the standard 50-seat Raketa. On short-range commuter services, additional passengers are seated around the promenade deck aft, and others are permitted to stand. The high density traffic version accommodates up to 100 passengers

Aft foil assembly comprising the foil, three supporting struts and bearing for the inclined propeller shaft of the Raketa passenger ferry

November 1961, the prototype carried 300 passengers between Gorki and Moscow in 14 hours. Although a heavy autumn storm was encountered en route the craft was able to continue under way at a cruising speed of 40 knots through several large reservoirs with waves running as high as 8ft.

FOILS: The foil system comprises a bow and rear foil with the outer struts of the bow assembly carrying two additional planing subfoils.

HULL: The hull is welded in AlMg-61 aluminium magnesium alloy. Adoption of an all-welded unit construction facilitated prefabrication of sections at the Sormovo shipyard and elsewhere, the parts being sent to other yards in the USSR for assembly. One yard used for assembling Sputniks is at Batumi, on the Caspian Sea.

POWER PLANT: Power is supplied by four 850hp M-50 water-cooled, supercharged V-type diesels, each driving its own propeller shaft and controlled electro-hydraulically from the forward wheelhouse.

ACCOMMODATION: Passengers are accommodated in three saloons, a well-glazed fore compartment seating 68, and central and aft compartments each seating 96. On short, high frequency services, the seating is increased to 108 in the latter compartments by the substitution of padded benches instead of adjustable aircraft-type seats. Two separate off-duty cabins are provided for the five-man crew. The cabins are attractively finished in pastel shades and fully insulated against heat and sound. Full fire fighting and other emergency provisions are made and in addition to lifebelts for all passengers and members of the crew, two inflatable rubber boats are carried.

DIMENSIONS
Length overall: 47·9m (157ft 2in)
Beam overall: 9m (29ft 6in)
Draft, hullborne: 1·3m (4ft 3in)
   foilborne: 0·9m (2ft 10in)
WEIGHTS
Displacement fully loaded: 110 tons
PERFORMANCE
Cruising speed: 75km/h (41 knots)

STRELA

Developed from the Mir and intended for services across the Black Sea, the prototype Strela (Arrow) completed its acceptance trials towards the end of 1961. The craft, which was designed and built in Leningrad, was first put into regular passenger service between Odessa and Batumi, and later between Yalta and Sevastapol. More recently a Strela has been operating a service between Leningrad and Tallinn. It covers the distance in four hours, ninety minutes faster than the express train service connecting the two ports. Only two craft of this type have been built.

Two 970hp 12-cylinder V-type M-50 F3 diesels driving twin screws give the Strela a cruising speed of 75km/h (40 knots). The craft has trapeze type surface-piercing bow foils with a horizontal centre section between the main struts, and can operate in sea state 4.

It carries 82-94 passengers in airliner type seats.

DIMENSIONS
Length overall: 29·3m (96ft 1in)
Beam overall: 8·3m (26ft 4in)
Draft, hullborne: 2·25m (7ft 7in)
   foilborne: 1·2m (3ft 11in)
WEIGHTS
Displacement, fully loaded: 46 tons
PERFORMANCE
Cruising speed: 40 knots
Sea state capability: 1·22m (4ft) waves
Range of operation: 740km (460 miles)
Time to reach service speed from stop: 130 seconds
Distance from full speed to stop: 234m (768ft)
Full speed ahead, to full speed astern: 117m (383ft)

VIKHR (WHIRLWIND)

Seagoing version of the 100-ton Sputnik, Vikhr employs the same hull and is one of the most powerful passenger hydrofoils operating today. Described as a "Coastal liner", it is

Bow foil and planing stabiliser foils of the 58-seat Raketa

100-ton Sputnik, first of the Soviet Union's large hydrofoil passenger ferries

Prototype Strela during trials off the Yalta coast

designed to operate during hours of daylight on inshore services on the Black Sea up to 50km (31 miles) from the coast. The craft was launched in 1962 and is currently in service on the Odessa-Herson route.

FOILS: Compared with the Sputnik, innovations include more sharply swept back foils, a form of stability augmentation, and an amidship foil, in addition to those fore and aft, to increase seaworthiness and stability. The bow and rear foils and their struts are in stainless steel, foil and stabiliser are made in aluminium magnesium alloy.

HULL: Similar to the Sputnik. Two steps are aligned with the flare of the sides. Hull and superstructure are of welded AlMg-61 aluminium magnesium alloy.

ACCOMMODATION: There are three passenger saloons, seating a total of 268 passengers. The forward saloon seats 78, the central saloon seats 96, and the aft 94. At the rear of the central cabin is a large buffet and bar, beneath which is the engine room. From the bar double doors lead to the off-duty quarters for the seven-man crew.

In high seas, passengers board from the stern, across the promenade deck. In normal conditions, embarkation takes place through a wide passageway across the vessel between the fore and middle saloons. Seats are arranged in rows of four abreast across each cabin with two aisles, each 1m (3ft 4in) wide, between, to ease access to the seats.

POWER PLANT: Power is supplied by four 1,200hp M50-F3 diesel engines, with DGKP (diesel generator, compressor pump) auxiliary engines. Each engine drives a three-bladed propeller via a reverse gear and its own inclined stainless steel shaft. The central shafts are inclined at 12° 20′ and the side shafts at 13° 13′.

An overriding control valve is fitted to the control systems of the main engines, so that the fuel gauges of all four can be controlled simultaneously. This makes it possible to maintain a uniform load on the engines immediately the craft becomes foilborne, thus increasing the life of the engines. The craft can operate satisfactorily with one engine out.

CONTROLS: The wheelhouse is equipped with an electro hydraulic remote control system for the engines, reverse gear, fuel supply etc. Twin balanced rudders are hydraulically operated by two separate systems—main and emergency.

SYSTEMS, ELECTRICAL: Power supply is 24V dc. A 1kW dc generator is attached to each

Vikhr employs the same hull as the Sputnik and is designed for regular year round services on the Black Sea

of the engines and these supply power when operating. Two KG-5·6, 5·6kW generators are included in the auxiliary unit and supply power when at rest. They can also be used when under way for supplying the heating plant or when the 1kW generators are inoperative. Four 12V acid storage batteries, each of 180Ah capacity and connected in series to provide 24V, supply power during stops.

COMMUNICATIONS: A radio transmitter/receiver is installed in the wheelhouse for ship-shore and inter-ship communication on r/t, also a receiver. A ship's broadcast system is also installed with speakers in the passenger saloons.

NAVIGATION: Equipment includes radar, and a radio direction finding unit, both with displays in the wheelhouse.

DIMENSIONS
Length overall: 47·54m (156ft)
Beam: 9m (29ft 6in)
Height of hull to awning deck: 5·54m (18ft 2in)
Draft hullborne: 4·1m (13ft 6in)
 foilborne: 1·5m (4ft 11in)

WEIGHTS
Displacement, fully loaded: 117·5 tons

PERFORMANCE
Max speed: 78km/h (43 knots)

Cruising speed: 66km/h (35·8 knots)
Cruising range: 386km (240 miles)
Max wave height in foilborne condition: 1·5m (4ft 11in)
Time to reach service speed from stop: 190 seconds
Distance from full speed to full stop: 300m (984ft)
Distance from full speed ahead to full speed astern: 224m (735ft)

VOLGA 70

First export version of the Molnia sports hydrofoil, the Volga 70 incorporates various design refinements including a completely redesigned bow foil.

Powered by a 90hp Volvo Penta diesel engine it was introduced at the end of 1972. The cruising speed is four km/h slower than that of the earlier model, but engine maintenance is easier and the acquisition of spares is simplified in many parts of the world. This model has been purchased by companies and individuals in the USA, West Germany, Sweden, Netherlands and Singapore.

A new export model of the Volga is due to be introduced in 1981. It will succeed both the Volga 70 and the Volga-275 described in *Jane's Surface Skimmers 1978.*

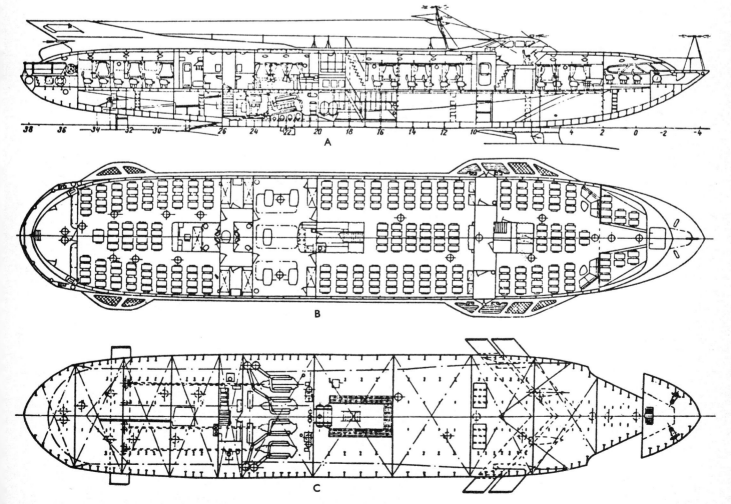
Internal arrangement of Vikhr. a. profile; b. main deck plan; c. holds

FOILS: The foil system consists of a bow foil with stabilising sub-foil and a rear foil assembly. The foils are of stainless steel.

HULL: Built in sheet and extruded light alloy, the hull is divided into three compartments by metal bulkheads. The forepeak is used for stores, the midship compartment is the open cockpit and the aft compartment houses the engine and gearbox.

ACCOMMODATION: Seats are provided for six—a driver and five passengers. The controls, instruments, magnetic compass and radio receiver are grouped on a panel ahead of the driver's seat. A full range of safety equipment is provided, including life jackets for six, life line, fire extinguisher and distress flares. A folding awning can be supplied.

POWER PLANT: Power is supplied by a single Volvo Penta AQD 32A/270TD diesel with a steerable outboard drive delivering 106hp at 4,000rpm. Fuel capacity is 120 litres (26·4 gallons), sufficient for a range of 150 miles.

SYSTEMS, ELECTRICAL: 12V dc. Starting, instrument and navigation lights and siren, are provided by an engine-mounted generator and an acid stowage battery.

Volga 70, a six-seat hydrofoil taxi and runabout powered by a 106hp Volvo Penta diesel. Volgas have been exported to 44 countries since 1972. Production is officially stated to have run into "several thousand"

DIMENSIONS
Length overall: 8·55m (28ft 1in)
Beam: 2·1m (6ft 10⅝in)
Height above water when foilborne: 0·98m (3ft 2⅝in)
Draft hullborne: 0·92m (3ft)
      foilborne: 0·52m (1ft 8½in)

WEIGHTS
Loaded displacement: 1,930kg (4,255lb)
Light displacement: 1,350kg (2,977lb)
PERFORMANCE
Max speed: 30 knots
Cruising speed: 28 knots
Range: 241km (150 miles)

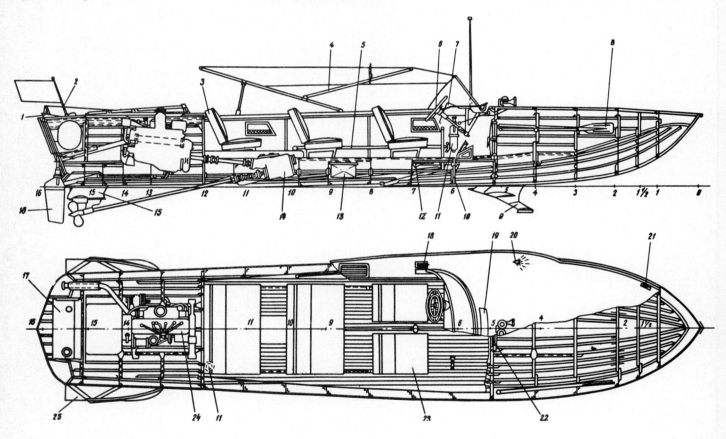

Inboard profile and plan of Volga
1 stern light; 2 flag pole; 3 bench seat; 4 awning; 5 dog hook; 6 steering column; 7 instrument panel; 8 oar; 9 bow foil assembly; 10 anchor line; 11 fire extinguisher OY-2; 12 anchor; 13 storage battery; 14 reduction and reverse gear; 15 rear foil assembly; 16 steering and rudder gear; 17 fuel tank; 18 cleat; 19 air intake; 20 side running light; 21 fairlead; 22 cover of first bulkhead hatch; 23 seat; 24 M652-Y six-cylinder automotive engine; 25 foilguard

UNITED STATES OF AMERICA

BOEING MARINE SYSTEMS
A Division of the Boeing Company
Head Office: PO Box 3707, Seattle, Washington 98124, USA
Telephone: (206) 655 3200
Officials:
Robert E Bateman, *Vice President and General Manager, Boeing Marine Systems*

Boeing Marine Systems, now a separate operating division of the Boeing company, was formed in 1959 to conduct research, development, design, manufacture and the testing of high performance marine vehicles systems. Boeing's entry into the hydrofoil field was announced in June 1960, when the company was awarded a US

$2 million contract for the construction of the US Navy's 120-ton PCH-1 High Point, a canard design which was the outcome of experiments with a similar arrangement in the US Navy test craft Sea Legs.

Boeing has also built a jet-driven hydroplane, the HTS, for testing foil models at full-scale velocity; the Fresh-1, a manned craft for testing superventilating or supercavitating foils at speeds between 60–100 knots and a waterjet test vehicle, Little Squirt. Descriptions of Fresh-1 and Little Squirt appear in *Jane's Surface Skimmers 1970-71* and earlier editions. The company also completed a highly successful waterjet-propelled gunboat, the PGH-2 Tucumcari, for the US Navy's Ship Systems Command. Its operational

trials included several months of combat evaluation in Viet-Nam as part of the US Navy's coastal surveillance force. Data provided by the vessel assisted the design and development of the NATO/PHM, which is a 'scaled up' Tucumcari, and the Jetfoil commercial hydrofoil.

High Point was modified by Boeing during 1972 to incorporate a new automatic control system, new struts and foils, a new diesel for hullborne propulsion and a steerable forward strut to provide improved manoeuvrability. The craft was returned to the US Navy in a new configuration, identified as Mod-1, in March 1973. In its revised form it is employed as a testbed for hydrofoil weapons compatibility.

In April 1975, the PCH was operated by the

Pegasus, first of the Boeing/NATO PHM (Patrol Hydrofoil Missile) class vessels, was commissioned into service with the US Navy on 9 July 1977, becoming the first hydrofoil to be officially designated a United States Ship (USS *Pegasus*). All other USN hydrofoils are operated by test commands and are not officially part of the fleet. Main armament comprises eight RGM-84A Harpoon anti-ship missiles and one rapid-fire 76mm cannon. Top speed is in excess of 50 knots

US Coast Guard for one month as part of a continuing research and development programme to evaluate high-speed water craft for the US Coast Guard use. Operating in Puget Sound and around San Francisco, the craft was employed on fisheries patrol, marine environmental protection and search and rescue missions.

On 19 January 1973, the keel was laid for the first 110-ton 250-seat Model 929-100 Jetfoil passenger ferry. The hull was assembled in a former 727 assembly building at Renton, Washington, and the first craft was launched on 29 March 1974 on Lake Washington, which is adjacent to the plant. Ten Jetfoils of this type are in commercial service. Jetfoil 0011, which was launched in June 1978, is the first Jetfoil of improved design. This new version, known as the Model 929-115 has improved performance, payload and reliability. Six of the new craft are in service, with additional Model 929-115s scheduled to begin services in 1981.

An order for the first fast patrol craft version of the Jetfoil was placed by the Royal Navy in 1978. This is basically a modified commercial Jetfoil, named HMS *Speedy,* and built on the commercial Jetfoil production line. It is a 117-ton craft with the top passenger deck removed. Two Allison 501-K20A gas turbines are installed for foilborne operation and two Allison 8V92T1 diesels for hullborne operation, giving added time on-station and increased endurance. HMS *Speedy* was launched in July 1979 and commissioned by the Royal Navy on 14 June 1980.

The company is at present examining the possibility of exporting both civil and military versions of the Jetfoil on a modular basis, with the customer purchasing a basic hull, which would contain all the essential systems, and installing his own superstructure.

In April 1973, US Naval Ship Systems Command awarded the company a US $42,602,384 contract for the design and development of the 235-tonne NATO PHM missile-equipped patrol boat, under the terms of which Boeing was to build the lead craft for the US Navy for evaluation.

The PHM was the first US Navy craft to be designed on the basis of a co-operative technical interchange between the United States and its allies within NATO.

The first PHM, *Pegasus,* was launched on 9 November 1974. Delivery to the US Navy took

PCH-1 High Point launching a McDonnell Douglas RGM-84A-1 Harpoon anti-ship missile during tests on the Joint US/Canadian Range, Nanoose, Canada, in January 1974

PCH-1 bearing the insignia of the US Coast Guard, which operated the vessel during the month of April 1975 as part of a continuing research and development programme to evaluate high-speed water craft for S & R missions, fisheries patrol and marine environmental protection

place in late 1976 and the craft completed its acceptance trials at Seattle in early June 1977.

In August 1977 it was announced by the US Defense Secretary that the US Navy will receive five more PHMs between April 1981 and March 1982. US$85·2 million has been appropriated to date for PHM development and US$272·7 million for the procurement of the five follow-on craft. On delivery the vessels will be assigned to a PHM squadron operating with the Sixth Fleet in the Mediterranean.

Interested observers in the PHM programme include the navies of Canada, Australia, Denmark, the Netherlands, France, Greece, Turkey and the United Kingdom.

Design studies are now being completed for bigger and faster hydrofoils including the 1,300–1,500-ton Destroyer Escort Hydrofoil (DEH), a vessel capable of open ocean missions and of crossing the Atlantic without refuelling.

PCH-1 HIGH POINT

General design of the PCH-1 High Point was specified by the US Navy's Bureau of Ships, with responsibility for detail design and construction assigned to Boeing. The ship was accepted by the US Navy in August 1963 and based at the Puget Sound Naval Shipyard at Bremerton, Washington. Since then it has been undergoing a wide range of tests to evaluate the performance of an inshore hydrofoil ASW system.

High Point had a major modification and overhaul by Boeing in 1972 and was returned to the US Navy in March 1973. The new configuration is identified as Mod-1. In its revised form it is employed as a weapons testbed to evaluate PHM missile ship equipment and weapons and ASW devices. Two RGM-84A-1 Harpoon blast test vehicles were successfully launched from the deck of the vessel while foilborne at 40 knots off British Columbia on the US-Canadian Nanoose range during December 1973–January 1974.

Both firings were conducted in normal sea conditions and moderate winds, the first being made while foilborne with the vessel straight and level, and the second while turning foilborne at 5 degrees/second. The dynamic stability of the craft was measured throughout the tests and the gas turbine was monitored to establish any possible harmful effects caused by the blast of the Aerojet-General 300lb solid-propellant booster employed in the launch. The success of the test confirmed the suitability of the launch canister design for use on the PHM and other hydrofoils.

During April 1975, the PCH-1 was employed by the US Coast Guard in Puget Sound and off San Francisco. It undertook a number of duties, from fisheries patrol to search and rescue missions, as part of a programme to evaluate high-speed water craft for possible use by the US Coast Guard.

FOILS: Submerged fixed incidence canard foil system, with 68% of the foil area located aft, and trailing-edge flaps on all foils for lift control, is a scaled-up version of that employed on Sea Legs. The foil struts retract vertically into the hull. Foils are of built-up construction in HY-80 weldable steel, and struts are in HY-130 steel.

HULL: Hull and superstructure are of all-welded, corrosion resistant 5456 aluminium. Integral plate stiffener extrusions are extensively used for decks and portions of the sides not having excessive curvature.

ACCOMMODATION: A crew of 18 is carried to provide a three-section watch: on duty at any given time are one officer of the deck/helmsman, one lookout on bridge, one radar operator and one navigator required in combat information centre, and two engineers on watch in main control. The wheelhouse seats two operators on the port and the helmsman on the starboard side. In addition there are seats for two observers. Crew accommodation is ventilated and heated only. Entry is via four watertight doors in the deckhouse and two watertight hatches on main deck.

POWER PLANT: Foilborne propulsion is provided by two Proteus Model 1273 gas turbines, each rated at 4,250hp maximum and 3,800hp continuous. The turbines are located aft and take

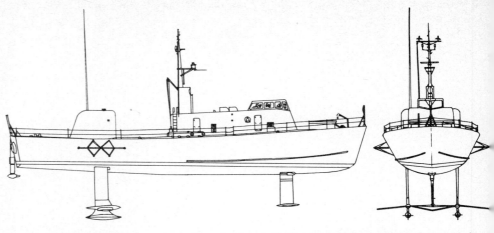

Outboard profile and bow-on view of the PCH-1 High Point in its Mod-1 configuration. Note the shallow M aft foil, which has two ailerons and two trailing edge flaps. Output of each of the two Proteus 1273 gas turbines has been uprated to 4,250shp

PHM-1 *Pegasus* underway hullborne, with foils extended. When the foils are fully retracted for long-range cruising and slow-speed manoeuvring, the craft is propelled by the two waterjet pumps of a hullborne propulsion system, powered by two 800hp Mercedes-Benz diesels

air through the two towers housing the retracted foil struts. The exhaust is discharged directly aft through the transom. Each gas turbine is coupled to a pair of contra-rotating, subcavitating five-bladed propellers, 34in in diameter, through two right-angle gearboxes one at the top of each aft strut and the others in each of the underwater nacelles.

Hullborne propulsion is supplied by a single GM 12-V-71 (N75) rated at 525hp for continuous operation. The engine is coupled to a 1,092mm (43in) diameter propeller through a retractable outdrive unit, which is steerable through 360 degrees and rotates about the axis of the horizontal shaft for retraction.

CONTROLS: Attitude and foilborne stability are controlled by an automatic control system, the heart of which is a computer. This governs motion of the trailing-edge flaps and the steerable forward strut in response to inputs from ultrasonic height sensors, position and rate gyros, accelerometers, feedback on control surface positions and helm commands. The system is active and all control surfaces are continuously moving in response to computer commands. On the bow foil, which is of single inverted tee (T) configuration, lift is varied by two trailing-edge flaps driven by a single actuator. The aft foil, of shallow M configuration, has two ailerons and two trailing-edge flaps. Each flap and its corresponding aileron are driven by a single hydraulic actuator.

Pitch is controlled by the flaps on the forward and aft foils. The gains in the control system were selected to provide automatic trim. Roll is controlled by differential operation of the flaps on the aft foil system. A roll to steer system causes the vessel to perform banked turns. Hullborne steering is accomplished by rotation of the hull-

borne propulsion unit about a vertical axis. This unit can also be rotated upward 87 degrees about a longitudinal axis to eliminate its drag during foilborne operation.

The attitude control is entirely automatic except for steering. The take-off procedure on the PCH-1 is simply to set the desired flying height, then advance the throttles. At a gross weight of 117 tons take-off occurs at 24 knots with 3,750 total horsepower delivered to the transmission system, the speed stabilising at 40 knots at that power setting. Minimum foilborne speed is 24 knots. At a cruising speed of 44 knots 4,400hp is required, with propellers turning at 1,350rpm.

SYSTEMS, ELECTRICAL: 100kW (450V, 60Hz).

HYDRAULICS: 3,000psi ship's service for hullborne steering, strut and foil extension/retraction, engineering auxiliaries, and separate 3,000psi system for foilborne control surfaces.

ELECTRONICS: Raytheon Pathfinder 1605 radar, UHF and HF radio transceivers.

ARMAMENT: Two fixed twin-tube Mk 32 torpedo tubes mounted on main deck at waist of ship.

DIMENSIONS

Length overall, hull: 35·28m (115ft 9in)
    waterline, hull: 33·65m (110ft 5in)
Hull beam: 9·14m (30ft)
Beam overall with foilguards: 11·71m (38ft 5in)
Draft hullborne: 2·62m (8ft 7in)
Freeboard: 2·67m (8ft 9in)

WEIGHTS

Light displacement: 99·6 tons
Normal take-off displacement: 127·2 tons
Useful load (fuel, water, etc): 27·6 tons

PERFORMANCE
Max speed foilborne: 50 knots
  hullborne: 25 knots
Cruising speed foilborne: 30-40 knots
  hullborne: 8 knots

PGH-2 TUCUMCARI

A 58-ton waterjet-propelled hydrofoil gun-boat, the PGH-2 was ordered from Boeing by the US Navy's Ship Systems Command in 1966, under a US $4 million, fixed price PGH (Patrol Gunboat Hydrofoil) programme. The craft was designed, constructed and tested in 23 months and delivered on schedule to the US Navy on 7 March 1968.

The craft operated with both the US Navy Pacific Fleet Amphibious Command, San Diego, and the Atlantic Amphibious Forces, Norfolk, Virginia. Its operational trials included several months of combat evaluation in Viet-Nam as part of the US Navy's 24-hour coastal surveillance force in Operation Market Time.

In 1971 the craft was deployed to Europe for operation with the US Sixth Fleet in the Mediter-ranean following a series of demonstrations for officials of NATO navies.

In November 1972, Tucumcari ran aground in the Caribbean, seven miles east of Puerto Rico, while conducting night-time operations with amphibious forces. No crewmen were killed or seriously injured. Due to damage sustained while removing the craft from the coral reef, the craft was struck from the list of active US Navy vessels and sent to the US Naval Research and Development Center where it has been emp-loyed for structural evaluation and fire contain-ment tests. A full technical description of the vessel appeared in *Jane's Surface Skimmers 1974-75* and earlier editions.

BOEING NATO/PHM

The NATO Hydrofoil Fast Patrol Ship Guided Missile (NATO/PHM) originated in mid-1969 when C-in-C South presented to NATO a requirement for a large number of fast patrol boats to combat the threat posed by missile-armed fast patrol boats in the Mediterranean.

The concept of a common fast patrol boat was studied, and in September 1970 it was decided that the submerged foil craft of 140 tons pro-posed by the US Navy was the vessel most suited to NATO mission requirements. In October 1971, the United States indicated that it would proceed at its own expense with the design of the vessel and share the results of the studies with those nations wishing to purchase PHMs. It also offered to conduct all aspects of design and development, contracting and management in co-operation with governments entering into project membership. Costs would be reimbursed only by those nations engaged in the project.

Letters of intent, acknowledging design and cost scheduled obligations, were provided by Italy and West Germany in April and May 1972, respectively. Sudden and extreme changes in the US government's attitude regarding PHM pro-duction in recent years had a markedly negative effect on the continued programme participation by West Germany. Tentative moves were made by Congress to delete four of the five production craft from the programme early in 1976. When, in February 1977, the new Secretary of Defense announced to the West German Government that the United States was terminating the PHM programme, the West German navy decided it had no option but to terminate participatory effort in production design, called back its project office personnel and embarked on the ordering of conventional fast patrol craft. By the time Con-gress had completed its 1977 action refusing to rescind prior year appropriated PHM funding, the situation was irreversible and West Germany was no longer an active partner.

Statements made in mid-1978 suggest, how-ever, that the US Departments of Defense and State are currently seeking to promote renewed participation in the PHM Programme by the USA's NATO allies. Although only three gov-ernments decided to participate actively in the

Pegasus launching a test missile during operational and technical evaluation. The firing, conducted by the US Navy at Port Hueneme, California, was to test the structure of the PHM's Harpoon anti-ship missile system. The evaluation included the testing of the Mk 94 fire control system and the 76mm OTO Melara dual-purpose rapid-fire cannon

Pegasus during an operational exercise. A Boeing three-axis automatic control system regulates the height of the PHM's hull above the waves. The ACS also introduces the correct amount of bank and steering to coordinate turns in full

Impression of a projected Coast Guard variant of PHM. Hydrofoils of this type can easily be converted to perform such roles as anti-submarine warfare, fisheries law enforcement and the protection of offshore resources

initial stages, future project membership is not restricted. Interested observers include Canada, Denmark, the Netherlands, France and the United Kingdom. Greece and Turkey have also considered participation. Japan is also expressing interest in purchasing or building PHMs.

In November 1971, the US Navy awarded Boeing a US $5·6 million contract for the pre-liminary design of a 230-ton craft and the pur-chase of mechanical and electronic components for at least two of the vessels. Seventeen months later, Boeing was awarded a US $42,607,384 contract for the design and development of the PHM for NATO navies. Under the terms of the contract the first craft, the *Pegasus*, was built for the US Navy.

Pegasus was launched on 9 November 1974, and made its first foilborne flight on 25 February 1975. *Pegasus* achieved its classified designed

speed, completed the Navy-conducted phase of testing its weapons, and then began operational evaluation in the San Diego area in the autumn of 1975.

It completed its acceptance trials during the first week of June 1977 and was commissioned into service on 9 July 1977, becoming the first hydrofoil officially designated a United States Ship (USS *Pegasus*). Rear Admiral John Bulkely, USN, In-Service Trial President recorded that she had demonstrated 'superb reliability throughout her trial with no major or significant breakdowns or failures'.

In October 1977 it was announced that the US Navy will receive five more PHMs between April 1981 and March 1982. Designated Patrol Com-batants — Missile (Hydrofoils), they will be assigned to a PHM squadron operating with the Sixth Fleet in the Mediterranean.

The first squadron of PHMs will consist of the USS *Pegasus* and her five sister ships, *Taurus, Aquila, Aries, Gemini* and *Hercules,* now under construction, plus the PHM Mobile Logistic Support Group (MLSG) and the Squadron commander's staff. An interim MLSG has been established to support *Pegasus* and comprises one officer and 28 enlisted personnel operating from six standard 40ft containers and three road-able trailers outfitted to provide shop, office and training space and stowage for spares and food stores. During the second phase of the squadron build-up a converted 1178 Class LST, to be known as a Hydrofoil Support Ship (AGHS) was to be made available. This would have provided all the facilities available from the van complex plus the basic fuel and other services now provided from ashore.

However the AGHS has been deleted from the US Navy budget, although the support need remains. One possible alternative would be the use of selected DD 963 Spruance Class destroyers to carry the PHM Mobile Logistics Support Group and equip the PHM to undertake portions of the DD 963 helicopter (LAMPS) mission. This would dramatically increase the surface warfare capability of each of the two classes of ship. It would release the PHM from any restrictions on its mobility and deployment and improve the all-weather ASW capability of the DD 963.

Four of the production craft will be armed with a 75mm OTO Melara dual-purpose rapid fire cannon and eight Harpoon anti-ship missiles in two four-tube lightweight canister launchers. Armament for the fifth craft will be installed after delivery. Construction of PHM-2 *Hercules* began in May 1974 but was stopped in 1975. This will be the last to be delivered in March 1982. PHM-3, the first of the follow-on craft to be completed, is scheduled to be delivered in April 1981, followed by PHM-4 in June, PHM-5 in October and PHM-6 in January 1982. All five craft will be built by Boeing Marine Systems at its hydrofoil assembly plant at Renton, Washington, adjacent to Lake Washington. USS *Pegasus* is now operationally assigned to the Atlantic Fleet at Key West, Florida, as of August 1980.

The PHM has sufficient design flexibility to allow for individual variations by any country.

PHMs under construction at Boeing's hydrofoil assembly plant, Renton, Washington. In the foreground PHM-3 *Taurus*, due for delivery in April 1981 and, behind, PHM-4 *Aquila*, due to be delivered in June 1981

These variations will be primarily in the weapons systems installed, and the participating nations, current and future, can acquire the standard PHM carrying whatever combat equipment is determined necessary to meet national requirements.

PHM's potential in terms of strategic mobility was demonstrated between 30 September and 1 October 1975, when *Pegasus* completed the 1,225 nautical miles from Seattle to San Diego in the record-breaking time of less than 34 hours, which included a refuelling stop at Eureka, California.

With the aid of midway refuelling the craft is capable of crossing oceans with fast carrier task groups, convoys of merchant ships and amphibious assault groups. With three underway refuellings, it can cross the Atlantic from Massachusetts to the United Kingdom at an average speed of 30 knots in 4·2 days, or it could cross from Norfolk, Virginia to Cadiz in 4·6 days with four underway refuellings.

PHM is designed to be self-supporting at sea for a period of five days. For extended periods, or during intensive operations, it could be refuelled with either JP-5 or Naval Distillate (DFM) by

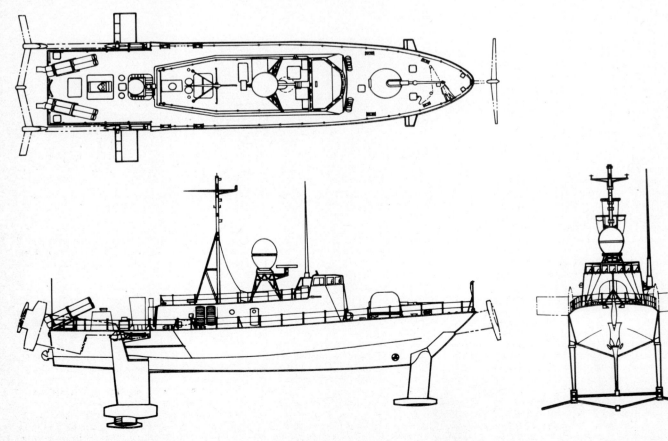

General arrangement of NATO PHM

oilers, major combatants and carriers.

It can be easily adapted for such roles as anti-submarine warfare, fisheries law enforcement and the protection of offshore resources.

The standard PHM is approximately 40·5m (132ft 10in) long, has a beam of 8·6m (28ft 2in) and a full load displacement of about 241 tonnes (238 tons). Foilborne range is in excess of 500n miles at speeds in excess of 40 knots in 8–12ft seas. The hull form and size, the major structural bulkheads and decks, foils and struts, waterjets, pumps, controls and main propulsion machinery are identical. The auxiliary equipment and arrangements, deckhouse and crew accommodation are also of standard design, but variations in the latter are possible to suit the manning requirements of individual countries.

FOILS: Fully-submerged canard arrangement with approximately 32% of the dynamic lift provided by the bow foil and 68% by the aft foil. The aft foil retracts rearwards and the bow foil retracts forward into a recess in the bow. Bow doors preserve the hull lines when the forward foil is either fully extended or retracted. The foils and struts are in 17-4 PH stainless high strength steel. Both forward and aft foils are welded assemblies consisting of spars, ribs, and skin. Flaps are fitted to the trailing edges to provide control and lift augmentation at take-off and during flight. The bow foil system incorporates a strut that rotates to provide directional control and reliable turning rates in heavy seas.

The shallow M or inverted double pi configuration of the aft foil is designed for improved hydroelastic and turning characteristics. The primary strut structure consists of spars, ribs and skin welded into watertight assemblies. The struts are designed as beam columns, and rigidly attached to the foil support structure at the hull.

The struts are attached to the hull with pivot pins that allow the foils to rotate clear of the water. Hydraulic actuators are used for retraction and extension, mechanical stops and position locks being employed to secure the foils in either position.

CONTROLS, FOILBORNE: The helm, throttle and an automatic control system (ACS) provide continuous dynamic control during take-off, foilborne operation and landing. Once take-off is complete, the ACS requires no attention on the part of the crew. It controls the craft by sensing craft attitude, motion rates and acceleration, then comparing them electronically with desired values. Any deviations are processed by analogue control computer which generates electrical commands causing hydraulic actuators to reposition the control surfaces, thus minimising detected errors. The foilborne control surfaces are trailing edge flaps on each of the foils, plus the rotating bow foil strut which acts as the foilborne rudder.

Manual controls and displays for both hullborne and foilborne conditions are concentrated at the helm station and include the wheel, a foil-depth selector, a foil-depth indicator, a ship-heading indicator and a heading holding switch.

CONTROLS, HULLBORNE: Steering control in the hullborne mode is provided by steerable nozzles which rotate electro-hydraulically in response to the wheel. An automatic heading control, similar to that employed for foilborne operation is incorporated, together with the necessary heading reference provided by the gyrocompass.

POWER PLANT, FOILBORNE: The foilborne propulsion system comprises a single 18,000shp, co-axial two-stage, two-speed waterjet, driven through two sets of reduction gears by a single General Electric LM 2500 marine gas turbine, developed from the GE TF39, which powers the USAF's C-5 transport and the DC-10 Trijet.

Both the foilborne and hullborne propulsion systems were designed by Aerojet Liquid Rocket Company, Sacramento, California, under a Boeing contract.

The single foilborne propulsion pump is capable of handling 90,000 gallons/min and the two hullborne pumps will each operate at approximately 30,000 gallons/min.

Engine installation and removal for overhaul is

Cu Na Mara, a Boeing Jetfoil 929-115 operated by B+I Line between Dublin and Liverpool

Passenger accommodation is fully air-conditioned and arranged on two decks. This photograph was taken in the upper passenger saloon of Jetfoil 002 *Madeira*, one of the seven Jetfoils operated by Far East Hydrofoil Co, Hong Kong, on its Hong Kong-Macao service. Seats are provided on this particular model for 284 passengers. Cruising speed is 45 knots (83·3km/h; 51·8mph)

accomplished through hatches located in the main deck between the deckhouse and exhaust outlet.

The vessel is capable of operation on JP-5 or diesel fuel.

POWER PLANT, HULLBORNE: Twin Aerojet waterjet pumps powered by two 800hp Mercedes-Benz 8V331TC80 diesels propel the vessel when hullborne. Each waterjet propulsor has nozzle steering and reversing buckets. The hullborne system provides long-range cruising and slow speed manoeuvring, while the gas turbine is available when required for high-speed foilborne operation.

HULL: Hull and deckhouses are all-welded structures in AL 5465 alloy.

ACCOMMODATION: Crew will average 21 officers and men, but will vary according to the armament carried. Accommodation on the US Navy version is provided for four officers—the commanding officer has a separate cabin—three chief petty officers and 14 enlisted men. The superstructure accommodates the bridge, which contains steering and engine control consoles and is elevated to provide a 360 degree view. A short ladder from the bridge leads down to the command and surveillance deckhouse that accommodates the fire control, radar, communications and navigation equipment. The size of the deckhouse provides flexibility in accommodating various national equipment requirements. The space aft of the superstructure and forward of the foilborne engine exhaust is used to erect rigging for replenishment and refuelling.

Below the main deck, about one third of the PHM's length is devoted to crew accommodation, the forward third is occupied by the primary gun, automatic loader mechanism, ammunition storage and forward foil, and the after third is occupied by the unmanned machinery spaces.

All manned spaces are equipped with a recirculating air conditioning system to give a maximum air temperature of 27°C at 55% relative humidity in summer, and a minimum inside temperature of 18°C in winter. The officers'

staterooms, crew quarters and lounge/messing area are fully air-conditioned, the temperature being controlled by individual thermostats in the spaces concerned.

SYSTEMS, ELECTRICAL: Ship's service electric plant comprises two AiResearch Ship Service Power Units (SSPUs), with ME831-800 gas turbines as prime movers driving 250kVA, 400Hz, 450V generators. Each SSPU also drives an attached centrifugal compressor for starting the LM 2500 engine and two hydraulic pumps for the ship's hydraulic system. One is capable of handling the entire electrical load, the second is provided as a standby. Through the use of static power conversion equipment, limited three-phase, 60Hz ac power and 28V dc is available for equipment requirements. In port, the craft can utilise shore power, or use its own auxiliary power unit for this purpose as well as battery charging and emergency use of navigation and radio equipment.

HYDRAULICS: 3,000psi to actuate the hull-borne and foilborne controls, foil retraction and hullborne engine starting. Dual hydraulic supply is provided to each service with sub-system isolation fore and aft in the event of major damage.

FIRE EXTINGUISHING: Dry chemical equipment throughout craft, and a fixed total flooding-type Freon 1301 system.

WEAPONS/FIRE CONTROL: Either WM-28 radar and weapons control system or US model, the Mk 92. Both systems embody a combined fire control and search antenna system, mounted on a single stabilised platform and enclosed in a fibre-glass radome. The Italian Argo system can also be installed.

TARGETING/MISSILE WARNING: Automatic classification ESM (electronic warfare support measures) set is installed for missile warning and over-the-horizon targeting of enemy surface units.

GUNS: Standard primary gun is the OTO Melara 76mm gun, which is unmanned and automatically controlled by the fire control system. The craft can also be delivered with secondary guns. If

specified two Mk 20 Rh 202 20mm AA cannon can be provided, one each, port and starboard, adjacent to the fire control antenna structure.
MISSILES: The prototype carries eight Harpoon missiles in two four-tube lightweight canister launchers, but Exocet, Otomat, Tero or any smaller missile system can be installed. Space is provided aft to accommodate the four launchers, port and starboard, in parallel pairs. The launchers are deck-fixed in elevation and azimuth.

Armament of the standard US Navy version will be eight McDonnell Douglas RGM-84A Harpoon anti-ship missiles in lightweight container launchers; one Mk 75 Mod 1 76mm cannon and one Mk 92 Mod 1 GFCS (Mk 94 on PHM-1) and two Mk 34 Chaff launchers.
COMMAND, CONTROL AND COMMUNICATIONS: True motion navigation radar; OMEGA navigation equipment; gyro compass; dead reckoning tracer; Tactical and Navigation Collision Avoidance System (TANCAV); speed log; depth sounder/recorder; AN/SPA-25B repeater consoles (2); integrated intercom/announcing/exterior communications system; HF, UHF and VHF communications (teletype and voice) IFF system, ESM system.

The basic PHM design allows for a growth of approximately five tons in full load displacement to enhance mission capability. Areas under consideration include sonar, torpedoes, improved surface-to-surface missiles and low-light-level TV, all of which appear to be feasible without having an adverse effect on its current capabilities.

The following details apply to the model under construction for the US Navy.
DIMENSIONS
Length overall,
　foils extended: 40·5m (132ft 10in)
　foils retracted: 44·3m (145ft 4in)
Beam max, deck: 8·6m (28ft 2in)
Max width across foils: 14·5m (47ft 6in)
Draft,
　hullborne, foils retracted: 2·3m (7ft 6in)
　hullborne, foils extended: 7·1m (23ft 2in)
　foilborne, normal: 2·5m (8ft 2in)
WEIGHTS
Displacement, full load including margins: 241 tonnes
PERFORMANCE
Max speed foilborne: in excess of 50 knots
Cruising speed,
　foilborne, sea state 0–5: in excess of 40 knots
　hullborne: 11 knots
Sea state: can negotiate 10ft seas at speeds in excess of 40 knots
Range, foilborne: in excess of 600n miles
　hullborne: in excess of 1,800n miles

BOEING JETFOIL 929-100

This is a 110-ton waterjet-propelled commercial hydrofoil for services in relatively rough waters. It employs a fully-submerged, automatically-controlled canard foil arrangement and is powered by two 3,710hp Allison 501-K20A gas turbines. Normal foilborne cruising speed is 42 knots.

Typical interior arrangements include a commuter configuration with up to 350 seats and a tourist layout for 190-250 tourists plus baggage.

The company is also evaluating various utility models with open load decks suitable for search and rescue duties, offshore oil-rig support and firefighting. Two utility derivatives for offshore rig crew and priority/emergency cargo support are showing great potential. They are 50 and 100 seat crew/supply boat versions with considerable cargo capacity for supporting rigs within 50–250n miles from shore.

Eleven commercial Jetfoils are currently in service: seven with Far East Hydrofoil Co Ltd, Hong Kong; two with Sado Kisen Kaisha, Japan; one with B+I Line between Dublin, Ireland, and Liverpool, England and one with Flying Princess Transportation Corp of Victoria, British Columbia between Seattle, Washington and Victoria.

An order has been placed by Alimar, the Argentinian operator for one Jetfoil to operate in the River de la Plata area and RMT, the Belgian state-owned ferry company, will begin operation

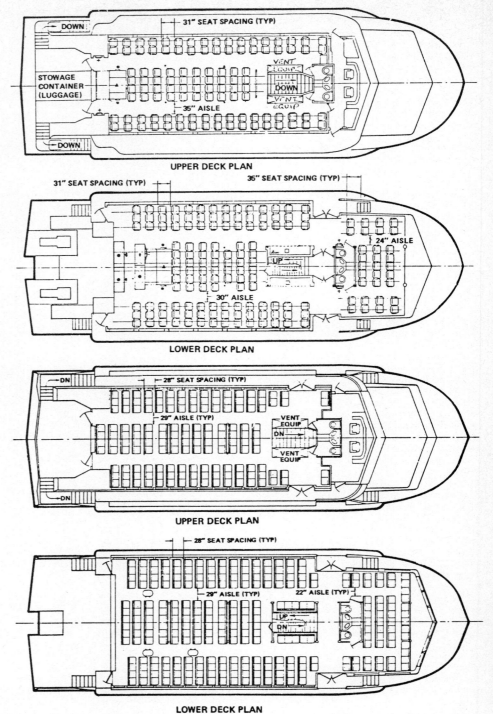

UPPER DECK PLAN

LOWER DECK PLAN

UPPER DECK PLAN

LOWER DECK PLAN

Typical interior arrangements on the Jetfoil include a commuter configuration with 350 seats. Seats are track mounted to facilitate spacing changes, removal or replacement. Food and beverage service units can be installed

of two Jetfoils between Dover, England and Ostend in 1981.

Additionally, HMS *Speedy*, an Ocean Patrol Hydrofoil (OPH) derivative of the Jetfoil is now in operation for the Royal Navy in a protection role in the North Sea. HMS *Speedy* was launched in July 1979 and upon completion of the final outfitting by Vosper Thornycroft (UK) Ltd, was commissioned by the Royal Navy on 14 June 1980.

By 31 May 1980 Jetfoils had logged 339,199,410 passenger miles during 71,355 underway hours with a dispatch reliability of 97 per cent.

Keel-laying of the first Jetfoil took place at the company's Renton, Washington, plant on 19 January 1973, and the craft was launched on 29 March 1974. After testing on Puget Sound and in the Pacific, the craft was delivered to Pacific Sea Transportation Ltd for inter-island services in Hawaii. High speed foilborne tests began in Puget Sound in mid-July and it was reported that the vessel attained a speed of 48 knots during its runs.

During a rigorous testing programme to prove the boat's design and construction, Jetfoil One operated for 470 hours, including 237 hours foilborne. The latter phase of testing was conducted in the rough waters of the straits of Juan de Fuca and the Pacific Ocean, where it encountered wave swells as high as 30ft, winds gusting up to 60 knots and wave chop averaging six feet high.

The first operational Jetfoil service was successfully initiated on 25 April 1975 by Far East Hydrofoil Co, of Hong Kong, with Jetfoil 002, *Madeira*. Prior to this, the Jetfoil received its ABS classification, was certificated by the Hong Kong Marine Department and passed US Coast Guard certification trials, although a US Coast Guard certificate was not completed since the craft would not be operating in US waters.

The first US service began in Hawaii on 15 June 1975 with the first of three Jetfoils, 003 *Kamehameha,* starting inter-island runs. By the end of the summer all five Jetfoils were in service. The tenth Jetfoil was launched in May 1977. An active world-wide marketing programme is under way to sell these high-speed craft, which are currently priced at US $10 million.

Jetfoil 0011, launched in June 1978, is the first Jetfoil of improved design. Many of the improvements incorporated in this new version, the Model 929-115, are based on operating experience accrued over the past three years and will add to the Jetfoil's performance, payload and reliability.

FOILS: Fully submerged canard arrangement with a single inverted tee strut/foil forward and a three-strut, full-span foil aft. The forward foil assembly is rotated hydraulically through 7 degrees in either direction for steering. All foils have trailing-edge flaps for controlling pitch, roll and yaw and for take-off and landing. Hydraulically-driven foil flap actuators control the variation in flap positions through linkages between actuators and flap hinge points. Foils and struts retract hydraulically above the waterline, the bow foil forward, and the rear foil aft. All structural components of the foil/strut system are in 15·5PH corrosion resistant all-welded steel construction.

CONTROLS: The craft is controlled by a three-axis automatic system while it is foilborne and during take-off and landing. The system senses the motion and position of the craft by gyros, accelerometers and height sensors, signals from which are combined in the control computer with manual commands from the helm. The resulting computer outputs provide control-surface deflections through electro-hydraulic servo actuators. Lift control is provided by full-span trailing edge flaps on each foil. Forward and aft flaps operate differentially to provide pitch variation and height control. Aft flaps operate differentially to provide roll control for changes of direction.

The vessel banks inwardly into all turns, to ensure maximum passenger comfort. The ACS introduces the correct amount of bank and steering to coordinate the turn in full. Turn rates of up to 6 degrees per second are attained within 5 seconds of providing a heading change command at the helm.

Three basic controls only are required for foilborne operation. The throttle is employed to set the speed, the height command lever to set the required foil depth, and the helm to set the required heading. If a constant course is required, a "heading hold" circuit accomplishes this automatically.

For take-off, the foil depth is set, the two throttles advanced, and the hull clears the water in about 60 seconds. Acceleration continues, until the craft automatically stabilises at the command depth and the speed dictated by the throttle setting. The throttle setting is reduced for landing, the craft settling as the speed drops. The speed normally diminishes from 45 knots (cruising speed) to 15 knots in about 30 seconds. In emergencies more rapid landings can be made by the use of the height command lever to provide hull contact within two seconds.

HULL: Hull and deckhouse in marine aluminium. Aircraft assembly techniques are used, including high-speed mechanised welding processes.

POWER PLANT: Power for the waterjet propulsion system is supplied by two Allison 501-K20A free-power gas turbines, each rated at 3,300shp at 27°C (80°F) at sea level. Each is connected to a Rocketdyne Powerjet 20 axial-flow pump through a gearbox drive train. The two turbine/pump systems are located in their own bays, port and starboard, separated by the slot in the hull into which the central water strut retracts for hullborne operation. The system propels the craft in both foilborne and hullborne modes. When foilborne, water enters through the inlet located at the forward lower end of the aft centre foil strut. At the top of the duct, the water is split into two paths and enters into each of the two axial flow pumps. It is then discharged at high pressure through nozzles in the hull bottom.

The water path is the same during hullborne operations with the foils extended. When the foils are retracted, the water enters through a flush inlet located in the keel. Reversing and steering for hullborne operation only are accomplished by

Military version of Jetfoil in anti-ship/coastal patrol configuration

Jetfoil with superstructure designed for law and treaty enforcement applications

In the counter-insurgency role, the Jetfoil would carry two fully-equipped twelve-man SEAL (sea-air-land) teams. A twin 30mm rapid-fire cannon would provide defensive armament

reverse-flow buckets located immediately aft of the water exit nozzles. A bow thruster is provided for positive steering control at low forward speeds.

A 15,140 litre (4,000 gallon) integral fuel tank supplies the propulsion turbine and diesel engines. Recommended fuel is Diesel No 2. The tank is fitted with a 5cm (2in) diameter fill pipe and fittings compatible with dockside refuelling equipment. Coalescent-type water separating fuel filters and remote-controlled motor-operated fuel shut-off valves are provided for fire protection.

ACCOMMODATION: Passenger accommodation is fully air-conditioned and arranged on two decks, which are connected by a wide, enclosed stairway. The cabins have 914mm (3ft) wide aisles and 2·06m (6ft 9in) headroom. In the commuter configuration 1·58m³ (56ft³) per passenger is provided and 1·87m³ (66ft³) in the tourist configuration. Floors are carpeted and 61cm (2ft) seats are provided. Lighting is indirect and adjustable from the wheelhouse. Interior noise is near conversation level (below 68 dB SIL). Passengers are entertained and informed by a public announcement system. Each deck

level has two wc/washbasin units. Drinking water dispensers are located on each passenger deck.

Quality of the ride in the craft is comparable with that of a Boeing 727 airliner. The vertical acceleration at the centre of gravity is designed to be no more than 0·04 G, with lateral acceleration less than that of the vertical. Angles of pitch and roll will be less than 1 degree RMS. Passenger discomfort in an emergency landing is prevented by a 'structural fuse', which limits deceleration to less than 0·4 G longitudinally and 0·8 G vertically so that a passenger would not be thrown from his seat in the event of the craft striking a major item of floating debris at full speed. The 'structural fuse', when actuated, causes the foil and strut to rotate backwards, protecting the system from sustaining significant damage. The fuses can be reset while under way in some cases, depending on the degree of impact.

Crew comprises a captain and first officer plus cabin attendants.

SYSTEMS, ELECTRICAL: 60Hz, 440V ac electrical system, supplied by two diesel-driven generators rated at 62·5kVA each. Either is capable of supplying all vital electrical power. 90kVA capacity shore connection facilities provided, and equipment can accept 50Hz power. Transformer rectifier units for battery charging provide 28V dc from the ac system.

HYDRAULICS: 210·9kg/cm² (3,000psi) system to actuate control surfaces. Each pump is connected to a separate system to provide split system redundancy in the event of a turbine, pump, distribution system or actuator malfunctioning.

EMERGENCY: Craft meets all applicable safety regulations of the US Coast Guard and SOLAS. Hull provides two-compartment subdivision and a high degree of stability. Life rafts and life jackets are provided.

NAVIGATION: Equipment includes radar. A low-light-level television system covering potential collision zone is available as an optional extra.

DIMENSIONS
Length overall, foils extended: 27·4m (90ft)
   foils retracted: 30·1m (99ft)
Beam overall, max: 9·5m (31ft)
Draft hullborne,
   foils retracted: 1·5m (4ft 10in)
   foils extended: 5m (16ft 4in)
WEIGHTS
Displacement: 110 tons
PERFORMANCE
Max speed: 50 knots
Normal service speed: 42 knots
Turning radius at 45 knots: less than 304·8m (1,000ft)
Normal endurance at cruising speed: 4 hours
Max endurance: 8 hours
Max wave height foilborne: 3·65m (12ft)

BOEING 929-115

The last of the Jetfoil 929-100 series was the 0010 *Flying Princess II*. The first of the improved 929-115 series, Jetfoil 0011 *Mikado*, was launched at Renton, Washington on 29 June 1978, and is now operated by Sado Kisen in the Sea of Japan.

A number of detail changes have been made in order to comply with the new international novel craft code, but most have been made in the light of operating experience over the past three years. As a result the new model Jetfoil will have an increased payload, greater reliability and be easier to maintain. Some of the modifications are listed below.

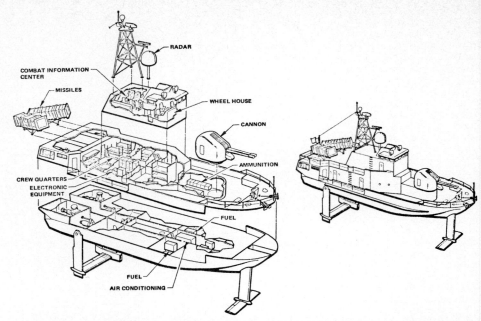

Projected 117-ton fast patrol boat version of the Jetfoil. The company is examining the possibility of exporting the Jetfoil on a modular basis with the customer purchasing a basic hull, which will contain the power plant and all the necessary systems, and installing his own superstructure

FOILS: External stiffeners on the foil struts have been eliminated; the retracted angle of the aft foil has been raised in order to lift the foil 330mm (13in) clear of the calm water level at 111 long tons, and the bow foil has been changed from constant section to tapered planform for improved performance. Stress levels have been reduced for extended life.

CONTROLS: Heading hold (autopilot) installed as basic equipment. Automatic control system "Autotrim" is improved to reduce steady state pitch and depth errors to negligible values. This reduces or completely eliminates the need for foil angle of incidence adjustments. A higher thrust bow-thruster is fitted and the navigation radar is now installed on a pedestal between the captain and first officer so that it can be swivelled for viewing from either position.

HULL: The bow structure design has been simplified to provide equivalent strength with increased payload and bulkhead 2 has been revised for decreased stress levels. Based on a seven-minute evacuation time in case of fire the following fire protection provisions have been made:

Fibreglass is used for thermal insulation where required throughout the passenger accommodation areas.

Aluminium ceiling panels, window reveals and air conditioner sleeves are employed throughout, together with aluminium doors and frames.

One-half inch thick Marinite is employed in machinery spaces, with US Coast Guard-type felt added wherever required for insulation to comply with 30 minute fire test.

Carpet, seat fabrics and lining materials meet

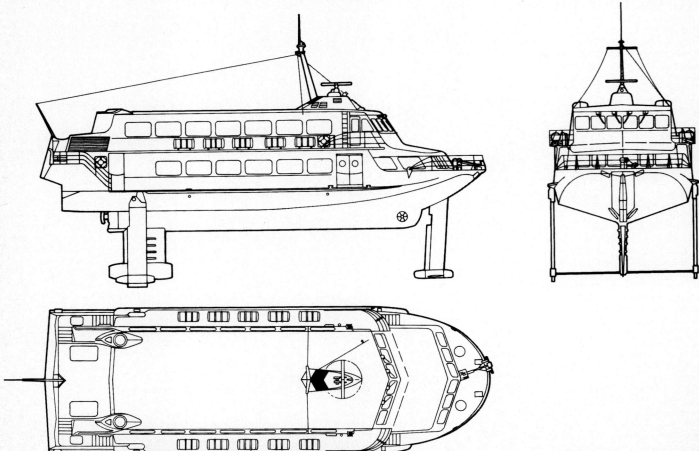

General arrangement of Boeing Jetfoil Model 929-115 passenger ferry

low flame spread, toxicity and smoke requirements of US Coast Guard and Department of Trade, United Kingdom.

POWER PLANT: The propulsion system has been uprated to operate at 2,200 maximum intermittent pump rpm with an increase of 3 tons in maximum gross weight.

ACCOMMODATION: Seats of revised design are fitted; environmental control unit has been located forward to increase payload and aid servicing, stairway to upper deck has a round handrail for better grip.

SYSTEMS, ELECTRICAL: DC system is now located in the wheelhouse to comply with new dynamically supported craft rules. AC panels relocated to be closer to equipment served to reduce wire runs. Redundant power sources are provided from either diesel generator for services to 24V dc emergency loads and loads essential for foilborne operation. Emergency 24V dc lights have been added in lavatories and aft machinery areas. Daylight signalling lamps with self-contained batteries are provided.

HYDRAULICS: System is now consolidated with one manifold and reduced piping.

AIR CONDITIONING: Machinery moved forward to space above the main stairway and forward machinery space to improve operation and servicing.

DIESEL FUEL SYSTEM: Separate fuel systems have been provided for the propulsion engines and diesel generators. This allows alternate fuels to be used in the turbines and greatly simplifies the plumbing system.

SEAWATER SYSTEM: Cooling water for the propulsion system has been separated from the remainder of the system. This simplifies the system and improves its reliability.

MISCELLANEOUS: Originally the hull corrosion prevention system was based on the isolation of dissimilar metals and ship-to-shore grounding. The new approach uses dockside impressed current, resistance-controlled shorting of struts and foils to the hull, additional pod anodes and electrical isolation. Other changes include a changeover to titanium seawater piping, a change in seawater pump materials and protective painting added to the hydraulic system.

DIMENSIONS
Length overall, foils extended: 27·4m (90ft)
Beam, max: 9·5m (31ft)
Draft,
    foils extended: 5·2m (17ft)
    foils retracted: 1·7m (5ft 6in)
Height (without retractable mast),
    hullborne, above mean waterline: 12·8m (42ft)
    foilborne, at 2·4m (8ft) foil depth: 15·5m (51ft)
WEIGHTS
Fully loaded displacement: 115 long tons
PERFORMANCE
Design cruising speed: 43 knots (80km/h; 50mph)

JETFOIL OCEAN PATROL HYDROFOIL (ROYAL NAVY)

The first ocean patrol hydrofoil (OPH) has been delivered to the Royal Navy for use in an offshore protection role in the North Sea. Named HMS *Speedy,* the craft is a modified Model 929-115 commercial Jetfoil and was built on the commercial Jetfoil production line. This concept has now evolved into a new model, 929-201, incorporating the well-tested commercial Jetfoil systems into a basic military platform. Power for foilborne operation is provided by two Allison 501-K20A gas turbines and two Allison 8V92T1 diesels are installed for hullborne operation, giving increased on-station time and endurance.

Externally the craft resembles the projected Boeing Offshore Jetfoil, with the top passenger deck removed to provide an open deck measuring 4·87 × 7·31m (16 × 24ft) which is occupied by two semi-inflatable dinghies on davits. Light weapons will be carried. Displacement is 117 tons.

Launching was on 9 July 1979 with delivery in November 1979 for final outfitting by Vosper Thornycroft (UK) Ltd and delivery to the Royal Navy in June 1980.
DIMENSIONS: As for Jetfoil Model 929-115.

HMS *Speedy*, Jetfoil ocean patrol hydrofoil (OPH), which was delivered to the Royal Navy in June 1980

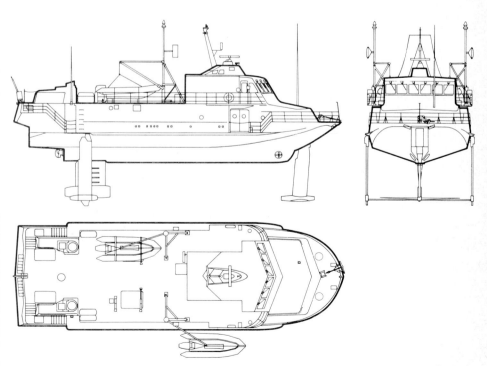

General arrangement of the Boeing Jetfoil ocean patrol hydrofoil (OPH) supplied to the Royal Navy for use in the offshore protection role in the North Sea

MILITARY JETFOIL

New configurations evolving from the production of HMS *Speedy* include the following variants:

TROOP TRANSPORT

In this configuration the Jetfoil can fly 250 troops and their equipment 300n miles in 7 hours. Since it draws only 1·8m in the hullborne mode with foils retracted, it can use most docking facilities.

CARGO CARRIER

Up to 35 tons of high-priority cargo can be flown up to 600n miles without refuelling. With seats and carpeting removed the lower deck provides 230m³ of storage space. Access is through forward and aft doors on both sides of the superstructure. The forward doors are 2m high by 1·5m wide and the aft doors 2m high by 1m wide. A special door 2m high by 3·5m wide is optional. In addition to lower deck cargo, up to 96 troops can be seated on the upper deck.

MEDICAL EVACUATION

Up to 213 litter cases with their attendants can be evacuated at a time. Special facilities are provided on board for the treatment of emergency cases while underway. Conversion from the standard Jetfoil configuration can be accomplished in 4 hours. Seats are removed and replaced with litter stanchions from a medical evacuation kit which can be stowed aboard for emergency use.

FISHERIES AND OFFSHORE RESOURCES PROTECTION

This version, which can be either sea- or shore-based can be equipped for search and rescue duties, law and treaty enforcement, anti-smuggling patrol and similar missions.

COUNTER INSURGENCY VEHICLE

Two fully equipped twelve-man patrols, complete with inflatable dinghies, can be carried by this variant. Its defensive armament, mounted above bridge level for maximum field of fire, comprises a twin 30mm rapid-fire cannon.

ANTI-SHIP/COASTAL PATROL CRAFT

Intended as a fast, economical weapons platform, this version is armed with six anti-ship missiles on two triple-tube lightweight launchers plus a single OTO Melara 76mm rapid fire cannon for air defence, together with launchers for rapid blooming off-board chaff (RBOC). The combat system level of automation, similar to that of the PHM, is such that one man, unassisted, can simultaneously engage air and surface targets with guns and missiles respectively. A 12-man crew would be carried.

MODULAR JETFOIL

In November 1974 Boeing announced that consideration was being given to the export of Jetfoils on a modular basis. One approach would

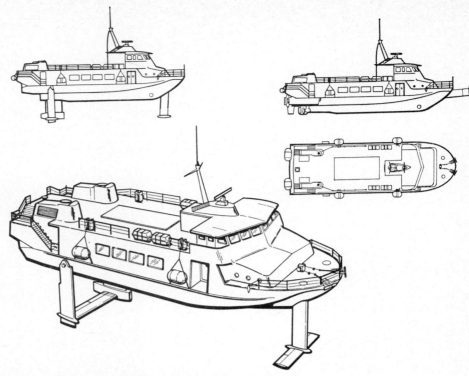

Offshore oil rig support model of the Boeing Jetfoil Model 929-100

be to supply operators, both commercial and military, with the basic Jetfoil hull, complete with foils, powerplant and control system, and the operator would arrange to install his own superstructure.

This would give them access to craft embodying the latest developments in hydrofoil technology and permit them to add superstructure tailored to their own particular needs. Variants would range from passenger ferries and utility craft for offshore marine operations, to coastguard patrol vessels and missile gunboats.

The modular concept is expected to appeal in particular to lesser developed countries, since by completing the craft locally, a useful saving in hard currency could be realised. A substantial amount of the superstructure could be riveted together by fairly low-skilled labour.

Maintenance requirements are expected to be reasonably low. The Allison 501-K20A gas turbines have a life of 18,000 hours, and the Boeing autopilot, the most sensitive part of the system, has a life expectancy of three to four years under normal operating conditions, allowing 3,000 hours in service each year.

Allison is willing to negotiate contract rates for

servicing the gas turbines at a fixed-rate per operating hour.

Boeing states that modifications could be made to the design to allow the installation of alternative engines, such as the Rolls Royce Tyne or Proteus, should countries like the United Kingdom prefer them.

Weapons suitable for the military models include the OTO Melara 76mm rapid-fire cannon and the Emerson 30mm cannon, the Argo control system and the Otomat, Exocet, Penguin and Gabriel anti-ship missiles.

Another Boeing concept is the regional final assembly centre, a number of which would be established around the world in order to supply customers with complete vessels made up from imported hulls and superstructures. At the same time the arrangement would meet the growing demand in lesser developed areas for greater participation in industrial programmes.

The centres, which would not be owned or operated by Boeing, would simply be involved with their importation, assembly and marketing. Likely areas for the establishment of these centres include the Caribbean, Greece, Iran, Japan, Taiwan, Indonesia and Scandinavia.

DAK HYDROFOILS

PO Box 1747, Sausalito, California 94965, USA
Officials:
David A Keiper, *Proprietor and Chief Designer*

Dak Hydrofoils is currently designing and developing simple low-cost hydrofoil conversion kits for outboard powerboats. These are based on those available from the company for existing racing catamarans.

The arrangement employs identical lateral foils, positioned in a similar location, plus a fully-submerged stern foil. Lighter craft will have a simple foil beneath the outboard engine. Heavier craft, of up to 680·38kg (1,500lb) loaded weight, have a retractable 152mm (6in) chord foil supported by twin struts.

The propeller is lowered by a combination of

A 12ft dinghy equipped with DAK hydrofoils for an owner in New Zealand. Power is supplied by a 9·5hp engine

engine shaft extension or extensions, and/or lowering the engine by means of parallel bars.

DYNAFOIL INC

881 West 16th Street, Newport Beach, California 92663, USA
Telephone: (714) 645 3201
Officials:
David J Cline, *Chairman*
James M Dale, *Secretary/Treasurer*
Paul D Griem, *Executive Vice President*

Dynafoil, Inc was formed in December 1971 to develop the Dynafoil sport craft. The development of this vehicle began in late 1970 with the construction of IRMA 1, the foil configuration of which has been the foundation for all subsequent work. Patents for the foil configuration have been applied for in all the main consumer countries, and have been granted in the USA.

DYNAFOIL MARK I

This fibreglass-hulled sports hydrofoil is a marine counterpart to the motorcycle and snowmobile. The bow foil is mounted at the base of a handlebar-equipped steering head and the handling characteristics are similar to those of a motorcycle. Production began in June 1975.
FOILS: Canard configuration with a fully sub-

merged main foil located aft and bearing 60% of the load and small incidence-controlled twin-delta foil forward. The angle of incidence is controlled mechanically by a curved planing control foil to achieve a constant flying height. Both the control foil and the bow foils rotate on pitch axes located forward of their centre of hydrodynamic lift. In normal flight the trailing edge of the control foil skims the water surface, while the twin delta bow and foil maintains its designed angle of incidence. If the bow rises too high above the mean water line, the control foil pitches upwards, allowing the foils to operate in a neutral position, in which it generates little or no lift. Conversely, downward pitch at the bow decreases the angle of attack of the control foil, which, through a link-age system causes the bow foils to increase its incidence angle, thus restoring normal flight. The aft foil has anhedral to prevent tip breeching and ventilation and is set above the propeller. The foils are in cast 356-T6 aluminium while the struts are of fibreglass. Both foils retract fully, the bow foil rotating upwards and rearwards, the aft foil rearwards and upwards against the transom.
CONTROLS: Steering is accomplished by turning the front foil strut. All turns enter a fully co-ordinated bank.
HULL: Two-stage deep V hull comprises two fibreglass mouldings bonded together at the belt-line. After bonding, all voids not employed for functional components are filled with 2lb density polyurethane foam providing 600lb of buoyancy.
ACCOMMODATION: Open cockpit with a motorcycle pillion-style seat for two.
POWER PLANT: The Mark I is available with a choice of two engines—either a 340cc, 26hp, or a high performance 440cc, 36hp, two-cylinder, two-stroke Xenoah engine. Power is delivered to the outdrive through a 90 degree gearbox mounted inboard. The overall gear ratio is 1·75:1. Final drive is through a bevel gear at the base of the rear strut. The propeller, made by Michigan Wheel, is of three-bladed subcavitating design in cast aluminium. A single 18·92 litre (5 US gallon) fuel tank is located amidships, with a refuelling neck on the outside hull at the bow.
DIMENSIONS
Length overall, hull: 2·13m (7ft)
   foils retracted: 2·43m (8ft)
   foils extended: 2·13m (7ft)
Beam overall,
   foils retracted: 1·06m (3ft 6in)
   foils extended: 1·06m (3ft 6in)
Draft hullborne,
   foils retracted: 304mm (1ft)
   foils extended: 914mm (3ft)
Draft foilborne: 457mm (1ft 6in)
Freeboard: 355mm (1ft 2in)
Height overall: 1·06m (3ft 6in)
   hullborne: 609mm (2ft)
WEIGHTS
Light displacement: 158·75kg (350lb)
Normal take-off displacement: 272·14kg (550lb)
Max take-off displacement: 362·85kg (800lb)
PERFORMANCE
Max speed, foilborne: 64·36km/h (40mph)
   hullborne: 8·04km/h (5mph)
Cruising speed,
   foilborne: 48·28km/h (30mph)
   hullborne: 8·04km/h (5mph)
Designed endurance and range at cruising speed, approx: 104·6km (65 miles)
Turning radius at cruising speed: 4·57m (15ft)
Fuel consumption at max speed: 9–22·7 litres/hour (2–5 gallons/hour)
SEA TEST: Craft has been tested in 3-4ft chop and 8-10ft swells.
PRICE: $1,995, plus options.

MILITARY DYNAFOIL

Tentative interest has been shown in a military version of the Dynafoil Mk II. Feasibility studies are being undertaken by the company but no construction timetable has yet been established. Power would be supplied by a 700hp turbo-charged V-8 automotive engine. Hydraulic foil retraction is envisaged.
DIMENSIONS
Length overall: 7·62m (25ft)

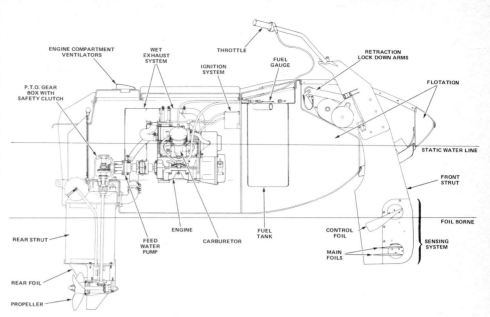

Inboard profile of the Dynafoil Mark I showing the power plant and transmission arrangements

Dynafoil Mark I two-seat sports hydrofoil

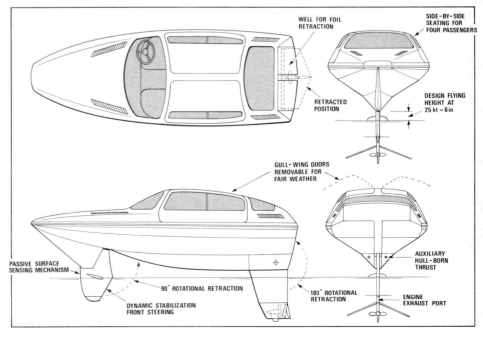

Dynafoil Mk II—a four-seater employing the same basic foil configuration as the Dynafoil Mk I. The gull-wing doors of the fully enclosed cabin can be removed for fair weather operation. Both foils are fully retractable

WEIGHTS
Max take-off displacement: 2,722kg (6,000lb)
Light displacement: 1,814kg (4,000lb)

PERFORMANCE
Cruising speed: 96km/h (60mph)

MARK III

As an intermediate step towards construction of the larger Mark II, the company is currently operating a 12ft development prototype utilizing a hydrofoil configuration identical to the Mark I. Known as Mark III, this vehicle is undergoing evaluation trials to ascertain performance characteristics prior to construction of the Mark II. It has already achieved its design goal of foilborne operation at 453·57kg (1,000lb) gross vehicle weight, and has reached a speed of 35mph when powered by a 45hp engine.

EDO CORPORATION, GOVERNMENT PRODUCTS DIVISION

13-10 111th Street, College Point, New York 11356, USA
Officials:

L M Swanson, *Director, Air MCM Applications*

Edo Corporation has developed a foil-equipped catamaran MCM system which speeds the process of magnetic mine clearance and reduces the hazards of mine sweeping operations. The system, the Edo Mark 105, is designed to be towed by the US Navy's RH-53D Sea Stallion and other heavy-lift helicopters of similar size and performance. The first unit formed to operate Mk 105 Airborne Minesweeping Gear was the HM-12 helicopter mine countermeasures squadron, which operated off North Viet-Nam to clear mines from the entrance to the port of Haiphong and undertook the aerial sweeping of the Suez Canal during the spring of 1974. The operation—code named Nimbus Star—was said to have been a complete success.

It has been stated that a mine can be detonated almost immediately beneath the Mk 105 without the craft sustaining major structural damage.

If required the equipment can be towed behind a BHC BH.7 amphibious hovercraft or other suitable ACV. Tests with this arrangement have been undertaken in the UK and USA.

It is reported that ten RH-53D Sea Stallions, together with towed sweeping equipment, have been supplied to the Naval Air Transport Battalion, Iran.

Advantages claimed for the system include the following: lower acquisition and maintenance costs; fewer operating personnel required; low equipment vulnerability and bigger areas cleared within a given time.

Normally the helicopter/seasled combination is conveyed to the affected area aboard an amphibious assault craft. The helicopter lifts-off with the sled at the end of a line, lowers it into the water, extends its foils, and sets off to sweep the minefield.

The towline, which is 137·16m (450ft) long, also serves as an electric cable for carrying control signals to the sled, and as a fuel transfer line in the case of extended operations.

A portable winch in the helicopter is used to handle the craft, the sweep cables and the towing cable during launching and retrieval. The system can be operated from either ships or shore bases equipped with crane facilities and small boats for handling the sweep cables which stream out behind the seasled.

In 1978, it was announced that Edo engineers are working on a new system called the Lightweight Magnetic Sweep (LMS). Development is being undertaken for US Naval Air Systems Command. The Edo LMS is designed to enhance the US Navy's airborne minesweeping capabilities now provided by the Edo Mk 105. It is said to offer a substantial advance in performance compared with previous systems.

Mk 105 AIRBORNE MINESWEEPING GEAR

The Mk 105 is a helicopter-towed, magnetic minesweeping system mounted on a 8·38m (27ft 6in) long catamaran seasled. Foils are fitted to permit high speed operation and provide improved seakeeping performance. Aboard the craft is a turbogenerator which provides energy for the magnetic sweep cables and powers a hydraulic pump for foil retraction.
FOILS: Surface-piercing tandem configuration with two inverted V foils forward and two aft, balancing the loading between them. High-riding pitch control subfoils of similar configuration are located ahead of the two bow foils. Bow and stern

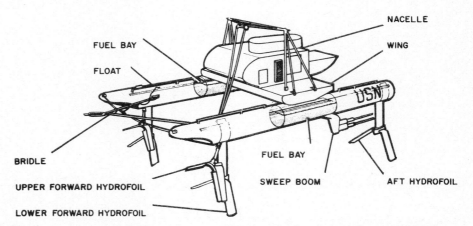

Surface-piercing tandem foil system of the Edo Mk 105 and the high-riding pitch-control subfoils

Edo Mk 105 towed by an RH-53D Sea Stallion helicopter

foils are rotated for retraction and extension by a self-contained hydraulic system.
HULL: Catamaran hull comprising two tubular pontoons of light metal alloy construction, connected by an aerofoil section platform on which is mounted a gas-turbine powered electric generator set and the retrieval rig structure to which handling lines are attached. The two ends of the towing bridle are attached to the inward faces of the twin pontoon hulls forward of the platform. Wheels are attached to the underside of the pontoons to facilitate deck handling. Fuel for the turbogenerator set is carried in two centrally located tanks, one in each pontoon.
TOWING AND OPERATION: The 137·16m (450ft) long towing cable terminates in an electrical connector and fuel fitting. As well as providing the towing links between the platform and the helicopter, all electrical commands and supplementary fuel pass through the cable. The cable consists of an electrical core containing 19 individual conductors, around which is a double layer of steel wire. Surrounding this is a hose, and fuel flows through the annular space between the inner diameter of the hose and the steel wire reinforcement.

The 27ft 6in long sled is generally carried aboard an Amphibious Assault Ship (LPH) or Amphibious Transport Dock (LPD), which also act as a mobile base for the helicopters. The helicopter lifts the sled off the deck then lowers it into the water to enable the sweepgear streaming operation to be completed.

The tow cable is then picked up and the sled is towed, foilborne, into the sweep area. Once in the area, the sled can be towed at lower speeds, hullborne, to simulate a displacement vessel and its magnetic (or in the case of the Mk 106, combined magnetic and acoustic) signature.
SYSTEMS: A gas-turbine generator set, mounted within a nacelle on the platform provides energy for the generation of the magnetic field. The complete power pack comprises a gas-turbine driven ac generator, a rectifier, a controller containing the waterborne electronics and batteries to power the electronics system.
MAGNETIC SWEEP CABLE: This is attached to the after end of the sweep boom located on the underside of the port pontoon. It comprises an upper electrode attached to the end of a trailing cable and a lower electrode fitted to the boom fin. The potential between the electrodes, employing the water as a conductor, produces a magnetic field which simulates that of a ship.

The Edo Mk 105, probably the most sophisticated of all mine countermeasures systems, has been under development for some years. It comprises a helicopter and a towed hydrofoil sea sled, on which is mounted a turbogenerator that energises magnetic sweep cables, thus simulating the magnetic field of a ship

CONTROL PROGRAMMER: Located in the helicopter this is the only manned station employed in the system. It contains the airborne electronics and all the controls and instrumentation necessary.

The console contains the fuel transfer control panel, turbine indicators, hydrofoil and sweep boom actuators and the generator controls and indicators.

From the console the operator can start and stop the turbine, raise and lower the foils and control the magnetic influences generated through the conductor cables trailed behind the sled.

DIMENSIONS
Length overall: 8·38m (27ft 6in)
Beam,
  catamaran structure only: 3·53m (11ft 7in)
  across foils: 6·4m (21ft)
Height, foils extended,
  to top of retrieval rig: 5·26m (17ft 3in)
  to top of nacelle: 4·11m (13ft 6in)
  foils retracted, to base of wheels: 3·5m (11ft 6in)

WEIGHTS
Empty: 2,504kg (5,522lb)
Gross: 2,917kg (6,432lb)

PERFORMANCE
Towing speeds and sea state capability: not available

Mk 106

An earlier airborne minesweeping system was the Mk 104, which can also be carried, towed and recovered by helicopters. This is used to detonate acoustic mines. It comprises a venturi tube and a water-activated turbine which rotates a disc to reproduce a ship's acoustic signature. The latest model in the series combines the duties of the Mk 104 and 105 to provide both acoustic and magnetic influences and is known as the Mk 106.

GRUMMAN AEROSPACE CORPORATION

Bethpage, New York 11714, USA
Telephone: (516) 752 3681, Management and technical staff
  (516) 575 6090, Marketing
Telex: GRUMAIRBETHPAGENY 961430
Officials:
G M Skurla, *Chairman and President*
R L Caporali, PhD, *Vice President, Development*
W G Wohleking, *Director, Advanced Marine Systems*
D L Walsh, *Director, Marketing*
V Beck, *Manager, Marine Marketing*

Grumman entered the hydrofoil field in 1956 when it acquired Dynamic Developments Inc, producer of the experimental XCH-4, built for the Office of Naval Research in 1955. Powered by two aircraft engines with air propellers, this 8-ton vessel established a world speed record for hydrofoil craft by exceeding 145km/h (78 knots). In 1958 Grumman designed and built the XCH-6 Sea Wings, also for the Office of Naval Research. Sea Wings was the first hydrofoil to employ both supercavitating foils and a supercavitating propeller and attained speeds in excess of 60 knots.

In 1960, Grumman was awarded a contract by the Maritime Administration for the design and construction of the HS *Denison*, an 80-ton open ocean research vessel which was launched in June 1962. This craft (described in the 1967-68 edition) was operated at speeds above 60 knots, demonstrated good foilborne manoeuvrability and seakeeping ability in rough water.

Grumman also completed the guidance design for the 328-ton, 64·6m (212ft) AGEH Plainview for the US Navy. The foils for this ship were the forerunners of those used on the Dolphin, the PGH-1 Flagstaff, and the more recent Flagstaff Mk II.

The primary purpose of Plainview was to establish the possibility of operating large hydrofoils in high sea states, and explore many possible mission assignments including ASW, hydrographic data collection, surveillance, search and rescue and escort duties.

In December 1972, it was equipped with a single missile container and launched three NATO-configured Sea Sparrow missiles during rough water trials off the coast of Washington.

An overhaul of Plainview was completed in 1977, and the vessel scheduled to be used in the evaluation of platform and weapon systems for future large hydrofoils of the US Navy. However, due to budget limitations, it was de-activated in late June 1978.

Two Dolphin I class hydrofoils were built for Grumman by Blohm & Voss, Hamburg, but development of this class has now discontinued. In September 1968, the PGH-1 Flagstaff, the Grumman designed and built hydrofoil gunboat, was delivered to the US Navy. Between April and June 1971, it was employed on 152mm (6in) gun-firing trials.

A series of underwater explosion tests were also conducted with the Flagstaff in an experiment aimed at obtaining data on the shock responses of hydrofoil craft. The Flagstaff was the first and is so far the only hydrofoil to have undergone such tests. Following extended evaluation by the US Coast Guard the vessel was de-activated in September 1978.

The company is now concentrating on the development of improved variants of Flagstaff and Dolphin class hydrofoils for use by both foreign navies and Coast Guards as well as domestic interests, and on large combatant hydrofoil ships for the US Navy.

In 1975, an updated and stretched version of PGH-1 was announced—the Flagstaff Mk II. With an overall length of 25·6m (84ft 0in), 3·44m (11ft) longer than the PGH-1, this model can accommodate a variety of the latest naval weapon systems. Main propulsion is supplied by an Allison 501-KF marine gas turbine. Maximum foilborne speed is 50 knots.

In December 1977, a contract was awarded to Grumman for the detail design and construction of two 100-tonne missile patrol craft, variants of the Mk II design. While details of the programme are classified, the design variant is currently in production.

PGH-1 FLAGSTAFF

The 67·5 ton PGH-1 Flagstaff hydrofoil gunboat was launched on 9 January 1968. It underwent preliminary trials in July 1968, and was delivered and placed in service at West Palm Beach in September 1968.

For five and a half months it underwent operational trials in South Viet-Nam. Between 1 September 1969 and 19 February 1970, Flagstaff was employed on various missions in Phase II of "Opeval" and "Market Time", operating from Da Nang.

Grumman's PGH-1 Flagstaff hydrofoil patrol gunboat equipped with 152mm howitzer

Between November and December 1970 the craft was modified to mount a 152mm M551 gun from a Sheridan light tank on its foredeck. The gun fires conventional 6in shells or Shillelagh missiles and has a laser rangefinder giving instant accurate ranging. It is capable of hitting a target at a range of up to 6·43km (4 miles).

Between November 1974 and February 1975 the vessel underwent evaluation by the US Coast Guard in a number of missions including: enforcement of laws and treaties; fisheries and contraband enforcement; search and rescue; marine environmental protection; servicing aids to navigation and marine science activities.

In October 1976, the PGH-1 was transferred permanently to the US Coast Guard and recommissioned as a US Coast Guard cutter. Designated WPGH-1, the Flagstaff saw service in Coast Guard District 1 (New England area) where it was being employed to evaluate further the use of hydrofoils for Coast Guard missions and to augment the fisheries patrol in that area.

At the conclusion of the hydrofoil evaluation programme the Coast Guard deactivated the craft.

FOILS: Fully-submerged system of conventional configuration, split forward, and a single foil aft. About 70% of the weight is supported by the twin forward foils and 30% by the aft foil. Foil section is sub-cavitating, 16 series. All three foils are incidence-controlled and operated by an AiResearch hydropilot. The stern foil strut rotates ±3 degrees for steering and all three retract completely clear of the water. Foils (by Potvin Kellering) are forged 6061-T652 aluminium and struts (by Blohm & Voss) are 4130 and HY80 steel. Foil area is 9·29m² (100ft²).

HULL: The hull structure is of combined welded and riveted corrosion resistant 5456 aluminium. The pilot house roof is of fibreglass sandwich. All frames and bulkheads are welded assemblies and transverse framing is used throughout.

POWER PLANT: The main engine is a 3,550hp Rolls-Royce Tyne Mk 621/10 gas turbine, flat rated to 90°F. Power is transmitted through a mechanical right-angle drive to a KaMeWa 1·14m (45in) diameter, three-bladed super-cavitating, controllable pitch propeller. Nominal rpm at cruising speed, 1,000. Hullborne power is supplied by two 202hp GM 6V diesels driving twin Buehler 419mm (1ft 4½in) diameter water-jets, equipped with ±35 degree steering and reversing nozzles.

SYSTEMS, ELECTRICAL: Ship's service generator sets: twin GM 4-53N diesels with Delco 120V, 50kW, 62·5kVA, three-phase Delta, 60Hz at 1,800rpm. Emergency power (generators inoperable): 2 sets batteries 200Ah, 24V, for autopilot, gyroscope and navigation lights, all automatically switched.

RADIO: VHF and HF transceivers.

RADAR AND NAVIGATION: Decca TM626 at navigator's station and repeater at commander's station. Bendix ADF-162A automatic direction finder, Raytheon 726 depth sounder, Arma Mk 26 hydrocompass, Chesapeake EM-log speed log, Bendix prototype DRAI and DRT navigation system.

FIREFIGHTING AND DAMAGE CONTROL: Diesel-driven 50 gallons/min bilge pump, plus 50 gallons/min diesel-driven deck service pump, portable electric 250 gallons/min pumps and hand pump. Deck SW connection for fighting fires on other craft. Walter Kidde central CF BR fire extinguishing system in two 251lb cylinders. Four portable 2½lb Ansul Foray Combo Pacs.

ARMAMENT: Main battery (until November 1970): single 40mm Mk 3 Mod 0 rapid-firing cannon. Machine guns: two twin mounts .50 calibre Mk 56 Mod 0. Mortar: One 81mm Mk 2 Mod 0. Small arms: M16 rifles (11), .38 calibre pistols, 12 gauge shotguns. New main gun battery to June 1973: 152mm M551 howitzer, firing conventional 6in shells or Shillelagh missiles. Laser rangefinder. Main gun battery has been removed. Current Coast Guard armament consists of single .50 calibre mount forward and small arms.

WPGH-1 Flagstaff bearing the insignia of a US Coast Guard Cutter. The craft was transferred to the US Coast Guard in October 1976 for extended evaluation in Coast Guard District 1 (New England area)

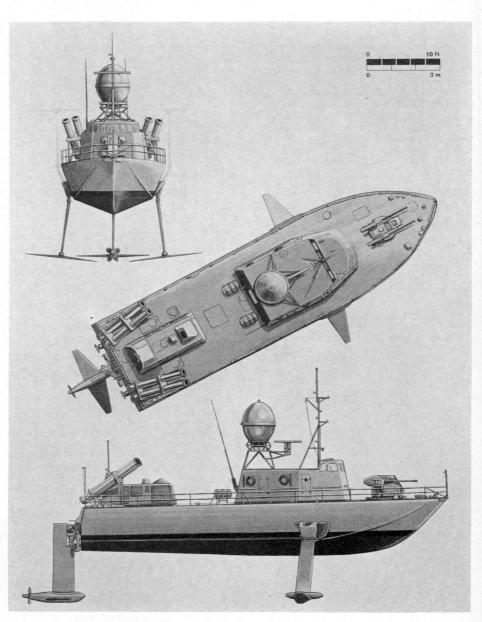

Outboard profile, Grumman Mk II (single, 3,980hp Allison 501-KF marine has turbine)

DIMENSIONS
Length overall, hull: 22·2m (73ft)
  foils extended: 26·36m (86ft 6in)
  foils retracted: 27·1m (89ft)
Hull beam: 6·5m (21ft 5in)
Extreme beam, foils retracted tip-to-tip: 11·28m (37ft 1in)
Draft, foils extended, static: 4·26m (13ft 11in)

Nominal draft foilborne: 1·72m (5ft 8in)
WEIGHTS
Displacement, fully loaded, as delivered: 67·5 long tons
1971, with 152mm howitzer: 72 long tons
PERFORMANCE
Cruising speed, foilborne: in excess of 40 knots
  hullborne: in excess of 7 knots

FLAGSTAFF Mk II

This new model has been designed for a variety of naval and military roles and can be fitted with a wide range of weapons. A number of variants are available with differing payloads and endurances. One model, intended for patrolling exclusive economic zones, is known as the Enforcer. It can operate at 45 knots in lower sea state 5 and offers a six-fold increase in the number of investigatory contacts possible with conventional patrol vessels. The chief differences between this craft and its predecessor lie in the installation of a more modern, higher horsepower gas turbine; a longer hull; an improved foil system and the installation of new foilborne automatic control and foilborne transmission systems. The fully loaded displacement has been increased to 100 tonnes. Maximum useful load (payload and fuel) is over 34 tonnes. Two Mk IIs are currently under construction and negotiations are in progress with a number of navies for additional craft. The prototype is due to be launched in the spring of 1981.

FOIL SYSTEM: Fully submerged system of conventional configuration, comprising twin inverted T foils forward and a single inverted T foil aft. Approximately 70% of the load is supported by the two forward foils and 30% by the

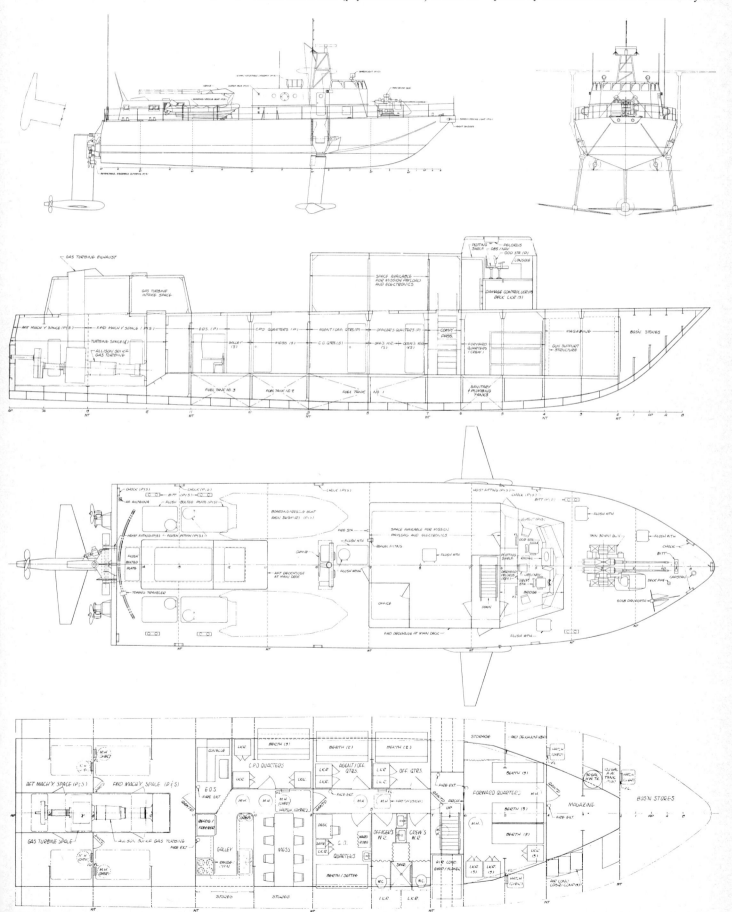

Outboard and inboard profiles and deck views of the Mk II offshore patrol boat

aft foil. All three foils are incidence controlled and operated by an ACS employing electro-hydraulic actuators. The stern foil power strut, together with the propeller, rotates ±5 degrees for steering and all three foil/strut units retract completely clear of the water for hullborne man-oeuvring. The foils are of machined aluminium and the struts are in HY130 steel. Break joints are incorporated on the two forward struts, so that should either of them strike large items of debris each would break clean at the point of its connection to its yoke. A shear bolt releases the aft strut permitting it to rotate rearwards and upwards above the transom.

HULL: Fabricated in 5086 and 5456 aluminium alloys. Frames and bulkheads are welded assemb-lies. Bottom, side, and deck plating consists of large panels of wide-ribbed extrusions welded to the frames and bulkheads.

ACCOMMODATION: Ship manning varies with the mission and weapons fitted. Minimum operating crew normally comprises three to four men; helmsman, engineer, deck officer/navigator and, if needed, a look-out. A nominal crew com-plement of 15 can be accommodated in terms of berthing, and messing facilities. All normally manned spaces are fully heated and air con-ditioned. The forward superstructure accommo-dates the bridge, which contains steering and engine control consoles and is elevated to give a 360 degree view. Entry to the deckhouse is via two 660mm × 1·52m (2ft 2in × 5ft) watertight doors, one port, one starboard. An emergency exit is located aft, behind the pilothouse on the weather deck. Escape hatches are provided in the living spaces.

POWER PLANT: FOILBORNE: A 3,980hp (con-tinuous) Allison 501-KF marine gas turbine. Power is transmitted to a supercavitating con-trollable pitch propeller through a Grumman Z drive transmission. Overall reduction 14 : 1.

HULLBORNE: Twin retractable outdrives. Three-bladed stainless steel 660mm (26in) fixed-pitch propellers driven through geared transmission by integrally-mounted Rexroth hydraulic motors.

FUEL: All installed prime movers will operate on JP-5, diesel No 2 or equivalent fuel. Tank for fuel provided. Underway refuelling facilities can be incorporated.

SYSTEMS, ELECTRICAL: Supplied by two 200kW, 120/208V, 400Hz three-phase generators driven by 550hp Pratt & Whitney ST-6 gas turbine APUs. Each generator is cap-able of supplying normal ship electrical load and can be operated in parallel during battle condi-tions.

HYDRAULICS: A 3,000psi system, driven by four pumps located on both the hullborne and foilborne prime movers, provides control power for hullborne and foilborne operation and tur-bine starting.

CONTROLS: An automatic control system stabilises the Mk II in foilborne operations. This system consists of: dual radar height sensors, an inertial sensor, a digital processor, displays and controls. Both flat or co-ordinated turns and plat-forming or contouring modes can be selected by the helpsmen.

FIRE EXTINGUISHING: A manual over-ride automatic Freon extinguishing system is installed in machinery spaces.

ELECTRONICS: Navigation and communica-tions equipment will vary with specific customer preferences. A true motion radar, a stable ele-ment gyro-compass, hullborne and foilborne speed logs and fathometers are recommended.

ARMAMENT: Typical armament would include surface-to-surface missiles of the Harpoon, Gab-riel, Otomat, Exocet or Penguin type; either one or two 30mm to 40mm gunmounts; sensors and fire control equipment and an integrated control centre.

DIMENSIONS

Length, overall (hull moulded): 25·62m (84ft)
  between perpendiculars: 23·4m (76ft 9in)
  overall (foils retracted): 31·79m (104ft 4in)
  overall (foilborne): 29·81m (97ft 10in)
Beam, hull moulded: 7·32m (24ft)
  foils retracted (extreme): 12·95m (42ft 6in)
  foilborne (extreme): 12·45m (40ft 10in)

Grumman Mk II with four Gabriel missiles, Emerlec 30mm gun and two twin 20mm cannon mounts in port and starboard gun tubs

Model of Mk II with foils retracted. Armament of this variant comprises eight Harpoon missiles and two twin 30mm gun mounts

Grumman Mk II multi-role military hydrofoil

Draft (full load), foils system retracted: 1·45m (4ft 9in)
  foils system, extended: 4·83m (15ft 10in)
  foilborne (nominal): 1·7m (5ft 7in)
Surface search radar height, hullborne: 9·99m (32ft 10in)
  foilborne: 12·13m (39ft 10in)

WEIGHTS

Light displacement: 66 tonnes
Full load displacement: 100 tonnes
Normal fuel load: 16 tonnes

PERFORMANCE

Max intermittent speed: 52 knots
Most economical speed: 42 knots
Foilborne operating envelope (normal): 35-48 knots

Max hullborne speed: 9·5 knots
Range at 42 knots: 750-1,150n miles
Specific range at 42 knots: 47-55n miles per tonne

AG(EH)-1 PLAINVIEW

The 328-ton AG (EH)-1—the designation means auxiliary general experimental hyd-rofoil—was built by the Lockheed Shipbuilding & Construction Company, Seattle, Washington. It has been used by the US Navy's Hydrofoil Systems Testing Unit, Bremerton, Washington to investigate the performance of a large seagoing hydrofoil under operational conditions. The guidance design and preparation of contract specifications were undertaken by Grumman under the direction of the Bureau of Ships.

A contract for detailed design and construction was awarded to Lockheed Shipbuilding and Construction Company in June 1963 and the hull was launched in June 1965. The craft successfully completed her maiden flight on 21 March 1968 at Puget Sound and was officially delivered to the US Navy on 1 March 1969. It was given the US Navy classification "In Service, Special" in March 1969 and US Navy research and development trials are continuing. Due to budget limitations, de-activation was due to begin in late July 1978.

FOILS: The foil system is fully submerged and automatically controlled by a Hamilton Standard autopilot system similar to that used in High Point. The foil arrangement is of conventional type with 90% of the weight carried on the two main foils and the remainder on the aft foil. The three foils, which have considerable sweep and taper, are geometrically similar with an aspect ratio of three. The swept back leading edges help to delay cavitation and facilitate the shedding of seaweed and other neutrally buoyant debris. They also reduce impact loads associated with water entry after foil broaching. The main foils have some dihedral while the tail foil is flat.

Total foil area is 509ft², and foil loading is 1,460lb/ft² maximum. Foils are constructed in welded HY80 steel.

In February 1976, Grumman Aerospace delivered a new tail strut fabricated in HY130 steel. HY130 is being considered by the US Navy as a material for future large hydrofoils.

The main foils are extended, retracted and locked in each terminal position by means of a hydraulically-operated activating arm connected to the upper part of the strut. The two foils are synchronised to be raised and lowered together in the transverse plane. The aft foil operates in a similar manner, but can be raised and lowered independently.

Foil lift variation is by change in the incidence angle; each can move through +11 degrees to —4 degrees. The single aft foil controls pitch angle.

The aft foil strut rotates for use as a rudder. Steering can be flat (rudder only) or fully coordinated, using differential main foil angles for banked turns, with the aft strut trailing.

HULL: The hull is almost completely fabricated in 5456 aluminium alloy. All deck, side and bottom plating is made from integrally stiffened, aluminium extruded planks. The hull is predominantly welded construction with the exception of the pilot house and certain longitudinal hull seams that act as crack stoppers.

The hull shape is designed to minimise the structural loadings due to wave impact and the bow shape has been developed for this specific purpose. Bottom deadrise is carried to the transom with the same objective.

ACCOMMODATION: Crew of 25, comprising 4 officers and 21 enlisted men. The pilothouse, CIC compartment, living, messing and berthing spaces are air-conditioned. Sanitary and washroom areas, galley, displacement and main engine room are all mechanically ventilated. In the wheelhouse, the pilot's position is on the left, with the principal instrumentation; the co-pilot is on the right, and the observer between and slightly aft. Entry to the deckhouse is via three standard US Navy quick-acting aluminium doors—one aft port and one forward starboard on the main deck, and one aft on the lower deck. Emergency equipment includes seven-man liferafts, seven life-rings, four aircraft markers, one kapok heaving line and emergency scuttles, port and starboard.

POWER PLANT: Foilborne propulsion is supplied by two General Electric LM 1500s (marine version of the J-97), each of 14,500hp continuous rating, connected by shafting and gearing to two four-bladed 1·52m (5ft) diameter supercavitating titanium propellers at the end of the propulsion pods on the main foils. The hydrodynamic design of the propellers was undertaken by Hydronautics Inc, and they were built by Hamilton Standard. The blades are bolted to the hubs and each blade is replaceable. The air inlet

AG (EH)-I Plainview, 328-ton US Navy ocean-going hydrofoil warship research vessel, moored in Puget Sound with foils retracted. Two four-bladed propellers at the end of the pods on the main foil struts propel the vessel when foilborne

Maximum foilborne speed of the Plainview, which is powered by two 14,500hp GE LM 1500s, is in excess of 50 knots. It is designed to operate in sea state 5 conditions and has undergone trials in 2·43-3·04m (8-10ft) waves off Victoria, British Columbia

In the interests of weight economy, the Plainview's hull is built largely from specially extruded aluminium planks, each 12·19m (40ft) in length and 0·635m (2ft 1in) in width. Struts and foils are built in HY80 and HY130 steel alloys. The bow shape is designed to minimise structural loadings due to wave impact

New AG (EH)-I Plainview aft foil assembly, comprising strut, pod and foil

for the main turbines is introduced at the top of the deckhouse. Because of the need to prevent ingestion of water or saltspray into the gas turbines, there are lowered deflectors over the inlet opening, followed by a bank of sheet metal spray separators.

There is a dam for solid water separation and four right-angle turns before the air reaches the engine bellmouths.

The hullborne powerplants are two General Motors V12-71 diesels each rated at 500hp. Each diesel drives aft through a shaft to a right-angle gear drive resembling a large outboard motor, mounted on the side of the hull. Each of these right angle drives is retractable about a horizontal axis and steerable about a vertical axis through 360 degree rotation. A 1·34m (4ft 5in) diameter five-bladed subcavitating propeller is mounted at the end of each right-angle drive.

Auxiliary power is supplied by two GMC V8-71 engines driving two 100kW generators.

AIR CONDITIONING: The pilothouse, CIC compartment, living, messing and berthing spaces are air-conditioned during the cooling season by a 15-ton capacity Trane type compressor system. Sanitary and washroom areas, galley, displacement engine room, main engine room, windlass room and the engineer's control booth are all mechanically ventilated.

HYDRAULICS: 3,000psi operates foils, steering, extension, retraction and locking of struts and anchor windlass and starts propulsion diesels.

ELECTRONIC SYSTEMS: Raytheon Pathfinder radar with AN/SPA-25 repeater, AN/WRC-1B Bendix radio, AN/URC-58 radio RF Comm Inc, two AN/ARC-52X Collins radios.

ARMAMENT: Six Mk 32 torpedo tubes in two tri-mounts, port and starboard, aft of the deckhouse. One Mk 44 torpedo stowed in each tube. Single missile canister fitted in late 1972 for demonstration launching of three NATO-configured Sea Sparrow missiles.

Project for a 1,330-ton ocean-going hydrofoil frigate with a fixed fully-submerged foil system

DIMENSIONS

EXTERNAL

Length overall, hull: 64·61m (212ft)
  foils retracted: 68·17m (223ft 8in)
  foils extended: 66·75m (219ft ½in)
Length waterline, hull: 62·48m (205ft 1¾in)
Hull beam: 12·31m (40ft 5in)
Beam overall, foils retracted: 25·19m (82ft 8in)
  foils extended: 21·59m (70ft)

Draft hullborne, foils retracted: 1·9m (6ft 3in)
Freeboard,
  forward: 4·72m (15ft 6in)
  aft: 2·29m (7ft 6½in)
Height to top of mast: 16·69m (54ft 9½in)

WEIGHTS
Light displacement: 265 tons
Normal take-off: 290 tons
Max take-off: 328 tons

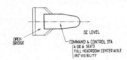

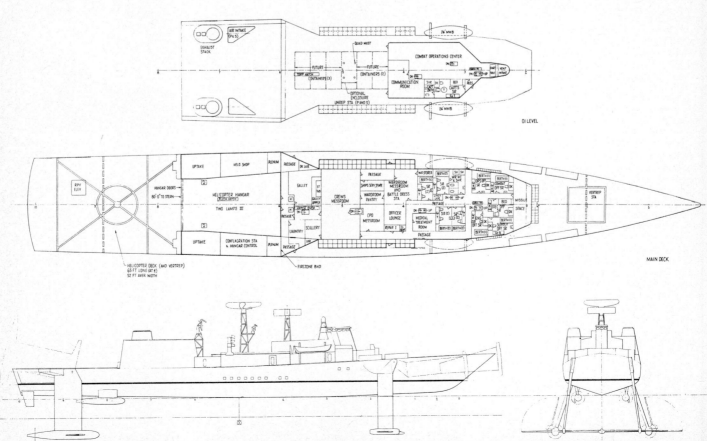

Outboard profile and deck views of a projected 2,400-tonne air capable hydrofoil warship. This design accommodates a variety of weapon systems, and provides for the operation of two LAMPS III ASW helicopters and the launching and recovering of RPVs

PERFORMANCE
Max speed foilborne: in excess of 50 knots
Cruising speed foilborne: 42 knots
Max speed hullborne: 13·4 knots
Cruising speed hullborne: 12 knots
Max permissible sea state and wave height in
foilborne mode: (design sea state) Beaufort 5,
sea state 5

OCEAN HYDROFOIL COMBATANT

Since September 1974, Grumman Aerospace
Corporation has been involved in the exploration
of the potential of hydrofoil ships to fulfill the role
of ocean combatants for the US Navy.

Preliminary designs have been completed for
ships ranging in displacement from 1,330 to
1,625 tonnes. A variety of foil configurations
have been investigated including fixed and totally
retractable systems. Foilborne ranges in the
order of 3,000n miles, speeds in excess of 50
knots and continuous operations in sea state six
are being considered. Sustained operation will be
possible from zero to maximum foilborne speed.

Foilborne power for the designs under consideration will be provided by twin General Electric
LM 2500 gas turbines, with optional gas turbines
for hullborne operation. Power is transmitted
through mechanical Z-drives to supercavitating
CP propellers for foilborne operation and CRP
propellers when hullborne. Hull construction is
all-welded aluminium. Foil and struts are in HY
130 steel. New composite material is under consideration for foil fabrication.

Multiple combat systems are under study,
including vertical launch missiles and air capability. The larger designs under study may employ
VTOL aircraft to provide long-range identification for shipboard missiles and surveillance
up to 400 nautical miles from the ship.

HYD-2

In March 1977 Grumman delivered to the US
Navy the conceptual design of a 2,400-tonne air
capable hydrofoil ship, to be known as the
HYD-2. This design accommodates a variety of
weapon systems and provides for the launching,
retrieving, and servicing of two LAMPS III
helicopters.

FOILS: Fully-submerged canard arrangement
with approximately 40% of the load carried by
the bow foil and 60% by the aft foil. Fuel burn-off
increases the percentage of the load on the bow
foil, assisting the maintenance of favourable pitch

Impression of HYD-2, Grumman's proposal for a 2,400-tonne air capable hydrofoil for the US Navy

stability throughout the loading range. For hullborne operation the bow foil rotates forwards
and upwards clear of the waterline and the rear
foil rotates aft.
POWER PLANT: Foilborne power is provided
by two Turbo Power and Marine Systems Inc FT9
Marine gas turbines, each rated at 43,000shp
maximum intermittent and 37,000shp maximum
continuous at 4,000rpm and 27°C (80°F). Hullborne power is supplied by a single General
Electric LM500 gas turbine, rated at 5,100shp
maximum intermittent and 4,650shp maximum
continuous at 7,000rpm at 27°C (80°F). All three
units are located aft of amidship and drive four
propellers, two foilborne and two hullborne,
through a combined transmission. All four propellers are identical in blade design to facilitate
servicing and replacement. The hullborne propellers are reversible and variable in pitch to reduce
take-off drag, while the foilborne propellers are
variable in pitch to reduce drag when operating
hullborne.
HULL: Incorporates continuous main (weather)
and second decks and a partial lower platform
deck. Hold beneath the load deck is divided into
13 major watertight compartments.
ACCOMMODATION: Crew will vary according to the nature of the missions for which the
craft is employed and the type of weapons installed. Accommodation is provided for 155 officers
and enlisted personnel, allowing for the in-
service growth of the crew by 15 members above

the anticipated initial manning of 140. All
accommodation is located amidships in the area
of least motion.
SYSTEMS, ELECTRICAL: Three Lycoming
T35 gas turbines are fitted, each rated at
2,800shp continuous at 15,000rpm, two to drive
generators for normal ship's services, one for
emergency use and anchor operation.
WEAPONS: Two LAMPS III helicopters operated from pad aft of superstructure. Pad is also
employed for launching and recovering remotely
piloted vehicles (RPVs). Vertically launched
weapons, located principally in mounts located
fore and aft, along both sides of the hull and
inboard, amidship.
DIMENSIONS
Length between perpendiculars (hull): 97·54m
(320ft)
Length overall, foils retracted: 111·17m (364ft
9in)
foils extended: 106·85m (350ft 7in)
Beam overall, foils retracted (tips folded):
24·69m (81ft)
foils extended: 35·62m (116ft 10½in)
Max beam (hull): 15·87m (52ft 1in)
Operational draft, foils retracted: 5·72m (18ft
9in)
hullborne, foils extended: 13·41m (44ft)
Draft (nominal), foilborne: 5·43m (17ft 10in)
Radar height above water (nominal),
foilborne: 24·99m (82ft)
hullborne: 17·07m (56ft)

HYDROFOILS INCORPORATED

PO Box 115, Red Bank, New Jersey 07701, USA
Telephone: (201) 842 1260
Officials:
Kenneth E Cook, *President*

Hydrofoils Incorporated has designed a
fibreglass-hulled two-seater, the Mirage, for
powerboat racing. The company, in conjunction
with the American Power Boat Association, is
examining the possibility of establishing a new
racing class which would lead to the inception of a
water counterpart to multi-turn Grand Prix road
racing.

One of the company's latest projects is a 8·53m
(28ft) patrol hydrofoil employing foils of similar
configuration to those of Mirage.

Work is also under way on a new craft, powered by a 1,500hp engine for an attempt on the
world hydrofoil speed record.

Performance of the Mirage is said to compare
favourably with that of other high performance
craft. At the time of going to press, production
quantities and the retail price were in the process
of being settled. Preliminary details are given
below.

MIRAGE

This novel recreational craft is intended as a
water-borne equivalent to a two-seater sports
car. One major objective has been to produce a
craft capable of tight, high-speed turns, thus
permitting boats of this type to race on relatively

Note the novel canard arrangement incorporating an inverted V main foil with a conventional V foil forward.
Wing-shaped stabilisers on the main foils limit the degree of immersion of the main foil thereby maintaining
the hull at a negative angle of attack, and preventing the craft from blowing over at high speed

small courses. The prototype is fitted with a
350in³ Chevrolet automobile engine, but a wide
range of alternative petrol engines can be fitted.
FOILS: Surface-piercing canard configuration.
About 75% of the load is borne by the inverted V
foil aft and the remainder on the small conventional V foil at the bow. Wing-shaped stabiliser
foils are attached to the inverted V main foil at
calm water line level to limit the degree of foil
immersion, maintaining the hull at a negative
angle of attack to prevent kiteing and blowover at
high speed. Foils are of supercavitating design
and fabricated in high strength aluminium. Small

rudder surfaces are attached at right angles to
main foil. Various sizes available. Rudder design
is a compromise between maximum steering
capability and optimum fin effect to limit yaw,
roll and drift in high-speed turns. The aft foils
hinge upwards for towing, reducing the overall
beam to conform with state trailer laws.
HULL: Planing type hull. Moulded fibreglass
structure with aluminium frames and sitka spruce
stringers.
ACCOMMODATION: Open cockpit with twin
upholstered bucket seats for driver and one passenger.

POWER PLANT: Single 350in³ Nicson marine conversion engine installed aft of the cockpit. Output is transferred via a Casalle vee-drive to a Stellings chrome-plated high-performance two-bladed propeller. Drive is air, water and oil-cooled and provides forward and neutral quick-change. Ten different gear ratios are available from 1·03:1 to 1·37:1. Total fuel capacity is 15 gallons.

CONTROLS: Craft heading is controlled by twin rudders operated from the cockpit by a steering wheel. There is also a foot-operated throttle and a gear shift lever. The boat is equipped with an automatic bilge pump.

SYSTEMS, ELECTRICAL: 12V dc starter, alternator and voltage regulator.

DIMENSIONS
Length overall, hull: 5·02m (16ft 6in)
Beam overall: 3·96m (13ft)
 hull: 2·43m (8ft)
Draft, hullborne: 0·91m (3ft)
 foilborne: 457mm (1ft 6in)
WEIGHTS
Displacement: 816·42kg (1,800lb)
PERFORMANCE
Max speed: 129km/h (80mph)
PRICE: The Mirage is available both as a complete craft or in kit form. A kit information package is available at US$7.

28ft PATROL HYDROFOIL

Hydrofoils Incorporated is completing a design study for the Department of Fisheries, Canada, for a 8·53m (28ft) patrol hydrofoil, with living and sleeping accommodation for a crew of four. Foil configuration is similar to that of the Mirage. Power will be supplied by either a single or twin engines driving marine propellers through V-drive shafts or retractable outboard drives.

A provisional three-view drawing accompanies this entry.

DIMENSIONS
Length overall, hull: 8·53m (28ft)
 foils retracted: 9·14m (30ft)
 foils extended: 9·14m (30ft)
Hull beam: 3·63m (11ft 11in)
Beam overall, foils extended: 5·79m (19ft)
Draft static, foils retracted: 0·609m (2ft)
 foils extended: 2·13m (7ft)
Draft foilborne: 0·67m (2ft 6in)
Height overall, foilborne: 3·04m (10ft)
 static: 1·82m (6ft)

40ft FERRY

Work has started on a 20-passenger, 40ft long light ferry which could also be employed to service offshore oil rigs.

Hull of Mirage is in moulded glass fibre with an aluminium frame

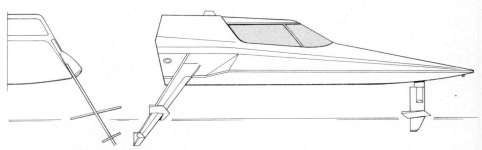

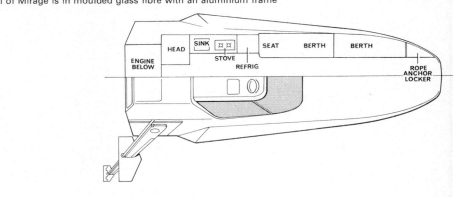

Design study for a 8·53m (28ft) patrol hydrofoil completed by Hydrofoils Inc

Two-seat Mirage racing hydrofoil during tests

SAILING SKIMMERS

JAPAN

KANAZAWA INSTITUTE OF TECHNOLOGY

Department of Mechanical Engineering, Kanazawa Institute of Technology, PO Kanazawa-South, Ishikawa-Ken 921, Japan
Telephone: 0762 48 1100
Officials:
Yutaka Masuyama, *Researcher*

The Hydrodynamic Department of Mechanical Engineering, Kanazawa Institute of Technology, has been studying sailing hydrofoil craft since 1975. Three experimental craft have been built. Ichigo-tei was completed in 1975 and tested in 1976; employing data obtained from this craft, Hi-Trot II was built and tested in 1977 and Hi-Trot III was tested in 1979.

ICHIGO-TEI

This is a basic test rig to investigate the manoeuvrability, stability and balance of sails and foil systems. The Ichigo-Tei has a specially designed catamaran hull, to which two surface-piercing bow foils and one stern foil are attached.
FOILS: The bow foils are of three-rung ladder configuration with removable outer rungs. The stern foil is of trapeze configuration with the rudder mounted immediately aft. Foil loading during a normal take-off is bow foils 60% and stern foil 40%. The foils, struts and rudder are fabricated in glass fibre and polyester resin. Foil section throughout is Göttinger 797, with 170mm (6·7in) chord.
HULL: Marine plywood sheathed with glass fibre and polyester resin.
SAIL: Sloop rig with a 10·2m² (110ft²) mainsail borrowed from the Hobie-cat 14, and a jib sail of 3·7m² (40ft²) borrowed from the Snipe.
DIMENSIONS
Length overall: 4·46m (14ft 8in)
    waterline: 4·2m (13ft 9in)
Hull beam: 2·2m (7ft 3in)
Width overall across foils: 4·3m (14ft 1in)
Draft afloat (fixed foils):   0·96m (3ft 2in)
    foilborne: 0·5-0·4m (1ft 8in-1ft 4in)
WEIGHTS
Empty: 140kg (309lb)
PERFORMANCE
Take-off speed: 6 knots with 11-knot wind
Max speed foilborne: 9 knots with 14-knot wind

HI-TROT II

Employing data gathered during the test programme conducted with Ichigo-tei, the Kanazawa Institute of Technology design team built the Hi-Trot II. The hull is longer than that of the earlier craft, but the chief difference, apart from the adoption of a simpler foil system, is the use of a rotating sail rig.
FOILS: The split bow foil is of surface-piercing V-type, with cantilevered extensions, set at 40 degrees dihedral, at the apex. The bow foil section is ogival, with 250mm (9·8in) chord and a 12% thickness-to-chord ratio. The aft foil is of inverted T type and the complete foil and strut assembly rotates for use as a rudder. About 80% of the load is carried by the bow foils, and the remaining 20% by the stern foil. Foils, struts and rudder are all fabricated in glass fibre, carbon fibre and epoxy resin.
HULL: Plywood structure sheathed with glass fibre and epoxy resin.
SAIL: Comprises three sail panels in parallel, each 4·2m², mounted in parallel. An air rudder

Ichigo-tei, Kanazawa Institute's test craft, during trials. Take-off speed is 7 knots

Hi-Trot II foilborne. Note the air rudder attached to the central sail panel which automatically adjusts the attack angle of all three sails to the wind

automatically adjusts the attack angle of the sails to the wind. Each panel has a wing section, and though the section is symmetrical, it can form a camber on either side by bending at 40% chord length. The leading edge of each wing is covered with thin aluminium sheet while the trailing edges are covered with terylene cloth. Wing frames are of plywood and polystyrene foam sandwich and provide the necessary buoyancy to prevent the craft from capsizing should it turn on its side. The surface of each wing is spray painted with polyurethane paint.
DIMENSIONS
Length overall: 5·1m (16ft 9in)
    waterline: 4·95m (16ft 3in)

Hull beam: 2·68m (8ft 10in)
Beam, overall (fixed foils):   5·45m (17ft 11in)
Draft afloat (fixed foils):   1·1m (3ft 7in)
    foilborne: 0·55-0·4m (1ft 10in-1ft 4in)

WEIGHTS
Empty: 250kg (551lb)

PERFORMANCE
Take-off speed: 7 knots with 15-knot wind
Max speed foilborne: 11 knots with 17-knot wind
SEA TEST: The craft has been tested in 10-20 knot winds. Due to mechanical problems, tests could not be undertaken in wind speeds exceeding 20 knots. Improvements are being made to remedy this.

HI-TROT III

During 1978 the Kanazawa Institute of Technology design team constructed and tested a third craft, Hi-Trot III. The major difference between it and Hi-Trot II is the use of two parallel soft wing sails.

FOILS: The split bow foil is of surface-piercing Y-type, and the aft foil is of inverted T type as on the Hi-Trot II. Up to 90% of the load is carried by the bow foils, and the remaining 10% by the stern foil. Foils are of GFRP sandwich construction with polyurethane foam core and reinforced by carbon fibre.

HULL: Plywood structure sheathed with glass fibre and epoxy resin.

SAIL: Comprises two parallel soft wing sails specially developed for Hi-Trot III, each 8m². Total sail area 16m².

DIMENSIONS
Length overall: 5·08m (16ft 8in)
   waterline: 4·95m (16ft 3in)
Hull beam: 0·3m (1ft)
Beam overall, foils retracted: 3·74m (12ft 3in)
   foils extended: 6·84m (22ft 5in)
Draft afloat, foils retracted: 0·2m (8in)
   foils extended: 1m (3ft 3in)
Draft foilborne: 0·4m (1ft 4in)
WEIGHTS
Empty: 255kg (562lb)
PERFORMANCE: Hi-Trot III takes-off at 8 knots in a 15-knot wind and accelerates to 15 knots rapidly. The maximum speed attained during trials was 21 knots in an 18-knot wind (1·2 times wind speed).

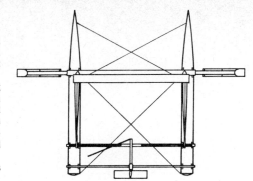
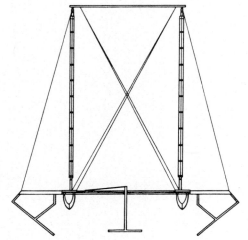
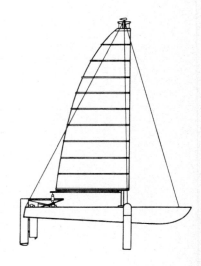

General arrangement of Hi-Trot III sail hydrofoil test craft

Top speed attained by Hi-Trot III during trials is 21 knots in an 18-knot wind (1·2 times wind speed)

POLAND

INSTYTUT LOTNICTWA (AVIATION INSTITUTE)

02-256 Warszawa, Al Krakowska 110/114, Poland

Telephone: 460993
Telex: 81-537

Dr Jerzy Wolf is employing an ultra-light wing, constructed by the Aviation Institute while undertaking research on agricultural aircraft, as a sail for an experimental "skimmer" sailing craft.

The wing raises the hull above the water surface and also acts as a sail.

The object of Dr Wolf's experiments is to develop a sailing vessel which offers a higher speed than that attained by current sailing hydrofoils.

Z-76 Sailing Skimmer undergoing tests

The wing, which has inherent directional and lateral stability, is hinged to the mast top, slightly ahead of the centre of pressure, and pulls the craft obliquely, in a similar way to a kite of high lift/drag ratio. The angles of attack and roll are controlled by lines or push-pull rods connected to a control cross-bar. Craft heading is controlled by a conventional water rudder.

Dr Wolf's Z-70 and Z-71 sailing craft are described in *Jane's Surface Skimmers 1976-77* and earlier editions.

ZAGLOSLIZG (SAILING SKIMMER)

Developed from the Z-70 and Z-71, the Z-73 employs a modified Cadet class dinghy hull, equipped with a high aspect ratio centreboard and rudder.

During 1974, several further modifications were made to the sailwing, including the addition of a bow stabiliser to assess the advantages of a canard configuration, and a horizontal stabiliser surface to assess the value of a conventional configuration.

The mast was moved aft of the cockpit, and foot-operated rudder bar steering was installed.

Based on the test results, a further development model—the Z-76—is being built, the wing of which will also be used as an ultra-light, tailless hang-glider.

The wing, covered in dacron, incorporates a light vertical stabiliser, and has inherent directional and lateral stability.

Altitude control is based on a combination of incidence and heel angle control. Excessive altitude results in increased drift and a loss of speed and lift. This leads to a restoration of normal trim, with the hull riding at a predetermined height above the water level. The restoring forces are described as being similar to those of a V-foil sailing hydrofoil.

DIMENSIONS
Length overall, hull: 3·2m (10ft 6in)
Beam: 1·3m (4ft 3in)
Draft, centreboard lowered: 1·2m (3ft 11in)
Sailwing span: 6·5m (21ft 4in)
Aspect ratio: 4·7:1
Stabiliser area: 1·2m² (13ft²)
WEIGHTS
Empty: 68kg (150lb)
Gross: 150kg (330lb)
Sailwing: 10kg (22lb)
PERFORMANCE (Design)
Lift/drag ratio, sailing: approx 8:1
Max angle of wing setting: 60 degrees
Horizontal lift/drag ratio for 45 degree heel: 3·5:1
Lift/drag ratio of centre board and rudder: 2·1:1
Wind velocity for take-off: 6·5m/s (21ft/s)
Minimum speed for take-off: 45km/h (27mph)
Optimum airborne speed: 60km/h (36mph)

UNITED KINGDOM

BEN WYNNE

Glyn Artro Farm, Llanbedr (Mer), Gwynedd LL45 2LY, Wales

MAYFLY

In 1972, the Royal Yachting Association inaugurated the Sailing Speed Record competition and since then has held this event annually in Portland Harbour, England. One of the successful craft to emerge from these trials has been the one-man hydrofoil catamaran *Mayfly*. She was originally designed and built by Philip Hansford to compete in the A class sail area category (up to 13·94m²) and was sailed in early competitions by James Grogono, who pioneered hydrofoil sailing in the UK with his converted Tornado class catamaran *Icarus* in 1969. *Mayfly* was acquired by Wynne for the 1976 event during which she raised her record for the class to 21·1 knots. After this she was taken to workshops at the University of Newcastle-upon-Tyne, where with the help of Dr V Hill new bow foils were designed and built in time for the 1977 competition. The boat has been gradually developed over the years to its present form described below.
FOILS: Aeroplane configuration with surface-piercing bow foils and a single fully-submerged 'inverted-T' rudder foil strut assembly aft. All foils are made of aluminium and retract. The cantilever member of the bow foils has a design lift coefficient of 0·4 and was machined from solid by numerical control to a low drag aerofoil section. The turned down tips reduce leeway at high speeds. The inverted-T rudder/foil assembly is of hollow construction fabricated from aluminium plates rolled to form a symmetrical bi-ogival section 10-12% thick. All foils are fitted with full chord antiventilation fences.
HULLS: These were purpose built with low freeboard to reduce weight and windage and are lightly constructed from 3mm plywood forming a round bilge hull, with joints held by fibreglass tape. The hulls are joined by a forward and an aft tubular aluminium cross beam. A specially tailored sail cloth 'trampoline' is stretched between the beams and hulls to give an aerofoil section bridge deck. The bow foils are mounted directly onto the forward crossbeam and may be retracted or lowered in one minute. They are rotated forwards and upwards for hullborne sails or mooring with wire and bottle screw to fix the angle of incidence. The rear foil is mounted centrally on a third cross beam and swings forwards and upwards to retract. Sitting out 'wings' are currently fitted to enable the helmsman to move his weight further to windward thus permitting a sail sideforce of up to 85% of the all-up weight including crew.
RIG: A single soft sail is used having an area of 13·2m² (142ft²). It is fully battened and is set on an over rotating wingmast.

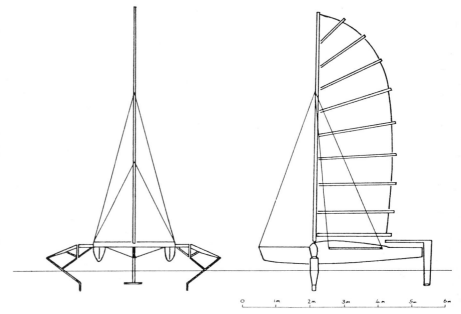

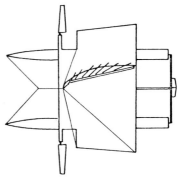

Mayfly, a catamaran sailing hydrofoil. *Mayfly* has held the A Class World Speed Record since its inception and established the current record of 23 knots in 1977

DIMENSIONS
Length overall: 4·8m (15ft 9in)
Beam overall: 5·1m (16ft 8¾in)
Draft hullborne: 1·0m (3ft 3in)
foilborne: 0·6m (1ft 11in)
Mast height: 7·0m (22ft 11in)

WEIGHTS
All-up (less crew): 118kg (260lb)

PERFORMANCE: *Mayfly* requires a 12-14-knot breeze to fly. Once foilborne in marginal conditions, she has little difficulty in staying up and is highly manoeuvrable. At speed she takes on an aeroplane-like sensitivity to control movements and the only sounds are a whine from the rig and the hiss of water rushing past the foils. In flat water, foiling to windward is possible on courses to within approximately 60 degrees of the true wind. However, the maximum speed is reached on a course about 120 degrees to the true wind when, under favourable conditions with smooth water and a medium breeze, she can reach twice the windspeed.

Mayfly has held the A Class World Speed Record since its inception and established the current record of 23 knots in 1977.

UNITED STATES OF AMERICA

DAK HYDROFOILS

PO Box 1747, Sausalito, California 94965, USA

Officials:

David A Keiper, *Proprietor and Chief Designer*

Design of the Williwaw, the world's first seagoing sailing hydrofoil, began in 1963. Construction of the craft, which is based on a specially designed trimaran hull, began in May 1966 and tests started in November 1967.

After nearly three years of trials along the California coast, Williwaw, manned by David Keiper and one other crew member, successfully completed a 16-day passage between Sausalito, California and Kahului Harbour, Maui, Hawaii, in September 1970—the first ocean crossing by the hydrofoil sailboat.

Heavy seas and strong winds were encountered on the first two days of the voyage, during which the craft made 200 miles per day. At times the craft attained 25 knots, but light winds in mid-ocean prevented the craft from making the passage in record time.

The craft entered chartered sailing yacht service in March 1971, operating from Hanalei, Hawaii and before returning to Sausalito, California, completed about 2,000 miles of inter-island sailing around Hawaii, mainly in open sea conditions.

Williwaw was entered in the Pacific Multihull Association speed trials held in Los Angeles Harbour on 9 May 1975. Average speed was determined over a 229m (250yd) course, planned so that the true wind was approximately 10 to 20 degrees aft of the beam. On one run, with a reasonably steady wind of 17 knots, Williwaw averaged 17·5 knots over the course. On another run, with a stronger wind of 24 knots, under gusty and turbulent conditions with 1½ft very short wave chop, Williwaw averaged 18·5 knots.

The foils stabilised the craft perfectly. The bow kept up high in all runs, while various racing catamarans of 14 to 38ft experienced serious problems with bow burying. Two catamarans capsized. The three-man crew on Williwaw stood on the windward deck, holding onto the shrouds, while the crews of the catamarans had to lie down and hold on tight to avoid being thrown overboard.

Various modifications to the craft were undertaken during 1974-75, and in the summer of 1975 a second series of sea trials were undertaken in the South Pacific, to test these modifications.

Williwaw sailed to Hawaii again in June 1975. Wind was generally light until deep within the tradewind region. In heavy tradewind squalls with the boat running down steep 15ft seas, the foils were found to stabilise perfectly and the bow was never submerged.

On a run from Hanalei, Hawaii to Whangaroa, New Zealand, made between November and December 1975, with stopovers in Samoa and Tonga, moderate trade winds were experienced during the first 2,000 miles of the voyage and generally light winds during the last 2,000 miles. During the first 12 days of the voyage, the foils were left set continuously. Over one ten-day period, the craft completed 1,650 miles, including a doldrums crossing. Self-steering was used for most of the way, with the helm tied. Only the working sail area of 380ft² was used.

The return trip from New Zealand to Hawaii was made via Rarotonga and Penrhyn in the Cook Islands. When the craft left New Zealand, a disturbed south west air stream was generating 35-knot squalls, day and night. Seas were very irregular and the boat would occasionally slam into walls of water at speeds in excess of 20 knots. About 500 miles from the New Zealand coast one freak wave encountered was 35-40ft high, and had a slope greater than 45 degrees. The trough was flat-bottomed, with no rounding between the slope and the trough. Descending the slope, the bow was well above the surface. After impact there was no tendency for the stern to lift

Williwaw sailing in San Francisco Bay before her historic trans-ocean voyage to New Zealand

Williwaw in Auckland harbour, with foils retracted

The bow remained under for about two seconds before it emerged and the boat started moving again. Waves such as this have been known to pitchpole yachts, monohull and multihull, but the hydrofoil trimaran showed no such tendency.

Williwaw operated sailing excursions from Hanalei, Hawaii, during the summers of 1971, 1975 and 1976. By the end of August 1976, it had completed 19,000 miles of sailing.

Economic conditions permitting, Dak Hydrofoils hopes to begin the full-scale marketing of ready-to-install foil sets for a variety of multihulls in 1981.

WILLIWAW

A prototype sailing hydrofoil, Williwaw has a specially designed trimaran hull attached to which are four foils—a deep V-foil at the bow, a ladder foil at the stern, and one laterally outboard of each of the port and starboard pontoons. The stern foil pivots and serves as a rudder when hullborne.

The craft accommodates two-three passengers, together with cruising supplies.

It is able to remain fully foilborne for unlimited distances in moderate seas as long as there is adequate wind power.

Various modifications and improvements were made to the craft during 1974-75. These included the addition of streamlined fairings at the four main intersections of the lifting surfaces and struts on the bow foil, the installation of a retractable leeboard for improved windward performance in light airs, and the facing of various aluminium foil fittings with stainless steel to prevent wear and tear around the shear/fastening bolts.

FOILS: The bow foil, of surface-piercing V configuration, is mounted between the pontoon bows and that of the main hull. Foils, supporting struts and sub-foil elements, are of welded aluminium, with a protective coating of vinyl. Foil section is NACA 16-510 with 152·4mm (6in) chord throughout the system. The foils have fairly high aspect ratio. Foil loading during a normal take-off is: bow foil 40%, stern foil 20% and leeward lateral foil 40%, depending on sail heeling forces. Dihedral of the bow foil is 30-50 degrees.

The lateral foils, which are not as deep as the bow and stern foils, are of four-rung ladder type, and have 35 degrees dihedral. The stern foil is of three-rung ladder configuration with zero dihedral at rest, but craft heel gives it 10-15 degrees dihedral. Under most conditions the rungs are fully submerged. The entire stern foil pivots for steering action. Shear bolts protect bow and stern foils from damage if debris is struck.

Foil retraction arrangements are as follows:

After the removal of shear bolts the bow foil swings forward and upwards through 90 degrees; the lateral foils swing outwards and over, and are laid flat on the deck through a second pivot axis, and the stern foil swings aft and over through 180 degrees. Retraction of the bow and lateral foils is achieved through the use of a simple block and tackle.

CONTROL: A tiller-operated, combined stern foil and rudder controls direction in foilborne mode; paired struts, also tiller operated, provide rudder control when hullborne.

HULL: Lightweight, but robust trimaran hull with small wing deck to avoid aerodynamic lift. Marine ply structure sheathed with glass fibre. Built-in attachment points for foils. Mast supported by main frame.

ACCOMMODATION: The craft is designed for two to three people, with cruising supplies, but has flown with nine aboard. The deep cockpit accommodates the helmsman and one crew member. The cockpit, which provides adequate shelter from the strong winds developed by high-speed sailing, forms the entrance to main and stern cabins. The main cabin seats four comfortably. There are two berths in the main cabin and one in the stern cabin. The main cabin also includes a galley, shelving and a marine head. There is generous stowage space in the pontoon hulls.

SAIL AND POWERPLANT: Sail power alone on prototype, but a small outboard auxiliary engine can be fitted if required. Total sail area is 35·3m² (380ft²).

SYSTEMS, ELECTRONICS: Radio direction finder normally carried.

DIMENSIONS

EXTERNAL

Length overall, hull: 9·54m (31ft 4in)
   waterline, hull: 8·53m (28ft)
   overall, foils retracted: 10·05m (33ft)
   overall, foils extended: 9·75m (32ft)
Hull beam:
   main hull at water line: 0·91m (3ft)
   hull overall, foils retracted: 4·97m (16ft 4in)
Beam, overall, foils extended: 7·62m (25ft)
Draft afloat, foils retracted: 0·4m (1ft 4in)
   foils extended: 1·21m (4ft)
Draft foilborne: 0·45-0·76m (1ft 6in-2ft 6in)
Freeboard: 0·61m (2ft)
Pontoon deck: 475-762mm (1ft 6in-2ft 6in)
Main hull deck: 762mm-1·06m (2ft 6in-3ft 6in)
Height overall to masthead: 11·88m (39ft)

INTERNAL

Cabin (wheelhouse, galley, toilet included):
   length: 8·53m (28ft)
   max width: 4·87m (16ft)
   max height: 1·62m (5ft 4in)
   volume: 13·78m³ (480ft³)

WEIGHTS

Light displacement: 997·88kg (2,200lb)
Normal take-off displacement: 1,360kg (3,000lb)
Max take-off displacement: 1,632kg (3,600lb)
Normal payload: 362·8kg (800lb)
Max payload: 635kg (1,400lb)

PERFORMANCE (in steady wind and calm water, with normal payload)

Take-off speed: normally 12 knots. Craft is able to take-off with a 12-knot beam wind and accelerate to 18-20 knots
Max speed foilborne: 30 knots
Cruising speed foilborne: 12-25 knots
Max permissible sea state and wave height in foilborne mode: sea state almost unlimited at 12 knot average speed with wind aft of beam. Foils well behaved in all conditions met so far. Sails reefed down in heavy conditions to maintain comfort and ease of handling. Craft shows no tendency to pound.
Turning radius at cruising speed: 45·72m (150ft)
Number of seconds and distance to take-off: 5 seconds in strong wind, two boat lengths
Number of seconds to stop craft: 8 seconds, turning dead into wind
SEA TESTS: Craft operated in strong winds and breaking seas including steep 15-20ft seas in Pacific en route to New Zealand and one freak

Hobie-16 Dak-foil conversion with foils retracted

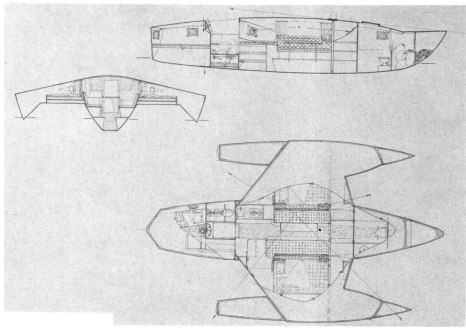

Inboard profile and deck plan of the Pacific Express 35 hydrofoil racing/cruising trimaran

wave 35-40ft high with 45-50 degree slope. It has completed a return voyage from the California coast to Hawaii, and a second Pacific voyage from California to New Zealand and back to Hawaii. By the end of August 1976, the craft had covered 19,000 miles.

Speed is significantly more than wind speed in conditions of steady wind and calm water. The craft can match wind speed in moderate seas, but not in heavy seas. In heavy seas, broad reaching or beam, it has averaged 15 knots for hours at a time, winds gusting to Force 5 and 6. Speeds may climb to 30 knots or drop to 5 knots, depending upon local wind and waves. Acceleration and decelerations are gradual and not objectionable. The ride is far smoother than that of displacement multihulls.

PACIFIC EXPRESS 35

Successor to Williwaw, the Pacific Express is a second generation hydrofoil cruising trimaran. It is designed to be sailed solo when necessary, and avoid many of the problems inherent in conventional trimarans—pounding, broaching, tunnel interference, quick motion, pitchpoling, poor control and poor self-steering in heavy seas.

The craft is wider than its predecessor, has fully buoyant float hulls, is equipped with a more efficient hydrofoil system and has a slightly greater load-carrying capacity.

It is designed to operate in a wide variety of conditions, from heavy storm seas to light airs. In heavy seas, with foils set, it is exceptionally stable and capable of high speeds.

The length, 10·66m (35ft), is the shortest in which it is convenient to have full standing headroom as well as a flush deck. Through its proportionately wider hulls, it should be able to exceed true wind speed more substantially than Williwaw and be able to fly fully foilborne at about 50 degrees from the true wind. The boat should be able to beat to windward with complete comfort for the crew.

In light airs and calms, with foils retracted, the craft makes the most of the available wind.

FOILS: Configuration similar to that of Williwaw. Foils have a 152mm (6in) chord and are fabricated in heavily anodised aluminium extrusions. Bolts, washers, etc, are in stainless steel. Bow and lateral foil are fixed while sailing. Tiller-operated combined stern foil and rudder controls craft direction when foilborne. All four foils retract manually after the removal of sheer bolts.

HULL: Main hull bottom and topside, triple diagonal wood strips, remainder in plywood. All wood saturated with epoxy.

SAIL: Sail area as a cutter 650ft². Sloop working sail area 485ft².

DIMENSIONS
Length, overall: 10·66m (35ft)
   waterline, static: 9·65m (31ft 8in)
Beam, foils retracted: 6·7m (22ft)
Mast height: 12·19m (40ft)
Draft, foils retracted: 457mm (1ft 6in)
   (static) foils extended: 1·52m (5ft)
Outboard projection of lateral foils: 1·21m (4ft)

WEIGHTS
Normal loaded displacement: 1,814kg (4,000lb)

PERFORMANCE
Top speed, strong wind, flat water: 45 knots

Normal foilborne speed range: 13-30 knots
Speed to become fully foilborne: 13 knots
Speed to become half foilborne: 9 knots
Wind required to become fully foilborne, in flat water: 11-12 knots

in average seas: 12-15 knots
Average hull clearance at high speed: 0·6m (2ft)
Max sea state for foilborne operation: unlimited
In heavy seas, sails are reefed in order to obtain a good balance between speed, comfort and safety.

DONALD NIGG

7924 Fontana, Prairie Village, Kansas 66208, USA
Telephone: (913) 642 2002

Development of the Flying Fish began in 1963 at Lake Quivira, an inland lake in Kansas. Donald Nigg believed that if the pitchpole moment and vertical stability problems could be solved, the front-steering three-point suspension system typical of the modern ice-yacht offered several advantages. Previous craft had often used three-point suspension, but all appear to have used rear steering. To develop this new approach, Exocoetus, an experimental platform was built. It was evolved through three distinct versions during 1964-67 and established the basic feasibility.

Interest in the experiments resulted in numerous requests for plans, but although the craft was ideal as a development platform, it was not a design suitable for home construction. In response to these requests the Flying Fish was developed.

To keep the costs to a minimum, the craft is designed to carry a sail area of 100-150ft². It was anticipated that most of those interested in building a sailing hydrofoil would be small boat sailors, owning a boat carrying a mainsail of this size. The design thus allows the builder to share the sail and rigging with an existing dinghy.

A true development class of sailing hydrofoil has been slow to emerge, but the Flying Fish may mark the beginning of such a class. The Amateur Yacht Research Society, Hermitage, Newbury, Berkshire, England, is promoting the design as a development class.

Sets of plans for the Flying Fish have been supplied to potential builders in many countries, including Brazil, Canada, Greece, Australia, the USA, the United Kingdom and Italy.

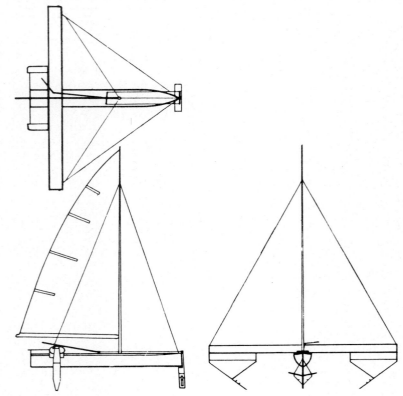

Nigg Flying Fish

FLYING FISH

First of a development class of sailing hydrofoils, the Flying Fish has been specially developed for home builders. Built mainly in wood and with a length overall of 5·02m (16ft 6in), it has a maximum foilborne speed of more than 30 knots.

The estimated cost of constructing a craft of this type, less sail and rigging (the 125ft² mainsail and rigging from a Y-Flyer were used for the prototype illustrated), is US$250.

FOILS: The foil configuration is surface piercing and non-retractable with 16% of the weight supported by the V bow foil and the remaining 84% by the outrigged main foils. The latter are also of the V type, with cantilevered extensions at the apex. Total foil area is 1·42m² (15·3ft²) and the foil loading is 300lb/ft² max at 30 knots. The front foil and its supporting strut are built in aluminium and oak, and the main foil is in oak only.
STEERING: A basic feature of the design is the use of front rather than rear steering. Directional control is provided by the movement of the hinged bow foil.
HULL: This is an all-wooden structure built in fir plywood, ¼in thick and sealed. Torque load is carried by the skin, and bending loads are carried by the skin and the internal beam structure.

The crossbeam provides stability when in dock and in a displacement condition at low speeds. At 2-3 knots the horizontal safety foils at the top of the V of the rear foils provide interim foil stabilisation up to the take-off speed of 5 knots and prevent dragging an end of the crossbeam in the

Topping 20 knots on a close reach in a light wind

water. At foilborne speeds the safety foils preclude the possibility of an end of the crossbeam being driven into the water by sudden heeling.

RIG: A cat rig of 9·2-13·9m² (100-150ft²) area is recommended.

DIMENSIONS
Length overall, hull (plus boom overhand at rear, dependent on sail plan): 5·02m (16ft 6in)
waterline, hull: 4·87m (16ft)
Beam: 6·09m (20ft)
Draft afloat (fixed foils): 1·06m (3ft 6in)
foilborne: 304-762mm (12-30in) over operating speed range
Height, approx: 7·3m (24ft)

PERFORMANCE
Max speed foilborne: over 30 knots
design cruise range: optimised for 20-30 knots
Max speed hullborne: 5 knots
Minimum wind for take-off: 10 knots
Number of seconds and distance to take-off (theoretically approx): 3s with 15·2m (50ft) run in favourable wind
Number of seconds and distance to stop craft (theoretically approx): can land from 20 knots in 45·6m (150ft) in about 6 seconds

SEA TEST: The craft has been tested in 10-25 knot winds, on both sheltered inland lakes and on ocean bays, with a maximum chop of about 18in. Speeds up to approximately 30 knots have been attained.

HYDROFOIL OPERATORS

ALBANIA
ALBANIAN NAVY

Type(s): Hu Chwan (White Swan) Class, 32 (Shanghai)
Operating areas: Coastal waters

ARGENTINA
ALIMAR SanciyF

Avda Cordoba 1801 (Esq Callao), Codigo Postal 1120, Buenos Aires, Argentina
Telephone: 42-4498/3924
Telex: 121510 Almar
Type(s): PT 50, 3 (Rodriquez)
Route: Buenos Aires-Colonia; Colonia-Montevideo

AUSTRALIA
PUBLIC TRANSPORT COMMISSION OF NEW SOUTH WALES

Head Office: Ferry Division, No 2 Jetty, Circular Quay, Sydney, New South Wales 2000, Australia
Telephone: 27 9251
Telex: NSWTC AA25702
Terminal Offices: No 2 Jetty, Circular Quay
Telephone: 27 9251
Manly Wharf, Manly. **Telephone:** 977 3028
Officials:
T F Gibson, *General Manager*
W Heading, *Superintendent Engineer*

OPERATIONS: Routes served and frequency. Sydney to Manly, 7 miles, every 20 minutes between 7am and 7pm
Approximate number of passengers carried during year: 2 million.
CRAFT OPERATED
PT 50 (Rodriquez) *Fairlight*, 140 passengers, built 1966
PT 50 (Rodriquez) *Long Reef*, ex *Freccia di Mergellina*, 140 passengers, built 1968
PT 50 (Rodriquez) *Palm Beach*, ex *Patane*, 140 passengers, built 1969
PT 50 (Rodriquez) *Dee Why*, 140 passengers, built 1970
RHS 140 (Navaltecnica) *Curl Curl*, 140 passengers, built 1972

TIRES PTY LTD

Corner Junction Road and Gray Terrace, Rosewater, Outer Harbour, South Australia, Australia
Type(s): Aquavion Waterman, 1
Route(s): Port Adelaide to Outer Harbour. Hourly service. Also educational and scenic tours of Port River, Adelaide.

AUSTRIA
SCHIFFSWERFT KORNEUBURG

Korneuburg, Austria
Type(s): Raketa, 1 (Sormovo)
Route(s): Danube

BELGIUM
REGIE TRANSPORTES MARITIME (RTM)

Type(s): Jetfoil 929-115, 2
Route(s): Ostend-Dover
This state operator of Belgian ferry routes announced in November 1979 that it was to operate two Jetfoil 929-115 boats on a route between Ostend (Belgium) and Dover, beginning in April 1981. The Belgian Government is paying BFr825 million (£13·35 million) for the two Jetfoils and expects to spend a further BFr75 million (£1·21 million) on terminal facilities for them. The route length is about 64 nautical miles and will take Jetfoil about 1 hour and 40 minutes. RTM already operates several car ferries on this route and the adjacent Folkestone/Ostend route.

BOLIVIA
CRILLON TOURS LTD

PO Box 4785, Av Comacho 1223, La Paz, Bolivia
Telephone: 350363, 374566/67
Telex: BX 5296, BV 2557
Cables: Critur
Officials:
Darius Morgan, *General Manager*
Helmut Kock, *Hydrofoil Designer and Consultant*
Type(s): Albatross (Honold) 4, modified by Helmut Kock; Bolivia Arrow (Kock-Crillon Tours) 1; Seaflight H-57, 1
Route(s): Lake Titicaca

BRAZIL
AEROBARCOS DO BRASIL, Transtur

Transportes Maritimos e Turismo SA, Transtur, Avenida Amaral Peixoto 71—11th floor, Niteroi—R-J, Brazil
Telephone: 719-7070
Telex: 217171 JTMH BR
Type(s): PT 20, 8 (Rodriquez); RHS 110, 1 (Navaltecnica)

BULGARIA
KORABOIMPEX

128 D Blagoev Blvd, Varna, Bulgaria
Type(s): Kometa, 11; Raketa, 1; Meteor, 4 (Sormovo)
Route(s): Bourgas-Nesetow-Varna; Danube, between Rousse and Silistra

CANADA
ROYAL HYDROFOIL CRUISES

25 Queen's Quay, East Marine, Terminal 27, Toronto, Ontario M5E 1A1, Canada
Type(s): PT 150, 3 (Westermoen)
Route(s): Toronto-Youngstown

CHINA (PEOPLE'S REPUBLIC)
NAVY OF THE CHINESE PEOPLE'S REPUBLIC

Type(s): Hu Chwan Class, 140 plus (Shanghai)
Operational areas: Coastal waters

CUBA
MAR-PORT

Calle 21 y O, Vedado, Havana, Cuba
Type(s): Kometa M, 5 (Sormovo)
Route(s): Batabano—Nueva Gerona

DENMARK
A/S DAMPSKIBSSELSKABET ØRESUND

Havnegade 49, DK-1058 Copenhagen, Denmark
Telephone: 01 14 77 70, 01 12 80 88
Telex: 45-27502 Sundet DK
Type(s): PT 50, 8 (5 Rodriquez, 3 Westermoen)
Route(s): Copenhagen-Malmö, Sweden

EGYPT
THE GENERAL NILE COMPANY FOR RIVER TRANSPORT

39 Kasr El-Nil Street, Cairo, Egypt
Telephone: 54517/18
Cables: Naknahri Cairo
Type(s): PT 20, 3 (Rodriquez)
Route(s): Abu Simbel-Asswan

FINLAND
PAIJANTEEN KANTOSIIPI OY

Type(s): Raketa, 1 (Sormovo)
Route(s): Lahti-Jyvaskyla, across Lake Paijane

FRANCE
VEDETTES ARMORICAINES

Ier Eperon, 56 rue d'Aiguillon, Brest Cedex, France
Type(s): Kometa, 1 (Sormovo)

GERMANY, DEMOCRATIC REPUBLIC
SCHIFFACOMMERS

Doberaner Str 44-47, Rostock 1, German Democratic Republic
Type(s): Kometa, 3 (Sormovo)

GERMANY, FEDERAL REPUBLIC
WATER POLICE

Type(s): PT 4, 3 (West German shipyard)
Route(s): Patrol service on the Rhine

KÖLN DÜSSELDORFER SHIPPING CO (KD German Rhine Line)

Frankenwerft 15, D-5000 Cologne 1, Federal Republic of Germany
Type(s): Raketa, 1 *Rhine Arrow* (Sormovo)
Route(s): Dusseldorf/Cologne, Koblenz and Mainz

One of seven Jetfoils operated by Far East Hydrofoil Co Ltd on the 36n mile route between Hong Kong and Macao

GREECE
CERES HELLENIC SHIPPING ENTER-PRISES LTD

Akti Miaouli 69, Piraeus, Greece
Companies: Ceres Flying Hydroways Ltd, Ceres Hydrofoils Limited and Ceres Express Ltd.
Type(s): Kometa-M, 9 plus 6 (Sormovo)
Route(s): Piraeus to islands in the Cyclades group

SOLAM HELLAS

Piraeus, Greece
Type(s): Kometas (Sormovo)
Route(s): Piraeus to Hydra, Spetiai, Syros, Paros, Antiparos, Amagos, Asypalea, Nissyros, Symi and Rhodes.

HONG KONG
HONG KONG MACAO HYDROFOIL CO

Han Seng Bank Building, 77 de Voeux Road Central, Hong Kong
Type(s): PT 50, 4 (Rodriquez); RHS 140, 5 (Navaltecnica)

FAR EAST HYDROFOIL CO LTD

36th Floor, Connaught Centre, Connaught Road, Hong Kong
Telephone: H-243176
Telex: 74200 SEDAM HX
Officials:
Stanley Ho, *Managing Director*
K B Allport, *Group Manager*
Robert Ho, *Manager*
D Hill, *Technical Manager*
Type(s): PT 50, 4, *Guia, Penha, Taipa, Balsa* (Hitachi Zosen);
RHS 110, 3, *Cerco, Praia, Cacilhas* (Navaltecnica);
RHS 160, 1, *Lilau* (Navaltecnica);
PTS 75 Mk III, 2, *Rosa* (Vosper Thornycroft), *Patane* (Supramar Pacific Shipbuilding Co Ltd);
Jetfoils, 7, *Madeira, Santa Maria, Flores, Corvo, Pico, São Vincente* and *Azores* (Boeing).
Route(s): Hong Kong-Macao, distance 36n miles by the Southern Route. Services half-hourly, sunrise to sunset, ie 16,000 trips per annum. Approximate total number of passengers carried per year, 3,000,000. Since the Jetfoils were introduced into service on 25 April 1975, the seven Jetfoils operating on the Hong Kong-Macao route had carried (up to 31 May 1980) 5,742,694 passengers.

HUNGARY
MAHART MAGYAR HAJÓZASI RT

Apáczai Csere János utca 11, H-1052 Budapest V, Hungary
Type(s): Raketa; Meteor, 1; Voskhod (Sormovo)
Route(s): Budapest-Vienna, Dunaújváros-Budapest, Budapest-Esztergom

INDONESIA
SUNDAHARYA CORP, JAKARTA

Type(s): PT 20 (Rodriquez)
Route(s): Indonesian coast

IRAN
MINISTRY OF DEFENCE

Type(s): Kometa, 2 (Sormovo)
Operating area: Persian Gulf

IRELAND
B + I LINE

12 North Wall, Dublin, Ireland
   This Irish ferry operator operates a single Jetfoil 929-115 on a route between Dublin and Liverpool and is considering adding a second to the service in 1981.
Type(s): Jetfoil 929-115, 1 (Boeing)
Route(s): Dublin-Liverpool (from April 1980)

Nibbio, first of six Sparviero class hydrofoils under construction for the Italian Navy

RHS 160 operated between Brindisi and Corfu by Aliscafi SNAV

Freccia delle Valli, one of three RHS 150s operated by the Italian Ministry of Transport

ISRAEL
ISRAELI NAVY

Type(s): Flagstaff, 1 (Grumman)
Duties: Coastal patrol, convoy escort
A licence for the series production of these craft in Israel is being negotiated. Once her own needs have been met, Israeli-built craft would be made available for export.

ITALY
ITALIAN NAVY

Type(s): Sparviero Class, 2 completed, plus 5 on order (Alinavi)
Route(s): Coastal patrol

ALISCAFI SNAV, SpA

Cortina del Porto, IS XI, 98100 Messina, Italy
Type(s): PT 20, 7; PT 50, 8 (Rodriquez)
Route(s): Messina-Reggio-Isole-Lipari, Naples-Capri-Ischia
Type(s): RHS 160, 1 (Navaltecnica)
Route(s): Brindisi-Corfu
Type(s): RHS 150, 1 (Rodriquez)
Route(s): Milazzo-Eolian Islands

SAS, TRAPANI

Via Evrialo 9, 91100 Trapani, Italy
Type(s): PT 50, 1; PT 20, 3 (Rodriquez)
Route(s): Trapani-Egadi Islands

ADRIATICA DI NAVIGAZIONE SpA

Zattere 1411, 30123 Venice, Italy
Telephone: 704322
Telex: 41045 Adrnav
Type(s): PT 50, 1 (Rodriquez); RHS 160, 2 (Navaltecnica)
Route(s): Termoli-Isole Tremiti; Ortona-Vasto-Isole Tremiti; Brindisi-Corfu; Otranto-Corfu

MINISTRY OF TRANSPORT, MILAN

Via L Ariosto 21, 20145 Milan, Italy
Type(s): PT 20, 2 (Rodriquez); RHS 70, 10 (Navaltecnica); RHS 150, 3 (Navaltecnica)
Route(s): Lake Garda, Lake Como, Lake Maggiore

NAVIGAZIONE LAGO MAGGIORE—GG

Viale F Baracca 1, 28041 Arona, Italy
Type(s): PT 20, 2 (Rodriquez); RHS 70, 2 (Navaltecnica)
Route(s): Lake Maggiore

COMPAGNIA DI NAVIGAZIONE

Piazza Volta 44, 22100 Como, Italy
Type(s): PT 20, 2 (Rodriquez); RHS 70, 2 (Navaltecnica); RHS 150, 1 (Navaltecnica)
Route(s): Lake Como

G & R SALVATORI, NAPLES

Type(s): PT 50, 2 (Westermoen)
Route(s): Naples-Capri

CAREMAR
COMPAGNIA REGIONALE MARITIMA SpA

Molo Beverello 2, Naples, Italy
Type(s): RHS 140, 1; RHS 160, 2 (Navaltecnica)

SIREMAR
SICILIA REGIONALE MARITIMA SpA

Via Crispi 120, Palermo, Sicily
Telephone: 240801/211916
Telex: 91135 Siremar
Type(s): RHS 160, 2 (Navaltecnica)
Route(s): Palermo—Ustica

TOREMAR
TOSCANA REGIONALE MARITIMA SpA

Scali del Corso 5, Livorno, Italy
Type(s): RHS 140, 1 (Navaltecnica)

AGIP SpA

S Donato Milanese, Milan, Italy
Telephone: 53531
Telex: 31246 ENI
Type(s): PT 20, 1; PT 50, 1 (Rodriquez)

JAPAN
BOYO KISEN CO LTD

134-6, Yanai, Yanai-shi, Yamaguchi, Japan
Type(s): PT 50, 1 (Hitachi); PT 20, 1 *Shibuki No 2* (Hitachi)
Route(s): Yanai—Matsuyama

ISIZAKI KISEN CO LTD

Fukae, Ohaki-cho, Saeki-gun, Hiroshima-ken, Japan
Type(s): PT 50, 1 *Kosei* (Hitachi)
Route(s): Hiroshima-Kure-Matsuyama
Type(s): PT 50, 1 (Hitachi)
Route(s): Hiroshima-Kure-Matsuyama
Type(s): PT 20, 1 *Kinsei* (Hitachi)
Route(s): Onomichi-Matsuyama
Type(s): PT 20, 1 *Tsobasamaru* (Hitachi)
Route(s): Hiroshima-Kure-Matsuyama
An additional PT 50 was delivered to the company during 1977.

MAYEKAWA TRADING CO LTD

3-22-1 Aobadai, Meguru-ku, Tokyo, Japan
Type(s): Kometa, 1 (Sormovo)

MEITETSU KAIJO KANKOSEN CO

99-1, Shinmiyasaka-cho, Atsuta-ku, Nagoya, Japan
Type(s): PT 50, 2 *Osyo* and *Kaio* (Hitachi)
Route(s): Gamagori-Nishiura-Irako-Toba, and Nagoya-Shinogima-Irako-Toba (summer)
Type(s): PT 20, 1 *Hayabusamaru* (Hitachi)
Route(s): Gamagori-Nishiura-Irako-Toba and Kowa-Himagajima-Shinojima (summer)

NICHIMEN CO LTD
(KINKOWAN FERRY CO LTD)

Type(s): PT 50, 1 *Otori No 3* (Hitachi)
Route(s): Kajiki-Kagoshima-Ibusuki

NISSHO-IWAI CO LTD
(HANKYU LINES CO LTD)

Type(s): PT 50, 2 *Zuiho* and *Houo* (Hitachi)
Route(s): Koke-Tokushima

HANKYU LINES CO LTD

Type(s): PT 20, 2 *Amatsu* and *Kasugano* (Hitachi)
Route(s): Kobe-Naruto

HITACHI ZOSEN

Type(s): PT 20, 1; ST 3, 1 (Rodriquez)
Route(s): Japanese coast

SADO KISEN KAISHA

353, Oazaminato, Ryotsu-shi, Niigata, Japan
Type(s): Jetfoil 929-100, 1; Jetfoil 929-115, 1 (Boeing)
Route(s): Niigata, Honshu Island and Ryotsu, Sado Island, Sea of Japan
Route distance: 63km (34n miles)

SETONAIKAI KISEN CO LTD

Ujinakaigan 1-12-23, Minami-ku, Hiroshima, Japan
Type(s): PT 50, 3 *Wakashio*, *Otori No 1* and *Otori No 2* (Hitachi)
Route(s): Onomichi-Setoda-Imabari and Hiroshima-Kure-Matsuyama
Type(s): PT 50, 1 *Kondoru* (Hitachi)
Route(s): Hiroshima-Kure-Matsuyama
Type(s): PT 50, 1 (Hitachi)
Route(s): Onomichi-Setoda-Imbari
Type(s): PT 50, 4 *Hibiki No 1*, *No 2* and *No 3* and *Shibuki No 1* (Hitachi)
Route(s): Onomichi-Setoda-Omishima-Imbari and (*Shibuki No 1*) Yanai-Matsuyama

KOREA, REPUBLIC
HAN RYEO DEVELOPMENT CO LTD

25-5 1-Ka, Chungmu-Ro, Chung-ku, Seoul, Republic of Korea
Telephone: 28-7145/28-8889
Telex: HANRYEO K24856
Type(s): PT 20, 1 (Rodriquez); PT 20, 2 (Hitachi)
Route(s): Busan-Yeosu

MOROCCO
CIE MARITIME D'HYDROFOILS "TRANSTOUR"

54 boulevard Pasteur, Ier Etage, Tangier, Morocco
Type(s): Kometa, 3 (Sormovo)
Route(s): Tangier-Algeciras, Tangier-Gibraltar, Tangier-Tarifa

NEW ZEALAND
HYDROFOIL CRUISES LTD

PO Box 58, Queenstown, New Zealand
Type(s): *Meteor III*
Route(s): Lake Wakatipu, South Island

NORWAY
BRAATHENS SAFE

Oslo, Norway
Braathens SAFE is to purchase two Boeing Jetfoils for offshore oil rig support in the North Sea. A joint Braathens-Boeing study will determine the best configuration of the Jetfoil Model 929-115 for the safe and comfortable transport of crews to the oil platforms. The Jetfoils will also be employed in the transfer of high priority cargo to the rigs. The Jetfoil will operate in conjunction with a new system of transferring crews to and from oil rigs developed by Kongsberg Engineering A/S of Norway.

DE BLA OMNIBUSSER A/S

Type(s): PT 20, 2 (Westermoen)
Route(s): Oslofjord

DET STAVANGERSKE DAMPSKIBS-SELSKAB

PO Box 40, N-4001 Stavanger, Norway
Telephone: 200 20
Telex: 33022 DSDP N
Type(s): PT 50, 1; PT 20, 1 (Rodriquez); RHS 140, 1 (Navaltecnica)
Route(s): Stavanger-Haugesund-Bergen

HARDANGER SUNNHORDELANDSKE DAMPSKIBSSELSKAB

Box 268, N-5001 Bergen, Norway
Telephone: 215070
Telex: 42607 HSD N
Type(s): PT 20, 1 (Westermoen); RHS 140, 1 (Navaltecnica)
Route(s): Bergen-Tittelsness

PAKISTAN
PAKISTAN NAVY

Type(s): Hu Chwan, 6 (Shanghai)
Duties: Coastal patrol and strike missions

PHILIPPINES
TOURIST HOTEL AND TRAVEL CORPORATION

Type(s): PT 20, 2 (Rodriquez)
Route(s): Manila-Corregidor

PHILIPPINE NAVY

Headquarters, Roxas Boulevard, Manila, Philippines
Type(s): PT 20, 2 (Rodriquez); PT 32, 2 *Bontoc*, *Baler* (Hitachi)
Route(s): Coastal patrol

POLAND
NAVIMOR

Ul Matejkl 6, Gdansk, Poland
Type(s): Kometas, 10; Meteors, 4; Raketas, 3
Route(s): Szczecin-Swinoujscie; Szczecin-Stralsund, Copenhagen, Malmö and Strassuitz, also Kolobrzeg and Stralsund

ROMANIA
ROMANIAN NAVY

Type(s): Hu Chwan, 10
Operating area: Coastal waters

SPAIN
TRANSMED
COMPANIA TRASMEDITERRANEA SA

Madrid, Spain
Type(s): Jetfoil (07 *Flying Princess*), to be replaced by Boeing Jetfoil 929-115 018 in the spring of 1981. A second Jetfoil 929-115 will be added to the service in the autumn of 1981.
Route(s): Las Palmas-Santa Cruz

SRI LANKA
SRI LANKAN NAVY

Type(s): Waterman, 1 (International Aquavion)
Duties: Communications and patrol

SWEDEN
SVENSKA REDERIAKTIEBOLAGET ÖRESUND

PO Box 177, S-20121 Malmö 1, Sweden
Telex: 32632 SROMT 5
Type(s): PT 50, 2 (Rodriquez); RHS 140, 1 (Navaltecnica)
Route(s): Copenhagen-Malmö

TANZANIA
TANZANIA NAVY

Dar es Salaam, Tanzania
Type(s): Hu Chwan, 4 (Shanghai)
Duties: Coastal patrol

TURKEY
SEJIR DENIZYOLLARI LTD

34-A Canbulat, Sokak, Girne, Mersin 10, Turkey
Type(s): PT 20, 1; PT 50, 1 (Rodriquez)
Route(s): Turkey-Cyprus

MED SHIPPING

Type(s): Kometa-M, 2 (Sormovo)
Route(s): Turkey-Cyprus

UNION OF SOVIET SOCIALIST REPUBLICS
MINISTRY OF THE RIVER FLEET

The Soviet Ministry of the River Fleet operates hydrofoil passenger ferries on practically all the major rivers, lakes, canals and reservoirs from Central Russia to Siberia and the Far East.

In 1958, when hydrofoils were first introduced to the rivers of the USSR, they carried ten thousand passengers. By 1968 the number of passengers carried had grown to three million. During the 1969-70 navigation season there were 80 hydrofoil services on the Volga alone, operated by vessels of the Raketa, Meteor, Sputnik and Burevestnik series. There are now more than 150 hydrofoil passenger services in the Soviet Union and it was stated that during 1972 the 200 craft operating these services carried about 20 million passengers.

In addition to craft on inland waterways employing the Alexeyev shallow draft submerged foil system, Strela-type craft, with surface-piercing foils, operate in the Gulf of Finland, and supported by Kometas and Vikhrs, provide year-round services between ports on the Black Sea.

Four new hydrofoil passenger ferry designs are being put into production—the Cyclone, a seagoing, waterjet-propelled ferry with seats for 250 and capable of 40 knots, the Typhoon, a gas turbine powered 90-seat vessel with fully submerged, autostabilised foils, the Voskhod (Sunrise), a Raketa replacement and the Albatros. The Voskhod provides greater comfort and improved facilities for passengers and crew and air-conditioning will be installed. As with the Raketa, a family of variants will be available to suit a wide variety of operating and traffic conditions. Fastest of the series is reported to be the Voskhod-3, powered by a gas turbine and capable of 43 knots.

The Albatros has the same overall dimensions as the Kometa, but its engines will be mounted aft, its foils will be controlled by an automatic control system and the standard version will seat 150 passengers.

The Raketa has given excellent service and has extremely low operating costs. The cost of carrying passengers on the craft is stated to be lower than that of either displacement-type passenger ferries or automobiles. Similar low-cost operation is demonstrated by the 260-passenger Sputnik on the Moscow-Astrakhan route. It has been

found that the cost of operating a Sputnik on this service is only 8% of that of the latest displacement-type passenger ferry of the United Volga Steamship Line. Time saving is one of the most important considerations. In many cases, hydrofoils take passengers to their destinations faster than trains. For example, a Raketa service covers the 800km (516 miles) from Gorki to Kazan in 12 hours, while trains take 20 hours for the same journey. Price of the ticket is the same, however, whether the journey is undertaken by hydrofoil or rail.

The Meteor service from Moscow to Sormovo takes 13 hours 40 minutes to cover 900km (559 miles). A conventional passenger ship requires about three days to cover this distance.

In 1976 sea trials confirmed that the Kometa can operate successfully in Arctic waters. Tests conducted off the Kola Peninsula and Kamchatka, in the Soviet Far East, demonstrated that the craft is capable of navigating through areas with broken ice without sustaining damage.

A number of Soviet commercial hydrofoils are now being equipped for night operations.

In 1977 it was announced that the number of hydrofoils operating on Soviet waterways exceeded 3,000. Nearly two-thirds of these are likely to be Molnia, Volga and Nevka hydrofoils which are used throughout the Soviet Union as water taxis.

SOVIET FRONTIER POLICE

Some twenty-five Pchela patrol hydrofoils, derived from the Strela passenger ferry, are in service with the KGB Frontier Police in the Baltic, Caspian and the Black Sea areas.

SOVIET NAVY

First hydrofoil warship to enter service with the Soviet Navy was the wooden-hulled P 8-class torpedo boat, which was equipped with bow foils and a gas-turbine booster engine. These have now been retired. In the spring of 1973, the first sightings were made of a larger craft, a 230-ton fast patrol boat given the NATO code-name Turya. This vessel, which is equipped for ASW work, is based on the hull of the Osa missile craft. The design employs a fixed surface-piercing bow

foil only. Powered by three 5,000hp diesels it has a top speed of about 45 knots under calm conditions. Production is in hand at three Soviet naval shipyards.

Latest hydrofoils to be built for the Soviet Navy are the Sarancha, a 330-tonne missile-armed fast strike craft, the Babochka, a 400-tonne fast patrol boat equipped for anti-submarine warfare and the 220-ton Matka, a replacement for the Osa II displacement missile craft.

UNITED KINGDOM
CONDOR LTD

4 North Quay, St Peter Port, Guernsey
Telephone: 0481 24604
Telex: 4191275 (a/b DILIG G)
Type(s): RHS 140, 1 (Navaltecnica); RHS 160, 1 (Navaltecnica)
Route(s): Guernsey-Sark-Jersey-St Malo-Alderney

RED FUNNEL GROUP

12 Bugle Street, Southampton, Hampshire SO9 4LJ, England
Telephone: 0703 22042
Telex: 47388 Chamcom G (Attn Red Funnel)
Type(s): RHS 70, 2 (Navaltecnica); RHS 70, 1 (Rodriquez)
Route(s): Southampton-Cowes

ROYAL NAVY

The first Jetfoil patrol hydrofoil has been ordered by the Royal Navy for use in the fisheries protection role in the North Sea. Basically the craft is a modified Model 929-115 commercial Jetfoil, named HMS Speedy, and has been built on the commercial Jetfoil production line. It is a 117-ton craft with the top passenger deck removed. Two semi-inflatable dinghies will be carried together with light weapons. HMS Speedy was launched in July 1979 and after outfitting in the UK, was delivered to the Royal Navy in June 1980.

HMS *Speedy*, employed by the Royal Navy in the offshore protection role in the North Sea

UNITED STATES OF AMERICA
DEPARTMENT OF THE NAVY, NAVAL SEA SYSTEMS COMMAND (NAVSEA)

The Boeing/NATO PHM, Patrol Hydrofoil, Guided Missile, is a NATO project, sponsored by the US Navy. It is being developed by NAVSEA PMS 303.

The first craft, the PHM-1 *Pegasus*, was accepted by the US Navy's Board of Inspection and Survey in June 1977 and is now serving with the Atlantic Fleet. A further five PHMs are scheduled for delivery to the US Navy over the eleven month period between April 1981 and March 1982.

SEA WORLD

1720 South Shores Road, Mission Bay, San Diego, California 92109, USA
Telephone: (714) 222 6363

This company operates three 28-seat hydrofoils, *Sea World II, III* and *IV* (Sprague Engineering Co) on seven minute sightseeing tours around Mission Bay. The craft were the first built on the West Coast to be licensed by the US Coast Guard for commercial use.

US NAVAL SHIP RESEARCH AND DEVELOPMENT CENTER

Type(s): High Point, PCH-1; Plainview AGEH-1 (de-activated June 1978)
Purpose: US Navy hydrofoil development programme

URUGUAY
BELT SA

Head Office: Cerrito 467, Montevideo, Uruguay
Type(s): RHS 140, 2 (Navaltecnica)
Route(s): Montevideo-Colonia

VENEZUELA
COMPANIA SHELL

Type(s): PT 20, 3 (Werf Gusto)
Route(s): Offshore oil drilling operations on Lake Maracaibo

PHM-1 *Pegasus* during test firing of Harpoon anti-ship missiles

TOURISMO MARGARITA, CA

Type(s): Jetfoil, 2 (Boeing)
Route: Puerto La Cruz-Isle of Margarita
This operator's two Jetfoils began services on 18 January 1977 and have carried (up to 30 June 1979) 323,617 passengers and reached 5,328 hours underway.

YUGOSLAVIA
SPLIT AIRPORT/INTEREXPORT

Split, Yugoslavia
Type(s): Kometa, 11 (Sormovo)
Route(s): Adriatic coastal services; tourist and passenger ferry services between Italy and Yugoslavia

CENTROTOURIST

Beograd, Yugoslavia
Type(s): Raketa, 2 (Sormovo)
Route(s): Adriatic coastal services

RUDNAP

Beograd, Yugoslavia
Type(s): Meteor, 4 (Sormovo)
Route(s): Adriatic coastal services

ZAIRE
NAVAL FORCE

Bases: Matadi and Lake Tanganyika
Type(s): Hu Chwan, 3 (Shanghai)

FAST CATAMARANS

NORWAY

WESTAMARIN A/S

PO Box 143, 4501 Mandal, Norway
Telephone: 042-62 222
Telex: 16514

Westamarin A/S was established in 1960, under the name of Westermoen Hydrofoil, to produce, develop and market high speed surface vessels for commercial and military use. In 1970 the company introduced the Westamaran, an asymmetric catamaran based on a semi-planing hull of welded marine aluminium. Three versions, the Westamaran 86, 95 and 100 have been built to date. Larger models for passenger and offshore support duties are projected. A Super Westamaran based on the Westamaran 86 has also been built under licence by Mitsui in Japan.

WESTAMARAN 86

Over 20 Westamaran 86s have so far been built. Most are in service in Scandinavia, fitted out for 140-167 passengers. Three of the vessels operating in Norway are equipped to carry 94-100 passengers and up to six tonnes of freight. The main powerplants are two MTU 1,100hp diesels.
DIMENSIONS
Length: 26·7m (89ft)
Beam: 9·0m (29ft)
Draught: 1·2m (4ft)
WEIGHTS
Gross tonnage: 200 tons
Net tonnage: 135 tons
PERFORMANCE
Max speed: 28 knots
Range: 235n miles

WESTAMARAN 95

A longer version of the Westamaran 86, the Westamaran 95 can carry up to 190 passengers. Two SACM 1,800hp diesels give the 29·1m (95ft 6in) vessel a maximum speed of 32 knots. Some ten Westamaran 95s have been delivered to operators in Norway, Denmark, Italy, Spain and Yugoslavia. A 30m (98ft 6in) Westamaran 95 has also been developed. Powered by two Avco Lycoming 3,350hp gas turbines driving waterjet units, it can carry 205 passengers at speeds of up to 40 knots.

WESTAMARAN 100T

The largest Westamaran vessel so far built, the Westamaran 100T can seat up to 260 passengers. Two Avco Lycoming TF40 gas turbines, each producing 4,000hp, driving Rocketdyne PJ24 waterjet units give the vessel a maximum speed of 38 knots. The prototype was used for six months during summer 1980 on services between the Channel Islands and France.

WESTAMARAN OPERATORS

Denmark
Operator: A/S D/S Øresund
Base: Copenhagen
Vessels: *Tumleren* (W95)
   Tunen (W95)
   Tranen (W95)

France
Operator: Service Maritime Carteret-Jersey
Base: Carteret
Vessels: *Pegasus* (W86)

Operator: Soc Anon des Bateaux de la Cote d'Emeraude les Vedettes Blanches
Base: St Malo
Vessels: *Belle de Dinard* (W86)

Italy
Operator: Alilauro Aliscafi de Tirrano SpA
Base: Naples
Vessels: *Martini Bianco* (W95)

Highland Seabird, one of more than twenty Westamaran 86s in service. It seats 140-167 passengers

Stern view of *Highland Seabird.* Powered by two 1,100hp MTU diesels, the vessel cruises at 28 knots

Netherlands
Operator: BV Terschellinger Stoomboot Mij
Base: Terschelling
Vessels: *Koegelwieck* (W86)

Norway
Operator: A/S Haanes Rederi
Base: Kristiansand
Vessels: *Westjet* (W95T)

Operator: A/S Haugesund D/S
Base: Haugesund
Vessels: *Haugesund* (W86)*
   Storesund (W86)
*Passenger/cargo version

Operator: A/S Troms Fylkes D/S
Base: Tromso
Vessels: *Fjorddronningen* (W86)
   Fjordkongen (W86)
   Fjordprinsessen (W86)

Operator: Det Stavangerske D/S
Base: Stavanger
Vessels: *Fjorddrott* (W86)
   Mayflower (W86)
   Sauda (W86)

Operator: DSD/Hardanger Sunnhordlandske D/S
Base: Bergen
Vessels: *Drauplner* (W86)
   Sleipner (W95)
   Sunnhordland (W95)
   Tedno (W86)
   Vingtor (W95)

Operator: Finnmark Fylkesrederi & Ruteselskap
Base: Hammerfest

Vessels: *Byrilen* (W86)*
   Hornog (W86)
*Passenger/cargo version

Operator: Fosen Trafikklag A/S
Base: Trondheim
Vessels: *Hertugbussen* (W86)
   Kongsbussen (W86)
   Olavsbussen (W86)

Operator: Fylkesbaatane i Sogne og Fjordane
Vessels: *Fjordrrins* (W86)
   Fjordglytt (W86)
   Fjordtroll (W86)

Operator: Oygarden & Sotra Rutelag
Vessels: *Oygar* (W86)*
*Passenger/cargo version

Operator: Sattens D/S
Base: Bodo
Vessels: *Steigtund* (W86)

United Kingdom
Operator: Condor Ltd
Base: Guernsey
Vessels: *Condor 6* (W100T)
Operated for six months trial period during summer 1980

Operator: Western Ferries (Argyll)
Base: Glasgow
Vessels: *Highland Seabird* (W86)

Yugoslavia
Operator: Union Dalmacijou Ooura Flota
Base: Split
Vessels: *Mediteran* (W95)

UNITED KINGDOM

JETCAT MARKETING LTD

31 Southampton Row, London WC1B 5HJ, England
Telephone: 01-404 4321
Telex: 8812583

The Jetcat JC-F1 is a low resistance, non-planing, diesel-powered, waterjet propelled catamaran with very shallow draught designed and built by Marinteknik Verkstads AB, of Sweden, for Jetcat Ltd, Jersey. Trials of the prototype started in November 1980.

JETCAT JC-F1

The Jetcat JC-F1 is mainly constructed in specially designed corrosion-resistant aluminium alloy extrusions welded together to form the hull plating, bulkheads and frames.

PROPULSION: Two MTU 12V 396 TC 82 1,408bhp diesels drive KaMeWa S-62 waterjets with steering nozzles able to deflect the waterjet stream ±30 degrees. All propulsion machinery is housed within the hulls, assisting in the provision of a low centre of gravity.

HULL: The very narrow hulls are of symmetrical form and are interchangeable, being mounted to the underside of the bridging structure by anti-vibration mountings. Both hulls are divided into the required number of watertight compartments as stipulated by the classification and regulatory authorities.

ACCOMMODATION: Seating for normal ferry operations is provided for 197 passengers, although up to 220 seats can be installed in the saloon. Projected versions of the Jetcat include a 329-seat, double-deck vessel and a passenger/car variant.

DIMENSIONS
Length: 29·8m (97ft 9in)
Beam: 9·4m (30ft 10in)
Height: 7·0m (23ft)
Draught: 1·14m (3ft 9in)
WEIGHTS
Displacement: 73 tonnes
Nominal max payload: 16·75 tonnes
Fuel: 5·88 tonnes
PERFORMANCE
Cruising speed: 32·5 knots
Range with max payload: 153n miles

Model of standard Jetcat 197-seat passenger ferry

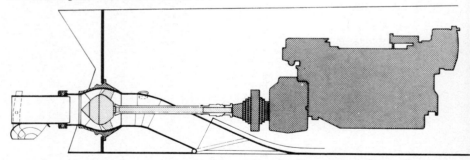

General arrangement of standard Jetcat JC-F1

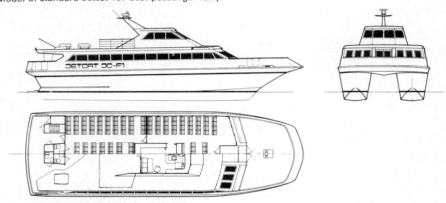

Propulsion arrangement on Jetcat. Two 1,408bhp MTU 12V 396 TC 82 high speed marine diesels drive two KaMeWa S-62 waterjet units

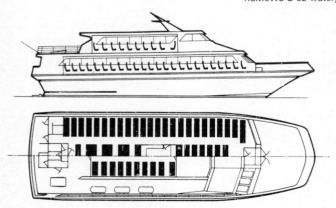

329-seat, double-deck variant of Jetcat

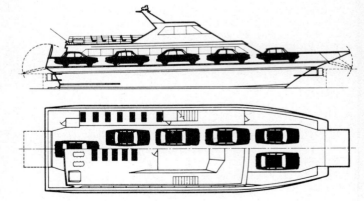

Passenger/car ferry variant

SEMI-SUBMERGED CATAMARANS

JAPAN

MITSUI ENGINEERING & SHIPBUILDING CO LTD

6-4 Tsukiji 5-chome, Chuo-ku, Tokyo, Japan
Telephone: (03) 544-3451/3910
Telex: J22821/Jss924

MARINE ACE

Mitsui began its high speed semi-submerged catamaran development programme (SSC) in 1970. Since 1976 the programme has been operated in conjunction with the Japanese Marine Machinery Development Association (JAMDA). In 1977, following extensive research and model tests, Mitsui built the experimental 18·37-tonne Marine Ace in order to obtain practical experience with this hull form. In 1979, the first SSC high-speed passenger craft for practical use, the SSC Mesa 80, was launched. She was only the second such vessel to be built, the first being the US Navy's SSP *Kaimalino* range support vessel, designed to operate in the rough seas off the Hawaiian islands.

PROPULSION: Motive power for the Marine Ace is supplied by two sets of V-type four-cycle petrol engines, each developing 200bhp at 3,700rpm. Each drives via a vertical intermediate transmission shaft and bevel gear a three-bladed fixed-pitch propeller, one at the end of each of the two torpedo-like hulls. Tank capacity: ballast 11·01m³ (2,420 gallons), fuel oil 1·45m³ (320 gallons).

AUTOMATIC MOTION CONTROL SYSTEM: Four sets of fin stabilisers, driven by hydraulic servo motors, reduce ship motion in heavy seas.

DIMENSIONS
Length overall: 12·35m (40ft 6in)
  registered: 11·95m (39ft 2in)
Beam max: 6·5m (21ft 4in)
  at load line: 5·8m (19ft)
Designed full load draft: 1·55m (5ft 1in)
WEIGHTS
Full load displacement: 18·37 tonnes
Gross tonnage: about 29 tonnes
PERFORMANCE
Speed, max cruising revolutions, full load draft: about 18 knots

MESA 80

Developed jointly by Mitsui Engineering & Shipbuilding Co Ltd, and the Japanese Marine Machinery Development Association (JAMDA), the 27-knot Mesa 80 is the world's first commercial semi-submerged catamaran. Although the Mesa 80 has been designed as a high-speed passenger ferry it can be built to suit a wide variety of alternative applications, from oceanographic survey to offshore crewboat. Despite her small size, the overall length is just under 36m (118ft), the vessel provides a stable ride in seas with 3·5m (11ft 6in) waves. It is expected to operate with nearly 100% regularity under the sea conditions found in the coastal ferry service areas of Japan.

PROPULSION: Main engines are two Fuji-SEMT marine diesels, each developing 4,050hp at 1,475rpm. Each drives via a vertical transmission shaft and bevel gear a three-blade fixed-pitch propeller. Two 206·25kVA generators provide electrical power.

HULL: Built in marine grade aluminium alloy.
ACCOMMODATION: Crew of seven. Passenger seats provided for 446.
AUTOMATIC MOTION CONTROL SYSTEM: Four sets of fin stabilisers driven by hydraulic servo motors reduce ship motion in heavy seas.

DIMENSIONS
Length overall: 35·9m (117ft 9in)
Beam: 17·1m (56ft 1in)
Depth: 5·84m (19ft 2in)
Designed draft: 3·15m (10ft 4in)

18·37-tonne Marine Ace built by Mitsui to obtain practical experience of the SSC hull form

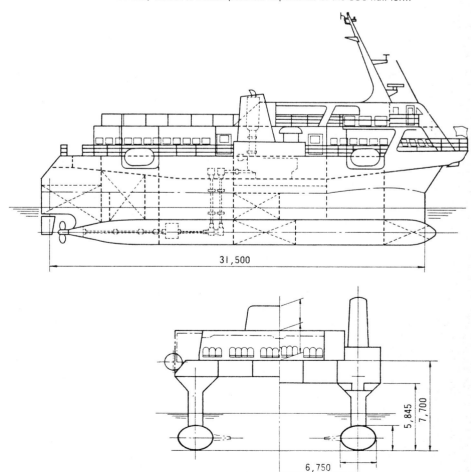

31,500

5,845
7,700

6,750

General arrangement of MESA 80, high speed semi-submerged catamaran passenger ferry

WEIGHTS
Gross tonnage: 670 tonnes approx

PERFORMANCE
Max speed: about 27 knots

Mitsui MESA 80, the world's first commercial semi-submerged catamaran

Powered by two Fuji-SEMT diesels, MESA 80 seats up to 446 passengers and has a maximum speed of 27 knots

UNITED STATES OF AMERICA

SEMI-SUBMERGED SHIP CORPORATION

417 Loma Larga Drive, Solana Beach, California 92075, USA
Telephone: (714) 481 6417
Telex: 695482

SSSCO was founded by Dr Thomas G Lang, the inventor of the semi-submerged ship (S³). Basically the S³ consists of two parallel torpedo-like hulls attached to which are two or more streamlined struts which pierce the water surface and support an above-water platform. Stabilising fins are attached near the after end of each hull, and a pair of smaller fins are located near their forward ends.

Semi-submerged ship technology has been proved over the past five years by the 190-ton SSP *Kaimalino*, a US Navy developed range-support vessel which has been operating in the rough seas off the Hawaiian islands since 1975. Following private development, Dr Lang introduced the concept into the US Navy in 1968 and holds several basic patents in the field. He led the Navy's first research work, and initiated and developed the hydrodynamic design for the stable semi-submerged platform (SSP), the world's first high-performance, open-ocean semi-submerged ship.

The US Navy's present SWATH (Small Waterplane Area Twin Hull) ship programme is

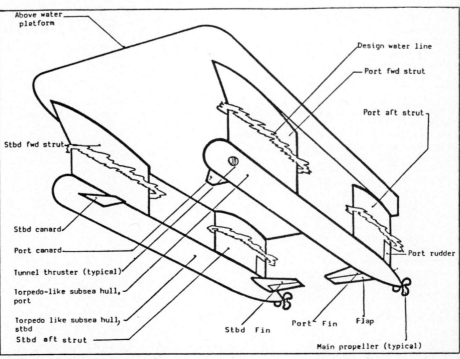

Semi-submerged ship (S³) concept

based on the S³ concept. The performance features that set S³s apart from conventional vessels are: greatly reduced motions with sustained speed even in heavy seas, lower hydrodynamic drag and reduced power requirements at moderate to high speeds, and far superior course-keeping characteristics at all sea headings. S³s have excellent manoeuvrability at speed, when operating in confined harbours and when station-keeping.

The control surfaces of the S³ designs enable them to ride smoothly through the water. Controllable bow planes, or canard fins, can be operated collectively or differentially. Used together, canards and fins control heave, pitch and roll. Twin rudders provide directional control at high speed. Twin screws and thrusters provide differential thrust at low speed, to help in delicate, close-in manoeuvres. The screws may have variable and reversible-pitch blades.

Typical vessel designs include: crew change vessels, ferries, intervention vessels, multifunction support vessels and diving support vessels, etc, from 100 tons to 10,000 tons and more. SSSCO has an exclusive agreement with British Shipbuilders covering the development of the S³ in European and Mediterranean areas and an exclusive agreement with Manderstam Technical Services covering marketing and technical assistance.

SSP KAIMALINO

SSP *Kaimalino*, a US Navy range-support vessel has operated from near calm conditions to beyond sea state 6 at speeds of up to 25 knots. Her motion is small relative to a conventional monohull either when at rest or underway. The SSP has made smooth transits in 4·57m (15ft) swells without any impacts; however, in short, steep 3·66m (12ft) waves, occasional bow impacts have occurred. No structural damage has occurred, even during storm conditions when 7·62-9·14m (25-30ft) high waves were encountered.

DIMENSIONS
Length: 27·0m (80ft)
Beam (at mid section): 14·0m (46ft)
Height: 9·7m (32ft)
WEIGHTS
Displacement: 190 tons
Max payload (including fuel): 50 tons
PERFORMANCE
Max speed: 25 knots
Range at max speed and payload: 400n miles

CREW CHANGE VESSEL (CCV)

One of the recent projects proposed by Semi-Submerged Ship Corporation is a 2,100-ton payload vessel designed to service offshore oil and gas deposits. A smooth ride is to be expected in 6·7m (22ft) waves at 30 knots in the North Sea. Her high speed capability would also help the vessel to participate in the emergency evacuation of personnel. Additionally, vessels of this type have characteristics which make them ideal for transferring passengers when station-keeping with offshore installations.

PROPULSION: Propulsive power would be furnished by two 27,000hp marinised gas turbines, probably installed in the lower hulls. This location would be favourable, not only from the point of view of weight distribution, but also because it would reduce noise and vibration levels for the passengers. For servicing and replacement the powerplants would be removed from the lower hulls via the air intake ducting in the aft struts. Each gas turbine would drive a controllable and reversible-pitch propeller (CRP). Not only would these eliminate the need for reversing clutches and clutch brakes, but they would make a substantial reduction in the stopping time and greatly enhance manoeuvrability and docking capabilities. Maximum engine efficiency could be maintained for varying sea states, wind and load conditions by adjusting the propellers for optimum pitch. It also permits the operation of only one engine in an emergency and for slow speed operation.

190-ton SSP *Kaimalino*, the US Navy-developed range-support vessel. The world's first high-performance open ocean semi-submerged ship, it has been operating off the Hawaiian islands since 1975

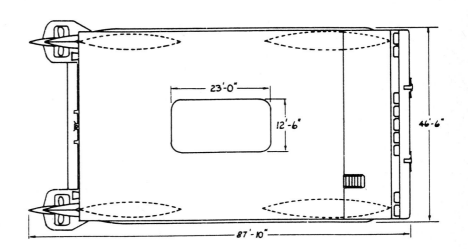

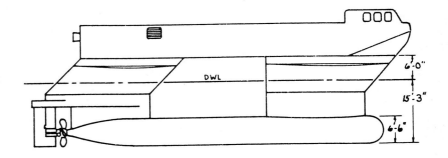

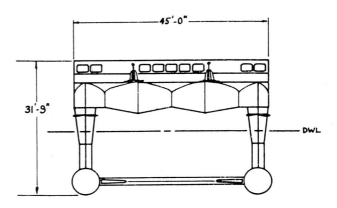

General arrangement of SSP *Kaimalino*

AUTOMATIC MOTION CONTROL SYSTEM: If waves are restricted to the strut region the resulting changes in buoyancy due to their passing is small. Automatically controlled bow fins or canards and stabilising fins at the stern are operated collectively or differentially to dampen heave, pitch and roll. Since there will always be some speed and heading in which resonance will occur in each of the heave, pitch and roll motions an automatic motion control system has been developed to minimise resonance problems in comparison to those encountered by monohulls and other types of semi-submerged ships which lack fins. Signals are supplied to a central computer unit by a gyrostabilised inertial reference platform, static pressure taps on the lower hull and manual inputs from the helmsman control unit. The helmsman control unit allows the captain to select the desired heading, to trim the vessel in pitch and roll and to engage or disengage the AMCS at will. Manual override is available at any time. The automatic control system is effective at speeds as low as 8 knots.

Canards and fins are attached between the lower hulls and extend inboard. This avoids the need for their retraction while drawing alongside berths and other vessels and while manoeuvring in harbour.

HULL: The hull cross-structure, bow and bottom sides are designed to accept and minimise the force of impacts. It is possible to flood or loose either or both sub-sea hulls without experiencing anything worse than becoming an unpowered barge which will float quite adequately.

ACCOMMODATION: Arrangements to suit the requirements of the operator and the particular service for which the vessel is intended. In typical configuration accommodation would be provided for a total complement of 25 in single berth cabins. Single class saloons would be provided for up to 400 passengers. Since the vessel is designed to operate on short haul routes no sleeping accommodation is provided. Features will include a 49-seat cinema and a large refreshment lounge.

The vessel will be able to accommodate a Sikorsky S-61N helicopter which can be used to transfer passengers to and from offshore structures or for the transport of injured personnel. It is claimed that it is an ideal emergency vessel and can respond to disasters in severe weather conditions and at a speed which no other vessel in the North Sea can duplicate.

DIMENSIONS
Length: 74·5m (245ft)
Beam: 27·1m (89ft)
Height: 15·2m (50ft)
WEIGHTS
Displacement: 2,100 tons
PERFORMANCE
Cruising speed: 35 knots
Max speed: 38 knots
Draft: 6·7m (22ft)
Range: 500-1,000n miles
Endurance: 7 days

HIGH SPEED FERRY

An S³ ferry would provide a smooth, level ride through sea state 5 and into sea state 6 for up to 600 passengers and 130 vehicles. In rough water operations, passengers would experience far less rolling and pitching motions than at present. There should be little, if any, incidence of seasickness. The S³ ferry design is highly manoeuvrable and is easy to dock.

DIMENSIONS
Length: 103m (340ft)
Beam: 39·5m (130ft)
Height: 25·8m (88ft)
WEIGHTS
Displacement: 3,200 tons
PERFORMANCE
Cruising speed: 20-25 knots

RAPID INTERVENTION VESSEL (RIV)

Because of her high speed, a S³ RIV would be able to reach potential disaster areas extremely quickly. During a full scale emergency, due to the vessel's excellent seakeeping qualities, seriously injured personnel could be air lifted to shore hospitals even under severe weather conditions. The S³ RIV would be fitted with fire monitors to meet international safety requirements.

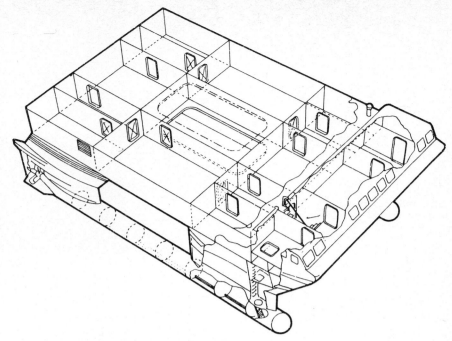

Cutaway showing basic hull configuration of SSP *Kaimalino*

Impression of Semi-Submerged Ship Corporation's 2,100-ton crew change vessel (CCV), designed to service offshore oil and gas deposits

DIMENSIONS
Length: 74·5m (245ft)
Beam: 27·1m (89ft)
Height: 15·2m (50ft)
WEIGHTS
Displacement: 2,100 tons
PERFORMANCE
Cruising speed: 16 knots
Max speed: 25 knots

S³ MULTIFUNCTION SUPPLY AND SUPPORT VESSEL (MSSV)

The S³ MSSV is designed to operate as a supply vessel servicing the offshore complexes in the North Sea during the winter season. Able to operate in 10·6-12·2m (35-40ft) seas, she could deliver vital supplies when no other type of supply vessel (except possibly conventional slow semi-submersibles) could operate. Available deck area would be 2,500m² (26,900ft²). A central well would be provided to handle equipment such as look-out/observation submersibles, transfer modules and underwater remote control vessels (RCVs) during the summer season.

DIMENSIONS
Length: 93·3m (307ft)

Beam: 40·1m (132ft)
Draft: 10·6m (35ft)
WEIGHTS
Displacement: 6,000 tons
PERFORMANCE
Cruising speed: 16 knots

DIVING SUPPORT VESSEL

The diving system of the S³ DSV may have a depth capability of up to 500m (1,650ft) for up to eight divers. A hyperbaric rescue lifeboat is provided on deck. Diving bell handling is through a diving moonpool in the front starboard strut. A central well can support observation/look-out submersibles, RCVs, ADS etc. A fully redundant DP system is provided.

DIMENSIONS
Length: 74·5m (145ft)
Beam: 27·1m (89ft)
Draft: 6·7m (22ft)
WEIGHTS
Displacement: 2,000 tons
PERFORMANCE
Cruising speed: 16 knots
Endurance: 2 weeks

POWER PLANTS AND PROPULSION SYSTEMS

CANADA

PRATT & WHITNEY AIRCRAFT OF CANADA LTD

PO Box 10, Longueuil, Quebec J4K 4X9, Canada

Officials:
E L Smith, *President*
R H Guthrie, *Vice President, Industrial and Marine Division*
L D Caplan, *Executive Vice President*
K H Sullivan, *Vice President, Marketing*
G P Ouimet, *Vice President, Finance*
J P Beauregard, *Vice President, Materials and Procurement*
C J Pascoe, *Vice President, Counsel*
R C Abraham, *Vice President, Production*
E H Schweitzer, *Vice President, Commuter Operations*
J C R Nicholson, *General Manager, Helicopter and Systems Division*
R J Losch, *Vice President, Product Support*
C B Wong, *Vice President, Engineering*
A L Tontini, *Vice President, Personnel*
P Henry, *Director of Communications*

In addition to its compact range of low-power aircraft turbines (eg the PT6A turboprop, PT6B, PT6T and T400 turboshafts, and JT15D turbofan), Pratt & Whitney Aircraft of Canada Ltd also manufactures a marine derivative of the PT6, the ST6 series of turboshafts. These engines are rated at 550shp and upwards, and are installed in a number of ACV and hydrofoil vessels. The US prototype Surface Effect Ship SES-100B is equipped with three ST6J-70s to power its eight lift fans, and two ST-60 series engines power the Canadian research hydrofoil Proteus. Two ST6T-75 Twin-Pac® turbines power the Bell Aerospace Canada Voyageur hovercraft and a single ST6T-75 provides power in that company's Viking craft. A series of larger Voyageurs for the US Army designated LACV-30 are powered by ST6T-76 engines.

Including aero-engine installations, over 16,000 of this series of gas turbines have been delivered. Between them they have accumulated running experience in excess of 45 million hours.

ST6 gas turbine

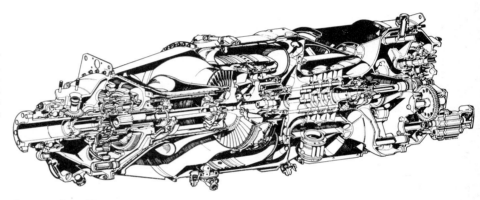

Cutaway of the ST6-70. The model illustrated, the ST6J-70, differs from the ST6K-70 only in the main reduction gearbox

ST6 MARINE GAS TURBINE

ST6 marine gas turbines are designed and manufactured by Pratt & Whitney Aircraft of Canada Ltd. Details of the engine specifications are given below:

TYPE: A simple cycle free turbine engine with a single spool gas generator and a multi-stage compressor driven by a single stage turbine. Burner section has an annular combustion chamber with downstream injection. The single stage-free turbine is connected to the output shaft via a reduction gearbox.

ST6 ENGINE DATA SUMMARY
Sea Level Standard Pressure at 15°C (59°F) Inlet Temperature

IMPERIAL MEASURE

Model	Maximum		Intermediate		Normal		Output	Length	Width	Height	Weight
	shp	sfc*	shp	sfc*	shp	sfc*	rpm (max)	(in)	(in)	(in)	(lb)
ST6J-70	620	0·64	580	0·65	510	0·67	2,200	62	19	19	350
ST6K-70	620	0·64	580	0·65	510	0·67	6,230	60	19	19	317
ST6L-77	811	0·589			654	0·62	33,000	52·2	19	19	306
ST6J-77	750	0·608	650	0·631	550	0·66	2,200	62	19	19	379
ST6K-77	690	0·62	620	0·64	550	0·66	6,230	60	19	19	350
ST6L-80	1,065	0·58	955	0·60	840	0·62	30,000	59·4	19	19	360
*ST6T-76	1,850	0·615	1,645	0·627	1,440	0·65	6,600	66·4	44·4	31·6	730

METRIC MEASURE

Model	Maximum		Intermediate		Normal		Output	Length	Width	Height	Weight
	kW	sfc*	kW	sfc*	kW	sfc*	rpm (max)	(mm)	(mm)	(mm)	(kg)
ST6J-70	463	0·389	433	0·395	380	0·407	2,200	1,575	483	483	159
ST6K-70	463	0·389	433	0·395	380	0·407	6,230	1,524	483	483	144
ST6L-77	605	0·358			488	0·377	33,000	1,326	483	483	139
ST6J-77	560	0·371	485	0·384	410	0·401	2,200	1,575	483	483	172
ST6K-77	515	0·377	463	0·389	410	0·401	6,230	1,524	483	483	159
ST6L-80	794	0·353	712	0·365	627	0·377	30,000	1,509	483	483	164
*ST6T-76	1,380	00·374	1,227	0·381	1,074	0·395	6,600	1,687	1,128	803	332

*sfc = lb/hp/h (imperial)
   = kg/kWh (metric)

The ST6T-75 and ST6T-76 Twin Pac® are dual engines with the two engines mounted side-by-side and coupled to a twinning reduction gear.

AIR INTAKE: Annular air intake at rear of engine with intake screen.

COMPRESSOR: Three axial-flow stages, plus single centrifugal stage. Single-sided centrifugal compressor with 26 vanes, made from titanium forging. Axial rotor of disc-drum type with stainless steel stator and rotor blades. Stator vanes are brazed to casing. The rotor blades are dove tailed to discs. Discs through-bolted with centrifugal compressor to shaft. Fabricated one-piece stainless steel casing and radial diffuser.

COMBUSTION CHAMBER: Annular reverse-flow type of stainless steel construction, with 14 Simplex burners. Two glow or spark plug igniters.

GAS GENERATOR: Single-stage axial. Rotor blades mounted by fir tree roots.

POWER TURBINE: Single or dual-stage axial. Rotor blades mounted by fir tree roots.

BEARINGS: Gas generator and power turbine supported by one ball bearing and one roller bearing each.

SHAFT DRIVE: Single, or two-stage planetary

ST6J-77 seen from above

reduction gear or direct drive, depending on engine model. Torque measuring system incorporated with reduction gearing.

FUEL GRADE: Diesel Nos 1 and 2 and Navy diesel or aviation turbine fuel.

JET PIPE: Single port exhaust discharging vertically upwards or at 60 degrees port or starboard of vertical. Alternatively twin ports discharging horizontally on some models.

ACCESSORY DRIVES: Mounting pads on accessory case including for starter or starter-generator and tacho-generator. Also tacho-generator drive on power section.

LUBRICATION SYSTEM: One pressure and four scavenge gear type pumps driven by gas generator rotor. Integral oil tank.

OIL SPECIFICATIONS: Type 2 synthetic lube oil PWA-521 MIL-L-23699.

FRANCE

CLUB FRANÇAIS DES AÉROGLISSEURS

41 and 43 rue Aristide Briand, 45130 Meung sur Loire, France

Club Français des Aéroglisseurs is marketing special propulsion units for high performance lightweight air cushion vehicles. The units, given the name Diagloo, comprise adapted 600 and 1200cc Citroen air-cooled, automotive engines, driving a 1·4m (4ft 7⅛in) diameter, two-bladed Merville propeller via a reduction and reverse gearbox. Engine outputs are 32·5bhp (33cv) and 56cv at 5,750rpm.

The 33cv units weigh 100kg (220lb) and the 56cv unit 160kg (352 lb). Each is supplied complete with an aerodynamically profiled hood. Series production has begun.

Diagloo propulsion unit for light sports ACVs

SOCIÉTÉ TURBOMÉCA

Head office and works: Bordes 64320 Bizanos (Pyrénées Atlantiques), France
Paris office: 1 rue Beaujon, 75008 Paris, France
Officials:
J R Szydlowski, *President and Director General*

The Société Turboméca was formed in 1938 by MM Szydlowski and Planiol to develop blowers, compressors and turbines for aeronautical use.

In 1947 the company began development of gas turbines of low power for driving aircraft auxiliaries and for aircraft propulsion.

Many of Turboméca's production series aircraft turbines have been adapted to industrial and marine duties including installation in French air cushion vehicles of various types. General descriptions follow of the main Turboméca turbine engines at present in production or under development. Reference is also made to air cushion vehicle and hydrofoil installations.

TURBOMÉCA ARTOUSTE

The Artouste is a single-shaft turboshaft engine which has been manufactured in quantity in two versions, the 400shp Artouste IIC and the 563shp Artouste IIIB. The 590shp Artouste IIID

1,300shp Turboméca Turmo IIIC free-turbine turboshaft, two of which will power the projected Aérospatiale SA 800 mixed-traffic hydrofoil ferry

has also been developed. More than 1,500 of the earlier Artouste II were built to power the Sud-Aviation Alouette II helicopter. The Artouste II has a single-stage centrifugal compressor, annular reverse-flow combustor and two-stage axial

turbine. In the second generation Artouste III in which the pressure ratio is increased from 3·88 : 1 to 5·2 : 1, a single-axial stage compressor has been added ahead of the centrifugal impeller. The turbine also has an additional stage.

A single Artouste drives the two propulsion airscrews on the Naviplane BC 8.

The following description refers to the Artouste IIIB.

TYPE: Single-shaft axial-plus-centrifugal turboshaft.

COMPRESSOR: Single-stage axial plus single-stage centrifugal compressor. Two diffusers, one radial and the other axial, aft of compressor. Pressure ratio at 33,500rpm at S/L 5·2 : 1. Air mass flow 4·3kg/s (9·5lb/s) at 33,500rpm at S/L.

COMBUSTION CHAMBER: Annular type, with rotary atomiser fuel injection. Torch igniters.

TURBINE: Three-stage axial type. Blades integral with discs. Row of nozzle guide vanes before each stage.

JET PIPE: Fixed type.

STARTING: Automatic with 4,000W starter-generator. Two Turboméca igniter plugs.

DIMENSIONS
Length: 1,815mm (71·46in)
Width: 520mm (20·47in)
Height: 627mm (24·68in)

WEIGHT: Dry equipped: 182kg (401lb)

PERFORMANCE RATING: 563shp at 33,500rpm

FUEL CONSUMPTION at T-O and max continuous rating: 322g (0·71lb) ehp/h

TURBOMÉCA TURMO

The Turmo is a free-turbine engine available in both turboshaft and turboprop versions spanning the 1,200 to 2,000shp power bracket. First generation Turmo IIIC and E series have a single-stage axial plus single-stage centrifugal compressor, annular reverse-flow combustor, two-stage axial compressor-turbine, and mechanically-separate single- or two-stage power turbine. Second-generation Turmo XII engines have an additional axial compressor stage and other refinements. By December 1978 more than 2,286 Turmo engines had been built.

Main versions of the Turmo at present in production or under development include: Turmo IIIC₇: derived from the Turmo IIIB, this model (with two-stage power turbine) has a 1,610shp at maximum contingency rating and powers early Sud-Aviation SA 321 Super-Frelon three-engined military helicopters. Two will power the projected Aérospatiale 46-ton patrol boat hydrofoil under development for the French navy.

The Turmo IIIF also powers the Turbotrains of SNCF.

Turmo IVC: based on the Turmo IIIC, this is a special version with a single-stage power turbine and powers the Sud-Aviation SA 330 Puma twin-engined military helicopter. The engine has a maximum contingency rating of 1,558shp.

Turmo IIIC₇: this model (which reverts to the standard two-stage power turbine) is in the same series as the Turmo IIIC and E and has a maximum emergency rating of 1,610shp. It is installed in Sud Aviation SA 321 F and J Super-Frelon civil three-engined helicopters.

Turmo IIIC₂: embodies new materials for the gas generator turbine, and offers an emergency rating of 1,610shp.

Turmo IIIE₃: two, each rated at 1,282shp, power the Bertin/Société de l'Aérotrain Orléans 250-80 tracked air cushion vehicle. Both engines drive a ducted seven-bladed 2·3m (7ft 7in) diameter Ratier-Figeac FH-201 hydraulically operated reversible-pitch propeller for propulsion. The Turmo IIIE is rated at 1,580shp.

Turmo IIIF: this model has been in production since 1970 to power the production version of the SNCF Turbotrain operating on the Paris-Caen-Cherbourg, Lyon-Nantes, Lyon-Strasbourg, Lyon-Bordeaux and Bordeaux-Toulouse runs.

In the United States it is employed in the AMTRAK locomotives on the Chicago-St Louis run and in Iran it is employed on locomotives on the Teheran-Mashed line.

Turmo IIIN₈: rated at 1,250shp, this version powered the twin-engined SEDAM Naviplane N 300 marine air cushion vehicle. The engines are cross-coupled to drive two three-bladed 3·6m (11ft 10in) diameter Ratier-Figeac FH 195-196 hydraulically-operated variable-pitch propellers

Turboméca Turmo XII which has an additional axial compressor stage

889shp Turboméca Turmastazou XIV free-turbine turboshaft

for propulsion and two 11-bladed 1·85m (6ft 3in) diameter Ratier-Figeac FD 155 hydraulically-operated variable-pitch axial fans for lift.

Turmo XII: developed from the Turmo IIIC this second-generation model has a two-stage axial compressor ahead of the centrifugal stage. With a maximum continuous rating of 1,610shp, the Turmo XII is in operation on an RTG Turbotrain in France.

Two Turmo IIIC series engines with a combined installed power of 2,564shp, are to power the projected Aérospatiale SA 800 second-generation hydrofoil.

TURMO IIIC₇

TYPE: Free-turbine axial-plus-centrifugal turboshaft.

AIR MASS FLOW: 6·2kg (13·71lb)/s

DIMENSIONS
Length: 1,976mm (77·8in)
Width: 693mm (27·3in)
Height: 717mm (28·2in)

WEIGHT Dry with standard equipment: 325kg (715lb)

PERFORMANCE RATINGS
T-O: 1,550shp
Max continuous: 1,292shp

FUEL CONSUMPTION
At T-O rating: 273g (0·6lb)/shp/h
At max continuous rating: 291g (0·64lb)/shp/h

TURBOMÉCA MARBORÉ

The Marboré single-shaft turbojet has been built in greater numbers than any other Turboméca engine. By December 1978 over 9,000 400kg (880lb) thrust Marboré IIs and 480kg (1,058lb) thrust Marboré VIs had been manufactured by Turboméca and its licensees for trainer aircraft and target drone applications. Of this total, 5,489 Marboré engines were manufactured by Turboméca. In both these versions the engine comprises a single-stage centrifugal compressor,

annular reverse-flow combustor and single-stage axial turbine.

Two Marborés power the H.890 hydrofoil test platform currently under development by Aérospatiale for the French Ministry of National Defence.

A Marboré II powers the lift system of the SEDAM Naviplane BC 8 marine ACV. The exhaust gases are ducted along channels designed to entrain additional air to augment the efflux.

MARBORE VI

DIMENSIONS
Length, with exhaust cone but without tailpipe: 1,416mm (55·74in)
Width: 593mm (23·35in)
Height: 631mm (24·82in)

WEIGHT Dry equipped: 140kg (309lb)

PERFORMANCE RATINGS
T-O: 480kg (1,058lb) st at 21,500rpm
Cruising: 420kg (925lb) st at 20,500rpm

SPECIFIC FUEL CONSUMPTION
At T-O rating: 1·09
At cruising rating: 1·07

TURBOMÉCA ASTAZOU

The Astazou is another of the later generation Turboméca engines, incorporating the experience gained with earlier series and making use of new design techniques. It has an extremely small gas-producer section and has been developed both as a turboshaft and as a turboprop driving a variable-pitch propeller.

The compressor consists of one or two axial stages followed by a centrifugal stage, with an annular combustion chamber and three-stage turbine. Accessories are mounted on the rear of the main intake casing. Pressure ratio is 6:1 and air mass flow 2·5kg/s (5·5lb/s) for the two-stage compressor engines, and 8 : 1 and 3·4kg/s (7·4lb/s) for the three-stage compressor engines respectively. In the turboshaft version, the rpm of the output shaft is 5,922.

Well over 2,500 Astazou engines of various types have been built. The following are the main Astazou variants:

Astazou II. This is a 535hp turboprop (with two-stage compressor) which powers a version of the Naviplane N 102.

Astazou IIA. A 523shp turboshaft (two-stage compressor) version powering the Sud-Aviation SA 318C Alouette II Astazou helicopter. A 450 shp Astazou provides power for the integrated lift and propulsion system of the SEDAM Naviplane N 102 marine ACV. The engine drives a 1·7m (5ft 7in) diameter axial lift fan and two three-bladed variable-pitch propellers for propulsion.

Astazou IIIN. Rated at 592hp, this is the definitive version (two-stage compressor).

Astazou IV. New version especially designed for industrial duty and in particular to form, associated with a Jeumont-Schneider ac generator, a 300kW generating set. It is installed in the RTG turbotrains made in France, USA and Iran. It is also being tested by the French Navy.

Astazou XIV (alias AZ14). Current major production turboshaft version (with three-stage compressor) rated at 852shp. The engine is the standard power plant for the Naviplane N 102.

The B version is installed in the Alouette III helicopter and the H version in the SA 342 Gazelle helicopter.

Astazou XVI (alias AZ16). First Turboméca production engine to embody the company's new air-cooled turbine. Rated at 913shp for Jetstream aircraft and the FMA IA 58 Pucará counter-insurgency aircraft of the Argentine Air Force.

Astazou XVIII. An uprated version of the Astazou XVI with take-off power of 1,554ehp and sfc of 232g (0·512lb)/ehp/h.

A turboshaft version is installed in the SA 360 Dauphin helicopter. Thermodynamic power: 1,032shp, sfc of 260g (0·57lb)/shp/h.

Astazou XX. This later version has an additional axial compressor stage, and is rated at take-off at 1,350ehp for an sfc of 219g (0·49lb)/ehp/h.

Turboshaft version has 1,295shp thermodynamic power, with sfc of 228g (0·51lb)/shp/h.

ASTAZOU IIIN
DIMENSIONS
Length: 1,433mm (56·3in)
Basic diameter: 460mm (18·1in)
WEIGHT Dry equipped engine: 147·5kg (325lb)
PERFORMANCE RATINGS
T-O: 592shp at 43,500rpm
Max continuous: 523shp at 43,500rpm
FUEL CONSUMPTION
At T-O rating: 284g (0·627lb)/shp/h
At max continuous rating: 292g (0·644 lb)/shp/h

TURBOMÉCA BASTAN
A compact single-shaft turboprop in the 1,000 to 2,000shp power bracket, the Bastan has its main application in the Nord 262. The 1,065ehp Bastan VIC powering the original 262 series aircraft, comprises a single-stage axial compressor plus single-stage centrifugal compressor, annular reverse-flow combustor and three-stage axial turbine, and is equipped with water-methanol injection. A new version of the Bastan VIC4 is under development with a rating of 1,085shp. The higher rated Bastan VII is capable of maintaining its 1,135ehp T-O power up to an ambient temperature of 40°C. This version is entering production to power the new 262C and incorporates an additional axial compressor stage.

BASTAN VII
DIMENSIONS
Length: 1,911mm (75·2in)
Width: 550mm (21·7in)
Height: 802mm (31·6in)
WEIGHT Dry basic engine: 290kg (639lb)
PERFORMANCE RATINGS: T-O and max continuous: 1,135ehp
FUEL CONSUMPTION: At T-O and max continuous ratings: 259g (0·572lb)/shp/h

TURBOMÉCA TURMASTAZOU
This is a new free-turbine direct-drive turboshaft comprising the Astazou XIV single-shaft gas generator section provided with a mechanically-independent power turbine. The Astazou turbine has two stages in place of its normal three, and the power turbine has two stages also. Development is underway of the 889shp Turmastazou XIV with a view to its use in twin-engined helicopters. The engine has also been proposed for the Bertin/Société de l' Aérotrain Orléans tracked ACV.

Turmastazou XVI. This version introduces the Turboméca air-cooled turbine, and gives a take-off rating of 1,015shp for an sfc of 231g (0·51lb)/shp/h.

TURMASTAZOU XIV
DIMENSIONS
Length: 1,371mm (54in)
Width: 440mm (17·3in)
Height: 553mm (21·8in)
WEIGHT Dry equipped engine: approx 155kg (341lb)
PERFORMANCE RATINGS
T-O: 889shp
Max continuous: 792shp

GERMANY, FEDERAL REPUBLIC

MTU
Motoren-und Turbinen-Union Friedrichshafen GmbH

Olgastrasse 75, Postfach 2040, D-7990 Friedrichshafen, Federal Republic of Germany
Telephone: (07541) 2071
Telex: MTUFH 0734360
Officials:
Dr Oec pupl Ernst Zimmermann, *President*
Dr Ing Hans Dinger, *Executive Vice President*
Dr Ing Peter Beer, *Director*
Hubert Dunkler, *Director*
Dr Ing Wolfgang Hansen, *Director*
Gunther Welsch, *Director*

The MTU-group of companies, formed in 1969 by MAN AG and Daimler-Benz AG, consists of MTU-München GmbH and MTU-Friedrichshafen GmbH.

MTU-Friedrichshafen comprises the two plants of the previous Maybach Mercedes-Benz Motorenbau GmbH at Friedrichshafen and is owned by MTU-München GmbH. MTU-München, in turn is owned equally by MAN and Daimler-Benz.

The areas of responsibility of the two MTU companies are as follows:
MTU-München:
Development, production and support of lightweight, advanced-technology gas turbines mainly for aircraft applications.
MTU Friedrichshafen:
Development, production and application of high-performance diesel engines.

MTU-Friedrichshafen is today the development and production centre for high-performance diesel engines of Maybach, MAN and Mercedes-Benz origin and as such embodies the experience of these companies in diesel engine technology. In addition to diesel engines, MTU-Friedrichshafen is responsible for sales and application of industrial and marine gas turbines.

MTU diesel engines for hydrofoil and hovercraft propulsion

Engine model	Speed rpm	Overload Power (available for limited time during take-off) kW	hp (metric)	Engine weight (dry) (basic engine) kg	lb
6 V 331 TC 82	2250	525	715	1850	4080
8 V 331 TC 82	2250	700	950	2310	5100
12 V 331 TC 82	2250	1050	1430	3210	7080
6 V 396 TB 83	1900	630	855	2060	4540
8 V 396 TB 83	1900	840	1140	2570	5670
12 V 396 TB 83	1900	1260	1710	3570	7870
12 V 652 TB 81	1460	1440	1960	5020*	11070*
16 V 652 TB 81	1460	1920	2610	6520*	14380*
12 V 538 TB 82	1760	1780	2420	5150	11360
16 V 538 TB 82	1760	2380	3240	6700	14770
20 V 538 TB 82	1760	2980	4050	9000	19840

*Weight of engine with light alloy housing

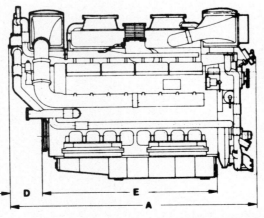
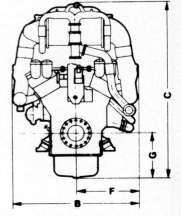

Outline Dimensions

Engine type	A	B	C	D	E	F	G
12V 652 TB 81	2557	1697	2120	289	1944	900	580
16V 652 TB 81	3122	1697	2256	275	2498	900	625

For applications in hydrofoils and hovercraft, MTU offers the following engines:
  331 engine family
  396 engine family
  652 engine family
  538 engine family
The table provides some details of the various engines with regard to speed, output and weight. The listed outputs are guideline figures only and are dependent upon the type of application, ie military or commercial, its operating profile etc, and will therefore be specified for each case individually.
The stated outputs are based on following ambient conditions:
  Air intake temperature 27°C
  Seawater temperature 27°C
  (up to 32°C seawater temperature for 331 type engines)
  Barometric pressure: 1,000mb
In addition, MTU projects and delivers complete propulsion systems, including gear shafts and propellers as well as combined power plants such as CODOG and CODAG systems.

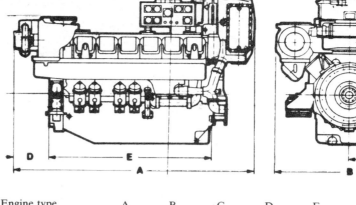

Engine type	A	B	C	D	E	F	G
6V 331 TC 82	1620	1396	1280	257	1023	711	475
8V 331 TC 82	1848	1404	1280	257	1251	719	475
12V 331 TC 82	2436	1446	1440	319	1707	723	535
6V 396 TB 83	1620	1458	1398	275	1023	735	475
8V 396 TB 83	1848	1442	1398	275	1251	719	475
12V 396 TB 83	2436	1506	1525	335	1707	753	535

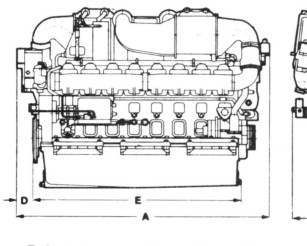

Engine type	A	B	C	D	E	F	G
12V 538 TB 82	2545	1640	2230	220	1820	820	760
16V 538 TB 82	3160	1640	2305	450	2265	820	595
20V 538 TB 82	3800	1640	2320	340	3260	820	665

RHEIN-FLUGZEUGBAU GmbH

Postfach 408, D-4050 Mönchengladbach 1, Federal Republic of Germany
Telephone: (02161) 66 20 31
Telex: 08 525 06
Officials:
Dipl Volksw W Kutscher, *Commercial Director*
Dipl Ing A Schneider, *Technical Director*

RFB has developed a fan thrust pod module for wing-in-ground-effect machines, gliders, air cushion vehicles and air-propelled boats.

By combining rotary engines of the Wankel type with a ducted fan, the company has produced an extremely compact power unit which can be mounted on either a fuselage or a wing in much the same way as gas-turbine pods. The air cooling system permits prolonged ground running when necessary with full throttle.

The system has been fitted to the L13 Blanik glider and also to boats.

SG 85

Length: 1,200mm (3ft 11½in)
Width max: 750mm (2ft 5½in)
Height, including 200mm connection: 1,000mm (3ft 3⅜in)
Inside shroud diameter: 650mm (2ft 1⅜in)
Weight: 58kg (127·8lb)
Power: 50hp
Static thrust at 5,400rpm (with muffler installed): 90kg (198·4lb)
Noise level with full throttle at 304·8m (1,000ft) altitude: 54 dB (A)

RFB Fan Pod Type SG 85

Rotor: 3-blades-rotor in fibre-reinforced plastic with erosive protection.
Shroud: plastic.
Engine cowling: glass fibre reinforced plastic.
Engine: Rotary engine KM 914/2V-85 ('Wankel' system; two coupled engines 25hp each) with electric starter 12V, generator, exhaust-gas system and complete assembly sets ready for installation.

Connection: Metal-construction as pylon having a connection-part.

Fuel: mixture 1:30

Fuel consumption:
  full throttle 5,500rpm: 15 litres/h (3·3 gallons/h)
  cruising speed 5,000rpm: 11·5 litres/h (2·5 gallons/h)

SG 85 thrust pod mounted on an Espadon Canot 422 inflatable dinghy, built by Etablissements Georges Hennebutte

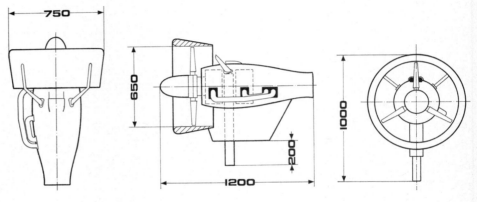

RFB Fan Pod, incorporating a Wankel rotary engine

VOLKSWAGEN (GB) LIMITED
(Incorporating Audi NSU (GB) Limited)

Volkswagen House, Brighton Road, Purley, Surrey CR2 2UQ, England
Telephone: 01-668 4100
Telex: 263226

TYPE 122

The air-cooled petrol engines powering over 20 million Volkswagen cars and vehicles are also produced as industrial power units in which role they have been proved reliable and economical in millions of hours running. There are three versions available, the Type 122 developed from the 1,192cc Volkswagen car engine; the 1,584cc Type 126A developed from the 1,500cc van engine; and the 1,795cc Type 127 developed from the 1,700cc car engine.

TYPE: Air-cooled four-cylinder, horizontally-opposed four-stroke petrol engine available with or without governor.

CYLINDERS: Four separate cylinders of special grey cast iron, with integral cooling fins. Cast aluminium heads, one for each two cylinders, with shrunk-in sintered steel valve seats and bronze valve guides. Bore 77mm (3·032in). Stroke 64mm (2·52in). Cubic capacity 1,192cc (72·74 in³). Compression ratio 7·3 : 1.

CRANKCASE: Two-part magnesium pressure casting with enclosed oil sump and flange for mounting the engine on machine or pedestal.

CRANKSHAFT: Forged, with hardened journals, mounted in three aluminium bearings and one three-layer, steel-backed bearing (No 2).

CONNECTING RODS: Forged steel, I-section shank. Three-layer, steel-backed, lead-bronze big-end bearing shells with white metal running surfaces.

PISTONS: Aluminium with steel inserts, two compression rings and one scraper ring.

CAMSHAFT: Grey cast iron, with three steel-backed, shell-type bearings in crankcase, driven by helical gears.

Volkswagen Type 127 industrial engine

VALVES: One inlet and one exhaust valve per cylinder. Exhaust valves have special armoured seating surfaces. 'Rotocap' valve rotating devices can be fitted on request.

COOLING: Radial fan, driven by belt from crankshaft. Protective grille on fan intake.

LUBRICATION: Forced feed gear-type pump. Full flow, flat tube oil cooler in fan airstream. Oil capacity 2·5 litres (4·4 pints).

CARBURETTOR: Downdraft Solex 26 VFIS on engine with governor. Downdraft Solex 28 PCI with accelerator pump, on engine without governor. Both have choke for cold starting.

IGNITION: Magneto, fully waterproofed and suppressed.

PLUGS: Bosch W145 T1.

FUEL: RON 87.

STARTING: Hand cranking lever or electric starter.
GOVERNOR: Centrifugal type, operating on carburettor throttle, driven by toothed belt.
EXHAUST SYSTEM: Cylindrical muffler located transversely at bottom of engine, with exhaust pipes from cylinders and damper pipe with short tail pipe.
MOUNTING: By four bolts in the crankcase flange.
COUPLING: Engine is connected to driven shaft by a clutch or flexible fixed-coupling.
PEDESTALS AND TRANSMISSIONS: Suitable flange pedestals, with or without couplings or clutches, can be supplied as well as gearboxes with direct drives or drives of various ratios for clockwise or anti-clockwise rotation.
DIMENSIONS
Length: 740·5mm (29·2in)
Width: 748mm (29·4in)
Height: 665·5mm (26·2in)
WEIGHT Dry with standard equipment: approx 93·5kg (205lb)
PERFORMANCE RATINGS: Continuous rating: 34bhp DIN at 3,600 output rpm
FUEL CONSUMPTION
At 20bhp at 2,000 output rpm: 242g (0·534lb)/bhp/h
At 30bhp at 3,600 output rpm: 268g (0·59lb)/bhp/h

OIL CONSUMPTION: Approx 20 to 35cc/h at 3,000 output rpm

TYPE 126A
TYPE: Air-cooled four-cylinder, horizontally-opposed four-stroke petrol engine available with or without governor. Construction generally similar to Type 122 with following exceptions:
CYLINDERS: Bore 85·5mm (3·543in). Stroke 69mm (2·717in). Cubic capacity 1,584cc (96·5in³). Compression ratio 7·7 : 1.
CARBURETTOR: Downdraft Solex 26 or 28 VFIS on engine with governor. Downdraft Solex 32 PCI on engine without governor.
DIMENSIONS
Length: 723mm (28·5in)
Width: 760mm (29·9in)
Height: 675·5mm (26·5in)
WEIGHT Dry with standard equipment: approx 100kg (220lb)
PERFORMANCE RATINGS: Continuous rating: 46bhp DIN at 3,600 output rpm
FUEL: 90 octane minimum
FUEL CONSUMPTION
At 28bhp at 2,000 output rpm: 225g (0·496lb)/bhp/h
At 44bhp at 3,600 output rpm: 255g (0·562lb)/bhp/h
OIL CONSUMPTION: Approx 25 to 40 cc/h at 3,000 output rpm

TYPE 127

TYPE: Air-cooled, four-cylinder, horizontally-opposed four-stroke petrol engine of low profile design.
CYLINDERS: Bore 93mm (3·74in). Stroke 66mm (2·165in). Cubic capacity 1,795cc (109·53in³). Compression ratio 7·3 : 1.
CRANKCASE: Aluminium, pressure die cast.
COOLING: Radial fan on crankshaft.
CARBURETTOR: Downdraft Solex 32 PCI or two Downdraft Solex 34PDSIT.
IGNITION: 12V battery.
DIMENSIONS
Length: 829mm (32·64in)
Width: 960mm (37·8in)
Height, without air cleaner: 556mm (21·89in)
WEIGHT Dry with standard equipment: 124kg (273lb)
PERFORMANCE RATINGS
Max continuous ratings at 4,000rpm:
    single carburettor: 62bhp DIN
    twin carburettor: 68bhp DIN
FUEL: 90 octane minimum
FUEL CONSUMPTION
At 3,000 output rpm: 230g (0·506lb)/bhp/h
At 4,000 output rpm: 255g (0·561lb)/bhp/h

ITALY

CRM FABBRICA MOTORI MARINI

Via Manzoni 12, 20121 Milan, Italy
Telephone: 708 326/327
Telex: 334382 CREMME
Cables: Cremme
Officials:
G Mariani, *Director*
Ing B Piccoletti, *Director*
Ing S Rastelli, *Director*
S Sussi, *Director*

CRM has specialised in building lightweight diesel engines for more than thirty years. The company's engines are used in large numbers of motor torpedo boats, coastal patrol craft and privately-owned motor yachts. More recently, the engines have also been installed in hydrofoils.

During the 1960s the company undertook the development and manufacture of a family of 18-, 12- and 9-cylinder diesel engines of lightweight high-speed design, providing a power coverage of 300bhp to 1,350bhp. These comprise the 18-cylinder CRM 18 D/2 and 18 D/S-3 of 1,050 to 1,350bhp with mechanically-driven supercharging and turbo-driven supercharging respectively and its cylinders arranged in an unusual W arrangement of three banks of six cylinders each; the 12-cylinder CRM 12 D/S-2 of 900bhp with two banks of six cylinders and first in the new series to introduce turbo-charging; and the 715bhp CRM 9 D/S-2 with a W arrangement of three banks of three cylinders and offering the option of turbo-charging or natural aspiration.

All engines available in a magnetic version, the disturbance of their magnetic field being reduced to insignificant amounts, for special applications.

Details of these engines are given below.

CRM 18

First in CRM's new series of lightweight high-speed diesels, the CRM 18 is an 18-cylinder unit with its cylinders arranged in a W form comprising three banks of six cylinders. Maximum power is 1,050bhp at 1,900rpm with mechanically-driven supercharging and 1,350bhp at 2,075rpm with exhaust gas turbo-charging. One 1,050bhp 18 D/2 engine powers the Finnish Tehi 70-passenger Raketa-type hydrofoil.

The following description relates to the mechanically supercharged CRM 18 D/2 and turbo-supercharged CRM 18 D/S-3.
TYPE: 18-cylinder in-line W type, four-stroke, water-cooled mechanically-supercharged (CRM

CRM 18 D/S-3 marine diesel rated at 1,350bhp at 2,075rpm

18 D/2) or turbo-supercharged (CRM 18 D/S) diesel engine.
CYLINDERS: Bore 150mm (5·91in). Stroke 180mm (7·09in). Swept volume 3·18 litres (194·166in³) per cylinder. Total swept volume 57·3 litres (3,495in³). Compression ratio 16·25 : 1. Separate pressed-steel cylinder frame side members are surrounded by gas-welded sheet metal water cooling jacket treated and pressure-coated internally to prevent corrosion. Cylinders are closed at top by a steel plate integral with side wall to complete combustion chamber. Lower half of cylinder is ringed by a drilled flange for bolting to crankcase. Cylinder top also houses a spherical-shaped pre-combustion chamber as well as inlet and exhaust valve seats. Pre-combustion chamber is in high-strength, heat and corrosion resistant steel. A single cast light alloy head, carrying valve guides, pre-combustion chambers and camshaft bearings bridges each bank of cylinders. Head is attached to cylinder bank by multiple studs.
PISTONS: Light alloy forgings with four rings, top ring being chrome-plated and bottom ring acting as oil scraper. Piston crowns shaped to withstand high temperatures especially in vicinity of pre-combustion chamber outlet ports.

CONNECTING RODS: Comprise main and secondary articulated rods, all rods being completely machined I-section steel forgings. Big-end of each main rod is bolted to ribbed cap by six studs. Big-end bearings are white metal lined steel shells. Each secondary rod anchored at its lower end to a pivot pin inserted in two lugs protruding from big-end of main connecting rod. Both ends of all secondary rods, and small ends of main rods have bronze bushes.
CRANKSHAFTS: One-piece hollow shaft in nitrided alloy steel, with six throws equi-spaced at 120 degrees. Seven main bearings with white metal lined steel shells. Twelve balancing counterweights.
CRANKCASE: Cast light alloy crankcase bolted to bed plate by studs and tie bolts. Multiple integral reinforced ribs to provide robust structure. Both sides of each casting braced by seven cross ribs incorporating crankshaft bearing supports. Protruding sides of crankcase ribbed throughout length.
VALVE GEAR: Hollow sodium-cooled valves of each bank of cylinders actuated by twin camshafts and six cams on each shaft. Two inlet and two outlet valves per cylinder and one rocker for each pair of valves. End of stem and facing of

exhaust valves fitted with Stellite inserts. Valve cooling water forced through passage formed by specially-shaped plate welded to top of cylinder.

FUEL INJECTION: Pumps fitted with variable speed control and pilot injection nozzle.

PRESSURE CHARGER: Two mechanically-driven centrifugal compressors on CRM 18 D/2, or two exhaust gas turbo-driven compressors on CRM 18 D/S-3.

ACCESSORIES: Standard accessories include oil and fresh water heat exchangers; fresh water tank; oil and fresh water thermostats; oil filters, fresh water, salt water and fuel hand pumps; fresh water and oil temperature gauges; engine, reverse gear and reduction gear oil gauges; pre-lubrication, electric pump and engine rpm counter. Optional accessories include engine oil and water pre-heater, and warning and pressure switches.

COOLING SYSTEM: Fresh water.

FUEL: Fuel oil having specific gravity of 0·83 to 0·84.

LUBRICATION SYSTEM: Pressure type with gear pump.

OIL: Mineral oil to SAE 40 HD, MIL-L-210GB.

OIL COOLING: By salt water circulating through heat exchanger.

STARTING: 24 volt 15hp electric motor and 85A, 24 volt alternator for battery charge, or compressed air.

MOUNTING: At any transverse or longitudinal angle tilt to 20 degrees.

REVERSE GEAR: Bevel crown gear wheels with hydraulically-controlled hand brake.

REDUCTION GEAR: Optional fitting with spur gears giving reduction ratios of 0·561 : 1, 0·730 : 1 and 0·846 : 1. Overdrive ratio 1·18 : 1.

PROPELLER THRUST BEARING: Incorporated in reduction gear or in overdrive. Axial thrust 3,003kg (6,620lb) at 1,176rpm.

DIMENSIONS
Length: 2,960mm (116·5in)
Width: 1,350mm (53·15in)
Height: 1,304mm (51·33in)

WEIGHTS
DRY
Engine: 1,665kg (3,690lb)
Reverse gear, generator and starter: 410kg (900lb)
Reduction gear or overdrive, with propeller thrust bearing: 150kg (330lb)
Total: 2,225kg (4,920lb)

PERFORMANCE RATINGS
CRM 18 D/S-3:
Max power: 1,350bhp at 2,075rpm
Intermittent service: 1,250bhp at 2,020rpm
Continuous service: 1,040bhp at 1,900rpm
FUEL CONSUMPTION: CRM 18 D/S-3 at continuous service rating: 0·17kg (0·37lb)/bhp/h
OIL CONSUMPTION: CRM 18 D/S-3 at continuous service rating: 0·003kg (0·007lb)/h

CRM 12D/S-2

Second in the new CRM series of lightweight diesels is the 900bhp 12-cylinder 12 D/S-2 with two banks of six cylinders set at 60 degrees to

CRM 12D/SS-YE marine diesel engine rated at 1,375bhp at 2,075rpm

form a V assembly. The bore and stroke are the same as in the CRM 18 series, and many of the components are interchangeable, including the crankshaft, bedplate, cylinders and pistons. The crankcase and connecting rod-assemblies are necessarily of modified design; the secondary rod is anchored at its lower end to a pivot pin inserted on two lugs protruding from the big-end of the main connecting rod. The fuel injection pump is modified to single block housing all 12 pumping elements located between the cylinder banks.

A major innovation first developed on the 12 D/S (and later provided for the other engines in the series) was the introduction of an exhaust gas driven turbo-charger. This involved a complete revision of the combustion system and all components comprising the cylinder heads. Conversion to turbo-charging avoided the mechanical power loss expended in driving the blower, and enabled a greater volume of air to be forced into the cylinders. The effect on specific fuel consumption was a reduction to around 160 to 170g (0·35—0·37lb)/bhp/h in conjunction with exhaust temperatures not exceeding 530°C (986°F) at maximum rpm. Two Holset turbochargers are fitted.

TYPE: 12-cylinder in-line V type, four-stroke water-cooled, turbo-supercharged diesel engines.

DIMENSIONS
Length: 2,530mm (99·6in)
Width: 1,210mm (47·64in)
Height: 1,204mm (47·4in)

WEIGHTS
DRY
Engine: 1,240kg (2,735lb)
Reverse gear, generator and starter: 410kg (900lb)
Reduction gear or overdrive, with propeller thrust bearing: 150kg (330lb)
Total: 1,800kg (3,965lb)

PERFORMANCE RATINGS
Max power: 900bhp at 2,035rpm
Intermittent service: 850bhp at 2,000rpm
Continuous service: 750bhp at 1,900rpm
FUEL CONSUMPTION: At continuous service rating: 0·18kg (0·4lb)/bhp/h

CRM 12D/SS-YE

As a development of 12D/S-2, the 12D/SS-YE is available for applications where a high rating is required, but space is limited.

Dry sump and wet sump versions are available for installation in engine-rooms with limited space available.

TYPE: Twelve cylinder V-60°, four stroke water-cooled, turbo-supercharged and inter-cooled diesel engine.

DIMENSIONS
Length: 2,642mm (104in)
Width: 1,210mm (47·63in)
Height, dry sump: 1,299mm (51·14in)
Height, wet sump: 1,427mm (56·18in)

WEIGHTS
DRY
Engine: 1,440kg (3,180lb)
Reverse gear, generator and electric starter: 410kg (903·9lb) (compressed air starter optional)
Reduction gear: 150kg (330·6lb) (optional)

PERFORMANCE RATINGS
Max power: 1,375bhp at 2,075rpm
Intermittent power: 1,250bhp at 2,010rpm
Continuous power: 1,085bhp at 1,920rpm
FUEL CONSUMPTION: At continuous service rating: 0·170kg (0·38lb)/bhp/h

CRM NON-MAGNETIC DIESEL ENGINES

Non-magnetic versions of all CRM diesel engines, are also available. These have extremely low magnetic perturbation fields.

FIAT/AIFO
Applicazioni Industriali Fiat-OM
Via Carducci 29, 20123 Milan, Italy
Telephone: 877006/7/8, 898351/2/3
Telex: 311-531 I

AIFO Carraro V12SS, 700hp 12-cylinder diesel engines are installed in the H57 60-passenger hydrofoil ferries built by Seaflight, Messina.

CARRARO V12SS

TYPE: Pre-chamber injection, V-form 12-cylinder, turbocharged and inter-cooled four-stroke diesel engine.

OUTPUT: Basic engine, 700bhp; maximum shaft output 650hp at 1,500rpm.

BORE AND STROKE: 142 × 180mm (5·59 × 7·09in).

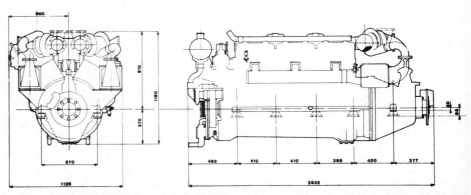

Fiat-Carraro V12SS 700hp marine diesel. Two of these 12-cylinder water-cooled and supercharged engines power the Seaflight H57 hydrofoil passenger ferry

FUEL INJECTION: Bosch type pumps and centrifugal governor; fuel feeding pumps; fuel cartridge filters.

ENGINE COOLING: By fresh water into closed circuit with thermostatic control valve.

OIL COOLING: By salt water circulating through a heat exchanger.

STARTING: 6hp starting motor and 600W generator for battery charging.

LUBRICATION: By gear pump.

REVERSE GEAR: Hydraulically operated, with brake on transmission.

REDUCTION GEAR: Standard ratios, 1·5 : 1-2 : 1.

WEIGHT Dry: 2,200kg (4,120lb)

8280 SRM

FIAT/AIFO has also released details of the eight-cylinder 550hp 8280 SRM engine, which is available for marine operations.

DIMENSIONS

Length: 1,935mm (76·18in)
Width: 1,195mm (47·05in)
Height: 1,170mm (46·06in)

FIAT/AIFO 8280 SRM 8-cylinder marine diesel, rated at 550hp at 2,400rpm

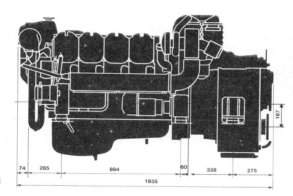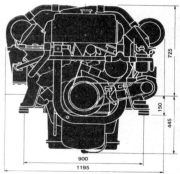

FIAT/AIFO 8280 SRM marine diesel

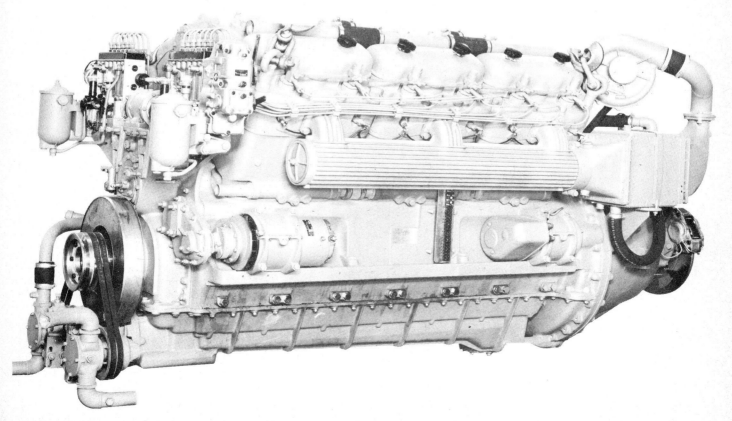

FIAT/AIFO-Carraro V12SS, 700hp supercharged 12-cylinder marine diesel engines

UNION OF SOVIET SOCIALIST REPUBLICS

A IVCHENKO

This design team headed by the late general designer Ivchenko is based in a factory at Zaporojie in the Ukraine, where all prototypes and pre-production engines bearing the 'AI' prefix are developed and built. Chief designer is Lotarev and chief engineer Tichienko. The production director is M Omeltchenko.

First engine with which Ivchenko was associated officially was the 55hp AI-4G piston-engine used in the Kamov Ka-10 ultra-light helicopter. He later progressed via the widely used AI-14 and AI-26 piston-engines, to become one of the Soviet Union's leading designers of gas-turbine engines.

Two AI-20s in de-rated, marinised form and driving two three-stage waterjets power the Burevestnik, the first Soviet gas-turbine hydrofoil to go into series production, and a single AI-24 drives the integrated lift/propulsion system of the Sormovich 50-passenger ACV.

1,750hp Ivchenko AI-23-CI marine gas turbine

IVCHENKO
AI-20

Ivchenko's design bureau is responsible for the AI-20 turboprop engine which powers the Antonov An-10, An-12 and Ilyushin Il-18 airliners and the Beriev M-12 Tchaika amphibian.

Six production series of this engine had been built by the spring of 1966. The first four series, of which manufacture started in 1957 were variants of the basic AI-20 version. They were followed by two major production versions, as follows:

AI-20K. Rated at 3,945ehp. Used in Il-18V, An-10A and An-12.

AI-20M. Uprated version with T-O rating of 4,190ehp (4,250 ch e). Used in Il-18D/E, An-10A and An-12.

Conversion of the turboprop as a marine power unit for hydrofoil waterjet propulsion (as on the Burevestnik) involved a number of changes to the engine. In particular it was necessary to hold engine rpm at a constant level during conditions of varying load from the waterjet pump—and it was also necessary to be able to vary the thrust from the waterjet unit from zero to forward or rearwards thrust to facilitate engine starting and vessel manoeuvring.

Constant speed under variable load was achieved by replacing the engine's normal high pressure fuel pump with a special fuel regulator pump—and the waterjet pump was modified to have a variable exit area and was fitted with an air valve enabling a variable amount of air to be passed into the intake just ahead of the pump rotor. With less air passing through the waterjet, unit load on the engine increased, and vice versa if the air flow was increased by opening the air valve.

The fuel regulator pump was designed to maintain engine rpm constant and to regulate output while the AI-20 was driving the waterjet unit. Steady running conditions were shown to be satisfactorily maintained by the engine under all operating conditions—and rpm and turbine temperature were held within the limits laid down for the aircraft turboprop version: engine rpm did not fluctuate outside ±2·5% of its set speed when loading or unloading the waterjet unit.

During development of the marinised AI-20, the normal aircraft propeller and speed governor were removed and the turboprop was bench tested over the full range of its operating conditions. This demonstrated that the engine performed in a stable manner throughout, from slow running to normal rpm. These tests were run initially using aviation kerosene Type TS-1 fuel, and then diesel fuels Types L and DS.

Following satisfactory results on the bench, the test engine was mounted on a self-propelled float-ing test bed equipped with a waterjet propulsion unit. Further tests with this configuration were also satisfactorily concluded, including starting checks with varying degrees of submersion of the pump section of the waterjet unit.

Electrical starting of the engine up to slow running speed (equal to approximately 25% of rated rpm) was shown to take 70 to 85 seconds. For starting and ignition at ambient conditions below 10°C, fuel pre-heating is employed and modified igniters are fitted. With this equipment, starts have been achieved down to minus 12°C.

Based on this experience, the marinised AI-20 for the twin-engined Burevestnik was rated at 2,700hp at 13,200rpm. At this power output, the hydrofoil achieved speeds of up to 97km/h (60mph). Specific fuel consumption was 320-330g (0·71-0·73lb)/hp/h.

Testing with the Burevestnik revealed a number of operating characteristics of the vessel: when the two AI-20s were running while the vessel was moored or manoeuvring, residual exhaust thrust from the turbines occurred and this is required to be balanced by a negative, or reverse thrust from the waterjet by partially closing the unit's nozzle flaps. This increased the load on the engine however, and caused a rise in fuel consumption.

Also, experience showed that with a normal start following a series of wet starts, any fuel which had accumulated in the jet pipe became ignited. This resulted in a sharp rise in turbine temperature and back pressure, and flame emerged from the ejection apertures into the engine compartment and exhaust nozzle. To circumvent this, the ejection apertures were covered with a metal grid, and a spray of water is provided at the exhaust nozzle prior to starting.

Based on an overhaul life for the turboprop AI-20 of several thousand hours, special techniques have been applied to the marinised version to increase its service life. These include the use of high quality assembly procedures for the engine, efficient design of the air intake and exhaust duct, adoption of appropriate procedures for starting and on-loading of the main and auxiliary turbines at all ambient temperature conditions—and by the utilisation of highly-skilled servicing methods of the installation during operation.

The AI-20 is a single-spool turboprop, with a ten-stage axial-flow compressor, cannular combustion chamber with ten flame tubes, and a three-stage turbine, of which the first two stages are cooled. Planetary reduction gearing, with a ratio of 0·08732 : 1, is mounted forward of the annular air intake. The fixed nozzle contains a central bullet fairing. All engine-driven accessories are mounted on the forward part of the compressor casing, which is of magnesium alloy.

The AI-20 was designed to operate reliably in all temperatures from −60°C to +55°C at heights up to 10,000m (33,000ft). It is a constant speed engine, the rotor speed being maintained at 21,300rpm by automatic variation of propeller pitch. Gas temperature after turbine is 560°C in both current versions. TBO of the AI-20K was 4,000 hours in the spring of 1966.

WEIGHT

DRY
AI-20K: 1,080kg (2,380lb)
AI-20M: 1,039kg (2,290lb)

PERFORMANCE RATINGS

Max T-O:
AI-20K: 4,000ch e (3,945ehp)
AI-20M: 4,250ch e (4,190ehp)
Cruise rating at 630km/h (390mph) at 8,000m (26,000ft):
AI-20K: 2,250ch e (2,220ehp)
AI-20M: 2,700ch e (2,663ehp)

SPECIFIC FUEL CONSUMPTION

At cruise rating:
AI-20K: 215g (0·472lb)/hp/h
AI-20M: 197g (0·434lb)/hp/h

OIL CONSUMPTION Normal: 1 litre (1·75 pints)/h

IVCHENKO
AI-24

In general configuration, this single-spool turboprop engine, which powers the An-24 transport aircraft, is very similar to the earlier and larger AI-20. Production began in 1960 and the following data refers to engines of the second series, which were in production in the spring of 1966.

A single marinised version, developing 1,800shp, drives the integrated lift/propulsion system of the Sormovich 50-passenger ACV.

An annular ram air intake surrounds the cast light alloy casing for the planetary reduction gear, which has a ratio of 0·08255 : 1. The cast magnesium alloy compressor casing carries a row of inlet guide vanes and the compressor stator vanes and provides mountings for the engine-driven accessories. These include fuel, hydraulic and oil pumps, tacho-generator and propeller governor.

The ten-stage axial-flow compressor is driven by a three-stage axial-flow turbine, of which the first two stages are cooled. An annular combustion chamber is used, with eight injectors and two igniters.

The engine is flat-rated to maintain its nominal output to 3,500m (11,500ft). TBO was 3,000 hours in the spring of 1966.

LENGTH (overall): 2,435mm (95·87in)
WEIGHT Dry: 499kg (1,100lb)
PERFORMANCE RATING: Max T-O with water injection: 2,859ch e (2,820ehp)

SUDOIMPORT

ul. Kaliaevskaja 5, Moscow K-6, USSR

Soviet industry has developed a variety of marine diesel engines, selected models of which have been installed in the Krasnoye Sormovo series of hydrofoil craft. Most popular of these are the 1,100hp M401 powering the Kometa hydrofoil, and the 1,200hp M50 powering the Byelorus, Chaika, Meteor, Mir, Raketa, Sputnik, Strela and Vikhr hydrofoils. A third marine diesel engine is the 3D12 with a continuous rating of 300hp. A version of this engine is installed in the Nevka hydrofoil, now in series production in Leningrad.

These and other marine diesels are available through Sudoimport, USSR marine export, import and repair organisation.

TYPE M 400

TYPE: Water-cooled, 12-cylinder, V-type four-stroke supercharged marine diesel engine.
CYLINDERS: Two banks of six cylinders set at 30 degrees, each bank comprising cast aluminium alloy monobloc with integral head. Pressed-in liner with spiral cooling passages comprises inner alloy steel sleeve with nitrided working surface, and outer carbon steel sleeve. Each monobloc retained on crankcase by 14 holding-down studs. Bore 180mm (7·09in). Stroke 200mm (7·87in). Cubic capacity 62·4 litres (3,810in³). Compression ratio 13·5 : 1.
SUPERCHARGING: Single-stage centrifugal supercharger, mechanically driven and providing supercharging pressure of at least 1·55kg/cm² (22lb/in²) at rated power.
CRANKCASE: Two-part cast aluminium alloy case with upper half carrying cylinder monoblocs, and transmitting all engine loads.
CYLINDER HEADS: Integral with cylinder monoblocs.
CRANKSHAFT: Six-crank seven-bearing crankshaft in nitrided alloy steel with split steel shells, lead bronze lined with lead-tin alloy bearing surface. Spring damper at rear end reduces torsional vibrations.
CONNECTING RODS: Master and articulated rods, with master connected to crankshaft by split big end with lead bronze lining. Articulated rods connected by pin pressed into eye of master rods.
PISTONS: Forged aluminium alloy with four rings, upper two of which are of trapeziform cross-section. Alloy steel floating gudgeon pin. Piston head specially shaped to form combustion chamber with spherical cylinder head.
CAMSHAFTS: Two camshafts acting direct on valve stems.
VALVES: Four valves in each cylinder, two inlet and two exhaust. Each valve retained on seat by three coil springs.
COOLING: Forced circulation system using fresh water with 1 to 1·1% potassium bichromate added. Fresh water pump mounted on forward part of engine. Fresh water, and lubricating oil leaving the engine are cooled by water-to-water and water-to-oil coolers, in turn cooled by sea water circulated by engine-mounted sea water pump.
SUPERCHARGING: Single-stage centrifugal supercharger, mechanically driven and providing supercharging pressure of at least 1·55kg/cm² (22lb/in²) at rated power.
LUBRICATION: Comprises delivery pump together with full-flow centrifuge; twin-suction scavenge pump, double gauze-type strainers at inlet and outlet to oil system; and electrically-driven priming pump to prime engine with oil and fuel.
FUEL INJECTION: Closed-type fuel injection with hydraulically-operated valves, giving initial pressure of 200kg/cm² (2,845lb/in²). Each injector has eight spray orifices forming 140 degree conical spray. High pressure 12-plunger fuel injection pump with primary gear pump. Two filters in parallel filter oil to HP pump.
STARTING: Compressed air system with starting cylinder operating at 75 to 150kg/cm² (1,067 to 2,134lb/in²) two disc-type air distributors and 12 starting valves.

Sudoimport M400

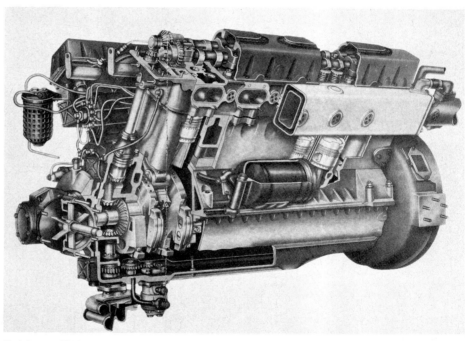

Sudoimport 3D12

GOVERNOR: Multi-range indirect-action engine speed governor with resilient gear drive from pump camshaft. Governor designed to maintain pre-set rpm throughout full speed range from minimum to maximum.
EXHAUST SYSTEM: Fresh water-cooled exhaust manifolds fastened to exterior of cylinder blocs. Provision made for fitting thermocouple or piezometer.
REVERSING: Hydraulically-operated reversing clutch fitted to enable prop shaft to run forwards, idle or reverse with constant direction of crankshaft rotation.
MOUNTING: Supports fitted to upper half of crankcase for attaching engine to bedplate.
DIMENSIONS
Length: 2,600mm (102·36in)
Width: 1,220mm (48·03in)
Height: 1,250mm (49·21in)
PERFORMANCE RATINGS
Max: 1,100hp at 1,800rpm
Continuous: 1,000hp at 1,700rpm

FUEL CONSUMPTION: At continuous rating: not over 193g (0·425lb)/hp/h
OIL CONSUMPTION: At continuous rating: not over 6g (0·013lb)/hp/h

TYPE 3D12

TYPE: Water-cooled, 12-cylinder, V-type, four-stroke marine diesel engine.
CYLINDERS: Two banks of six cylinders in jacketed blocks with pressed-in steel liners. Bore 150mm (5·9in). Stroke 180mm (7·09in). Cubic capacity 38·8 litres (2,370in³). Compression ratio 14 to 15 : 1.
CRANKCASE: Two-part cast aluminium alloy case with upper half accommodating seven main bearings of steel shell, lead bronze lined type. Lower half carries oil pump, water circulating pump and fuel feed pump.
CYLINDER HEADS: Provided with six recesses to accommodate combustion chambers. Each chamber is connected via channel to inlet and outlet ports of cylinder bloc.

CRANKSHAFT: Alloy steel forging with seven journals and six crankpins. Pendulum anti-vibration dampers fitted on first two webs to reduce torsional vibration.

CONNECTING RODS: Master and articulated rods of double-T section forged in alloy steel. Master rod big-end bearings have steel shells, lead bronze lined. Small end bearings of master rods and both bearings of articulated rods have bronze bushes.

PISTONS: Aluminium alloy.

CAMSHAFTS: Carbon steel camshafts with cams and journals hardened by high frequency electrical current.

COOLING: Closed water, forced circulation type incorporating centrifugal pump, self suction sea water pump and tubular water cooler.

LUBRICATION: Forced circulation type with dry sump, incorporating three-section gear pump, oil feed pump, wire-mesh strainer with fine cardboard filtering element and tubular oil cooler.

FUEL INJECTION: Rotary fuel feed pump, twin felt filter, plunger fuel pump with device to stop engine in event of oil pressure drop in main line. Closed-type fuel injectors with slotted filters. Plunger pump carries variable-speed centrifugal governor for crankshaft rpm.

STARTING: Main electrical starting system, with compressed air reverse system.

REVERSE-REDUCTION GEAR: Non-co-axial type with twin-disc friction clutch and gear-type reduction gear giving optional ratios, forwards, of 2·95 : 1, 2·04 : 1 or 1·33 : 1, and 2·18 : 1 astern.

DIMENSIONS
Length: 2,464mm (97·01in)
Width: 1,052mm (41·42in)
Height: 1,159mm (45·63in)
WEIGHT Dry fully equipped: 1,900kg (4,189lb)
PERFORMANCE RATING: Continuous 300hp at 1,500rpm
FUEL CONSUMPTION: At continuous rated power: 176g (0·388lb)/hp/h
OIL CONSUMPTION: At continuous rated power: not over 9g (0·02lb)/hp/h

M401A

The M401A, fitted to the Voskhod and the latest variants of the Kometa and Raketa, is based on the M50. The new engine is more reliable than its predecessor and its development involved the redesigning of a number of units and parts, as well as the manufacturing of components with a higher degree of accuracy, which necessitated the employment of the latest engineering techniques.

The engine is manufactured in left hand and right hand models. These differ by the arrangement on the engine housing of the fresh water pump drive and the power take-off for the shipboard compressor.

TYPE: Water-cooled, 12-cylinder, V-type four-stroke supercharged marine diesel.

CYLINDERS: Two banks of six cylinders set at 60 degrees. Monobloc is a solid aluminium cast-

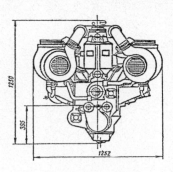
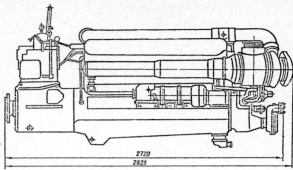

M401A water cooled 12-cylinder, V-type four-stroke supercharged marine diesel

ing. Pressed into monobloc are six steel sleeves with spiral grooves on the outer surface for the circulation of cooling water. Bore 180mm (7·09in). Stroke 200mm (7·87in). Compression ratio 13·5 : 0·5.

CRANKCASE: Two-piece cast aluminium alloy case with upper half carrying cylinder monoblocs and transmitting all engine loads.

CYLINDER HEADS: Integral with cylinder monobloc.

CRANKSHAFT: Six-crank, seven bearing crankshaft in nitrided alloy steel with split steel shells, lead-tin bronze lined with lead tin alloy bearing surface.

CONNECTING RODS: Master and articulated rods, with master connected to the crankshaft by split big end, lined with lead tin bronze. Articulated rod connected to crankshaft by a pin pressed into its eye ring.

PISTONS: Forged aluminium alloy with five rings. Top two steel rings, one cast iron of rectangular section and the two bottom rings, in cast iron and steel, are oil control rings fitted in a common groove.

CAMSHAFTS: Two, acting directly on valve stems.

VALVES: Four in each cylinder, two inlet and two exhaust. Each retained on seat by three coil springs.

SUPERCHARGING: Two, Type TK-18H superchargers, each comprising an axial-flow turbine and a centrifugal compressor mounted on a common shaft with a vane diffuser and volute. A silencer can be installed on the compressor air inlet. Turbine casing cooled with fresh water from the diesel engine cooling system.

GOVERNOR: Multi-range indirect action engine speed governor with resilient gear drive from pump camshaft. Designed to maintain preset rpm throughout full speed range.

LUBRICATION: Delivery pump with full-flow centrifuge, scavenge pump, double gauge strainers and electrically driven priming pump to power engine with oil and fuel.

COOLING: Double-circuit forced circulation system using fresh water with 1 to 1·1% potassium bichromate to GOST2652-71. Fresh water

pump mounted on engine. Fresh water and lubricating oil leaving engine are cooled by water-to-water and water-to-oil coolers in turn cooled by sea water circulated by engine-mounted sea water pump.

STARTING: Compressed air system with two disc-type air distributors and twelve starting valves.

REVERSING: Hydraulically operated reversing clutch to enable propeller shaft to run forwards, idle or reverse. Manual control available in emergency.

Rated power at ahead running under normal atmospheric conditions and at rated rpm: 1,000hp
Rated rpm at ahead running: 1,550
Max hourly power at maximum rpm: 1,100hp
Max rpm at ahead running: 1,600
Max power at astern running: 250hp
Minimum rpm at astern running (with the diesel engine control lever at reverse stop): 750
Max specific fuel consumption at rated power (with operating generator, hydraulic pump and the power take-off for compressor): 172 g/ehp/h+ 5%
Max specific oil burning losses at rated power: 5 g/ehp/h
Fuel:
Diesel fuel Grade (GOST 4749—49) Oil MC-20 (GOST 4749—49) with additive (GOST 8312-57) 3% in weight
Sense of power take-off flange rotation (if viewed from turbo-supercharger):
of right hand diesel engine: clockwise
of left hand diesel engine: counter-clockwise
Operating life (until major overhaul): 2,500 hours
Diesel engine dimensions:
length: (with muffler at intake) 2,825mm (111·1in)
length: (without muffler at intake) 2,720mm (107in)
width: 1,252mm (49·29in)
height: 1,250mm (49·21in)
Weight (dry) with all units and pipe lines mounted: 2,000kg (4,409lb)

UNITED KINGDOM

PAXMAN DIESELS LIMITED
(a management company of GEC Diesels Limited)

Hythe Hill, Colchester, Essex CO1 2HW, England

Manufactured at the Colchester Works of Paxman Diesels Ltd are three of the world's most advanced diesel designs; the V-form 'Ventura', built in 6, 8, 12 and 16-cylinder sizes covering 450 to 2,400bhp, the RP200 built in 8, 12 and 16 cylinder sizes covering 1,000-4,500bhp, and the Paxman 'Deltic'—an 18-cylinder engine of unique triangular configuration—in powers from 1,500 to 4,000shp. These engines, with their compact overall dimensions and low unit weight, are particularly suitable for the propulsion of high-speed craft including hydrofoils and hovercraft.

The 'Ventura' is being incorporated in several current designs for hydrofoils and rigid sidewall ACVs.

VENTURA (YJ) AND VALENTA (RP200) DIESELS

TYPE: Ventura engines: Direct injection 60 degree, V-form 6, 8, 12 and 16-cylinder, turbocharged or turbocharged and after-cooled four stroke diesel engine. Valenta engines: Direct injection, V-form 8, 12, 16 and 18 cylinder, turbocharged and water-cooled, four-stroke engine.
OUTPUT: Ventura engines: 450-2,400bhp, 1,000-1,600rpm. Valenta engines: 1,000-4,560bhp, 1,000-1,600rpm.
BORE AND STROKE: 197 × 216mm (7·75 × 8·5in).
SWEPT VOLUME (per cylinder): 6·57 litres (401in³).

HOUSING: Fabricated high quality steel plate.

CRANKSHAFT AND MAIN BEARINGS: Fully nitrided shaft carried in aluminium tin pre-finished steel-backed main bearings. Engine fully balanced against primary and secondary forces.

CONNECTING RODS: Fork and blade type with steel-backed, aluminium tin lined large end (forked rod) and steel-backed, lead bronze lined, lead tin flashed bearings (blade rod).

PISTONS: Conventional aluminium alloy, oil cooled with Alfin bonded insert for top ring. Three compression rings and one oil control ring (Ventura): Three compression rings and one oil control ring (Valenta).

CYLINDER HEAD: High grade casting carrying four valve direct injection system.

LINERS: Wet type seamless steel tube, chrome plated bore and water side surface honeycombed for surface oil retention.

FUEL INJECTION: External Monobloc pumps located below air manifolds (Ventura); single unit pumps (Valenta). Pump plungers and camshaft lubricated from main engine pressure system. Feed and injection pump driven from engine drive and gear train; a fuel reservoir and air bleed system fitted. Injectors of the multi-hole type spray fuel into the toroidal cavity in the top of piston. Injectors retained by clamp and are external to head cover (Ventura); sleeved connection inside cover (Valenta).

GOVERNOR: Standard hydraulic 'Regulateurs Europa' unit with self-contained lubricating oil system; mechanical, electrical or pneumatic controls. Alternative makes available.

PRESSURE CHARGING AND INTER-COOLING: Napier water-cooled exhaust-gas-driven turboblowers mounted above engine. Air to water intercooler of Serck manufacture for after-cooled versions.

LUBRICATION: Pressure lubrication to all bearing surfaces; separate pressure and cooling pumps (Ventura): single pump system (Valenta). Oil coolers mounted externally and integral with engine (fresh water-cooled (Ventura); sea water cooled (Valenta)). Full flow single or duplex oil filter can be supplied. Centrifugal filters fitted as standard (Ventura).

FRESH WATER COOLING: Single pump at free end, shaft-driven from drive end gear train. Thermostatic control valve mounted above pump, giving quick warm-up and even temperature control of water and oil circuits (Ventura); oil thermostat (Valenta).

EXHAUST: Single outlet from turboblower(s). Dry type manifolds (Ventura); watercooled manifolds (Valenta).

STARTING: Air, electric or hydraulic starting.

FUEL: Gas oil to BS.2869/1970 Class A1 and A2 or equivalent, and certain gas turbine fuels. Other classes of fuel subject to specification being made available.

LUBRICATING OIL: Oils certified to MIL-L-46152 (with a TBN of not less than nine).

OPTIONAL EXTRA EQUIPMENT: Gearboxes, starting control systems, and all associated engine ancillary equipment necessary for marine applications.

Paxman 18-cylinder Valenta marine diesel developing 4,500bhp

Deltic charge-air cooled, turbo-charged diesel engine with integral reverse reduction gear, developing 4,000shp

DELTIC DIESEL

TYPE: 18-cylinder, opposed piston, liquid cooled, two-stroke, compression ignition. Three banks of six cylinders in triangular configuration.

OUTPUT: Covers horsepower range of 1,500-4,000shp. Charge-cooled engine rating up to 3,000shp continuous at 1,800rpm. Half hour sprint rating up to 4,000shp at 2,100rpm. Weight/power ratio 3·94lb/shp.

BORE AND STROKE: Bore 130·17mm (5·125in). Stroke 184·15mm × 2 (7·25in × 2) (opposed piston).

SWEPT VOLUME: (total): 88·3 litres (5,284in³).

COMBUSTION SYSTEM: Direct injection.

PISTONS: Two piece—body and gudgeon pin housing. Gudgeon pin housing with fully floating gudgeon pin shrunk into body and secured with taper seated circlip. Body skirt and gudgeon pin housing in light alloy, piston crown in 'Hidurel' material. Oil cooled. Three gas, two oil control and one scraper ring.

CONNECTING RODS: Fork and blade type with steel backed, lead bronze, lead flashed, indium infused thin-wall bearings. Manufactured from drop forgings, machined and polished all over.

CRANKSHAFTS: Three crankshafts machined from forgings and fully nitrided. Each shaft fitted with viscous type torsional vibration damper. Each crankpin carries one inlet and one exhaust piston, thus the loading on all crankpins is identical and reciprocating forces are balanced within the engine.

CRANKCASES AND CYLINDER BLOCKS: Three crankcases and three cylinder blocks arranged in the form of an inverted equilateral triangle all of light alloy construction. Crankcases substantially webbed and carrying each crankshaft in seven, thin-wall, steelbacked, lead bronze, lead flashed indium infused main bearings. Cylinder blocks each carry six 'wet' liners, have integrally cast air inlet manifolds and mount the injection pumps camshaft casings.

CYLINDER LINERS: 18 'wet' type liners machined from hollow steel forgings, bores chrome plated with honeycomb process applied, finished by lapping. Coolant side flash tin plated. In areas of liquid contact with exhaust coolant-area, flash chrome plated.

TURBOCHARGER: Geared-in type, single stage, axial flow turbine and single-sided centrifugal compressor mounted on common shaft. Light alloy main castings. Charge-cooled engines have charge-air coolers (one for each cylinder block) incorporated within the overall dimensions of the turbocharger unit.

PHASING GEAR: To combine the output from the three crankshafts. A light alloy gear casing containing an output gear train linked to the crankshafts by quill-shafts and passing the torque to a common output gear. All gears hardened and ground and carried in roller bearings. Gear train also provides drives for auxiliary pumps and engine governor.

FUEL SYSTEM: Pressurised system from engine driven circulating pump supplying 18 'jerk' type fuel injection pumps one per cylinder mounted in banks of six on camshaft casings secured to each cylinder block. Each pump supplies a single injector per cylinder.

LUBRICATION: Dry sump system with engine driven pressure and scavenge pumps. Twin pressure oil filters engine mounted.

COOLING: Closed circuit system with engine driven circulating pump. Engine mounted circulating pumps for sea-water system for cooling coolant heat exchanger and oil cooler, also for charge-air coolers.

STARTING: Air starting to six cylinders of one bank.

MOUNTING: Four points by resilient mounting units.

REVERSE GEAR: Marine reverse reduction gearbox incorporating a hydraulic friction clutch can be supplied as an integral unit.

ROLLS-ROYCE LIMITED
(Industrial & Marine Division)

PO Box 72, Ansty, Coventry, Warwickshire CV7
9JR, England
Telephone: 0203 613211
Telex: 31637

In April 1967 Rolls-Royce Limited formed a
new division merging the former industrial and
marine gas-turbine activities of Rolls-Royce and
Bristol Siddeley. The new division was known as
the Industrial & Marine Gas-Turbine Division of
Rolls-Royce.

In May 1971 the present company, Rolls-
Royce Limited, was formed combining all the
gas-turbine interests of the former Rolls-Royce
company.

It offers a wider range of industrial and marine
gas turbines based on aero-engine gas generators
than any other manufacturer in the world. It has
available for adaptation a large selection of the
gas turbines being developed and manufactured
by the Rolls-Royce Derby Engine Division, the
Bristol Engine, and Small Engine Divisions.
Marinised gas turbines at present being produced
and developed by the company include the
Gnome, Proteus, Tyne, Olympus and Spey.

Over 2,017 of these marine and industrial
engines are in service or have been ordered for
operation around the world. Twenty-three navies
and nine civil operators have selected the company's marine gas turbines to power naval craft,
following the initial orders from the Royal Navy
in the late 1950s.

HYDROFOILS: The Boeing PCH High Point is
powered by two Proteus gas turbines while single
Proteus turbines power the CNR-Alinavi
Swordfish. A Tyne powers the Grumman
designed PGH-1 Flagstaff and the Super Flagstaff. Rolls-Royce marine gas turbines can also
be specified as alternative power plants for the
modular version of the Boeing Jetfoil.

HOVERCRAFT: The Gnome powers the BHC

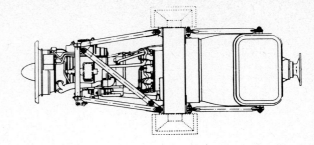

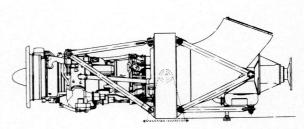

Tyne RM2 configuration

Rolls-Royce Marine Tyne RM2D rated at 6,000bhp

SR.N5 and SR.N6. The Proteus powers the
SR.N4, the BH.7 and the Vosper Thornycroft
VT 2.

MARINE GNOME

TYPE: Gas turbine, free-turbine turboshaft.
AIR INTAKE: Annular 15°C.
COMBUSTION CHAMBER: Annular.
FUEL GRADE
  DERD 2494 Avtur/50 Kerosene.
  DERD 2482 Avtur/40 Kerosene.
Diesel fuel: BSS 2869 Class A, DEF 1402 or
NATO F75
TURBINE: Two-stage axial-flow generator tur-
bine and a single-stage axial-flow free power tur-
bine.

BEARINGS: Compressor rotor has a roller bearing at the front and a ball bearing at the rear. Gas
generator turbine is supported at the front by the
compressor rear bearings, and at the rear by a
roller bearing.

Single stage power turbine is supported by a
roller bearing behind the turbine disc and by a
ball bearing towards the rear of the turbine shaft.
JET PIPE: Exhaust duct to suit installation.
ACCESSORY DRIVES: Accessory gearbox
provides a drive for : the fuel pump, the hydro-
mechanical governor in the flow control unit, the
centrifugal fuel filter, the dual tachometer and
the engine oil pump.
LUBRICATION SYSTEM: Dry sump.
OIL SPECIFICATION: DERD 2487.

BOEING PCH-1 HIGH POINT

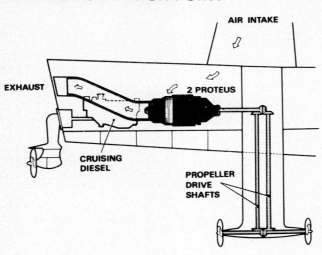

GRUMMAN PGH-1 FLAGSTAFF

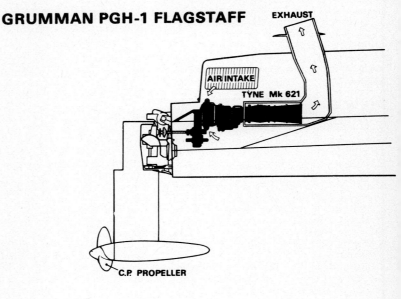

ITALIAN NAVY SWORDFISH

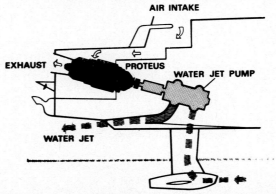

Rolls-Royce marine gas turbines are employed on the PCH-1 High Point, the PGH-1 Flagstaff and the Swordfish hydrofoils

MOUNTING: Front: three pads on the front frame casing, one on top, one on each side. Rear: without reduction gearbox, mounting point is the rear flange of the exhaust duct centre-body. With reduction gearbox mounting points are provided by two machined faces on the reduction gearbox.
STARTING: Electric.
DIMENSIONS
Length: 1,667mm (72·8in)
Width: 462mm (18·2in)
Height: 527mm (20·75in)
PERFORMANCE RATINGS
Max: 1,420bhp
Ratings are at maximum power-turbine speed, 19,500rpm. A reduction gearbox is available giving an output speed of 6,650rpm.
SPECIFIC FUEL CONSUMPTION
Max: 271g (0·597lb)/bhp/h
OIL CONSUMPTION
0·67 litres (1·2 pints)/h
Power turbine: 0·84 litres (1·5 pints)/h

MARINE OLYMPUS

Gas generator and single stage power turbine. Powered by the Marine Olympus, the TM3 module is a fully equipped enclosed power unit used for high speed operation by navies for modern warships.
TYPE: Gas turbine, two-shaft turbojet.
AIR INTAKE: Annular 15°C.
COMBUSTION CHAMBER: Eight.
FUEL GRADE: Diesel fuel BSS 2869 Class A. DEF 2402 or NATO F75.
TURBINE
ENGINE: Two stage, each stage driving its own respective compressor—5 stage low pressure or 7 stage high pressure.
POWER: Single stage axial flow.
BEARINGS: Compressor rotor forward end supported by a roller bearing and rear end by a duplex ball bearing.
The power turbine rotor assembly and mainshaft are supported as a cantilever in two white metal bearings housed in a pedestal.
JET PIPE: Exhaust duct to suit installation.
ACCESSORY DRIVES: Power turbine. Accessories are mounted on the main gearbox which is a separate unit transmitting the turbine's power output to the propeller shaft. These include pressure and scavenge oil pumps. Speed signal generator, iso-speedic switch and rpm indicator are driven by the pedestal-mounted accessory gearbox.
LUBRICATION SYSTEM: The gas generator has its own integral lubrication system which is supplied with oil from a 122·74 litre (27 gallon) tank. Components in the system are: a pressure pump, main scavenge pump, four auxiliary scavenge pumps and an oil cooler.
Power turbine: Bearings are lubricated and cooled by a pressure oil system.
OIL SPECIFICATION: Gas generator: D Eng RD 2487. Power turbine: OEP 69.
MOUNTING: The mounting structure depends on the customer's requirements for a particular application.
STARTING: Air or electric.
DIMENSIONS
GAS GENERATOR
Length: 3·6m (11ft 9in)
Width: 1·29m (4ft 3in)
POWER TURBINE
Length: 3·9m (12ft 9in)
Width: 2·4m (8ft)
Height: 3m (9ft 9in)
COMPLETE UNIT
Length: 6·8m (22ft 3in)
Width: 2·4m (8ft)
Height: 3m (9ft 9in)
WEIGHTS
Gas generator: 2,948·35kg (6,500lb)
Complete unit: 20·32 tonnes (20 tons)
PERFORMANCE RATING: Max: 29,600bhp at max power-turbine speed of 5,660rpm
SPECIFIC FUEL CONSUMPTION: Max: 211g (0·466lb)/bhp/h
OIL CONSUMPTION
GAS GENERATOR
Max: 0·84 litres (1·5 pints)/h
Power turbine: 0·84 litres (1·5 pints)/h

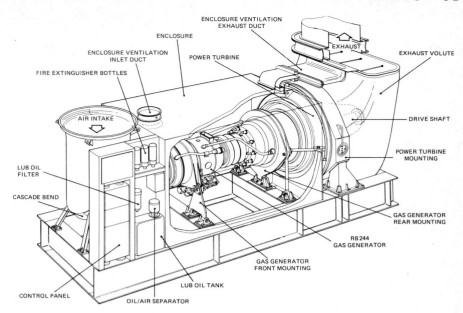

Rolls-Royce SM1A, rated at 16,750bhp

MARINE PROTEUS

TYPE: Gas turbine, free-turbine turboprop.
AIR INTAKE: Radial between the compressor and turbine sections of the engine. 15°C.
COMBUSTION CHAMBERS: Eight, positioned around the compressor casing.
FUEL GRADE: DEF 2402—Distillate diesel fuel.
TURBINE: Four stages coupled in mechanically independent pairs. The first coupled pair drive the compressor, the second pair form the free power turbine, which drives the output shaft.
BEARINGS: HP end of compressor rotor is carried by roller bearing, the rear end by a duplex ball bearing. Compressor turbine rotor shaft is located by a ball thrust bearing, as is the power turbine rotor.
JET PIPE: Exhaust duct to suit installation.
ACCESSORY DRIVES: All accessories are driven by the compressor or power turbine systems. Compressor driven accessories are: compressor tachometer generator, fuel pump and centrifugal oil separator for the breather. The power turbine tachometer generator and governor are driven by the power turbine. The main oil pressure pump and also the main and auxiliary scavenge pumps are driven by both the compressor and power turbines through a differential gear.
LUBRICATION SYSTEM: The engine is lubricated by a single gear type pump connected by a differential drive to both the compressor and power turbine systems.
OIL SPECIFICATION: OEP 71. DERD 2479/1 or DERD 2487 (OX 38).
MOUNTING: Three attachment points comprise two main trunnions one on each side of the engine close to the diffuser casing and a steady bearing located beneath the engine immediately aft of the air intake. Engines are supplied with integrally-mounted reduction gears giving maximum output shaft speeds of 5,240, 1,500 or 1,000rpm depending on the gearbox selected.
DIMENSIONS
Length: 2,870mm (113in)
Diameter: 1,067mm (42in)
WEIGHT Dry: 1,414kg (3,118lb)
PERFORMANCE RATINGS
Sprint: 5,000bhp
Max: 4,500bhp
SPECIFIC FUEL CONSUMPTION: At max rating: 256g (0·566lb)/bhp/h
OIL CONSUMPTION: Average: 0·28 litres (0·5 pints)/h

MARINE TYNE RM2D

Gas generator and two-stage power turbine.
TYPE: Gas turbine, two-shaft turboprop.
AIR INTAKE: Annular. 15°C.
COMBUSTION CHAMBER: Cannular containing ten flame tubes.

FUEL GRADE: Diesel fuel Grade A. DEF 2402B AVCAT.
TURBINE
ENGINE: Two-stage, each stage driving its own respective compressor—six-stage low pressure and nine-stage high pressure.
POWER: Two-stage, axial flow free turbine.
BEARINGS: Compressor rotor forward end supported by a roller bearing and at the rear end by a thrust ball location bearing.
The power turbine front stubshaft is supported on a roller bearing and the rear on a thrust bearing.
JET PIPE: Exhaust duct to suit installation.
ACCESSORY DRIVES: Engine and power turbines accessories are mounted on the external wheelcase of the engine and the primary gearbox accessories gearcase.
LUBRICATION SYSTEM: The gas generator lubricating oil system comprises fuel pump, scavenge pumps, filters, and magnetic plugs. The primary gearbox is also fed from the gas generator lubricating oil system.
OIL SPECIFICATION: DERD 2487
MOUNTING: The forward engine mounting comprises two cantilever frames constructed of tubular members, one each side of the engine. The frames are joined by a diagonal strut across the uppermost members.
The reduction gearbox is supported in a similar way by three tubular steel supports, one either side and one beneath the gearbox. The ends of the engine and gearbox supports are attached to the central main engine support frame by means of spherical bearings. The centre of the unit is supported through a dogged ring into the main central frame.
STARTING: Air or electric.
DIMENSIONS
Length: 4,013mm (158in)
Width: 1,270mm (50in)
Height: 1,400mm (54in)
WEIGHT: 2,815kg (6,200lb)
PERFORMANCE RATINGS
Max 6,000bhp (6,083cv) at max power turbine speed of 14,500rpm (primary gearbox output speed as required).
SPECIFIC FUEL CONSUMPTION
Max: 204·5g (0·451lb)/bhp/h

MARINE SM1A AND SM2B

The Marine SM1A and SM2B power units have been based on the Rolls-Royce RB244 gas generator derived from the Spey aero engine.
Both units offer high efficiency (in excess of 34%) and up to date features. They have been designed to fill the gap in the range of current marine gas turbines, and cater for a wide range of marine propulsion applications in the 1980s.
The SM1A unit has been designed for the

larger vessel, such as frigates, cruisers, destroyers etc, and the SM2B is for the lighter craft, such as hydrofoils, hovercraft and patrol boat applications.

The SM series of marine gas turbine has been under development since 1972 in a programme sponsored by the British Ministry of Defence.
TYPE: Marine gas turbine, incorporating two independently driven compressors, an axial-flow free-power turbine and exhaust volute, all on a lightweight mounting frame.
GAS GENERATOR CHARACTERISTICS
AIR INTAKE: Direct entry, fixed, without intake guides.
LP COMPRESSOR: 5 axial stages.
HP COMPRESSOR: 11 axial stages.
COMBUSTION SYSTEM: Turbo-annular type with ten interconnected straight flow flame tubes.
TURBINES: Impulse reaction, axial-type. Two HP and two LP stages.

EXHAUST: Fixed volume.
STARTING: Air/gas starter motor.
FUEL SYSTEM: Hydromechanical high pressure system with automatic acceleration and speed control.
FUEL GRADE: Diesel fuel Grade 'A', DEF 2402 or NATO F75.
LUBRICATION SYSTEM: Self-contained gear pump filters and chip detectors.
POWER TURBINE: Two-stage free axial-flow turbine.
DIMENSIONS
SM1A UNIT
Length: 7·46m (22ft 9in)
Width: 2·286m (7ft 6in)
Height: 3·073m (10ft 7in)
SM2B UNIT
Length (air intake flare to drive coupling): 6·063m (19ft 10½in)
Width: 2·286m (7ft 6in)

Height: 2·768m (9ft 1in)
GAS GENERATOR CHANGE UNIT DRY
Length: 2·667m (8ft 9in)
Max diameter: 910mm (3ft)
WEIGHTS
Estimated weight
 SM1A: 19,295kg (42,500lb)
 SM2B: 9,080kg (20,000lb)
Estimated dry weight of gas generator change unit: 1,406kg (3,100lb)
NOMINAL PERFORMANCE
*Max power: 17,100bhp (12·75MW)
*Specific fuel consumption: 0·239kg/kWh (0·393lb/bhp/h)
*Based on LCV of fuel of 43,125kJ/kg (18,540btu/lb)
No power off-takes
No intake or exhaust duct losses
Ambient air temperature of 15°C (59°F) and a pressure of 101·3kPa (14·7lbf/in²)

UNITED STATES OF AMERICA

AVCO LYCOMING
Avco Lycoming Division of Avco Corporation

550 South Main Street, Stratford, Connecticut 08497, USA
Telephone: (203) 378 8211
Telex: 964242
Officials:
Joseph S Bartos, *Vice President and General Manager, Lycoming Division*
Martin J Leff, *Vice President, Marketing and Product Support*
John W Treat, *Vice President, Manufacturing*
Charles Kuintzle, *Vice President, Engineering*
Donald Weidhuner, *Senior Vice President, Programs*

The Avco Lycoming Division, Stratford, is the turbine engine manufacturing division of the Avco Corporation.

Avco Lycoming manufactures a wide range of gas-turbine engines for helicopter, commuter jet, tanks and tracked vehicles, as well as for marine and industrial applications. Marine versions of the large turboshaft and turbofan T55 family are designated the TF25 and TF40.

TF25
The current production version of the TF25 is a high-speed shaft-turbine engine, with output shaft speed equal to power turbine speed. Integral oil tank and cooling system. An earlier TF25 powered the Vosper Thornycroft VT1, the Coastal Patrol Interdiction Craft (CPIC-X) and the Mitsui MV-PP15 155-seat hover ferry.
AIR INTAKE: Side inlet casting of aluminium alloy supporting optional reduction gearbox and front main bearings. Provision for intake screens.
COMPRESSOR: Seven axial stages followed by a single centrifugal stage. Two-piece aluminium alloy stator casing with one row of inlet guide vanes, and seven rows of steel stator blades, bolted to steel alloy diffuser casing to which combustion chamber casing is attached. Rotor comprises seven stainless steel discs and one titanium impeller mounted on shaft supported in forward thrust ball bearings and rear roller bearing. TF25 pressure ratio is 6 : 1.
COMBUSTION CHAMBER: Annular reverse flow type. Steel outer shell and inner liner. Twenty-eight fuel burners with downstream injection.
FUEL SYSTEM: Woodward fuel control system. Gear-type fuel pump, with gas producer and power shaft governors, flow control and shut-off valve.
FUEL GRADE: MIL-J-5624 grade JP-4, JP-5, MIL-F-46005 or marine diesel standard and wide-cut kerosene.
TURBINE: Two mechanically-independent axial-flow turbines. First turbine with single-stage drives compressor, has cored-out cast steel blades and is flange-bolted to outer co-axial drive shaft. Hollow stator vanes. Second, two-stage

Avco Lycoming TF25 marine/industrial gas turbine engine of 2,500shp

Avco Lycoming TF40 direct drive two-stage, free-power marine/industrial gas turbine, rated at 4,000shp continuous and 4,600shp boost power

turbine drives output shaft, has solid steel blades and is mounted on inner co-axial drive shaft.
EXHAUST UNIT: Fixed area nozzle, with inner cone, supported by six radial struts.
ACCESSORIES: Electric, air or hydraulic starter. Bendix-Scintilla TGLN high-energy ignition unit. Four igniter plugs.
LUBRICATION: Recirculating type. Integral oil tank and cooler.
OIL GRADE: MIL-L-17808, MIL-L-23699.
DIMENSIONS
Length: 1·27m (50·1in)
Width: 0·87m (34·4in)
Height: 1·11m (43·8in)
WEIGHT Dry: 600kg (1,324lb)
PERFORMANCE RATINGS
Max intermittent (peak): 3,000shp
Max continuous (normal): 2,500shp
FUEL CONSUMPTION At max continuous rating: 0·62sfc 198 US gallons/h

TF40

The TF40 engine is a scaled-up TF25 with higher mass flow. It has a four-stage turbine section and variable-incidence inlet guide vanes. The first two compressor stages are transonic, and new atomising fuel nozzles are fitted.

Both the Jeff A (Aerojet General) and Jeff B (Bell Aerospace) AALCs employ earlier model TF40s. Jeff A employs six, each developing 3,350shp continuous. Four drive individual, steerable ducted propellers, and the remaining two drive separate centrifugal lift fans. In the case of Jeff B, the six engines are arranged in two groups of three, located port and starboard. Each trio drives a single propeller and lift system through integrated gears.

Other craft now powered by TF40s include the SEDAM N 500, which employs two for lift and three, mounted in separate nacelles, for propulsion, a twin hull waterjet ferry now in service in Scandinavia, two PSMM Mk 5 CODAG gunboats for Taiwan, each equipped with three TF40s and three DDA 12V 149 diesel engines, and two private yachts.
AIR INTAKE: Side inlet casting of aluminium alloy housing internal gearing and supporting power producer section and output drive shaft. Integral or separately mounted gears are operational. Provision for intake filters and/or silencers.
COMPRESSOR: Seven axial stages followed by a single centrifugal stage. Two-piece aluminium alloy stator casing, with one row of inlet guide vanes, and seven rows of steel stator blades bolted to steel alloy casing diffuser, to which combustion chamber casing is attached. Rotor

Cutaway of the Avco Lycoming TF40 marine/industrial gas turbine rated at 4,000shp continuous, 4,600shp 'boost' power

comprises seven stainless steel discs and one titanium impeller mounted on shaft supported in forward thrust ball bearing and rear roller bearing. TF40 pressure ratio is 7·2 : 1.
COMBUSTION CHAMBER: Annular reverse flow type. Steel outer shell and inner liner. Twenty-eight fuel burners with downstream injection.
FUEL SYSTEM: Woodward fuel control system. Gear-type fuel pump, with gas producer and power shaft governors, flow control and shut-off valve.
FUEL GRADE: MIL-T-5624, JP-4, JP-5; MIL-F-16884 diesel, standard and wide-cut kerosene.
TURBINE: Two mechanically-independent axial-flow turbines. First turbine, with two stages, drives compressor. It has cored-out cast steel blades and is flange-bolted to outer co-axial drive shaft. Hollow stator vanes. Second two-stage turbine drives output shaft. It has solid steel blades and is mounted on inner co-axial drive shaft. (Other features include: integral cast first

turbine nozzle, cooled first turbine blades in both first and second stages, second turbine vane cooling, and second turbine disc and blade cooling).
EXHAUST UNIT: Fixed area nozzle, with inner cone, supported by six radial struts.
ACCESSORIES: Electric, air or hydraulic starter. Bendix-Scintilla TGLN high-energy ignition unit. Four igniter plugs.
LUBRICATION: Recirculating type. Integral oil tank and cooler.
OIL GRADE: Synthetic base oils.
DIMENSIONS
Length: 1·32m (52·2in)
Width: 0·88m (34·4in)
Height: 1·11m (43·8in)
PERFORMANCE RATINGS
Max intermittent (at 15°C (59°F)—sea level): 4,600shp
Max continuous (at 15°C (59°F)—sea level): 4,000shp
FUEL CONSUMPTION: At max continuous rating: 0·54sfc 255 US gallons/h
OIL CONSUMPTION: 454g/h (1lb/h)

BRIGGS AND STRATTON CORPORATION

PO Box 702, Milwaukee, Wisconsin 53201, USA
Officials:
Frederick P Stratton Jr, *President and Chief Executive Officer*
Laverne J Socks, *Executive Vice President*
L William Dewey Jr, *Executive Vice President*
James L Bunda, *Vice President of Engineering*
Robert K Catterson, *Vice President of Research*
J Byron Smith, *Vice President of Production*
James F Sullivan, *Vice President Sales*

Central Service Distributors for Great Britain and Ireland:
Autocar Electrical Equipment Co Ltd, 16 Rippleside Commercial Estate, Ripple Road, Barking, Essex, England

Briggs & Stratton is a major American supplier of low-power four-stroke gasoline engines, an important application of which is in motor lawn mowers of both US and European manufacture. Several installations of Briggs & Stratton in ACVs have been made. These include the American Bartlett M-8 Flying Saucer, a small lightweight craft powered by a single 3hp Briggs & Stratton engine mounted above a central plenum chamber driving a two-bladed Banks-Maxwell Mod 30-14 30in diameter pusher propeller; and Coelacanth Gemco's Pluto two-seat

Engines offered by Briggs & Stratton

Series No	Bore (in)	Stroke (in)	Displacement	hp	Net weight (lb)
Vertical crankshaft types					
92500	2⁹/₁₆	1³/₄	9.02	3.0	19¹/₂
92900	2⁹/₁₆	1³/₄	9.02	3.5	19³/₄
110900	2²⁵/₃₂	1⁷/₈	11.39	4.0	21
111900	2²⁵/₃₂	1⁷/₈	11.39	4.0	24³/₄
130900	2⁹/₁₆	2⁷/₁₆	12.5	5.0	30³/₄
170700	3	2³/₈	16.7	7.0	43¹/₂
190700	3	2³/₄	19.44	8.0	44
191700	3	2³/₄	19.44	8.0	49
220700	3⁷/₈	2³/₈	22.04	10.0	59¹/₄
252700	3⁷/₁₆	2⁵/₈	24.36	11.0	59¹/₄
Horizontal crankshaft types					
60100	2³/₈	1¹/₂	6.65	2.0	22¹/₄
80200	2³/₈	1³/₄	7.75	3.0	24
80300	2³/₈	1³/₄	7.75	3.0	25¹/₄
100200	2¹/₂	2¹/₈	10.4	4.0	29¹/₂
111200	2²⁵/₃₂	1⁷/₈	11.39	4.0	25¹/₂
130200	2⁹/₁₆	2⁷/₁₆	12.5	5.0	30³/₄
170400	3	2³/₈	16.7	7.0	44¹/₂
190400	3	2³/₄	19.44	8.0	45
220400	3⁷/₁₆	2⁵/₈	24.36	10.0	63¹/₄
252400	3⁷/₁₆	2⁵/₈	24.36	11.0	63¹/₄
253400	3⁷/₁₆	2⁵/₈	24.36	11.0	68¹/₂

test vehicle which has two 7hp Briggs & Stratton engines each driving 42in fans, one for lift and a second for propulsion.

Briggs & Stratton is an acknowledged technological leader in the small engine field. In 1953 the company introduced a 2hp aluminium alloy engine which gave the industry an engine significantly lighter and less costly than the cast iron ones then in use. Over the years the company has developed and added to this line with successively higher horsepower aluminium alloy engines. Today, this line extends from 2 to 16hp.

All of the company's engine manufacturing facilities are located in the Milwaukee area. The aluminium alloy engines are assembled at the principal manufacturing plant in Wauwatosa which has over two million square feet of production space. The cast iron engines are assembled at the Milwaukee plant. Engine components are produced at both factories and at the two foundries in West Allis.

Recently, Briggs & Stratton purchased the Faryman Diesel GmbH & Co KG of Lampertheim, West Germany, which manufactures single and two-cylinder air and liquid cooled diesels offering from 5hp to 26hp.

Engines offered by Briggs & Stratton

Series No	Bore (in)	Stroke (in)	Displacement	hp	Net weight (lb)
Two cylinder types					
401417 (ducted)	$3^7/_{16}$	$2^5/_{32}$	40.00	16.0	$91^1/_2$
401417	$3^2/_{16}$	$2^5/_{32}$	40.00	16.0	$81^1/_2$
401717	$3^2/_{16}$	$2^5/_{32}$	40.00	16.0	$91^1/_2$
422437 (ducted)	$3^7/_{16}$	$2^9/_{32}$	42.33	18.0	93
422431	$3^7/_{16}$	$2^9/_{32}$	42.33	18.0	83
421707 (ducted)	$3^7/_{16}$	$2^9/_{32}$	42.33	18.0	93
Cast iron types					
233400	3	$3^1/_4$	22.97	9.0	$91^1/_4$
243430	$3^1/_{16}$	$3^1/_4$	23.94	10.0	96
326430	$3^9/_{16}$	$3^1/_4$	32.4	16.0	$106^1/_2$

CATERPILLAR TRACTOR CO

Industrial Division, Peoria, Illinois 61602, USA

Caterpillar Tractor Co Ltd is the UK subsidiary of the Caterpillar Tractor Co, a leading US manufacturer of diesels, which has supplied engines worldwide equivalent to hundreds of millions of diesel horsepower. Engines are sold for marine, electrical power and industrial applications, and are supported by more than 900 Caterpillar dealer facilities for parts and service; more than 14,000 dealer servicemen provide a 24-hour service to diesel operators. The engines are designed to give a high degree of component interchangeability.

MODELS 3304T, 3306T and 3306TA

TYPE: Four and six cylinder, straight in-line, four-stroke, water-cooled, turbo-charged, (plus after cooling on 3306TA) diesel engines. Counterclockwise rotation when viewed from the rear.
CYLINDERS: Bore 121mm (4·75in). Stroke 152mm (6in). Total swept volume 3304T 6·9 litres (425in³), 3306T and 3306TA 10·5 litres (638in³). Compression ratio 17·5 : 1. Cylinder liners cast from Molybdenum alloy iron, induction hardened full depth water cooling and specifically designed to give life equal to engine.
TURBO CHARGER AND AFTER COOLER: Single stage centrifugal air compressor driven by single stage centripetal turbine energised by exhaust gases. 3306TA has watercooled after cooler interposed between compressor air delivery and cylinder manifold. Complete system doubles air flow rate to cylinders and reduces exhaust temperature.
ACCESSORIES: Include fuel priming pump, 24 or 30-32 volt alternator, starter, hydraulic starting, air starting etc.
STARTING AND CONTROL SYSTEMS: Mechanical governor charging alternator 12 volt, electric start 12 volt.
GEAR RATIOS
3304 1·97:1; 2·96:1; 3·79:1; 4·48:1.
3306 2:1; 2·95:1; 3·83:1; 4·50:1.
DIMENSIONS
WITH GEAR
3304T
Length: 1,613mm (63·5in)
Width: 913mm (36in)
Height: 1,051mm (41·4in)
3306T
Length: 2,125mm (83·7in)
Width: 924mm (36·4in)
Height: 1,217mm (47·9in)
3306TA
Length: 2,019mm (79·5in)
Width: 934mm (36·8in)
Height: 1,108mm (43·6in)

Caterpillar 3406 Marine Generator set

PERFORMANCE RATINGS
3304T
Max intermittent: 160hp (shaft)
Max continuous: 121hp (shaft)
3306T
Max intermittent: 243hp (shaft)
Max continuous: 184hp (shaft)
3306TA
Max intermittent: 281hp (shaft)
Max continuous: 228hp (shaft)
FUEL CONSUMPTION
AT MAX CONTINUOUS RATING
3304T: 28·8 litres/h (7·6 US gallons/h)
3306T: 41·6 litres/h (11 US gallons/h)
3306TA: 50·7 litres/h (13·4 US gallons/h)

MODELS 3406T and TA, 3408T and TA, 3412T and TA

The basic features of these models are in general similar to the D330 and D333 series, with the following main differences.
TYPE: Eight and twelve 65 degree V in-line (3412 and 3408) and six cylinder straight in-line (3406) four-stroke, water-cooled, turbo-charged, after-cooled diesel engines. Counterclockwise rotation when viewed from the rear.
CYLINDERS: Bore 137mm (5·4in). Stroke 152mm (6in); except **3406** at 165mm (6·5in). Total swept volumes **3412** 27 litres (1,649in³); **3408** 18 litres (1,099in³); **3406** 14·6 litres (893in³).

TURBO-CHARGER AND AFTER-COOLER: As for Model 3306.

STANDARD EQUIPMENT: Hydromechanical governor. Fuel, oil pressure, temperature and service hour gauges. Gear-driven fuel priming, fuel transfer and water jacket pumps.

ACCESSORIES: These include heat exchangers, sea water pumps, air starting, hydraulic starting, 24 or 32 volt starting generator and glow plugs.

COOLING SYSTEM: Water jacket with pump.

CRANKSHAFT: Unique **3408** offset crankshaft produces smooth even spaced 90 degree V type power delivery from 65 degree V layout.

GEAR RATIOS
3412 2·0:1; 2·94:1; 3·54:1; 4·0:1; 4·67:1; 5·88:1; 7·08:1
3408 2:1; 2·5:1; 3:1; 3·5:1; 4·5:1; 6:1
3406 2:1; 2·5:1; 3:1; 3·5:1; 4·5:1; 6:1

DIMENSIONS
WITH GEAR
3412TA
Length: 3,309mm (130·3in)
Width: 1,270mm (50in)
Height: 1,647mm (64·9in)
3408TA
Length: 2,188mm (86·1in)
Width: 1,231mm (48·5in)
Height: 1,481mm (58·3in)

3406TA

Length: 2,385mm (93·9in)
Width: 1,011mm (39·8in)
Height: 1,562mm (61·5in)

WEIGHTS

TOTAL WITH GEAR

3412TA: 3,809kg (8,400lb)
3408TA: 2,371kg (5,228lb)
3406TA: 2,046kg (4,510lb)

PERFORMANCE RATINGS

SHAFT

3406T

Max intermittent: 315hp
Max continuous: 242hp

3406TA

Max intermittent: 364hp
Max continuous: 267hp

3408T

Max intermittent: 412hp
Max continuous: 291hp

3408TA

Max intermittent: 460hp
Max continuous: 354hp

3412T

Max intermittent: 436hp

3412TA

Max continuous: 504hp

FUEL CONSUMPTION

3406T: 53·8 litres/h (14·2 US gallons/h)
3406TA: 59·9 litres/h (15·8 US gallons/h)
3408T: 59·2 litres/h (15·6 US gallons/h)
3408TA: 75·6 litres/h (20 US gallons/h)
3412T: 89·3 litres/h (23·6 US gallons/h)
3412TA: 110·5 litres/h (29·2 US gallons/h)

MODEL D348

Basic features of these models are in general similar to the earlier series, with the following main differences.

TYPE: Twelve cylinder 60 degree V in-line four-stroke, water-cooled, turbo-supercharger-aftercooled diesel engine. Counterclockwise rotation viewed from rear.

CYLINDERS: Bore 137mm (5·4in). Stroke 165mm (6·5in). Total swept volume 29·3 litres (1,786in³). Compression ratio, 16·5 : 1. One-piece nickel-chrome alloyed grey iron cast cylinder block, precision bored and milled. Conventional studs on V models are complemented by extra length studs extending into bearing saddle area.

TURBO-SUPERCHARGER AND AFTER-COOLER: Turbo-charger similar to 3304 and 3306 models with addition of water-cooled aftercooler interposed between compressor air delivery and cylinder manifold. System doubles rate of airflow to engine and lowers exhaust temperatures.

ACCESSORIES: Hydro-mechanical governor gear-driven fuel priming and transfer pumps, gear-driven jacket-water pump.

COOLING SYSTEM: Jacket water pump minimum flow 22·1 litres/s (350 gallons/min).

GEAR RATIOS: **D348** 2·00 : 1; 2·94 : 1; 3·54 : 1; 4·00 : 1; 4·767:1; 5·88:1 and 7·07:1, **D349** 2 : 1; 2·94 : 1; 3·54 : 1; 4·67 : 1. All ratios at 1,800 engine continuous rpm.

DIMENSIONS

WITH GEAR

D348

Length: 2,963mm (116·4in)
Width: 1,527mm (60·12in)
Height: 1,938mm (76·3in)

WEIGHTS

DRY WITH GEAR

D348: 5,146kg (11,335lb)

PERFORMANCE RATINGS

D348

Max at 2,000rpm: 920hp (flywheel)
Continuous at 1,800rpm: 725hp (flywheel)
FUEL CONSUMPTION: D348: 144 litres/h (38 gallons/h) at 725hp

MODEL 3208

TYPE: Eight cylinder 90 degree V in-line, four-

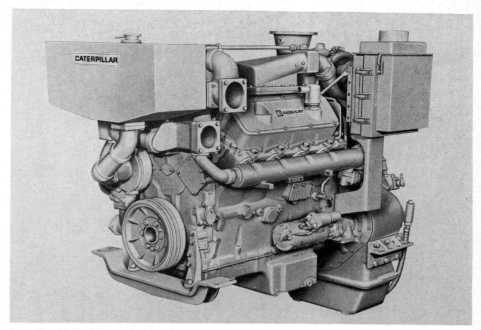

Caterpillar Model 3412 marine diesel engine

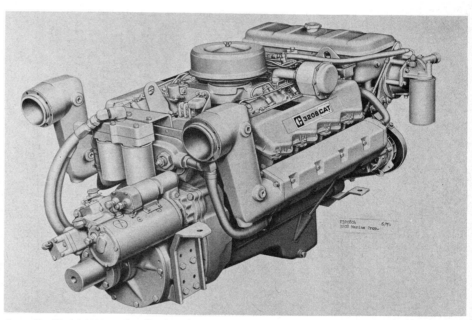

Caterpillar Model 3208 marine diesel engine

stroke, water-cooled naturally separated diesel engine.

CYLINDERS: Bore 114mm (4·5in). Stroke 127mm (5in). Total swept volume 10·4 litres (636in³). Compression ratio 16·5 : 1.

CRANKSHAFT: Forged, lightened, total hardened, 90 degree V results in balanced power strokes for smooth running. Regrindable at overhaul if needed.

CONNECTING RODS: Forged H-section rods. Computer-controlled grinding to precise balance.

FUEL SYSTEM: Fuel is fed from low pressure transfer pump to manifold. Separate pumps plunger for each cylinder driven by own crankshaft. System incorporates priming pump fuel filter and automatic variable timing.

COOLING SYSTEM: Water jacket cooling plus expansion tank with copper/nickel tube sea water exchanger. Jacket and sea water pumps are incorporated.

LUBRICATION SYSTEM: Gear driven six lobe oil pump passes oil through cooler and filters to oil gallery, supplying direct lubrication to all

bearing surfaces. The system employs positive crankshaft ventilation.

STARTING AND CONTROL SYSTEMS: 12 volt electric start and charging. Mechanical governor.

ACCESSORIES: Include marine gears, exhaust risers, 24 volt charging and starting system, gauges and instruments.

GEAR RATIOS: 1·50 : 1; 1·97 : 1; 2·50 : 1; 2·96 : 1 or 1·54 : 1; 2·00 : 1; 2·47 : 1 which are limited to pleasure craft applications.

DIMENSIONS

WITH GEAR

Length: 1,504mm (59·2in)
Width: 928mm (36·5in)
Height: 920mm (36·2in)

WEIGHT

Total: 816kg (1,800lb)

PERFORMANCE RATING

Max intermittent: 203hp (shaft)
Max continuous: 146hp (shaft)

FUEL CONSUMPTION: At max continuous rating: 29·9 litres/h (7·9 US gallons/h).

CUMMINS ENGINE COMPANY INC

Cummins Engine Company Inc, 1000 Fifth Street, Columbus, Indiana 47201, USA

Cummins Engine Company Ltd, Coombe House, St Georges Square, Maldon Road, New Maldon, Surrey, England

The Cummins Engine Company was formed in 1919 in Columbus, Indiana. It produces a wide range of marine diesel engines which are now manufactured and distributed internationally. In addition to manufacturing plants in the United States, the company also produces diesel engines in Brazil, India, Japan, Mexico and the United Kingdom. All these plants build engines to the same specifications thus ensuring interchangeability of parts and the same quality standards.

Cummins marine diesels power the Seaflight 46 (two VT8N-370-Ms) hydrofoil, and the Hovermarine 216 sidewall hovercraft.

On the latter, two VT8-370-Ms, each derated to 320bhp, supply propulsive power, and a single V-504-M, derated to 185bhp, drives the lift fans.

MODEL V-555-M

Horsepower: 240
Governed rpm: 3,300
Number of cylinders: 8
Bore and stroke: 117×104mm (4⅝×4⅛in)
Piston displacement: 9·095 litres (555in³)
Operating cycles: 4
Crankcase oil capacity: 22·73 litres (5 gallons)
Coolant capacity: 44 litres (9·5 gallons)
Net weight (engine less gear): 839·2kg (1,850lb)
BEARINGS: Precision type, steel backed inserts.
CAMSHAFT: Single camshaft controls all valve and injector movement. Induction hardened alloy steel with gear drive.
CAMSHAFT FOLLOWERS: Roller type for long cam and follower life.
CONNECTING RODS: Drop forged, 170·7mm (6·72in) centre to centre length. Taper piston pin end reduces unit pressure.
COOLER, LUBRICATING OIL: Tubular type, jacket water cooled.
CRANKSHAFT: High tensile strength steel forging. Bearing journals are induction hardened.
CYLINDER BLOCK: Alloy cast iron with removable wet liners. Cross bolt support to main bearing cap.
CYLINDER HEADS: Two, one each bank. All fuel lines are drilled passages. Individual intake and exhaust porting for each cylinder. Corrosion resistant inserts on intake and exhaust valve seats.
DAMPER, VIBRATION: Compressed rubber type.
FUEL SYSTEM: Cummins self adjusting system with integral flyball type governor. Camshaft actuated injectors.
GEAR TRAIN: Heavy duty, located rear of cylinder block.
LUBRICATION: Force feed to all bearings. Gear type pump.
PISTONS: Aluminium, cam ground, with two compression and one oil ring.
PISTON PINS: 38·1mm (1½in) diameter, full floating.
THERMOSTAT: Dual, modulating by-pass type.
VALVES: Dual intake and exhaust each cylinder. Each valve 41·3mm (1⅝in) diameter.
STANDARD EQUIPMENT:
CORROSION RESISTOR: Mounted, Cummins spin-on type, checks rust and corrosion, controls acidity, and removes impurities from coolant.
DIPSTICK, OIL: Port side when viewing engine from drive end.
ELECTRICAL EQUIPMENT: 12V, 58A ac system. Includes starting motor, alternator, regulator, magnetic switch and starting switch.
EXCHANGER, HEAT: Tubular type, mounted.
FILTERS: Cummins. Lubricating oil full flow paper element type, mounted. Fuel, spin-on, mounted.

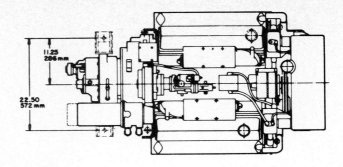

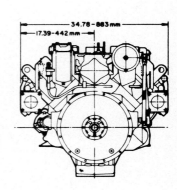

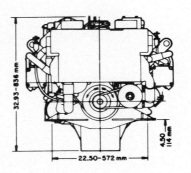

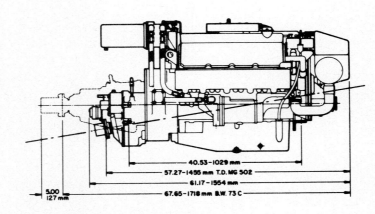

Cummins 8-cylinder V-555-M diesel, rated at 240hp

FLYWHEEL: For reverse and reduction gear.
GOVERNOR: Mechanical variable speed type.
HOUSING, FLYWHEEL: SAE No 3
INTAKE AIR: Silenced.
MANIFOLD, EXHAUST: Two, fresh water cooled.
PAN, OIL: Aluminium, rear sump type, 5 US gallon capacity.
PUMP, COOLANT: Belt driven, centrifugal type, 80 gallons/min at 3,300rpm.
PUMP, RAW WATER: Belt driven rubber impeller type, 48 gallons/min at 3,300rpm.
SUPPORT, ENGINE: Marine type, front and rear.

MODEL V-903-M

Horsepower: 295
Governed rpm: 2,600
Number of cylinders: 8
Bore and stroke: 139·7×120·6mm (5½×4¾in)
Piston displacement: 14·8 litres (903in³)
Operating cycles: 4
Oil pan capacity: 5 US gallons
Engine coolant capacity: 54·5 litres (12 gallons)
Net weight with standard accessories: 1,270kg (2,800lb)
BEARINGS: Precision type, steel backed inserts. Five main bearings, 95·2mm (3¾in) diameter. Connecting rod 79·3mm (3⅛in) diameter.

CAMSHAFT: Single camshaft controls all valve and injector movement. Induction hardened alloy steel with gear drive.
CAMSHAFT FOLLOWERS: Roller type for long cam and follower life.
CONNECTING RODS: Drop forged. Taper piston pin end provides superior load distribution and maximum piston crown material.
COOLER, LUBRICATING OIL: Tubular type, jacket water cooled.
CRANKSHAFT: High tensile strength steel forging. Bearing journals are induction hardened. Fully counterweighted.
CYLINDER BLOCK: Alloy cast iron with removable wet liners.
CYLINDER HEADS: Two, one each bank. All fuel lines are drilled passages. Individual intake and exhaust porting for each cylinder.
DAMPER, VIBRATION: Compressed rubber type.
FUEL SYSTEM: Cummins wear-compensating system with integral, flyball type, mechanical variable speed governor. Camshaft actuated injectors.
LUBRICATION: Force feed to all bearings. Gear type pump.
MAIN BEARING CAPS: Cross bolted for rigidity.
PISTONS: Aluminium, cam ground, with two compression and one oil ring.

PISTON PINS: 44·4mm (1¾in) diameter, full floating.

THERMOSTAT: Single unit, modulating by-pass type.

VALVES: Dual intake and exhaust each cylinder. Each valve 47·9mm (1⅞in) diameter. Heat and corrosion resistant face on all valves.

STANDARD EQUIPMENT:

CLEANER, AIR: Silencer type.

CORROSION RESISTOR: Cummins. Mounted. Throw-away unit. Checks rust and corrosion, controls acidity, and removes impurities from coolant.

DIPSTICK, OIL: Port side when viewing engine from drive end.

ELECTRICAL EQUIPMENT: 12V, 55A ac system. Includes starting motor alternator, regulator, and starting switch.

EXCHANGER, HEAT: Tubular type, mounted.

FILTERS: Cummins. Lubricating oil, full flow replaceable paper element type, mounted. Fuel, paper element throw-away type, mounted.

FLYWHEEL: For reverse and reduction gear.

GEAR, MARINE: Capitol 4HE-10200, 2:1 reverse and reduction gear with propeller shaft companion flange.

GOVERNOR: Mechanical variable speed type.

HOUSING, FLYWHEEL: SAE No 2.

MANIFOLD, AIR INTAKE: Two, located on inside of engine Vee.

MANIFOLD, EXHAUST: Two, fresh water cooled, with outlet to rear.

PAN, OIL: Aluminium, front sump type, 5 US gallon capacity.

PUMP, COOLANT: Gear driven, centrifugal type, 78 gallons/min at 2,600 rpm.

PUMP, RAW WATER: Gear driven, 61 gallons/min at 2,600 rpm.

SUPPORT, ENGINE: Marine type, 571mm (22½in) centres.

MODEL KTA-1150-M

Power rating, max: 388kW (520bhp)
Governed rpm: 1,950
Power rating, continuous: 350kW (470bhp)
Governed rpm: 1,800
Number of cylinders: 6
Bore and stroke: 159 × 159mm (6¼ × 6¼in)
Piston displacement: 18·86 litres (1,150in³)

Operating cycles: 4
Lube system oil capacity: 59 litres (15·5 US gallons)
Coolant capacity: 34·9 litres (9 US gallons)
Net weight, dry: 1,725kg (3,800lb)

AFTERCOOLER: Two. Jacket water cooled.

BEARINGS: Precision type, steel backed inserts. Seven main bearings 140mm (5½in) diameter. Connecting rod 102mm (4in) diameter.

CAMSHAFT: Single camshaft controls all valve and injector movement. Induction hardened alloy steel with gear drive.

CAMSHAFT FOLLOWERS: Roller type for long cam and follower life.

CONNECTING RODS: Drop forged 290mm (11·4in) centre to centre length. Rifle drilled for pressure lubrication of piston pin. Taper piston pin end reduces unit pressures.

CRANKSHAFT: High tensile strength steel forging. Bearing journals are induction hardened. Fully counterweighted.

CYLINDER BLOCK: Alloy cast iron with removable, wet liners.

CYLINDER HEADS: Individual cylinder heads. Drilled fuel supply and return lines. Corrosion resistant inserts on intake and exhaust valve seats.

FUEL SYSTEM: Cummins PTᴛᴍ self adjusting system with integral flyball type governor. Camshaft actuated injectors.

GEAR TRAIN: Heavy duty, induction hardened, located at front of cylinder block.

LUBRICATION: Force feed to all bearings, gear type pump. All lubrication lines are drilled passages, except pan to pump suction line.

PISTONS: Aluminium, cam ground, with two compression and one oil ring. Oil cooled.

PISTON PINS: 61mm (2·4in) diameter, full floating.

TURBOCHARGER: Scroll diffuser, side mounted.

VALVES: Dual intake and exhaust each cylinder. Each valve 56mm (2·22in) diameter. Heat and corrosion resistant face on intake and exhaust valves.

STANDARD EQUIPMENT:

AIR CLEANER: Two stage dry type for vertical mounting.

COOLER, LUBRICATING OIL: Plate type, jacket water cooled.

CORROSION RESISTOR: Fleetguard, mounted, dual spin-on type.

DAMPER, VIBRATION: Viscous type.

DIPSTICK, OIL: Mounted on either port or starboard side of engine.

DRIVE, ALTERNATOR: High capacity, poly-v belt arrangement driven from accessory drive pulley.

ELECTRICAL EQUIPMENT: 24 or 32 volt positive engagement starting motor and 24 or 32 volt ignition proof alternators with built-in voltage regulators.

EXHAUST OUTLET CONNECTIONS: Straight or 90 degree turbo exhaust connection for adapting 127mm (5in) piping.

EXCHANGER, HEAT: Copper-nickel tubular type, engine mounted.

FILTERS: Fleetguard. Lubricating oil: spin-on, full flow, paper element type, mounted on either port or starboard side of engine and by-pass type, not mounted. Fuel: dual spin-on, paper element type, mounted.

FLYWHEEL: For 356 to 457mm (14 to 18in) over centre clutch, reverse and reduction gear.

GEAR, MARINE: Twin Disc MG-521: 2·19 : 1, 3·03 : 1, 4·09 : 1. Twin Disc MG-527: 3·86 : 1, 5·18 : 1. Capitol HP 6900 : 2·5 : 1. Capitol HP 7700 : 3·5 : 1, 4·5 : 1. Capitol HP 28000: 5·16 : 1, 6 : 1.

GOVERNOR: Mechanical variable speed.

HOUSING, FLYWHEEL: SAE O with marine mounting pads.

MANIFOLD, EXHAUST: Water cooled.

PAN, OIL: Aluminium, rear sump type, 37·9 litres (10 US gallon) capacity.

PANEL, INSTRUMENT: Not mounted. Includes ammeter, tachometer or hour meter, lube oil temperature gauge, oil pressure gauge and engine water temperature gauge.

POWER TAKE-OFF: Front mounted. Twin Disc clutch models SP-114 for up to 112kW (150hp) and SL-214 for up to 161kW (215hp).

PUMP, COOLANT: Gear driven, centrifugal type 700 litres/min (185 gallons/min) at 1,950rpm.

SHIELD, BELT: For alternator drive.

STARTING AID: Manual ether cold start aid.

SUPPORT, ENGINE: Three point marine type, front cover, and marine gear.

DETROIT DIESEL ALLISON
(Division of General Motors Corporation)

General Offices: PO Box 894, Indianapolis, Indiana 46206, USA
Telephone: (317) 244 1511

Detroit Diesel Allison has been active in the development of gas turbines for aircraft, industrial and marine use for many years. Production of the first Allison gas turbine began in the 1940s, when the company built the power plant for the P-59, the first jet-powered aircraft to fly in the United States.

Later, the Allison T56 turboprop aircraft engine was developed. It demonstrated outstanding reliability and the same basic design has been adapted for industrial and marine applications. In the early 1960s, the first Allison 501-K gasturbine powered electric powerplant went into service. Today, almost 660 501-K industrial series engines are used not only in electric powerplants but also in industrial and marine applications. The two-shaft marine engine powers the Boeing Jetfoil, Halter crewboats and more recently has been installed in Westermoen catamarans and the Grumman M161 hydrofoil for primary propulsion.

ALLISON 501-K SERIES

The Allison 501-K series industrial gas turbine incorporates a 14-stage axial-flow compressor, with bleed valves to compensate for compressor surge.

Of modular design, it comprises three main

Detroit Diesel Allison 501-KF two-shaft marine gas turbine

sections: the compressor, combustor and turbine. Each section can be readily separated from the other. Modular design provides ease in handling and servicing of the engine.

The first stage of the four-stage turbine section

is air-cooled, permitting the engine to be operated at higher than normal turbine inlet temperatures.

The combustor section of the 501-K consists of six combustion chambers of the through-flow type, assembled within a single annular chamber. This multiple provides even temperature distribution at the turbine inlet, thus eliminating the danger of hot spots.

The 501-K Series engines are available in either single-shaft or free turbine design.

The lightweight, compact size of the 501-K lends itself to multiple engines driving a single shaft through a common gearbox, or as a gas generator driving a customer-furnished power turbine.

The engine can be operated on a wide range of liquid fuels. Designation of the marine model is 501-KF, a brief specification for which follows. Dimensions are shown on the accompanying general arrangement drawing.

Exhaust gas temperature: 535°C (994°F)
Inlet air flow: 26,000cfm
Exhaust air flow: 81,000cfm
Engine jacket heat rejection: 6,000 Btu/min
Lube heat rejection (Gasifier): 1,270 Btu/min
Max liquid fuel flow: 6,365 litres (360ghp)
Liquid fuel: DF-1, DF-2 per Allison EMS66
Lubricant: Synthetic oil per Allison EMS 35 and 53
Specific fuel consumption: 0·24 litre (0·503lb)/hp/h
Required Auxiliaries:
25hp starter
20-29V dc electrical power
Power take-off shaft and couplings
Temperature and speed controls from engine-furnished signals
Oil cooler
Auxiliary lube pump
Compressor inlet sensor
Gauge panel, meters and associated components
Engine exhaust diffusing tailpipe

ALLISON 570-K

A new 7,000hp gas turbine designed as a prime mover in the industrial and marine fields, the 570 series is a front drive, two-shaft gas turbine. It is currently in full operation and entered production in 1978. The model 570 represents General Motors' newest entry in the industrial & marine markets and is a derivative of the US Army's heavy lift helicopter (HLH) engine.

The 570 engine uses a variable geometry, 13-stage, axial flow compressor with a compression ratio of 12·1:1; the inlet guide vanes and the first five stages of status are variable. The compressor is directly coupled to a two-stage axial flow turbine and the vanes and blades of both stages are air-cooled. A power turbine drives the output shaft at the front end of the engine through a torque senser assembly located on the engine's centreline. The air foils of the power turbine are solid and do not require air cooling.

The 570 is operated by a full authority electronic control which features automatic starting sequence, speed governing, turbine temperature limiting, vibration sensing etc.

All production 570 engines are fully marinised using materials and coatings selected after more than ¼ million hours of marine experience with Boeing Jetfoils and DD 963 'Spruance' class destroyers.

The 570-K engine incorporates many technological advances and these have resulted in the unit having the lowest specific fuel consumption (SFC) of any turbine in its hp class. At maximum rated power of 7,170hp, the engine's SFC is 0·46lb/hp/h. This low level is maintained over a wide range of output power and speed; at 50% power the SFC increases by only 7%.

A larger version, designated the model 570-KB was due to enter production in mid-1980. A three-stage power turbine will be used and the unit will have a maximum power rating of 8,312hp with an SFC of 0·405lb/hp/h.

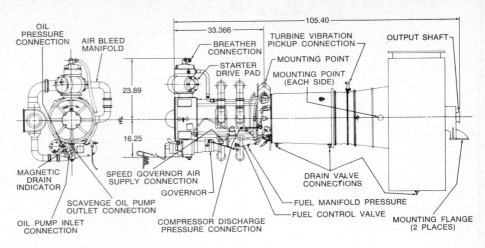

General arrangement of Allison 501-KF two-shaft marine gas turbine

Side view of Allison 501-KF two-shaft marine gas turbine

Allison 570-KF marine gas turbine

570-KA (two-stage) and 570-KB (three-stage) Gas Turbines

	Maximum		Continuous	
	570-KA	*570-KB*	*570-KA*	*570-KB*
Power (shp)				
15°C (59°F)	7,170	8,132	6,445	7,665
26·7°C (80°F)	6,610	7,644	5,890	6,876

570-KA (two-stage) and 570-KB (three-stage) Gas Turbines

	Maximum		Continuous	
	570-KA	570-KB	570-KA	570-KB
Fuel consumption (59°F)				
g/hp/h	210	184	209	186
lb/hp/h	0·462	0·405	0·460	0·409
Power turbine temperature				
°C	850	837	802	802
°C	1,562	1,538	1,477	1,475
Compression ratio	12·1	12·8	11·3	12·3
Corrected airflow				
kg/s	19·4	20·1	18·1	19·6
lb/s	42·8	44·3	40·0	43·3
Power turbine speed (rpm)	11,500	11,500	11,500	11,500
Weight				
kg	612	676	612	676
lb	1,350	1,490	1,350	1,490
Length				
m	1·83	1·90	1·83	1·90
in	72	75	72	75

Performance is subject to 5% guarantee factors.

DOBSON PRODUCTS CO

2241 South Ritchey, Santa Ana, California 92705, USA
Telephone: (714) 557 2987
Officials:
Franklin A Dobson, *Director*

Franklin Dobson has been building and marketing light ACVs in kit and factory-built form since 1963.

His company is now specialising in the design and construction of light ACV components evolved after a more thorough engineering approach. The components include reversible-pitch propellers and fans—the main purpose of which is to provide light craft with adequate braking—and suitable ducts, screens, etc.

Preliminary details of the company's first 0·91m (3ft) diameter, variable-pitch two-bladed propeller are given below.
DIMENSIONS
Diameter: 0·91m (36in)
Chord: 104mm (4·25in)
Blades: 2

Solidity (at 0·6 radius): 0·125
Pitch range: 60 degrees (nom +40, −20)
Max shaft diameter: 28mm (1·25in)
Design rpm: 3,000
Max rpm: 3,250
Horsepower required: 7-10
Max static thrust (with shroud): 34·01kg (75lb) (forward or reverse)
Max thrust at 60mph: 22·67kg (50lb)

A duct with integral screen, suitable for use with this propeller, is also under development.

THE GARRETT CORPORATION
AiResearch Manufacturing Company of Arizona

111 South 34th Street, Phoenix, Arizona 84010, USA

Telephone: (602) 267 3011

Officials:
Jack Marinick, *Vice-President and Manager*
Donald I Cauble, *Assistant Manager*
Malcolm E Craig, *Sales Manager*

The Garrett Corporation is the world's largest manufacturer of small gas-turbine engines for commercial, military, marine and industrial application, as well as a leading producer of air turbine starters, air motors, pneumatic valves and control systems for aircraft and aerospace applications.

ME990-3

The Garrett ME990-3 is a fully marinised gas turbine, rated at 6,250shp maximum. A free turbine, it has been designed for propulsion, pump and compressor drives and to power generator sets for primary and secondary power. Features are ease of maintenance and facilities for the replacement of modules in situ. Fitted with optional shock mounts, it satisfies the shock requirements of MIL-S-901C, Grade A, Class III.
TYPE: Simple cycle, two-shaft, free turbine.
COMPRESSOR: Two-stage centrifugal.
COMBUSTION CHAMBER: Single, annular.
TURBINE: Two-stage axial gas generator. Three-stage axial power turbine.
FUEL GRADES: VV-F-800, DF-A, DF-1 or DF-2; ASTM-D-975, 1-D or 2-D; ASTM-D-2880, 1-GT or 2-GT; ASTM-D-1655, Jet A, Jet A1 or Jet B; MIL-T-5624, JP4 or JP5.
ACCESSORIES: Integral within the gearbox.
DIMENSIONS
Length: 3·04m (120in)
Width: 1·60m (63in)
Height: 1·21m (48in)
WEIGHT Dry: 2,835kg (6,250lb) including integral gearbox and accessories, insulation blankets and electronics package. Shock mounts (optional) 454kg (1,000lb)
PERFORMANCE RATING
At ISO standard conditions with accessory power losses and no inlet or exhaust pressure losses normal power is 5,600shp at 7,200rpm power turbine speed.
System output speed: 3,600rpm

831-800

Garrett also has a fully marinised gas-turbine engine with a continuous power rating of 690shp and an intermittent rating of 800shp. This unit, designated 831-800, is currently in service on the Boeing PHM hydrofoil, providing secondary power. It is also in use in several other commercial and military applications.
TYPE: Simple-cycle, single shaft.
COMPRESSOR: Two-stage centrifugal.
COMBUSTION CHAMBER: Single, reverse-flow.
TURBINE: Three-stage axial.
FUEL GRADES: DF1 and DF2 per ASTM-D-975, VV-F-800, MIL-F-16884 and MIL-R-46005, Jet A, A-1 and B per ASTM-D-1665; JP-4 and JP-5 per MIL-F-5624 and VV-K-211.
DIMENSIONS
Length: 1,829mm (72in)
Width: 991mm (39in)
Height: 864mm (34in)
WEIGHT Dry: 680·4kg (1,500lb)
POWER RATING
Continuous SLS: 690shp
Standby: 800shp
Rated rotor speed: 41,730rpm (max)
System output speed constant speed, two output pad speed of 8,000rpm and two at 3,600rpm

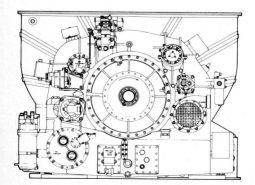
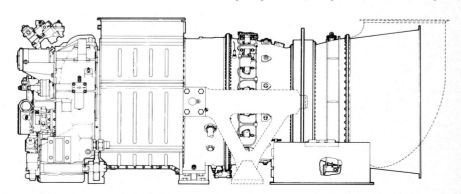

Garrett ME990-3 marinised gas turbine, rated at 6,250shp maximum and 5,600shp normal. Dashes indicate optional shock mountings and exhaust diffuser

GENERAL ELECTRIC COMPANY AIRCRAFT ENGINE GROUP

1000 Western Avenue, West Lynn, Massachusetts 01910, USA

Officials:

Fred O MacFee, Jr, *Vice President and Group Executive*

J W Sack, *Counsel*

The General Electric Company's Dr Sanford A Moss operated the first gas turbine in the United States in 1903 and produced the aircraft turbosupercharger, first flown in 1919 and mass-produced in the Second World War for US fighters and bombers.

The company built its first aircraft gas turbine in 1941, when it began development of a Whittle-type turbojet, under an arrangement between the British and American Governments.

Since that time, General Electric has produced and licensed over 83,000 aircraft gas turbine engines with more than 176 million hours of operation.

Three General Electric gas turbines have been marinised for marine service, the LM100, the LM1500 and the LM2500. The LM100 powers the Bell SK-5 air cushion vehicle, the LM1500 powers the 300-ton AG(EH)-1 Plainview and 17 US Navy patrol gunboats and the LM2500 is specified for powering various classes of ships in 12 navies around the world.

LM2500

The LM2500 marine gas turbine is a two-shaft, simple cycle, high efficiency engine, derived from the GE military TF39 and civil CF6 high by-pass turbofan engines for the US Air Force C-5 transport and DC-10, 747 and A300B commercial jets. The engine incorporates the latest features of compressor, combustor, and turbine design to provide maximum progression in reliability, parts life, and time between overhaul. The engine has a simple cycle efficiency of more than 35% which is due to the most advanced cycle pressures, temperatures and component efficiencies in marine gas turbine production today.

The LM2500 marine gas turbine has been specified for the foilborne power of the joint US Navy/NATO Patrol Hydrofoil Missile (PHM), six ships being built by the Boeing Company, Seattle, Washington. The engine is also specified for the lift engines for the US Navy's 3,000-ton 3KSES. Rohr Marine Inc, has been awarded the contract for the detailed design of this large Surface Effect Ship.

Other world naval applications of the LM2500 include: US Navy's DD 963 Spruance-class destroyers, FFG-7 Perry-class frigates, Australian and Spanish Navy FFG-7 frigates, Italian, Venezuelan, Peruvian and Egyptian LUPO-class fast frigates, West German Navy frigates, a South Korean Navy frigate, and patrol gunboats and corvette size ships for the Indonesian, Saudi Arabian and Danish navies.

Total operating time of LM2500 engines in marine service is now over 250,000 hours.

Two LM2500s power the Gas Turbine Ship (GTS) *Admiral William M Callaghan* roll-on/roll-off cargo vessel. The ship has over 90,000 operating hours to date with the LM2500 engine.

TYPE: Two-shaft, axial flow, simple cycle.

AIR INTAKE: Axial, inlet bellmouth or duct can be customised to installation.

COMBUSTION CHAMBER: Annular.

FUEL GRADE: Kerosene, JP4, JP5, Diesel, heavy distillate fuels and natural gas.

TURBINE: Two-stage gas generator, six-stage power.

JET PIPE: Vertical or customised to fit installation.

OIL SPECIFICATION: Synthetic Turbine Oil (MIL-L-23699) or equal.

MOUNTING: At power turbine and compressor front frame.

STARTING: Pneumatic, hydraulic.

GE LM2500 gas turbine

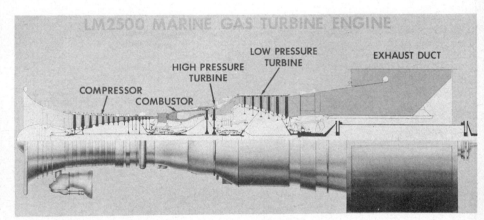

Internal arrangements of GE LM2500 marine gas turbine

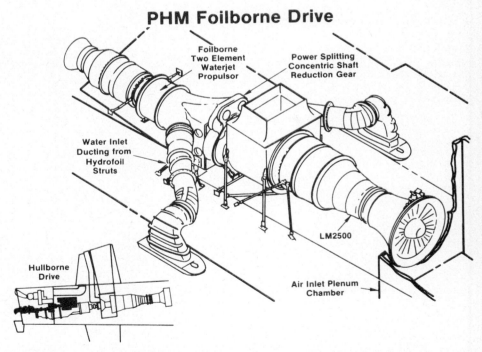

LM2500 installation aboard PHM. The LM2500 was selected to provide PHM with foilborne propulsion power in 1972. A joint development effort of the US Navy, Federal Republic of Germany and Italy, the builder's sea trials of PHM were completed in October 1977 and the first vessel was commissioned in 1978

DIMENSIONS
Length: 6,630mm (261in)
Width: 2,133mm (84in)
Height: 2,133mm (84in)

PERFORMANCE RATINGS: 30,000shp at 15°C (59°F) at sea level
SPECIFIC FUEL CONSUMPTION: 0·171kg (0·376lb)/hp/h

ROCKETDYNE DIVISION
ROCKWELL INTERNATIONAL

6633 Canoga Avenue, Canoga Park, California
91304, USA
Telex: 698478
Officials:
H Lee Barham, *Marketing Manager, Waterjet Propulsion*

Technology gained in the design and manufacture of high-performance pumps for the US space programme enabled Rocketdyne to develop a new family of waterjet propulsion systems, called Powerjet TM 16, 20 and 24. These systems employ advanced-design, axial-flow pumping elements to produce compact, lightweight waterjet propulsors. Simplicity of design minimises the number of components necessary in the units, while allowing accessibility for servicing or replacement of seals and bearings. All components are designed to meet American Bureau of Shipping requirements and have been built of materials selected for their resistance to cavitation damage, and seawater and galvanic corrosion.

Rockwell Powerjet 20s power the sixteen Boeing Jetfoils currently in service. On each Jetfoil, dual PJ20s, each driven by a Detroit Diesel Allison 501-K20A gas turbine rated at 3,840hp deliver a 24,000 gallons/min water flow.

Jetfoils operate regularly at a cruising speed of 45 knots in 12ft seas to transport passengers between Hong Kong and Macao; Sado Island and Niigata in Japan; London to Ostend, Belgium; Brighton to Dieppe, France; Liverpool to Dublin; Seattle to Victoria, Vancouver Island, BC; and a patrol boat version has been delivered to the British Royal Navy.

The vessels in service have carried passengers over 330 million passenger miles, during which the Powerjet 20 units have logged in excess of 140,000 pump hours.

Other new vessels to employ Rocketdyne Powerjets include the *American Enterprise*, the world's first turbine/waterjet-powered fast offshore crew and supply boat, which has achieved speeds in excess of 35 knots during trials. Power is supplied by two Powerjet 16 waterjet pumps direct-driven by Detroit Diesel Allison Model 16V-92T engines, developing 860shp each, and one Powerjet 24 pump on the centreline driven by a Detroit Diesel Allison Model 501-KF gas turbine, rated at 5,430hp maximum output. *Fortuna*, a private yacht designed by Don Shead Ltd is capable of exceeding 50 knots, powered by two Powerjet 16s direct-driven by MTU 8V 331 TC 92s and a single Powerjet 24 powered by a Lycoming Super TF40. The *Condor 6*, built by Westmarin and powered by two Powerjet 24 pumps and Lycoming Super TF40s, is operated on the Channel Islands to France routes by Condor Ltd.

POWERJET 20

TYPE: Single-stage, axial-flow.
APPLICATION: Designed for hydrofoils and high-speed craft at 3,840hp and medium- to high-speed craft at lower horsepower. Two Powerjet 20 propulsion units, each driven by an Allison 501-K20A gas turbine through a 6·37:1 reduction gearbox, power the Boeing 929 Jetfoil, a 106-ton, 45-knot passenger-carrying hydrofoil. In this application, the gearbox is used in conjunction with an over/under configuration, which results in a compact installation. Input horsepower to the gearbox is 4,000 at 13,380rpm.
ACCESSORY DRIVE: For the Boeing Jetfoil, Powerjet 20 is coupled to a gearbox that provides two pads for accessory drive. The first pad supplies power for the boat's hydraulic system, while the second directs power to gearbox, pump, and turbine lubrication and scavenge pump.
PRIME MOVERS: Diesels and gas turbines up to 4,000hp.
LUBRICATION SYSTEM: External recirculating supply, with 2·5 to 3·5 gallons/min flow at 55 to 70psi provided by a gerotor-type pump that contains both pressure and scavenge cavities.

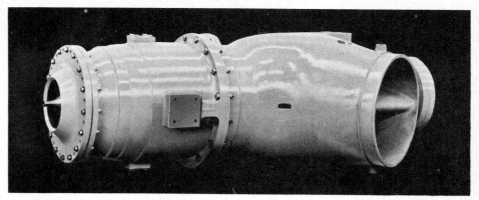

Powerjet 20, designed for hydrofoils and high-speed craft with diesels and gas turbines developing up to 3,840hp. Pump flow rate is 24,000 gallons/min

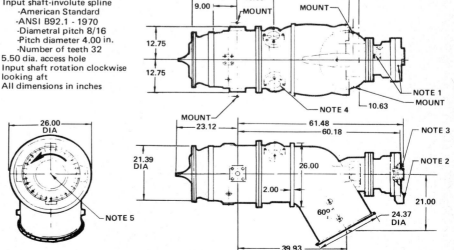

Twin Powerjet 20s installed in the Boeing Jetfoil

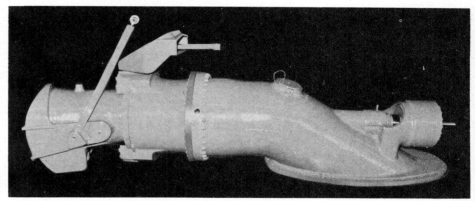

Powerjet 16, single-stage axial-flow waterjet pump for diesels and gas turbines developing between 700 and 1,575hp

ENGINEERING NOTES
1. Lube oil in (external supply)
2. Lube oil out
3. Input shaft-involute spline
   -American Standard
   -ANSI B92.1 - 1970
   -Diametral pitch 8/16
   -Pitch diameter 4.00 in.
   -Number of teeth 32
4. 5.50 dia. access hole
5. Input shaft rotation clockwise looking aft
6. All dimensions in inches

General arrangement of Powerjet 20, two of which are installed in the Boeing Jetfoil

LUBE OIL GRADE
MIL-L-23699
MIL-L-2106
Diesel crankcase oil—API (D Series)
Automobile differential oil—API (M Series)
SPECIFICATION
Operating range:
  Input hp: 3,840 (4,320hp also available)
  Input shaft speed: 2,145rpm
  Total inlet head: 7·92m (26ft)
  Pump flowrate: 24,750 gallons/min
Propulsion pump weight:
  Dry: 707·6kg (1,560lb)
  Wet: 961·6kg (2,120lb)

POWERJET 16
TYPE: Single-stage, axial-flow.
APPLICATION: Designed for high propulsive
efficiency at moderate speeds in all types of hull
configurations.
PRIME MOVERS: Diesels and gas turbines
developing between 700 and 1,575hp. Four
inducer trims are available for direct coupling to
most marine diesels.
LUBRICATION SYSTEM: Integrated recir-
culating system.
LUBE OIL GRADE
MIL-L-9000
MIL-L-17331
MIL-L-2105
Society of Automotive Engineers Gear Oils
Society of Automotive Engineers Motor Oils
SPECIFICATION
Operating Range:

	Trim Number			
	1	2	3	4
Max hp, up to:	1,575	1,575	1,575	1,306
Input shaft speed rpm, up to:	2,310	2,530	2,630	2,650
Nominal input direct drive, hp:	1,025	900	800	815
Nominal input shaft speed, rpm:	2,000	2,100	2,100	2,260
Total inlet head, ft, minimum:	30·1	22	22	22
Pump flowrate (at 30 knots), gallons/min:	18,200	16,700	16,700	16,700

Propulsion pump weight:
Dry: 1,027kg (2,265lb)
Wet: 1,141kg (2,515lb)
Steering vector: ±22 degrees
Reverse thrust: 50% of forward gross thrust to a
  maximum of 1,025hp

POWERJET 24
TYPE: Single-stage, axial-flow.
APPLICATION: Designed for high-propulsive
efficiency at moderate to high speeds.
PRIME MOVERS: Diesels and gas turbines
developing up to 5,790hp.
LUBRICATION SYSTEM: External recirculat-
ing supply requiring 3·8 to 4·2 gallons/min flow at
55 to 70psi.
LUBE OIL GRADE
MIL-L-9000
MIL-L-17331
MIL-L-2105
Society of Automotive Engineers Gear Oils
Society of Automotive Engineers Motor Oils
SPECIFICATION
Operating range:
Input: 5,790hp
Input shaft speed: 1,853rpm
Total inlet head: 13·1m (43ft) at 1,640rpm
Pump flowrate (at 30 knots): 45,000 gallons/min
Propulsion pump weight
Dry: 2,358kg (5,200lb)
Wet: 2,767kg (6,100lb)
Steering vector: ±22 degrees
Reverse thrust: 50% of forward gross thrust to a
  maximum of 1,830hp

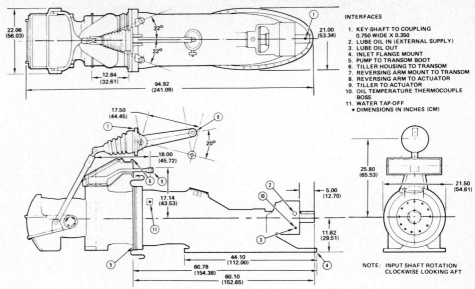

Powerjet 16, for diesels and gas turbines delivering between 700 and 1,575shp

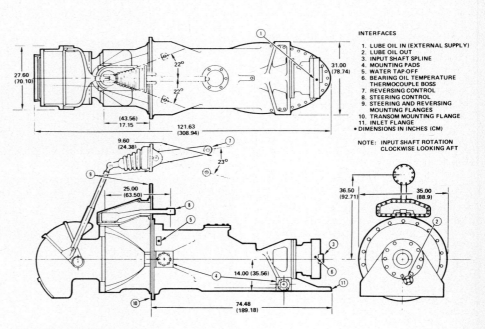

Powerjet 24 for diesels and gas turbines developing up to 5,790shp

Two Powerjet 24 units power the *Condor 6* Westamarin ferry

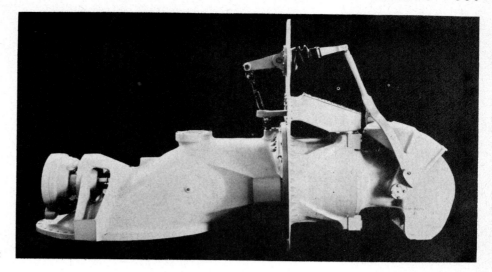

Powerjet 24 unit

SCORPION INC

Crosby, Minnesota 56441, USA
Telephone: (218) 546 5123
Telex: 294452
Officials:
Charles A Srock, *OEM and Export Manager*

The company is now manufacturing and marketing the Cuyuna range of axial-fan cooled twin-cylinder engines, developing 29-40hp.

The engines are serviced through a network of 2,000 independent service outlets and central distributors throughout the USA and Canada.

CUYUNA AXIAL-FAN TWIN-CYLINDER ENGINES

Models 295, 340, 400 and 440

Features of this range include a standard mounting for all models to ease installation; low engine profile with built-in shrouding; lightweight construction to reduce overall vehicle weight and high interchangeability of all parts. Crankshafts, crank cases, blower assemblies, magnetos, recoil starters and hardware items are fully interchangeable, thus reducing spare parts inventory requirements and lowering maintenance costs. Specifications for the four standard productions are given in the accompanying table.

Type	Twin Cylinder Axial-Fan Cooled			
Model	295	340	400	440
Bore	2·185in	2·362in	2·559in	2·658in
Stroke	2·362in	2·362in	2·362in	2·362in
Displacement	290cc	339cc	389cc	428cc
Compression Ratio		12·5 : 1		
Max Torque		6,500 rpm		
Brake hp/rpm	29hp	32hp	38hp	40hp
	6,500/7,000rpm	6,500/7,000rpm	6,500/7,000rpm	6,500/7,000rpm
Base Mounting Hole Thread		⁷/₁₆—14 UNC		
Cylinder		Aluminium with Cast Iron Sleeve		
Connecting Rod Bearing Upper		Needle		
Connecting Rod Bearing Lower		Needle		
Connecting Rod Material		Forged Steel		
Main Bearing		4 Heavy Duty Ball Bearings (1 Dual Row Bearing, PTO)		
Ignition		Bosch		
Lighting Coil		12V, 150W		
Contact Breaker Gap		0·014in to 0·018in		
Ignition Setting Before TDC		0·102in to 0·112in (Cam Fully Advanced)		
Spark Plug Thread		14 × 1·25mm (¾in) Reach		
Gap		0·016in to 0·020in		
Type		Bosch W-260-T-2		
		(or) Champion N-3		
Rotation		Counter-clockwise viewed from PTO End		
Fuel-Oil Mixture		40:1 (1 pint to 5 gallons)		
Lubrication		Premium Gasoline & Cuyuna 2 Cycle Engine Oil		
Carburettor Type		2¹⁵/₁₆in Centre to Centre Bolt Dimension		
Starter		Rewind Type, Standard; Electric, Optional		
Rope Material		Nylon		
Weight		62lb		

Horsepower ratings established in accordance with specifications SAE-J 607.

Engines will produce no more than 78dB when used with Cuyuna approved carburettor/muffler/intake silencer systems, according to SAE-J192 specifications.

UNITED TECHNOLOGIES CORPORATION POWER SYSTEMS DIVISION
(Gas Turbine Operations)

1690 New Britain Avenue, Farmington, Connecticut 06032, USA
Telephone: (203) 677 4081
Officials:
Rolf Bibow, *President, Power Systems Division*
M J Knapp, *Vice President and General Manager, Gas Turbine Operations*
R F Nordin, *Director of Sales*
D Caplow, *Director of Special Projects*

United Technologies Power Systems Division (Turbo Power and Marine Systems Inc), designs and builds industrial and marine gas turbine power plants and related systems utilising the FT4 Modular Industrial Turbine. It also provides a systems support for each of its installations.

Canadian sales of the FT4 are handled by Pratt & Whitney Aircraft of Canada Limited (qv) which also manufactures and sells the ST6 marine gas turbine.

Power Systems Division efforts have resulted in over 1,200 Modular Industrial Turbines supplied or on order in the USA and in 26 other countries. The turbines will supply more than 35 million hp for electric power generation, gas transmission and industrial drives as well as for marine propulsion.

MARINE GAS TURBINES

PSD's FT4 marine gas turbines were first used for boost power in military vessels, including two Royal Danish Navy frigates, twelve US Coast Guard Hamilton Class high endurance cutters and four Canadian Armed Forces DDH-280 Iroquois Class destroyers. Another boost power application of the FT4 is in the Fast Escort and ASW vessel *Bras d'Or* also built for the Canadian Armed Forces. Another application is for two new 12,000-ton Arctic ice breakers for the US Coast Guard. With three FT4 marine gas turbines, these vessels are capable of maintaining a continuous speed of three knots through ice 6ft thick, and are able to ram through ice 21ft thick.

PSD's marine gas turbines are used for both the main and boost propulsion in the four Canadian DDH-280 destroyers. These are the first military combatant vessels to be designed for complete reliance on gas turbine power. PSD's marine gas turbines are also used in a military surface effect ship programme.

FT4 gas turbines are also used as the main propulsion unit in the *Finnjet*, a high-speed Finnlines passenger liner. *Finnjet* has cut the Baltic crossing time in half, routinely maintaining 30 knots, with an engine availability over 99%.

UTC/PSD MARINE POWER PAC

The photograph shows an FT4 marine gas turbine completely packaged as a marine power pac ready for installation, with the minimum of interface connections to be made. Each is built upon a rigid mounting frame and includes a housing and gas turbine mounting system, together with controls, accessory equipment, wiring and piping. A remote control system is also provided. Installation is simple. Since all the equipment is pretested at the factory before shipment, time required for checkout after installation is minimised.

The gas generator portion of the gas turbine is easily removed for servicing. With a spare gas generator to replace the one removed for servicing, the ship's power plant can be changed in a matter of hours.

The FT4 gas turbine comprises the gas generator and the power (free) turbine. The independent power turbine accepts the kinetic energy of the gas generator and converts it to mechanical energy through a shaft which extends through the exhaust duct elbow.

GAS GENERATOR

TYPE: Simple-cycle two-spool turbine. A low pressure compressor is driven by a two-stage turbine and a high pressure compressor is driven by a single turbine. The burner section has eight burner cans which are equipped with duplex fuel nozzles.

AIR INTAKE: Cast steel casing with 18 radial struts supporting the front compressor bearing and equipped with a bleed air anti-icing system.

LOW PRESSURE COMPRESSOR: Nine-stage axial flow on inner of two concentric shafts driven by two-stage turbine and supported on ball and roller bearings.

HIGH PRESSURE COMPRESSOR: Seven-stage axial flow on outer hollow shaft driven by single-stage turbine and running on ball and roller bearings.

COMBUSTION CHAMBER: Eight burner cans located in an annular arrangement and enclosed in a one piece steel casing. Each burner has six duplex fuel nozzles.

TURBINES: Steel casing with hollow guide vanes. Turbine wheels are bolted to the compressor shafts and are supported on ball and roller bearings. A single-stage turbine drives the high compressor and a two-stage turbine drives the low compressor.

POWER TURBINE: The gas turbine is available with either clockwise or counter-clockwise rotation of the power turbine. Desired direction of rotation specified by customer. Power turbine housing is bolted to gas generator turbine housing. The three-stage turbine shaft assembly is straddle mounted and supported on ball and roller bearings. The output shaft is bolted to the hub of the power turbine rotor and extends through the exhaust duct.

BEARINGS: Anti-friction ball and roller bearings.

ACCESSORY DRIVE: Starter, fluid power pump, tachometer drives for low compressor, high compressor and free turbine.

LUBRICATION SYSTEM: Return system and scavenge pumps with internal pressure, 3·09 kg/cm² (45 psi).

LUBRICATING OIL SPECIFICATIONS: Type 2 synthetic lube oil PWA-521.

MARINE APPLICATIONS: Meets installation, high shock and ships seaway motion requirements.

STARTING: Pneumatic or hydraulic.

DIMENSIONS

Length: 8,788mm (346in)
Width: 2,438mm (96in)
Height: 2,794mm (101in)

UTC/PSD Marine Power Pac with an FT4 Modular Industrial Turbine

Current production model of the FT4 marine gas turbine, rated at 48,300shp maximum intermittent and 38,600shp base load

PERFORMANCE DATA: FT4 MARINE GAS TURBINE

Rating	Power Output (1)	Specific Fuel Consumption (2)
Max Intermittent	48,300shp	197g (0·435lb)/shp/h
Max Continuous	43,800shp	200g (0·440lb)/shp/h
Normal	38,600shp	204g (0·450lb)/shp/h

(1) All ratings at 3,600rpm shaft speed, 15°C (59°F) and sea level.
(2) Based on fuel with LHV of 18,500 Btu/lb.

FUEL SPECIFICATIONS
Light Distillate (Naphtha): PWA-532(1)
Aviation Grade Kerosene: PWA-522(1)
Marine Diesel: PWA-527(1)

Heavy Distillate: PWA-539
(1) Covered by TPM-FR-1 for series engine
Treated crude and residual oil refer to manufacturer.

ACV and HYDROFOIL LICENSING AUTHORITIES

ARGENTINA
ACVs and Hydrofoils
Prefectura Naval Maritima
  Paseo Colon 533
  Buenos Aires
  Argentina

AUSTRALIA
ACVs and Hydrofoils
Department of Transport
  GPO Box 1839Q,
  Melbourne,
  Victoria 3001,
  Australia

State Licensing Authorities
New South Wales
Ministry of Motor Transport
  Rothchild Avenue,
  Rosebery,
  Sydney,
  New South Wales 2000,
  Australia

Queensland
Department of Harbours and Marine
  231 Turbot Street,
  Brisbane,
  Queensland 4000,
  Australia

South Australia
Department of Marine and Harbors
  293 St Vincent Street,
  Port Adelaide,
  South Australia 5015,
  Australia

Tasmania
Navigation and Survey Authority of
  Tasmania
  1 Franklin Wharf,
  Hobart,
  Tasmania 7000,
  Australia

West Australia
Harbour and Light Department
  Crane House,
  6 Short Street,
  PO Box 402,
  Fremantle,
  West Australia 6160,
  Australia

AUSTRIA
ACVs and Hydrofoils
Bundesministerium für Handel Gewerbe und
  Industrie
  Stubenring 1,
  Vienna 1,
  Austria
Telephone: 57 66 55

BELGIUM
ACVs and Hydrofoils
Ministry of Communications
  Administration de la Marine et de la Naviga-
  tion Intérieure
  rue d'Arlon 104,
  B-1040 Brussels,
  Belgium
Telephone: 02/230 02 57

CANADA
ACVs
Chief, Air Cushion Vehicle Division Marine
  Safety Branch

Canadian Coast Guard,
Transport Canada,
Tower A,
Place de Ville,
Ottawa,
Ontario K1A ON5,
Canada

DENMARK
ACVs and Hydrofoils
Government Ships Inspection Service
  Snorresgade 19,
  DK-2300 Copenhagen S,
  Denmark

EGYPT
ACVs
The Arab General Organisation for Air Trans-
  port
  11 Emad El Din Street,
  Cairo,
  Egypt

FIJI
ACVs and Hydrofoils
Director of Marine
  Marine Department,
  PO Box 326,
  Suva,
  Fiji

FINLAND
Board of Navigation
  Vurorimiehenkatu 1,
  PO Box 158,
  SF-00141 Helsinki 14,
  Finland

FRANCE
ACVs and Hydrofoils
Secrétariat Général de la Marine Marchande
  3 Place de Fontenoy,
  75700 Paris,
  France
Telephone: (1) 567 55 05
Telex: 250 823 Minimar Paris

GAMBIA
ACVs and Hydrofoils
Ministry of Works and Communications
  Banjul,
  Gambia

GERMANY (Federal Republic)
ACVs and Hydrofoils
See-Berufsgenossenschaft
  Ships Safety Department
  Reimerstwiete 2,
  D-2000 Hamburg 11,
  Federal Republic of Germany

GHANA
The Shipping Commissioner
  Ministry of Transport and Communications,
  PO Box M.38,
  Accra,
  Ghana

GREECE
ACVs and Hydrofoils
Ministry of Mercantile Marine
  Merchant Ships Inspection Services,
  Palaiologou 1 str,
  Piraeus,
  Greece

HUNGARY
Közlekedési-és Postaügyi Minisztérium
  Hajózási Föosztály,
  Hajózási Felügyelet,
  Budapest V, Apáczai Csere János utca 11,
  Hungary

ICELAND
Directorate of Shipping
  PO Box 484,
  Reykjavik,
  Iceland

INDIA
ACVs and Hydrofoils
Directorate General of Shipping
  Bombay,
  India

INDONESIA
ACVs and Hydrofoils
Department of Transport, Communications and
  Tourism
  8 Medan Merdelka Barat,
  Jakarta-Pusat,
  Indonesia

IRELAND
ACVs and Hydrofoils
Department of Tourism and Transport
  Kildare Street,
  Dublin 2,
  Ireland

ISRAEL
ACVs and Hydrofoils
Ministry of Transport
  Division of Shipping and Ports,
  102 Ha'atzmauth Road,
  PO Box 33993,
  Haifa,
  Israel

ITALY
ACVs and Hydrofoils
Ministero della Marina Mercantile
  Ispettorato Tecnico,
  Viale Asia,
  00100 Rome,
  Italy

IVORY COAST
ACVs and Hydrofoils
Ministère des Travaux Publics et des Transports
  BP V6,
  Abijan,
  Ivory Coast

JAMAICA
The Marine Board
  Collector General's Department,
  PO Box 466,
  Newport East,
  Kingston,
  Jamaica

JAPAN
ACVs and Hydrofoils
Japanese Ministry of Transportation
  2-1-3 Kasumigaseki,
  Chiyoda-ku,
  Tokyo,
  Japan

KOREA (REPUBLIC)
Ministry of Transportation
1-3 Do-dong,
Choong-ku,
Seoul,
Republic of Korea

KUWAIT
ACVs and Hydrofoils
Department of Customs and Ports
PO Box 9,
Kuwait

LEBANON
ACVs and Hydrofoils
Ministère des Travaux Publics
Direction des Transports,
Beirut,
Lebanon

LUXEMBOURG
ACVs
Ministère des Transports,
19-21 boulevard Royal,
Luxembourg
Telephone: 4794-1

MADAGASCAR
ACVs and Hydrofoils
Ministère de l'Amina
Jement du Territoire,
Anosy,
Antananarivo,
Madagascar

MALAWI
The Ministry of Transport and Communications
Private Bag 322,
Capital City,
Lilongwe 3,
Malawi

MALAYSIA
The Ministry of Transport
Wisma Perdana,
Jalan Dungun,
Kuala Lumpur,
Malaysia
Telephone: 948122
Cables: Transport

MEXICO
ACVs and Hydrofoils
Departamento de Licencias
Direction de Marina Mercante,
Dr Mora No 15,
3er Piso,
Mexico 1,
Mexico

MOROCCO
Ministère des Travauxs Publics
Rabat,
Morocco

NETHERLANDS
ACVs and Hydrofoils
Ministerie van Verkeer en Waterstaat
Directoraat-Generaal Scheepvaart en Maritieme
Zaken,
Scheepvaartinspectie,
NW Buitensingel 2,
Postbus 20902,
2500 EX 's-Gravenhage (The Hague),
Netherlands

NEW ZEALAND
*ACVs and Hydrofoils (Certificates of Construc-
tion and Performance)*
Operating approval and licences:
Ministry of Transport
Marine Division,
Private Bag,
Wellington 1,
New Zealand
Hovercraft regulations currently being
drafted. Among other things these will require
hovercraft over a certain size to be licenced for
commercial operation. The administration of all
legislation for hovercraft and hydrofoils is the
responsibility of the above.

NORWAY
ACVs and Hydrofoils
Norwegian Maritime Directorate
Thv Meyersgt 7,
PO Box 8123-Dep,
Oslo 1,
Norway

SOUTH AFRICA
Department of Transport
Private Bag X193
Pretoria 0001,
South Africa

SPAIN
ACVs and Hydrofoils
Subsecretaria de la Marina Mercante
Ruiz de Alacron No 1,
Madrid 14,
Spain

SWEDEN
ACVs and Hydrofoils
The National Swedish Administration of Ship-
ping and Navigation
Sjöfartsverket,
S-601 78 Norrköping
Sweden

SWITZERLAND
*Cantonal licensing authorities for ACVs and Hyd-
rofoils*
Lake Zurich
Seepolizei/Schiffahrtskontrolle des Kantons
Zürich
Seestrasse 87,
CH-8942 Oberrieden,
Switzerland
Seepolizei-und Gewässerschutzkommissariat
der Stadt Zurich
Bellereivestrasse 260,
CH-8008 Zurich,
Switzerland

Lake Constance
Schiffahrtskontrolle des Kantons Thurgau,
Zürcherstrasse 254,
CH-8500 Frauenfeld,
Switzerland
Schiffahrtskontrolle des Kantons St Gallen,
Kornhaus,
CH-9400 Rorschach,
Switzerland
Kantonale Schiffahrtskontrolle
Klosterstrasse 9,
CH-8200 Schaffhausen,
Switzerland

Lake Lucerne
Schiffsinspektorat des Kantons Luzern
Gibraltarstrasse 3,
CH-6002 Lucerne,
Switzerland

Lake Geneva
Departement de Justice et Police Service de
la Navigation
Place Bourg-de-Four 1,
CH-1200 Geneva,
Switzerland
Departement de la Justice, de la Police et des
Affaires Militaire,
Service de la Police Administrative,
Place du Château 6,
CH-1001 Lausanne,
Switzerland

Lake Lugano
Ufficio Cantonale della Circolazione
Servizio Navigazione,
CH-6528 Camorino,
Switzerland

Lake Neuchatel
Departement de Police
CH-2000 Neuchatel,
Switzerland

Lake Thoune and Lake Brienz
Direktion für Verkehr, Energie- und Wasser-
wirtschaft des Kantons Bern
Verkehrsamt,
Rathausplatz 1,
CH-3011 Bern,
Switzerland

TURKEY
ACVs and Hydrofoils
T C Ulastirma Bakanligi
Deniz Ulaştirmasi Genel Müdürlügü,
Ankara,
Turkey
T C Ulastirma Bakanligi
Marmara Bolgesi Liman ve Denizisleri
Müdürlügü,
Karaköy-Istanbul,
Turkey

UNITED KINGDOM
*Hovercraft – Certification Issue of Type Safety,
Experimental and Export Certificates. Approval
of persons or organisations from whom the CAA
may accept reports on the design, construction,
maintenance or repair of hovercraft or elements
thereof. Approval of hovercraft items and equip-
ment.
Publication of "British Hovercraft Safety
Requirements"
Technical enquiries to:*
Hovercraft Department
Airworthiness Division
Civil Aviation Authority,
Brabazon House,
Redhill,
Surrey RH1 1SQ,
England
Telephone: Redhill 65966
Telex: 27100

Publications:
Civil Aviation Authority
Printing and Publication Services
Greville House,
3 Gratton Road,
Cheltenham,
Gloucestershire GL50 2BN,
England
Telephone: 0242 35151

*Hovercraft and Hydrofoils
Hovercraft Operating Permits and Hydrofoil
Passenger Certificates*
Department of Trade
Marine Divison,
Sunley House,
90-93 High Holborn,
London WC1V 6LP,
England
Telephone: 01-405 6911
Telex: 264084

UNITED STATES OF AMERICA
ACVs and Hydrofoils
Department of Transportation
Commandant (G-MMT-4),
US Coast Guard,
Washington DC 20593,
USA

VENEZUELA
Ministerio de Communicaciones
Dirección General de Transporte y Tránsito
Maritimo
Avenida Urdaneta,
Esquina Carmelitas,
Caracas 1010,
Venezuela

YUGOSLAVIA
Yugoslav Federal Economic Secretariat
Transport Department,
Bulevar AVNOJ-a 104,
Belgrade,
Yugoslavia

CLUBS AND ASSOCIATIONS

THE HOVERCLUB OF GREAT BRITAIN LTD

As Britain's national organisation for light hovercraft, the Hoverclub exists to encourage the construction and operation of light, recreational hovercraft by private individuals, schools, colleges, universities and other youth groups. The Hoverclub's major role in recent years has been its organisation of several national race meetings at sites throughout Britain. At these events sixty or more light hovercraft may compete for National Championship points over land and water courses at meetings held in the grounds of stately homes, or at reclaimed gravel workings.

In addition to national race meetings, the Hoverclub also performs the important task of providing its own members and prospective hovercraft builders with useful advice and information through its publications and a technical enquiries office.

PUBLICATIONS
Light Hovercraft, monthly
Light Hovercraft Handbook, annual. Prime reference book for the design, construction and safe operation of small recreational hovercraft.
Guide to Model Hovercraft
Light Hovercraft Design, Construction and Safety Requirements

Richard Cresswell cornering at Stanford Hall in his own 96km/h 'Eccles'

A growing activity within the Hoverclub has been the pastime of hovercruising which involves travelling by single or more usually multi-seat light hovercraft along rivers, canals, lochs or coastlines. Many hovercraft constructors see this activity as one offering the ability to explore areas which are not accessible by other means of transport. Hovercruises and holidays have been arranged in Scotland and Wales.

HOVERCLUB COUNCIL 1980-81
G G Harding, *President*
K Oakley, *Chairman*
T Sherlock, *Secretary*
V Garman, *Treasurer*
N Beale
N MacDonald
W Sherlock
K Smallwood
Mrs M Smart
R Smart
Mrs J Waddon
K Waddon

The Hoverclub's main address for initial enquiries related to membership and publication is:
Mrs J Waddon, Hoverclub Information Officer,
45 St Andrews Road, Lower Bemerton,
Salisbury, Wiltshire
Telephone: 0722 3424
Addresses of the various branches of the Hoverclub throughout Britain are listed below:

CHILTERNS
C Sanders,
8 Belsize Square, London NW3

EAST ANGLIAN
B Hill,
10 Fenland Road, Reffley Estate, Kings Lynn, Norfolk

LONDON
B Horsman,
5 Beeches Close, Uckfield, Sussex

NORTH WEST
Rev W G Spedding,
26 Milverton Close, Lostock, Bolton, Lancs

SCOTTISH
W S Sharp,
1 Coates Place, Edinburgh EH3 7AA

WELSH
Mrs H Riley,
11 Normandy Way, Chepstow, Gwent

WESSEX
Mrs J Waddon,
45 St Andrews Road, Lower Bemerton, Salisbury, Wiltshire

OTHER BODIES
ESSEX
E W Sangster,
53 Elm View Road, Benfleet, Essex SS7 5AR

MIDLANDS HOVERCLUB
Mrs B Kemp,
10 Long Acre, Bingham, Nottingham

SOUTHERN HOVERCLUB
A Bliault,
17 Southampton Road, Paulsgrove, Hampshire

NATIONAL SCHOOLS HOVERCRAFT ASSOCIATION

The National Schools Hovercraft Association was formed in 1975 to provide a focal point for the growing interest from schools and colleges in building and operating recreational hovercraft. Each year the Schools Association, together with the BP Oil Ltd, the Boy Scouts Association and the Hoverclub of Great Britain, organise a National Schools Hovercraft Championship. This competition allows many light hovercraft built by school groups to be evaluated over land and water circuits.

J Kemp
10 Long Acre, Bingham, Nottingham

THE HOVERCRAFT SOCIETY

Rochester House, 66 Little Ealing Lane, London W5 4XX, England
Telephone: 01-579 9411
Officers:
Sir Christopher Cockerell, *President*
R L Wheeler, *Vice President*
J E Rapson, MBE, *Vice President*
W F S Woodford, OBE, *Vice President*
E G Tattersall, *Chairman*
P H Winter, *Hon Treasurer*
P A Bartlett, *Secretary*

Formed in 1971, the Hovercraft Society was the UK constituent member of the 'International Air Cushion Engineering Society'. Its membership is drawn from ACV manufacturers, ferry operators, design groups, government departments and agencies, financial and insurance organisations, consultants, journalists and universities. Membership of the Society is open to persons engaged in hovercraft related fields in the UK and overseas. Currently the Society has over 250 members.

In addition to its programme of regular meetings, at which papers are presented on the technical, commercial, design, operating and military aspects of hovercraft and air cushion devices, THS also produces a regular monthly *Hovercraft Bulletin*. This publication contains the latest up-to-date information on hovercraft activities throughout the world. From time to time the Society also organises visits to hovercraft manufacturing or component factories for its members.

At the Society's headquarters in London a collection of hovercraft films is held, together with a library of books, periodicals, papers and reports on the subject of hovercraft.

In autumn 1980 the society published its first set of *Proceedings*, known as *The Hovercraft*, containing ten papers given to THS during the 1980 session.

THE BRITISH SMALL HOVERCRAFT MANUFACTURERS' ASSOCIATION

c/o Rochester House, 66 Little Ealing Lane, London W5 4XX, England
Telephone: 01-579 9411
Officers:
P V McCollum, *Chairman*
A Blunden, *Hon Secretary*

Established during the summer of 1979 to form a trade association for the manufacturers of the smaller sizes of hovercraft (under 10 metres overall length), the BSHMA has already accomplished some of its original objectives in gaining recognition by various British government departments, agencies and official organisations such as the Civil Aviation Authority's Hovercraft Department and NRDC.

THE HOVERCLUB OF AMERICA INC

Box 234, Uniontown, Ohio 44685, USA

Officers:
Chris Fitzgerald, *President*
Paul Esterle, *Vice President*
Dennis N Benson, *Secretary & Treasurer*
Mike Clare, *Director*
Wayne Moore, *Director*
Bob Windt, *Director*

Membership of the HoverClub of America, Inc, is available at US $10 pa.

Following a general meeting of the members of the American Hovercraft Association on 29 May, 1976, it was agreed to reorganise the Association into the HoverClub of America, Inc. Subsequently the HoverClub of America has been incorporated under the State Laws of Indiana and six national directors appointed and elected to serve for one year.

In the United States the HoverClub of America organises race meetings, rallies and other events for members possessing hovercraft, and also publishes a monthly newsletter.

TERRE HAUTE, INDIANA
Steve Anten,
2804 Garfield Avenue, Terre Haute, Indiana 47804

PENNSYLVANIA/OHIO
Stan Sykes,
1970 Weston, Youngstown, Ohio 44514

TUSTIN, CALIFORNIA
Ray Kemp,
15012 Red Hill Avenue, Tustin, California 92680

CORDOVA, ILLINOIS
Bob Windt,
1204 3rd Street, Cordova, Illinois 61242

TOLEDO, OHIO
Terry Chapman,
Box 111, Swanton, Ohio 43558

JACKSONVILLE, ILLINOIS
Leonard Fisher,
785 E College, Jacksonville, Illinois 62650

ANCHORAGE, ALASKA
Hank Sayler,
7400 Silver Birch Drive, Anchorage, Alaska 99502

TAMPA/ST PETERSBURG, FLORIDA
Dee Anders,
1915 Fern Street, Tampa, Florida 33604

JACKSONVILLE, FLORIDA
Marc Marchioli,
414 Sherry Drive, Atlantic Beach, Florida 32211

MEMPHIS, TENNESSEE
Guy R Pilce,
6090 Selkirk, Memphis, Tennessee 38138

INTERNATIONAL HOVERCLUBS

HOVER CLUB OF AUSTRALIA
H B Standen, *Hon Secretary*
GPO Box 1882, Brisbane, Queensland 4001, Australia

FÉDÉRATION FRANÇAIS DES CLUBS d'AÉROGLISSEURS
41-43 rue Aristide-Briande, 45130 Meung-sur-Loire, France
Member Clubs:

CLUB FRANÇAIS DES AÉROGLISSEURS
41-43 rue Aristide-Briande, 45130 Meung-sur-Loire, France

AÉROGLISSEURS D'ILE DE FRANCE
107 boulevard de Charonne, 75011 Paris, France

COUSS' AIR TOURAINE
81 rue Michelet, 37000 Tours, France

AÉROGLISSEURS D'OC
51 avenue Louis Abric, 34400 Lunel, France

ANJOU-BRETAGNE AÉROGLISSEURS
4 rue de la Maladrerie, 49220 Le Lion D'Angers, France

CLUB AÉROGLISSEURS RHÔNE-ALPES
8 rue de Richelieu, 69100 Villeurbanne, France

AÉROGLISSEURS VAL DE METZ
18 rue des Près-Argancy, 57640 Vigy, France

AÉROGLISSEURS OPALE
30 rue de Canal-Pinche Faline, 80230 St Valery/Somme, France

HOVER CLUB OF TRINIDAD & TOBAGO
N Seal, *President*
1 Richardson Street, Point Fortin, Trinidad

HOVERCRAFT CLUB OF NEW ZEALAND
K F Leatham, *Hon Secretary*
MacDonald Road, Pokeno, New Zealand

HOVER CLUB OF CANADA
R Fishlock
103 Doane Street, Ottawa, Ontario K2B 6GY, Canada

HOVER CLUB OF JAPAN
Information from Masahiro Mino, Senior Director, Aerodynamics Section, Nihon University at Narashino, 7-1591 Narashinodai, Funabashi, Chiba-Ken, Japan

SWEDISH HOVERCLUB
(Svenska Svävarklubben)
Garry Olsson, *Secretary*
Odensalvägen 72, S-195 00 Marsta, Sweden

THE INTERNATIONAL HYDROFOIL SOCIETY

17 Melcombe Court, Dorset Square, London NW1 6EP, England
Telephone: 01-723 4285 & 01-935 8678
Officers:
Dott Ing Leopoldo Rodriquez, *President*
Th Pellinkhof, *Chairman*
Michael Eames, *Vice President*
Juanita Kalerghi, *Vice President*
Mark Thornton, *Vice President*

The International Hydrofoil Society was founded in 1970 to advance study and research into both powered and sailing hydrofoils, and is ruled by a Council which meets in London. There are at present members in 27 countries, as well as a North American Chapter known as IHS-NA. A newsletter is published four times a year and in addition, *High-Speed Surface Craft (incorporating Hovering Craft & Hydrofoil)*, as the 'official organ' of the Society, includes an IHS section. Hydrofoil topics are discussed at regular meetings and the Society holds a library of related material at 51 Welbeck Street, London W1.

ACV AND HYDROFOIL CONSULTANTS

ACV CONSULTANTS

NIGERIA

Hovermarine Services (Nigeria) Ltd

PO Box 116, 19th Floor, Western House, Broad Street, Lagos, Nigeria
Officials:
Alhaji Waziri Ibrahim, *Chairman*
J Tunde Johnson, *Director*
J B Oluntunde, *Director*
A Odofin

General consultancy services for ACVs, route surveys, route proving, applications studies, performance assessments. Agents for Hovermarine Transport Ltd.

UNITED KINGDOM

Air Cushion Equipment (1976) Ltd

15-35 Randolph Street, Shirley, Southampton SO1 3HD, England
Telephone: 0703 776468
Telex: 477537
Officials:
J D Hake, *Chairman*
L A Hopkins, *Director*
R C Gilbert, *General Manager*
R R Henvest, *Works Manager*

Air Cushion Equipment (1976) Ltd offers its services as design engineers and technical consultants for air cushion and for water cushion systems. Past experience has involved investigations into systems using both water and air as the cushion fluid.

Water cushions have involved investigating skirt systems up to 15 bar and the various effects of these systems for operating within the industrial sector. Air cushion and skirt systems have been studied with cushion pressures up to 0·75 bar having skirt geometries which can be fitted to structures of various types.

An air cushion oil storage tank movement service is offered on a world wide basis together with an additional tank stressing service to verify structural integrity.

The company offers its own services and those of its licensed contractors for the movement of heavy, dense and awkward structures as well as its manufacturing facilities for the production of flexible structures and skirt systems.

Air Vehicles Ltd

Head Office: 1 Sun Hill, Cowes, Isle of Wight, England
Yard: Dinnis' Yard, High Street, Cowes, Isle of Wight, England
Telephone: 098 382 3194 & 4739
Officials:
P H Winter, MSc, *Director*
C D J Bland, *Director*
C B Eden, *Director*

Air Vehicles Ltd, formed in 1968, has a wide experience of all types of hovercraft and hovercraft operation, and can offer a full range of services as consultants.

Particular fields where Air Vehicles Ltd has specialised knowledge are:
1. manufacture and operation of small hovercraft up to 14 seats. Several craft have been built and the latest AV Tiger is also offered for charter;
2. design and construction of ducted propellers. Sizes have ranged from 4ft 6in diameter used on AV Tiger, ducts for SR.N6 and two large ducts of 9ft overall diameter delivered to the USA early 1976;
3. design, operation and site surveys for hoverbarges, particularly for ship-to-shore cargo. The first 350-ton hoverbarge on the Yukon River in Alaska was designed and commissioned by Air Vehicles Ltd.

Approved by the Civil Aviation Authority, the company can design and undertake modifications to larger craft. Typical of this work is the conversion to hoverfreighter configuration of SR.N5 and SR.N6. The company also offers two SR.N5 hovercraft for charter as well as the AV Tiger eight to ten seat hovercraft and the new Tiger S, 12-14 seater.

The company's association with Hoverwork Ltd enables it to call on the company's world-wide experience of hovercraft operations. A special feature of Air Vehicles' consultancy is a complete on-site survey and a feasibility study of all types of hovercraft which is undertaken for a fixed fee. Several of these have been completed for hoverbarge projects in various parts of the world.

British Rail Hovercraft Limited

50 Liverpool Street, London EC2P 2BQ, England
Telephone: 01-247 7600
Officials:
J M Lefeaux, *Managing Director*
A J Tame, *Marketing Director*
P A Yerbury, *Technical Director*
D H C Sumner, *Finance Manager*
Capt D Meredith, *Operations Manager*

British Rail Hovercraft Limited is the most experienced commercial hovercraft operator in the world. It is the only company to have operated commercially both amphibious and non-amphibious craft on estuarial and open water services.

Studies have been conducted on behalf of clients in many parts of the world and the company is able to provide a route costing and viability appraisal service based on "real time" operating experience.

Leslie Colquhoun and Associates

7 Daryngton Avenue, Birchington, Kent, England
Telephone: 0843 43085

Leslie Colquhoun and Associates was formed in 1973 to provide a hovercraft transport consultancy service using the unique experience of L R Colquhoun who has been closely associated with the hovercraft industry since 1959. This experience involved the testing, development and marketing of Vickers Ltd hovercraft projects from 1959-1965, and from 1966-1973 the setting up and running of Hoverlloyd's Ramsgate to Calais hovercraft service with the SR.N6 and SR.N4. Mr Colquhoun was Managing Director of the company when he resigned in December 1972 to set up the consultancy.

The consultancy is contracted to Hoverlloyd and has completed on their behalf a report on the company's SR.N4 cross Channel operations for the SESPO PM17 office of the Department of the US Navy.

Further work has been contracted in UK, France, Hungary, America, Iran and Malaysia.

The consultancy also provides assistance to International Hoverservices Ltd.

Through a close association with Comasco International Ltd the consultancy is involved in pollution and waste disposal schemes using both chemical and incineration processes.

Peter G Fielding, CEng, FRAeS

Branches:
United Kingdom: 20 Warmdene Road, Brighton, East Sussex BN1 8NL, England
Telephone: 0273 501212
Dock House, Niton Undercliff, Ventnor, Isle of Wight PO38 2NE, England
Telephone: 0983 730 252
USA: 1701 North Fort Myer Drive, Suite 908, Arlington, Virginia 22209, USA
Telephone: (703) 528 1092
7910 Woodmont Avenue, Suite 1103, Bethesda, Maryland 20014, USA
Telephone: (301) 656 5991

Consultant in air cushion systems, air cushion operations, and air cushion technology since 1959 to the US Army, the US Navy, US Department of Defense, the Advanced Research Projects Agency-DOD, US Department of Commerce-Maritime Administration, the Office of Naval Research, the US Naval Ships Research and Development Center, the US Army TRECOM, the Executive Office of the President USA, the US Navy-Chief of Naval Operations, the US Marine Corps, the Institute for Defense Analysis, the Center for Naval Analysis, the Bell Aerosystems Corporation, the Aerojet Corporation, the Research Analysis Corporation, Science Applications Incorporated, Hoverlift Applications Incorporated, Booz-Allen Applied Research Incorporated, Associated Consultants International Inc, and SeaSpan Inc. Services for the above organisations have included state of the art reports, technical and economic analysis, route surveys, environmental impact studies, subsystem analysis, operational plans, test plans, mission studies, advanced technology estimates, test site selection, cost analysis, structural and materials analysis and market research.

Assignments completed include:
1. Review and assessment of the Arctic SEV advanced technology programme for the Advanced Research Projects Agency, US Dept of Defense.

2. Analysis of "paddle wheel" propulsion and sealing systems for SES, for SA Inc McLean, Virginia, USA.
3. 'The Surface Effect Vehicle (SEV) in Search and Rescue Missions in Alaska'—for the Research Analysis Corporation, McLean, Virginia, USA.
4. 'An Assessment of the Technological Risk and Uncertainty of Advanced Surface Effect Vehicles (SEV) for the Arctic'—for the US Naval Ships Research and Development Center, Carderock, Maryland, USA.
5. 'An Evaluation of Advanced Surface Effect Vehicle Platforms Performing Military Missions in the Arctic'—for Science Applications Inc, La Jolla, California, and Arlington, Virginia, USA.
6. 'An Exhaustive Bibliography of Air Cushion Subjects' for the Research Analysis Corporation, McLean, Virginia, USA.
7. 'Preliminary Findings of the Economic Suitabilities of the Surface Effect Ship to Various Routes in the US'—for SEASPAN Inc, Washington DC, USA.
8. 'Appraisal of Heavy Lift Systems for Commercial Applications'—for Hoverlift Applications Inc, Arlington, Virginia, USA.
9. Results and Implications of the Advanced Projects Agency, US Department of Defense, Surface Effect Vehicles Programme—for Science Applications Inc, Arlington, Virginia, USA.

Hovercraft Consultants Limited

Forest Lodge West, Fawley Road, Hythe, Southampton, Hampshire SO4 6ZZ, England
Telephone: 0703 843178
Officials:
J E Rapson, MBE, *Managing Director*
J P Towndrow, *Director*
S M Rapson, *Secretary and Director*

Hovercraft Consultants Limited offers a comprehensive information and advisory service to the hovercraft and related industries. The company is headed by John Rapson, MBE, who has been continuously involved in hovercraft technology since 1956.

The nucleus of the HCL team was formed by former employees of Hovercraft Development Limited who specialise in cushion technology. In addition to their considerable combined experience, further technical and commercial assistance is provided by other members of the consultancy. This enables the company to undertake a full range of services, not only in the field of hovercraft technology, but also in areas of marine and general engineering. The company maintains many of the unique services offered by HDL in the past, particularly the hovercraft information service, pioneered by the Technical Unit. This service, however, has been streamlined by the use of a computerised data retrieval system.

Meeting rooms, telexing and copying facilities and general secretarial assistance are also available to HCL clients.

Hoverwork Limited

12 Lind Street, Ryde, Isle of Wight PO33 2NR, England
Telephone: 0983 5181
Telex: 86513 (A/B Hoverwork Ryde)
Officials:
C D J Bland, *Managing Director*
D R Robertson, *Director*
E W H Gifford, *Director*
A C Smith, *Director*
R G Clarke, *Director*
G M Palin, *Secretary*

Hoverwork Limited is a subsidiary of Hovertravel Limited and was formed in 1966. The company provides crew training and charter facilities for all available types of ACVs, thus bridging the gap between the operators and manufacturers.

Hoverwork and its parent, Hovertravel, own the largest fleet of hovercraft available for charter in the world. Types include the SR.N6, the SR.N6 freighter, SR.N5 passenger/freighter and the AV.2. In recent years the company has concentrated on providing craft for seismic, gravity and hydrographic survey work in shallow water areas and terrain impossible to other forms of transport.

The company, jointly with Hovertravel Limited, offers a route feasibility investigation service.

P N Structures Limited

Marine and Engineering Division
30A Sackville Street, Piccadilly, London W1X 1DB, England
Telephone: 01-734 2578
Telex: 261709
Officials:
Theo Pellinkhof, *Chairman*
Karin M Adeler, *Director*
David J Rimmer, *Secretary*
José Romero Sánchez, *Associate (Spain)*

Consultancy in the fields of economic transport systems and air cushion applications, including air-supported structures (airdomes).

Selection and indication of solutions for various transport problems. Also the selection of amphibious craft, hydrofoils, catamarans and a variety of types from a range of planing hulls to more conventional hull designs, to meet clients' specific requirements.

Selection of air cushion platforms and conveyor belts to facilitate cost-saving load moving.

A wide area of industrial and technological resources will be made available to clients.

R A Shaw

(Managing Director Hoverprojects Limited)
Fell Brow, Silecroft, Millom, Cumbria LA18 5LS, England
Telephone: 0657 2022

Consultancy services to governments, local authorities and private enterprise on all aspects of fast transport with special emphasis on hovercraft and hydrofoils. Services include financial, economic and operational assessments in all conditions and new designs to meet particular requirements.

Contracts have included:
1. A study for the State of Washington to assess the feasibility of introducing hovercraft and hydrofoils into the Puget Sound ferry system.
2. A feasibility appraisal of proposed hovercraft operations in British Columbia.
3. Reporting to a local authority on prospects of establishing a hoverport within their borough.
4. A study for the Greater London Council on fast passenger services on the Thames.
5. Three independent studies on the potential for hovercraft in the Venetian lagoon.
6. Examination of world potential market for hovercraft.
7. Design and economics of 1,000-ton river hovercraft.
8. Planning and operating consultancy for Airavia Ltd and Speed Hydrofoils Ltd for hydrofoils on the River Thames.

Work currently includes:
1. Design of a main river terminal in the Thames in front of St Paul's to cater for all forms of river passenger craft and to include a helistop.
2. Advising a shipping company on proposed hydrofoil services on the Thames estuary and to the continent.

Robert Trillo Limited

28a St Thomas St, Lymington, Hampshire SO4 9NF, England
Telephone: 0590 75098
Officials:
R L Trillo, CEng, FIMechE, FRAeS, AFAIAA, AFCASI, *Managing Director,* Author and Distributor "Marine Hovercraft Technology"
A U Alexander, *Secretary*

Operating since 1969 as a consultancy, engaging principally in technology and economics concerned with air cushion vehicles, high speed marine craft and amphibious vehicles. The firm has worked for industry and government departments in a number of countries and has undertaken transport feasibility studies, preliminary design investigations, design of light hovercraft and experimental investigations. Other work has been concerned with the aerodynamic design of five ducted propeller installations including the SR.N6 and Skima 12 hovercraft, and the Aerospace Developments AD 500 airship. Two light hovercraft have been designed for French companies, one of which, the Transfutur 4-seat Windlord is now in quantity production. Commissions have included work in Australia, Canada, Denmark, France, Sweden, the UK and USA and have covered economics and engineering studies, designs of craft and appraisal of investment opportunities. The firm publishes bi-monthly bibliography services on air cushion and hydrofoil systems and on high speed ground transportation and urban rapid transit systems.

Affiliate member of Northern Associates Reg'd, Canada, Canadian Arctic consulting group.
Representatives:
Canada:
Vice Admiral K L Dyer, RCN Rtd, Dyer & Associates, Suite 708, 77 Metcalfe Street, Ottawa K1P 5L6, Canada

Denmark:
Leif Hansen, A B C Hansen Comp A/S, Hauchsvej 14, DK-1825 Copenhagen V, Denmark

UNITED STATES OF AMERICA

Aerophysics Company

3500 Connecticut Avenue NW, Washington DC 20008, USA
Telephone: (202) 244 7502
Officials:
Dr Gabriel D Boehler, *President*
William F Foshag, *Chief Engineer*

Aerophysics Company was formed in 1957 to conduct fundamental research of the ground effect principle. Dr Boehler had previously performed private feasibility work with M Beardsley. Since then, Aerophysics has undertaken work in various areas of ACV design, including skirt design, control techniques, parametric analysis, conceptual and design studies, studies of ACV lift air systems including various types of blowers and propulsion systems.

Booz-Allen & Hamilton Inc

245 Park Avenue, New York, New York 10017, USA

General management consulting and technology management consulting world-wide, including: strategy management, organisation planning, marketing and marketing research, computer systems and software, manufacturing systems and technology and operations management; new product, process and equipment development; transportation and airport planning and engineering; and defence planning and research.

Davidson Laboratory
Stevens Institute of Technology

Castle Point Station, Hoboken, New Jersey 07030, USA
Telephone: (201) 420 5300
Officials:
Dr J P Breslin, *Director*
Dr D Savitsky, *Deputy Director*

Organised in 1935 as the Experimental Towing Tank, the Laboratory is active in basic and applied hydrodynamic research, including smooth water performance and manoeuvrability; seakeeping, propulsion and control of marine vehicles including ACV, SES and hydrofoil craft. Special model test facilities are available to investigate the dynamic behaviour of all types of vessels and platforms in smooth water and waves.

Doty Associates, Inc

451 Hungerford Drive, Rockville, Maryland 20850, USA
Telephone: (301) 424 0270
Officials:
Donald L Doty, *President and Technical Director*
Eugene H Brown, *Vice President and Director, Energy Systems Group*
William B Humphrey, *Vice President and Director, Defense Systems Group*

Doty Associates, Inc is a privately-owned, small business firm founded in 1968. The firm specialises in financial management, project control, weapon system analysis, test planning and evaluation, operations research, cost and economic analyses for Department of Defense and other government and state agencies.

Since its founding, the firm has been engaged in providing engineering services to the US Navy on a number of high technology programmes. These programmes include both the 2K and 3K Surface Effect Ship (SES) designs, the PHM Hydrofoil, the Sea Control Ship and the Vertical Support Ship (VSS). In addition, the firm is actively involved in Naval V/STOL aviation studies.

Forrestal Laboratory

Princeton University, Princeton, New Jersey 08540, USA
Officials:
T E Sweeney

Research prototypes (ACVs).

Gibbs & Cox

40 Rector Street, New York, New York 10006, USA
Telephone: (212) 487 2800
Arlington Office: 2341 Jefferson Davis Highway, Arlington, Virginia 22202, USA
Telephone: (703) 979 1240
Newport News Office: Rouse Tower, 6060 Jefferson Avenue, Newport, Virginia 23605, USA
Telephone: (804) 380 5800

Project management, co-ordination and consultation on conceptual and preliminary designs, contract drawings and specifications and construction drawings for commercial or naval ships of the SES/ACV or submerged hydrofoil systems, destroyers, escorts, frigates, corvettes and VTOL/Helo carriers.

Global Marine Inc

811 West 7th Street, Los Angeles, California 90017, USA
Telephone: (213) 680 9550
Global Marine Development Inc
PO Box 3010, 2302 Martin Street, Newport Beach, California 92663, USA
Telephone: (714) 752 5050
Officials:
R C Crooke, *President*
R B Thornburg, *Vice President, SP*
S B Wetmore, *Vice President, Engineering*

Wholly-owned subsidiaries:
Arctic Systems Ltd, Calgary, Alberta, Canada
Arctic Engineers & Constructors, Houston, Texas, USA

Global Marine Inc was incorporated in 1959, and is engaged primarily in offshore drilling and engineering. However, in 1968 the company undertook an engineering feasibility study directed towards developing equipment and techniques for drilling in Arctic areas. This engineering study led to the selection of ACT (Air Cushion Transport) units as the most feasible for operating in the area. Global Marine has a continuing design, sales and operations programme directed towards various size ACT (Air Cushion Transport) drilling rigs with various drilling capabilities. The programme is handled by Global Marine Development Inc which is a wholly-owned subsidiary of Global Marine Inc.

Global Marine constructed the ACT-100 in Canada in 1971. This unit was test operated in the Arctic during 1971, and was test operated by the Canadian government in connection with the Mackenzie River Highway and by Imperial Oil Ltd in connection with its offshore winter drilling operations in 1973-74. Design work on larger ACV drilling rigs continues.

Hydronautics, Incorporated

7210 Pindell School Road, Howard County, Laurel, Maryland 20810, USA
Telephone: (301) 776 7454
Officials:
Marshall P Tulin, *Chairman of the Board*
Phillip Eisenberg, *President and Chief Executive Officer*
Virgil E Johnson, Jr, *Senior Vice President*
Alex Goodman, *Senior Vice President*
Philip A Weiner, *Vice President and Secretary*
Harvey Post, *Treasurer*

The company was founded in July 1959, and has undertaken research, development and design of air cushion vehicles, hydrofoil craft and other high speed marine vehicles as well as advanced propulsion systems, under US Government and industrial contacts. Hydronautics has its own ship model basin and high speed water channel suitable for the evaluation of air cushion vehicles and hydrofoils.

Institute for Defense Analyses (IDA)

400 Army-Navy Drive, Arlington, Virginia 22202, USA
Telephone: (703) 558 1000

Performs interdisciplinary studies and analysis for agencies of the US Government, systems analysis, operations research, economics, policy analysis and studies of advanced technology and its applications.

E K Liberatore Company

567 Fairway Road, Ridgewood, New Jersey 07450, USA
Officials:
E K Liberatore, *Head*

Formed in 1964, the company specialises in systems engineering, vehicle design and in operations in the fields of ACVs, SESs and VTOL aircraft. Work includes requirements, integration, analysis, design, costing, FAA and other certification, route and market surveys and methodology. Current projects in the areas of helicopter development; proposal preparation; development of non-expendable energy systems for pumping water and generating electricity; and proposals for the State of Alaska. The company participated in the Aerophysics lift-fan programme for the US Navy/Rohr 3KSES (1979). It also prepared a social manifesto to be published by Morgan and Morgan in late 1980, of which some of the basic concepts were disclosed in a paper in *Jane's Surface Skimmers 1969-70*.

George E Meese

194 Acton Road, Annapolis, Maryland 21403, USA
Telephone: (301) 263 4054

SES structures.

M Rosenblatt & Son, Inc

350 Broadway, New York, New York 10013, USA
Telephone: (212) 431 6900
Officials:
Lester Rosenblatt, *President*
P W Nelson, *Executive Vice President*
E F Kaufman, *Vice President and Manager, Western Division*
N M Maniar, *Vice President and Technical Director*
L M Schlosberg, *Vice President and Design Manager*

M Rosenblatt & Son, Inc is an established naval architectural and marine engineering firm with over 30 years of proven experience in all phases of ship and marine vehicle design.

With offices in 10 US cities and abroad, the firm is close to the entire shipbuilding community and has a thorough understanding of its problems and needs. Its experience covers programme management and inspection of construction, as well as design.

A major portion of the company's design activities has been and is for the US Navy. Completed assignments are of the broadest possible variety covering research and development, feasibility studies, and conceptual and detail design for all classes of major combatants, auxiliaries, and high performance craft. In addition, the company has provided extensive design services for the conversion, overhaul, and repair of naval combatants, auxiliaries, submarines, amphibious warfare supply and landing craft.

The service to the maritime industry includes a wide variety of tasks covering the new and modification design of oceanographic ships, containerships, tankers, general cargo ships, dredges, bulk carriers, drilling platforms and ships, survey vessels, pipe-laying barges, and a great variety of supporting craft.

Typical ACV assignments include:

1. ARPA Advanced Surface Effect Vehicles

Conceptual studies, parametric studies and propulsion machinery analysis for phase 'O' studies of Advanced Surface Effect Vehicles for Advanced Research Project Agency. Work performed for American Machine and Foundry Company.

2. JSESPO Surface Effect Ship Testcraft

Conceptual and feasibility design studies of candidate SES vehicles for the JSESPO sizing study for second generation SES testcraft in the 1,000 to 3,000-ton range. The work included studies of various candidate versions of SES to identify and evaluate their unique operational and design capabilities; technological assessment of various structural materials and systems; preparation of a proposed development programme with required supporting research and development. Work performed for Joint Surface Effect Ship Program office.

3. Amphibious Fleet Conceptual Studies

Conceptual design studies of various types of ships for future amphibious fleets, including submarine, displacement, planing hydrofoil and ACV type ships. Studies included technological assessment of performance of the concepts, taking into account various operational capabilities, including speed, propulsion systems, manning, weapons, materials, payloads and costs. Work performed for Stanford Research Institute under basic contract with ONR.

4. The Surface Effect Ship, Advanced Design and Technology

A 283-page text book covering drag, structure, propulsion, transmission, propulsors, stability, lift systems, seals, auxiliaries, weights, parametric analysis, and sample problems. Each topic is discussed including design procedures and equations. The book was prepared for the US Navy Surface Effect Ships Project Office.

5. 2,000-ton Surface Effect Ship

Trade-off studies, system design parameters, equipment selection, system diagrams, hullborne stability in connection with a complete design proposal. The scope of work included hullborne structural design criteria, electrical power generating and distribution, heating, ventilating, air conditioning, hull appurtenances, piping systems, hotel and auxiliary machinery arrangements. Work performed for the Lockheed Missiles and Space Co, and the Surface Effect Ship Project Office.

6. ACV Amphibian

Conceptual design of a 20-ton capacity air cushion lighter, with retractable wheels, for US Army Mobility Equipment Research and Development Center.

Science Applications, Inc

1200 Prospect Street, La Jolla, California 92037, USA
Telephone: (714) 454 3811

Science Applications, Inc provides technical consulting, systems integration, and operations services in a wide range of fields in defence, energy and environment. In the field of air cushion vehicles, the company has experience in field operations, engineering consulting, and control systems. The company specialises in applications studies and economic analyses for any type of operation involving air cushion systems and heavy lift helicopter operations. The company employs 3,000 technical specialists and has offices in 36 states throughout the United States.

Stanford Research Institute

Menlo Park, California 94025, USA
Telephone: (415) 326 6200
Officials:
Robert S Ratner, *Director Transportation and Industrial Systems Center*

Operational and strategic management assistance, operational trade-off studies; economic and system evaluations; simulation applications, scheduling and routing systems.

Martin Stevens

Woodhull Cove, Oldfield Village, Setauket, Long Island, New York 11733, USA

Mechanical design, drive systems.

Systems Exploration Inc

3687 Voltaire Street, San Diego, California 92106, USA
Telephone: (714) 297 5404
Officials:
Dale K Beresford
Erwin J Hauber

Consultants to the US Navy on ACV, SES and hydrofoil test and development programmes.

Water Research Company

3003 North Central Avenue, Suite 600, Phoenix, Arizona 85012, USA
Telephone: (602) 265 7722
Officials:
Richard R Greer, *President, Member of American Society of Naval Engineers*

The Water Research Company was formed in 1972 to consolidate activities surrounding the patents held or applied for by Richard R Greer relating to various aspects of water-borne vehicles. The company has subsequently prepared conceptual studies on a class of winged surface effect vessels (WSEV) intended to fill a variety of US Navy and commercial freight applications. The conclusions of this study were published in the *Naval Engineers' Journal, April 1974,* and further comprehensive conclusions also setting forth energy savings and use of alternate fuels were published in *Jane's Surface Skimmers 1975-76* . Present efforts are directed to providing assistance in related research activities and further research studies.

Wheeler Industries Inc

Executive Office: Board of Trade Building, Suite 403, 1129 20th Street NW, Washington DC 20036, USA
Telephone: (202) 659 1867
Telex: 89 663

Systems Research Center: Wheeler Building, Suite 700, 1120 19th Street, NW, Washington DC 20036, USA
Telephone: (202) 223 1938

Other offices: Hayes Building, Suite 334 & 618, 2361 South Jefferson Davis Highway, Arlington, Virginia 20362, USA
Telephone: (703) 521 5005 and (703) 920 8686

Officials:
E Joseph Wheeler, Jr, *President and Chief Executive Officer*
George W Glatis, *Vice President, Operations and Corporate Development*
Roy G Shults, *Director, Systems Research Center*
Robert H Fillmore, *Director, Accounting*

Wheeler Industries Inc, is a privately-owned, small business firm that was founded in 1966 and specialises in systems engineering for ship, air, electronic, and deep ocean systems, as well as oceanographic and environmental research. Since its establishment, the company has continuously provided technical, engineering, and management support, primarily in the ship acquisition areas, to the US Navy. This support has encompassed a wide range including top level management plans, ship acquisition plans, technology assessments and forecasts, subsystem analysis and trade-offs, development and acquisition requirements and specifications, programme budgeting, development of hydrofoil design data, and hydrofoil strut/foil hydrodynamic load criteria and data. Currently, the company has one of the largest high speed surface ship teams in the United States. A team of experienced engineers has been assembled which is fully capable of providing the engineering, technical, design, and management services associated with hydrofoils. The company has expanded its organisation to provide technical and management services to the US Navy for air cushion vehicles and surface effect ships.

The technical and operational functions and capabilities are co-ordinated by the Systems Research Center. Under the Director of the Center, permanently assigned Project Managers (for ship, electronic, and oceanographic systems) form engineering task teams for the duration of a contract or included task(s), supported as necessary by technical support (clerical, graphics, editorial, and reproduction) personnel. This approach provides maximum management visibility and control over each task, and provides optimum response to customers while minimising costs.

HYDROFOIL CONSULTANTS

SWITZERLAND

Dr Ing E G Faber

Weinberglistrasse 60, CH-6000 Lucerne, Switzerland
Telephone: (041) 44 33 20
Telex: 78 670 DATAG-CH

Consultant in marine engine plant planning, marine engineering and marine technology, with special emphasis on high-speed and hydrofoil craft.

GENERAL: Feasibility studies, cost estimates, specifications, plant descriptions, project co-ordinations.

CONCEPTUAL AND PRELIMINARY DESIGNS: Engine and auxiliary plants, piping systems and hydraulics, electrical and monitoring systems, ventilation and air conditioning systems, noise insulation.

TECHNICAL EXPERTISE: Speed estimates and hydrodynamics problems, waterjet propulsion, analysis of ship structure, vibration and shock isolation, acceptance tests and damage survey.

Supramar Hydrofoils AG

Ausserfeld 5, CH-6362 Stansstad, Switzerland
Telephone: (041) 61 31 94
Telex: 78228 Supra CH
Officials:
Baron Hanns von Schertel, *President*
Dipl Ing Harry Trevisani, *General Manager*
Dipl Ing Eugen Schatté, *Research and Development*
Jürg Bally, *Board Member*
Ernst Schneider, *Board Member*

Supramar was founded in Switzerland in 1952 to develop on a commercial basis the hydrofoil system introduced by the Schertel-Sachsenberg Hydrofoil Syndicate and its licensee, the Gebrüder Sachsenberg Shipyard.

From this early date Supramar have provided a consultancy service on a world-wide basis covering not only their hydrofoil vessels but also other aspects of fast marine transportation. Their scientists have delivered papers to most of the world's leading professional bodies.

The company has been under contract to many Governments and military services.

UNITED KINGDOM

P N Structures Ltd

Marine and Engineering Division

See main entry under ACV consultants.

H H Snowball

30 Lismore Road, Croydon, Surrey, England

Founder, in 1968, of Airavia Ltd, the first company to represent Sudoimport hydrofoils in the West. Founder, Speed Hydrofoils Ltd, which introduced Raketa hydrofoils on scheduled services on the River Thames in 1974. Consultant Bataan-Manila Ferry Services, Hydrofoil Exploration Services, etc. Crew training arranged, also feasibility studies of projected hydrofoil routes.

UNITED STATES OF AMERICA

Davidson Laboratory
Stevens Institute of Technology

See main entry under ACV consultants.

Doty Associates, Inc

See main entry under ACV consultants.

Gibbs & Cox

See main entry under ACV consultants.

W A Graig

307 Troy Towers, Union City, New Jersey 07087, USA
Telephone: (201) 864 3993

W A Graig, Ingénieur Civil de l'Aéronautique (Ecole Nationale Supérieure de l'Aéronautique, France). Registered Prof Engineer (Ohio, USA).

W A Graig (formerly Grunberg) is the inventor of the Grunberg foil system, first patented in 1935. His approach provided the basis for the Aquavion series and many other designs, and his influence is still to be found in vessels in production today.

The Grunberg principle of inherent angle of attack variation is fully compatible with Forlanini's concept of area variation. Both can be incorporated in the same structure and in a number of modern hydrofoils the two principles work in association.

Hoerner Fluid Dynamics

PO Box 342, Brick Town, New Jersey 08723, USA
Officials:
S F Hoerner
Dr Ing Habilitatus

Hydrodynamicist of hydrofoils "Sea Legs" and "Victoria", since 1951. Author of "Fluid-Dynamic Drag" (1965) and "Fluid-Dynamic Lift" (1975).

Hydronautics Incorporated

See main entry under ACV consultants.

M Rosenblatt & Son Inc

See main entry under ACV consultants.

Typical hydrofoil assignments include:
AG(EH)

Preliminary design and naval architectural services for preparation of proposal for design and construction of 300-ton AG(EH) Hydrofoil Research Vessel—for Lockheed Aircraft Corp.
Hydrofoil (LVH)

Provided naval architectural services, including development of lines, powering predictions, stability curves and loading criteria for design and development of a 37ft Landing Force Amphibious Support Vehicle Hydrofoil (LVH)—for Lycoming Division, Avco Corporation.
Hydrofoil Amphibian

Conceptual design of a 60-ton capacity hydrofoil lighter with retractable wheels for US Army Mobility Equipment Research and Development Center.
Patrol Vessel

Portion of contract design and complete detail design for construction of a 100-ton, second generation hydrofoil patrol vessel for Grumman Aerospace Corp.

Stanford Research Institute

See main entry under ACV consultants.

Systems Exploration, Inc

See main entry under ACV consultants.

Water Research Company

See main entry under ACV consultants.

Wheeler Industries Inc

See main entry under ACV consultants.

GLOSSARY

ACS. Automatic control system. See **foil systems, submerged**

ACV. Air cushion vehicle

AIO. Action information organisation. See also **CIC,** combat information centre. Position allocated to computerised tactical and weapon control centre on light naval craft

AMPS. Arctic marine pipelaying system: method of laying pipelines in ice-covered Arctic waters employing skirted air cushion barge as icebreaker devised after Arctic Engineers successfully and continuously broke ice up to 0·68m (27in) thick using 250-ton ACT-100 platform. On contact with ice sheet, skirt rises above it, maintaining its seal. As ice sheet enters cushion zone, water level beneath is depressed by air pressure. Having lost flotation support, ice becomes cantilevered ledge and when it reaches its critical length, it breaks off into water below and is then thrust aside by plough-like deflector

ANVCE. (US Navy) Advanced Naval Vehicles Concepts Evaluation Project

APU. Auxiliary power unit

AQL. Aéroglisseur à quille latérale: ship-size seagoing air cushion vehicle employing rigid sidewalls and flexible seals fore and aft to contain air cushion

ASW. Anti-submarine warfare

A to N. Aids to navigation

abeam. Position of another craft at side or beam

actuator. Unit designed to translate sensor information and/or computer instructions into mechanical action. Energy is transferred to control surfaces hydraulically, pneumatically or electrically

aeration. See **air entry**

Aérobac. Mixed passenger/car ferries and freighters designed by Bertin and SEDAM

aerodynamic lift. Lifting forces generated by forward motion through atmosphere due to difference in pressure between upper and lower surfaces

aerodynamic profile drag. See **drag**

aerodynamic yaw angle. Angle in horizontal plane between relative air direction and craft centreline

Aerofoil boat, also **winged hull.** Name given by late Dr Alexander M Lippisch, inventor and aircraft designer, to his range of aerodynamic ramwing machines

aéroglisseur. Air-glider: range of passenger-carrying amphibious ACVs designed by Société Bertin & Cie in conjunction with Société d'Études et de Développement des Aéroglisseurs Marins (SEDAM)

aeroplane foil system. Arrangement in which main foil is forward of CG to support 75% to 85% of load, and auxiliary foil, supporting remainder, is aft as tail assembly

Four aerostatic-type air cushion vehicles. Each is supported by air put under pressure by a fan or fans and contained beneath the vehicles by flexible skirts or sidewalls. **Top left:** 3KSES; **top right:** 220-ton Soviet Aist; **centre:** 300-ton BHC SR.N4 Mk 3 and **bottom:** Sedam's 260-ton N 500

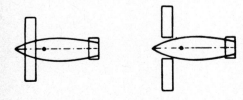

Aeroplane or conventional foil systems. Main foil may be divided into two to facilitate retraction

aerostatic lift. Lift created by self-generated cushion of pressurised air, put under pressure by fan or fans and contained beneath vehicle's structure by flexible seals or sidewalls

aérosuspendu. Air-suspended: form of suction-suspended monorail designed in France by Maurice Barthalon for mass public transportation on urban and suburban routes. Vehicle is suspended from its track by an air lift system in which pressure is sub-atmospheric. Propulsion is by linear induction motor

Aérotrain. Range of tracked air cushion vehicles under development in France by Société de l'Aérotrain

air bleed (ACV). Method of preventing "plough in" on skirted ACV by bleeding air from cushion through vent holes on outer front of skirt to reduce water drag by air lubrication

air bleed (hyd). See **air stabilisation.** Occasionally used instead of aeration or air entry

air cushion vehicle. Vehicle capable of being operated so that its weight, including payload, is wholly or significantly supported on a continuously generated cushion or 'bubble' of air at higher than ambient pressure. The air bubble or cushion is put under pressure by a fan or fans and generally contained beneath vehicle's structure by flexible skirts or sidewalls. In USA large or ship-size air cushion vehicles are called **surface effect ships** or **surface effect vessels.** There are two main types of air cushion vehicle, those supported by a self-generated cushion of air and those dependent on forward motion to develop lift. The former are designated aerostatic and the latter aerodynamic.

Aerodynamic craft include the *ram-wing,* the *channel-flow wing* and the *wing-in-ground-effect.* The *ram-wing* (a) can be likened to a short-span wing with sidewalls attached to its tip. The wing trailing edge and the sidewalls almost touch the water surface. At speed, lifting forces are generated by both the wing and the ram pressure built up beneath. One of the first concepts utilising a *channel-flow* wing (b) was the Columbia, designed in the USA by Vehicle Research Corporation in 1961 (*Jane's Surface Skimmers 1967-68*). The design featured a peripheral jet sidewall system for use at low speeds and an aerofoil shaped hull to provide lift at high speeds during forward flight. The side curtains of the peripheral jet were to be retained to seal the high pressure "channel" of air developed beneath from the low pressure airflow above and along the sides of the craft, down to the water surface. A 30ft long manned model of the Columbia was successfully tested in 1964.

The *wing-in-ground-effect* (c) is essentially an aircraft designed to fly in close proximity to the earth's surface, in order to take advantage of the so-called "image" flow that reduces induced drag by about 70%. In the Soviet Union this type of machine is known as an Ekranoplan.

Aerostatic-type air cushion vehicles can be divided into two categories—plenum chamber craft and peripheral or annular jet craft. *Plenum chamber craft* (d) employ the most simple of surface effect concepts. Air is forced from the lift fan directly into a recessed base where it forms a cushion which raises the craft. The volume of air pumped into the base is just sufficient to replace the air leaking out beneath the edges.

Variants of this category include the *skirted plenum craft* (e), in which a flexible fabric extension is hung between the metal structure and the surface to give increased obstacle and overwave clearance capability. The Naviplane and Terraplanes designed by Bertin and SEDAM employ separately fed multiple plenum chambers, each surrounded by lightweight flexible skirts. Skirted plenum chamber types are also favoured by builders of light air cushion vehicles because of their relatively simple design and construction.

Another variant is the *sidewall* ACV (f), in which the cushion air is contained between solid sidewalls or skegs and deflectable seals, either solid or flexible, fore and aft. Stability is provided by the buoyancy of the sidewalls and their planing forces. One of the derivatives of the sidewall type is the *Hydrokeel* (g) which is designed to plane on the after section of its hull and benefit to some degree from air lubrication.

In *peripheral* or *annular jet craft* (h) the ground cushion is generated by a continuous jet of air channelled through ducts or nozzles around the outer periphery of the base. The flexible skirts fitted to this type can take the form either of an extension to the outer wall of the duct or nozzle only, or an extension to both outer and inner walls. In the latter form it is known as a *trunked annular jet* (i).

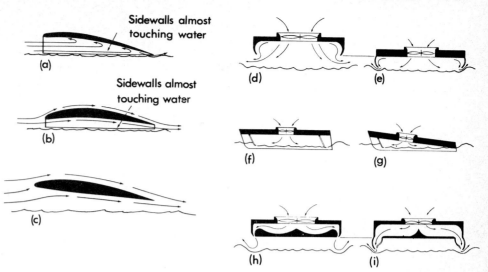

Sidewalls almost touching water

Sidewalls almost touching water

(a) ram wing; (b) channel-flow wing; (c) wing-in-ground-effect; (d) plenum chamber; (e) plenum chamber with skirt; (f) captured air bubble; (g) hydrokeel; (h) annular jet; (i) trunked annular jet

air entrainment. See **air entry**

air entry. Entry of air from atmosphere that raises low pressures created by flow due to foil's cambered surface

air gap area. Area beneath skirt through which air is able to leak from cushion

air gap (effective hoverheight). Air gap area divided by skirt periphery

air gap (local). Distance between local skirt hem and surface when craft is riding on its cushion

air momentum drag. Drag created by acceleration of air forming cushion from static to speed of hovercraft underway, relative to surrounding air

air pad. Part of air pallet assembly into which compressed air is introduced and allowed to escape in continuous flow through communicating holes in diaphragm

SEDAM Amphibarges

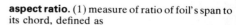

Air pad with flexible plastic diaphragm

air pallet, also **hoverpallet.** Air cushion supported load-carrying structure which bleeds continuous low pressure volume of air between structure and reaction surface, creating air film

air-port system. See **control ducts**

air-rider. Alternative generic name for air cushion vehicles or weight-carrying structures lifted off surface by cushion or film of air

air stabilised foils. See **foil systems**

amidships. (1) Midway between stem and stern of hull. (2) abbreviated to **midships** and meaning rudder or helm is in mid-position

amphibarge. Range of amphibious air cushion barges, self-propelled or towed, designed in France by SEDAM,

angle of attack. Angle made by mean chord line of aero- or hydrofoil with flow

angle of incidence. Angle made by mean chord line of hydrofoil in relation to fixed struts or hull

anti-bounce web. Tensioned skirt membrane connected between upper and lower bag points to restrain self-sustained vibration or 'bounce'

Aquavion type foil. Adapted from Grunberg system: about 85% of load is carried by mainfoil slightly aft of CG, 10% by submerged aft stabiliser foil, and remainder on pair of planing subfoils at bow. Planing subfoils give variable lift in response to wave shapes, whether skimming over or through them, and so trim angle of hull in order to correct angle of attack of main foil

articulated air cushion vehicle. Modular type load-carrying platform designed by Charles Burr of Bell Aerospace. Skirted platforms can be joined to form variety of ACVs of different load-carrying capacities

aspect ratio. (1) measure of ratio of foil's span to its chord, defined as

$$\frac{\text{span}^2}{\text{total foil area}}$$

(2) for ACVs defined as $\frac{\text{cushion beam}}{\text{cushion length}}$

attack craft. Small warship fitted with at least two major weapons

athwart, athwartship. Transversely across the hull from one side to other

axial flow lift fan. Fan generating airflow for lift that is parallel to axis of rotation

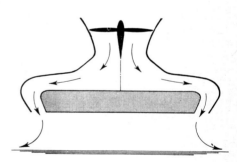

Axial flow lift fan

BTC. Buoyancy tank clearance. See **clearance**

backstrap. Fabric strap used to secure lift jet exit nozzle in flexible skirt at correct angle

baffle plates. See **fences**

bag perimeter. Perimeter of sideskirt bag or loop from outer to inner hinge, or from outer loop attachment to inner tie attachment of superstructure

ballast system. Method of transferring water or fuel between tanks to adjust fore and aft trim. In Mountbatten class ACVs, four groups of tanks, one at each corner, are located in the buoyancy tanks. Ring main facilitates rapid transfer of fuel between tanks as ballast and also serves as refuelling line

Three aerodynamic air cushion vehicles. Like aeroplanes, these craft depend upon forward speed to develop lift. A dynamic air cushion is formed between the vehicle and its supporting surface below. **Left to right:** The Soviet ESKA-1, two-seat river rescue craft; the Lippisch Rhein-Flugzeugbau X-113 Am and a Soviet experimental wing-in-ground-effect machine designed by the late Robert Oros di Bartini

base ventilated foil. System of forced ventilation designed to overcome reduction in lift/drag ratio of foil at supercavitating speeds. Air is fed continuously to upper surface of foil un-wetting surface and preventing formation of critical areas of decreased pressure. Alternatively air may be fed into cavity formed behind square trailing edge

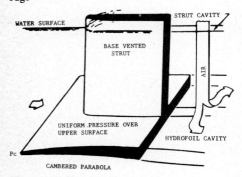

Base ventilated foil

beam. Measurement across hull at given point

beam-on. Sideways movement of craft, ie at 90° angle of yaw

Beaufort Scale. Scale of wind forces described by name and range of velocity and classified as from force 0 to force 12, or strong hurricanes to force 17. See **sea state**

bilge. Point of hull where side and bottom meet. Also water or fuel accumulated in bilges

bilge system. Pumping system to dispose of water and other fluids accumulated in bilges. In ACVs bilge systems are installed to clear buoyancy tanks. Small craft generally have hand-operated pump which connects directly to pipes in tanks. Larger craft, like 200-300-ton BHC Mountbatten, because of large number of buoyancy compartments, have four electrically driven pumps, each of which can drain one compartment at a time

block speed. Route distance divided by block time

block time, also **trip time.** Journey time between lift off and touchdown

boating. ACV when operating in displacement condition. Boating or **semi-hover** mode is used in congested terminal areas, when lift power and spray generation is kept to minimum. Some craft have water surface contact even at full hover for stability requirements

bow-up. Trim position or attitude when craft is high at bow. Can be measured by eye or attitude gyro

breast, to. To take waves at 90 degrees to their crests

Breguet range. Approximate range of craft based on average values of propulsion efficiency, specific fuel consumption and ratio of initial to final gross weight, assuming constant lift-to-drag ratio

broach, to. Sudden breaking of water surface by foil, or part of foil, resulting in loss of lift due to air flowing over foil's upper surface

to broach to. To swing sideways in following seas under wave action

bulkheads. Vertical partitions, either transverse or longitudinal, which divide or sub-divide hull. May be used to separate accommodation areas, strengthen structure, form tanks or localise fires or flooding

buoyancy. Reduction in weight of floating object. If object floats its weight is equal to (or less than) weight of fluid displaced

buoyancy chamber. Structure of which the weight and all loads which it supports is equal to (or less than) weight of water it displaces

buoyancy, reserve. Buoyancy in excess of that required to keep undamaged craft afloat. See **buoyancy**

buoyancy tubes. Inflatable tubular members providing reserve buoyancy. May be used as fenders if fitted to outer periphery of craft

CAA. Civil Aviation Authority

CAB. Captured air bubble. See **air cushion vehicle**

CIC. Combat information centre

cp. Centre of pressure

CP shifter. Control system which moves centre of pressure of supporting cushion(s) relative to CG of ACV to augment a craft's natural stability in pitch and roll

CPIC. Coastal patrol interdiction craft

CWL. Calm water line

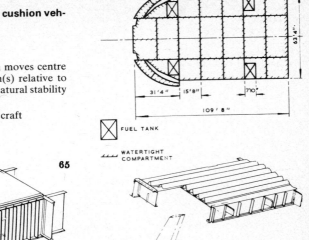

Typical buoyancy tank unit on the SR.N4. The basic structure of the SR.N4 is the buoyancy chamber, built around a grid of longitudinal and transversal frames, which form 24 watertight sub-divisions for safety. Below, the SR.N4 buoyancy tank layout

camber. (1) convexity on upper surface of deck to increase strength and/or facilitate draining. (2) convex form on upper surface of foil: high-speed flow over top surface decreases pressure and about two-thirds of lift is provided by this surface

canard foil system. Foil arrangement with main foil of wide span near stern, aft of CG, bearing about 65% of weight, and small central foil at bow

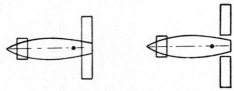

Canard foil configuration. Main foil area may be divided in to two to facilitate retraction

captain. Senior crew member aboard a hovercraft. Defined as the person designated by the operator to be in charge of a hovercraft during any journey, under the UK government's "The Hovercraft (Application of Enactments) Order 1972". Equivalent in rank to airliner or ship's captain. Alternative terms: pilot, driver, helmsman, coxswain and ACV operator

captured air bubble craft (see also **sidewall craft** and **surface effect ship**). Vessel in which cushion (or air bubble) is contained by rigid sidewalls and flexible bow and stern skirts. Occasionally used for any air cushion craft in which air cushion (or air bubble) is contained within cushion periphery with minimal air leakage

cavitation. Formation of vapour bubbles due to pressure decrease on upper surface of foil or back of propeller's blades at high speeds. Non-stable cavities or cavitation bubbles of aqueous vapour form near foil's leading edge and extend down stream expanding and collapsing. At points of collapse positive pressure peaks can rise to 20,000psi causing erosion and pitting of the metal. Cavitation causes unstable water flow over foils resulting in abrupt changes in lift and therefore discomfort for those aboard.

Foil sections being developed either delay onset of cavitation by reduced camber, thinner sections, or sweepback, or if craft is required to operate at supercavitating speeds, stabilise cavitation to provide smooth transition between sub-cavitating and super-cavitating speeds

centrifugal flow lift fan. Cushion lift fan which generates airflow at right angles to axis of rotation

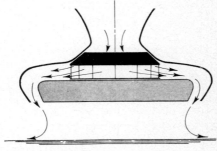

Centrifugal flow lift fan

chain ties. Chains used to maintain correct shape of air jet exit nozzle on flexible skirt

chip bag. Skirt segment, generally at rear of craft, with additional wall on side facing into cushion to prevent water scooping

chord. Distance between leading and trailing edges of foil section measured along chord-line

chord-line. Straight line joining leading and trailing edges of foil or propeller blade section

classification. Commercial seagoing and amphibious craft are classified by mode and place of construction by Lloyd's Register of Shipping for the UK. Other classification societies include Registro Italiano Navale, Germanischer Lloyd, Det norske Veritas, American Bureau of Shipping and the Japanese Ministry of Transport.

clearance. Distance between hard structure, eg buoyancy tank, and surface

coastal vessel. Vessel able to operate in up to sea state 5 and which would normally seek shelter in gales

cones. Cone-shaped fingers often fitted to rear of skirt bags to minimise scooping

continuous nozzle skirt. See **skirt**

contour, to. Motion of air cushion vehicle or hydrofoil when more or less following wave profile

control ducts, also **puff ports, thrusters** and **yaw ducts.** Controlled apertures in skirt system, or cushion supply ducting, through which air can be expelled to assist control at low speeds

craft. Vessel with one main deck in hull

critical depth speed. Overwater speed at which theoretical wavemaking behaviour changes, with discontinuity in wavemaking drag

critical speed. Low speed at which hovercraft, moving beam-on, is most vulnerable to overturn, generally when close to or slightly beneath primary hump speed for beam-on motion

cross-flow. Flow of air, transversally or longitudinally within air cushion

curtain. Fluid flow issuing from ducts or nozzles beneath hovercraft, either to contain or divide a cushion

cushion. Volume of higher than ambient pressure air enclosed between bottom of air cushion vehicle and its supporting surface by rigid structure, air curtains, skirts or combination of all three

cushion area. Area of cushion in planform at supporting surface

cushion beam. Maximum width of air cushion in planform at supporting surface

cushion borne. Craft borne above sea or land surface by its air cushion

cushion length. Maximum length of air cushion in planform at supporting surface

cushion length, mean. Defined as:
$$\frac{\text{cushion area}}{\text{cushion beam}}$$

cushion pumping. See **wave pumping**

cushion seal. Air curtains, sidewalls, skirts, water-jets or other means of containing or sealing air cushion to minimise leakage of trapped air

cushion stiffness. Slope of curve of applied moment plotted against angle. See **roll and pitch stiffness**

cushion system. Means by which cushion(s) of air beneath hovercraft is maintained and controlled

cushion thrust. Thrust obtained by deflection of cushion air

DEF spec. Standard of specification for military equipment operated by UK

DTNSRDC. (US Navy) David W Taylor Naval Ships Research and Development Center

DWL. Displacement water line.

deadrise. Angle with horizontal made at keel by outboard rise of vessel's hull form at each frame

delta wing. Triangular aircraft wing designed and developed by Dr Alexander Lippisch and more recently employed by him in his series of Aerofoil Boats. Applied also in Soviet Union because of its high aerodynamic qualities and stability for range of Ekranoplan aerodynamic ram-wings

differential pressure rate. Rate of change of cushion pressure differential across cushion divider with roll or pitch angle

diffuser-recirculation. See **recirculation system**

direct operating cost. Cost of operating craft, excluding company overheads and indirect costs

displacement. Weight in tons of water displaced by floating vessel. Light displacement: craft weight exclusive of ballast

ditch, to. To set down hovercraft, while still in motion, by deliberate collapse of cushion

Doppler, navigator. Automatic dead reckoning device which gives continuous indication of position by integrating speed derived from measuring Doppler effect of echoes from directed beams of radiant energy transmitted from vessel

down-by-the-head. Trim or sit of craft with bow more deeply immersed than stern. Opposite is 'down-by-the-stern'

draft, draught. Depth between water surface and bottom of craft. Under the Ministry of Transport Merchant Shipping (Construction) rules, 1952, draught is defined as vertical distance from moulded base line amidships to sub-division load waterline

draft, draught marks. (1) marks on side of craft showing depth to which it can be loaded. (2) figures cut at stern and stem to indicate draft and trim

drag. (1) ACVs: aerodynamic and hydrodynamic resistances resulting from aerodynamic profile, gain of momentum of air needed for cushion generation, wave making, wetting or skirt contact.
(2) hydrofoils: hydrodynamic resistances resulting from wave making, which is dependent on craft shape and displacement, frictional drag due to viscosity of water, total wetted surface and induced drag from foils and transmission shafts and their supporting struts and structure, due to their motion through water

drift angle. Difference between course and track of craft

ECCM. Electronic counter-countermeasures: ability of search radar installation to overcome enemy jamming, chaff and other countermeasures

ESKA. (Russian) Ekranolytny Spasatyelny Kater Amphibiya (screen-effect amphibious lifeboat): series of small wing-in-ground-effect machines developed by Central Laboratory of Lifesaving Technology, Moscow. Also known as Ekranolyet or Nizkolet (skimmer)

ESM. Electronic support measures: active, passive and analysing electronic equipment, including chaff launchers and flare dispensing systems

efficiency (propulsive). Ratio of useful work performed (ie thrust times relative velocity through air or water) to total input power

Ekranoplan. (Russian, from *ekran*, a screen or curtain, and *plan*, principal supporting surface of aeroplane) Types of ACV in USSR raised above their supporting surfaces by dynamic lift. Western equivalent, wing-in-ground-effect machines (WIG), aerodynamic ram-wings and power-augmented ram-wings.

elevator. Movable aerodynamic control surface used on small hovercraft to provide degree of fore and aft trim control. Elevator surfaces are normally in slipstream of propulsive units to provide some control at low speed

extended-range vessel. Small warship capable of up to 14 days' continuous unsupported operation away from base at 14-18 knots patrol speeds for 2,500-4,000 nautical miles or vessel capable of over 1,000 nautical miles at maximum speed

FPB. Fast patrol boat

Fences on the bow foil of a Supramar hydrofoil

FWL. Foilborne water line

fast vessel. Vessel capable of 25-35 knots

fences. Small partitions at short intervals down upper and lower surfaces of hydrofoil tending to prevent air ventilation passing down to destroy lift, attached in direction of flow

fetch. Distance given wind has blown over open water or distance upwind to nearest land

finger. One of a series of flexible sheet members forming lower part of seal of hovercraft cushion boundary

fire zone. Compartment containing full supply and ignition source which is walled with fire resisting material and fitted with independent fire warning and extinguishing system

fixed annual cost. Major component of a vehicle's direct operating cost: depreciation, craft insurance and operating and maintenance crew salaries, all incurred regardless of whether craft is operated or not

flare. Upward and outward curvature of freeboard at bow, presenting additional, rising surface to oncoming waves

flexible skirt. See **skirt**

flying bridge. Navigating position atop wheel or chart house

foilborne. (Hydrofoil) with hull raised completely out of water and wholly supported by lift from foil system

foil flaps. (a) trailing edge flaps for lift augmentation during take-off and to provide control forces, (b) upper and lower flaps to raise cavitation boundary

foil systems. Foil systems in current use are generally either **surface piercing, submerged** or **semi-submerged.** There are a number of craft with hybrid systems with a combination of submerged and surface piercing foils, recent examples being the Supramar PT 150 and the de Havilland FHE-400.

surface piercing foils are more often than not V-shaped, the upper parts of the foil forming the tips of the V and piercing the surface on either side of the craft. The V foil, with its marked dihedral is area stabilised and craft employing this configuration can be designed to be inherently stable, and, for stability, geometry dependent.

The forces restoring normal trim are provided by the area of the foil that is submerged. A roll to one side means the immersion of increased foil area, which results in the generation of extra lift to counter the roll and restore the craft to an even keel.

Equally, a downward pitching movement at the bow means an increase in the submerged area of the forward foil, and the generation of extra lift on this foil, which raises the bow once more. Should the bow rise above its normal water level the lift decreases in a similar way to restore normal trim. This type of foil is also known as an **emerging foil system.**

As the V-foil craft increases its speed, so it generates greater lift and is raised further out of the water—at the same time reducing the wetted area and the lift. The lift must be equal to the weight of the craft, and as the lift depends on the speed and wetted foil area, the hull rides at a predetermined height above the water level.

ladder foils. Also come under the heading surface piercing, but are rarely used now. This is one of the earliest foil arrangements and was used by Forlanini in his 1905 hydro-aeroplane, which was probably the first really successful hydrofoil. In 1911 Alexander Graham Bell purchased Forlanini's patent specifications and used his ladder system on his Hydrodomes, one of which, the HD-4, set up a world speed record of 61·5 knots in 1919. Early ladder foils, with single sets of foils beneath the hull, fore and aft, lacked lateral stability, but this disadvantage was rectified later by the use of two sets of forward foils, one on each side of the hull. The foils were generally straight and set at right angles to their supporting struts, but were occasionally of V configuration, the provision of dihedral preventing a sudden change of lift as the foils broke the surface. Both the V foil and the ladder systems are self-stabilising to a degree. The V foil has the advantage of being a more rigid, lighter structure and is less expensive.

Primary disadvantages of the conventional surface-piercing systems in comparison with the submerged foil system are: (a) the inability of V-foil craft without control surfaces to cope with downward orbital velocities at wave crests when overtaking waves in a following sea, a condition which can decrease the foil's angle of attack, reducing lift and cause either wave contact or a stall; (b) on large craft the weight and size of the surface-piercing system is considerably greater than that of a corresponding submerged foil system; (c) restoring forces to correct a roll have to pass above the centre of gravity of the craft, which necessitates the placing of the foils only a short distance beneath the hull. This means a relatively low wave clearance and therefore the V foil is not suited to routes where really rough weather is encountered.

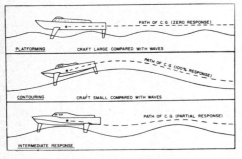

Comparison of platforming and contouring modes, and intermediate response of craft equipped with fully submerged, automatically controlled foil system

shallow-draft submerged foil system. This system which incorporates the Grunberg angle of attack variation approach, is employed almost exclusively on hydrofoils designed and built in the Soviet Union and is intended primarily for passenger carrying craft used on long, calm water rivers, canals and inland seas. The system, also known as the immersion depth effect system, was evolved by Dr Rostislav Alexeyev. It generally comprises two main horizontal foils, one forward, one aft, each carrying approximately half the weight of the vessel. A submerged foil loses lift gradually as it approaches the surface from a depth of about one chord, which prevents it from rising completely to the surface. Means therefore have to be provided to assist take-off and prevent the vessel from sinking back into the displacement mode. Planing subfoils, port and starboard, are therefore provided in the vicinity of the forward struts, and are so located that when they are touching the water surface, the main foils are submerged at a depth of approximately one chord.

submerged foils. These have a greater potential for seakeeping than any other, but are not inherently stable to any degree. The foils are totally immersed and a sonic, mechanical or air stabilisation system has to be installed to maintain the foils at the required depth. The system has to stabilise the craft from take-off to touch-down in heave and all three axes—pitch, roll and

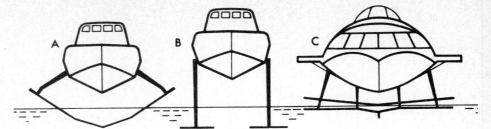

Foil systems in current use. A surface piercing, B submerged and C shallow draft submerged

yaw. It must also see that the craft makes co-ordinated banked turns in heavy seas to reduce the side loads on the foil struts; ensure that vertical and lateral accelerations are kept within limits in order to prevent excessive loads on the structure and finally, ensure a smooth ride for the passengers and crew.

The control forces are generated either by deflecting flaps at the trailing edge of the foil or varying the incidence angle of the entire foil surface. Incidence control provides better performance in a high sea state.

The key element of a typical automatic control system is an acoustic height sensor located at the bow. The time lag of the return signal is a measure of the distance of the sensor from the water.

Craft motion input is received from dual sonic ranging devices which sense the height above the water of the bow in relation to a fixed reference; from three rate gyros which measure yaw, pitch and roll; from forward and aft accelerometers which sense vertical acceleration fore and aft and from a vertical gyro which senses the angular position of the craft in both pitch and roll. This information is processed by an electronic computer and fed continuously to hydraulic actuators of the foil control surfaces, which develop the necessary hydrodynamic forces for stability producing forces imposed by wave action manoeuvring and correct flight.

mechanical incidence control. The most successful purely mechanically operated incidence control system is the Hydrofin autopilot principle, designed by Christopher Hook, who pioneered the development of the submerged foil. A fixed, high-riding crash preventer plane is mounted ahead of and beneath the bow.

The fixed plane, which is only immersed when the craft is in a displacement mode, is also used as a platform for mounting a lightweight pitch control sensor which is hinged to the rear.

The sensor rides on the waves and continu-

ously transmits their shape through a connecting linkage to vary the angle of incidence of the main foils as necessary to maintain them at the required depth. A filter system ensures that the craft ignores small waves and that the hull is flown over the crests of waves exceeding the height of the keel over the water.

Two additional sensors, trailing from port and starboard immediately aft of the main struts, provide roll control. The pilot has overriding control through a control column, operated in the same manner as that in an aircraft.

air stabilisation system. A system designed and developed by Baron Hanns von Schertel of Supramar AG, Lucerne. Air from the free atmosphere is fed through air exits to the foil upper surface and under certain conditions the lower surface also (ie into the low pressure regions). The airflow decreases the lift and the flow is deflected away from the foil section with an effect similar to that of a deflected flap, the air cavities extending out behind producing a virtual lengthening of the foil profile. Lift is reduced and varied by the quantity of air admitted, this being controlled by a valve actuated by signals from a damped pendulum and a rate gyro. The pendulum causes righting moments at static heeling angles. If exposed to a centrifugal force in turning, it causes a moment, which is directed towards the centre of the turning circle, thereby avoiding outside banking (co-ordinated banking). The rate gyro responds to angular velocity and acts dynamically to dampen rolling motions.

force time effectiveness. Time to land effective landing force ashore

fore peak. Space forward of fore collision bulkhead, frequently used as storage space

frames. Structure of vertical ribs or girders to which vessel's outside plates are attached. For identification frames are numbered consecutively, starting aft

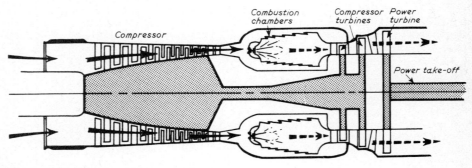

Free power turbine

These military hydrofoil designs illustrate three different foil systems. **Left to right:** The De Havilland Canada MP-100, a 100-ton missile craft with its inherently stable 'canard' surface-piercing system, incorporating a trapeze configuration main foil aft; the 83·5 ton Flagstaff II with incidence-controlled fully submerged foils in "aeroplane" configuration and the Boeing NATO/PHM. The latter has a fully submerged canard system with 32% of the dynamic lift provided by the bow foil and 68% by the aft foil. Lift control is provided by trailing edge flaps on each foil

freeboard. Depth of exposed or free side of hull between water level and freeboard deck. Degree of freeboard permitted is marked by load lines

freeboard deck. Deck used to measure or determine loadlines

free power turbine. Gas turbine on which power turbine is on separate shaft from compressor and its turbine

full hover. Condition of ACV at its design hoverheight

furrowing. Condition of foilborne operation of hydrofoil caused by contact of lower part of hull and keel with crests of larger waves. Contact is brief and does not prevent craft from remaining foilborne. See also **hull cresting**

GEM. Ground effect machine.

grp. Glass-reinforced plastics

gross tonnage. Total tonnage of vessel, including all enclosed spaces, estimated on basis of 100ft² = 1 ton

ground effect machine. Early generic term for ACVs of all types

Grunberg foil system. First patented in 1936, the Grunberg principle of inherent angle of attack variations comprises a "stabiliser" attached to the bow or a forward projection from the latter, and behind this a "foil". Both foil and stabiliser can be "split" into several units. The lift curve of the stabiliser, plotted against its draft, is considerably steeper than its corresponding foil lift curve. Hence as the operational conditions (speed, weight, CG travel) change, the foil sinks or rises relative to the stabiliser, automatically adjusting its angle of attack. The "foil" is set at an appropriate angle of incidence in order to prevent it from approaching the interface. The system is fully compatible with Forlanini's concept of area variation and both can be incorporated in the same structure

HATS. Harbour acceptance trials: equipment trials undertaken in harbour

HDL. Hovercraft Development Ltd

HYSWAS. Hydrofoil small waterplane area ship

hard chine. Hull design with topsides and bottom meeting at an angle, rather than curving to round bilge

hard structure. Any structure (hard or flexible but excluding skirts) which may create a capsizing or righting moment when in contact with water

head sea. Sea approaching from direction steered

heave. Vertical motion of craft in response to waves

heave stiffness. Rate of change of restoring force in heave direction with displacement in that direction

heel. (a) Incline or list in transverse direction while under way. (b) Lower end of mast or derrick. (c) Point where keel and stern post meet

Helibarge. System devised by Walter A Crowley (USA) combining helicopter and air cushion barge. Helicopter's downwash rotor pressurises air cushion

hemline. Lowest peripheral edge of hovercraft skirt

high-speed vessel. Vessel with top speed of 36 knots and over

hinge spacing (horizontal). Horizontal distance between inner and outer 'hinges' or attachment points to structure

hinge spacing (vertical). Vertical distance between inner and outer 'hinges' or attachment points to structure

hourly running cost. Part of direct operating cost incurred when craft is operated, ie, fuel, maintenance and overhauls

hoverbarge. Fully buoyant, shallow-draft hovercraft built for freight carrying. Either self-propelled or towed

hovercraft. (a) Originally craft using patented peripheral jet principle invented by Sir Christopher Cockerell, in which air cushion is generated and contained by jet of air exhausted downward and inward from nozzle at periphery at base

of vehicle. (b) Classification in USA for skirted plenum chamber and annular jet-designs. (c) In British Hovercraft Act 1968, a vehicle designed to be supported when in motion wholly or partly by air expelled from vehicle to form cushion of which boundaries include ground, water or other surface beneath vehicle

hover height. Vertical height between hard structure of ACV and supporting surface when vehicle is cushion-borne

hover-listen. ACVs employed for ASW operating at low speeds to detect target

hover pallet. See **air pallet**

hoverplatform. Non self-propelled hovercraft designed primarily to convey heavy loads across terrain impassable to wheeled and tracked vehicles under load

Mackace 50-ton hoverplatform

hoverport. Defined by British Hovercraft Act 1968 as any area, whether land or elsewhere, which is designed, equipped, set apart or commonly used for affording facilities for arrival and departure of hovercraft

hoversled. Vehicle for operation on ice and snow combining features of air cushion vehicle with skis or pontoons. Contact between vehicle's skis and supporting surface beneath gives better directional control than on most conventional skirted ACVs operating over ice and snow

hovertrailer. Steel structure platform around which is fitted flexible segmented skirt, cushion lift being provided by fans. Devised by Air Cushion Equipment Ltd and Hover Systems Ltd, system is designed to increase load capacity of tracked and wheeled vehicles many times. In cases where it is impossible for tow vehicle to operate, trailer can be winched

hull cresting. Contact of hydrofoil's hull with waves in high seas

hull slamming. Contact of hydrofoil's hull with water following foil broach. See **broach, to**

Hovertrailer with payload of 6·7 tons at 100lb/ft²

hump. "Hump" formed on graph of resistance against speed of displacement vessel or ACV. Maximum of "hump" corresponds to speed of wave generated by hull or air depression

hump speed. Speed over water at which there is peak value of wave-making drag. In general there will be several hump speeds, the highest being 'primary hump speed'

Hydrodynamic yaw angle. Angle in horizontal plane between longitudinal axis of hovercraft and instantaneous direction of motion relative to local water surface

hydrofoils. Small wings, almost identical in section to those of aircraft, and designed to generate lift. Since water is 815 times denser than air, same lift as aeroplane wing is obtained for only $1/815$ of area (at equal speeds)

hydrofoil small waterplane area ship. Projected hybrid vessel comprising a single submerged hull with fully submerged foil system and upper hull structure supported by vertical strut or struts. At low speeds craft is supported by buoyancy of submerged hull, strut, and lower section of upper hull. At speed dynamic lift generated by foil system raises upper hull out of water with reduction of waterplane area of strut

hydroskimmer. Experimental air cushion vehicles built under contract to US Navy Bureau of Ships. Preference was given to this name since it gave craft sea-service identity

IOC. (US Navy) Initial operational capability

IOT&E. (US Navy) Initial operational testing and evaluation

inclined shaft. Marine drive shaft used in small V foil and shallow-draft submerged foil craft, with keels only limited height above mean water level. Shaft is generally short and inclined at about 12-14 degrees to horizontal. On larger craft, designed for operation in higher waves, need to fly higher necessitates alternative drive arrangements such as vee drive and Z-drive, water jet system or even air propulsion

indirect operating cost. Costs incurred apart from running craft including advertising, buildings, rents, rates and salaries for terminal staff other than those employed for craft maintenance

induced wave drag. Drag caused by hollow depressed in water by ACV's air cushion. As craft moves forward depression follows beneath, building up bow wave and causing wave drag as in displacement craft until hump speed has been passed

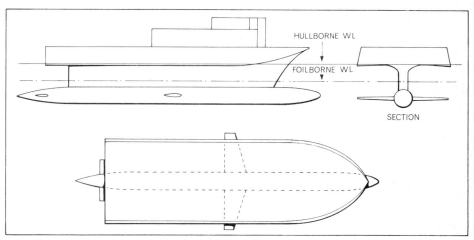

HULLBORNE WL

FOILBORNE WL

SECTION

Hydrofoil small waterplane area ship (HYSWAS)

inshore vessel. Vessel able to operate in up to sea state 3. It would normally not operate in conditions above sea state 5 and would need to seek shelter in gales

integrated lift-propulsion system. ACV lift and propulsion system operated by a common power source, transmission and power-sharing system allowing variation in division of power

JP-4. Liquid fuel, based on kerosene, used widely in gas turbines

keel. (a) "backbone" of hull. (b) extension of ACV's fore-and-aft stability air jet, similar in construction and shape to skirt, and taking form of inflated bag

knitmesh pads. Thick, loosely woven pads of either metal or plastic wire in engine's air intake to filter out water and solid particles from engine air

LCG. Longitudinal distance measurement (from appropriate datum) of CG

LIMRV. Linear induction motor research vehicle

land, to. At end of runs hydrofoils and ACVs are said to "settle down" or "land"

landing pads. Strong points protruding below rigid bottom of hovercraft which support vehicle at rest on land. Can also provide attachment points for towing equipment, lifts and jacks

leading frequency of sea waves. See **significant wave height.** Sea wave of greatest energy content

leakage rate. Rate at which air escapes from air cushion, measured in cubic metres or cubic feet per second

lift fan. See also **axial flow lift fan** and **centrifugal flow lift fan.** Fan used to supply air under pressure to air cushion, and/or to form curtains

lift off. To rise from ground on air cushion

linear induction motor. Linear induction motors show considerable promise as a means of propulsion for tracked skimmers, and are now under development in France, the United Kingdom, West Germany, Italy, Japan, the United States and USSR. An attractive feature of this method of electric traction is that it does not depend upon the vehicle having contact with the track or guideway.

The motor can be likened to a normal induction motor opened out flat. The "stator" coils are attached to the vehicle, while the "rotor" consists of a flat rail of conductive material which is straddled by the stator poles. The variable frequency multi-phase ac current required for the linear motor can either be generated aboard the vehicle or collected from an electrified track.

Although the mounting of the stators on the vehicle appears to be preferred in Europe at present they can also be built into the guideway. In this case the rotor, in the form of a reaction rail, would be suspended from the vehicle. It would be of sufficient length to span several of the fixed stators simultaneously to avoid jerking

load factor. Relationship between payload capacity available and capacity filled

long-range vessel. Small warship capable of up to 7 days' continuous unsupported operations away from base, at 14 to 18 knots patrol speed for 1,500 to 2,500 nautical miles

longitudinal framing. Method of hull construction employing frames set in fore and aft direction or parallel to keel

loop. Abbreviated form of bag skirt with large openings over segments so there is little pressure difference between loop and cushion. May or may not include sheet of material inboard of segment inner attachments. There is no definitive demarcation as to when bag becomes loop

MCM. Mine countermeasures

MIL spec. Standard of specification for military equipment operated by US Navy

maglev. Magnetic levitation

mean bag pressure. Mean pressure in bag or loop relative to atmospheric pressure

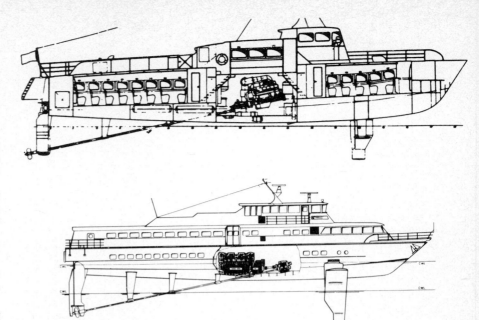

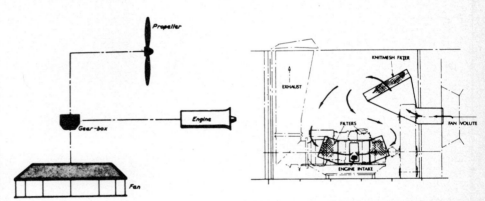

Sectional views showing inclined shaft **(top)** on the PT 50 and vee drive system employed on the PT 150

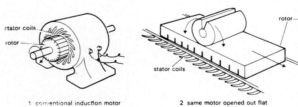

Integrated lift-propulsion system

Gas turbine air filtration path on Vosper Thornycroft VT 1, showing the knitmesh filter pad

Principle of linear induction motor

1 conventional induction motor   2 same motor opened out flat   3 rail between moving stator coils

medium-range vessel. Small warship capable of up to 3 days' operation from base, patrolling up to 1,500 nautical miles at economical speed or vessel capable of up to 500 nautical miles at maximum speed

medium speed vessel. Vessel capable of 18-24 knots or more

multiple skirt. System devised by late Jean Bertin, employing number of separate flexible skirts for his system of individually fed, multiple air cushions

multi-role craft. Small warship with facilities for fitting range of interchangeable weapons at short notice (up to six hours)

Naviplane. Overwater or amphibious air cushion vehicles developed in France by SEDAM

net tonnage. Total tonnage of craft based on cubic capacity of all space available for carrying revenue-producing cargo less allowance for areas needed to operate craft

nibbling. Catching of skirt, usually bow fingers, on surface being traversed, indication of possible 'plough-in' developing

OPEVAL. (US Navy) Operational evaluation

ocean vessel. Vessel able to operate in gales

offshore vessel. Vessel able to remain operational in up to sea state 7 and which can remain at sea in gales

orbital motion. Orbital or circular motion of water particles forming waves. Circular motion decreases in radius with increasing depth. Peculiar sequence of motion causes illusion of wave translation. In reality water moves very little in translation. Circular directions are: up at wave front, forward at crest, down at wave back and back at trough

PAR. Power augmented ram-wing

PPI. Plan position indicator: radar display and presentation giving view as seen from above in plan form

pvc. Polyvinylchloride

PTO. See **power take off unit**

patrol craft. Small warship fitted with light armaments

payload weight. Weight of revenue earning load, excluding crew and fuel

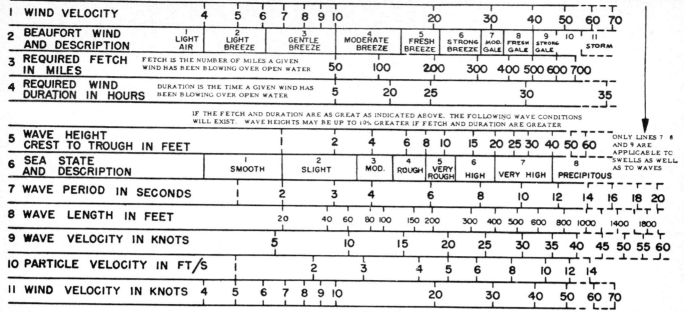

1	**WIND VELOCITY**	4	5	6	7	8	9	10		20		30	40	50	60	70							
2	**BEAUFORT WIND AND DESCRIPTION**	LIGHT AIR	2 LIGHT BREEZE	3 GENTLE BREEZE			4 MODERATE BREEZE	5 FRESH BREEZE	6 STRONG BREEZE	7 MOD. GALE	8 FRESH GALE	9 STRONG GALE	10	11 STORM								
3	**REQUIRED FETCH IN MILES**	FETCH IS THE NUMBER OF MILES A GIVEN WIND HAS BEEN BLOWING OVER OPEN WATER		50		100		200		300	400	500	600	700								
4	**REQUIRED WIND DURATION IN HOURS**	DURATION IS THE TIME A GIVEN WIND HAS BEEN BLOWING OVER OPEN WATER		5		20	25			30			35									

IF THE FETCH AND DURATION ARE AS GREAT AS INDICATED ABOVE, THE FOLLOWING WAVE CONDITIONS WILL EXIST. WAVE HEIGHTS MAY BE UP TO 10% GREATER IF FETCH AND DURATION ARE GREATER

5	**WAVE HEIGHT CREST TO TROUGH IN FEET**	1	2	4	6	8	10	15	20	25	30	40	50	60	ONLY LINES 7 8 AND 9 ARE APPLICABLE TO SWELLS AS WELL AS TO WAVES
6	**SEA STATE AND DESCRIPTION**	1 SMOOTH	2 SLIGHT	3 MOD.	4 ROUGH	5 VERY ROUGH	6 HIGH	7 VERY HIGH	8 PRECIPITOUS						
7	**WAVE PERIOD IN SECONDS**	1	2	3	4	6	8	10	12	14	16	18	20		
8	**WAVE LENGTH IN FEET**	20	40	60	80	100	150	200	300	400	500	600	800	1000	1400	1800
9	**WAVE VELOCITY IN KNOTS**	5	10	15	20	25	30	35	40	45	50	55	60		
10	**PARTICLE VELOCITY IN FT/S**	1	2	3	4	5	6	8	10	12	14				
11	**WIND VELOCITY IN KNOTS**	4	5	6	7	8	9	10	20	30	40	50	60	70	

Chart of sea state conditions. Corresponding values lie on a vertical line

peripheral jet. See **air curtain** and **hovercraft**

peripheral jet cushion system. Ground cushion generated by continuous jet of air issued through ducts or nozzles around outer periphery of base of craft. Cushion is maintained at above ambient pressure by horizontal change of momentum of curtain

peripheral trunk. See **skirt**

pitch. Rotation or oscillation of hull about transverse axis in seaway. Also angle of air or water propeller blades

pitch angle. Pitch craft adopts relative to horizontal datum

pitch attitude. Instantaneous angle between surface **(roll attitude)** traversed and longitudinal (lateral) datum of craft

pitch stiffness. Rate of change of restoring pitch moment with pitch angle. Slope of applied pitch moment versus pitch angle diagram

platform, to. Approximately level flight of hydrofoil over waves lower than calm water hull clearance

plenum. Space or air chamber beneath or surrounding lift fan or fans through which air under pressure is distributed to skirt system

plenum chamber cushion system. Simplest air cushion concept: cushion pressure is maintained by pumping air continuously into recessed base without use of peripheral jet curtain

"plough in". Bow down attitude resulting from bow part of skirt contacting surface and progressively building up drag. Unless controlled can lead to serious loss of stability and possibly overturning

With skirt's front outer edge dragging on water towards centre of craft ('tuck under') there is marked reduction in righting moment of cushion pressure. As downward pitch angle increases, stern tends to rise from surface and excessive yaw angles develop. Considerable deceleration takes place down to hump speed and danger of roll over in small craft is accentuated by following waves which further increase pitch angle

Solutions include vent holes on a skirt's outer front to reduce drag through air lubrication, and bag skirt which automatically bulges outwards on contact with water, delaying tuck under and providing righting moment

porpoising. Oscillatory motion in pitch and heave of high-speed planing hull craft caused by incorrect trim rather than wave action

power augmented ram-wing. Wing-in-ground-effect machine designed so that the propulsion system exhaust is directed into the space between the wing and the surface to lift the wing clear of the water at zero speed. Current research is also aimed at employing power augmentation in conjunction with end plates to provide a low speed or hover capability. Advantages include the avoidance of the high hydrodynamic drag experienced by craft with relatively high wing loadings during take-off and the high impact loadings encountered during take-off and landing. Use of the PAR system would also provide surface mobility over short ranges or under high sea state conditions which would normally prevent take-off. The system is expected to avoid the need for large hydrodynamic hulls for WIGs since the wing volume on winged hull types and others with deep aerofoil sections, could also be used for buoyancy

power take off unit. Unit for transmitting power from main engine or engines, generally for auxiliary services required while craft is under way, such as hydraulics, alternators and bilge pumps

puff ports. See **control ducts**

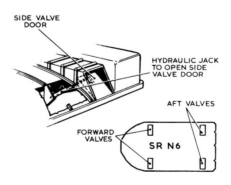

SIDE VALVE DOOR

HYDRAULIC JACK TO OPEN SIDE VALVE DOOR

AFT VALVES

FORWARD VALVES

SR N6

Puff port arrangement on BHC SR.N6

ram wing. See **air cushion vehicles**

recirculation system. Air curtain employing recirculating air flow, which is maintained within and under craft

reliability factor. Percentage relationship between number of trips scheduled and those achieved

rise height. Distance which hovercraft rises from flat hard ground to being fully cushion-borne

river vessel. Non-seagoing craft able to operate in up to sea state 5

Ro-ro. Roll-on roll-off: ships and air cushion vehicles with decks providing straight-through loading facilities, ie with cargo ramps or loading doors fore and aft

roll. Oscillation or rotation of hull about longitudinal axis

roll attitude. Angle of roll craft adopts relative to longitudinal datum

roll stiffness. Rate of change of restoring roll moment with roll angle. Slope of applied roll moment versus roll angle diagram

running time. Time during which all machinery has been in operation, including idling time

SATS. Sea acceptance trials: weapons trials undertaken at sea under dynamic conditions

SES. See **surface effect ship**

SEV. Surface effect vehicle (USA) air cushion vehicles of all types. (USSR) large sea- or ocean-going wing-in-ground-effect machines

SSM. Surface-to-surface: ship-to-ship missile system

SSP. Semi-submerged platform craft

SSPU. Ship's service power unit

SWATH. Small waterplane area twin-hull craft

Savitsky flap. Hinged vertical control flaps employed for foil lift variation, attached to trailing edge of foil struts, and canted out at angle. The flaps are attached mechanically to the trailing-edge flaps on the foil. At the normal flying height only the lower part of the Savitsky flap is submerged.

As more of the flap becomes submerged due to increased wave height, the moment of the flap increases causing it to raise the foil flap, thus increasing lift and restoring normal inflight attitude and flying height. The system can be adjusted to react only to lower-frequency layer waves. The system is employed on the Atlantic Hydrofoils *Flying Cloud* and *Sea World*. It was invented by Dr Daniel Savitsky of the Davidson Laboratory

sea loiter aircraft. Aircraft capable of loitering on or under the sea for extended periods of time are currently being investigated by the US Navy which foresees a significant operational potential for this type of machine. Applications would include anti-submarine warfare, command, communications and control and strategic missile carrier

seal. See **cushion seal**

sea state. Scale of sea conditions classified from state 1, smooth, to state 8, precipitous, according to the wind duration, fetch and velocity, also wave length, period and velocity

segment. Flexible sheet member of lower part of hovercraft cushion boundary seal (see **finger**) or individual sections of bag skirt

semi-submerged propeller. Concept for partially submerged, supercavitating propeller on ship-size air cushion vehicles, driven through sidewall transom. Advantages include considerable drag reduction due to absence of inclined shafts and supporting structures, and possibly elimination of propeller erosion resulting from appendage cavity impingement

service speed. Cruising speed obtained by average crew in average craft on given route

set down. Lower air cushion vehicle onto its landing pads

short-range vessel. Small warship capable of up to 36 hours' continuous operation and which can cover up to 600 miles at economical speed or vessel capable of covering up to 250 nautical miles at maximum speed

sidewall. Rigid structure extending along side of craft and forming part of cushion seal

sidewall vessel. ACV with cushion air contained between immersed sidewalls or skegs and transverse air curtains or skirts fore and aft. Stability is provided by buoyancy of sidewalls and their planing forces

significant. Arithmetic means of highest third of set of measurements, eg wave heights or lengths

significant wave height. Sea waves are composed of different frequencies and have different wave heights (energy spectrum). A wave with the leading frequency of this spectrum and energy content is called the significant wave. It is from this wave that the significant wave height is measured

skirt. Flexible fabric extension between ACV's metal structure and surface to give increased obstacle and overwave clearance capability for small air gap clearance and therefore reduced power requirement. Skirt deflects when encountering waves or solid obstacles, then returns to its normal position, air gap being increased only momentarily. On peripheral jet ACVs skirt is flexible extension of peripheral jet nozzle with inner and outer skins hung from inner and outer edges of air duct and linked together by chain ties or diaphragms so that they form correct nozzle profile at hemline

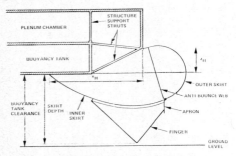

BHC fingered bag skirt

skirt, bag. Simple skirt design consisting of inflated bag. Sometimes used as transverse and longitudinal stability skirts

skirt depth. Designed vertical distance from craft hard structure to finger tip

skirt, finger. Skirt system designed by British Hovercraft Corporation, consisting of fringe of conical nozzles attached to base of bag or loop skirt. Each nozzle or finger fits around air exit hole and channels cushion air inwards towards bottom centre of craft

skirt, segmented. Conceived by Hovercraft Development Ltd's Technical Group, this skirt system is employed on the HD.2, Vosper Thornycroft VT1, VT2 and many new craft either under design or construction. It is also being employed for industrial applications, including hoverpallets and hovertrailers.

The flexible segments are located around the craft periphery, each being attached to the lower edge of a sheet of light flexible material, which inflates to an arc shape, and also to the craft hard structure.

The system enables the craft to clear high waves and obstacles as the segments occupy a substantial part of the full cushion depth. No stability skirts or other forms of compartmentation are necessary. A smooth ride is provided as the skirt has good response due to low inertia.

The cushion area can be the same as the craft hard structure plan area. The skirt inner attachment points can be reached without jacking the craft up from its off-cushion position, simplifying maintenance

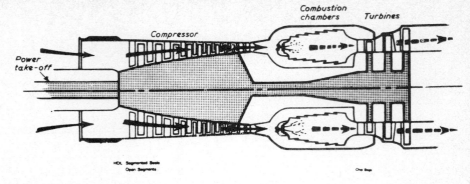

Single shaft gas turbine

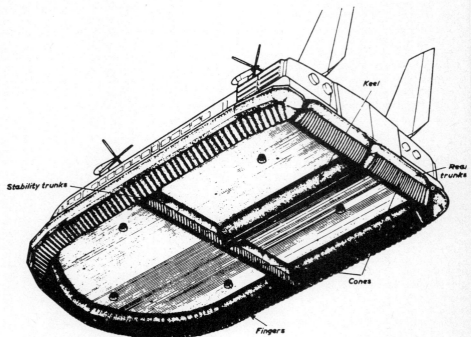

Underside of SR.N4 showing stability skirts

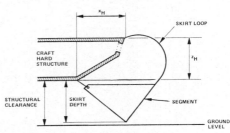

HDL segmented skirt

skirt shape transition. Change from finger only in water contact to state in which bag or loop component is in contact and fingers are flattened

skirt shifting. Control system in which movement of centre of area of cushion is achieved by shifting skirt along one side, which tilts craft. Pitch and roll trim can be adjusted by this method

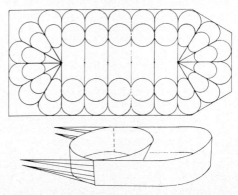

SEDAM skirt system

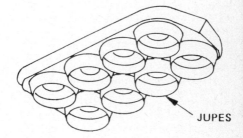

Bertin skirt

split foil. Main foil system with foil area divided into two, either to facilitate retraction, or to permit location of control surfaces well outboard, where foil control and large roll correcting moments can be applied for small changes in lift

stability curtain. Transverse or longitudinal air curtains dividing air cushion in order to restrict cross flow of air within cushion and increase pitch and roll stability. Also **stability skirt**

standard speed vessel. Patrol vessel capable of speeds of up to 18 knots

strake. (a) permanent band of rubber or other hard wearing material along sides of craft to protect structure from chafing against quays, piers and craft alongside. (b) lengths of material fitted externally to flexible skirt and used to channel air downwards to reduce water drag

strike craft. Small warship fitted with at least one major weapon, plus light defensive armament

submerged foil system. Foil system employing totally submerged lifting surfaces. Depth of submergence is controlled by mechanical, electronic or pneumatic systems which alter angle of incidence of foils or flaps attached to them to provide stability and control. See **foil systems**

supercavitating foil. General classification given to foils designed to operate efficiently at high speeds while fully cavitated. Since at very high speeds foils cannot avoid cavitation, sections are being designed which induce onset of cavitation from leading edge and cause cavities to proceed downstream and beyond trailing edge before collapsing. Lift and drag of these foils is determined by shape of leading edge and under-surface

surface effect ship. Large ship-size ACV. Generally applied in USA and United Kingdom to large sidewall craft. See **air cushion vehicles**

surface piercing ACV. Craft with rigid sidewalls that penetrate water surface. Air cushion is contained laterally by sidewalls and at bow and stern by flexible seals. See **sidewall vessel** or **surface effect ships**

surf zone. Area from outer waves breaking on shore to limit of their uprush on a beach

TECHEVAL. (US Navy) Technical evaluation

TLACV. Track-laying air cushion vehicle: ACV vehicle employing looped caterpillar-like tracks for propulsion. Air cushion and seals may be between flexible tracks, as on Soviet MVP-3 series, or can form broad belt or track that loops round complete air cushion

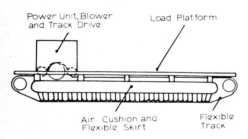

Track laying air cushion vehicle operating on a broad track that loops around the air cushion

TLRV. Tracked levitated research vehicle

take-off speed. Speed at which hydrofoil hull is raised clear of water, dynamic foil lift taking over from static displacement or planing of hull proper

tandem foils. Foil system in which area of forward foils is approximately equal to that of aft foils, balancing loading between them

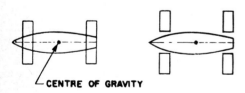

Tandem foil system. The foil areas can be "split" into two to facilitate retraction

terramechanics. Study of general relationship between performance of off-road vehicle and its physical environment

thickness-chord ratio. Maximum thickness of foil section in relation to its chord

thruster. Controlled aperture through which air or water can be expelled to assist control at low speeds

Tietjens-type foil. Forward swept (surface piercing) main foil almost amidships and slightly ahead of CG. It was intended that pronounced sweep of V foils would result in increasing area of foil further forward coming into use to increase bow up trim of craft when lift was lost. Considerable length of unsupported hull ahead of CG meant craft was constantly in danger of "digging in" in bad seas and was highly sensitive to loading arrangements

transcavitating foil. Thin section foil designed for smooth transition from fully wetted to super-cavitating flow. By loading tip more highly than

SURFACE EFFECT SHIP CONFIGURATIONS

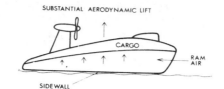

Ram wing SES

Wing-in-ground-effect

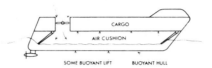

Aircat SES with wide buoyant hulls

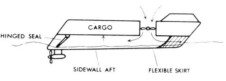

Hybrid SES with rigid sidewalls and bow skirt

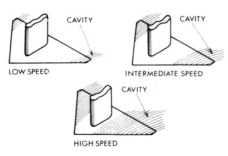

Air-lubricated hull or hydrokeel SES

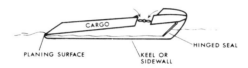

Transit foil operation

root cavitation is first induced at tip, then extends spanwise over foil to roots as speed increases

transisting foil. See **transcavitating foil**

transit foil. See **transcavitating foil**

transom. Last transverse frame of ship's structure forming stern board

transverse framing. Steel frames running athwartships, from side to side, instead of fore and aft

trapped air cushion vehicle. Concept for skirt-type SES with 20ft skirts separated from water surface by thin film of air lubrication

trim. Difference between drafts forward and aft in displacement vessel and by extension, ACV and hydrofoil hull attitude relative to line of flight

trim angle. Pitch or roll angle which results under steady running conditions

tuck-under. Action of skirt being pulled back under structure as result of local drag forces

tunnel hull. Racing boat with tunnel-shaped hull designed to employ the advantages of aerodynamic lift as in ram-wing or channel-flow wing ACV

variable-pitch propeller. Propeller with blades which can be rotated about their longitudinal axes to provide forward or reverse thrust

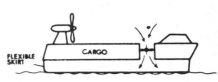

Air-propelled amphibious SES

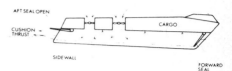

Airjet SES, propelled by cushion thrust

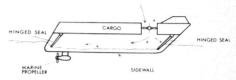

Sidewall SES. Also known as a Captured Air Bubble or CAB Type

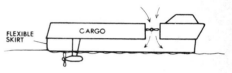

Water-propelled, semi-amphibious SES

ventilation. See **air entry**

VCG. Vertical height measurement (from appropriate datum) to CG

water wall ACV. Craft employing a curtain of water to retain its air cushion instead of air curtain

waterjet propulsion. Now applied to a propulsion system devised as an alternative to super-cavitating propellers for propelling high speed ship systems. Turbines drive pumps located in the hull, and water is pumped through high velocity jets above the water line and directed astern. The system weighs less than a comparable super-cavitating propeller system and for craft with normal operating speeds above 45 knots it is thought to be competitive on an annual cost basis. First high speed applications include the Soviet Burevestnik and Chaika hydrofoils, the Aerojet-General SES-100A testcraft and two products of the Boeing Company—the PGH-2 hydrofoil gunboat and the NATO PHM.

Waterjets are also being employed for propulsion at relatively low speeds. In the Soviet Union the Zarya shallow-draught waterbus (24 knots) and the Gorkovchanin sidewall ACV are propelled by waterjets. In the USA the PGH-1 and PGH-2 hydrofoils use waterjets for hullborne propulsion. The jet can be turned easily to give side propulsion to facilitate docking which is not so easy for a normal propeller

wave height. Vertical distance from wave trough to crest or twice wave amplitude

wave length. Horizontal distance between adjacent wave crests

wave making drag. Drag due to creation of waves by moving hovercraft pressure system

wave pumping. Alternating increase and decrease of volume of pressurised air in ACV's cushion, caused by passage of waves or other objects through cushion

wave velocity. Speed at which wave form travels along sea surface. (The water itself remaining without forward movement)

weights. There are no generally accepted standards with respect to ACV and SES weights, except that small ACVs tend to follow aircraft practice and large types follow ship practice. The hydrofoil concepts are ship orientated. A consistently used format aids in evaluating the concept and permits usage on, or direct comparison with other designs. Format 1, below is according to US Naval practice and is suitable for all sizes of ACVs, SESs, and hydrofoils. The actual terminology used for the totals is optional, so that the nomenclature can be consistent with the size of the vessel. In presenting results, the units (short tons, long tons, metric tons, pounds, etc) should be clearly indicated.

Format 2 is used by the hovercraft industry in the United Kingdom. This emphasises equipment options, and by breaking down the expendable or useful load, the payload/range performance can be readily determined. It is also useful in defining first costs and operating costs

wetting drag. Drag due to immersion of parts of craft in water, eg skirts and sidewalls, usually considered to include drag due to creation of spray. In practice forms residual drag when aerodynamic and wave-making components are subtracted from total drag measured

winged hull. See **Aerofoil boat**

wing-in-ground-effect. See **air cushion vehicle**

yaw angle. Rotation or oscillation of craft about vertical axis

yaw ducts. See **control ducts**

Z-drive. Drive system normally employed on hydrofoils to transmit power from engine in hull to screw through horizontal shaft leading to bevel gear over stern, then via vertical shaft and second bevel gear to horizontal propeller shaft, thus forming propeller "Z" shape

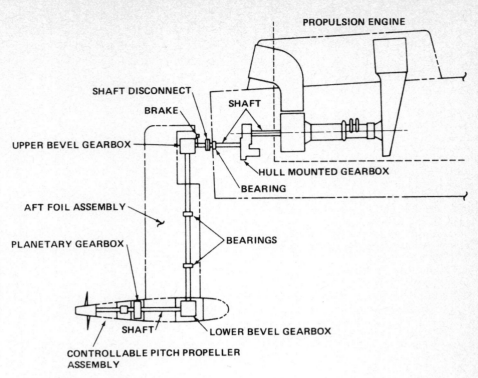

Z-drive system on Grumman Flagstaff II

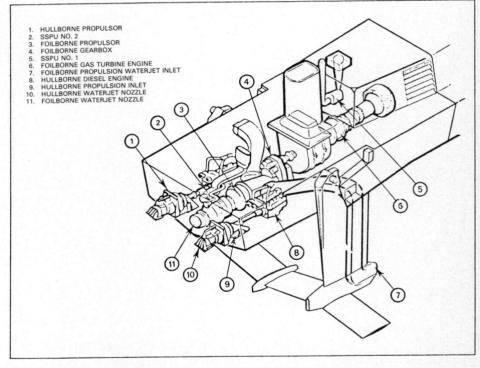

1. HULLBORNE PROPULSOR
2. SSPU NO. 2
3. FOILBORNE PROPULSOR
4. FOILBORNE GEARBOX
5. SSPU NO. 1
6. FOILBORNE GAS TURBINE ENGINE
7. FOILBORNE PROPULSION WATERJET INLET
8. HULLBORNE DIESEL ENGINE
9. HULLBORNE PROPULSION INLET
10. HULLBORNE WATERJET NOZZLE
11. FOILBORNE WATERJET NOZZLE

Waterjet propulsion system employed on the Boeing/NATO PHM missile-armed fast patrol craft in service with the US Navy

HOVERCRAFT WEIGHT TERMS

Format 1

Group	Typical Items
1 Hull (or structure)	Basic structure, planting, frames, stringers, scantlings, decks, foundations, fittings, super-structure, doors and closures.
2 Propulsion	Engines, turbines, propellers, fans, gearboxes, shafting, drive systems, associated controls, nuclear plant, associated fluids.
3 Electrical	Power generation, switching, lighting, load canters, panels, cable.
4 Communication and Control	Communications (internal, external) and navigation equipment, military electronics, computers, displays (note ship controls are in Group 5).
5 Auxiliary Systems	Fuel, heating, ventilation, fresh water, ship controls, rudder, cushion seal (flexible or articulated), plumbing, oil, fire extinguishing, drainage, ballast, mooring, anchoring, hydro-foils distilling plant.
6 Outfit and Furnishings	Hull fittings, marine hardware, ladders, furnishings, boats, rafts, preservers, stowages, lockers, painting, deck covering, hull insula-tion, commissary equipment, radiation shield-ing (other than at reactor area).
7 Armament	Weapons, mounts, ammunition stowage, handling systems, special plating.
Total: Light Ship or Light Displacement or Empty Weight	(sum of the above items).
Variable Load or Useful Load	Operating personnel and effects, cargo, freight, fuel, passengers, baggage, water, ammuni-tion, aircraft, stores, troops, provisions.
Full Load Displacement or Load Displacement or Gross Weight or All Up Weight	(sum of empty weight and useful load).

Format 2

Standard Bare Weight

(1) Weight of structure, power plants & sys-tems considered to be integral parts of the standard craft
(2) Oil (turbine engines only)
(3) Full hydraulic/pneumatic/cooling etc sys-tems
(4) Essential standard equipment common to all customer requirements
(5) Unusable fuel
(6) Other unconsumable liquids

Customer Equipment Weight

(1) Flight crew seats
(2) Flight crew emergency equipment
(3) Soundproofing, trim, partitions, floor cov-ering etc in payload areas
(4) Passenger seats, tables, lockers and other furnishings
(5) Heating, ventilating and air conditioning
(6) Toilet and washing facilities
(7) Galley facilities
(8) Domestic water supply (inc toilet)
(9) Fire precautions in payload areas
(10) Marine equipment
(11) Life rafts and containers
(12) Life jackets and stowages
(13) Emergency equipment (axes, first aid etc)
(14) Radio
(15) Radar
(16) Navaids
(17) Intercommunication and internal broad-casting
(18) Racking (for 14-17)
(19) Weapon and system installations
(20) Signalling equipment, distress flares etc
(21) Environmental equipment
(22) Long range tankage and system

Basic Weight

Variable Load

(1) Crew
(2) Crew's baggage and equipment
(3) Purser's equipment
(4) Role equipment
(5) Non-consumable liquid ballast

Expendable Load (other than usable fuel)

(1) Oil (piston engines only)
(2) Domestic, humidifying, windscreen water
(3) Other liquid/gaseous consumables
(4) Ammunition, missiles, etc
(5) Food, drink, bonded stores, etc
(6) Boarding parties and their equipment

Payload

(1) Passengers
(2) Vehicles
(3) Freight

Usable Fuel

(1) Main fuel
(2) Reserve fuel
(3) Long range fuel

Operating Weight

Zero Fuel Weight

All-up Weight

BIBLIOGRAPHY

AIR CUSHION VEHICLES

ACVs IN NORTH AMERICA

ACV Icing Problems, J R Stallabras and T R Ringer (National Research Council). Seventh Canadian Symposium on Air Cushion Technology, June 1973.

Air-Cushion Vehicles, Operational use in the Arctic, G Ives. *Petroleum Eng,* Vol 45 No 1, January 1974.

Air Cushion Vehicles and Soil Erosion, P Abeels. International Society for Terrain-Vehicle Systems 5th International Conference, Detroit, Houghton, Michigan, June 1975.

Arctic Development Using Very Large ACVs, J L Anderson (NASA Lewis Laboratories). Seventh Canadian Symposium on Air Cushion Technology, June 1973.

Arctic Operational Experience with SR.N6 engaged in Hydrographic Survey and Cushioncraft CC-7, L R Colby and G M Yeaton (Polar Continental Shelf Project, DEMR). Fourth Canadian Symposium on Air Cushion Technology, 1970. publ Canadian Aeronautics and Space Institute.

Arctic Transportation, Operational and Environmental Evaluation of an ACV in Northern Alaska, G Abele and J Brown (US Army Cold Region Research Engineering Laboratory). ASME Conference, Mexico City, September 1976. Paper 76-Pet-41 ASME. (Also in *Transactions of Journal of Pressure Vessels Technology,* Vol 99, February 1977, pp 176-182).

The Arctic Surface Effect Vehicle Program, J V Kordenbrock and C W Harry. 59th Annual Meeting of American Society of Naval Engineers, Washington DC, May 1976.

Continuing Advances with Air Cushion Icebreaking, M A Ball, (Transport Canada). Tenth CASI Symposium on Air Cushion Technology, October 1976.

Dynamic Performance of an Air-Cushion Vehicle in a Marine Environment, J A Fein, A H Magnuson and D D Moran (Naval Ship Research and Development Center, Bethesda, Maryland). AIAA/SNAME Advanced Marine Vehicle Conference, San Diego, California, February 1974.

Development of the Canadian Air-Cushion Vehicle Industry, R G Wade (Ministry of Transport, Ottawa). AIAA/SNAME Advanced Marine Vehicle Conference, San Diego, California, 25-28 February 1974.

Economics of Air Cushion Icebreaker Bow Platforms Applied to Commercial Navigation in the Upper Great Lakes Basin—A Case Study, M Tapiero and J Udell (Transportation Development Centre, Transport Canada). 12th CASI Symposium on Air Cushion Technology, 25-27 September 1978.

Effects of Hovercraft Operation on Organic Terrain in the Arctic, Gunars Abele (US Army Cold Regions Research and Engineering Laboratory). Hovering Craft, Hydrofoil and Advanced Transit Systems Conference, Brighton, May 1974.

Environmental Effects of ACV and other Off-Road Vehicle Operations on Tundra, G Abele and W E Rickard (US Army Cold Region Research and Engineering Laboratory). Seventh Canadian Symposium on Air Cushion Technology, June 1973.

High Speed Method of Air Cushion Icebreaking, R W Robertson (Transport Canada). Tenth CASI Symposium on Air Cushion Technology, October 1976.

Hovercraft Operations in the Arctic, the Activities of Voyageur 003 Between Hay River, Northwest Territories, Canada and Umiat, Alaska, N Ray Sumner Jr (Science Applications, Inc), 1651 Old Meadow Road, McLean, Virginia 22101, USA. November 1974.

Icebreaking with Air-Cushion Technology, Report National Research Council of Canada, NRC Associate Committee on Air-Cushion Technology, 1975.

Improvements in Ice-breaking by the use of Air Cushion Technology, R G Wade, R Y Edwards and J K Kim. Eastern Canada Section of SNAME Symposium Ice Tech 75, Montreal, April 1975.

Model Tests of an Arctic Surface Effect Vehicle over Model Ice, E J Lecourt, T Kotras and J Kordenbrock. Eastern Canadian Section of SNAME Ice Tech 75 Symposium, Montreal, April 1975.

NCTL's Voyageur Experience, B Meade (Northern Transportation Co). Seventh Canadian Symposium on Air Cushion Technology, June 1973.

Operational Evaluation of the SK-5 in Alaska, R A Liston and B Hanamoto (US Army Cold Region Research and Engineering Laboratory). Seventh Canadian Symposium on Air Cushion Technology, June 1973.

Operational Test and Evaluation of Air Cushion Vehicle Icebreakers for River Ice Environment, J Brick (ORI Inc), C W Prichett (US Coast Guard) and B Dennis (Chi Associates Inc). 12th CASI Symposium on Air Cushion Technology, 25-27 September 1978.

Small Air Cushion Vehicle Operation on Floating Ice under Winter Condition, R J Weaver and R O Romseier (Dept of the Environment). Seventh Canadian Symposium on Air Cushion Technology, June 1973.

AIR CUSHION LANDING SYSTEMS

ACLS for a Commercial Transport, T D Earl (Bell Aerospace Textron). Society of Automotive Engineers Meeting, 30 April-2 May 1974.

Air-Cushion Landing Systems Development on a Buffalo Aircraft, C J Austin (The De Havilland Aircraft Co of Canada Ltd). CASI Flight Test Symposium, Edmonton, Alberta, March 1975.

Characteristics of an Air-Cushion Landing System Incorporating an Inelastic Trunk, A B Boghani and K M Captain (Foster Miller Associates) and D N Wormley (MIT). 12th CASI Symposium on Air Cushion Technology, 25-27 September 1978.

The Development and Flight Testing of the XC-8A Air Cushion Landing Systems, D J Rerez (US Air Force Wright Patterson Base). SAE Aerospace Engineering & Manufacturing Mtg, 29 November-2 December, 1976. Paper 760920.

Elastically Retracting ACLS Trunks, T D Earl (Bell Aerospace Textron). *Canadian Aeronautics and Space Journal,* Vol 21 No 5, pp 169-173, May 1975.

Further Developments in Surface Effect Take-Off and Landing System Concepts, A E Johnson, F W Wilson and W B Maguire (NSRDC). Sixth CASI Symposium on Air Cushion Technology, Ontario, June 1972.

Landing on a Cushion of Air, J H Brahney (Wright Patterson Air Force Base). *Astronautics & Aeronautics,* pp 58-61, February 1976.

Tests on the Air Cushion Landing System Buffalo Aircraft, Captain T Clapp (US Air Force). Tenth CASI Symposium on Air Cushion Technology, October 1976.

The Potential of an Air Cushion Landing Gear in Civil Air Transport, T D Earl (Bell Aerosystems Co). Second Canadian Symposium on Air Cushion Technology, 1968. publ Canadian Aeronautics and Space Institute.

AIR CUSHION LOAD CARRIERS

Air and Water Cushion Lift Systems, G Parkes (Hoverlift Systems Ltd). Tenth CASI Symposium on Air Cushion Technology, October 1976.

Air Cushion Towed Raft Evaluation Project—Current Trials, J E Laframboise (Transportation Development Agency). Seventh Canadian Symposium on Air Cushion Technology, June 1973.

An Amphibious Hover Platform for Civil Engineering uses, D G W Turner (Mackace Ltd). Hovering Craft, Hydrofoil and Advanced Transit Systems Conference, Brighton, May 1974.

A Track Laying Air-Cushion Vehicle. R Wingate Hill (NSW Dept of Agriculture, Agricultural Engineering Centre, Glenfield, NSW, Australia). *Journal of Terramechanics,* Vol 12 No 3/4, 1975, pp 201-216.

Development of a Track Laying Air Cushion Vehicle, J R Goulburn and R B Steven (University of Belfast). Hovering Craft, Hydrofoil and Advanced Transit Systems Conference, Brighton, May 1974.

Movement of Heavy Loads, L A Hopkins (Air Cushion Equipment Ltd). Seventh Canadian Symposium on Air Cushion Technology, June 1973.

On the Applications of Air Cushion Technology to Off-Road Transport, Dr J Y Wong (Carleton University). Sixth CASI Symposium on Air Cushion Technology, Ontario, June 1972.

Road Fleet Operation of Air Cushion Assisted Vehicles—An Evaluation of Technical & Economic Problems, D Eyre (Saskatchewan Research Council) and A Jones (Jones & Associates). 12th CASI Symposium on Air Cushion Technology, 25-27 September 1978.

The Drag and Roll/Pitch Stability of Hoverferries at Low Speed over Water, H S Fowler (NRC of Canada). High-Speed Surface Craft Conference, Brighton, June 1980.

The Role of the Non-Self Propelled Air Cushion Vehicle, L A Hopkins (Air Cushion Equipment Ltd). Sixth CASI Symposium on Air Cushion Technology, Ontario, June 1972.

Towed Air Cushion Rafts, J Doherty, G Morton and C R Silversides (National Research Council of Canada). NRC Associate Committee on Air-Cushion Technology, Ottawa, Canada, 1975.

AIR LUBRICATED HULLS

The Application of the Air Cushion Principle to Very Large Vessels—A Case for Further Research, J W Grundy, Naval Architect. Hovering Craft, Hydrofoil and Advanced Transit Systems Conference, Brighton, May 1974.

COMMERCIAL OPERATION

A Successful Operation, E Jones (Hoverlloyd Ltd). Second International Hovering Craft and Hydrofoil Conference, Amsterdam, May 1976.

Air Cushion Vehicles in the Gulf Offshore Oil Industry: A Feasibility Study, J M Pruett (Louisiana State University, Baton Rouge). Final Report on Sea Grant Project (NOAA Contract 04-3-158-19), December 1973.

Air Cushion Vehicles in the Petroleum Industry—A Potential User's Perspective, N W Miller (Petro Canada). 12th CASI Symposium on Air Cushion Technology, 25-27 September 1978.

Air Cushion Vehicles in Support of the Petroleum Industry, Wilfred J Eggington and Donald J Iddins (Aerojet-General Corporation). American Petroleum Institute Meeting, Shreveport, Louisiana, March 1969.

Commercial Operation of Hovercraft, J Lefeaux (BR Seaspeed). Second International Hovering Craft and Hydrofoil Conference, Amsterdam, May 1976.

Developing an Operational Role for Air Cushion Vehicles in the Canadian Coast Guard, T Melhuish (Canadian Coast Guard). 12th CASI Symposium on Air Cushion Technology, 25-27 September 1978.

Hovercraft in the Canadian Coast Guard, T F Melhuish (Canadian Coast Guard). High-Speed Surface Craft Conference, Brighton, June 1980.

ACV PROJECTS

ACV Technology Programs at Aerojet-General, R W Muir (Aerojet-General Corporation). Third Canadian Symposium on Air Cushion Technology, June 1969. publ Canadian Aeronautics and Space Institute.

An Update on Large SES Progress, G E Rich (Lockheed). High-Speed Surface Craft Conference, Brighton, June 1980.

Control of a Single Propeller Hovercraft, with Particular Reference to BH.7, R L Wheeler (British Hovercraft Corporation Ltd). Fourth Canadian Symposium on Air Cushion Technology, June 1970. publ Canadian Aeronautics and Space Institute.

Current Canadian Developments Related to Low Speed, Heavy Lift ACVs, R Dyke (Hoverlift Systems Ltd). 12th CASI Symposium on Air Cushion Technology, 25-27 September 1978.

Development of Surface Effect Technology in the US Industry, John B Chaplin (Bell Aerospace Company). AIAA/SNAME/USN Advanced Marine Vehicles Meeting, Annapolis, Maryland, July 1972.

Future Hovercraft, J M George (British Hovercraft Corporation). TIMG Presentation, London 1977.

Resultats d'Exploitation des Aéroglisseurs Marins "Naviplane", P F Guienne (Bertin et Cie). Seventh Canadian Symposium on Air Cushion Technology, June 1973.

Maintenance by Design, D J Vitale (NSSC). High-Speed Surface Craft Conference, Brighton, June 1980.

Stretching the Hovermarine HM.2, A J English (Hovermarine Transport Ltd). *Hovering Craft and Hydrofoil,* Vol 16 No 5, February 1977.

Shore-to-Shore Lightering with the Voyageur, R W Helm (Bell Aerospace Canada Textron). Tenth CASI Symposium on Air Cushion Technology, October 1976.

Status of Super-4, R Wheeler (BHC). AIAA/SNAME Conference on Advance Marine Vehicles, 1979.

The 260-tons French Amphibious Hovercraft 'Naviplane N.500', P F Guienne (SEDAM). AIAA/SNAME Advanced Marine Vehicles Conference, San Diego, April 1978.

The VT.2 100-ton Amphibious Hovercraft, A Bingham (Vosper Thornycroft Ltd). Second International Hovering Craft and Hydrofoil Conference, Amsterdam, May 1976.

Turning Technology into Fleet Capability, J Benson and R Kennefick (NSRDC). High-Speed Surface Craft Conference, Brighton, June 1980.

Voyageur Trials and Operating Experience, T F Melhuish (Bell Aerospace Canada). Seventh Canadian Symposium on Air Cushion Technology, June 1973.

DESIGN

A Comparison of Some Features of High-Speed Marine Craft, A Silverleaf and F G R Cook (National Physical Laboratory). Royal Institution of Naval Architects, March 1969.

A method for the preliminary sizing of Lift Fan Systems, Applicable to Large Hovercraft, W B Wilson (Webb Institute of Naval Architecture, Glen Cove, New York). Naval Ship Engineering Center of the US Navy, Propulsion Systems Analysis Branch, Technical Report 6144E-75-126, February 1975.

Aerodynamic Challenges for the Faster Interface Vehicles, P R Shipps (Rohr Corporation). Sixth CASI Symposium on Air Cushion Technology, Ontario, June 1972.

Lateral Stability of a Dynamic Ram Air Cushion Vehicle, P V Aidala (Transportation Systems Center, Cambridge, Massachusetts). DOT-TSC-FRA-74-6. FRA-ORD/D-75-6. PB-236-516/1WT, August 1974.

On the Determination of the Hydrodynamic Performance of Air-Cushion Vehicles, S D Prokhorov, V N Treshchevski and L D Volkov (Kryloff Research Institute, Leningrad). Ninth Symposium on Naval Hydrodynamics, Paris, August 1972.

Predicting the Unpredictable, E G Band (Band Lavis). High-Speed Surface Craft Conference, Brighton, June 1980.

Ram-Wing Surface Effect Boat, Capt R W Gallington (USAF, US Air Force Acadamy, Colorado). Advanced Marine Vehicle Meeting, AIAA/SNAME/USN, Annapolis, Maryland, July 1972.

Some Aspects of Optimum Design of Lift Fans, T G Csaky (NSRDC). Sixth CASI Symposium on Air Cushion Technology, Ontario, June 1972.

Some Design Aspects of an Integrated Lift/Propulsion System, D Jones (Jones, Kirwan and Associates). Sixth CASI Symposium on Air Cushion Technology, Ontario, June 1972.

The Lift Air Requirements of ACVs over Various Terrain, H Fowler (NRC of Canada). 12th CASI Symposium on Air Cushion Technology, 25-27 September 1978.

Trade-Off Methodology for Evaluation of Design Alternatives of Air Cushion Vehicles, O Gokcek and J H Madden (Aerojet General Corporation). Sixth CASI Symposium on Air Cushion Technology, Ontario, June 1972.

Design and Operation of Centrifugal, Axial-flow and Crossflow fans. Translated from German, Edited by R S Azad and D R Scott, Pergamon Press 1973.

EXTERNAL AERODYNAMICS

The External Aerodynamics of Hovercraft, Professor E J Andrews (College of Aeronautics, Cranfield). Royal Aeronautical Society Rotorcraft Section, April 1969.

LIGHTWEIGHT ACVs

Amphibious Hovercraft: The Little Ones are growing up, M A Pinder (Pindair Ltd). *Hovering Craft and Hydrofoil,* Vol 14 No 9, pp 5-9, June 1975.

Control and Guidance of Light Amphibious Hovercraft up to a Gross Weight of 5,000lbs, R L Trillo (Robert Trillo Ltd). Seventh Canadian Symposium on Air Cushion Technology, June 1973.

Small Hovercraft Design, P H Winter (Air Vehicle Developments). Institution of Production Engineers (Southampton Section). International Hovercraft Conference, 1968.

Small Hovercraft Structure, A J English (Sealand Hovercraft Ltd). Hovering Craft, Hydrofoil and Advanced Transit Systems Conference, Brighton, May 1974.

The Evaluation of Light Hovercraft, B J Russell. *Hovering Craft and Hydrofoil,* Vol 17 No 4, pp 8-12, January 1978.

MILITARY APPLICATIONS and OPERATING EXPERIENCE

ACV Military Applications—Experience and Potential, J B Chaplin (Bell Aerosystems Company). Third Canadian Symposium on Air Cushion Technology, June 1969. publ Canadian Aeronautics and Space Institute.

Air Cushion Vehicles in a Logistical Role, Col H N Wood (Ret) (US Army Combat Development Command Transportation Agency). Fourth Canadian Symposium on Air Cushion Technology, 1970. publ Canadian Aeronautics and Space Institute.

Amphibious Assault Landing Craft JEFF(A), E F Davison (Aerojet) and M D Fink (NSRDC). High-Speed Surface Craft Conference, Brighton, June 1980.

Demonstrated Performance of the Amphibious Assault Landing Craft JEFF(B), A Coles (Bell) and M Kidd (NSRDC). High-Speed Surface Craft Conference, Brighton, June 1980.

Development of the SR.N6 Mk 5 Vehicle-carrying Hovercraft, Major M H Burton (Dept of Trade and Industry, UK). Seventh Canadian Symposium on Air Cushion Technology, June 1973.

Hovercraft in Mine Counter Measures, C M Plumb and D K Brown (DG Ships, MOD). High-Speed Surface Craft Conference, Brighton, June 1980.

Military Hovercraft, R Old (British Hovercraft Corporation Ltd). Second International Hovering Craft and Hydrofoil Conference, Amsterdam, May 1976.

SES-100 Test Program, C Raleigh (SESTF). AIAA/SNAME Conference, 1976. Paper 76-860.

Seakeeping Characteristics of the Amphibious Assault Landing Craft, A H Magnuson and R F Messal. AIAA/SNAME Conference, 1976. Paper 76-865.

Some Military Applications of Small Hovercraft, G W Shepherd (SAS Developments Ltd). Second International Hovering Craft and Hydrofoil Conference, Amsterdam, May 1976.

UK Military Hovercraft, Commander N T Bennett, AFC, RN (Interservice Hovercraft Unit). Institute of Production Engineers, Second International Hovercraft Conference, April 1971.

Testing the JEFF Craft—An Interim Report, M Brown (D W Taylor NS R & D Centre) and Margaret Bullock (ORI Inc). AIAA/SNAME Conference on Advanced Marine Vehicles, 1979.

Test Evaluation and Cost Effectiveness of an Air Cushion Vehicle in a Logistics Support Role for the US Army, F D DeFilippis (MERDC). High-Speed Surface Craft Conference, Brighton, June 1980.

The Amphibious Hovercraft as a Warship, R L Wheeler (British Hovercraft Corporation). RINA Small Warship Symposium, London, March 1978.

The US Army LACV-30 Program, J Sargent (US AME R & D Command) and C Faulkner (Bell). AIAA/SNAME Conference 1976. Paper 76-866.

The US Navy Surface Effect Ship Acquisition Project, E H Handler. *Hovering Craft and Hydrofoil,* Vol 17 No 3, pp 4-10, December 1977.

The US Navy 3000-LT Surface Effect Ship Programme, G D McGhee (Rohr Marine Inc). 85th Meeting of SNAME, New York, November 1977.

LEGISLATION and REGULATIONS

Canadian Air-Cushion Vehicle Legislation and Regulation, J Doherty (Ministry of Transport Canada). Ninth Canadian Symposium on Air Cushion Technology, Ottawa, October 1975.

Hovercraft Noise. publ The Noise Advisory Council, London, 1980.

Operating Legislation for ACVs, Captain J Doherty (Department of Transport). Second Canadian Symposium on Air Cushion Technology, June 1968. publ Canadian Aeronautics and Space Institute.

United States Requirements for Commercial Surface Effect Ships, W A Cleary Jr and Lt D H Whitten (US Coast Guard). Second Canadian Symposium on Air Cushion Technology, June 1968. publ Canadian Aeronautics and Space Institute.

A Review of the Report of the ARB Special Committee on Hovercraft Stability & Control, J G Wrath (Civil Aviation Authority). Tenth CASI Symposium on Air Cushion Technology, October 1976.

POWERPLANTS

Design Performance and Operational Features of the LM500, Dr H E Fogg and Dr L Maccaferri. High-Speed Surface Craft Conference, Brighton, June 1980.

Epicyclic Gearboxes for High-Speed Marine Craft, R Hicks. publ The Hovercraft Society, London, 1980.

Gas Turbine Power for Large Hovercraft, P A Yerbury (BR Seaspeed). *Proc Symposium Gas Turbines,* London, pp 117-124, February 1976.

Gas Turbine Installations for Air Cushion Vehicle Lift and Propulsion Power, G H Smith (Avco Lycoming). ASME Gas Turbine Conference, Philadelphia, March 1977. Paper 77-GT-71.

The Selection of the Optimum Powerplant for the Air Cushion Vehicle, R Messet (United Aircraft of Canada Ltd). Fourth Canadian Symposium on Air Cushion Technology, June 1970. publ Canadian Aeronautics and Space Institute.

Some Aspects of Free Turbine Engine Hovercraft Control, W Bloomfield and T B Lauriat (Avco Corporation Lycoming Division). Institute of Production Engineers, Second International Hovercraft Conference, April 1971.

PRODUCTION

Hovercraft from a Shipbuilder, A E Bingham (Vosper Thornycroft Ltd). Hovering Craft, Hydrofoil and Advanced Transit Systems Conference, Brighton, May 1974.

The Production of Air Cushion Vehicles, E F Gilberthorpe (British Hovercraft Corporation). Institution of Production Engineers (Southampton Section), International Hovercraft Conference, April 1968.

RESEARCH and DEVELOPMENT

Air Appraisal of Present and Future Large Commercial Hovercraft, R L Wheeler (British Hovercraft Corporation Ltd). Royal Institution of Naval Architects, October 1975.

CAA Paper 75017, Report of the ARB Special Committee on Hovercraft Stability and Control, Civil Aviation Authority, London, 1975.

A Decade of Development—The SR.N6 Family of Hovercraft, R L Wheeler (British Hovercraft Corporation). Hovering Craft, Hydrofoil and Advanced Transit Systems Conference, Brighton, May 1974.

Development of Hovermarine Transport Vehicles, E G Tattersall (Hovermarine Transport Ltd). Institute of Production Engineers, Second International Hovercraft Conference, April 1971.

The Development of Marine Hovercraft with special reference to the Construction of the N500, P F Guienne (SEDAM). Second International Conference Transport-Expo, Paris, April 1975.

The Drag of a Sidewall ACV over Calm Water, R Murao (Ministry of Transport, Japan). Second International Hovering Craft and Hydrofoil Conference, Amsterdam, May 1976.

General Survey of the Studies and Testing Techniques that led to the definition of N500 Performance, G Herrouin and Y Boccarodo (SEDAM). Second International Hovering Craft and Hydrofoil Conference, Amsterdam, May 1976.

Hovercraft Research on the Cranfield Whirling Arm Facility, P A T Christopher and K H Lim (Cranfield Institute). High-Speed Surface Craft Conference, Brighton, June 1980.

Hovercraft Research and Development, R L Wheeler (British Hovercraft Corporation Ltd). Institute of Production Engineers, Second International Hovercraft Conference, April 1971.

Hovercraft Noise, 3 papers presented at a symposium organised by the Hovercraft Society and The Royal Aeronautical Society, London. publ The Hovercraft Society, 1980.

Optimum Speed of an Air Cushion Vehicle—A Naviplane N500 Application, P F Guienne (SEDAM). *Hovering Craft and Hydrofoil,* Vol 16 No 9-10, 1977.

Power-Augmented-Ram Landing Craft, F H Krause (DTNSRDC). High-Speed Surface Craft Conference, Brighton, June 1980.

Research and Development Work Associated with the Lift and Propulsion of Air Cushion Vehicles, J G Russell (Dowty Rotol Ltd). Hovering Craft, Hydrofoil and Advanced Transit Systems Conference, Brighton, May 1974.

Research into the Profitability of the Design and Construction of the N.500, P F Guienne (SEDAM). Second International Hovering Craft and Hydrofoil Conference, Amsterdam, May 1976.

Response of Air Cushion Vehicles to random seaways and the inherent distortion in scale models., D R Lavis, R J Bartholomew and J C Jones. *Journal of Hydronautics,* Vol 8, p 83, July 1974.

Some Aspects of Hovercraft Dynamics, J R Richardson (NPL Hovercraft Unit). Institution of Production Engineers, Second International Hovercraft Conference, April 1971.

Techniques of Model Testing Hovercraft, B Clarke (BHC). *The Hovercraft Proceedings,* Vol 1, 1980. publ The Hovercraft Society, London.

The Definition of Sea State for Hovercraft Purposes, NPL Hovercraft Sea State Committee Report 2, National Physical Laboratory (HU Report 8), April 1969.

STRUCTURAL DESIGN

Development of Stability Standards for Dynamically-Supported Craft—A Progress Report, D R Lavis (Band Lavis). High-Speed Surface Craft Conference, Brighton, June 1980.

A Method of Testing Models of Hovercraft on Open Waters, Prof L Koblinski and Dr M Krezelewski (Ship Research Institute, Technical University of Gdansk). Institute of Production Engineers, Second International Hovercraft Conference, April 1971.

Static and Dynamic Analysis of the 3KSES Hull Structure, Messrs Havel, Dent, Phillips & Chang (Bell Aerospace). AIAA/SNAME Conference, 1976. Paper 76-858.

Prediction of Hydrodynamic Impact Loads Acting on SES and ACV Structure, E G U Band, D R Lavis and J G Giannotti. AIAA/SNAME Conference, 1976. Paper 76-868.

SYSTEMS

An Accumulator Control System for Alleviating SES Craft Heave motions in waves, P Kaplan and T P Sargent (Oceanics Inc) and James L Decker (US Navy Surface Effect Ships Project Office, Washington DC). Advanced Marine Vehicle Meeting AIAA/SNAME/USN, Annapolis, Maryland, July 1972.

An Investigation of the Roll Stiffness Characteristics of three Flexible Slanted Cushion Systems, Messrs Sullivan, Hinchey and Delaney (Toronto University, Institute for Aerospace Studies). UTIAS Report No 213, 1977.

Characterisation and Testing of Skirt Materials, Dr R C Tennyson and J R McCullough (Toronto University, Institute for Aerospace Studies). Seventh Canadian Symposium on Air Cushion Technology, June 1973.

The Design and Operating Features of Vosper Thornycroft Skirts, R Dyke (Vosper Thornycroft Ltd). Second International Hovering Craft and Hydrofoil Conference, Amsterdam, May 1976.

Deterioration of Hovercraft Skirt Components on Craft Operating over Water, M D Kelly, J Morris and E R Gardner (Avon Rubber Co Ltd). Hovering Craft, Hydrofoil and Advanced Transit Systems Conference, Brighton, May 1974.

Evolution of Integrated Lift, Propulsion and Control in the Aeromobile ACV, Dr W R Bertelsen (Bertelsen Manufacturing Co). Third Canadian Symposium on Air Cushion Technology, June 1969. publ Canadian Aeronautics and Space Institute.

Experience of Using the Gas Turbine Engine for the Propulsion of the Fully Amphibious Air Cushion Vehicle, M L Woodward (Rolls-Royce (1971) Ltd). Sixth Canadian Symposium on Air Cushion Technology, Ontario, June 1972.

The French Technique of Aéroglisseurs Marins, C Marchetti (SEDAM). Second Canadian Symposium on Air Cushion Technology, June 1968. publ Canadian Aeronautics and Space Institute.

Hovercraft Control, B J Russell (AMTE). High-Speed Surface Craft Conference, Brighton, June 1980.

Hovercraft Skirts, R L Wheeler (British Hovercraft Corporation). Hovering Craft, Hydrofoil and Advanced Transit Systems Conference, Brighton, May 1974.

Hovercraft Skirt Design Requirements, J Rapson (HDL). 12th CASI Symposium on Air Cushion Technology, 25-27 September 1978.

Hovercraft Skirt Materials, Dr E Gardner (Avon Processed Polymers). 12th CASI Symposium on Air Cushion Technology, 25-27 September 1978.

Iceater 1-The Air Cushion Icebreaker, J C Snyder (Global Marine) and M Ball (Canadian Coast Guard). Offshore Technology Conference, Houston, May 1977.

The Influence of Plenum Chamber Obstructions on the Performance of a Hovercraft Lift Fan, G Wilson, Dr D J Myles and G Gallacher (National Engineering Laboratory). Third Canadian Symposium on Air Cushion Technology, June 1969. publ Canadian Aeronautics and Space Institute.

Jets, Props and Air Cushion, Propulsion Technology and Surface Effect Ships, Alfred Skolnick and Z G Wachnik (Joint Surface Effect Ships Program Office). The American Society of Mechanical Engineers. Gas Turbine Conference and Products Show, March 1968.

Low Temperature Effects on the Abrasion Behaviour of Coated Fabrics, R C Tennyson and A A Smailys (University of Toronto, Institute for Aerospace Studies). Tenth CASI Symposium on Air Cushion Technology, October 1976.

Pneumatic Power Transmission Applied to Hovercraft, J F Sladey Jr and R K Muench (United States Naval Academy and Naval Ship Research and Development Centre). Sixth CASI Symposium on Air Cushion Technology, Ontario, June 1972.

Power Optimization of the Captured Air Bubble Surface Effect Ship, K F Richardson (Naval Postgraduate School). AD-A039341, December 1976.

Power Transmission System of Hovercraft MV-PP1, MV-PP5 and MV-PP15, T Yamada, O Tamano, T Morita, K Horikiri, H Hirasawa and M Fujiwasa (Mitsui Shipbuilding & Engineering Co). Proc International Symposium on Marine Engineering, Tokyo, November 1973. Technical Paper Vol Ser 2-4, pp 13-23. publ Marine Engineers Society in Japan, Tokyo, 1973.

Ride Improvement Systems for Sidewall Hovercraft, M Barnesley and J Ruler. publ The Hovercraft Society, London, 1980.

Seakeeping Trials of the BH.7 Hovercraft, A H Magnusson. Naval Ship R & D Report SPD-574-01, August 1975.

Skirt Design and Development on the Naviplane, G Herrouin and A Lafant (Dubigeon Normandie/SEDAM). High-Speed Surface Craft Conference, Brighton, June 1980.

Surface Effect Vehicle Propulsion: A Review of the State of the Art, J B Chaplin, R G Moore and J L Allison (Bell Aerospace). Sixth Canadian Symposium on Air Cushion Technology, Ontario, June 1972.

Water-Jet Propulsion, S Kuether and F X Stora (Tamco Ltd, US Army Mobility Equipment, R & D Center). Second Canadian Symposium on Air Cushion Technology, 1968. publ Canadian Aeronautics and Space Institute.

Waterjet Propulsion for High Speed Surface Ships, P Duport, M Visconte and J Merle (SOGREAH). Ninth Symposium on Naval Hydrodynamics, Paris, August 1973.

SURFACE EFFECT SHIPS

An Analysis of Desired Manoeuvring Characteristics of Large SEVs, W Zeitfuss Jr and E N Brooks Jr (Naval Ship Research and Development Centre, Washington DC). Advanced Marine Vehicle Meeting, AIAA/SNAME/USN, Annapolis, Maryland, July 1972.

Applications of Surface Effect Ships, Lt Cdr P Lindley (Vosper Hovermarine). High-Speed Surface Craft Conference, Brighton, June 1980.

Crew/Combat System Performance Requirements in the Operational Environment of Surface Effect Ships, A Skolnick. *Naval Engineers Journal,* Vol 86 No 6, pp 15-32, December 1974.

Current State-of-the-Art of Waterjet Inlet Systems for High Performance Naval Ships, R A Barr and N R Stark. Hydronautics Inc, Tech Rep 7224-5, December 1973.

Domain of the Surface Effect Ship, W J Eggington and N Kobitz. Eighty-third Annual Meeting of SNAME, New York, November 1975. Paper NB 11.

Large High Speed Surface Effect Ship Technology, P J Mantle (Aerojet-General Corporation). Hovering Craft, Hydrofoil and Advanced Transit Systems Conference, Brighton, May 1974.

The Nuclear Powered Ocean-Going SES, E K Liberatore (Aeromar Corporation). *Jane's Surface Skimmers, 1971-72.*

Ocean-Going Surface Effect Ships, W F Perkins (Ocean Systems Div, Lockheed Missiles & Space Co). Northern California Section of SNAME and Golden Gate Section of ASNE Meeting at Treasure Island Naval Station, 1974.

On the Wave Resistance of Surface Effect Ships, J C Trotinclaux. Eighty-third Annual Meeting of SNAME, New York, November 1975. Paper No 3.

Performance Predictions for Open Ocean ACVs and Surface Effect Ships, J A Tremills (Canadian Defence Research Establishment). 12th CASI Symposium on Air Cushion Technology, 25-27 September 1978.

SES Programme, Civil Application, J J Kelly (Bell-Halter). *Hovering Craft and Hydrofoil,* Vol 17 No 4, pp 26-36, January 1978.

Some Special Problems in Surface Effect Ships, Robert D Waldo (Aerojet-General Corporation). *Journal of Hydronautics,* July 1968. publ American Institute of Aeronautics and Astronautics.

Study of Heave Acceleration/Velocity Control for the Surface Effect Ship, AD-009 302/1WT. US Grant, Naval Postgraduate School, Monterey, California, December 1974.

Surface Effect Ship Habitability Familiarisation, W F Clement and J J Shanahan (Systems Technology Inc). Interim Tech Rep STI-1041-1, November 1973.

The US Navy's Large Surface Effect Ship, Commander Jerome J Fee and Eugene H Handler (US Navy). Tenth CASI Symposium on Air Cushion Technology, October 1976.

Surface Effect Ships in the Surface Navy, R C Truax. *US Navy Institute Proceedings,* Vol 99 No 12/850, pp 50-54, December 1973.

TRACKED AIR CUSHION VEHICLES

A Comparative Study of the Ride Quality of TRACV Suspension Alternatives, R A Lums (Wright-Patterson Air Force Base). AFIT-C1-78-2 AD-AO46 565/8WT, September 1977.

Aérotrain Tridim for Urban Transportation, Jean Bertin and Jean Berthelot (Bertin & Cie and Sté Aérotrain). Hovering Craft, Hydrofoil and Advanced Transit Systems Conference, Brighton, May 1974.

The Air-Cushion at High Speeds, F Steiner (Société de l'Aérotrain). Second International Conference Transport-Expo, Paris, April 1975.

Current Collection for High-Speed Transit Systems, Messrs Appleton, Bartam, MacMichael and Fletcher (International Research & Development Co Ltd). Second International Hovering Craft and Hydrofoil Conference, Amsterdam, May 1976.

Linear Propulsion by Electromagnetic River, Prof E R Laithwaite (Imperial College of Science and Technology). Hovering Craft, Hydrofoil and Advanced Transit Systems Conference, Brighton, May 1974.

The Operational Performance and Economics of URBA, M E Barthalon and L Pascual (SETURBA). Hovering Craft, Hydrofoil and Advanced Transit Systems Conference, Brighton, May 1974.

Tracked Air-Cushion Vehicle Suspension Models: Analysis and Comparison, D P Garg (Duke University, North Carolina) and B E Platin (MIT, Cambridge). *Vehicle System Dynamics (Holland),* Vol 2 No 3, November 1973.

ACV PUBLICATIONS, BOOKS and GENERAL LITERATURE
GENERAL INTEREST

This is the Hovercraft, Hugh Colver. publ Hamish Hamilton.

Hovercraft and Hydrofoils, Roy McLeavy. publ Blandford Press Ltd.

Hovercraft and Hydrofoils, Jane's Pocket Book 21, Roy McLeavy. publ Jane's Publishing Company.

The Hovercraft Story, Garry Hogg. publ Abelard-Schuman.

Hydrofoils and Hovercraft, Bill Gunston. publ Aldus Books.

Jane's Surface Skimmers (annual) edited by Roy McLeavy. publ Jane's Publishing Company.

TECHNICAL

Hovercraft Control and Stability. publ Dept of Industry, London, 1980

Hovercraft Design and Construction, Elsley & Devereax. publ David & Charles.

An Introduction to Hovercraft and Hoverports, Cross & O'Flaherty. publ Pitman Publishing/Juanita Kalerghi.

Light Hovercraft Handbook, (ed) Neil MacDonald. publ Hoverclub of Great Britain Ltd (available from 45 St Andrews Road, Lower Bemerton, Salisbury, Wilts).

A Guide to Model Hovercraft, (ed) Neil MacDonald. publ Hoverclub of Great Britain Ltd.

Marine Hovercraft Technology, Robert Trillo. publ Leonard Hill Books.

HOVERCRAFT PERIODICALS

Air-Cushion and Hydrofoil Systems Bibliography Service, (bimonthly) Robert Trillo Ltd, Broadlands, Brockenhurst, Hants SO4 7SX.

High-Speed Surface Craft, (monthly) Kalerghi Publications, 51 Welbeck Street, London W1M 7HE.

Light Hovercraft, (monthly) The Hoverclub of Great Britain Ltd, 45 St Andrews Road, Lower Bemerton, Salisbury, Wilts.

Hovercraft Bulletin, (monthly) The Hovercraft Society, Rochester House, 66 Little Ealing Lane, London W5 4XX.

Air Cushion Review, (monthly) Aristos Publications, 17 Southampton Road, Paulsgrove, Hants PO6 4SA.

SPECIAL INTEREST
The Law of Hovercraft, L J Kovats. publ Lloyd's of London Press Ltd, 1975.

HYDROFOILS
BOOKS
Hydrofoils, Christopher Hook and A C Kermode. publ Sir Isaac Pitman & Sons Ltd, London.

Hydrofoil Sailing, A J Alexander, J L Grogono and Donald J Nigg. publ Kalerghi Publications.

PAPERS, ETC
COMMERCIAL OPERATION
Jetfoil In Operation, V Salisbury (Boeing Marine Systems). AIAA/SNAME Conference on Advanced Marine Vehicles, 1979.

Operational Experience with USSR Raketa Hydrofoils on the River Thames, H Snowball (Hovermarine Transport Ltd). Second International Hovering Craft and Hydrofoil Conference, Amsterdam, May 1976.

Operating the PT150 Hydrofoil, J Presthus (Johns Presthus Rederi). Second International Hovering Craft and Hydrofoil Conference, Amsterdam, May 1976.

Running and Maintenance of Supramar Hydrofoils in Hong Kong, D Hay and N J Matthew (Institute of Marine Engineers). April 1970.

DESIGN
Bending Flutter and Torsional Flutter of Flexible Hydrofoil Struts, P K Beach, Y N Liu (US Naval Ship Research and Development Centre). Ninth Symposium on Naval Hydrodynamics, Paris, August 1972.

Canadian Advances in Surface Piercing Hydrofoils, N E Jeffrey and M C Eames (Defence Research Establishment Atlantic, Dartmouth, Nova Scotia). Advanced Marine Vehicle Meeting, AIAA/SNAME/USN, Annapolis, Maryland, July 1972.

Choice of Hydrofoil Propulsion, Dr D Di Blasi (Rodriquez Cantiere Navale). High-Speed Surface Craft Conference, Brighton, June 1980.

A Comparison of Some Features of High-Speed Marine Craft, A Silverleaf and F G R Cook (National Physical Laboratory). Royal Institute of Naval Architects, March 1969.

Design Optimization of Waterjet Propulsion Systems for Hydrofoils, R P Gill, M S Theseis (Massachusetts Institute of Technology). May 1972.

Flow Separation, Re-attachment and Ventilation of Foils with Sharp Leading Edge at Low Reynolds Number, R Hecker and G Ober. Naval Ship Research & Development Center Report 4390, III, May 1974.

A High-Speed Hydrofoil Strut and Foil Study, R Wermter and Y T Shen (Naval Ship Research & Development Center, Bethesda, Maryland). AIAA/SNAME Advanced Marine Vehicle Conference, San Diego, California, February 1974. Paper 74-310.

Hydroelastic Design of Sub-Cavitating and Cavitating Hydrofoil Strut Systems, Naval Ship Research & Development Center, Maryland, USA. NSRDC Report 4257. April 1974.

Hydrofoil Craft Designers Guide, R Altmann, Hydronautics Inc, Technical Report 744-1, March 1968.

Laminar Boundary-Layer Induced Wave Forces on a Submerged Flat-Plate Hydrofoil, *Journal of Hydronautics,* Vol 8 No 2, pp 47-53, April 1974.

Large Hydrofoil Ships Feasibility Level Characteristics, James R Greco (Naval Ship Engineering Center, Hyattsville, Maryland). Advanced Marine Vehicle Meeting, AIAA/SNAME/USN, Annapolis, Maryland, July 1972.

Navaltecnica Hydrofoils, Dott Ing Leopoldo Rodriquez (Navaltecnica) and Dott Ing Maurizo Piatelli (SMA). *Hovering Craft and Hydrofoil,* Vol 17 No 8-9, pp 4-12, May-June 1978.

Production PHM Hull Structure Productivity Design, Ottis R Bullock and Bryan Oldfield (Boeing Co). *Hovering Craft and Hydrofoil,* Vol 16, No 9-10, 1977.

Prospects for very High Speed Hydrofoils, A Conolly. San Diego Section of the Society of Naval Architects and Marine Engineers/The American Society of Naval Engineers joint meeting, 20 November 1974. Available from: Section Librarian, Cdr R Bernhardt, US Coast Guard, Code 240, Box 119, US Naval Station, San Diego, California 92136.

Special Problems in the Design of Supercavitating Hydrofoils, G F Dobay and E S Baker (Naval Ship Research and Development Center, Bethesda, Maryland). AIAA/SNAME Advanced Marine Vehicle Conference, San Diego, California, February 1974. Paper 74-309.

Typhoon—A Seagoing Vessel on Automatically Controlled Submerged Foils, I I Baskalov and V M Burlakov *(Sudostroyeniye). Hovering Craft and Hydrofoil,* October 1972.

NAVAL CRAFT
High Speed and US Navy Hydrofoil Development, D A Jewell (Naval Ship Research and Development Center, Bethesda, Maryland). AIAA/SNAME Advanced Marine Vehicle Conference, San Diego, California, February 1974. Paper 74-307.

HMCS Bras d'Or—Sea Trials and Future Prospects, M C Eames and T G Drummond (Defence Research Establishment Atlantic, Canada). Royal Institution of Naval Architects, April 1972.

Jetfoils As an Offshore Patrol Vessel, R T Crawley (Boeing Marine Systems). AIAA/SNAME Conference on Advanced Marine Vehicles, 1979.

Military Hydrofoils, Baron H von Schertel, Dipl Ing Egon Faber and Dipl Ing Eugen Schatté (Supramar AG). *Jane's Surface Skimmers 1972-73.*

Military Hydrofoils, G Myers (Boeing Marine Systems). *Hovering Craft and Hydrofoil,* Vol 17 No 1, pp 32-35, October 1977.

Mission Applications of Military Hydrofoils, Lt Cdr W C Stolgitis (US Navy) and R E Adler (R E Adler Consultants). High-Speed Surface Craft Conference, Brighton, June 1980.

The NATO PHM Programme, Cdr Karl M Duff, USN (Naval Ship Systems Command, Washington DC). Advanced Marine Vehicle Meeting, AIAA/SNAME/USN, Annapolis, Maryland, July 1972.

The Operational Evaluation of the Hydrofoil Concept in US Coast Guard Missions, R E Williams (US Coast Guard and Development Center). Second International Hovering Craft and Hydrofoil Conference, Amsterdam, May 1976.

PHM Hullborne Wave Tests, C J Stevens (Institute of Technology, Hoboken, New Jersey). Stevens Institute of Technology, Davidson Lab Rep R-1759, June 1974.

Research on Hydrofoil Craft, Prof Dr Siegfried Schuster (Director Berlin Towing Tank). International Hydrofoil Society Winter Meeting, 1971, *Hovering Craft and Hydrofoil,* December 1971.

Sparviero-'Swordfish'-Type Multi-Role Combat Hydrofoil, Dott Ing Francesco Cao (Cantieri Navali Riuniti). Mostra Navale Italiana, Genoa, Italy, May 1978.

The Role of the Hydrofoil Special Trial Unit (HYSTU) in the US Navy Hydrofoil Program, R E Nystrom (US Navy). Second International Hovering Craft and Hydrofoil Conference, Amsterdam, May 1976.

The "Swordfish" Type Hydrofoil Design Criteria and Operational Experience, M Baldi (Cantieri Navali Riuniti). Second International Hovering Craft and Hydrofoil Conference, Amsterdam, May 1976.

SEAKEEPING CHARACTERISTICS
Examining the Pitch, Heave and Accelerations of Planning Craft Operations in a Seaway, M Haggard and M Jones (Naval Sea Systems Command). High-Speed Surface Craft Conference, Brighton, June 1980.

Experimental Analysis on a Surface-Piercing Hydrofoil at Sea, Prof R Tedeschi, Dott Ing S Martellini and D G Mazzeo. High-Speed Surface Craft Conference, Brighton, June 1980.

Prediction of the Seakeeping Characteristics of Hydrofoil Ships, Irving A Hirsch (Boeing Company). AIAA/SNAME Advanced Marine Vehicles Meeting, Norfolk, Virginia, May 1967. Paper 67-352.

Wave Impacts on Hydrofoil Ships and Structural Indications, Messrs Drummond, Mackay and Schmitke. 11th Symposium on Naval Hydrodynamics, London 1976.

SYSTEMS
Heaving Motions of Ventilated Trapezoidal Hydrofoils, L F Tsen and M Guilbaud (University of Poitiers). Fourth Canadian Congress of Applied Mechanics, CANCAM '73, 28 May—1 June 1973, Ecole Polytechnique, Montreal.

Life Saving Systems for High-speed Surface Craft, D V Edwards, A J Burgess and M D Martin (RFD Inflatables). High-Speed Surface Craft Conference, Brighton, June 1980.

Importance of Rudder and Hull Influence at Cavitation Tests of High-Speed Propellers, O Rutgersson (Swedish Maritime Research Centre). High-Speed Surface Craft Conference, Brighton, June 1980.

The Longitudinal Behaviour of a Hydrofoil Craft in Rough Seas, M Krezelewski (Institute of Ship Research, Gdansk University). Hovering Craft, Hydrofoil and Advanced Transit Systems Conference, Brighton, May 1974.

On the Design of Propulsion Systems with Z-Drives for Hydrofoil Ships, A A Rousetsky (Kryloff Research Institute, Leningrad). Ninth Symposium on Naval Hydrodynamics, Paris, August 1972.

Waterjet Propulsion in High-Speed Surface Craft, G Venturini. High-Speed Surface Craft Conference, Brighton, June 1980.

RESEARCH AND DEVELOPMENT

A Theory for High Speed Hydrofoils, D P Wang and Y T Shen. Naval Ship R & D Centre Report SPD-479-14, June 1975.

The Design of Waterjet Propulsion Systems for Hydrofoil Craft, J Levy. Soc Naval Architects and Marine Engineers, *Marine Technology,* 2, 15-25 41, January 1965.

The Development of Automatic Control Systems for Hydrofoil Craft, R L Johnston and W C O'Neill (Naval Ship Research Development Centre, Bethesda, Maryland). Hovering Craft, Hydrofoil and Advanced Transit Systems Conference, Brighton, May 1974.

The Economics of an Advanced Hydrofoil System, A M Gonnella and W M Schultz (Hydrofoil Systems Organisation, The Boeing Company). *Hovering Craft & Hydrofoil,* November 1970.

The Effect of Nose Radius on the Cavitation Inception Characteristics of Two-Dimensional Hydrofoils, D T Valentine. Naval Ship Research & Development Center Report 3813, VI, July 1974.

An Examination of the Hazards to Hydrofoil Craft from Floating Objects, Christopher Hook. Society of Environmental Engineers Symposium, The Transport Environment, April 1969.

Key Problems Associated with Developing the Boeing Model 929-100 Commercial Passenger Hydrofoil, William Shultz (Boeing International Corporation). Hovering Craft, Hydrofoil and Advanced Transit Systems Conference, Brighton, May 1974.

The Large Commercial Hydrofoil and its Limits in Size and Speed, Baron H von Schertel (Supramar). Second International Hovering Craft and Hydrofoil Conference, Amsterdam, May 1976.

Model Resistance Data of Series 65 Hull Forms Applicable to Hydrofoils and Planing Craft, H D Holling and E N Hubble. Naval Ship Research & Development Center Report 4121, V, May 1974.

Nine Years' History of the Hitachi-Supramar Hydrofoil Boat, *Hovering Craft & Hydrofoil,* November 1970.

Parametric Survey of Hydrofoil Stunt Flutter, P K Besch and E P Rood. Naval Ship R & D Center Report 76-0050, March 1976.

Preliminary Propulsion Performance Estimates for an 80ft Hydrofoil Craft, D L Gregory. Naval Ship R & D Center Evaluation Report SPD-606-01, June 1975.

Selection of Hydrofoil Waterjet Propulsion Systems, Ross Hatte and Hugh J Davis (The Boeing Company). *Journal of Hydronautics,* Vol 1 No 1, 1967. publ American Institute of Aeronautics and Astronautics.

Survey of French Hydrofoil Programmes (in French), J L Vollot. *Bulletin de l'Association Technique Maritime et Aéronautique,* No 72, pp 229-248, 1972.

Twenty Years of Hydrofoil Construction & Operation, L Rodriquez (Cantiere Navaltecnica). Second International Hovering Craft and Hydrofoil Conference, Amsterdam, May 1976.

Waterjet Propulsion for Marine Vehicles, V E Johnson, Jr. AIAA Paper 64-306, 1964. publ American Institute of Aeronautics and Astronautics.

Waterjet Propulsion for Marine Vehicles, J Traksel and W E Beck. AIAA Paper 65-245, 1965. publ American Institute of Aeronautics and Astronautics.

SAILING SKIMMERS

The Basic Mechanics of Sailing Surface Skimmers and Their Future Prospects, Dr Jerzy Wolf (Aviation Institute, Warsaw). *Hovering Craft & Hydrofoil,* March 1972.

Hydrofoil Ocean Voyageur "Williwaw", David A Keiper, PhD, Hydrofoil Sailing Craft. Third AIAA Symposium on the Aero/Hydronautics of Sailing, November 1971.

Hydrofoil Sailing, James Grogono. Hovering Craft, Hydrofoil and Advanced Transit Systems Conference, Brighton, May 1974.

Mayfly—A Sailing Hydrofoil Development, J Grogono and J B Wynne. *The Naval Architect,* pp 131-132, July 1977.

A Record of Progress Made on a Purpose-built Hydrofoil Supported Sailing Trimaran, N Bose and R C McGregor (Glasgow University). High-Speed Surface Craft Conference, Brighton, June 1980.

A Sculling Hydrofoil Development, J Grogono. High-Speed Surface Craft Conference, Brighton, June 1980.

A Self-Tending Rig with Feedback and Compass Course, C Hook. *Hovering Craft & Hydrofoil,* Vol 14 No 10, pp 26-31, July 1975.

Surface Piercing vs Fully Submerged Foils for Sailing Hydrofoils: The Design and Development of Two Small Sailing Hydrofoils, D R Pattison and J B Wynne. High-Speed Surface Craft Conference, Brighton, June 1980.

Why Sailing Hydrofoils? Christopher Hook. Ancient Interface IV Symposium, American Institute of Aeronautics and Astronautics, January 1973.

ADDENDA

AIR CUSHION VEHICLES

CHINA

65-TONNE AMPHIBIOUS HOVERFERRY

Details of a passenger/car ferry version of the Chinese Navy's new 70-ton landing craft were revealed towards the end of 1980 when the Chinese Marine Design and Research Institution exhibited a model of the craft. An accompanying plaque gave the following information.

POWERPLANTS: Two 1,430hp and two 1,530hp engines which drive four air propellers and six Type 4-73 centrifugal fans.

DIMENSIONS
Length: 27·2m (89ft 3in)
Beam: 13·8m (45ft 3in)
Height: 9·6m (31ft 6in)
Cushion depth: 1·5m-1·8m (4ft 11in-5ft 11in)

WEIGHTS
All-up weight: 65 tonnes
Useful load: 15 tonnes

PERFORMANCE
Speed, calm water: 55 knots

Bow-on view of a model of China's new 65-tonne mixed traffic ferry

Power for this 55-knot amphibious ferry is supplied by four engines, two of 1,430hp and two of 1,530hp

FRANCE

BASSIN d'ESSAIS DES CARÈNES
Paris, France
Officials:
R V Balquet, *Chef de la Division Navies, Speciaux*

Studies for surface effect ships for the French Navy have been underway at Bassin des Carènes, Paris, since the early 1970s and have included vessels of up to 500 tonnes. The latest design proposal to emanate from the group is for a 200-tonne SES with a light helicopter capability to help patrol 200-mile exclusive economic zones. Other possible applications would include policing traffic in congested shipping lanes like the English Channel.

The configuration selected is the aéroglisseur à quilles latérales (AQL), the French term for the sidewall SES. Preliminary details of the basic design are given below.

NESSIE
(Navire à Effet de Surface de Surveillance des Intérêts Economiques)
LIFT AND PROPULSION: Motive power for the lift system is furnished by two 800hp MTU 8V 331 TC 81 or similar marine diesels, each of

which drives a centrifugal fan. The cushion-borne propulsion system comprises two 4,000shp SACM AGO 195 V16 CZ SHR or similar marine diesels, each driving a Rocketdyne PJ24 waterjet. Propulsion and lift systems, control systems, auxiliary equipment, diesel and helicopter fuel and the main storage areas would all be located in the sidewalls.

HULL: Construction mainly in corrosion resistant light alloy. Each sidewall would be divided into seven watertight compartments. Working and sleeping quarters and other installations located in a three-deck superstructure based on a main, upper and bridge deck. Gazelle helicopter would be accommodated in a telescopic hangar retracting into the rear of the superstructure.

ACCOMMODATION: Operating, living and sleeping quarters provided for a complement of 22 officers and men and two passengers or observers. Quarters would include a sick bay, control centre and technical centre.

EQUIPMENT: One Gazelle helicopter and two "Commando" type 150hp inflatable speedboats.

ARMAMENT: Two manually-operated 20mm

cannon, one port, one starboard, at sides of bridge.

DIMENSIONS
Length overall: 46m (151ft)
Beam overall: 13m (42ft 8in)
Draft on cushion: 1·1m (3ft 7in)
 off cushion: 3m (9ft 10in)

WEIGHTS
Hull and superstructure
 (including hangar): 56 tonnes
Fit out: 22 tonnes
Propulsion systems: 36 tonnes
Lift system: 14 tonnes
Electrical equipment: 7 tonnes
Other equipment: 4 tonnes
Armament: 8 tonnes
Non-consumable items: 1 tonne
Total structure
 (including 10-tonne margin): 148 tonnes
Crew: 2·5 tonnes
Diesel fuel: 35 tonnes
Helicopter fuel: 10 tonnes
Other consumable items: 4·3 tonnes
Ammunition: 1·2 tonnes
Total payload: 53 tonnes
Total weight: 201 tonnes

PERFORMANCE
ON CUSHION
Speed, sea/wind force 0: 40 knots plus
  force 2: 40 knots
  force 4: 30 knots
Range, sea/wind force 2: 960n miles
HULLBORNE
Speed: 15 knots
Range: 7 days at 12 knots

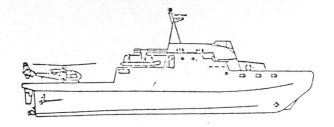

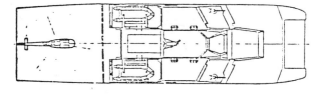

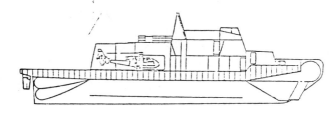

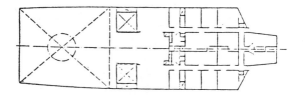

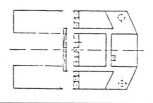

Elevations and general arrangement of NESSIE

GERMANY, FEDERAL REPUBLIC

GÜNTHER W JÖRG
Odenwaldring 24, 6101 Gross-Bieberau, Federal Republic of Germany
Telephone: 061 62 3624

A qualified and experienced pilot and aeronautical engineer, Günther W Jörg was for a number of years a constructor, works manager and development engineer for various West German vertical take-off and landing (VTOL) projects. He sees his Tandem Aerofoil Boat (TAB) concept as a means of providing fast, economical and comfortable travel over water, especially over great distances. His experiments began in the 1960s with a series of radio-controlled models. Wind tunnel tests were also undertaken and the results were checked by computer. The first Günther Jörg ramwing, a two-seater powered by a modified Volkswagen engine, was designed in 1973, and first flew in 1974. After an extensive test programme, a second craft was designed and performed its first flight in 1976. The craft, Jörg II, incorporated more than 25 design improvements and has travelled more than 10,000km (6,200 miles) to date and made several thousand take-offs and landings. During 1978-79, Jörg designed a glass fibre hulled four-six seater, Jörg III, which would have been put into series production in Poland had it not been for the current political tension. The first prototype was completed in 1980 and has been demonstrated on the Rhine. At the time of going to press designs were being prepared for bigger and faster craft capable of carrying heavier loads over greater distances.

First manned Tandem Aerofoil Boat during test flights on the Rhine in 1974. Named Jörg I the craft is powered by a 70hp Volkswagen engine and cruises at 100km/h

Jörg II, two-seat sports craft, flying up the Rhine near Mainz in 1980. Built in wood, the craft is powered by a 55hp engine and cruises at 115km/h

Stabilisation of the pitch and roll axes and maintaining the flying height of the TAB can be regulated independently by the ground/water surface reaction and therefore requires only a simple steering control for movement around the vertical axis. This basic requirement led to the development of a tandem wing configuration, the handling characteristics of which were tested at first on models and then in numerous tests on two-seat research craft. Tests showed that the tandem wings had good aerodynamic qualities, even above turbulent water, with or without water contact.

TABs have ample buoyancy and are seaworthy, even while operating at low speed (cruising in displacement condition). After increasing speed the craft lifts to the surface of the water and the resulting air cushion reduces the effects of the waves. After losing water contact the boat starts its ram wing flight at a height of 4-8% of the profile depth. A two-seater with a wingspan of 3·2m (10ft 6in) and a profile length of 3·05m (10ft), it will have a flying height above the water surface of 102-203mm (4-8in) at a speed of 96·6km/h (60mph). The low power requirement of this type of craft is achieved through the improved lift/drag ratio of a wing in ground effect as compared to free flight.

The main components of a Tandem Aerofoil Boat are: forward main wing; aft wing; vertical stabiliser and rudder; longitudinal tip fence/float; fuselage for passengers and/or cargo and the power plant. The latter comprises an engine with propeller or ducted propeller, which can be either mounted as a pod on the rear wing or as a unit integrated with the rear fuselage.

Additional equipment might include a retractable undercarriage, which would enable the craft, under its own power, to run on to dry land or move from land to water for take-off. Towing connections can be provided for water-skiing and an electrically operated anchor winch can be fitted.

The following operational possibilities are foreseen:

INLAND WATERWAYS AND OFFSHORE AREAS: Suitable for rescue boats, customs, police, coast guard units, patrol boats, high speed ferries, leisure craft.

COASTAL TRAFFIC: Large craft would be operated as fast passenger and passenger/car ferries and mixed-traffic freighters.

OVERLAND: Suitable for crossing swamps, flat sandy areas, snow and ice regions. Another possible application is as a high speed tracked skimmer operating in conjunction with a guide carriage above a monorail.

TAB SIZES

Smaller craft, displacing 1 ton or more, can travel over a surface at a height of 304mm (12in) or more at a speed of 96·6-144·8km/h (60-90mph).

Larger craft, weighing 10-50 tons will be able to fly at a height of 914mm to 1·98m (3ft to 6ft 6in) at a speed of 129-177km/h (80-110mph).

Coastal craft displacing more than 100 tons will fly at a height of 3·04m (10ft) or even higher.

The basic advantage of the TAB is its ability to transport passengers and freight far quicker than by conventional ship, rail or road transport. The ratio between empty weight and service load is about 2:1 but can with certainty be improved. Fuel consumption is 80 to 85% lower than that of a boat of similar construction.

Jörg I
Total wingspan: 4·1m (13ft 6in)
Length overall: 6·2m (20ft 4in)
Wing profile length: 2·5m (8ft 2in)
Max take-off weight: 700kg (1,543lb)
Passengers: 2
Cruising speed: 100km/h (62·1mph)
Installed power: 70hp
Average cruising height: 0·1m (4in)
Max flying height: 0·5m (20in)
Year of construction: 1973-74
Construction: grp/wood
Range: 300km (186 miles)

Jörg II flying above calm water at 100km/h. Take-off is quicker on rough water than calm water. Jörg II is able to fly above waves of 1m

Jörg III at the start of its trials on the Rhine in January 1980

One of 28 radio-controlled models used to gather data on the TAB concept

Radio-controlled model in flight at 65km/h (35mph)

Jörg II
Total wingspan: 3·28m (10ft 9in)
Length overall: 8·3m (27ft 3in)
Wing profile length: 3m (9ft 10in)
Max take-off weight: 670kg (1,477lb)
Passengers: 2
Cruising speed: 125km/h (77·7mph)
Installed power: 65hp
Average cruising height: 0·12m (4¾in)
Max flying height: 1m (3ft 3in)
Year of construction: 1975-76
Construction: wood
Range: 400km (248·5 miles)

Jörg III
Total wingspan: 5·3m (17ft 5in)
Length overall: 11·35m (37ft 3in)
Wing profile length: 4m (13ft 1in)
Max take-off weight: 1,800-2,000kg (3,968-4,409lb)
Passengers: 4-6
Cruising speed: 135km/h (84mph)
Installed power: 225-325hp
Average cruising height: 0·2m (8in)
Max flying height: 1·3m (4ft 3in)
Year of construction: 1978-79
Construction: grp
Range: 500-600km (310-373 miles)

TAB VII
Total wingspan: 7·9m (25ft 11in)
Length overall: 19·78m (65ft)
Max take-off weight: 10 tonnes
Passengers: 30 + 2 crew
Cruising speed: 135-196km/h (84-122mph)
Installed power: 2,500hp
Average cruising height: 0·72m (28½in)
Max flying height: 1·5m (4ft 11in)
Year of construction: 1980-81
Construction: aluminium
Range: 800-3,000km (497-1,864 miles) (according to installed power, speed and operating height)

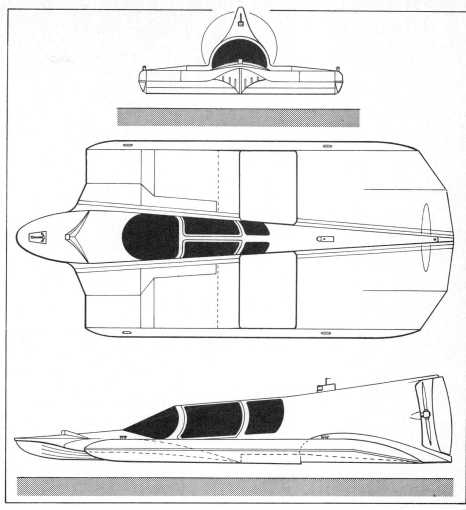

General arrangement of Jörg III, grp-hulled four-six seater

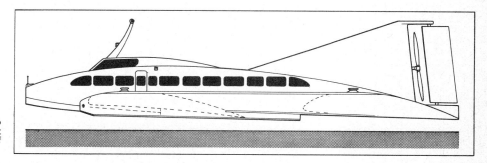

Profile of Jörg TAB VII, which will seat a crew of two and up to 30 passengers. At a height of 1·44m it would have a speed of 196km/h and a range of 800km

---

UNION OF SOVIET SOCIALIST REPUBLICS

MAGNUS 02-1

This new Soviet ram-wing single seater has been designed and built by students of the 'Bauman' Higher Technical School at Moscow especially to patrol inland waterways and for fishery protection duties. It is said to be particularly stable in flight and has a payload capacity of 130kg (287lb). Cruising speed is 55km/h (34mph) and flying height is 1·5m (4ft 11in).

MULTI-PURPOSE ACV

One of the latest Soviet amphibious hovercraft is designed for the support of geological surveys in the Soviet North and North east regions. References have been made in Soviet magazines to "trains" made up of hovercraft and other multi-terrain vehicles taking geologists deep into the Soviet hinterlands where small townships have been set up in support of the expeditions.

A model of one of these general purpose ACVs was exhibited in Moscow recently and is seen in the accompanying photograph. It was described as being "a new mobile gas-turbine electricity generating station".

Magnus 02-1 ram-wing

Magnus 02-1 single-seat ram-wing with a flying height of 1·5m

Multi-purpose hovercraft employed as a gas-turbine electricity generating station

UNITED KINGDOM

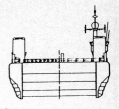

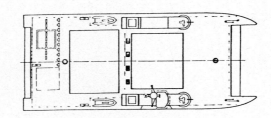

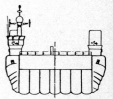

VOSPER HOVERMARINE LIMITED
HM 700 SERIES

Vosper Hovermarine has announced that an open water craft with considerable sea capacity and performance is being developed which will have an all-up weight of approximately 500 tons. The vessel, the Vosper Hovermarine 700, will have a cushion depth in excess of 6m (20ft) and will be fully stabilised to cope with sea conditions up to that severity. It is envisaged that as a quick response emergency vessel it would be powered with gas turbines to provide on-cushion speeds in excess of 50 knots and maintaining 40 knots in conditions of up to 4m (13ft) seas. A slower patrol speed in displacement mode would be provided by diesel engines for speeds of 17-20 knots. This craft would be capable of patrolling for long periods at sea and would have a range capability in the patrol mode in excess of 5,000 miles (about 2,000 miles on cushion at speeds in excess of 40 knots). With this capability it should be possible to relocate vessels quickly in a large area of operation.

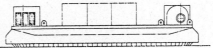

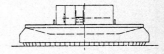

Vosper Hovermarine 700 offshore protection craft

ACV TRAILERS AND HEAVY LIFT SYSTEMS

FINLAND

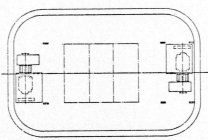

OY WÄRTSILÄ AB

Wärtsilä Helsinki Shipyard, SF-00150 Helsinki 15, Finland
Telephone: 90-1941
Telex: 12-1246 wht sf

The Wärtsilä Shipbuilding Division is part of the Wärtsilä Company, a diversified enterprise within the heavy engineering sector with a total of about 14,000 employees.

The Shipbuilding Division comprises the Turku Shipyards (Turku Shipyard and Perno Shipyard in Turku, Ylivieska Factory in Ylivieska and Kotka Shipyard in Kotka), and the Helsinki Shipyard in Helsinki.

Within the Shipbuilding Division the Turku Shipyards and the Helsinki Shipyard work in close co-operation, but being independent profit centres the yards have their own marketing and research and development responsibilities.

Financial and legal functions are managed by Wärtsilä's Central Administration in Helsinki, which carries out these duties for the corporate company. The managerial activities of the yards are co-ordinated by the top management of the division in Helsinki.

An additional asset for the Wärtsilä yards is the availability of extensive sub-contracting and specific know-how from Wärtsilä's other plants, whose production includes cranes, steering gears, castings and pipe assemblies. Diesels of Wärtsilä's own design are manufactured by the Vasa Factory.

Traditional products of the Helsinki Shipyards have been icebreakers, car and passenger ferries, and cruise liners, all types that demand considerable research and design support. The yard, which employs about 2,300 people, has been able to capture the greater part of the world's orders for icebreakers and by July 1979 had delivered 43 diesel-electric icebreakers, which covered the whole range from smaller harbour and lake icebreakers up to Arctic icebreakers of 26·5MW (36,000shp). Most of the icebreakers have been sold to the Finnish government and the USSR.

The yard's Arctic Design and Marketing Department (WADAM) is continuously engaged in feasibility studies and research on the development of ice-going tonnage and future transport needs in the Arctic and Antarctic areas. There is also an icebreaking model basin (WIMB) which performs research for Wärtsilä's own account and also accepts orders from outside interests.

The Helsinki shipyard built the world's largest and fastest passenger and car ferry, the GTS *Finnjet* of 24,600grt, 30·5 knots and 1,532 passengers.

General arrangement of PUC 40-900TP

Since the recent completion of a new investment programme at the yard, shipbuilding takes place in a 400,000m³ enclosed building hall, which can accommodate cruise liners up to 30,000grt and icebreakers up to 120MW (160,000shp). The necessary facilities are also available for the production of floating units such as hotels, hospitals, etc and naval craft in the 300 to 1,500-ton range.

POLAR UTILITY CRAFT

Wärtsilä's Helsinki Shipyard has developed a range of three fully-amphibious air cushion platforms to carry passengers, vehicles and cargo in an arctic environment.

The vehicles, known as the Polar Utility Craft (PUC) series, are:
PUC 40-900TP, a towed, 40-tonne capacity amphibious hoverbarge;
PUC 30-3000SP, a 30-tonne capacity ACV lighter with airscrew propulsion, and
PUC 22-2500SP, a 30-tonne capacity vehicle/passenger ferry which is designed chiefly for services in the Finnish archipelago during the partial icing conditions of the late autumn and spring.

Wärtsilä states that the three craft have been designed with an emphasis on reliability rather than high performance. They will operate in low temperatures across stretches of sea, water, ice and broken ice.

In addition to the design work undertaken by the yard, wide-ranging tests have been undertaken with models of different sizes and prototypes. The largest prototype or test platform built has an all-up weight of 41 tonnes and has been tested in a variety of different ice situations and in open water. Wärtsilä has also undertaken an extensive study of the behaviour and wear of different skirt hem materials when operating in low temperatures.

Oy Wärtsilä Ab, is best known for its icebreakers, most of which have been sold to the Finnish government and the USSR. The new ACV programme is aimed at the same two markets, although it should offer business potential in other regions, from Alaska and Canada to Arctic/Antarctic expeditions.

PUC 40-900TP

TYPE: Towed amphibious barge.

LIFT: Two 880kW marinised diesels, mounted one forward and one aft, each drive a single centrifugal fan to feed air to the segmented bag-type skirt system. Location of the two diesel/fan units can be changed to suit the demands for cargo space.

PROPULSION/CONTROLS: Towing cable.

HULL: Box-type hull in steel. Prototype has aluminium hull. Overall dimensions determined by the requirement that the craft or several of them should be carried in the hold or on the deck of a cargo ship. Craft is specially designed to operate in varying and difficult conditions in arctic coastal areas and coastal waters. Principal dimensions of the prototype differ slightly from the dimensions of PUC 40-900TP but both represent towable hover platforms of the same class.

PROTOTYPE

DIMENSIONS

Length overall: 18·5m (60ft 8in)
Beam overall: 12m (39ft 4in)
Height of hull side: 1m (3ft 3in)
Free deck space: 12 × 11·5m (39ft 4in × 37ft 9in)

WEIGHTS

Useful load: 40 tonnes
All-up weight: 40 tonnes

PERFORMANCE

Clearance height: 1·2m (3ft 11in)

PRODUCTION MODEL

DIMENSIONS

Length overall: 19·5m (64ft)
  hull: 18·5m (60ft 8in)
Beam overall: 13m (42ft 8in)
  hull: 12m (39ft 4in)
Height of hull side: 1m (3ft 3in)

WEIGHTS AND PERFORMANCE: As for prototype.

PUC 30-3000SP

TYPE: Self-propelled amphibious lighter designed to operate in arctic coastal areas and coastal waters. Can be carried on the deck or in the hold of a cargo ship. If required for use as a non-self-propelled hover barge for extended periods, the propellers can be disconnected and removed by undoing the bolt connections of the coupling.

LIFT AND PROPULSION: Integrated system powered by two 3,000kW marinised diesels. The output of the forward diesel is absorbed by two centrifugal lift fans and a single three-bladed ducted propeller mounted on the port forward quarter. Output of the aft diesel is absorbed by a single centrifugal lift fan and a single three-bladed ducted propeller mounted on the starboard aft quarter. It is stated that the diagonal location of the propellers provides good steering characteristics.

HULL: Steel construction. Can also be supplied in aluminium, in which case the payload capacity is higher or the required output for lift is lowered.

DIMENSIONS

Hull length: 18·5m (60ft 8in)
Beam: 12m (39ft 4in)
Height of hull side: 1m (3ft 3in)
Free deck space: 8 × 6·2m (26ft 3in × 20ft 4in)

WEIGHTS

Useful load: 30 tonnes
Total weight: 90 tonnes

PERFORMANCE

Speed in open waters: 8 knots
Clearance height: 1·2m (3ft 11in)

PUC 22-2500SP

The prototype of this 22-tonne capacity amphibious mixed-traffic ferry was ordered by the Finnish Directorate of Road and Naval Construction from the Wärtsilä Helsinki Shipyard on 17 January 1980 for delivery in 1981.

Bearing a superficial resemblance to the US Navy's Jeff (A) amphibious assault landing craft, the craft is designed for service in the Finnish archipelago and other similar areas during winter. It will carry up to 16 light motor vehicles or two buses or one heavy lorry and 50 passengers.

LIFT AND PROPULSION: Integrated system powered by four marinised diesels, each rated at 2,500kW. The engines are mounted one forward and one aft in each of the two sidestructures. Each diesel drives, via a main gearbox, a single centrifugal fan and via a bevel gear and vertical shaft a four-bladed pylon-mounted ducted propeller.

HULL: Built in marine grade aluminium.

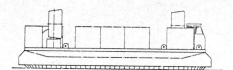
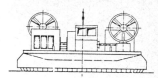

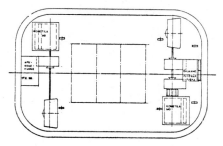

General arrangement of PUC 30-3000SP

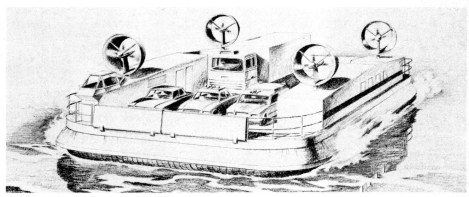

Impression of PUC 22-2500SP passenger/vehicle ferry

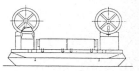

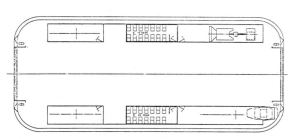

General arrangement of PUC 22-2500SP

Buoyancy raft type structure with port or starboard sidestructures. Each sidestructure contains two diesels, one forward, one aft, together with their associated fans, ducted propellers, transmission and auxiliary power systems. Hydraulically operated bow and stern loading ramps provide roll-on, roll-off through loading facilities.

SKIRT: 1m (3ft 3in) deep bag and segment type.

ACCOMMODATION: All controls are located in a raised bridge located well forward on the starboard superstructure. Passengers are seated amidships in two 25-seat cabins, one in each sidestructure.

DIMENSIONS

Length overall: 32m (105ft)
  hull: 31·2m (102ft 4in)
Beam overall: 14m (46ft)
  hull: 13m (42ft 8in)
Height overall: 7·2m (23ft 8in)
  hull side: 1m (3ft 3in)

WEIGHTS

Useful load: 22 tonnes

PERFORMANCE

Clearance height: 1m (3ft 3in)

POWER PLANTS AND PROPULSION SYSTEMS

ITALY

FIAT AVIAZIONE SpA

Marine & Industrial Products Department, Via Nizza 326, Turin, Italy
Telephone: 637287
Telex: 221320 FIATAV

The LM500 gas turbine is a compact high performance marine and industrial power unit in the 3,000 to 6,000 shaft horsepower class. General Electric's Marine and Industrial Engine Division and Fiat Aviazione SpA, in a co-operative undertaking initiated the design programme in July 1978. In January 1980 the first engine began full load testing, and the LM500 is now in production.

The LM500 is a simple-cycle, two-shaft gas turbine engine with a free power turbine. It incorporates a variable stator compressor, with excellent stall margin capability, driven by an air-cooled, two-stage turbine. It is derived from the TF34 high bypass turbofan aircraft engine which was designed for marine operation in the US Navy's S-3A aircraft and later incorporated in the US Air Force's A-10 aircraft, with the same materials and marine corrosion protection as employed in the very successful LM2500 marine gas turbine. The LM500 incorporates the latest in proven design technology and corrosion-resistant materials to provide a mature design with maximum reliability, component life and time between inspections and overhaul. The LM500 demonstrates higher efficiency than currently available gas turbines in its class and is suited for marine applications requiring light weight and fuel economy.

General Electric Company and Fiat Aviazione SpA, have designed the LM500 gas turbine to produce power for marine applications requiring significant fuel economy, compactness, light weight, minimum maintenance, high tolerance to fouling/deposits, and reliable operation. Such applications include military land craft, hydrofoils, air cushion vehicles, fast patrol boats, cruise power propulsion and on-board electric power generators.

LM500

The LM500 is a simple-cycle, two-shaft gas turbine engine. The single shaft gas generator consists of a 14-stage high pressure compressor with variable inlet guide vanes and variable stator vanes in the first five stages, an annular machined ring combustor with 18 externally mounted fuel injectors and an air-cooled, two-stage HP gas generator turbine. The free power turbine has four stages and the output shaft connecting flange is located at the air inlet end of the engine.

AIR INTAKE: The LM500 offers, as optional equipment, an air inlet collector to guide the inlet air from the customer's intake ducting into the engine. The inlet duct is made from aluminium and also provides the structural connection for the forward engine mounts or for the reduction gearbox containing the forward mounts.

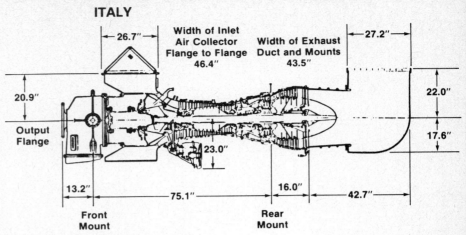
LM500 gas turbine with reduction gearbox

An off-engine inlet screen is also offered to prevent objects from entering the compressor.
COMPRESSOR: The compressor is identical to the TF34 and consists of the front frame, accessory drive assembly, compressor rotor and case/vane assembly. The front frame is an uncomplicated four strut aluminium casting and is designed to provide the compressor inlet flowpath, the forward structural support for the engine, support the forward bearings and seals for the gas generator and power turbine rotors, and support the accessory gearbox.
COMBUSTOR: The LM500 combustor is of the TF34 flight engine design. It is an annular through-flow combustor utilising a machined ring liner construction for long life. Metered fuel is distributed and introduced through 18 central, individually replaceable injectors.
HIGH PRESSURE TURBINE: The LM500 high pressure turbine is a two-stage, fully air-cooled design, identical to the TF34 turbine except for minor changes to improve performance and meet the requirements for marine and industrial applications.
POWER TURBINE: The LM500 power turbine is a four-stage, uncooled, high performance design incorporating aerodynamic and mechanical features and materials identical to the TF34 low pressure turbine. The power turbine rotor structural components are all made of inconel 718 material. The four turbine discs carry tip shrouded turbine blades that are attached to the discs with single tang dovetails. The blades are made of René 77 material with the first stage Codep coated. The durability of René 77 alleviates the need for coatings on the other stages. At operating gas temperatures 111°C (200°F) less than the TF34, the LM500 blades have virtually infinite stress rupture life. The structural integrity of the power turbine rotor has been demonstrated to a speed of 9,030rpm, 29% over the normal rated speed of the LM500 engine.

LUBRICATION: The LM500 lubricating oil system provides the following functions: lubricates and cools the gas turbine main bearings; supplies hydraulic fluid for the variable geometry actuation system and fuel metering valve actuator.

The main engine bearings are lubricated from an accessory gearbox-driven lube pump. The scavenge circuit is based on a dry sump system and each bearing sump is scavenged by a separate pump or pump elements driven off the accessory gearbox. All scavenge oil is filtered (coarse screens) prior to entry into the pump elements.

FUEL: The LM500 is designed to operate with marine diesel, diesel, and JP fuels. The fuel system consists of on-engine and off-engine components. Filtered fuel is supplied by the customer to the fuel pump, which is mounted on the accessory gearbox, where the fuel pressure is increased by a centrifugal boost element and then ported externally to an on-engine last chance fuel filter. From the filter the fuel is routed to an off-engine fuel regulating assembly (FRA) which meters the engine fuel flow according to signals received from the off-engine main electronic control assembly (MECA). Also included in the FRA are two fuel shut-off valves mounted in series for redundancy which are used to shut off the fuel to the engine during normal shutdowns and automatic shutdowns. Fuel is then routed to the on-engine fuel distributor which divides the fuel through separate hose assemblies to eighteen fuel injectors.

SPECIFICATION (basic engine)
Length overall: 2,184mm (86in)
Width: 864mm (34in)
Weight: 580kg (1,276lb)
(with optional inlet and axial exhaust duct, starter kit and output gearbox)
Length overall: 3,307mm (130·2in)
Width: 1,179mm (46·4in)
Weight: 1,031kg (2,269lb)

UNITED STATES OF AMERICA

AEROJET LIQUID ROCKET COMPANY MARINE SYSTEMS

PO Box 13222, Sacramento, California 95813, USA
Telephone: (916) 355 3011
Telex: 377-409 (ALRCSAC)
Officials:
J R Rowe, *Vice President, Programmes*

Aerojet Marine Systems' long experience in rotating machinery with requirements for high reliability, long life, maintainability and reasonable cost has been applied to developing and producing propulsion systems for new marine craft.

The simple, rugged design of Aerojet propulsors provides a number of advantages. Vessels can reduce draft, opening a larger percentage of the world's shorelines, bays, channels and rivers to navigation. Reductions in periodic maintenance and debris damage result in lower operating costs for the Aerojet waterjet. Additionally, because the propulsion force is also the steering force, Aerojet waterjet systems have superior steering and reversing capabilities disposing of the need for a conventional rudder and complex variable-geometry propellers.

The ability of Aerojet waterjets has been shown by long operating times on a number of craft. The company offers a wide array of currently available waterjet systems ranging from 800 to 18,000 horsepower, including the AJW 800, the AJW 6500 and the AJW 18000.

Aerojet operates one of the largest waterjet test facilities in the world. Existing test facilities include five separate test stands, two multi-million gallon lakes, a control centre and a 1·2 million gallon tank with controllable flow rates up to 100,000 gallons per minute. A 4 million gallon lake provides variable test conditions for large waterjets up to 25,000 horsepower.

For lower horsepower waterjets with steering and reversing capabilities, such as the PHM hullborne waterjet, a 2·5 million gallon facility with a controllable water level provides various suction head test parameters for start and run conditions.

Long duration testing at flow rates of over 100,000 gallons/min and thrust levels over 100,000lb st are achieved with a unique closed-loop facility system.

AJW-800

The AJW-800 waterjet is a ruggedly-built marine waterjet capable of operating over a wide horsepower range with a variety of marine diesel engines. The pump features an advanced single stage, mixed flow impeller operating at conservative suction specific speeds.

WEIGHTS
Wet (inlet flange to pump nozzle):
  1,220kg (2,690lb)
Dry: 660kg (1,455lb)

PERFORMANCE
RATED
Input power: 800mhp
Input speed: 900rpm
Inlet total head: 12m (39ft 4in)
Flow rate: 1·95m³/s (69ft³/s)
Thrust efficiency: 90%

SUCTION PERFORMANCE AT RATED SPEED
Inlet total head: 7·7m (25ft 3in)
Flow rate: 1·9m³/s (67ft³/s)
Thrust efficiency: 88·2%

AHEAD RATED THRUST
Static thrust (0° steering): 46·5kN
Max static side thrust (30° steering): 19·7kN
Ahead static thrust (30° steering): 32·8kN
Max steering actuator force (30° steering):
  14·8kN
Steering actuator stroke: 355mm (14in)

ASTERN RATED THRUST
Static thrust (0° steering): 23·4kN
Max static side thrust (30° steering): 11·7kN
Astern static thrust (30° steering): 20kN
Jet vertical lift thrust component: 24kN

AJW-6500

The AJW-6500 waterjet propulsion unit has been designed to meet the needs of 35-45 knot planing craft. The unit provides the low pump head rise and high flow rates required by this typical application. The resulting high overall propulsive efficiency is a very desirable benefit especially for commercial craft.

The AJW-6500 comprises the low speed or inducer pump stage of the operational foilborne propulsion unit of the US Navy PHM, the AJW-18000. Other components are shared between the two units such that a certain degree of interchangeability is achieved.

The AJW-6500 propulsor assembly is offered with an inlet elbow for a flush water inlet installation together with an advanced, short-coupled steering/reversing sub-system. Alternatively, the thrust reverser may be integrated with the boat hull giving an additional degree of freedom in propulsion system layout.

WEIGHTS
Dry: 3,629kg (8,000lb)
Wet: 5,897kg (13,000lb)

PERFORMANCE
RATED
Input power: 6,590mhp
Input speed: 790rpm
Inlet total head: 28·8m (94ft 6in)
Flow rate: 7·29m³/s (257ft³/s)
Thrust efficiency: 85%
Thrust (static): 236kN
*Net thrust (40 knots): 119kN
*With inlet drag

SUCTION PERFORMANCE AT RATED SPEED
Inlet total head: 7·6m (24ft 11in)

AJW-18000

The AJW-18000 is the world's largest operating waterjet propulsion unit. It represents over 26 years of experience within Aerojet in building high performance waterjets. The AJW-18000 is developed from the AJW-8000 and, like the AJW-8000, includes its own integral gearbox.

The parallel shaft two-speed gear-reduction system drives the two-stage, two-speed pump yielding a very high pump efficiency over a wide range of operating conditions. The pump features a bifurcated inlet for hydrofoil applications but can be made available with a single inlet for SES or planing hull applications. This unit has been employed as the foilborne propulsion unit for the US Navy PHM and has demonstrated high in-service reliability.

Aerojet waterjet AJW-800

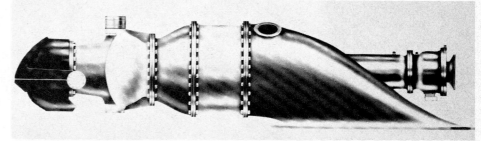

Aerojet waterjet AJW-18000

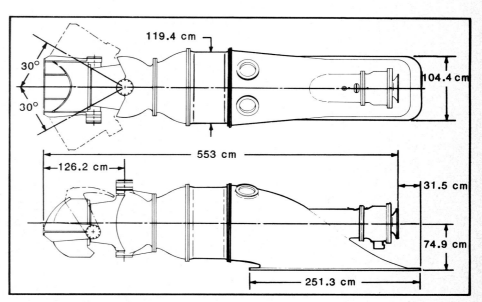

Aerojet waterjet AJW-18000

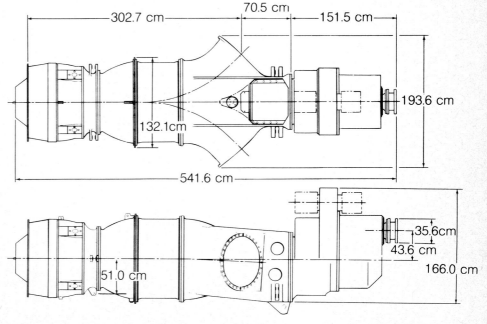

Aerojet waterjet AJW-6500

WEIGHTS
Dry: 5,700kg (12,566lb)
Wet: 8,000kg (17,637lb)

PERFORMANCE

RATED
Input power: 16,200mhp
Input speed with gearbox: 3,093rpm
  without gearbox, low speed: 714rpm
    high speed: 1,510rpm
Inlet total head: 11m (36ft 2in)
Flow rate: 5·93m³/s (209ft³/s)
Thrust efficiency: 87%
Thrust (static): 336kN
Thrust (45 knots): 240kN

SUCTION PERFORMANCE AT RATED SPEED
Inlet total head: 7·93m (26ft)
Flow rate: 5·75m³/s (203ft³/s)
Thrust efficiency: 84·3%

Aerojet waterjet AJW-6500, employed as main foilborne propulsor of the US Navy/Boeing PHM

INDEX

A

AALC Jeff (A) (Aerojet Liquid) 109
Jeff (B) (Bell) 115
AC-5 Beaver (Air Cushion Systems) 112
AC-44 (Air Cushion Systems) 112
AC 800 (Air Cushion Industries Ltd) 6
ACDS (Global Marine) 169
ACE (1976) LTD. 162, 197
ACT-100 (Global Marine) 168
ACT, 250-ton (Mackace) 164
ACV-4000 (Maridyne) 172
ACV SALES INC 5
ACV Tractors (VNII neftmash) 161
ACV Trailers (VNII neftmash) 161
AG (EH)-1 Plainview (Grumman) 290
AI-20 (Ivchenko) 322
-24 322
AJW-800 (Aerojet Liquid) 375
-6500 375
-18000 375
API-88 General Purpose Hovercraft (BHC) 69
ART-1 (Maritime Dynamics) 129
ART-10 130
AV Tiger (Air Vehicles) 63
AV Tiger S 63
ADRIATICA DI NAVIGAZIONE, SpA 303
AEROBARCOS DO BRASIL 147, 301
Aero-Caster Load Modules (Aero-Go) 201
Aeroduct System (Bertelsen) 191
Aero Glider (Kharkov) 58
AERO-GO INC 201
AEROJET LIQUID ROCKET COMPANY 109, 374
Aeromobile 16 (Bertelsen) 124
Aero-Pallets (Aero-Go) 202
Aero-Planks 202
Aero Sabre AS-2 (Airhover) 62
Mk I 61
Mk III 62
Mk IV 62
AÉROTRAIN, SOCIETE DE L' 176
Aérotrain 01 (Experimental) (Société de l'Aérotrain) 176
02 (Experimental) 177
I-80 (Full-scale) 177
I-80 HV ('Orléans') 178
S-44 178
Suburban 179
Urban 180
AERO VODOCHODY 12
AGIP SpA 303
Air Beams (Rolair) 209
Air Bearings 204
Air Bearings, Lightweight 209
Airboat IV (Survey Craft) (Aircushion Boat Co) 110
42 ft (Passenger ferry/freighter) 110
Air Car Model K (Dobson) 125
Aircraft Ground Testing Installation (Rolair Systems Inc) 206
AIRCUSHION BOAT COMPANY INC 110
AIR CUSHION EQUIPMENT (1976) LTD. 162, 197
Air Cushion Ferry, 160-ton (Mackace) 165
Air Cushion Heavy Load Transporter (BHC) 163
AIR CUSHION INDUSTRIES LTD 6
AIR CUSHION SYSTEMS (California) 112
AIR CUSHION SYSTEMS (Florida) 111
AIRESEARCH MANUFACTURING COMPANY (Garrett Corp) 335
AIRHOVER LTD 61
AIRMATIC ENGINEERING (UK) LTD. 196
AIR VEHICLES LTD 63
'Aist' (Krasnoye Sormovo) 43
ALASKA HOVERCRAFT INC 113
ALBANIAN NAVY 301
ALBERTO GIMENEZ DE LOS GALANES 36
ALIMAR SanciyF 301
ALISCAFI SNAV, SpA 302
Allison 501-K Series (Detroit Allison) 333
570-K 334
ALL-UNION OIL MACHINERY RESEARCH INSTITUTE, WEST SIBERIA (VNII neftmash) 160
Amficat 4 (Prototype) (Pintaliitäjäpalvelu) 13
4b 14
10 14
Amphibarge (SEDAM) 158
Amphibious Hoverferry, 65-tonne (Shanghai 708 Research) 368
Amphibious Passenger Ferry, 3-engined (Shanghai 708 Research) 10
ANGEVINIERE SA 14
Antonov An-2E (CLST) 40
Arctic Drill Barge System (Mackace) 167
Arcturus (Coelacanth) 38
Artouste (Turboméca) 314
Assault Landing Craft, 70-ton (Shanghai 708 Research) 9
Assembly line for Crawler Tractors (Rolair Systems Inc) 205
Astazou (Turboméca) 315
AUSTRALIAN LIGHT HOVERCRAFT SERVICES 1, 142
Automatic Modular Home Production Line (Rolair Systems Inc) 205
AVCO LYCOMING DIVISION OF AVCO CORPORATION 328
AVON INDUSTRIAL POLYMERS (MELKSHAM) LTD 163

B

B + I LINES 302
BARS-1 (Snow Leopard) (Neptun) 59
BH.7 Wellington Class (BHC) 72
Mk 4 (Logistic support) 73
Mk 5 (Combat) 73
Mk 5A (Combat/Logistics) 73
Mk 5A (Minehunter) 74
Mk 5A (Minesweeper) 74
BHC Mine clearance hovercraft 74
BU-75-VP (VNII neftmash) 161
Babochka (Krasnoye Sormovo) 257
BAHRAIN, MINISTRY OF THE INTERIOR 147
BAKER, BILL, VEHICLES LTD 64
Bartini T-Wings (Sormovo) 52
BASSIN d'ESSAIS DES CARÈNES 368
Bastan (Turboméca) 316
BATAAN-MANILA FERRY SERVICES CO 149
'BAUMAN' HIGHER TECHNICAL SCHOOL 371
BELGIUM, MINISTRY OF WORKS 147
Bell AL-30 8
BELL AEROSPACE TEXTRON CANADA 6
BELL AEROSPACE TEXTRON (USA) 114
BELL-HALTER INC 119
Bell-Halter 48 (Rodolf) 119
85 120
110 121
110 Dashboat 122
133 122
157 122
BELT SA 305
BERTELSEN INC 124, 190
BERTIN & CIE 16, 193
BIWAKO KISEN CO LTD 149
BLECHVERARBEITUNG, HELMUT FRANK 194
BOEING MARINE SYSTEMS 274
Boeing NATO/PHM 277
Bolivia Arrow (Kock) 211
BOYO KISEN CO LTD 303
BRAATHENS SAFE 303
Breeze (Sormovo) 44
BRIGGS AND STRATTON CORPORATION 329
BRITISH COLUMBIA GOVERNMENT 147
BRITISH HOVERCRAFT CORPORATION 65, 163, 199
BRITISH RAIL HOVERCRAFT LTD (SEASPEED) 150
Burevestnik (Sormovo) 262
Byelorus (Sormovo) 263

C

CLST (Central Laboratory of Lifesaving Technology) 38
CRM FABBRICA MOTORI MARINI 319
CRM 12 D/S-2 320
12 D/SS 320
18 319
CT 70 (Supramar) 254
CANADIAN ARMED FORCES 147
CANADIAN COAST GUARD HOVERCRAFT UNITS 147
CANADIAN HOVERWAYS 148
CANTIERI NAVALI RIUNITI (CNR) 217
Carraro V12SS (Fiat/AIFO) 320
Caspian (Mariisky Polytechnic) 58
CATERPILLAR TRACTOR 330
Caterpillar Tractor Engines 330
3208 331
3304 T 330
3306 T 330
3306 TA 330
3406 T 330
3406 TA 330
3408 T 330
3408 TA 330
3412 T 330
3412 TA 330
D 348 331
D 349 331
CENTRAL LABORATORY OF LIFE-SAVING TECHNOLOGY (CLST) 38
CENTROTOURIST 305
CERES HELLENIC SHIPPING ENTERPRISES 302
Cergy-Pontoise-La Défense Suburban Aérotrain (Aérotrain) 179
Chaika (Sormovo) 263
Chayka-1 (Sormovo) 45
CHINA (PEOPLE'S REPUBLIC) (NAVY) 148, 301
Chinook (Hover-Flight) 8
CLUB FRANCAIS DES AEROGLISSEURS 314
COELACANTH GEMCO LTD 37, 194
COMMAND MARINE, INC 153
COMPAGNIA DI NAVIGAZIONE, MILAN 303
COMPAGNIA REGIONALE MARITIMA, SpA 303
COMPANIA SHELL 305
CONDOR LTD 304
Contender (Alaska Hovercraft) 113
Cormorant (Osprey) 83
Crane (US Hovercraft) 140
Crew Change Vessel (CCV) (SSSCO) 311
CRILLON TOURS LTD 301
CUMMINS ENGINE COMPANY INC 332
Cuyuna Axial-fan Twin-cylinder Engines (Scorpion Inc) 339
CYCLONE HOVERCRAFT 78
Cyclone (Sormovo) 264

D

DHC-MP-100 (De Havilland) 212
ASW Patrol Craft 213
General Purpose 212
Gunboat 212
Missile craft 212
DTCN 214
DAK HYDROFOILS 284, 298
DAMPSKIBSSELSKAPET ORESUND 301
Dash 6 (Tropimere) 96
Dash 7 97
DE BLA OMNIBUSSER A/S, NORWAY 303
DE HAVILLAND AIRCRAFT COMPANY OF CANADA, LIMITED 211
Deltic Diesel (Paxman) 325
DEPARTMENT OF CIVIL AVIATION (NZ) 149
DEPARTMENT OF ENVIRONMENT AND NATIONAL RESEARCH COUNCIL (CANADA) 148
DEPARTMENT OF THE NAVY, NAVAL SEA SYSTEMS COMMAND (NAVSEA) 124, 305
DEPARTMENT OF INDUSTRY NATIONAL MARITIME INSTITUTE (UK) 151
DETROIT DIESEL ALLISON 333
DET STAVANGERSKE DAMPSKIBSSELSKAB 303
DIRECTION TECHNIQUE DES CONSTRUCTIONS NAVALES (DTCN) 214
Diving Support Vessel (SSSCO) 312
DOBSON PRODUCTS CO 125, 335
Dobson Air Car, Model H 125
DUBIGEON-NORMANDIE/SEDAM 17, 158
DYNAFOIL INC 284
Dynafoil Mk I 284
Mk II 285
Mk III 286

E

Eagle (US Hovercraft) 139
EDO CORPORATION GOVERNMENT PRODUCTS DIVISION 286
Edo Mk 105 Airborne Minesweeping Gear 286
Mk 106 287
EGYPTIAN NAVY 148
Ekranolet E-120 (CLST) 41
Ekranoplan Experimental (Krasnoye Sormovo) 50
Escapade (Orley) 16
Eska 1 (CLST) 39
Eska EA-06 (CLST) 40
Espadon (Hennebutte) 16
ETABLISSEMENTS NEU 194
Etel 422 (Hennebutte) 215

F

FB 24 Mosquito (Fanbird) 25
26 Mini 25
26 Super Mini 25
32 STD 25
32 Sports 25
36 SD 25
36 TD 25
FEI 5, 175
FM-AERODESLIZADORES 35
FM-AXZ-001 36
FV-10 Newpole (Fun Vehicle) 26
FABBRICA MOTORI MARINI (CRM) 319
FACULTY OF INDUSTRIAL ENGINEERING (FEI) 5, 175
Falcon (Osprey) 83
FALKE, HORST 23
Falke Racing Hovercraft 23
FANBIRD HOVERCRAFT 25
Fan-Jet Skimmer (Skimmers) 138
FAR EAST HYDROFOIL CO LTD 302
FEDERAL MINISTRY OF TRANSPORTATION (NIGERIA) 149
FIAT/AIFO 320
Fiat/Aifo 8280 SRM 321
FIAT AVIAZIONE SpA 374
FINLAND, BOARD OF ROADS AND WATERWAYS 148
Flagstaff Mk II (Grumman) 289
FLOMAT (AUST) PTY LTD 193
Floral 1 (Nihon University) 33
Flying Fish (Nigg) 300
FRENCH NAVY 148
RAILWAYS (SNCF) 148
FUN VEHICLE CO LTD 26
Furtivo 1 (Los Galanes) 36

G

G1 Cargo Hovercraft (FM-Aerodeslizadores) 35
G2 35

G + R SALVATORI 303
GP CONCESSIONAIRES LTD 78
Gardan G.10 (Angevinière) 15
GARRETT CORPORATION 335
Garrett 831-800 335
Gas Generator (United Technologies) 340
GDANSK SHIP RESEARCH INSTITUTE 239
GENERAL ELECTRIC COMPANY AIRCRAFT ENGINE GROUP 336
GENERAL NILE COMPANY FOR RIVER TRANSPORT 301
GERMAN FEDERAL REPUBLIC WATER POLICE 301
Glidercraft (Orley) 16
GLOBAL MARINE DEVELOPMENT INC 168
Gorkovchanin (Sormovo) 45
GRUMMAN AEROSPACE CORP. 287
'Gus' (Sormovo) 48

H

H.890 (SNIA) 215
H.891 (SNIA) 216
HDL Skirt Shift System (Hovercraft Development) 79
HFL-SEAGLIDE LTD 79
HL-101 Rubber Duck (Hoverlift) 155
-104 156
-105 156
-115 Salamander 156
-301 158
-533 Icebreaker 158
HM.2 Mk IV (Hovermarine Pacific) 27
HM.100F (Hovermarine Pacific) 27
HSST (JAL) 186
-01 187
-02 187
Commercial 188
H.V.4. (Hover Vehicles NZ) 34
HYD-2 (Grumman) 293
HANKYU LINES CO LTD 303
HAN RYEO DEVELOPMENTS CO LTD 303
HARDANGER SUNNHORDELANDSKE DAMPSKIBSSELSKAB 303
HELMUT FRANK BLECHVERARBEITUNG 194
HENNEBUTTE, GEORGES (Société d'Exploitation et de Développement des Brevets Georges Hennebutte) 16, 215
High Speed I-80 HV "Orléans" Aérotrain (Aérotrain) 178
High Speed Ferry (SSSCO) 312
HITACHI SHIPBUILDING & ENGINEERING CO 239
HITACHI ZOSEN 303
Hi-Trot II (Kanazawa) 295
Hi-Trot III (Kanazawa) 296
HONG KONG AND YAUMATI FERRY CO 148
HONG KONG MACAO HYDROFOIL CO 302
Horizonty Technicki (Warsaw Young Technicians) 35
Hoverbarges (Leningrad Central Design Bureau) 161
Hoverbird (US Hovercraft) 140
HOVERCRAFT DEVELOPMENT LIMITED 79
Hoverflex Amphibious Barges (Hoverlift) 158
HOVER-FLIGHT CANADA LTD 8
Hover Hawk (GP) 78
HOVERLIFT SYSTEMS LTD 155
HOVERLLOYD LTD 151
HOVERMAC HOVERCRAFT AUSTRALIA 1
Hovermac I 1
II 2
III 2
IV 2
Hovermarine 216 (Vosper Hovermarine) 99
216 (Hydrographic Survey Craft) 99
218 (Ferry) 100
218 (Port Patrol) 101
218 (Coastguard Vessel) 102
218 (Medicraft) 102
221 102
527 103
527MC 104
533OPV 104
700 series 372
HOVERMARINE PACIFIC CO LTD 27
Hover Modules (Mackace) 166
Hoverpads (BHC) 199
Hoverplatforms (Mackace) 165
HOVERSERVICES 80
HOVER TRAVEL LTD 152
HOVER VEHICLES (NZ) LTD 34
HOVERWORK LTD 152
Hu Chwan (White Swan) (Hutang) 214
Hurricane (Windcraft) 145
HUTANG SHIPYARD 214
Hydrofoil Catamaran Car Ferry, 200 T (Supramar) 255
HYDROFOIL CRUISES LTD 303
HYDROFOILS INC 293

I

Icarus II (Okrujnaye Polytechnic) 5
Iceater I (Global Marine) 170
Ichigo-Tei (Kanazawa) 295
Inceptor II SKI-16 Mk 1 (Stolkraft) 3
INGLES HOVERCRAFT ASSOCIATES LTD 80
INSTITUTE OF DIESEL LOCOMOTIVE ENGINEERING, MOSCOW 189
INSTYTUT LOTNICTWA (AVIATION INSTITUTE) 296
Intercepteur (Angevinière) 14
Interceptor (FM-Aerodeslizadores) 36
INTERNATIONAL HOVERSERVICES LTD 153
IRAN, MINISTRY OF DEFENCE 302
IRANIAN NAVY 149
IRAQI NAVY 149
ISIZAKI KISEN CO LTD 303
Islesman 1000 (Quantum) 88
ISRAELI NAVY 149, 302
ISRAEL SHIPYARDS LIMITED 216
ITALIAN INTERFORCE UNIT 149
ITALIAN NAVY 302
IVCHENKO, A 322
Ivchenko AI-20 322
AI-24 322

J

JAPAN AIR LINES 186
JAPANESE NATIONAL RAILWAYS 149
Jetfoil 929-100 (Boeing) 280
929-115 282
JETCAT MARKETING LTD 308
Jetcat JC-F1 308
Jetfoil Ocean Patrol Hydrofoil (OPH) (Boeing) 283
Jetstream (Skidaddle) 94
Jetstream 4-seater 94
6-seater 94
JETSTREAM SYSTEMS COMPANY 203
Jing-Sah River Passenger Ferry (Shanghai 708 Research) 11
Test Craft 10
JORDAN VALLEY AUTHORITY 149
JÖRG, GÜNTHER W 369
Jupiter (Coelacanth) 38

K

KTA-1150-M (Cummins) 333
KANAZAWA INSTITUTE OF TECHNOLOGY 295
Kestrel (Osprey) 84
Kestrel GT 84
KHARKOV MOTOR TRANSPORT TECHNICAL SCHOOL 58
KOCK, HELMUT 211
Kolkhida (Sormovo) 264
KOLN DUSSELDORFER SHIPPING CO 301
Komet (Transrapid-EMS) 185
Kometa (Sormovo) 264
ME 266
MT 267
KORABOIMPEX 301
KOREA TACOMA MARINE INDUSTRIES LTD 34
Korea Tacoma 8m SES 34
15m SES 34
18m SES 34
KRASNOYE SORMOVO SHIPYARD 41, 256
KYUSHU YUSEN CO LTD 149

L

LACV-30, Model 7467 (Bell) 118
LCAC Programme (Rohr) 135
LM500 (Fiat Aviazione) 374
LM 2500 (General Electric) 336
LMSES (Rohr) 135
LSES 136
LANDING CRAFT AIR CUSHION (LCAC) ACQUISITION PROGRAMME 126
LANGUEDOC-ROUSSILLON REGIONAL DEVELOPMENT BOARD 148
LAPAN 25
Lapan XH-01 25
Lebed (Sormovo) 46
LENINGRAD CENTRAL DESIGN BUREAU 161
LENINGRAD INSTITUTE OF ENGINEERING & CONSTRUCTION 195
Lestes 03 (Thilloy) 21
LIGHT HOVERCRAFT COMPANY (AUSTRALIA) 2
LIGHT HOVERCRAFT COMPANY (UK) 81, 200
LING SYSTEMS LTD 200
LOCKHEED-GEORGIA 128
Logistics Surface Effect Ship (Rohr) 136
LOS GALANES, ALBERTO GIMENEZ DE 36
Low pressure air systems (ACE) 162
LUKKARILA 12
Lukkarila Two-seater 12

M

M100 (Rodriquez) 230
150 235
200 236
300 236
600 236
M400 (Sudoimport) 323
M401A 324
ME 990-3 (Garrett) 335
MN.2 Research Craft (SEDAM) 20
MPI-15 Caspian (Mariisky Polytechnic) 58
18 58
M-RHS 150 Search and Rescue (Rodriquez) 229
M-RHS 150 Patrol Craft 230
MT 80 (Supramar) 253
250 253
MTU MOTOREN-UND TURBINEN-UNION FRIEDRICHSHAFEN GmbH 316
MV-PP1 (Mitsui) 32
-PP5 (50-seat ferry) 31
-PP5 Mk II 32
-PP15 (155-seat hoverferry) 29
MACKACE HOVERSYSTEMS 164
Magnus 02-1 (Bauman Higher Technical School) 371
MAHART MAGYAR HAJOZASIRT 302
MARAVEN SA 153
Marboré (Turboméca) 315
MARIDYNE 172
Maridyne ACV-4000 (Backhoe) 172
MARIISKY POLYTECHNICAL INSTITUTE 58
Marine Gas Turbines (United Technologies) 339
Marine Gnome (Rolls-Royce) 326
Olympus 327
Proteus 327
SM1A 327
SM2B 327
Tyne RM2D 327
MARINE TRANSPORT SERVICES CO 147
MARITIME DYNAMICS INC 129
MAR-PORT 301
Mars (Coelacanth) 38
Matka (Sormovo) 267
MAXCAT HOVERCRAFT 82
Maxcat 83
MAYEKAWA TRADING CO 303
Mayfly (Ben Wynne) 297
MEARS CONSTRUCTION LTD. 167
MED SHIPPING 304
MEITETSU KAIJO KANKOSEN KK 149, 303
Mesa 80 (Mitsui) 309
Meteor (Sormovo) 267
MILAN, MINISTRY OF TRANSPORT 303
MINISTRY OF THE INTERIOR, BAHRAIN 147
MINISTRY OF THE MERCHANT MARINE, LENINGRAD CENTRAL DESIGN BUREAU 161
MINISTRY OF THE RIVER FLEET (USSR) 150, 304
MINISTRY OF WORKS, BELGIUM 147
Mirage (Hydrofoils Inc) 293
Mistral 2 (Nihon University) 33
MITSUI ENGINEERING & SHIPBUILDING CO LTD 29, 160, 309
Molnia (Sormovo) 268
Mountbatten Class (SR.N4) (BHC) 65
Multifunction Supply and Support Vessel (SSSCO) 312

N

N73 (Nihon University) 33
NAT 85 (Supramar) 251
90 251
190 252
NATIONAL MARITIME INSTITUTE, DEPT OF INDUSTRY 151
NATO/PHM (Boeing) 277
Naval Amphibious Assault Craft (Sormovo) 47
NAVAL HOVERCRAFT TRIALS UNIT, HONG KONG 149
NAVAL HOVERCRAFT TRIALS UNIT, UK 153
Naval Research Hovercraft (Sormovo) 47
Naval Inland Water Craft (Shanghai 708 Research) 12
NAVIGAZIONE LAGO MAGGIORE-GG 303
NAVIMOR 303
Naviplane (SEDAM) 17
N300 (Multi-purpose transport) 18
N300 Mk II (Military) 19
N300 Mk II (Fast ferry) 19
N500 (Mixed-traffic hoverferry) 19
NAVSEA (Department of the Navy, Naval Sea Systems Command) 124, 305
NEOTERIC ENGINEERING AFFILIATES LTD 3
NEOTERIC USA INC 131
Neova II (Neoteric) 131
NEPTUN CENTRAL DESIGN BUREAU 59
Neptun AKVPR-001 59
NESSIE (Carène) 368
NEU, ETABLISSEMENTS 194
Nevka (Sormovo) 269
NEW SOUTH WALES, PUBLIC TRANSPORT COMMISSION 301
NEW ZEALAND DEPARTMENT OF CIVIL AVIATION 149
NICHIMEN CO LTD 303
NIGERIAN FEDERAL MINISTRY OF TRANSPORT (IND) 149
NIGG, DONALD 300
NIHON UNIVERSITY, NARASHINO 33
Nimbus Mk III (Surface Craft) 94
Mk IV 95
Mk V 95
NIPPON KAI KANKO FERRY 149
NISSHO-IWAI CO LTD 303
NORTH AMERICAN HOVERCRAFT COMPANY 132
NORTH SHORE FERRIES 149
NOVOCHERKASSK LOCOMOTIVE TECHNICAL INSTITUTE 190
NOVOCHERKASSK POLYTECHNIC 195

O

Odyssey 700 (Space Hovercraft) 9
OITA HOVERFERRY CO LTD 149
OKRUJNAYE POLYTECHNIC 5

Orion-01 (Sormovo) ... 48
ORLEY, Z O ... 16
OSPREY HOVERCRAFT LTD ... 83

P

PACT-50 (Global Marine) ... 171
PAR/WIG Project (Lockheed-Georgia) ... 128
PAT 20 (Supramar) ... 251
PAT 70 ... 251
PCH-1 High Point (Boeing) ... 276
PGA 1 Intercepteur (Angevinière) ... 14
PGH (NIGERIA) ... 149
PGH-1 Flagstaff (Grumman) ... 287
PGH-2 Tucumcari (Boeing) ... 277
PSL 003 (Angevinière) ... 14
PT 20 Mk II (Supramar) ... 241
20B Mk II ... 242
50 Mk II ... 243
PT 100 ... 248
PTL 28 (Supramar) ... 242
PTS 75 Mk III (Supramar) ... 245
150 Mk III ... 248
PUC 22-2500SP (Wärtsilä) ... 373
30-3000TP ... 373
40-900SP ... 372
Pacific Express (Dak Hydrofoils) ... 299
PAIJANTEEN KANTOSIIPI OY ... 301
PAKISTAN COAST GUARD AUTHORITY ... 149
PAKISTAN NAVY ... 303
Parawing Ekranoplans (CLST) ... 41
Patrol Hovercraft, 18 metre (Vosper) ... 105
Patrol Hydrofoil, 28ft (Hydrofoils Inc) ... 294
PAXMAN DIESELS LIMITED ... 324
Pchela (Bee) (Sormovo) ... 270
Phantom (Light Hovercraft) ... 81
PHILIPPINE NAVY ... 303
PHOENIX HOVERCRAFT CORPORATION ... 172
PINDAIR LTD ... 85, 168
PINTALIITAJAPALVELU (HOVERCRAFT SERVICE) ... 13, 148
PIPELINE CONTRACTORS INC ... 149
Plainview (Grumman) ... 290
Pluto (Coelacanth) ... 37
I, II (Test vehicle) ... 37
III (4-seater runabout) ... 37
Portable Piers (Rolair) ... 203
POWER BREEZE ... 132
Powerjet 16 (Rockwell) ... 338
20 ... 337
24 ... 338
PRATT & WHITNEY AIRCRAFT OF CANADA LTD ... 313

Q

QUANTUM HOVERCRAFT LTD ... 88

R

R-1001 MANTA (CLST) ... 40
RFB (Lippisch) X-113 Am Aerofoil Boat (Rhein-Flugzeugbau) ... 23
RFB X-114 Aerofoil Boat (Rhein-Flugzeugbau) ... 24
RHS 70 (Rodriquez) ... 220
70 Hydroil ... 227
110 ... 221
140 ... 222
140 Hydroil ... 228
150 ... 223
160 ... 223
160 Hydroil ... 228
200 ... 225
Aliyacht ... 226
Racing Hovercraft (Falke) ... 23
Raduga (Sormovo) ... 52
Raketa (Sormovo) ... 270
Rapid Intervention Vessel (SSSCO) ... 312
Rassvet (Dawn) (Krasnoye Sormovo) ... 52
RED FUNNEL GROUP ... 304
REGIE TRANSPORTES MARITIME (RTM) ... 301
RHEIN-FLUGZEUGBAU GmbH (RFB) ... 23, 317
River Rover (Ingles) ... 81
RIVTOW, VANCOUVER, BRITISH COLUMBIA ... 148
ROCKWELL INTERNATIONAL ROCKET-DYNE DIVISION ... 337
RODRIQUEZ CANTIERE NAVALE SpA ... 220
ROHR INDUSTRIES, INC ... 133
ROLAIR SYSTEMS INC ... 203
ROLAIR SYSTEMS (UK) LTD ... 200
ROLLS-ROYCE LTD (INDUSTRIAL & MARINE DIVISION) ... 326
ROMANIAN NAVY ... 240, 303
Rotary Air Tables (Airmatic) ... 196
ROTORK MARINE LTD ... 89
Rotork 512 Range ... 91
ROTTERDAM PORT AUTHORITY ... 149
ROYAL HYDROFOIL CRUISES ... 301
ROYAL NAVY (UK) ... 304
RUDNAP ... 305

S

SA-800 (SNIA) ... 216
SAS, TRAPANI ... 302
SES3 (Rohr Industries) ... 134
SES, 3K ... 134
SES-100A (Rohr Industries) ... 133
SES-100A (SES Acquisition Project) ... 138
SES-100B (Bell) ... 116
SES 4-5,000 ton (SEDAM) ... 21
SES, Light Multi-Purpose (Rohr) ... 135
SES Passenger Ferry, 23·5m (Sormovo) ... 54
25·6m (Sormovo) ... 54
SG 85 (RFB) ... 317
SK-5 Model 7255 (Bell) ... 115
SMT-1 (Warsaw Young Technicians) ... 35
SNCF ... 148
SR.N4 Mountbatten Class (BHC) ... 65
Mk 2 ... 65
Mk 3 'Super 4' ... 68
Mk 4 ... 76
(Hunter/disposal craft) ... 76
(Influence sweeper) ... 76
(Logistic support) ... 77
(Minelayer) ... 77
(Multi-role craft) ... 76
(Wire sweeper) ... 76
Military 4 ... 77
SR.N6 Winchester Class (BHC) ... 70
(Ducted propeller for) (Air Vehicles) ... 63
Mk 1S (Passenger ferry/general purpose) ... 71
Mk 2/3 (Military) ... 71
Mk 4 (Coastal defence) ... 71
Mk 6 ... 71
Mk 8 ... 71
SSP *Kaimalino* (SSSCO) ... 311
ST-3A Fully Submerged Foil Research Craft (Supramar) ... 251
ST6 (Pratt & Whitney) ... 313
STW 408 (Rotork) ... 90
STW 412 ... 90
SADO KISEN KAISHA ... 303
SALVATORI, G+R ... 303
Saphyr (DTCN) ... 214
Sarancha (Krasnoye Sormovo) ... 258
SAUDI ARABIAN COASTAL AND FRONTIER GUARD ... 150
Scarab I (Hoverservices) ... 80
II ... 80
8 ... 80
10-2 (Bill Baker) ... 64
10-4 (Bill Baker) ... 64
XI (Bill Baker) ... 64
SCHIFFACOMMERS ... 301
SCHIFFSWERFT KORNEUBURG ... 301
SCORPION INC ... 339
SEACONSTRUCT ... 35
Seahawk 500 (Sector) ... 93
SEAWORLD ... 305
SECTOR HOVERCRAFT LTD ... 93
SEDAM (Société d'Etudes et de Développement des Aéroglisseurs Marins, Terrestres et Amphibies) ... 17, 158
SEJIR DENIZYOLLARI LTD ... 304
SEMI-SUBMERGED SHIP CORPORATION (SSSCO) ... 310
SETONAIKAI KISEN CO LTD ... 303
SHANGHAI 708 RESEARCH INSTITUTE ... 9
SICILIA REGIONALE MARITIMAS SpA ... 303
Simple Cyclone (Cyclone) ... 78
SKIDADDLE LEISURE PRODUCTS ... 93
Skima (Pindair) ... 85
2 (Two-seater) ... 85
3 (Two/three-seater) ... 85
4 (Two/four-seater) ... 85
5 (Four/five-seater) ... 85
6 (Six-seater) ... 85
12 (Twelve-seater) ... 86
18 ... 87
25 ... 87
SKIMMERS INCORPORATED ... 138
SOCIEDADE TURISTICA PONTA DO ADOXE SARL ... 150
SOCIETE ANGEVINIERE ... 14
SOCIETE BERTIN ET CIE ... 16, 193
SOCIETE DE L'AEROTRAIN ... 175
SOCIETE MINIERE DE BAKWANGA ... 153
SOCIETE NATIONALE INDUSTRIELLE AEROSPATIALE ... 215
SOCIETE TURBOMECA ... 314
SOLAM HELLAS ... 302
SORMOVO, KRASNOYE ... 41, 256
Sormovich (Sormovo) ... 54
SOVIET ARMY ... 150
SOVIET FRONTIER POLICE ... 304
SOVIET MINISTRY OF THE RIVER FLEET ... 150, 304
SOVIET NAVY ... 150, 304
SPACE HOVERCRAFT LTD ... 9
Space Shuttle Solid Rocket Boosters (Rolair) ... 206
Spin Tank (Mackace) ... 166
SPLIT AIRPORT ... 305
Sputnik (Sormovo) ... 271
SRI LANKAN NAVY ... 304
STAVANGERSKE DAMPSKIBSSELSKAB ... 303
STOLKRAFT PTY LTD ... 3
Stolkraft Mk III ... 4
Stolkraft 25 metre Commuter Ferry ... 4
Strela (Sormovo) ... 272
Suburban Aérotrain Aérotrain S-44 (Aérotrain) ... 179
SUDOIMPORT ... 323
Sudoimport engines ... 323
3D12 ... 323
M 400 ... 323
M 401A ... 324
SUNDAHARYA CORP ... 302
Sunrider (Transcraft) ... 95
SUPRAMAR HYDROFOILS AG ... 240
SURFACE CRAFT LTD ... 94
SURFACE EFFECT SHIP ACQUISITION PROJECT ... 136
SVENSKA REDERIAKTIEBOLAGET ORESUND ... 304
Swordfish (CNR) ... 217

T

T.6 (Trans-Hover) ... 96
TAB VIII (Jörg) ... 370
TALAV (FEI) ... 175
TB 106 (Rotork) ... 92
TF 25 (Avco Lycoming) ... 328
40 ... 329
TACOMA, CITY OF ... 153
Tank moving (ACE) ... 163
TANZANIAN NAVY ... 304
Targa (Airhover) ... 62
TAYLORCRAFT TRANSPORT PTY LTD ... 4, 155
THILLOY, JACQUES M ... 21
Tiger Shark (Alaska Hovercraft) ... 113
TIRES PTY LTD ... 301
TOSCANA REGIONALE MARITIMA SpA ... 303
TOURISMO MARGARITA CA ... 305
TOURIST HOTEL AND TRAVEL CORPORATION ... 303
TRANSCRAFT LTD ... 95
TRANSFUTUR SA ... 22
TRANS-HOVER LTD ... 96
TRANSMED ... 303
TRANSPORT CANADA (ACV Division) ... 9
TRANSRAPID-EMS ... 183
Transrapid 02 Research Vehicle (Transrapid-EMS) . 184
03 Research Vehicle ... 184
04 ... 185
05 ... 185
06 ... 186
07 ... 186
08 ... 186
TRANSTOUR ... 303
Tridim Urban Transportation System (Aérotrain) .. 180
TRI-GLIDE (Airmatic) ... 197
TROPIMERE LTD ... 96
TUPOLEV, A N ... 59
Tupolev A-3 Amphibious Aerosledge ... 59
Turbo (Light Hovercraft) ... 82
TURBOMECA, SOCIETE ... 314
Turbo Super Hover Mk 5 (ACV Sales Inc) ... 5
TURISMO MARGARITA CA ... 153, 305
Turist (Sormovo) ... 55
Turmastazou (Turboméca) ... 316
Turmo (Turboméca) ... 315
Turntables (Airmatic) ... 196
Turya (Sormovo) ... 260
Typhoon (Sormovo) ... 260

U

UH-12S (Universal Hovercraft) ... 140
-12T ... 141
-12T2 ... 141
-13SA ... 141
-13T ... 141
-14B ... 142
-14T ... 142
-16S ... 142
-17S ... 142
-18S ... 143
-18T ... 144
-26S ... 144
UHO (Fanbird) ... 25
URBA (Compagnie d'Energétique Linéaire mb) ... 181
URBA 8 ... 182
20 ... 183
30 ... 183
UTC/P5D Marine Power Pac (United Technologies) ... 340
UNITED STATES HOVERCRAFT MANUFACTURING CO INC ... 139
UNITED TECHNOLOGIES CORPORATION POWER SYSTEMS DIVISION ... 339
UNIVERSAL HOVERCRAFT ... 140
US ARMY CORPS OF ENGINEERS ... 153
US ARMY MOBILITY EQUIPMENT R & D COMMAND (MERADCOM) ... 153
US COAST GUARD ... 153
US NAVAL SHIP RESEARCH AND DEVELOPMENT CENTER ... 305
US NAVY LCAC ACQUISITION PROGRAMME ... 153
US NAVY/US COAST GUARD ... 153

V

V-66 (Aero Vodochody) ... 12
V-555-M (Cummins) ... 332
V-903-M (Cummins) ... 332
VA (FEI) ... 5
VA-1 (FEI) ... 5
VNII neftmash ... 160
VT 2 (Vosper Thornycroft) ... 106
Fast missile ... 108
Logistic support craft ... 107
Mine countermeasures craft ... 108
Multi-role logistic support craft ... 108
Valenta (RP200) (Paxman) ... 324
Variable-Plan Sports Stadium (Rolair Systems Inc) . 204
VEDETTES ARMORICAINES ... 301
Ventura (YJ) (Paxman) ... 324
VENTURE AERO-MARINE ... 144
Venus (Coelacanth) ... 38

Vikhr (Whirlwind) (Sormovo) 272
Viking Model 7505 (Stretched) (Bell) 8
Volga 70 (Sormovo) 273
VOLKSWAGEN (GB) LTD 318
Volkswagen Type 122 318
   Type 126A 319
   Type 127 319
Voskhod 2 (Sormovo) 258
VOSPER HOVERMARINE LTD 99, 372
VOSPER PRIVATE LTD 240
VOSPER THORNYCROFT (UK) LTD 105
Vosper Thornycroft 18 metre
   Patrol Hovercraft 105
Voyageur Model 7467 LACV-30 (Bell) 118

W

WARSAW YOUNG TECHNICIANS CENTRE ... 35
WÄRTSILÄ AB, OY 372

Water Film Aero-casters (Aero-Go) 202
WATER RESEARCH COMPANY 145
Water Skate (ACE) 162, 197
Water Skate, Mini (ACE) 198
Water Spider II (Kanazawa) 28
WATER SPYDER MARINE LTD 213
Water Spyder 1A 213
   2B 213
   6A 213
Wellington Class (BH.7) (BHC) 72
Westamarin A/S 307
Westamaran 86 (Westamarin) 307
   95 307
   100T 307
Wetlands Drillbarge System
   (WDBS) (Phoenix) 173
Williwaw (Dak Hydrofoils) 298
Winchester Class (SR.N6) (BHC) 70
WINDCRAFT M & M INC 145
Windlord (Transfutur) 22
WYNNE, BEN 297

X

XR-1 Testcraft (Rohr Industries) 133
XR-1D Structural Loads Tests
   (SES Acquisition) 136
XR-1D Ride Control Systems 137
XR-3 137
XR-5 137

Y

YJ Ventura (Paxman) 324
YAEYAMA KANKO FERRY KK 149
Yukon Princess I (Mackace) 165
   II 165

Z

Z-76 (Instytut Lotnictwa) 297
Zagloslizg Z-73 (Instytut Lotnictwa) 297
ZAIRE NAVAL FORCE 305
Zarnitsa (Sormovo) 55
Zarya (Dawn) (Sormovo) 55

Printed in England by Netherwood Dalton & Co. Ltd., Huddersfield